Health Care Facilities Handbook

Health Care Facilities Handbook

EIGHTH EDITION

Edited by

Richard P. Bielen, P.E.

Chief Systems and Applications Engineer
National Fire Protection Association

With the complete text of the 2005 edition of NFPA 99, *Standard for Health Care Facilities*

NFPA®

National Fire Protection Association
Quincy, Massachusetts

Product Manager: Debra Rose
Developmental Editor: Dana Richards
Project Editor: Irene Herlihy
Copy Editor: Joyce Grandy
Composition: Modern Graphics, Inc.
Cover Design: Cameron, Inc.
Manufacturing Manager: Ellen Glisker
Printer: Edwards Brothers/MI

Notice Concerning Liability: Publication of this handbook is for the purpose of circulating information and opinion among those concerned for fire and life safety and related subjects. While every effort has been made to achieve a work of high quality, neither the NFPA nor the authors and contributors to this work guarantee the accuracy or completeness of or assume any liability in connection with the information and opinions contained in this handbook. The NFPA and the authors and contributors shall in no event be liable for any personal injury, property, or other damages of any nature whatsoever, whether special, indirect, consequential, or compensatory, directly or indirectly resulting from the publication, use of or reliance upon this work.

This handbook is published with the understanding that the NFPA and the authors and contributors to this handbook are supplying information and opinion but are not attempting to render engineering or other professional services. If such services are required, the assistance of an appropriate professional should be sought.

Notice Concerning Code Interpretations: This eighth edition of *Health Care Facilities Handbook* is based on the 2005 edition of NFPA 99, *Standard for Health Care Facilities.* All NFPA codes, standards, recommended practices, and guides are developed in accordance with the published procedures of the NFPA by technical committees comprised of volunteers drawn from a broad array of relevant interests. The handbook contains the complete text of NFPA 99 and any applicable Formal Interpretations issued by the Association. These documents are accompanied by explanatory commentary and other supplementary materials.

The commentary and supplementary materials in this handbook are not a part of the *Standard* and do not constitute Formal Interpretations of the NFPA (which can be obtained only through requests processed by the responsible technical committees in accordance with the published procedures of the NFPA). The commentary and supplementary materials, therefore, solely reflect the personal opinions of the editor or other contributors and do not necessarily represent the official position of the NFPA or its technical committees.

NFPA No.: 99HB05
ISBN: 0-87765-684-3
Library of Congress Card Catalog No.: 2005926802

Printed in the United States of America
05 06 07 08 09 5 4 3 2 1

Contents

Annexes

PART TWO
Supplements 659

Preface

NFPA 99, *Standard for Health Care Facilities,* is the result of the integration of 12 documents developed over a 40-year period by the Health Care Facilities Correlating Committee (formerly the Committee on Hospitals). However, it is not the only document applicable to health care facilities—there are some 50 other NFPA documents either that address, in whole or in part, health care facilities or that can be used by health care facilities to address emergency or fire safety issues.

In categorizing fire protection for health care facilities, two general divisions of fire protection can be identified:

- **Facility Fire Protection.** Facility fire protection features, such as hydrants, types of structural protection, length of exit travel distances, and detection and extinguishing systems, are built into or around a structure to minimize hazards. They generally do not require human intervention to provide safety.
- **Operational Fire Protection.** Operational fire protection practices, such as safe use of inhalation anesthetics, safe use of electricity, safe practices in laboratories, use of emergency electrical power, and emergency planning, are intended to minimize fire hazards once the health care facility is occupied. These practices definitely rely on human intervention to provide safety.

Some items (such as portable extinguishers, manual pull stations, and performance criteria for grounding systems) can be categorized into either of the aforementioned divisions. In general, NFPA 99 is concerned with operational fire protection for the many activities occurring in hospitals, ambulatory health care centers, clinics, medical and dental offices, nursing homes, and limited care facilities. NFPA 99 includes provisions for patient care areas (e.g., wards, intensive care units, operating suites, hyperbaric and hypobaric facilities), certain laboratories, several facility-wide systems, and overall emergency planning for a facility in the event of an emergency (fire or otherwise) that interrupts the delivery of patient care.

The effort to combine these 12 health care facility documents began in late 1979 at the suggestion of Marvin J. Fischer, then Chairman of the Health Care Facilities Correlating Committee and Vice-President for Facilities Planning and Engineering Services, Brookdale Hospital Medical Center, Brooklyn, New York. It was Mr. Fischer's firm belief that combining these individual documents into one cohesive document would benefit health care personnel and patients, as well as designers, builders, and enforcing authorities. The correlating committee agreed, but to assure consensus among those affected by the proposed change, the committee solicited public comments on the idea in 1981. With overwhelming support, in January 1982 the committee proceeded with the initial step of publishing a compilation of the latest editions of each of the documents into one bound volume. This compilation was designated NFPA 99, *Health Care Facilities Code.*

The 1984 edition of NFPA 99 was the next step in the process: integration of the previous individual documents into one new document, with a format revised to follow the NFPA *Manual of Style* (all definitions in one chapter; requirements in the main body of the text; recommendations in the annexes). The 1987 edition of NFPA 99 completed this integration process by restructuring text into a form that placed nonfacility-specific requirements in one section and facility-specific requirements into another section. (See Section 1.5 in Chapter 1 for details.) Once the reorganization of the document began, the creation of a handbook on NFPA 99 was a natural extension of the document. With so much material in one document, assistance in the form of commentary seemed the best method to share some of the history of this material as well as to provide additional information and guidance in applying the standard to present conditions.

Codes and standards by themselves can be difficult to understand for those not involved in their development. However, it is not practical to include in these documents complete information on the requirement-adoption process (e.g., the reasons behind requirements, the pros and cons, the voting, the striving for consensus, the research, the discussion). Annex material can help the reader to better understand the codes and standards development process; recently, rationales for the committee's decisions have been stressed. Handbooks present another vehicle for helping readers to better understand the requirements and recommendations of a document.

It is my hope that this eighth edition of the *Health Care Facilities Handbook* will continue to add to the store of knowledge on health care fire safety and will prove to be a useful resource for all those involved in protecting health care facilities from fire and associated hazards.

Acknowledgments

The eighth edition of the *Health Care Facilities Handbook* is the result of substantial contributions by many talented people. I am grateful to many colleagues who provided support and assistance. A number of experts from the field of health care facilities fire safety participated in preparing commentary. The valued members of this technical team include the following:

Mark Allen, Beacon Medical Products, Charlotte, NC

Saul Aronow, Waban, MA

Michael A. Crowley, The RJA Group, Inc., Houston, TX

Alan Lipschultz, Christiana Care Health System, Newark, DE

Susan B. McLaughlin, SBM Consulting, Ltd., Barrington, IL

Hugh O. Nash, Jr., Nash Lipsey Burch, LLC, Nashville, TN

Russell Phillips, Russell Phillips & Associates, Inc., Rochester, NY

Robert B. Sheffield, Wound Care Group, San Antonio, TX

Wilbur T. Workman, Undersea & Hyperbaric Medical Society, TX

I am grateful to Phil Long for providing his photographic expertise and to James R. Madden, director of engineering & facility repair at Children's Hospital Medical Center of Akron. He was most helpful in guiding us through the facility, wherein a number of the book's photographs were taken.

I am most grateful to Dana Richards, the developmental editor of this book, Joyce Grandy, the book's copy editor, and Irene Herlihy, the book's project editor, as well as to Debra Rose, the book's product manager, for their assistance, knowledge, perseverance, and friendship that kept this project on track.

Richard P. Bielen, P.E.

PART ONE

NFPA 99
Health Care Facilities
2005 Edition, with Commentary

Part One of this handbook includes the complete text and illustrations of the 2005 edition of NFPA 99, *Standard for Health Care Facilities.* The text and illustrations from the standard are printed in black, and they are the official requirements of NFPA 99. Line drawings and photographs from the standard are labeled "Figures."

Paragraphs that begin with the letter *A* are extracted from Annex A of the standard. Although printed in black ink, this nonmandatory material is purely explanatory in nature. For ease of use, Annex A material immediately follows the text paragraph to which it refers in this handbook.

In addition to standard text and annexes, Part One includes commentary that provides other background information for specific paragraphs in the standard. This insightful commentary takes the reader behind the scenes, into the reasons underlying the requirements. To readily identify commentary material, commentary text, captions, and tables are all printed in blue. So that the reader can easily distinguish between required illustrations from the standard and illustrations for the commentary, line drawings and photographs in the commentary are labeled "Exhibits."

This handbook also includes supplements. Part Two is comprised of three supplements, which explore, in greater detail than does the commentary, the background of selected topics related to NFPA 99.

NFPA 99 is the result of integrating 12 documents developed by the Health Care Facilities Correlating Committee (and its predecessor, the Committee on Hospitals) over a period of more than 40 years. The effort to combine those other documents into a stand-alone code began in 1979 at the suggestion of Marvin J. Fischer, who then chaired the Health Care Facilities Correlating Committee. The correlating committee solicited input and found overwhelming support for the idea of creating one cohesive document.

The first step, taken in 1982, was to compile the latest editions of relevant documents into one bound volume, designated as NFPA 99, *Health Care Facilities Code.* The 1984 edition integrated the individual documents into one new document that followed the *Manual of Style* (MOS) (e.g., all definitions in one chapter, requirements in the main body of the text, and recommendations in appendixes). By the 1987 edition, restructured text placed nonfacility-specific requirements in one portion and facility-

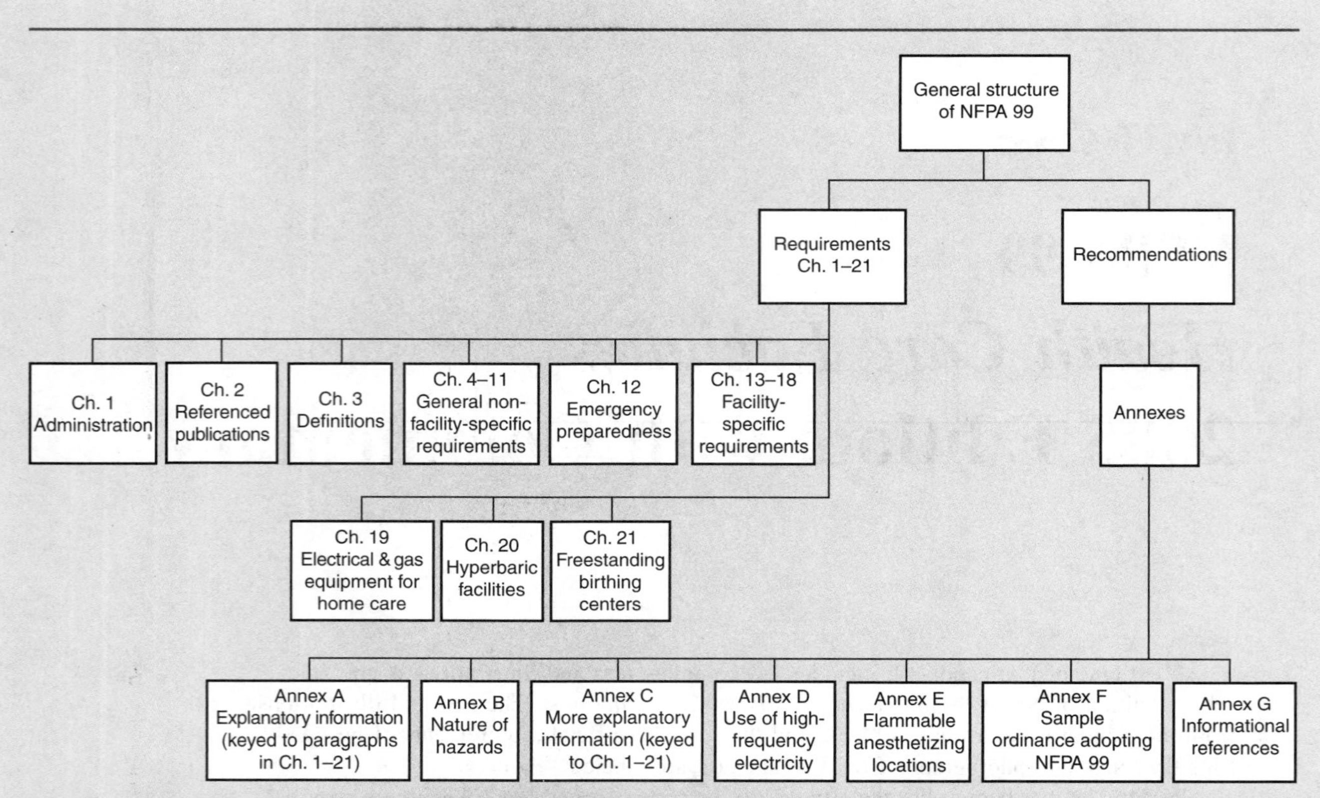

EXHIBIT 1 *How NFPA 99 is organized.*

specific requirements in another portion. This restructuring completed the integration process. (See Exhibit 1.)

The NFPA MOS underwent an update for the year 2000, mandating a major rewrite and reorientation of NFPA 99. In accordance with the structure of documents mandated by the MOS, the scope and purpose of each chapter of NFPA 99 are located in Chapter 1. To make this an internationally accepted document, all units of measure are expressed in the International System of Units (SI) with U.S. customary units of measure expressed in parentheses. For example, where 212°F was used, it will now appear as 100°C (212°F). The MOS brought other changes to the look of this standard. It required that each chapter be divided into sections, each with a section title. Consequently, each chapter has more section titles than in the past. Also, each paragraph must now contain only one requirement, whereas previous editions had many instances of multiple requirements within a single paragraph. These are now split into separate paragraphs, which are now numbered as subparagraphs under the applicable section. This reorganization should make the chapters easier to use.

Other MOS changes have had an impact on the technical content of the standard. These involve use of mandatory language, exceptions, and annexes (formerly called appendixes). The MOS requires that text of the standard use only mandatory language (e.g., *shall, shall not*) and that nonmandatory language (e.g., *should*) be deleted or moved to an annex as advisory text. In previous editions, there were several instances of nonmandatory language within the text of the standard. The committee gave careful consideration to these changes so that the intent of the standard is clear. In some paragraphs,

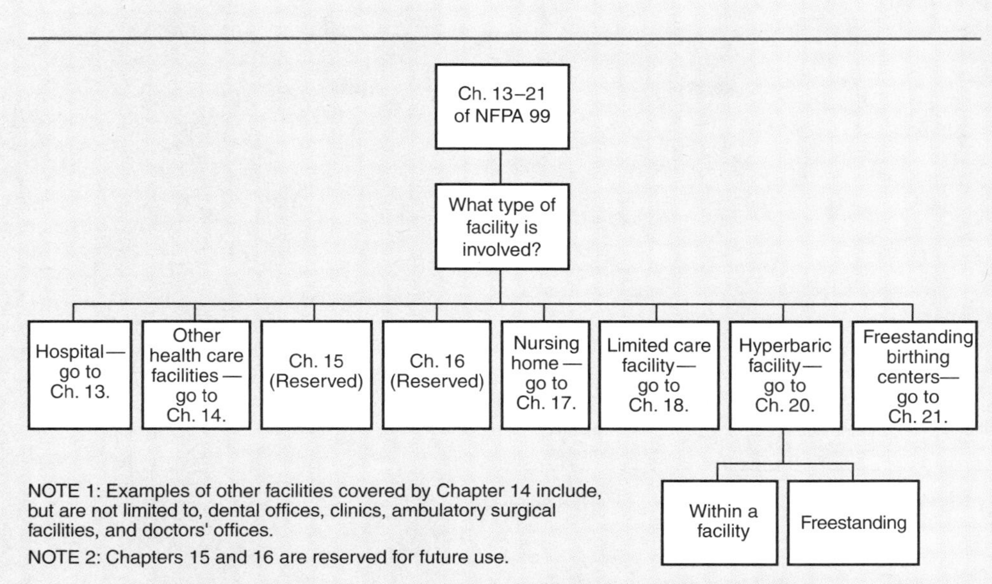

EXHIBIT 2 Finding a requirement in a health care facility.

nonmandatory language was changed to mandatory language to clarify that a particular issue was intended to be a requirement. In other paragraphs, nonmandatory language was moved to an annex to make it advisory text. Many paragraphs formerly contained explanatory material and supplementary information. This text has been moved to an annex, or deleted if it was determined to be redundant or unnecessary.

The use of exceptions is strongly discouraged by the MOS. Several exceptions in previous editions have been rewritten as requirements. The language of paragraphs was carefully chosen so that the original intent was not changed. Where there is an apparent change of intent in one of these paragraphs, it was a result of a separate committee action to address the technical content of that paragraph.

The numbering of paragraphs in the past two standards is substantially different from previous editions as a result of separating multiple requirements into different paragraphs, rewriting exceptions into new paragraphs, and moving text to annexes. The committee recognized that the location of a requirement (under a particular section/paragraph) can affect the interpretation of that requirement. Where new paragraphs or subparagraphs were created, the committee gave careful consideration to their location and numbering so that the intent of the requirements is clear. (See Exhibit 2.)

In addition to NFPA 99, some fifty other NFPA documents address the fire safety needs of health care facilities.

The 2005 edition of this handbook features icons, a tool designed to help users easily identify important elements in the text. Icons represent special information and have been added in the margins of the book next to the material they are identifying. These icons represent the following material:

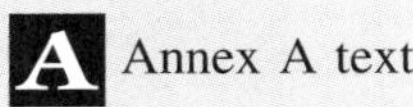

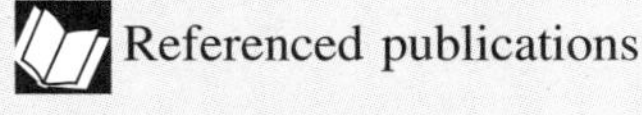

CHAPTER 1

Administration

Overview. The following commentary provides the reader with a general background of NFPA 99, including the former documents that contributed to it and how it came to be the standard it is today. It is important to review this history before moving on to the specifics of Chapter 1. Users of NFPA 99 who know and understand this general background will find that this information increases their ability to apply, interpret, and review the standard.

Use of the Term *Reserved*. The use of the term *reserved* in NFPA 99 does not indicate either the omission or imminent inclusion of text. New text may be added whenever the committee responsible for that material feels text is warranted or when public proposals recommending text are received and approved. In either instance, all proposals for new text have to go through the full NFPA adoption procedures before being incorporated.

Responding to Changing Needs. The health care facilities project itself is a product of changing needs in the health care field. In 1917, NFPA formed a committee to address the use of gases. In the 1930s, the problem of explosions in operating rooms due to changes in the way anesthesia was administered began to occur with alarming frequency. The Committee on Gases investigated the problem and developed recommendations for the safe use of anesthetic gases. In the 1940s, other problems involving electricity and equipment in hospital operating rooms became evident, and a separate Committee on Hospital Operating Rooms was established to address these situations.

Over the years, standards and guidelines for other aspects of hospital activities involving fire and explosion hazards (including electric shock and emergency electric power) were established. To reflect this more inclusive approach, the name of the committee was changed once more. This newly named Committee on Hospitals included standing subcommittees on anesthetizing agents, respiratory therapy, laboratories, essential electrical systems, safe use of electricity, medical-surgical vacuum systems, safe use of high-frequency electricity, disaster planning, and hyperbaric/hypobaric facilities.

By 1975, the breadth of the subcommittees had become so extensive that the role of the Committee on Hospitals shifted again, with its function becoming that of correlating the diverse activities of its eight subcommittees. Thus, the Health Care Facilities Correlating Committee (formerly the Committee on Hospitals) came into existence, and its subcommittees were elevated to technical committees.

By 1985, the Correlating Committee realized that to be more effective it would have to be able to make technical changes in the documents under its responsibility. Because, under NFPA procedures, Correlating Committees cannot make such technical changes, the Correlating Committee petitioned the Standards Council to discharge the Correlating Committee and technical committees under it and establish a new, balanced technical committee, with standing subcommittees under it. These subcommittees were not to be simply the previous technical committees; rather, they were to reflect the restructuring of NFPA 99.

The 1987 edition of NFPA 99 introduced several major changes in addition to the restructuring of the document, including the following: Material on hypobaric facilities was separated into a new document (NFPA 99B) because these facilities were no longer used for medical purposes; material on the home use of respiratory therapy (Appendix F in the 1984 edition of NFPA 99) was deleted entirely because the committee felt that publishing a simplified brochure was a better way to provide patients with this safety information. The text of NFPA 56F, *Standard on Nonflammable Medical Gas Systems,* 1983 edition, was incorporated into a chapter on gas and vacuum systems (Chapter 5 in the 2002 edition). NFPA 56F no longer exists as an individual document.

In the early 1990s, the NFPA Standards Council again studied the way committees were operating and established two structures for committees. The Technical Committee on Health Care Facilities reviewed the results and petitioned the Council to have the project restructured within this framework. A new Technical Correlating Committee on Health Care Facilities was established to supervise the efforts of the technical committees. A new Technical Committee on Administration was also created to handle issues that were beyond the scopes of the other technical committees. Most recently, the Technical Correlating Committee combined the Technical Committee on Anesthesia Services and the Technical Committee on Gas Equipment because of similarities in their activities. The Technical Committee on Gas Delivery Equipment now replaces the two.

Numerous technical changes were made throughout the 1990 edition of NFPA 99, while the 1993 edition incorporated more technical changes as well as structural changes to make the document more user-friendly. These structural changes included clearly separating requirements from recommendations by placing all "guidance" related to text into Notes or into Appendix A (now called Annex A) of the document. In addition, flowcharts were added to help explain how NFPA 99 was structured and how requirements could be found. Technical changes included the following: adding requirements and recommendations in Annex 2 (now called Annex E) to further prevent or minimize fires in operating rooms; making major changes to requirements in Chapter 4 (now Chapter 9) for installing, testing, and maintaining nonflammable medical piped gas systems; adding new sections on medical gases and dental vacuum requirements in Chapter 4 (now Chapter 5); changing leakage current limits of patient-care-related electrical appliances to correlate more closely with an international document on the subject; revising laboratory requirements to correlate more closely with NFPA 45, *Standard on Fire Protection for Laboratories Using Chemicals* [1]; changing essential electrical system requirements in ambulatory health care clinics and medical/dental offices; and extensively revising hyperbaric chamber requirements (now in Chapter 20).

In addition to structural changes to the 1996 edition, technical changes included the following: relocating all requirements on flammable anesthetics and anesthetizing locations to a then new Annex 2 (now Annex E) in the back of the document; replacing a previous annex with recommendations on emergency preparedness with requirements in a new Chapter 11 (now Chapter 12); adding a chapter on home health care, because more patients are being discharged from health care facilities with gas- and electric-powered devices; and revising load testing criteria for emergency generators by referencing NFPA 110, *Standard for Emergency and Standby Power Systems* [2], which has new requirements for such testing.

In the 1999 edition, the major structural change was to delete in its entirety the text of a chapter on ambulatory health care center requirements, and to replace it with requirements that apply to health care facilities other than hospitals, nursing homes, or limited care facilities. The committee made this change in concert with deleting in their entirety chapters on clinic requirements, and medical and dental office requirements. The purpose of this major change was to move away from chapters that based the required protection on a "label" or designation given to a building, because such a classification does not always provide a true description of what type of health care is being provided to patients in the structure.

The committee was aware that authorities having jurisdiction were having problems interpreting the appropriate applications because the then current definitions of some facilities were not accurate. For 1999, the committee believed that several chapters could be combined into a new "other" health care facility chapter and made a technical change to all chapters where the level of risk to the patient (based on life support) would determine the level (or complexity) of the systems (electrical, gas, vacuum, etc.) required in the facility.

In the 2002 edition, the chapter numbering was changed to conform to the most recent NFPA *Manual of Style* (MOS) [3]. The scope and administration sections were relocated to Chapter 1. The definitions were reviewed and correlated with the NFPA glossary of definitions.

The majority of the changes to the 2005 edition were to Chapter 5, Gas and Vacuum Systems. Several new joining methods were approved as well as a different compressor technology. The alarm system components were expanded to include a centralized computer system to monitor the gas and vacuum alarms. Chapter 12, Health Care Emergency Management, was revised to correlate with NFPA 1600, *Standard on Disaster/Emergency Management and Business Continuity Programs* [4].

1.1 Scope

Section 1.1 reflects the scopes of the 12 original individual documents from which NFPA 99 was created in 1984.

NFPA 99 covers facilities that treat humans. Freestanding veterinary facilities present many of the same hazards as hospitals, but they are not addressed in NFPA 99. This subject could be addressed in a separate document. (It should be noted that veterinary laboratories located within health care facilities as well as hyperbaric chambers used for animals are included and addressed in NFPA 99.)

1.1.1 The scope of this document is to establish criteria to minimize the hazards of fire, explosion, and electricity in health care facilities providing services to human beings.

1.1.2 Annex D covers principles of design and use of electrical and electronic appliances generating high-frequency currents for medical treatment in hospitals, clinics, ambulatory care facilities, and dental offices, whether fixed or mobile.

1.1.2.1 Areas Not Addressed The following areas are not addressed:

(1) Communication equipment, resuscitation equipment (e.g., defibrillators), or physiological stimulators (e.g., used for anesthesia, acupuncture)
(2) Experimental or research apparatus built to order, or under development, provided such apparatus is used under qualified supervision and provided the builder demonstrates to the authority having jurisdiction that the apparatus has a degree of safety equivalent to that described in Annex D

1.1.3 Annex E retains the established requirements that would be necessary for the safe use of flammable inhalation anesthetics should the use of this type of anesthetic be reinstituted.

1.1.4 Chapter 4, Electrical Systems, covers the performance, maintenance, and testing of electrical systems (both normal and essential) used within health care facilities.

Chapter 1 does not apply to all medical facilities or all situations. Those responsible for a particular medical facility, or for an individual patient care function within a medical facility, are urged to evaluate the application of this chapter in relation to their particular situation. If additional electrical supply features are installed, installation must be done in a manner consistent with the details and philosophy of this chapter.

This chapter is to be used in conjunction with NFPA 70, *National Electrical Code®* [5], particularly Article 517, which addresses health care facilities.

1.1.4.1 Areas Not Addressed in Chapter 4 The following areas are not addressed in NFPA 99, but are addressed in other NFPA documents:

(1) Specific requirements for wiring and installation on equipment are covered in NFPA 70, *National Electrical Code.*
(2) Requirements for illumination and identification of means of egress in health care facilities are covered in NFPA *101*, *Life Safety Code.*
(3) Requirements for fire protection signaling systems.

For requirements for signaling systems, see NFPA *101*®, *Life Safety Code*® [6], and *NFPA 72*®, *National Fire Alarm Code*® [7].

(4) Requirements for fire pumps are covered in NFPA 20, *Standard for the Installation of Stationary Pumps for Fire Protection*, except that the alternate source of power shall be permitted to be the essential electrical system.

For requirements for fire pumps, see NFPA 20, *Standard for the Installation of Stationary Pumps for Fire Protection* [8].

(5) Requirements for the installation of stationary engines and gas turbines are covered in NFPA 37, *Standard for the Installation and Use of Stationary Combustion Engines and Gas Turbines.*

1.1.5 Chapter 5, Gas and Vacuum Systems, covers the performance, maintenance, installation, and testing of the following:

(1) Nonflammable medical gas systems with operating pressures below a gauge pressure of 2068 kPa (300 psi)
(2) Vacuum systems used within health care facilities
(3) Waste anesthetic gas disposal (WAGD) systems, also referred to as scavenging
(4) Manufactured assemblies that are intended for connection to the medical gas, vacuum, or WAGD systems (also referred to as scavenging)

1.1.5.1 Areas Not Addressed in Chapter 5 Requirements for portable compressed gas systems are covered in Chapter 9, Gas Equipment.

1.1.6 Chapter 6, Environmental Systems, covers the performance, maintenance, and testing of the environmental systems used within health care facilities.

1.1.7 Chapter 7, Materials, covers the hazards associated with the use of flammable and combustible materials used within health care facilities.

1.1.8 Chapter 8, Electrical Equipment, covers the performance, maintenance, and testing of electrical equipment used within health care facilities.

1.1.9 Chapter 9, Gas Equipment, covers the performance, maintenance, and testing of gas equipment used within health care facilities.

1.1.10 Chapter 10, Manufacturer Requirements, covers the performance, maintenance, and testing, with regard to safety, required of manufacturers of equipment used within health care facilities.

1.1.11 Chapter 11, Laboratories, establishes criteria to minimize the hazards of fire and explosions in laboratories, as defined in Chapter 3.

1.1.11.1 Areas Not Addressed in Chapter 11 Subsection 1.1.11 is not intended to cover hazards resulting from any of the following:

(1) Chemicals
(2) Radioactive materials
(3)* Biological materials that will not result in fires or explosions

A.1.1.11.1(3) Although this subsection deals primarily with hazards related to fires and explosions, many of the requirements to protect against fire or explosion, such as those for hood exhaust systems, also serve to protect persons from exposure to nonfire health hazards of these materials.

1.1.12* Chapter 12, Health Care Emergency Management, establishes minimum criteria for health care facility emergency management in the development of a program for effective disaster preparedness, response, mitigation, and recovery.

A.1.1.12 Because no single model of an emergency management plan is feasible for every health care facility, this chapter is intended to provide criteria in the preparation and implementation of an individual plan. The principles involved are universally applicable; the implementation needs to be tailored to the specific facility.

1.1.13 Chapter 13, Hospital Requirements, addresses safety requirements of hospitals.

1.1.14 Chapter 14, Other Health Care Facilities, addresses safety requirements for facilities, or portions thereof, that provide diagnostic and treatment services to patients in health care facilities. Requirements for specific health care facilities are addressed in the following chapters:

(1) Hospitals — Chapter 13
(2) Nursing homes — Chapter 17
(3) Limited care facilities — Chapter 18

1.1.15 Reserved.

1.1.16 Reserved.

1.1.17 Chapter 17, Nursing Home Requirements, addresses safety requirements of nursing homes.

1.1.18 Chapter 18, Limited Care Facility Requirements, covers safety requirements of limited care facilities.

1.1.19 Chapter 19, Electrical and Gas Equipment for Home Care, addresses the requirements for the safe use of electrical and gas equipment used for home care medical treatment.

1.1.20* Chapter 20, Hyperbaric Facilities, covers the recognition of and protection against hazards of an electrical, explosive, or implosive nature, as well as fire hazards associated with hyperbaric chambers and associated facilities that are used, or intended to be used, for medical applications and experimental procedures at gauge pressures from 0 to 690 kPa (0 to 100 psi). Chapter 20 applies to both single- and multiple-occupancy hyperbaric chambers; to animal chambers, the size of which precludes human occupancy; and to those in which the chamber atmosphere contains an oxygen partial pressure greater than an absolute pressure of 21.3 kPa (3.09 psi) (0.21 atmospheres).

A.1.1.20 During the past 20 years there has been a widespread interest in the use of oxygen at elevated environmental pressure to increase the partial pressure of oxygen in a patient's tissues in order to treat certain medical conditions or to prepare a patient for surgery. These techniques are also employed widely for the treatment of decompression sickness (e.g., bends, caisson worker's disease) and carbon monoxide poisoning.

Recently, however, the level of knowledge and expertise has increased so dramatically that the codes are in need of updating. By the end of 1988, there were 218 hyperbaric facilities in operation in the U.S. and Canada. These facilities supported hyperbaric medical treatments for 62,548 patients between 1971 and 1987. As these facilities provide therapy for disorders indicated for treatment, these numbers will continue to increase. As the number of facilities increases, the number of patients treated will also increase.

Such treatment involves placement of the patient, with or without attendants, in a hyperbaric chamber or pressure vessel, the pressure of which is raised above ambient pressure. In the course of the treatment, the patient breathes up to 100 percent oxygen.

In addition to being used for patient care, these chambers also are being employed for research purposes using experimental animals and, in some instances, humans.

The partial pressure of oxygen present in a gaseous mixture is the determinate factor of the amount of available oxygen. This pressure will rise if the volume percentage of oxygen present increases, or if the total pressure of a given gas mixture containing oxygen increases, or if both factors increase. Because the sole purpose of the hyperbaric technique of treatment is to raise the total pressure within the treatment chamber, an increased partial pressure of oxygen always is available during treatment unless positive means are taken to limit the oxygen content. In addition, the patient is often given an oxygen-enriched atmosphere to breathe.

There is continual need for human diligence in the establishment, operation, and maintenance of hyperbaric facilities. It is the responsibility of the chief administrator of the facility possessing the hyperbaric chamber to adopt and enforce appropriate regulations for hyperbaric facilities. In formulating and administering the program, full use should be made of technical personnel highly qualified in hyperbaric chamber operations and safety.

It is essential that personnel having responsibility for the hyperbaric facility establish and enforce appropriate programs to fulfill the provisions of Chapter 20.

Potential hazards can be controlled only when continually recognized and understood by all pertinent personnel.

The purpose of this chapter is to set forth minimum safeguards for the protection of patients or other subjects of, and personnel administering, hyperbaric therapy and experimental procedures. Its purpose is also to offer some guidance for rescue personnel who are not ordinarily involved in hyperbaric chamber operation, but who could become so involved in an emergency.

Requirements cited in 1.1.20 are minimum ones. Discretion on the part of chamber operators and others might dictate the establishment of more stringent regulations.

1.1.21 Chapter 21, Freestanding Birthing Centers, addresses the requirements for the safe use of electrical and gas equipment, and for electrical, gas, and vacuum systems used for the delivery and care of infants in freestanding birthing centers.

1.2 Purpose

1.2.1 The purpose of this standard is to provide minimum requirements for the performance, maintenance, testing, and safe practices for facilities, material, equipment, and appliances, including other hazards associated with the primary hazards.

1.3 Application

In NFPA 99 and most other standards, requirements are not intended to be applied retroactively. They apply only to new equipment and construction. Existing facilities should be considered individually. This is not meant, however, to authorize or condone clearly hazardous conditions (i.e., those presenting a distinct hazard to life). Minimum requirements for existing equipment and construction are specifically and clearly indicated in many instances in the document.

The intent of 1.3.3 is to indicate clearly how Chapter 4 through Chapter 12 are linked to Chapter 13 through Chapter 19 and Chapter 21.

1.3.1 This document shall apply to all health care facilities.

1.3.2 Construction and equipment requirements shall be applied only to new construction and new equipment, except as modified in individual chapters. Only the altered, renovated, or modernized portion of an existing system or individual component shall be required to meet the installation and equipment requirements stated in this standard. If the alteration, renovation, or modernization adversely impacts existing performance requirements of a system or component, additional upgrading shall be required.

1.3.3 Chapters 13 through 19 specify the conditions under which the requirements of Chapters 4 through 12 shall apply in Chapters 13 through 19.

1.3.4 This document is intended for use by those persons involved in the design, construction, inspection, and operation of health care facilities and in the design, manufacture, and testing of appliances and equipment used in patient care areas of health care facilities. Nonflammable piped medical gases covered by this document include, but are not limited to, oxygen, nitrogen, nitrous oxide, medical air, carbon dioxide, and helium.

As specified in 1.3.4, the required use of NFPA 99 will depend on whether the document is adopted for use, and who adopts the document for use, including governmental and nongovernmental agencies or companies.

1.4 Equivalency

1.4.1 The authority having jurisdiction for the enforcement of this document shall be permitted to grant exceptions to its requirements.

Although authorities having jurisdiction can adopt and enforce voluntary standards that they consider appropriate (e.g., adopt and enforce requirements as written; issue waivers to specific facilities not meeting certain requirements; adopt a document but change certain requirements), 1.4.1 is intended to apply to the entire standard as a reminder to authorities that they can grant exemptions.

1.4.2 Nothing in this standard is intended to prevent the use of systems, methods, or devices of equivalent or superior quality, strength, fire resistance, effectiveness, durability, and safety to those prescribed by this standard. Technical documentation shall be submitted to the authority having jurisdiction to demonstrate equivalency. The system, method, or device shall be approved for the intended purpose by the authority having jurisdiction.

Paragraph 1.4.2 adds the concept of equivalency to the previous permission of allowing enforcing authorities (governmental and nongovernmental) to grant exceptions to requirements. This wording on equivalency is almost verbatim from Section 1.4 of the 2003 edition of NFPA *101, Life Safety Code,* with some additional information provided [6]. The authority having jurisdiction determines whether a submitter's "equivalency" is indeed equivalent.

1.5 Units and Formulas

1.5.1* Primary units will be trade units, secondary will be the conversion. Although it is common practice for medical appliances to have metric units on their dials, gauges, and controls, many components of systems within the scope of this document, which are manufactured and used in the United States, employ nonmetric dimensions. Since these dimensions (such as nominal pipe sizes) are not established by the National Fire Protection Association, the Technical Correlating Committee on Health Care Facilities cannot independently change them. Accordingly, this document uses dimensions that are presently in common use by the building trades in the United States.

The primary measurement unit in NFPA 99 is metric; U.S. customary units (inch/pound) are included in parentheses.

A.1.5.1 Trade units vary from SI to U.S. customary units depending on the equipment devices or material.

1.6 Standard Adoption Requirements

1.6.1 The effective date of application of any provision of this document is not determined by the National Fire Protection Association. All questions related to applicability shall be directed to the authority having jurisdiction.

1.6.2 Enforcement

This standard shall be administered and enforced by the authority having jurisdiction designated by the governing authority. *(See Annex F for a sample wording for enabling legislation.)*

Subsections 1.6.1 and 1.6.2 give the authority having jurisdiction the material to adopt this document as a local ordinance or code.

REFERENCES CITED IN COMMENTARY

1. NFPA 45, *Standard on Fire Protection for Laboratories Using Chemicals,* 2004 edition.
2. NFPA 110, *Standard for Emergency and Standby Power Systems,* 2005 edition.
3. NFPA, *Manual of Style for NFPA Technical Committee Documents,* July 2004 edition.
4. NFPA 1600, *Standard on Disaster/Emergency Management and Business Continuity Programs*, 2004 edition.
5. NFPA 70, *National Electrical Code®*, 2005 edition.
6. NFPA *101®*, *Life Safety Code®*, 2006 edition.
7. *NFPA 72®*, *National Fire Alarm Code®*, 2002 edition.
8. NFPA 20, *Standard for the Installation of Stationary Pumps for Fire Protection,* 2003 edition.

CHAPTER 2

Referenced Publications

Chapter 2 lists the referenced documents from NFPA, as well as publications of the following organizations:

- American National Standards Institute (ANSI)
- American Society of Mechanical Engineers (ASME)
- American Society of Sanitary Engineering (ASSE)
- ASTM (formerly known as the American Society for Testing and Materials)
- American Welding Society (AWS)
- Copper Development Association (CDA)
- Compressed Gas Association (CGA)
- Electrotechnical Commission (IEC)
- Instrumentation, Systems, and Automation Society (ISA)
- Manufacturer's Standardization Society of the Valve and Fittings Industry (MSS)
- Underwriters Laboratories (UL)
- U.S. government

2.1 General

The documents or portions thereof listed in this chapter are referenced within this standard and shall be considered part of the requirements of this document.

2.2 NFPA Publications. National Fire Protection Association, 1 Batterymarch Park, Quincy, MA 02169-7471.

NFPA 10, *Standard for Portable Fire Extinguishers,* 2002 edition.
NFPA 13, *Standard for the Installation of Sprinkler Systems,* 2002 edition.
NFPA 30, *Flammable and Combustible Liquids Code,* 2003 edition.
NFPA 37, *Standard for the Installation and Use of Stationary Combustion Engines and Gas Turbines,* 2002 edition.
NFPA 45, *Standard on Fire Protection for Laboratories Using Chemicals,* 2004 edition.
NFPA 51, *Standard for the Design and Installation of Oxygen–Fuel Gas Systems for Welding, Cutting, and Allied Processes,* 2002 edition.
NFPA 54, *National Fuel Gas Code,* 2002 edition.
NFPA 55, *Standard for the Storage, Use, and Handling of Compressed Gases and Cryogenic Fluids in Portable and Stationary Containers, Cylinders, and Tanks,* 2005 edition.
NFPA 58, *Liquefied Petroleum Gas Code,* 2004 edition.
NFPA 70, *National Electrical Code®*, 2005 edition.
NFPA 72®, National Fire Alarm Code®, 2002 edition.
NFPA 99B, *Standard for Hypobaric Facilities,* 2005 edition.
NFPA *101®*, *Life Safety Code®*, 2003 edition.
NFPA 110, *Standard for Emergency and Standby Power Systems,* 2005 edition.

NFPA 111, *Standard on Stored Electrical Energy Emergency and Standby Power Systems,* 2005 edition.
NFPA 220, *Standard on Types of Building Construction,* 1999 edition.
NFPA 255, *Standard Method of Test of Surface Burning Characteristics of Building Materials,* 2000 edition.
NFPA 326, *Standard for the Safeguarding of Tanks and Containers for Entry, Cleaning, or Repair,* 2005 edition.
NFPA 701, *Standard Methods of Fire Tests for Flame Propagation of Textiles and Films,* 2004 edition.
NFPA 704, *Standard System for the Identification of the Hazards of Materials for Emergency Response,* 2001 edition.
NFPA 1600, *Standard on Disaster/Emergency Management and Business Continuity Programs,* 2004 edition.

2.3 Other Publications

2.3.1 ANSI Publication. American National Standards Institute, Inc., 22 West 43rd Street, 4th floor, New York, NY 10036.

ANSI C84.1, *Electric Power Systems and Equipment — Voltage Ratings,* 1995.
ANSI Z66.1, *Specifications for Paints and Coatings Accessible to Children to Minimize Dry Film Toxicity,* 1964.
ANSI/NEMA WD 6, *Wiring Devices — Dimensional Requirements,* 2002.

2.3.2 ASME Publications. American Society of Mechanical Engineers, Three Park Avenue, New York, NY 10016-5990.

ANSI/ASME PVHO-1-1990, *Safety Standard for Pressure Vessels for Human Occupancy.*
ASME *Boiler and Pressure Vessel Code,* Sections VIII and IX, 2001.
ASME B1.20.1, *Pipe Threads, General Purpose,* 2001.
ANSI/ASME B16.50, *Wrought Copper and Copper Alloy Braze-Joint Pressure Fittings,* 2001.
ASME B31.3, *Pressure Process Piping,* 2002.
ASME B40.100, *Pressure Gauges and Gauge Attachments,* 1998.
ASME B16.22, *Wrought Copper and Copper Alloy Solder-Joint Pressure Fittings,* 2001.

2.3.3 ASSE Publications. American Society of Sanitary Engineering, 28901 Clemens Road, Suite 100, Westlake, OH 44145.

ASSE 6010, *Professional Qualifications Standard for Medical Gas Systems Installers,* 2001.
ASSE 6030, *Professional Qualifications Standard for Medical Gas Systems Verifiers,* 2001.

2.3.4 ASTM Publications. American Society for Testing and Materials, 100 Barr Harbor Drive, West Conshohocken, PA 19428-2959.

ASTM A 53, *Standard Specification for Pipe, Steel, Black and Hot-Dipped, Zinc-Coated, Welded and Seamless,* 1994.
ASTM B 32, *Standard Specification for Solder Metal,* 1996.
ASTM B 88, *Standard Specification for Seamless Copper Water Tube,* 2002.
ASTM B 280, *Standard Specification for Seamless Copper Tubing for Air Conditioning and Refrigeration Field Service,* 2002.
ASTM B 819, *Standard Specification for Seamless Copper Tube for Medical Gas Systems,* 2000.
ASTM B 828, *Standard Practice for Making Capillary Joints by Soldering of Copper and Copper Alloy Tube and Fittings,* 2002.
ASTM D 5, *Standard Test Method for Penetration of Bituminous Materials,* 1997.

ASTM D 2855, *Standard Practice for Making Solvent-Cemented Joints with Poly(Vinyl Chloride) (PVC) Pipe and Fittings,* 1996 (2002).
ASTM D 2863, *Standard Test Method for Measuring the Minimum Oxygen Concentration to Support Candle-like Combustion of Plastics (Oxygen Index)* (ANSI D2863), 1997.
ASTM E 136, *Standard Test Method for Behavior of Materials in a Vertical Tube Furnace at 750°C,* 1998.

2.3.5 AWS Publications. American Welding Society, 550 N.W. LeJeune Road, Miami, FL 33126.

ANSI/AWS A5.8, *Specification for Filler Metals for Brazing and Braze Welding,* 1992.
AWS B2.2, *Standard for Brazing Procedure and Performance Qualification,* 1991.

2.3.6 CDA Publication. Copper Development Association Inc., 260 Madison Avenue, New York, NY 10016.

Copper Tube Handbook.

2.3.7 CGA Publications. Compressed Gas Association, 4221 Walney Road, 5th Floor, Chantilly, VA 20151-2923.

GCA C-7, *Guide to the Preparation of Precautionary Labeling and Marking of Compressed Gas Containers,* 2004.
CGA G-4, *Oxygen,* 1996.
CGA G-4.1, *Cleaning Equipment for Oxygen Service,* 2004.
CGA G-6.1, *Standard for Insulated Carbon Dioxide Systems at Consumer Sites,* 2002.
CGA G-6.5, *Standard for Small, Stationary Insulated Carbon Dioxide Supply Systems,* 2001.
CGA G-8.1, *Standard for Nitrous Oxide Systems at Consumer Sites,* 1990.
CGA M-1, *Guide for Medical Gas Installations at Consumer Sites,* 2003.
CGA O2-DIR, *Directory of Cleaning Agents for Oxygen Service,* Edition 4.
CGA P-2.5, *Transfilling of High Pressure Gaseous Oxygen to be Used for Respiration,* 2000.
CGA P-2.6, *Transfilling of Liquid Oxygen to be Used for Respiration,* 1995.
CGA P-2.7, *Guide for the Safe Storage, Handling, and Use of Portable Liquid Oxygen Systems in Healthcare Facilities,* 2000.
CGA V-1, *Compressed Gas Association Standard for Compressed Gas Cylinder Valve Outlet and Inlet Connections* (ANSI B57.1), 2003.
CGA V-5, *Diameter-Index Safety System (Noninterchangeable Low Pressure Connections for Medical Gas Applications),* 2000.
CGA V-6, *Standard Cryogenic Liquid Transfer Connection,* 2000.

2.3.8 IEC Publication. Electrotechnical Commission, 3 rue de Varembé, P.O. Box 131, CH-1211 Geneva 20, Switzerland.

IEC 60601-1-2, *Medical Electrical Equipment — Part 1–2: General Requirements for Safety — Collateral Standard: Electromagnetic Compatibility — Requirements and Tests,* 2004.

2.3.9 ISA Publications. The Instrumentation, Systems, and Automation Society (ISA), 67 Alexander Drive, Research Triangle Park, NC 27709.

ANSI/ISA S-7.0.01, *Quaility Standard for Instrument Air,* 1996.
RP 12.6, *Installation of Intrinsically Safe Systems in Hazardous Locations,* 1995.

2.3.10 MSS Publications. Manufacturer's Standardization Society of the Valve and Fittings Industry, Inc., 127 Park Street NE, Vienna, VA 22180.

SP-58, *Pipe Hangers and Supports — Materials, Design, and Manufacture,* 2002.
SP-69, *Pipe Hangers and Supports — Selection and Application,* 2002.

2.3.11 UL Publication. Underwriters Laboratories Inc., 333 Pfingsten Road, Northbrook, IL 60062-2096.

UL 94, *Test for Flammability of Plastic Materials for Parts in Devices and Appliances,* 2001.

2.3.12 U.S. Government Publications. Document Automation and Production Service (DAPS), Building 4D, 700 Robbins Avenue, Philadelphia, PA 19111-5094. www.dodssp.daps.mil

MIL-Standard 104C, *Limit for Electrical Insulation Color.*

U.S. Government Commercial Standard 223-59, *Casters, Wheels, and Glides for Hospital Equipment.*

CHAPTER 3

Definitions

Chapter 3 lists the definitions used in this standard. Each definition in Section 3.3, General, identifies the Technical Committee responsible for its use. For example, the Technical Committee on Gas Delivery Equipment (GAS) is responsible for the definition of *aerosol*. Technical Committees may make changes to or add new definitions as needed to address their chapters.

3.1 General

The definitions contained in this chapter shall apply to the terms used in this standard. Where terms are not defined in this chapter or within another chapter, they shall be defined using their ordinarily accepted meanings within the context in which they are used. *Merriam-Webster's Collegiate Dictionary*, 11th edition, shall be the source for the ordinarily accepted meaning.

3.2 NFPA Official Definitions

3.2.1* Approved. Acceptable to the authority having jurisdiction.

A.3.2.1 Approved. The National Fire Protection Association does not approve, inspect, or certify any installations, procedures, equipment, or materials; nor does it approve or evaluate testing laboratories. In determining the acceptability of installations, procedures, equipment, or materials, the authority having jurisdiction may base acceptance on compliance with NFPA or other appropriate standards. In the absence of such standards, said authority may require evidence of proper installation, procedure, or use. The authority having jurisdiction may also refer to the listings or labeling practices of an organization that is concerned with product evaluations and is thus in a position to determine compliance with appropriate standards for the current production of listed items.

3.2.2* Authority Having Jurisdiction (AHJ). An organization, office, or individual responsible for enforcing the requirements of a code or standard, or for approving equipment, materials, an installation, or a procedure.

A.3.2.2 Authority Having Jurisdiction (AHJ). The phrase "authority having jurisdiction," or its acronym AHJ, is used in NFPA documents in a broad manner, since jurisdictions and approval agencies vary, as do their responsibilities. Where public safety is primary, the authority having jurisdiction may be a federal, state, local, or other regional department or individual such as a fire chief; fire marshal; chief of a fire prevention bureau, labor department, or health department; building official; electrical inspector; or others having statutory authority. For insurance purposes, an insurance inspection department, rating bureau, or other

insurance company representative may be the authority having jurisdiction. In many circumstances, the property owner or his or her designated agent assumes the role of the authority having jurisdiction; at government installations, the commanding officer or departmental official may be the authority having jurisdiction.

As pointed out in A.3.2.2, a health care facility can be the enforcing authority. Such authority, however, is possible only in the absence of any governmental regulations. To be sure, a facility can enforce more stringent requirements than the government, but this authority might not always be successful.

For an interesting discussion on this aspect of authority and enforcement of codes and standards, see "Electricity, Safety and the Patient" [1].

3.2.3* Code. A standard that is an extensive compilation of provisions covering broad subject matter or that is suitable for adoption into law independently of other codes and standards.

A.3.2.3 Code. The decision to designate a standard as a "code" is based on such factors as the size and scope of the document, its intended use and form of adoption, and whether it contains substantial enforcement and administrative provisions.

3.2.4 Guide. A document that is advisory or informative in nature and that contains only nonmandatory provisions. A guide may contain mandatory statements such as when a guide can be used, but the document as a whole is not suitable for adoption into law.

3.2.5 Labeled. Equipment or materials to which has been attached a label, symbol, or other identifying mark of an organization that is acceptable to the authority having jurisdiction and concerned with product evaluation, that maintains periodic inspection of production of labeled equipment or materials, and by whose labeling the manufacturer indicates compliance with appropriate standards or performance in a specified manner.

3.2.6* Listed. Equipment, materials, or services included in a list published by an organization that is acceptable to the authority having jurisdiction and concerned with evaluation of products or services, that maintains periodic inspection of production of listed equipment or materials or periodic evaluation of services, and whose listing states that either the equipment, material, or service meets appropriate designated standards or has been tested and found suitable for a specified purpose.

A.3.2.6 Listed. The means for identifying listed equipment may vary for each organization concerned with product evaluation; some organizations do not recognize equipment as listed unless it is also labeled. The authority having jurisdiction should utilize the system employed by the listing organization to identify a listed product.

3.2.7 Shall. Indicates a mandatory requirement.

3.2.8 Should. Indicates a recommendation or that which is advised but not required.

3.2.9 Standard. A document, the main text of which contains only mandatory provisions using the word "shall" to indicate requirements and which is in a form generally suitable for mandatory reference by another standard or code or for adoption into law. Nonmandatory provisions shall be located in an appendix or annex, footnote, or fine-print note and are not to be considered a part of the requirements of a standard.

3.3 General Definitions

3.3.1 ACFM. Actual cubic feet per minute. (PIP)

The term *actual cubic feet per minute* (ACFM) in 3.3.1, as used in NFPA 99 for hyperbaric chambers, indicates the amount of air used for ventilation at the pressure and temperature used in the chamber. In contrast, the term *standard cubic feet per minute* (SCFM) is understood as air at atmospheric pressure at sea level. (See the commentary following 3.3.163, SCFM.)

3.3.2 Adiabatic Heating. The heating of a gas caused by its compression. (HYP)

In general thermodynamic terms, adiabatic heating refers to an energy exchange process in which there is no external gain or loss of heat energy. As used in this standard, it refers to the special case of the rapid compression of a gas in which the mechanical energy input serves to raise the temperature of the gas, as in a compressor. An example of adiabatic heating is the rise in temperature of the environment within a hyperbaric chamber during rapid compression.

3.3.3 Aerosol. An intimate mixture of a liquid or a solid in a gas; the liquid or solid, called the dispersed phase, is uniformly distributed in a finely divided state throughout the gas, which is the continuous phase or dispersing medium. (GAS)

Previous editions of the standard contained a definition of *air, oil-free, dry (air for testing)* immediately after the definition of *aerosol.* At one time, this type of air was used for pressure-testing purposes and could be confused with medical air (see *medical air*). The use of dry, oil-free air for testing nonflammable medical gas pipelines was eliminated in 1993, and only dry, oil-free nitrogen is to be used. Because such air was no longer permitted for testing purposes, the definition was deleted to avoid confusion on the part of the installer.

3.3.4 Alarm Systems.

NFPA 99 recognizes three distinct types of alarms in Level 1 and Level 2 medical gas systems: master alarms, area alarms, and local alarms. Level 3 alarms are distinctive and lack the divisions of function required of Level 1 and Level 2. The actual operation of all alarms is very similar, including an audible component that can be cancelled, a visual component that is continuous when the alarm is active, and a test function. Requirements are found in 5.1.9 for Level 1 alarms, 5.2.9 for Level 2 alarms, and in 5.3.9 for Level 3 alarms.

3.3.4.1 Area Alarm System. A warning system within an area of use that provides continuous visible and audible surveillance of Level 1 and Level 2 medical gas and vacuum systems. (PIP)

Area alarms are typically those located in treatment areas at or near the nurses' station. They monitor and report on conditions for the benefit of the staff in that area — hence the term *area alarm.* They are sometimes called *zone alarms,* but this usage is incorrect. See 5.1.9.3 for requirements for area alarms. Area alarms are commonly found on the control panel of air or vacuum equipment.

3.3.4.2 Level 3 Alarm System. A warning system within an area of use that provides continuous visible and audible surveillance of Level 3 medical gas systems. (PIP)

The definition of *Level 3 alarm system* refers to a specific type of alarm commonly used in a small office–based medical gas system, such as in a dental office. Level 3 alarms reflect the lower complexity of a Level 3 system and the facilities in which they are typically installed. Requirements for a Level 3 alarm system are found in 5.3.9.

3.3.4.3 Local Alarm System. A warning system that provides continuous visible and audible surveillance of medical gas and vacuum system source equipment at the equipment site. (PIP)

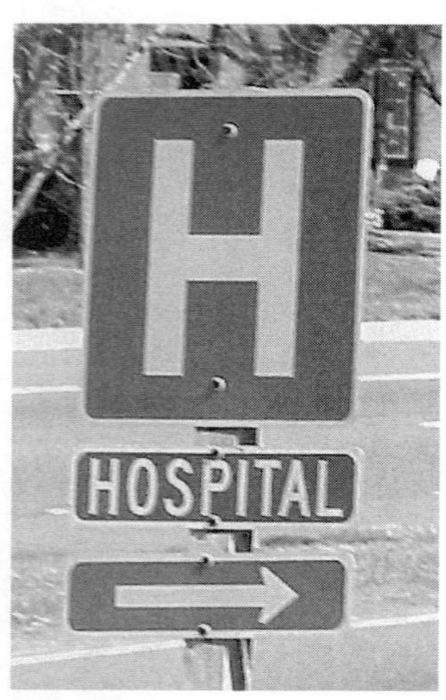

EXHIBIT 3.1 A hospital facility, one of the many kinds of health care facilities defined in Chapter 3. (Courtesy of Rob Swift and Prince William Hospital)

Local alarms are placed on or very near the source equipment they monitor and are "local" to that equipment — hence the term *local alarms.* They are sometimes referred to as "source alarms," which is perhaps more descriptive but can be confusing. See 5.1.9.5 for requirements for local alarms.

3.3.4.4 Master Alarm System. A warning system that monitors the operation and condition of the source of supply, the reserve source (if any), and the pressure in the main lines of each medical gas and vacuum piping system. (PIP)

The definitions of *area, local,* and *master alarms* have been included because the terms frequently have been misinterpreted in the past. The master alarm is the alarm used to indicate the condition of the sources of supply (which may be remote) at locations that are attended whenever the building is occupied and where the staff who can act to correct any failures will see them. In practice, these are also occasionally called *source alarms,* but the term *master alarm* is more conventional and is used in NFPA 99. See 5.1.9.2 for requirements and typical applications for this alarm type.

3.3.5 Alternate Power Source. One or more generator sets, or battery systems where permitted, intended to provide power during the interruption of the normal electrical service; or the public utility electrical service intended to provide power during interruption of service normally provided by the generating facilities on the premises. (ELS)

3.3.6 Ambulatory Health Care Center. A building or portion thereof used to provide services or treatment simultaneously to four or more patients that (1) provides, on an outpatient basis, treatment for patients that renders the patients incapable of taking action for self-preservation under emergency conditions without the assistance of others; or (2) provides, on an outpatient basis, anesthesia that renders the patients incapable of taking action for self-preservation under emergency conditions without the assistance of others. (ADM)

The definition in 3.3.6 correlates with NFPA *101®*, *Life Safety Code®* [2]. This term and other health care related terms used in both documents reflect the appropriate level of risk of each. (See Exhibit 3.1.)

The specific requirements for ambulatory health care centers are located in Chapter 14, Other Health Care Facilities.

3.3.7 Ampacity. The current, in amperes, that a conductor can carry continuously under the conditions of use without exceeding its temperature rating. (ELS)

3.3.8 Anesthetic. As used in this standard, applies to any inhalation agent used to produce relative analgesia or general anesthesia. (GAS)

Note the reference to inhalation as part of the definition of *anesthetic.*

3.3.9* Anesthetizing Location. Any area of a facility that has been designated to be used for the administration of nonflammable inhalation anesthetic agents in the course of examination or treatment, including the use of such agents for relative analgesia. *(See also 3.3.158, Relative Analgesia.)* (GAS)

A.3.3.9 Anesthetizing Location. For guidance on flammable anesthetizing locations, see Annex E.

This term is defined in a way to avoid the prior interpretation that a health care facility is considered an *anesthetizing location.* The key word is "designated." The administrative body must designate an area as an anesthetizing location before the requirements of 13.4.1 are applicable.

It is necessary for a facility to designate certain areas as anesthetizing locations so that it is clear to all which requirements are applicable to those particular locations within the facility. Regular administration of inhalation anesthetics in a location not administratively designated for such practice could have serious consequences.

This definition refers to areas where general anesthesia (i.e., inhalation anesthetics) is administered, not to areas where only local anesthetics are administered.

Recommendations for anesthetizing locations that use flammable inhalation anesthetics are located in Annex E, Flammable Anesthetizing Locations. Flammable inhalation anesthetics are rarely used in the United States. Precautions need to be taken if flammable anesthetics are ever reintroduced into the surgical operating arena in the United States.

3.3.10 Anoxia. A state of markedly inadequate oxygenation of the tissues and blood, of more marked degree than hypoxia. (HYP)

3.3.11 Appliance. Utilization equipment, generally other than industrial, normally built in standardized sizes or types, that is installed or connected as a unit to perform one or more functions. (ELE)

The definition of *appliance* used in this document agrees with that listed in NFPA 70, *National Electrical Code®* [3]. This definition encompasses many kinds of electrical end-use devices, from cord-connected devices such as a monitor to hard-wired devices such as a whirlpool bath or an X-ray machine. Larger physical plant equipment, such as pumps, air conditioners, and elevators, are generally not included.

How the device is used must be considered in determining the applicability of the provisions of this standard. Note that the Food and Drug Administration uses the term *device* as the generic term, but that term encompasses many other items, such as lenses and mercury thermometers, that have no electrical elements.

3.3.12* Applicator. A means of applying high-frequency energy to a patient other than by an electrically conductive connection. (ELE)

A.3.3.12 Applicator. In the given sense, an applicator is not an electrode because it does not use a conductive connection to the patient in order to function. A radio frequency "horn" of a diathermy machine is a typical applicator.

Other types of applicators might use electric or magnetic fields, such as coils, for inductive heating or power transfer, or capacitors for dielectric heating. High-frequency ultrasonic waves are also used for therapeutic heating, although they are not electromagnetic radiation.

3.3.13 Area of Administration. Any point within a room within 4.3 m (15 ft) of oxygen equipment or an enclosure containing or intended to contain an oxygen-enriched atmosphere. (GAS)

3.3.14* Atmosphere. The pressure exerted by, and gaseous composition of, an environment. (HYP)

A.3.3.14 Atmosphere. As employed in this standard, *atmosphere* can refer to the environment within or outside of a hyperbaric facility. When used as a measure of pressure, atmosphere is expressed as a fraction of standard air pressure [101.4 kPa (14.7 psi)]. *(See Column 1 of the Pressure Table in Annex D of NFPA 99B.)*

The term *atmosphere* has two distinct meanings. Its general meaning is the space occupied by gases surrounding a particular region, usually air at a particular pressure and temperature. The term also has a technical meaning, that of a unit of pressure, that is used extensively in Chapter 20, Hyperbaric Facilities. The context of the requirement determines which meaning is pertinent.

3.3.14.1 Ambient Atmosphere. The pressure and composition of the environment surrounding a chamber. (HYP)

It is important to be precise in describing the various atmospheres associated with hyperbaric operation (i.e., ambient and chamber). The term *composition* replaced *concentration* because composition includes concentration and is more technically correct in describing the atmosphere surrounding the chamber.

3.3.14.2 Atmosphere Absolute (ATA). The pressure of the earth's atmosphere, 760.0 mm Hg, 101.325 kPa, or 14.7 psia. Two ATA = two atmospheres. *(See also 3.3.14, Atmosphere.)* (HYP)

Understanding the concept of atmospheres absolute (ATA) is important in hyperbaric chamber operations. An atmosphere of pressure is equal to 33 ft of seawater (FSW), 101.4 kilo-Pascals (kPa) or 14.7 pounds per square inch (psi). Although a chamber can be pressurized to an internal pressure of two atmospheres (66 FSW or 202.8 kPa, or 29.4 psi), a person exposed to that pressure environment responds physiologically to a pressure equivalent of three ATA. Normal atmospheric pressure of one atmosphere or 101.4 kPa (14.7 psi) must be taken into account and added to the actual chamber atmosphere.

3.3.14.3* Atmosphere of Increased Burning Rate. Any atmosphere containing a percentage of oxygen or oxygen and nitrous oxide greater than the quotient of 23.45 divided by the square root of the total pressure in atmospheres. (HYP)

A.3.3.14.3 Atmosphere of Increased Burning Rate. The degree of fire hazard of an oxygen-enriched atmosphere varies with the concentration of oxygen and diluent gas and the total pressure. The definition contained in the current edition of NFPA 53, *Recommended Practice on Materials, Equipment, and Systems Used in Oxygen-Enriched Atmospheres* and in editions of NFPA 56D, *Standard for Hyperbaric Facilities*, prior to 1982, did not necessarily reflect the increased fire hazard of hyperbaric and hypobaric atmospheres.

The definition of atmosphere of increased burning rate used in Chapter 20 and in NFPA 99B, *Standard for Hypobaric Facilities*, defines an oxygen-enriched atmosphere with an increased fire hazard, as it relates to the increased burning rate of material in the atmosphere. It is based on a 1.2 cm/sec (0.47 in./sec) burning rate (at 23.5 percent oxygen at 1 atmosphere absolute) as described in Figure A.3.3.14.3.

This rate can be determined as follows:

$$\frac{23.45}{\sqrt{TP_{atmos}}}$$

where:

TP_{atmos} = total pressure in atmospheres

The definition of *atmosphere of increased burning rate* accounts for the special atmospheres now in use by military, nonmilitary, and private sector operators of hyperbaric and hypobaric chambers. It is based on actual test data under hyperbaric and hypobaric conditions.

The definition was added to more correctly reflect adherence of oxygen concentrations at levels below 23.5 percent. Virtually all modern hyperbaric chamber operations routinely monitor interior chamber oxygen levels and increase chamber ventilation rates as levels approach 23.5 percent. If oxygen levels cannot be maintained below this maximum, all hyperbaric chamber operations should be terminated. The current definition of *increased burning rates* reflects the fact that if a fire should occur, the rate of burning will be faster due to the increased partial pressure of oxygen found in a hyperbaric environment.

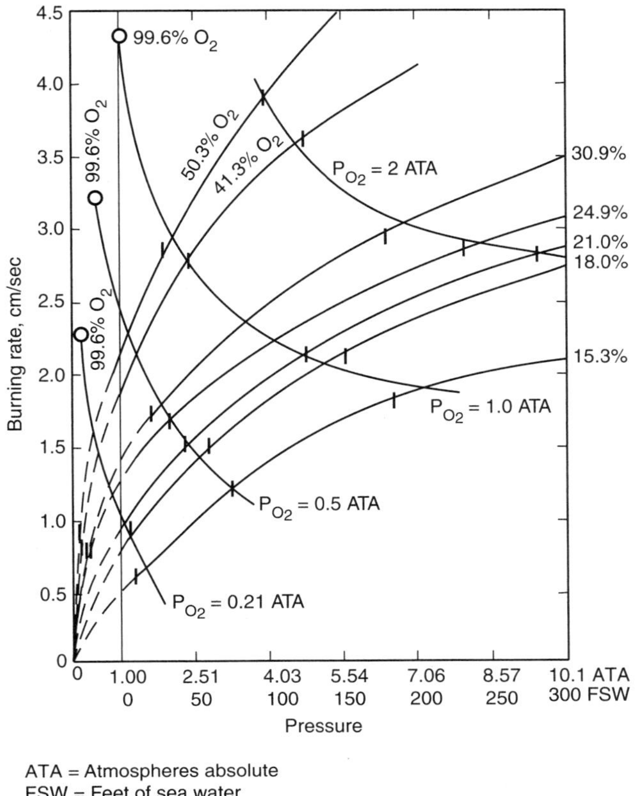

Figure A.3.3.14.3 *Burning Rates of Filter Paper Strips at an Angle of 45 Degrees in N_2–O_2 Mixtures. (Adapted from Figure 4 of "Technical Memorandum UCRI-720, Chamber Fire Safety.")*

3.3.14.4 Chamber Atmosphere. The environment inside a chamber. (HYP)

3.3.15 Automatic. Providing a function without the necessity of human intervention. (ELS)

3.3.16* Bends. Decompression sickness; caisson worker's disease. (HYP)

A.3.3.16 Bends. See C.20.1.3.4.2.

The term *bends* is commonly used to describe decompression sickness. Decompression sickness, a complex phenomenon that presents a variety of symptoms, depending on the severity of the case, has two general classifications: Type I (Mild) — pain only (usually associated with joint pain and skin manifestations); and Type II (Severe) — cerebral, spinal cord, vestibular, or cardiopulmonary injury. Although decompression sickness is usually associated with diving or hyperbaric operations, it is also possible to experience the bends from unprotected exposure to altitudes in excess of 5486 m (18,000 ft). (See the commentary following 3.3.31, *Decompression Sickness,* for additional information.)

3.3.17 Branch Circuit. The circuit conductors between the final overcurrent device protecting the circuit and the outlet(s). [**70,** 2005](ELS)

The definition of *branch circuit* conforms to that in NFPA 70 [3]. It refers to the wiring and does not include the overcurrent device or the outlet.

3.3.18 Branch Line. See 3.3.145, Piping.

3.3.19 Bulk System. An assembly of equipment, such as storage containers, pressure regulators, pressure relief devices, vaporizers, manifolds, and interconnecting piping, that terminates at the source valve of oxygen or 1452 kg (3200 lb) of nitrous oxide including unconnected reserves on the site. (PIP)

The term *bulk system* is derived from historic usage. The term itself is a poor description of what the system typically is and does. More descriptive (if equally bizarre sounding) is the U.K. term "V.I.E." for vacuum insulated evaporator. In essence, the bulk system as the term is used in the United States is a system of vessels and heat exchangers for storing gas in large quantities. This gas has typically been converted into a cryogenic liquid and is transported and stored in this extremely cold, liquid state. The V.I.E. or bulk system acts to gasify the liquid under controlled conditions and to deliver that gas to the facility.

However, note that NFPA 99's definition does not limit a bulk system to one that contains cryogenic liquid, but instead encompasses any system above a given total capacity. Although it is unlikely that a facility would attempt to keep this much gas in cylinders simply because of the acreage required to store it, NFPA 99 expects any system of this capacity — whether cylinder or liquid — to be treated according to the rules for a bulk system.

3.3.19.1 Bulk Nitrous Oxide System. An assembly of equipment as described in the definition of bulk oxygen system that has a storage capacity of more than 3200 lb (1452 kg) [approximately 28,000 ft^3 (793 m^3) (at normal temperature and pressure)] of nitrous oxide. (PIP)

3.3.19.2* Bulk Oxygen System. An assembly of equipment such as oxygen storage containers, pressure regulators, pressure relief devices, vaporizers, manifolds, and interconnecting piping that has a storage capacity of more than 566 m^3 (20,000 ft^3) of oxygen (at normal temperature and pressure) including unconnected reserves on hand at the site. (PIP)

A.3.3.19.2 Bulk Oxygen System. The oxygen containers can be stationary or movable, and the oxygen can be stored as gas or liquid. The bulk oxygen system terminates at the point where oxygen at service pressure first enters the supply line.

3.3.20 Cold Room. A refrigerated area large enough for personnel to enter. (LAB)

3.3.21 Combustible. Capable of undergoing combustion. (GAS)

3.3.22* Combustible Liquid. A liquid having a flash point at or above 37.8°C (100°F). Combustible liquids shall be subdivided as follows: (a) Class II liquids shall include those having flash points at or above 37.8°C (100°F) and below 60°C (140°F); (b) Class IIIA liquids shall include those having flash points at or above 60°C (140°F) and below 93°C (200°F); (c) Class IIIB liquids shall include those having flash points at or above 93°C (200°F). (LAB)

A.3.3.22 Combustible Liquid. See NFPA 30, *Flammable and Combustible Liquids Code*, for further information on flash point test procedures.

This definition uses the NFPA 30, *Flammable and Combustible Liquids Code* [4], criteria to describe flammable and combustible liquids.

3.3.23* Combustion. A chemical process (such as oxidation) accompanied by the rapid evolution of heat and light. (GAS)

A.3.3.23 Combustion. Combustion is not limited to a chemical reaction always involving oxygen. Certain metals, such as calcium and aluminum, will burn in nitrogen; nitrous oxide will support the combustion of phosphorus and carbon; and so on. However, this document deals with the more common process of fuels burning in air.

Exhibit 3.2 shows three zones of chemical reaction in oxygen/nitrogen mixture (similar to air). Around the 6 percent mark, oxygen paper strips will not burn due to lack of oxygen in the chemical reaction.

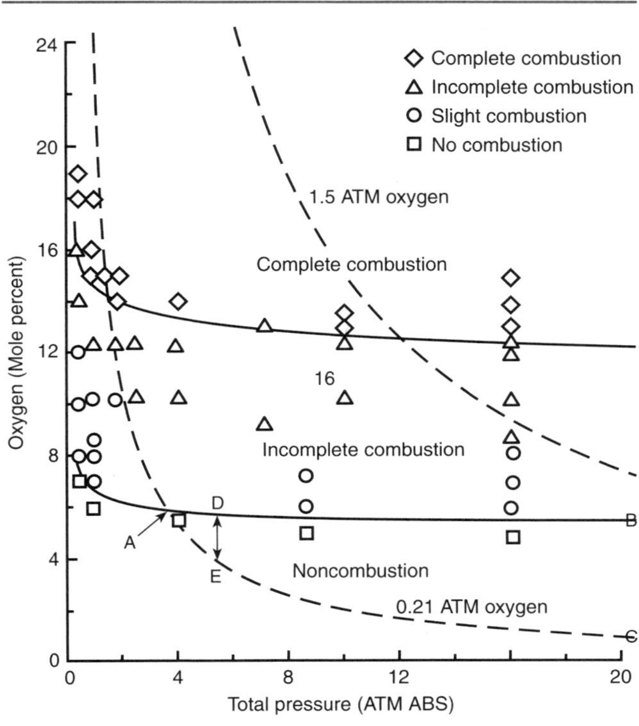

EXHIBIT 3.2 Three combustion zones for vertical paper strips in N_2–0_2 mixtures. (Courtesy of Technical Memorandum UCRI-721, Chamber Fire Safety [5])

3.3.24 Combustion Products. The gases, volatilized liquids and solids, particulate matter, and ash generated by combustion. (GAS)

Combustion products are also referred to as products of combustion in other NFPA documents. See B.4.2 for a discussion of the toxicological hazards of combustion products that result from materials subjected to fire. With the increased use of synthetic and plastic materials, the need for protection against the associated hazards grows. See also Chapters 2-6 and 2-13 in *The SFPE Handbook of Fire Protection Engineering* [6] and Chapters 8-1 and 8-2 in the *Fire Protection Handbook* [7].

3.3.25 Container. A low-pressure, vacuum-insulated vessel containing gases in liquid form. (GAS)

The term *container* is used in Chapter 9 to refer specifically to oxygen containers and is now widely accepted for this type of application. The term *cylinder* is reserved for high-pressure application.

3.3.26 Critical Branch. A subsystem of the emergency system consisting of feeders and branch circuits supplying energy to task illumination, special power circuits, and selected receptacles serving areas and functions related to patient care and that are connected to alternate power sources by one or more transfer switches during interruption of normal power source. (ELS)

A high degree of selectivity should be used when choosing loads to be connected to the critical branch, because this branch provides electric power to areas and equipment involved in the most critical patient care functions.

3.3.27 Critical Care Area. See 3.3.138, Patient Care Area.

3.3.28 Critical Equipment. That equipment essential to the safety of the occupants of the facility. (HYP)

3.3.29 Critical System. A system of feeders and branch circuits in nursing homes and custodial care facilities arranged for connection to the alternate power source to restore service to certain critical receptacles, task illumination, and equipment. (ELS)

The term *critical system* is used primarily in long-term facilities where life support systems are not normally used (see 4.5.2 on Type 2 essential electrical system distribution requirements). The critical system picks up those loads that allow the institution to maintain operational continuity.

3.3.30 Cylinder. A supply tank containing high-pressure gases or gas mixtures at pressures that can be in excess of 2000 psi gauge (13.8 kPa gauge). (GAS)

See the commentary following 3.3.25, *Container.*

3.3.31 Decompression Sickness. A syndrome due to evolved gas in the tissues resulting from a reduction in ambient pressure. (HYP)

Decompression sickness is a condition that develops when a person experiences a rapid reduction of pressure in his or her surrounding environment. For example, a scuba diver who ascends too rapidly from depth, without giving the body sufficient time to off-gas additional amounts of nitrogen that have saturated the body's tissues, will develop decompression sickness. This condition results from the elevated partial pressure of nitrogen in the breathing medium.

This evolution of inert gas produces a varying degree of symptoms based on the severity of the formation of inert gas "bubbles" in the bloodstream or tissues and their location in the body. Once bubbles have formed at depth, they respond to Boyle's law and increase in volume as the surrounding pressure is reduced.

This condition is also possible from exposure to altitudes in excess of 5486 m (18,000 ft). As an example, the occupants of an aircraft flying at an altitude of 10,668 m (35,000 ft) that suddenly loses cabin pressurization would be rapidly exposed to an altitude above 5486 m (18,000 ft) and their risk of developing decompression sickness would be increased. (See the commentary following 3.3.16, *Bends,* for additional information.)

3.3.32 Detonation. An exothermic reaction wherein the reaction propagates through the unreacted material at a rate exceeding the velocity of sound, hence the explosive noise. (GAS)

3.3.33* Direct Electrical Pathway to the Heart. An externalized conductive pathway, insulated except at its ends, one end of which is in direct contact with heart muscle while the other is outside the body and is accessible for inadvertent or intentional contact with grounded objects or energized, ground-referenced sources. (ELE)

A.3.3.33 Direct Electrical Pathway to the Heart. Electrodes, such as those used for pacing the heart, and catheters filled with conductive fluids, are examples of direct electrical pathways to the heart.

The conductive pathway can approach the heart by way of a venous or arterial catheter or by insertion through the chest wall.

3.3.34* Disaster. Within the context of this document, a disaster is defined as any unusual occurrence or unforeseen situation that seriously overtaxes or threatens to seriously overtax the routine capabilities of a health care facility. (HCE)

A.3.3.34 Disaster. A disaster can be either an event that causes or threatens to cause physical damage and injury to facility personnel or patients within the facility, or an event that requires expansion of facilities to receive and care for a large number of casualties resulting from a disaster that produces no damage or injury to the health care facility and staff, or a combination thereof.

Such a situation creates the need for emergency expansion of facilities, as well as operation of this expanded facility in an unfamiliar environment. Under this definition, the recognition of a disaster situation will vary greatly from one facility to another and from time to time in any given facility. Such recognition and concomitant activation of the Health Care Emergency Preparedness Plan is dependent on mutual aid agreements, facility type, geographic location, bed capacity, bed occupancy at a given time, staff size, staff experience with disaster situations, and other factors. For example, the routine workload of the emergency department of a large metropolitan general hospital would constitute a disaster, requiring activation of the Health Care Emergency Preparedness Plan, were this same workload to be suddenly applied to a small community hospital.

Disasters have a variety of causes, all of which should be considered for effective emergency preparedness planning. Among the most common are natural disasters such as earthquakes, hurricanes, tornadoes, and floods; mass food poisoning; industrial accidents involving explosion or environmental release of toxic chemicals; transportation accidents involving crashes of trains, planes, or automobiles with resulting mass casualties; civil disturbances; building fires; extensive or prolonged utility failure; collapse of buildings or other occupied structures; and toxic smogs in urban areas. Arson attempts and bomb threats have been made on health care facilities and should therefore be considered. Potential admission to the facility of high profile persons should be addressed. Although the last does not involve mass casualties or the potential of mass casualties, the degree of disruption of normal routine will be sufficient to qualify it as a disasterlike situation.

Disaster plans should reflect a facility's location from internal and external disasters. As an example, areas subject to frequent wildland fires should invoke countermeasures for smoke management and air quality maintenance.

Disasters, as noted, can come in many forms that vary in intensity and affect health care facilities differently. A disaster can be an event that occurs within the facility and threatens patients or personnel, such as a fire or power outage. Utility failures, geological events, and incidents involving mass casualties are examples of disasters that occur externally but that can also affect the health care facility. Terrorism is another form of external disaster that can place demands on a health care facility. Although facilities themselves are generally not targeted, they are expected to provide medical attention and other services when other facilities are attacked.

Thus, a *health care facility disaster* is any event that creates a volume of victims who will require a facility to institute special procedures and resources, such as altering staffing patterns and health care service. Additional information and communications systems will need to be instituted, and the overall activities of the facility will need to be adjusted to the demands of providing services to a high volume of injured victims.

Generically, a disaster is any situation that overwhelms or threatens the normal operational mode of an agency, complex, or system, including political subdivisions and their various arms.

Administratively, the President of the United States can declare the existence of a "disaster" in any affected locality after (1) the event has occurred, (2) the governor of the affected state has requested the declaration, and (3) the Federal Emergency Management Agency (FEMA) has made an evaluation that supports the request. This sequence is legally required before a presidential declaration is allowed. However, in response to the enormous destruction and lengthy interruptions caused by Hurricane Andrew, the federal government has accelerated and simplified these procedures and continues to look at other ways to further streamline the process.

3.3.35 D.I.S.S. Connector. A system of noninterchangeable medical gas and vacuum connectors complying with CGA V-5, *Diameter-Index Safety System (Noninterchangeable Low Pressure Connections for Medical Gas Applications).* (PIP)

CGA V-5, *Diameter-Index Safety System (Noninterchangeable Low Pressure Connections for Medical Gas Applications,* also known as the V-5 D.I.S.S. standard [8] is an internationally accepted standard for noninterchangeable, threaded, gas-specific connections, such as the one shown in Exhibit 3.3. It is limited to applications under 1380 kPa (200 psi) (see also 9.3.4). The higher-pressure applications use a Pin-Index Safety System (see 9.3.3 and A.9.5.1.2).

EXHIBIT 3.3 D.I.S.S. connector.

3.3.36* Double-Insulated Appliances. Appliances where the primary means of protection against electrical shock is not grounding. The primary means is by the use of combinations of insulation and separation spacings in accordance with an approved standard. (ELE)

A.3.3.36 Double-Insulated Appliances. Double-insulated appliances can be identified by a symbol consisting of a square within a square, or wording such as "double-insulated" marked on the appliance. Appliance packaging and documents may also provide identification. Although double-insulated appliances do not require a third wire or pin, some double-insulated appliances have a third conductor or pin solely for purposes of electro-magnetic compatibility (EMC).

Appliances that have grounding as the primary means of protection also use insulation and spacing as functional insulation. Double-insulation requires supplemental insulation as appropriately specified by testing laboratories. This supplemental insulation can become complex when there are such items as controls, connectors, and motor shafts that penetrate to the interior of the device. CAUTION: A simple coat of epoxy paint does not constitute supplementary insulation.

3.3.37 Electrical Life Support Equipment. Electrically powered equipment whose continuous operation is necessary to maintain a patient's life. (ELS)

How the term *electrical life support equipment* is defined and used in NFPA 99 is intended to ensure that electrical equipment requiring continuous electrical power for patient care will be operational if normal electric power is interrupted. (See 13.3.4, 14.3.4, etc.)

In some instances, the location of some equipment can have a bearing on whether it fits this term and definition. For example, a dialysis machine in a hospital would fall within the definition of this term, whereas one in an outpatient clinic probably would not.

3.3.38 Electrode. An electrically conductive connection to a patient. (ELE)

In the purest sense, an electrode is the terminal where electrical energy is transferred from a device to the patient or vice versa. However, the terminal must be connected by a cable or wire for the transfer to take place.

3.3.38.1 Active Electrode. An electrode intended to generate a surgical or physiological effect at its point of application to the patient. (ELE)

3.3.38.2 Bipolar Electrode. An electrode consisting of adjacent contacts (e.g., the two legs of a forceps) such that the current passes between the pair of contacts generating the intended effect. (ELE)

3.3.38.3* Dispersive Electrode. An electrode, intended to complete the electrical path between patient and appliance and at which no surgical effect is intended. (ELE)

A.3.3.38.3 Dispersive Electrode. This electrode is often called the grounding electrode, the "indifferent electrode," the "return electrode," the "patient ground plate," or the "neutral electrode."

This term *dispersive electrode* is used in electrosurgery. It is often called the "indifferent electrode," the "return electrode," the "patient plate," or the "neutral electrode." The term used by the International Electrotechnical Commission is *neutral electrode,* although the term is not intended to imply that it is related to the neutral conductor of the power supply system. The term is not used extensively in the United States because of this possible confusion.

3.3.39 Emergency Management. The act of developing procedures and plans to create effective preparedness, mitigation, response, and recovery during a disaster affecting a health care facility. (HCE)

Emergency management is a total program of responding to disasters. The term *emergency preparedness* was used in older editions but was not defined; *emergency management* is a more comprehensive term.

3.3.40 Emergency Oxygen Supply Connection. An assembly of equipment which permits a gas supplier to make a temporary connection to supply oxygen to a building which has had its normal source of oxygen disconnected. (PIP)

3.3.41 Emergency System. A system of circuits and equipment intended to supply alternate power to a limited number of prescribed functions vital to the protection of life and safety. (ELS)

3.3.42 Equipment Grounding Bus. A grounding terminal bus in the feeder circuit of the branch circuit distribution panel that serves a particular area. (ELE)

The equipment grounding bus is intended to provide a common connection point for all the equipment grounding conductors in a given patient area. One equipment grounding bus might serve several patient locations fed from the same branch-circuit distribution panel. It is not intended that an additional grounding bus be installed if an appropriate bus is already present.

3.3.43 Equipment System. A system of feeders and branch circuits arranged for delayed, automatic, or manual connection the alternate power source and that serves primarily 3-phase power equipment. (ELS)

Often, the equipment system serves heavy equipment that is 3-phase powered, such as pumps and fans. This type of equipment is necessary for the operation of the facility, but a brief interruption in service can be tolerated without serious consequences. Rapid transfer of these heavy loads to the alternate power source could cause large surges and further disrupt the system.

3.3.44 Essential Electrical System. A system comprised of alternate sources of power and all connected distribution systems and ancillary equipment, designed to ensure continuity of electrical power to designated areas and functions of a health care facility during disruption of normal power sources, and also to minimize disruption within the internal wiring system. (ELS)

3.3.45 Evacuation — Waste Gas. See 3.3.184, Waste Anesthetic Gas Disposal.

Evacuation is a term still often used in practice for what is now officially waste anesthetic gas disposal or WAGD. Although the term *WAGD* is clumsy and almost comical, the term *evacuation* has too many other medical meanings and is uncomfortably close in connotation to the term *suction.* See 3.3.184, *Waste Anesthetic Gas Disposal.*

3.3.46 Exposed Conductive Surfaces. Those surfaces that are capable of carrying electric current and that are unprotected, uninsulated, unenclosed, or unguarded, permitting personal contact. (ELE)

Such a current may be a leakage current or an unintended current resulting from a fault.

3.3.47* Failure. An incident that increases the hazard to personnel or patients or that affects the safe functioning of electric appliances or devices. (ELE)

A.3.3.47 Failure. Failure includes failure of a component, loss of normal protective paths such as grounding, and short circuits or faults between energized conductors and the chassis.

3.3.48 Fault Current. A current in an accidental connection between an energized and a grounded or other conductive element resulting from a failure of insulation, spacing, or containment of conductors. (ELS)

3.3.49 Feeder. All circuit conductors between the service equipment, the source of a separately derived system, or other power supply source and the final branch-circuit overcurrent device. (ELS)

3.3.50* Flame Resistant. The property of a material that passes the small-scale test in NFPA 701, *Standard Methods of Fire Tests for Flame Propagation of Textiles and Films.* (HYP)

A.3.3.50 Flame Resistant. A source of ignition alternate to the gas burner specified in NFPA 701, *Standard Methods of Fire Tests for Flame Propagation of Textiles and Films,* could be required for this test if it is to be performed in 100 percent oxygen at several atmospheres pressure.

This criterion applies to finishes and materials within hyperbaric and hypobaric chambers that must be flame resistant. For criteria concerning interior finishes, see 20.2.2.5.2. The supplementary annex information is intended to ensure compatibility of results for hyperbaric conditions.

3.3.51* Flammable. A combustible that is capable of easily being ignited and rapidly consumed by fire. (LAB)

A.3.3.51 Flammable. Flammables may be solids, liquids, or gases exhibiting these qualities. Many substances nonflammable in air become flammable if the oxygen content of the gaseous medium is increased above 0.235 ATA.

This definition in 3.3.51 expands on the definition of flammable that is based on a normal atmosphere and includes information peculiar to hyperbaric operation. See the commentary following 3.3.133, *Oxygen-Enriched Atmosphere,* for an explanation of how the value of 0.235 came to be used. See also 3.3.126, *Nonflammable.*

3.3.52 Flammable Gas. Any substance that exists in the gaseous state at normal atmospheric temperature and pressure and is capable of being ignited and burned when mixed with proper proportion of air, oxygen, or other oxidizers. (HYP)

The definition of *flammable gas* is from NFPA 326, *Standard for the Safeguarding of Tanks and Containers for Entry, Cleaning, or Repair* [9], because this definition has the broadest applicability of the four currently used in NFPA documents.

3.3.53 Flammable Liquid. A liquid that has a closed-cup flash point that is below 37.8°C (100°F) and a maximum vapor pressure of 2068 mm Hg (40 psi absolute) at 37.8°C (100°F). (LAB)

The definition in 3.3.53 is from NFPA 30, *Flammable and Combustible Liquids Code* [4].

3.3.54* Flash Point. The minimum temperature at which a liquid gives off vapor in sufficient concentration to form an ignitable mixture with air near the surface of the liquid within the vessel, as specified by appropriate test procedures and apparatus. (LAB)

A.3.3.54 Flash Point. See C.11.2.2.

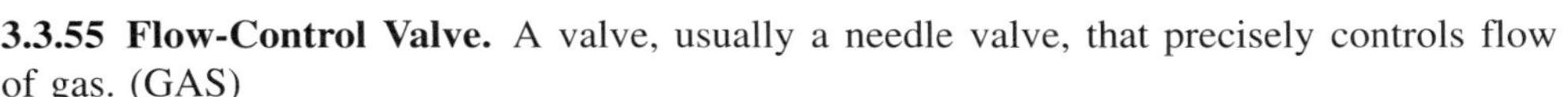

3.3.55 Flow-Control Valve. A valve, usually a needle valve, that precisely controls flow of gas. (GAS)

3.3.56 Flowmeter. A device for measuring volumetric flow rates of gases and liquids. (GAS)

It should be noted that some flowmeters, such as the one shown in Exhibit 3.4, can indicate the mean flow rates, in addition to the volumetric flow rate, of a substance being measured.

3.3.56.1 Pressure Compensated Flowmeter. A flowmeter indicating accurate flow of gas whether the gas is discharged into ambient pressure or into a system at nonambient pressure. (GAS)

3.3.57 Freestanding Birthing Center. A facility in which low-risk births are expected following normal, uncomplicated pregnancies, and in which professional midwifery care is provided to women during pregnancy, birth, and postpartum. (ADM)

3.3.58* Frequency. The number of oscillations, per unit time, of a particular current or voltage waveform. The unit of frequency is the hertz. (ELE)

A.3.3.58 Frequency. Formerly the unit of frequency was cycles per second, a terminology no longer preferred. The waveform can consist of components having many different frequencies, in which case it is called a complex or nonsinusoidal waveform.

3.3.59* Fume Hood. An enclosure designed to draw air inward by means of mechanical ventilation. (LAB)

A.3.3.59 Fume Hood. Laboratory fume hoods prevent toxic, flammable, or noxious vapors from entering the laboratory, present a physical barrier from chemical reactions, and serve to contain accidental spills.

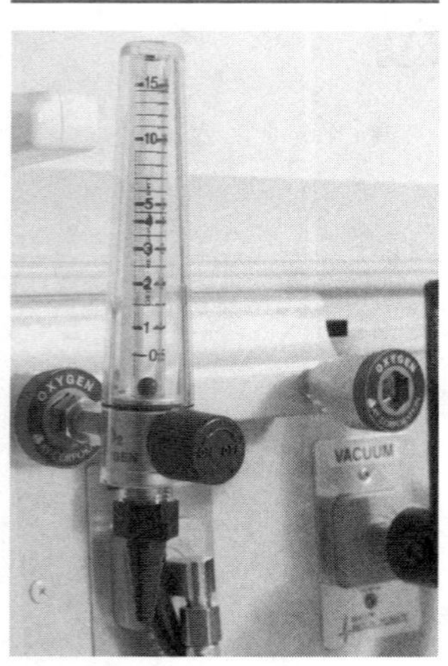

EXHIBIT 3.4 Flowmeter.

This definition does not include canopy hoods or recirculation laminar-flow biological-safety cabinets that are not designed for use with flammable materials.

The definition of *fume hood* does not include canopy hoods or recirculation laminar-flow biological-safety cabinets that are not designed for use with flammable materials.

3.3.60 Gas-Powered System. A Level 3 gas distribution system comprised of component parts including but not limited to cylinders, manifolds, air compressor, motor, receivers, controls, filters, dryers, valves, and piping that delivers compressed air or nitrogen at pressures less than 1100 kPa (less than 160 psi) gauge to power devices (e.g., hand pieces, syringes, cleaning devices) as a power source. (PIP)

The term *gas-powered system* applies to a system that is used primarily by dentists to drive pneumatic tools. It is related to, but different from, instrument air as used in Levels 1/2. See 3.3.80, *Instrument Air.* Note that it is NEVER used where the gas might be breathed, because the gas in fact may not even be air — it may be nitrogen. See 5.3.3.5 for requirements for gas-powered systems.

3.3.61 General Care Area. See 3.3.138, Patient Care Area.

3.3.62 Governing Body. The person or persons who have the overall legal responsibility for the operation of a health care facility. (ADM)

3.3.63 Ground-Fault Circuit Interrupter (GFCI). A device intended for the protection of personnel that functions to de-energize a circuit or portion thereof within an established period of time when a current to ground exceeds some predetermined value that is less than that required to operate the overcurrent protective device of the supply circuit. (ELS)

3.3.64 Grounding. See 3.3.65, Grounding System.

The issue of grounding in health care facilities has been controversial. Grounding is a means of providing a low-resistance pathway to ground (the point of relative voltage) for metal parts of appliances not intended to carry currents. If a fault should occur within the appliance that induces a voltage between these parts and ground, current would flow through the grounding means rather than some higher-resistance path, such as a person touching the metal part. A method for providing that low-resistance path has evolved in the form of a third conductor in the power cord of appliances and a third conductor in the building circuit wiring. Thus, a continuous low-resistance path is created between the noncurrent-carrying metal parts of appliances and earth ground (see Exhibit 3.5).

Questions regarding the reliability of the third conductor method of grounding intensified in the health care community when the number of electrical appliances used in health care

EXHIBIT 3.5 Grounding.

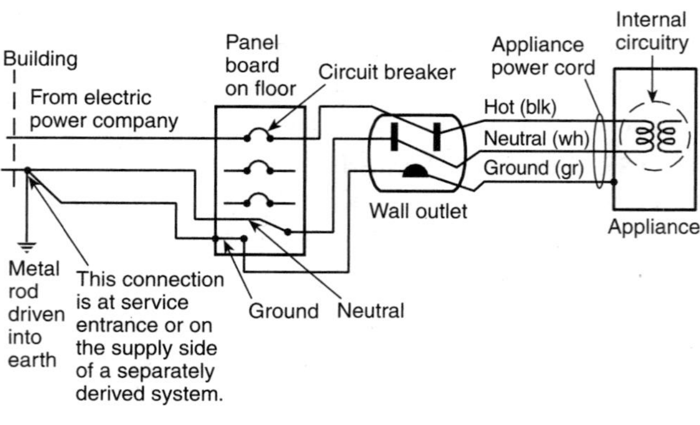

began to increase in the late 1960s. Instead of one or two electrical devices involved in any procedure, six or more might be attached to a patient. Some believed that this increase in electrical devices created a need for even more grounding mechanisms, whereas others insisted that better quality and maintenance of existing grounding methods was adequate. Equipotential grounding systems were tried, but the concept proved to be too restrictive. By listing only performance criteria, the methods used to reach required performance levels were left to the discretion of equipment designers. (See 4.3.3.1.1.)

Grounding is a concern because most electrical power systems are grounded; that is, a conductor is physically connected to earth. This grounding is not relevant to the operation of the electrical appliance as long as the voltage difference between the two power conductors is the operating voltage of the appliance. However, grounding (and identifying) one conductor has long been established as a safety measure so that events such as lightning or transformer faults will not raise both conductors to a high voltage level in relation to the physical earth.

Although this safety measure solved one problem, it created another hazard. Many conductors found in a building (e.g., structural steel, plumbing) are physically connected to the earth, an arrangement that effectively makes them electrically connected to one side of the power line. In addition, a person could be connected to earth via his or her body capacitance even without a direct conductive connection to a grounded object. Thus, the possibility exists that everyone is connected to one power conductor and all that is needed is one accidental connection to the other power conductor to experience a shock.

It can be argued that it would be safer not to have either conductor grounded. For example, for a wiring system of limited size, such as an isolated power system in an operating room, ungrounded systems can be practical. However, capacitive coupling and other problems in large systems, such as a system for an entire building, would defeat the objective of an isolated power system.

3.3.65* Grounding System. A system of conductors that provides a low-impedance return path for leakage and fault currents. (ELS)

A.3.3.65 Grounding System. It coordinates with, but can be locally more extensive than, the grounding system described in Article 250 of NFPA 70, *National Electrical Code.*

3.3.66 Hazard Current. For a given set of connections in an isolated power system, the total current that would flow through a low impedance if it were connected between either isolated conductor and ground. (ELS)

Hazard currents, defined in 3.3.66, are not currents that actually flow under normal conditions. Rather, they are currents that are predicted to be able to flow under certain circumstances (i.e., with one line solidly grounded). This is not to say that there is no leakage current under normal conditions, but this leakage current will always be less than the actual hazard current.

3.3.66.1 Fault Hazard Current. The hazard current of a given isolated power system with all devices connected except the line isolation monitor. (ELS)

3.3.66.2 Monitor Hazard Current. The hazard current of the line isolation monitor alone. (ELS)

3.3.66.3 Total Hazard Current. The hazard current of a given isolated system with all devices, including the line isolation monitor, connected. (ELS)

3.3.67* Hazardous Chemical. A chemical with one or more of the following hazard ratings as defined in NFPA 704, *Standard System for the Identification of the Hazards of Materials for Emergency Response:* Health — 2, 3, or 4; Flammability — 2, 3, or 4; Reactivity — 2, 3, or 4. (LAB)

A.3.3.67 Hazardous Chemical. For hazard ratings of many chemicals, see NFPA 49, *Hazardous Chemicals Data*, and NFPA 325, *Guide to Fire Hazard Properties of Flammable*

Liquids, Gases, and Volatile Solids, both available in NFPA's *Fire Protection Guide to Hazardous Materials. (See also C.11.2.3.)*

3.3.68* Health Care Facilities. Buildings or portions of buildings in which medical, dental, psychiatric, nursing, obstetrical, or surgical care are provided. (ADM)

A.3.3.68 Health Care Facilities. Health care facilities include, but are not limited to, hospitals, nursing homes, limited care facilities, clinics, medical and dental offices, and ambulatory health care centers, whether permanent or movable.

The definition of *health care facility* is consistent with that in NFPA *101* [2]. Note that for the purposes of NFPA 99, a portion of a building can be considered a health care facility. However, only that portion is considered a health care facility, not the entire building.

3.3.69 Home Care. Medical services (equipment) provided in residential occupancies. (ADM)

3.3.70 Hospital. A building or portion thereof used on a 24-hour basis for the medical, psychiatric, obstetrical, or surgical care of four or more inpatients. [***101***, 2003](ADM)

The definition of *hospital* is consistent with that in other NFPA documents, such as NFPA *101* [2].

3.3.71 Hospital-Based. In the interpretation and application of this document, physically connected to a hospital. (GAS)

Stand-alone "daytime" health care facilities that include inhalation anesthetizing locations can readily be classified as ambulatory health care facilities. Those ambulatory care facilities located adjacent to, or forming a portion of, a hospital are more difficult to classify. The definition of *hospital-based* reflects the conclusion that if an ambulatory health care facility that has an anesthetizing location is "physically connected" to a hospital, there is a reasonable chance that inpatients from the hospital will be operated on in the ambulatory care facility. For purposes of Chapter 14 and anesthetizing locations, "physically connected" means that a patient can be wheeled directly from the inpatient portion of the facility to the ambulatory health care facility without going outside or leaving the hospital premises.

3.3.72 Humidifier. A device used for adding water vapor to inspired gas. (GAS)

3.3.73 Hyperbaric. Facility, building, or structure used to house chambers and all auxiliary service equipment for medical applications and procedures at pressures above normal atmospheric pressures. (HYP)

3.3.74 Hyperbaric Oxygenation. The application of pure oxygen or an oxygen-enriched gaseous mixture to a subject at elevated pressure. (HYP)

Hyperbaric oxygenation is also known as *HBO*. Hyperbaric oxygen creates a more favorable oxygen diffusion gradient by providing increased tissue oxygen levels that are dissolved in the blood's plasma. The Undersea and Hyperbaric Medical Society defines HBO as "breathing 100 percent oxygen while pressurized in a hyperbaric chamber." HBO is used routinely to treat a variety of nonhealing wound conditions such as diabetic ulcers, failing skin flaps, and osteoradionecrosis of the mandible.

It should be noted that 100 percent oxygen is never administered at gauge pressures greater than 66 FSW (29.4 psi or 3 ATA). If this cardinal rule is violated, the person breathing oxygen at this pressure (or greater) will experience oxygen toxicity, a condition similar to a grand mal seizure.

3.3.75 Hypobaric. Facility, building, or structure used to house chambers and all auxiliary service equipment for medical applications and procedures at pressures below atmospheric pressures. (HYP)

3.3.76 Hypoxia. A state of inadequate oxygenation of the blood and tissue sufficient to cause impairment of function. [**99B,** 2005] (HYP)

3.3.77 Immediate Restoration of Service. Automatic restoration of operation with an interruption of not more than 10 seconds. (ELS)

Immediate restoration does provide for a brief interruption of power for 10 seconds. If a particular appliance or procedure cannot tolerate even this brief interruption, a method of bridging or eliminating this 10-second period might need to be provided through the use of an uninterrupted power supply (UPS).

3.3.78* Impedance. Impedance is the ratio of the voltage drop across a circuit element to the current flowing through the same circuit element. The unit of impedance is the ohm. (ELE)

A.3.3.78 Impedance. The circuit element can consist of any combination of resistance, capacitance, or inductance.

Impedance is frequency dependent and is stated as ohms at a particular frequency. The symbol for impedance is *Z.* Resistance, symbol *R,* is one element of impedance and is often frequency independent. The elements of impedance caused by inductance and capacitance are called reactance, symbol *X,* and are also measured in ohms.

3.3.79 Incident Command System (ICS). The combination of facilities, equipment, personnel, procedures, and communications operating within a common organizational structure that has responsibility for the management of assigned resources to effectively accomplish stated objectives pertaining to an incident or training exercise. [**1670,** 2004] (HCE)

Health care facilities need to use the incident command system (ICS) when managing disasters in order to function more efficiently in conjunction with the fire service, which also uses this method in its operations. NFPA 1600, *Standard on Disaster/Emergency Management and Business Continuity Programs* [10], is a reference document for ICS.

3.3.80 Instrument Air. For the purposes of this standard, instrument air is air intended for the powering of medical devices unrelated to human respiration (e.g., surgical tools, ceiling arms). Medical air and instrument air are distinct systems for mutually exclusive applications. Instrument air is a medical support gas that falls under the general requirements for medical gases. (PIP)

Note the distinction between instrument air and medical air (defined in 3.3.106). Instrument air is an alternative for nitrogen used to drive tools, power columns, dry glassware, and so on. Medical air is a pharmaceutical used for life support. See also 3.3.106, *Medical Air,* and 3.3.60, *Gas-Powered Systems.*

◀ **FAQ**
What is the difference between instrument air and medical air?

3.3.81 Intermittent Positive-Pressure Breathing (IPPB). Ventilation of the lungs by application of intermittent positive pressure to the airway. (GAS)

3.3.82* Intrinsically Safe. As applied to equipment and wiring, equipment and wiring that are incapable of releasing sufficient electrical energy under normal or abnormal conditions to cause ignition of a specific hazardous atmospheric mixture. (HYP)

A.3.3.82 Intrinsically Safe. Abnormal conditions can include accidental damage to any part of the equipment or wiring, insulation or other failure of electrical components, application of overvoltage, adjustment and maintenance operations, and other similar conditions.

It is very difficult to obtain medical equipment (monitors, etc.) that has been certified as intrinsically safe for operation in the hyperbaric environment.

3.3.83 Invasive Procedure. Any procedure that penetrates the protective surfaces of a patient's body (i.e., skin, mucous membrane, cornea) and that is performed with an aseptic field (procedural site). [Not included in this category are placement of peripheral intravenous needles or catheters used to administer fluids and/or medications, gastrointestinal endoscopies (i.e., sigmoidoscopies), insertion of urethral catheters, and other similar procedures.] (ELS)

3.3.84 Isolated Patient Lead. A patient lead whose impedance to ground or to a power line is sufficiently high that connecting the lead to ground, or to either conductor of the power line, results in current flow below a hazardous limit in the lead. (ELE)

The development of isolated patient leads resulted from the discovery and verification that very low levels of current in leads directly to the heart could disrupt its function. (See the commentary following 3.3.89, *Leakage Current.*) A non-isolated lead might not have sufficient impedance to keep even small leakage currents from affecting the heart.

The concept of an isolated lead refers not only to the physical wire that is connected to the patient but also to the wire as it is assembled to the appliance.

3.3.85* Isolated Power System. A system comprising an isolating transformer or its equivalent, a line isolation monitor, and its ungrounded circuit conductors. (ELS)

A.3.3.85 Isolated Power System. See NFPA 70, *National Electrical Code.*

When the problem of explosions in operating rooms was first addressed in the 1940s, an *isolated power system* (IPS) was one of the techniques used to reduce the occurrence of sparks in the operating room. With the development of nonflammable anesthetics, however, the necessity of continuing to adhere to requirements developed for use with flammable anesthetics began to be questioned.

Permitting (for anesthesia purposes) a grounded electrical system in nonflammable anesthetizing locations, however, soon created another set of questions concerning requirements for wet locations.

In NFPA 99, an additional level of electrical safety is required in wet locations. When all anesthetizing locations were required to have IPSs, it was not necessary to determine whether an anesthetizing location was also a wet location, because the required level of safety was already provided. However, when flammable anesthetics was eliminated, a new question had to be answered for each nonflammable anesthetizing location: Was it a wet location? It is still the responsibility of the individual health care facility to decide which, if any, anesthetizing locations should be considered wet locations. (See the commentary following 3.3.185, *Wet Locations.*)

3.3.86 Isolation Transformer. A transformer of the multiple-winding type, with the primary and secondary windings physically separated, that inductively couples its ungrounded secondary winding to the grounded feeder system that energizes its primary winding. (ELS)

Isolation transformers change a grounded electrical system to an ungrounded electrical system (see Exhibit 3.6) and provide an added level of protection against hazardous electric current flow for certain electrical faults within appliances. Thus, the connection to ground of one conductor of the electrical power system is eliminated (see the commentary following 3.3.64,

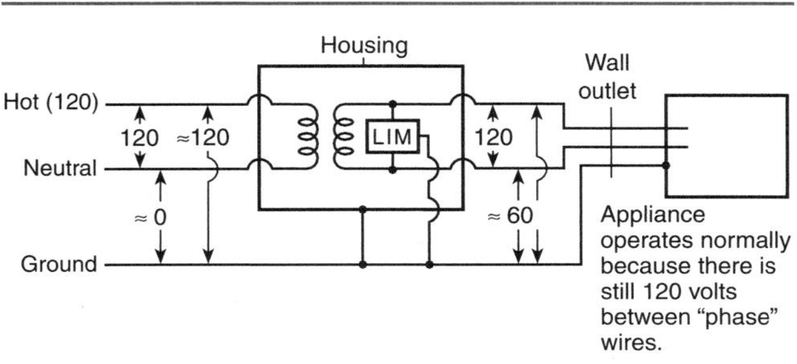

EXHIBIT 3.6 *Schematic of isolation transformer.*

Grounding), and two gross faults, rather than one, are required in order to cause a severe shock.

Where interruption of electrical power cannot be tolerated, a further advantage of an isolation transformer is that certain first faults within a device (e.g., line-to-ground) will not interrupt the flow of electricity to that device. This feature is especially important in areas such as operating rooms. A fault in a grounded electrical system, such as the phase (hot) conductor touching the chassis of a properly grounded appliance, would create a short circuit and trip (open) either the appliance's overcurrent protector or the branch-circuit breaker, removing power from the appliance or from all the appliances on that breaker. Such a fault in an ungrounded (isolated) electrical system would remove only one layer of protection, reducing the system to the equivalent of a conventionally grounded system but allowing the device to continue to be used if absolutely essential. A monitoring device (i.e., a line isolation monitor) can warn that a fault has occurred, and the fault can be identified without electrical power being interrupted. Note that a line-to-line fault will trip a circuit breaker whether the appliance is operating from an IPS or from a grounded system.

This added level of protection applies to gross macroshock effects (in the milliampere and ampere levels of current). It does not apply to microshock effects (in the microampere levels of current), because electrical systems usually have large enough capacitive couplings at these low current levels to negate the isolating effects of an isolation transformer.

Isolation transformers are built in various sizes. The units used in anesthetizing locations, for example, range up to 25 kVA. It is therefore necessary to know the approximate number of devices expected to be used and their power ratings when installing isolation transformer(s) in these locations. Otherwise, the transformer's circuit breaker overcurrent protection will sense too much current being drawn and will trip and cut off power to all devices connected to the circuit breaker.

When an isolation transformer is installed in a health care facility, it must be in conjunction with a line isolation monitor (LIM). (See 3.3.99, *Line Isolation Monitor.*) LIMs provide visual and audible indications of current flow between the output wires of the isolation transformer and ground as a result of coupling (resistive or capacitive). The LIM will alarm when this current passes above some preset value (now set at 5 mA maximum).

3.3.87* Laboratory. A building, space, room, or group of rooms intended to serve activities involving procedures for investigation, diagnosis, or treatment in which flammable, combustible, or oxidizing materials are to be used. (LAB)

A.3.3.87 Laboratory. These laboratories are not intended to include isolated frozen section laboratories; areas in which oxygen is administered; blood donor rooms in which flammable, combustible, or otherwise hazardous materials normally used in laboratory procedures are not present; and clinical service areas not using hazardous materials.

Diagnostic and/or therapeutic areas of health care facilities are often referred to as laboratories. For the purposes of this document, however, only those areas with the hazards indicated in the definition are considered laboratories. Note that a laboratory is not facility-dependent. Chapter 13 through Chapter 18 contain the application of requirements for laboratories.

Isolated frozen section laboratories are included in this definition if they use flammable liquids. They are not included if they do not use flammable liquids.

NFPA 45, *Standard on Fire Protection for Laboratories Using Chemicals* [11], is the primary reference document for construction requirements, and it applies to all health care laboratories that store or use flammable or combustible liquids in quantity. NFPA 45 should be consulted for details concerning those volumes that determine applicability. (See the discussion following A.11.1.)

3.3.88* Laboratory Work Area. A room or space for testing, analysis, research, instruction, or similar activities that involve the use of chemicals. This work area may or may not be enclosed. (LAB)

A.3.3.88 Laboratory Work Area. See NFPA 45, *Standard on Fire Protection for Laboratories Using Chemicals.*

The word *research* was added to the definition of the term *laboratory work area* to correlate the definition with that in NFPA 45 [11].

3.3.89 Leakage Current. Any current, including capacitively coupled current, not intended to be applied to a patient, that is conveyed from exposed conductive parts of an appliance to ground or to other accessible parts of an appliance. (ELE)

Leakage current is electric current as governed by Ohm's law:

$$I = \frac{V}{Z}$$

where:

I = current
V = voltage
Z = impedance

Current flow requires a closed circuit, and leakage current is peculiar in that the voltage is frequently the power line voltage and the circuit elements are unintended but inevitable capacitive coupling or faulty resistive insulation. A person can also form an unintended part of the circuit. See A.10.2.13.4.3 for an extensive discussion on the leakage current limits contained in Chapter 8 and Chapter 10.

Leakage current became a growing concern in the health care community in the 1960s when cardiovascular medicine and surgery began invading the heart with electrical and electromechanical probes. Researchers discovered that the heart's pumping action could be interrupted with very low levels of current, particularly at the power line frequency, 60 Hz. Many physical and physiological factors contribute to the susceptibility of the heart. The design and utilization of electro-medical equipment in health care facilities was dramatically altered by the recognition of these unintended leakage currents.

For further details of the effects of currents, see A.10.2.13.4.3 and B.1.2.2.1.

3.3.90 Level 1 Medical Piped Gas and Vacuum Systems. Systems serving occupancies where interruption of the piped medical gas and vacuum system would place patients in imminent danger of morbidity or mortality. (PIP)

The definition of *Level 1 Medical Piped Gas and Vacuum Systems* in 3.3.90 is often viewed as unsatisfactory because it is not concrete — for example, the definitions do not clearly say that such and such occupancy shall be piped Level ____. Although such black and white definitions would make enforcement easy, they would also force NFPA 99 hopelessly out of step with the pace of change in the medical field. The question of what level of system should be installed in a given occupancy can be determined only by careful consideration of the medical procedures for which the facility is being built. This definition is simply a concise statement of the principles underlying that decision.

A more detailed decision tree is offered in the occupancy chapters under 13.3.5, 14.3.5, 17.3.5, and 18.3.5.

3.3.91 Level 1 Vacuum System. A system consisting of central-vacuum-producing equipment with pressure and operating controls, shutoff valves, alarm warning systems, gauges, and a network of piping extending to and terminating with suitable station inlets at locations where patient suction could be required. (PIP)

A Level 1 vacuum system is dedicated for patient suctioning and is not intended for other purposes. Use for WAGD is not recommended. (See 3.3.184, *WAGD,* and 5.1.3.7 and its commentary for information on precautions.)

Chapter 13 through Chapter 18 list the "level" of vacuum systems required for various health care facilities.

3.3.92 Level 2 Medical Piped Gas and Vacuum Systems. Systems serving occupancies where interruption of the piped medical gas and vacuum system would place patients at manageable risk of morbidity or mortality. (PIP)

3.3.93* Level 3 Compressed Air System. A system of component parts, including, but not limited to, air compressor, motor, receiver, controls, filters, dryers, valves, and piping, that delivers compressed air <1100 kPa (<160 psi gauge) to power devices (hand pieces, syringe, cleaning devices, etc.) as a power source. (PIP)

A.3.3.93 Level 3 Compressed Air System. The system does not produce air to meet the medical requirements of medical air and is not intended to be used for air life support devices.

Air compressors are used to drive dynamic devices used for patient treatment. A Level 3 medical gas system is limited to oxygen and nitrous oxide only. Dental air used for drying teeth is not addressed in NFPA 99. A Level 3 compressor is used for gas-powered devices.

3.3.94 Level 3 Piped Gas Systems. Systems serving occupancies where interruption of the piped medical gas would terminate procedures but would not place patients at risk of morbidity or mortality. (PIP)

3.3.95* Level 3 Piped Vacuum System. A Level 3 vacuum distribution system that can be either a wet system designed to remove liquids, air–gas, or solids from the treated area; or a dry system designed to trap liquid and solids before the service inlet and to accommodate air–gas only through the service inlet. (PIP)

A.3.3.95 Level 3 Piped Vacuum System. The system is not intended for Level 1 vacuum applications. A wet piping system is designed to accommodate liquid, air–gas, and solids through the service inlet. A dry piping system is designed to accommodate air–gas only through the service inlet. [Liquid(s) and solid(s) are trapped before entering the service inlet.]

3.3.96 Life Safety Branch. A subsystem of the emergency system consisting of feeders and branch circuits, meeting the requirements of Article 700 of NFPA 70, *National Electrical Code*, and intended to provide adequate power needs to ensure safety to patients and personnel, and that is automatically connected to alternate power sources during interruption of the normal power source. (ELS)

3.3.97 Limited Care Facility. A building or portion of a building used on a 24-hour basis for the housing of four or more persons who are incapable of self-preservation because of age; physical limitations due to accident or illness; or limitations such as mental retardation/developmental disability, mental illness, or chemical dependency. (ADM)

3.3.98* Limited-Combustible Material. A material (as defined in NFPA 220, *Standard on Types of Building Construction*) not complying with the definition of noncombustible material that, in the form in which it is used, has a potential heat value not exceeding 8141 kJ/kg (3500 Btu/lb) and complies with one of the following: (a) materials having a structural base of noncombustible material, with a surfacing not exceeding a thickness of 3.2 mm (⅛ in.) and having a flame-spread rating not greater than 50 or (b) materials, in the form and thickness used, other than as described in (a), having neither a flame-spread rating greater than 25 nor evidence of continued progressive combustion and of such composition that surfaces that would be exposed by cutting through the material on any plane would have neither a flame-spread rating greater than 25 nor evidence of continued progressive combustion. (PIP)

A.3.3.98 Limited-Combustible Material. Materials subject to increase in combustibility or flame-spread rating beyond the limits herein established through the effects of age, moisture, or other atmospheric condition are considered combustible.

See NFPA 259, *Standard Test Method for Potential Heat of Building Materials.*

See NFPA 259, *Standard Test Method for Potential Heat of Building Materials* [12], for more information on limited-combustible material.

3.3.99 Line Isolation Monitor. A test instrument designed to continually check the balanced and unbalanced impedance from each line of an isolated circuit to ground and equipped with a built-in test circuit to exercise the alarm without adding to the leakage current hazard. (ELS)

The function of a line isolation monitor is to check the hazard current from an isolated circuit to ground. Note that hazard current is a predicted current, not one that is actually present.

This definition is in concert with that in NFPA 70 [3].

3.3.100* Liquid. Any material that has a fluidity greater than that of 300 penetration asphalt when tested in accordance with ASTM D 5, *Standard Test Method for Penetration of Bituminous Materials.* [**30,** 2003] (LAB)

A.3.3.100 Liquid. When not otherwise identified, the term *liquid* includes both flammable and combustible liquids. *(See also C.11.2.1.)*

3.3.101* Local Signal. A visible indication of the operating status of equipment. (PIP)

Local signals are not alarms, but rather might be considered as a kind of aid to the operator. The requirements for local signals are found in each source section 5.1.3.4.10.6, 5.1.3.4.12.9, 5.1.3.4.13.6, 5.3.1.4.15.5, and 5.1.3.8.10.2.

A.3.3.101 Local Signal. Examples would include a light to indicate a compressor is operating or a cylinder header is in use or a flag attached to a manual changeover valve to indicate which side is in use.

3.3.102 mA. Milliampere.

3.3.103 Manifold. A device for connecting the outlets of one or more gas cylinders to the central piping system for that specific gas. (PIP)

3.3.104* Manufactured Assembly. A factory-assembled product designed for aesthetics or convenience that contains medical gas or vacuum outlets, piping, or other devices related to medical gases. (PIP)

This definition reflects the addition of specific requirements for these potentially large and complex subcomponents of a medical gas system that are assembled in a factory and integrated into the medical gas system on site.

There was some confusion as to whether manufactured assemblies were an extension of the "piped system" or a separate "device" that plugged into the piped system. Therefore, not only was a definition for the term *manufactured assembly* added but criteria were also established for these units. The quantity and complexity of the piping that manufactured assemblies might contain can significantly affect the final testing, operation, and integrity of the complete system. The requirements in NFPA 99 are intended to ensure that the integrity of the piping does not diminish between the wall and the appliance interface because of the use of a "manufactured assembly" that creates a similar wall-like interface. (See 5.1.6 and B.2.2.)

A.3.3.104 Manufactured Assembly. Examples are headwalls, columns, ceiling columns, ceiling hung pendants, movable track systems, and so on.

Manufactured assemblies might include ceiling columns, booms, pendants, headwalls, horizontal trunking systems, movable columns, "power columns," prepiped benches, cabinetry with medical gases installed, preassembled wall sections, portable treatment rooms, modular operating rooms (ORs), modular patient rooms, and a plethora of other manifestations of prepiped and more or less movable equipment.

3.3.105 Mask. A device that fits over the mouth and nose (oronasal) or nose (nasal), used to administer gases to a patient. (GAS)

3.3.106* Medical Air. For purposes of this standard, medical air is air supplied from cylinders, bulk containers, medical air compressors, or has been reconstituted from oxygen USP and oil-free, dry nitrogen NF.

The definition of *medical air* has not changed as much as it might appear. Although the definition itself is simpler than in previous editions, most of the requirements that previously resided in the definition are now in the body of the text. (See 5.1.3.5.) Note that instrument air is used to drive tools, power columns, dry glassware, and so on. Medical air, by contrast, is a pharmaceutical used for life support.

A.3.3.106 Medical Air. Air supplied from on-site compressor and associated air treatment systems (as opposed to medical air USP supplied in cylinders) that complies with the specified limits is considered medical air. Hydrocarbon carryover from the compressor into the pipeline distribution system could be detrimental to the safety of the end user and to the integrity of the piping system. Mixing of air and oxygen is a common clinical practice, and the hazards of fire are increased if the air is thus contaminated. Compliance with these limits is thus considered important to fire and patient safety. The quality of local ambient air should be determined prior to its selection for compressors and air treatment equipment.

The "quality of air" might seem to be a subject that is outside the scope of this document and perhaps even that of NFPA. At issue is the problem of oil and water introduced into piped air systems by compressors. Oil poses a fire hazard if the air is blended with oxygen for respiratory support, in addition to affecting patient medical treatment. To address the problem, a set of criteria for medical air (i.e., air quality) that would define requirements and list performance criteria for compressor manufacturers was added.

◀ **FAQ**
Does the outside air supply need to meet USP specifications?

It should be noted that NFPA 99 does not require compressors to supply specification Grade D air. NFPA 99 also does not require the quality of outside, local air to meet Grade D air.

NFPA 99 does not require air treatment systems for medical air compressor systems because ambient air, taken from a location free from auto exhausts or other sources of pollution, is normally well within the limits required by Compressed Air/USP and the preceding definition. Compressors that comply with the definition of *medical air compressor* will not add contamination to the airstream and thus do not often require air treatment. (Liquid ring air compressors, it should be noted, use water to compress air, and the quality of the water source is of concern because of its effect on the air being compressed.)

Air quality does vary from place to place and from day to day and could in a few areas exceed the contaminant limits of USP air for unacceptably long periods. Variation can be determined only through knowledge of local conditions and air quality testing at the intake. A local office of the U.S. Environmental Protection Agency might be able to provide data on local conditions.

Where the quality of the intake air is unreliable, specific air treatment devices might be desirable. Where installed, these devices need to be monitored and maintained. Such devices add considerably to the purchase price and maintenance of the air system, but their use can offset even greater costs associated with the effects of untreated air on the patient and the piped air system.

3.3.107 Medical Air Compressor. A compressor that is designed to exclude oil from the air stream and compression chamber and that does not under normal operating conditions or any single fault add any toxic or flammable contaminants to the compressed air. (PIP)

Compressors can be designed to deliver the quality of air required for medical compressed air purposes. Factors such as the inherent design of the compressor and the way it is maintained will influence the extent to which oil or other contaminants are injected into the medical compressed air line during a compressor failure.

The term and definition reflects the critical importance of excluding toxic and potentially damaging elements from the medical air both for the safety of equipment, where pure oxygen is commonly added to the air, and for the safety of patients, who will often breathe the air without other filtration or purification. (See 3.3.106, *Medical Air.*)

Appropriate limitations and safety devices are listed in Chapter 5 for each accepted technology.

3.3.108* Medical/Dental Office. A building or part thereof in which the following occur: (1) Examinations and minor treatments/procedures are performed under the continuous supervision of a medical/dental professional; (2) Only sedation or local anesthesia is involved and treatment or procedures do not render the patient incapable of self-preservation under emergency conditions; (3) Overnight stays for patients or 24-hour operation are not provided. (ADM)

A.3.3.108 Medical/Dental Office. Examples include dental office/clinic, medical office/clinic, immediate care facility, and podiatry office.

3.3.109 Medical Gas. A patient medical gas or medical support gas. *(See also 3.3.143, Patient Medical Gas and 3.3.111, Medical Support Gas.)* (PIP)

3.3.110 Medical Gas System. An assembly of equipment and piping for the distribution of nonflammable medical gases such as oxygen, nitrous oxide, compressed air, carbon dioxide, and helium. (PIP)

3.3.111 Medical Support Gas. Piped gases such as nitrogen and instrument air that are used to support medical procedures by operating medical–surgical tools, equipment booms, pendants, and similar medical support applications.

3.3.112 Medical–Surgical Vacuum. A method used to provide a source of drainage, aspiration, and suction in order to remove body fluids from patients. (PIP)

3.3.113 Medical–Surgical Vacuum System. An assembly of central vacuum producing equipment and a network of piping for patient suction in medical, medical–surgical, and waste anesthetic gas disposal (WAGD) applications. (PIP)

3.3.114 Multiple Treatment Facility. A diagnostic or treatment complex under a single management comprising a number of single treatment facilities, which can be accessed one from the other without exiting the facility (i.e., does not involve widely separated locations or separate distinct practices). (ADM)

Note that the definition of *multiple treatment facility* is applied only in Level 3 occupancies. See also 3.3.169, *Single Treatment Facility.*

3.3.115 mV. Millivolt.

3.3.116 Nasal Cannula. Device consisting of two short tubes to be inserted into the nostrils to administer oxygen or other therapeutic gases. (GAS)

The definition of *nasal cannula* distinguishes it from *nasal catheter,* which is a slightly different apparatus for administering oxygen. See Exhibit 3.7.

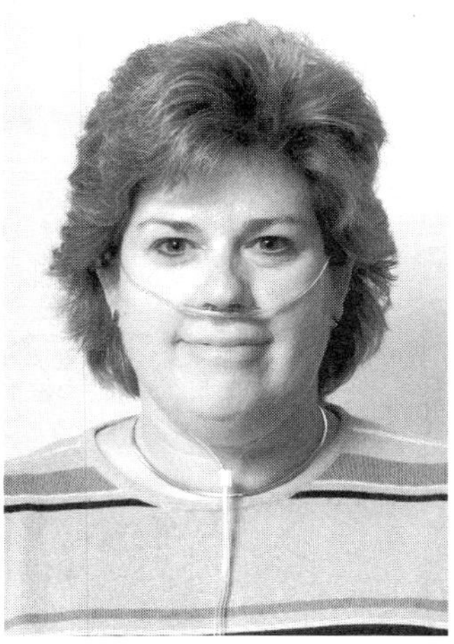

EXHIBIT 3.7 Nasal cannula.

3.3.117 Nasal Catheter. A flexible tube for insertion through the nose into the nasopharynx to administer oxygen or other therapeutic gases. (GAS)

3.3.118 Nebulizer. A device used for producing an aerosol of water and/or medication within inspired gas supply. (GAS)

3.3.119 Negative Pressure. Pressure less than atmospheric. (GAS)

The definition of *negative pressure* can apply to air within the body as well as that in the surrounding environment.

3.3.120 Nitrogen. An element that, at atmospheric temperatures and pressures, exists as a clear, colorless, and tasteless gas; it comprises approximately four-fifths of the earth's atmosphere. (GAS)

3.3.120.1 Nitrogen NF (Oil-Free, Dry). Nitrogen complying as a minimum with oil-free, dry nitrogen NF. (PIP)

Nitrogen is used for pipe joining and pressure-testing purposes (see 5.1.12). Grade NF is the nitrogen acceptable for use in pipes intended for medical application. Nitrogen is required to be oil-free because it is used in piped oxygen lines where particles of oil can be a fire hazard, as well as a hazard to patients.

Nitrogen NF is nitrogen as defined in the U.S. Pharmacopeia/National Formulary [13]. Because the USP is the standard for pharmaceutical purity in the United States and much of the world, Nitrogen NF has been argued to be a drug and therefore should not be available without a doctor's prescription. The initial storm this conflict generated appears to have subsided, and the gas is now widely available for the purpose intended in the standard, nitrogen purging and testing, per 5.1.10.5.5 and 5.3.10.7.5.

3.3.121* Nitrogen Narcosis. A condition resembling alcoholic inebriation, which results from breathing nitrogen in the air under significant pressure. (HYP)

A.3.3.121 Nitrogen Narcosis. See C.20.1.3.2.2.

Nitrogen, present in air in a concentration of almost 80 percent and under pressure, causes the condition of nitrogen narcosis.

When breathing air at increased pressures (either scuba or hyperbaric chamber air), the partial pressure of nitrogen increases accordingly. At depths greater than 100 FSW (partial pressure of nitrogen >2400 mm Hg), nitrogen narcosis becomes more prevalent. Symptoms include euphoria, fatigue, idea fixation, laughter, inability to reason normally, loss of fine movement, loss of judgment, overconfidence, and short-term memory impairment. In any diving operation, this condition can be fatal if not recognized. Routine hyperbaric chamber operations have virtually eliminated nitrogen narcosis as a cause of death.

3.3.122 Nitrous Oxide. An inorganic compound, one of the oxides of nitrogen. It exists as a gas at atmospheric pressure and temperature, possesses a sweetish smell, and is used for inducing anesthesia when inhaled. The oxygen in the compound will be released under conditions of combustion, creating an oxygen-enriched atmosphere. (GAS)

3.3.123 Noncombustible (Hyperbaric). An adjective describing a substance that will not burn in 95 ± 5 percent oxygen at pressures up to 3 ATA (44.1 psia). (HYP)

A distinction between noncombustibility in hyperbaric chambers and in hypobaric chambers is made to reflect the different atmospheric conditions that exist inside these chambers and the conditions under which substances are considered noncombustible in each.

Although 100 percent is normally the percentage used, 95 percent ± 5 percent is considered acceptable because of limitations on measuring techniques. [See 3.3.124, *Noncombustible (Hypobaric).*]

3.3.124 Noncombustible (Hypobaric). An adjective describing a substance that will not burn in 95 percent, plus or minus 5 percent oxygen at pressures of 101.325 kPa (760 mm Hg). (HYP)

3.3.125* Noncombustible Material. A material (as defined in NFPA 220, *Standard on Types of Building Construction*) that, in the form in which it is used and under the conditions anticipated, will not ignite, burn, support combustion, or release flammable vapors when subjected to fire or heat. (PIP)

A.3.3.125 Noncombustible Material. Materials reported as noncombustible, when tested in accordance with ASTM E 136, *Standard Test Method for Behavior of Materials in a Vertical Tube Furnace at 750°C*, are considered noncombustible materials.

3.3.126 Nonflammable. An adjective describing a substance that will not burn under the conditions set forth in the definition of flame resistant. (HYP)

3.3.127* Nonflammable Anesthetic Agent. Refers to those inhalation agents that, because of their vapor pressure at 37°C (98.6°F) and at atmospheric pressure, cannot attain flammable concentrations when mixed with air, oxygen, or mixtures of oxygen and nitrous oxide. (GAS)

A.3.3.127 Nonflammable Anesthetic Agent. It is possible to halogenate a compound and render it partially or totally nonflammable by the substitution of one or more halogens (e.g., fluorine, chlorine, bromine) for hydrogen. Thus halothane ($CF_3CHClBr$) is almost completely halogenated and is nonflammable. Methoxyflurane ($CHF_2CCl_2OCH_3$) is partially halogenated and is nonflammable in conditions encountered during clinical anesthesia (if it is heated, its vapor concentration will increase enough to burn). Fluroxene ($CF_3CH_2OCHCH_2$) is halogenated even less; it is flammable in concentrations of 4 percent or greater.

The following agents are considered flammable during conditions of clinical use in anesthesia:

(1) Cyclopropane
(2) Divinyl ether
(3) Ethyl chloride
(4) Ethylene
(5) Ethyl ether

The following agent is flammable during use in clinical anesthesia in higher concentrations: Fluroxene. Because fluroxene is flammable under certain conditions of use, it is listed as a flammable agent. Concentrations required for induction of anesthesia generally exceed

4 percent and are flammable. Maintenance of fluroxene anesthesia can be accomplished with concentrations of less than 4 percent, however.

The following agents are nonflammable during conditions of use in clinical anesthesia:

(1) Chloroform
(2) Halothane
(3) Methoxyflurane
(4) Nitrous oxide
(5) Trichloroethylene
(6) Enflurane

The list of nonflammable anesthetic agents is representative, not inclusive. Research is continuing into the development of other improved agents.

Any anesthetic agent that does not meet the definition of a nonflammable anesthetic agent is to be considered flammable because of its inherent properties or the manner in which it is used.

3.3.128* Nonflammable Medical Gas System. See 3.3.110, Medical Gas System.

A.3.3.128 Nonflammable Medical Gas System. See Chapter 5, Gas and Vacuum Systems.

3.3.129 Nursing Home. A building or portion of a building used on a 24-hour basis for the housing and nursing care of four or more persons who, because of mental or physical incapacity, might be unable to provide for their own needs and safety without the assistance of another person. (ADM)

3.3.130* Oxidizing Gas. A gas that supports combustion. (HYP)

A.3.3.130 Oxidizing Gas. Oxygen and nitrous oxide are examples of oxidizing gases. There are many others, including halogens.

3.3.131* Oxygen. An element that, at atmospheric temperatures and pressures, exists as a colorless, odorless, tasteless gas. (GAS)

A.3.3.131 Oxygen. Its outstanding property is its ability to sustain life and to support combustion. Although oxygen is nonflammable, materials that burn in air will burn much more vigorously and create higher temperatures in oxygen or in oxygen-enriched atmospheres.

3.3.131.1 Gaseous Oxygen. A colorless, odorless, and tasteless gas; also, the physical state of the element at atmospheric temperature and pressure. (GAS)

3.3.131.2* Liquid Oxygen. Exists at cryogenic temperature, approximately −184.4°C (−300°F) at atmospheric pressure. It retains all of the properties of gaseous oxygen, but, in addition, when allowed to warm to room temperature at atmospheric pressure, it will evaporate and expand to fill a volume 860 times its liquid volume. (GAS)

A.3.3.131.2 Liquid Oxygen. If spilled, the liquid can cause frostbite on contact with skin.

3.3.132* Oxygen Delivery Equipment. Any device used to transport and deliver an oxygen-enriched atmosphere to a patient. (GAS)

A.3.3.132 Oxygen Delivery Equipment. If an enclosure such as a mask, hood, incubator, canopy, or tent is used to contain the oxygen-enriched atmosphere, then that enclosure is considered to be oxygen delivery equipment.

3.3.133 Oxygen-Enriched Atmosphere. For the purpose of this standard, and only for the purpose of this standard, an atmosphere in which the concentration of oxygen exceeds 23.5 percent by volume. (HYP)

The normal percentage of oxygen in air is 20.9 percent, commonly expressed as 21 percent. The value of 23.5 percent reflects an error factor of ±2.5 percent. Such a margin of error is necessary because of the imprecision of gas measurement devices and the practicality of reconstituting air from gaseous nitrogen and oxygen. Hyperbaric chambers located in areas of potential atmospheric pollution cannot be pressurized with air drawn from the ambient atmosphere. Such chambers are supplied by "air" prepared by mixing one volume of oxygen with four volumes of nitrogen. It is impractical to reconstitute large volumes of air with tolerances closer than 21 percent ± 2.5 percent.

The standard does not intend to imply that the use of compressed air cylinders in normal atmospheric areas (i.e., outside hyperbaric chambers) would create an oxygen-enriched atmosphere. The compressed air expands as it leaves the cylinder, drops to normal atmospheric pressure, and is not oxygen-enriched.

This definition varies slightly from the one appearing in NFPA 53, *Recommended Practice on Materials, Equipment, and Systems Used in Oxygen-Enriched Atmospheres* [14], which states that the concentration of oxygen in the atmosphere exceeds 21 percent by volume or its partial pressure exceeds 21.3 kPa (160 torr). The scope of the definition is limited to the way the term is used throughout NFPA 99. The definition is independent of the atmospheric pressure of the area and is based solely on the percentage of oxygen. In defining the term, the issue of environments, such as a hyperbaric chamber, where the atmospheric pressure can vary, was taken into consideration. Under normal atmospheric conditions, oxygen concentrations above 23.5 percent will increase the fire hazard level. Different atmospheric conditions (e.g., pressure) or the presence of gaseous diluents, however, can actually increase or decrease the fire hazard level even if, by definition, an *oxygen-enriched atmosphere* exists. An oxygen-enriched atmosphere in and of itself does not always mean an increased fire hazard exists.

3.3.134 Oxygen Hood. A device encapsulating a patient's head and used for a purpose similar to that of a mask. *(See also 3.3.105, Mask.)* (HYP)

The oxygen hood was developed for those patients unable to breathe oxygen in a hyperbaric chamber through a more traditional mask. For example, patients who are undergoing mandibular reconstruction surgery and are unable to be fitted with an oronasal mask might use an oxygen hood. The clear, flexible hood either is attached to a rubber neck dam/ring assembly or is taped to the patient's skin to help prevent oxygen leaks into the chamber environment. Hood inflation is maintained with a delicate balance of supply (100 percent oxygen) and exhaust. The hood assembly is the most commonly used oxygen delivery device in Class A clinical hyperbaric medicine chambers.

3.3.135 Oxygen Index. The minimum concentration of oxygen, expressed as percent by volume, in a mixture of oxygen and nitrogen that will just support combustion of a material under conditions of ASTM D 2863, *Standard Test Method for Measuring the Minimum Oxygen Concentration to Support Candle-Like Combustion of Plastics (Oxygen Index).* (HYP)

3.3.136* Oxygen Toxicity (Hyperbaric). Physical impairment resulting from breathing gaseous mixtures containing oxygen-enriched atmospheres at elevated partial pressures for extended periods of time. (HYP)

There are two types of oxygen toxicity: pulmonary (called the Smith–Lorraine effect) and central nervous system (called the Paul Bert effect). Prolonged breathing of 60 percent to 100 percent oxygen for long periods of time can produce serious lung damage. Effects range from minor lung irritation to a pneumonia-like condition. Central nervous system oxygen toxicity occurs more rapidly than pulmonary toxicity and produces seizure activity similar to epileptic convulsions. Breathing 100 percent oxygen at 60 FSW for 30 continuous minutes will produce seizure activity in approximately 2 percent of the population.

Neither pulmonary nor central nervous system oxygen toxicity is a problem in routine hyperbaric chamber operations due to well-established safety practices.

A.3.3.136 Oxygen Toxicity (Hyperbaric). Under the pressures and times of exposure normally encountered in hyperbaric treatments, toxicity is a direct function of concentration and time of exposure. *(See also C.20.1.3.2.3.)*

3.3.137 Patient Bed Location. The location of a patient sleeping bed, or the bed or procedure table of a critical care area. (ELS)

The definition of *patient bed location* confirms the standard's intent that the general locations of examination and procedure tables in critical patient care areas (e.g., operating and delivery), as well as in recovery areas and the immediate area surrounding patient sleeping beds, are to be considered patient bed locations. This is an important distinction because NFPA 70, Section 517.33 and NFPA 99 (see 4.3.2.2) stipulate the number of normal and critical branch circuits and receptacles required at general care and critical care patient bed locations. NFPA 99 requires a normal receptacle at each critical care patient bed location so that a critical branch distribution system failure (i.e., transfer switch) will not black out the entire critical patient care area.

3.3.138* Patient Care Area. Any portion of a health care facility wherein patients are intended to be examined or treated. (ELE)

The definition of *patient care area* was enhanced to emphasize the need for area alarms in recovery and emergency rooms as required by 5.1.9.

A.3.3.138 Patient Care Area. Business offices, corridors, lounges, day rooms, dining rooms, or similar areas typically are not classified as patient care areas.

3.3.138.1* Critical Care Areas. Those special care units, intensive care units, coronary care units, angiography laboratories, cardiac catheterization laboratories, delivery rooms, operating rooms, postanesthesia recovery rooms, emergency departments, and similar areas in which patients are intended to be subjected to invasive procedures and connected to line-operated, patient-care–related electrical appliances.

A.3.3.138.1 Critical Care Areas. For the purpose of this standard, the use of intravenous needles or catheters used to administer fluids and/or medications, endoscopes, colonscopes, sigmoidscopes, and urinary catheters are not considered invasive.

3.3.138.2* General Care Areas. Patient bedrooms, examining rooms, treatment rooms, clinics, and similar areas in which it is intended that the patient will come in contact with ordinary appliances such as a nurse-call system, electric beds, examining lamps, telephones, and entertainment devices. (ELE)

A.3.3.138.2 General Care Areas. In such areas, patients could be connected to patient-care–related electrical appliances (such as heating pads, electrocardiographs, drainage pumps, monitors, otoscopes, ophthalmoscopes, intravenous lines, etc.).

3.3.139 Patient-Care-Related Electrical Appliance. An electrical appliance that is intended to be used for diagnostic, therapeutic, or monitoring purposes in a patient care vicinity. (ELE)

3.3.140 Patient Care Vicinity. A space, within a location intended for the examination and treatment of patients, extending 1.8 m (6 ft) beyond the normal location of the bed, chair, table, treadmill, or other device that supports the patient during examination and treatment and extending vertically to 7 ft 6 in. (2.3 m) above the floor. (ELE)

A *patient care vicinity* is an area within a room and does not extend through barriers such as walls, partitions, or floors. It is a fixed area that does not move with a patient through corridors, hallways, or waiting rooms. The term *patient care vicinity* more accurately conveys the intended meaning of a place where patients are actually cared for.

◀ **FAQ**
A patient care area consists of both critical care and general care, but what is a patient care vicinity?

The dimensions of a patient care vicinity are based on the possible reach of the patient or the reach of an attendant who might be touching the bed with one hand and touching a piece of apparatus with the other. The dimensions include a small safety factor in the event of unforeseen circumstances. Vertically, the dimension provides for the use of an IV pole, orthopedic frame, or similar vertically mounted attachments. Dimensional limits were established so that in a large room it would not be necessary to treat the entire room as the patient care vicinity. See Exhibit 3.8 through Exhibit 3.10.

Like many code provisions, the definition of patient care vicinity provides a definable baseline for applying safety regulations. Such a baseline prevents requirements that are too

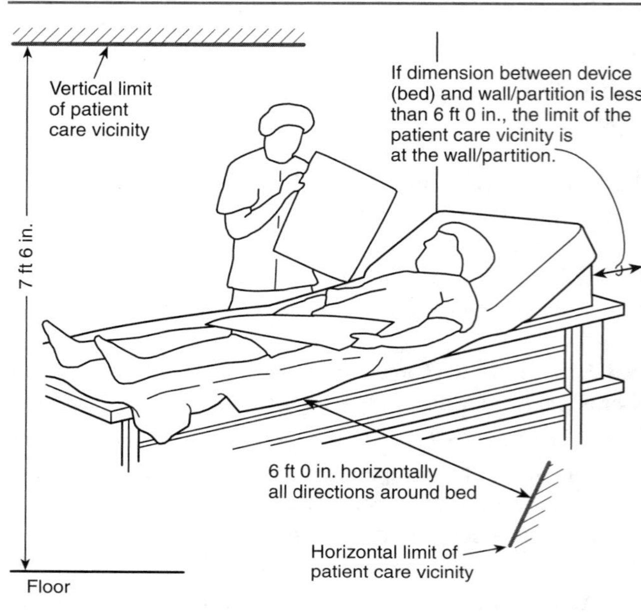

EXHIBIT 3.8 *A patient bed, one of the many kinds of patient care vicinities.*

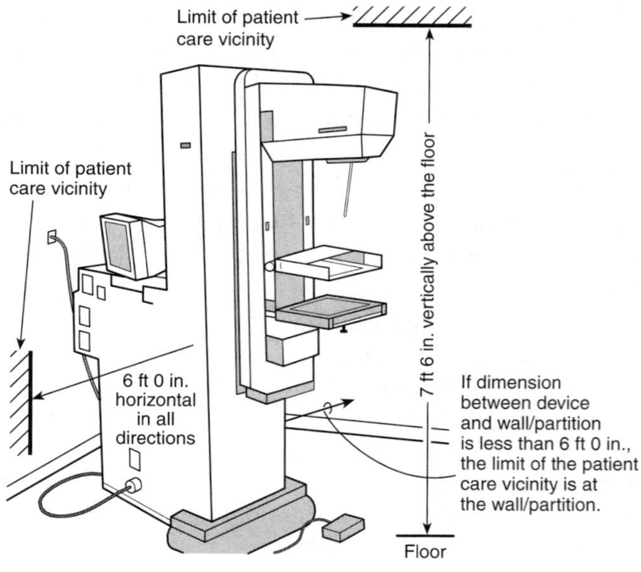

EXHIBIT 3.9 *A mammography machine, one of the many kinds of patient care vicinities.*

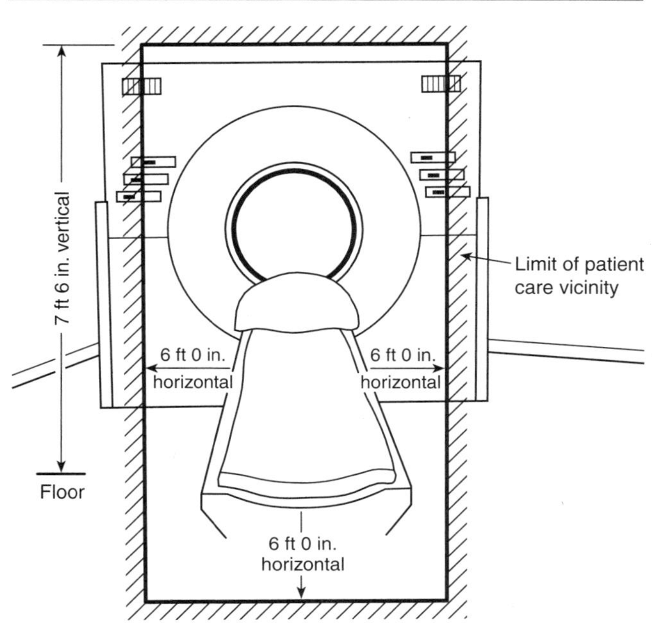

EXHIBIT 3.10 *An MRI (magnetic resonance imaging) unit, one of the many kinds of patient care apparatus.*

restrictive (e.g., the whole hospital considered a patient care vicinity) or too lenient (e.g., no need to designate any patient care vicinities).

3.3.141 Patient Equipment Grounding Point. A jack or terminal that serves as the collection point for redundant grounding of electric appliances serving a patient care vicinity or for grounding other items in order to eliminate electromagnetic interference problems. (ELE)

The reference to electromagnetic interference was considered necessary because it is a recognized problem, and proper grounding will reduce its effects.

3.3.142* Patient Lead. Any deliberate electrical connection that can carry current between an appliance and a patient. (ELE)

A.3.3.142 Patient Lead. This can be a surface contact (e.g., an ECG electrode); an invasive connection (e.g., implanted wire or catheter); or an incidental long-term connection (e.g., conductive tubing).

It is not intended to include adventitious or casual contacts such as a push button, bed surface, lamp, hand-held appliance, and so forth.

Also see 3.3.84, Isolated Patient Lead.

Patient lead is not intended to include adventitious or casual contacts such as a push button, bed surface, lamp, hand-held appliance, and so forth.

3.3.143 Patient Medical Gas. Piped gases such as oxygen, nitrous oxide, helium, carbon dioxide, and medical air that are used in the application of human respiration and the calibration of medical devices used for human respiration. (PIP)

3.3.144 Piped Distribution System. A pipeline network assembly of equipment that starts at and includes the source valve, warning systems (master, area, local alarms), bulk gas system signal actuating switch wiring, interconnecting piping, and all other components up to and including the station outlets/inlets. (PIP)

The term in 3.3.144 is also often applied to a vacuum system, even though that system flows to, rather than away from, the source.

3.3.145 Piping. The tubing or conduit of the system. The three general classes of piping are main lines, risers. and branch (lateral) lines. (PIP)

The definitions in 3.3.145.1 through 3.3.145.3 apply to both positive-pressure gas systems and negative-pressure vacuum systems because the layouts of the distribution systems of each are similar.

3.3.145.1 Branch (Lateral) Lines. Those sections or portions of the piping system that serve a room or group of rooms on the same story of the facility. (PIP)

3.3.145.2 Main Lines. The piping that connects the source (pumps, receivers, etc.) to the risers or branches, or both. (PIP)

3.3.145.3 Risers. The vertical pipes connecting the system main line(s) with the branch lines on the various levels of the facility. (PIP)

3.3.146 Plug (Attachment Plug, Cap). A device that, by insertion in a receptacle, establishes connection between the conductors of the attached flexible cord and the conductors connected permanently to the receptacle. (ELE)

3.3.147 Positive-Negative Pressure Breathing. Ventilation of the lungs by the application of intermittent positive-negative pressure to the airway. (GAS)

3.3.148 Pressure.

3.3.148.1 Absolute Pressure. The total pressure in a system with reference to zero pressure. (HYP)

3.3.148.2 Ambient Pressure. Refers to total pressure of the environment referenced. (HYP)

3.3.148.3 Gauge Pressure. Refers to total pressure above (or below) atmospheric. (HYP)

3.3.148.4 High Pressure. A pressure exceeding 200 psig (1.38 kPa gauge) (215 psia). (GAS)

3.3.148.5* Partial Pressure. The pressure, in absolute units, exerted by a particular gas in a gas mixture. (HYP)

A.3.3.148.5 Partial Pressure. The pressure contributed by other gases in the mixture is ignored. For example, oxygen is one of the constituents of air; the partial pressure of oxygen in standard air, at a standard air pressure of 14.7 psia, is 3.06 psia or 0.208 ATA or 158 mm Hg.

Dalton's law states, "In a mixture of gases the pressure exerted by each gas is the same as it would exert if it alone occupied the same volume; and the total pressure is the sum of the partial pressures of the component gases." This is an important gas law that should be understood. The effect of a component gas (such as carbon dioxide) could be insignificant at normal ambient pressure but extremely hazardous under hyperbaric conditions. For example, if 2 percent carbon dioxide exists at a chamber pressure of 5 ATA (132 FSW), it would have the same physiological effect as 10 percent breathed at sea level. Elevated partial pressures of carbon dioxide are thought to reduce one's tolerance to central nervous system oxygen toxicity.

3.3.148.6 Positive Pressure. Pressure greater than ambient atmospheric. (GAS)

3.3.148.7* Working Pressure. A pressure not exceeding 11.6 kg/cm^2 (200 psig). (GAS)

A.3.3.148.7 Working Pressure. A pipeline working pressure of 2.9 to 3.2 kg/cm^2 (50 to 55 psig) is conventional because medical gas equipment is generally designed and calibrated for use at this pressure.

3.3.149* Pressure-Reducing Regulator. A device that automatically reduces gas under high pressure to a usable lower working pressure. (GAS)

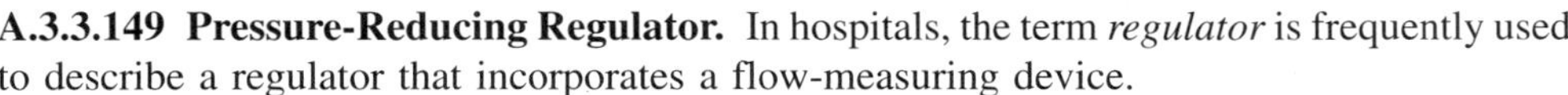

A.3.3.149 Pressure-Reducing Regulator. In hospitals, the term *regulator* is frequently used to describe a regulator that incorporates a flow-measuring device.

3.3.150 Procedure Room. Where the proceduralist is using instrumentation that requires constant observation and control.

3.3.151 psia. Pounds per square inch absolute, a unit of pressure measurement with zero pressure as the base or reference pressure. (HYP)

3.3.152* psig. Pounds per square inch gauge, a unit of pressure measurement with atmospheric pressure as the base or reference pressure. (HYP)

See the commentary following 3.3.14.2 for a discussion on *atmosphere absolute (ATA).*

A.3.3.152 psig. Under standard conditions, 0 psig is equivalent to 14.7 psia.

3.3.153 Quiet Ground. A system of grounding conductors, insulated from portions of the conventional grounding of the power system, that interconnects the grounds of electric appliances for the purpose of improving immunity to electromagnetic noise. (ELS)

3.3.154 Reactance. The component of impedance contributed by inductance or capacitance. The unit of reactance is the ohm. (ELE)

See the commentary following 3.3.78 for a discussion on *impedance.*

3.3.155* Reactive Material. A material that, by itself, is readily capable of detonation, explosive decomposition, or explosive reaction at normal or elevated temperatures and pressures. [**45**, 2004] (LAB)

A.3.3.155 Reactive Material. See Table C.11.2.3.3 for definitions of Reactivity 3 and Reactivity 4.

3.3.156 Reference Grounding Point. The ground bus of the panelboard or isolated power system panel supplying the patient care area. (ELE)

3.3.157* Refrigerating Equipment. Any mechanically operated equipment used for storing, below normal ambient temperature, hazardous materials having flammability ratings of 3 or 4. (LAB)

A.3.3.157 Refrigerating Equipment. It includes refrigerators, freezers, and similar equipment.

3.3.158 Relative Analgesia. A state of sedation and partial block of pain perception produced in a patient by the inhalation of concentrations of nitrous oxide insufficient to produce loss of consciousness (conscious sedation). (GAS)

In addition to procedures performed in hospital locations, conscious sedation is frequently used during dental procedures.

3.3.159* Remote. A Level 3 source of supply that is accessed by exiting the single or multiple treatment facility. (PIP)

A.3.3.159 Remote. A gas storage supply system can be remote from the single treatment facility, but all use points must be contiguous within the facility.

Note that remoteness is not a matter of distance; rather, it is based on whether one must use an exit to go from the use point treatment facility to the storage area.

3.3.160 Reserve Supply. Where existing, that portion of the supply equipment that automatically supplies the system in the event of failure of the operating supply. The reserve supply only functions in an emergency and not as a normal operating procedure. (PIP)

Reserve supply should not be confused with secondary supply. (See 3.3.173.4, *Secondary Supply.*)

3.3.161 Safety Can. An approved container, of not more than 18.9 L (5 gal) capacity, having a spring-closing lid and spout cover and so designed that it will safely relieve internal pressure when subjected to fire exposure. (LAB)

The definition for *safety can* is taken from NFPA 30, *Flammable and Combustible Liquids Code* [4].

3.3.162 Scavenging. An alternate term for WAGD often applied in Level 3. (PIP)

3.3.163 SCFM. Standard cubic feet per minute. (PIP)

The *SCFM* is a standard reference. In an actual gas flow situation, gas flow rate will be different as pressure and temperature change.

With regard to patient suction therapy and Level 1 vacuum systems, SCFM is the volume of air drawn into the vacuum system through patient drainage and aspiration equipment, the ambient room air, or both.

3.3.164 Selected Receptacles. A minimal number of receptacles selected by the governing body of a facility as necessary to provide essential patient care and facility services during loss of normal power. (ELS)

FAQ ▶
How many receptacles should be placed on the essential electrical system?

Although no specific number of receptacles is listed in Chapter 4, it is important to be judicious in selecting only the minimum number of receptacles for connection to the essential electrical system. Although it can be argued that any electrical receptacle might be needed in an emergency, prudent selection, based on need and past experience, is to be used.

The standard has emphasized that limiting the number of receptacles on the essential electrical system limits the load on generator sets. The administration (or its duly appointed representatives) of a facility is responsible for determining the number and location of receptacles on the essential electrical system.

Readers are reminded that not every receptacle is to be wired to the essential electrical system. The entire facility should not be placed on the essential electrical system.

3.3.165 Self-Extinguishing. A characteristic of a material such that, once the source of ignition is removed, the flame is quickly extinguished without the fuel or oxidizer being exhausted. (HYP)

3.3.166 Semipermanent Connection. A noninterchangeable connection, usually a D.I.S.S. connector, which is the termination of the pipeline and that is intended to be detached only for service. It is not the point at which the user makes connections or disconnections. (PIP)

This definition for *semipermanent connection* is applied only to the manufactured assembly, and is the point at which the assembly is connected to the physical pipeline. In the nature of a manufactured assembly, the connection is not used except when the assembly requires service, and thus has its own requirements and allowances. See 5.1.6 for requirements.

The copper pipelines to these assemblies are commonly terminated with an outlet (typically a D.I.S.S. connector) that is hidden behind or within the manufactured assembly. The connection between this pipeline outlet and the outlets at which the user makes connections (termed the *terminal*) is commonly made using flexible tubing (typically rubber hoses). Because these hoses and outlets are hidden, the flexible connections and outlets are accessible to maintenance personnel only when the manufactured assembly is disassembled.

This practice has created two distinct hazards. First, manufacturers are encouraging the installation of multiple station outlets to allow for convenient future connections. These station outlets are frequently not tested and certified, increasing the possibility of a latent cross connection that would be discovered only after the outlet is activated, which could be long after the system is in service. The second hazard results from the flexible assembly and connection hidden in the manufactured assembly. A leak or rupture would allow the development of an oxygen-enriched atmosphere that could have very serious consequences in a fire incident. (See 5.1.6 for requirements designed to mitigate these hazards.)

3.3.167 Service Inlet. The pneumatic terminus of a Level 3 piped vacuum system. (PIP)

The definitions of *service inlet* and *service outlet* (see 3.3.168) help to distinguish between an inlet for a Level 3 vacuum system and an inlet for a more critical level of patients, such as for a Level 1 vacuum system.

Note that the analog to a service inlet in Level 1, 2, or 3 medical gases (e.g., oxygen and nitrous oxide) is a "station outlet." Its counterpart in Level 1 and Level 2 vacuum is a "station inlet." In Level 3 Gas Powered Systems, its equivalent is a "service outlet." These four definitions are often misapplied.

3.3.168 Service Outlet. The pneumatic terminus of a piped gas system for other than critical, continuous duty, nonflammable medical life support type gases such as oxygen, nitrous oxide, or medical air. (PIP)

The equivalent to a service outlet in Level 1 and Level 2 medical gases is a "station outlet." The analog in Level 3 vacuum systems is a "service inlet." The counterpart in Level 1 and Level 2 vacuum systems is a "station inlet." These four definitions are often misapplied.

3.3.169* Single Treatment Facility. A diagnostic or treatment complex under a single management comprising a number of use points, but confined to a single contiguous group of use points (i.e., does not involve widely separated locations or separate distinct practices). (PIP)

Note the definition of *single treatment facility* is applied only in Level 3 occupancies. See also 3.3.114, *Multiple Treatment Facility.*

A.3.3.169 Single Treatment Facility. The definition of single treatment facility was established to take into consideration principally single-level installations or those of a practice that could be two-level, but are reached by open stairs within the confines of the single treatment facility. See Figure A.3.3.169.

3.3.170* Site of Intentional Expulsion. All points within 0.3 m (1 ft) of a point at which an oxygen-enriched atmosphere is intentionally vented to the atmosphere. (GAS)

A.3.3.170 Site of Intentional Expulsion. This definition addresses the site of intended expulsion. Actual expulsion can occur at other sites remote from the intended site due to disconnections, leaks, or rupture of gas conduits and connections. Vigilance on the part of the patient care team is essential to ensure system integrity.

For example, for a patient receiving oxygen via a nasal cannula or face mask, the site of expulsion normally surrounds the mask or cannula; for a patient receiving oxygen while enclosed in a canopy or incubator, the site of intentional expulsion normally surrounds the

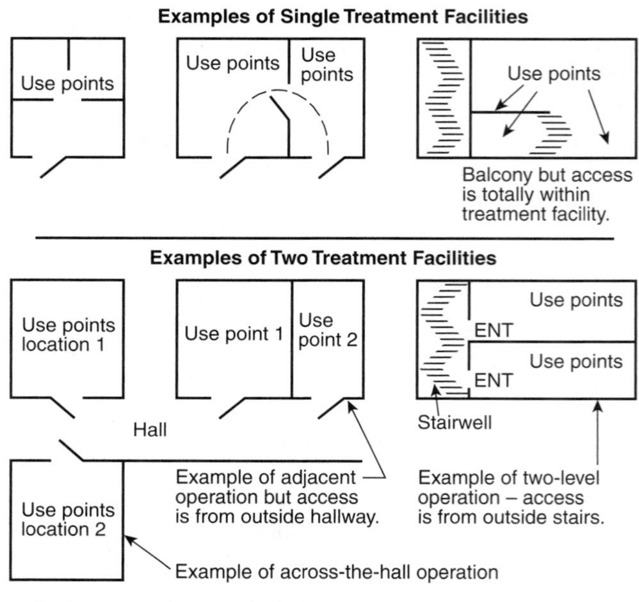

Figure A.3.3.169 *Examples of Treatment Facilities.*

openings to the canopy or incubator; for a patient receiving oxygen while on a ventilator, the site of intentional expulsion normally surrounds the venting port on the ventilator.

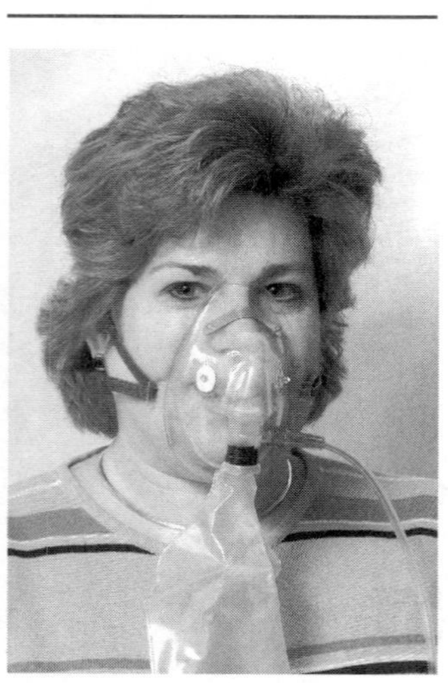

EXHIBIT 3.11 *A face mask used to provide oxygen to a patient.*

Paragraph A.3.3.170 calls attention to the unexpected type of failure, such as from equipment, and the unintentional type of failure, such as from human error. Any resulting hazards should be addressed without delay.

In Exhibit 3.11 a face mask is used to provide oxygen to a patient. The site of intentional expulsion is 0.3 m (1 ft) away from any point on the face mask.

The term *site of intentional expulsion* refers to intentional expulsion within the facility and does not refer to expulsion (exhaust) to the outside environment (as in building exhaust systems).

See also the commentary following 8.5.2.3.1, 9.6.1.2.3, and 10.2.9.3(4)(b).

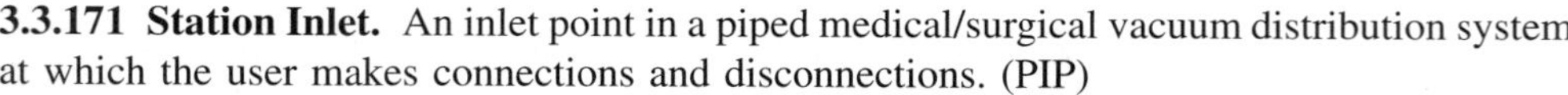

3.3.171 Station Inlet. An inlet point in a piped medical/surgical vacuum distribution system at which the user makes connections and disconnections. (PIP)

This term distinguishes between the end connector of Level 1 piped vacuum systems and the end connector of Level 1 piped gas systems.

Note that the equivalent to a station inlet in Level 3 vacuum systems is a "service inlet." The analog in Level 1 and Level 2 medical gases is a "station outlet," and its counterpart in Level 3 gas-powered devices is a "service outlet." These four definitions are often misapplied.

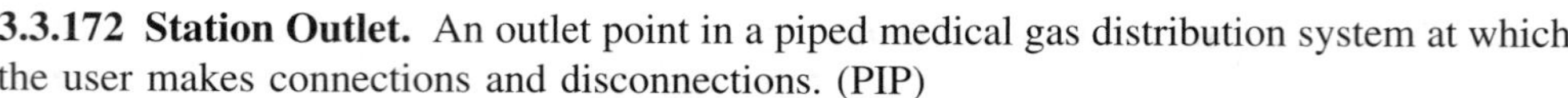

3.3.172 Station Outlet. An outlet point in a piped medical gas distribution system at which the user makes connections and disconnections. (PIP)

Note that the equivalent to a station outlet in Level 3 gas-powered systems is a "service outlet." The analog in Level 1 and Level 2 vacuum systems is a "station inlet," and its counterpart in Level 3 vacuum systems is a "service inlet." These four definitions are often misapplied.

3.3.173 Supply Source.

Supply source has the following subdefinitions for portions of the operating (overall) system: *Primary Supply, Reserve Supply,* and *Secondary Supply.*

> ***3.3.173.1 Operating Supply.*** The portion of the supply system that normally supplies the piping systems. The operating supply consists of a primary supply or a primary and secondary supply. (PIP)
>
> ***3.3.173.2 Primary Supply.*** That portion of the source equipment that actually supplies the system. (PIP)
>
> ***3.3.173.3 Reserve Supply.*** Where provided, that portion of the source equipment that automatically supplies the system in the event of failure of the primary and secondary operating supply. (PIP)
>
> ***3.3.173.4 Secondary Supply.*** Where provided, that portion of the source equipment that automatically supplies the system when the primary supply becomes exhausted. (PIP)

◀ **FAQ**
Is a secondary supply the same as a reserve supply?

The term *secondary supply* should not be confused with the term *reserve supply.* A secondary supply will, in the course of normal operation, be brought on-line once the *primary supply* has dropped below the amount or pressure required for normal operation. A reserve supply is used only in the event of the failure of both the primary and secondary supplies. (See 3.3.173.3, *Reserve Supply.*)

3.3.174 Support Gas. Nitrogen or instrument air that is used to support medical procedures by operating medical–surgical tools, equipment booms, pendants, and similar devices, and are not respired as part of any treatment. (PIP)

The definition of *support gas* addresses the use of nitrogen and instrument air to support medical procedures. Support gases would not come in direct contact with the patient.

3.3.175* Surface-Mounted Medical Gas Rail Systems. A surface-mounted gas delivery system intended to provide ready access for two or more gases through a common delivery system to provide multiple gas station outlet locations within a single patient room or critical care area. (PIP)

A.3.3.175 Surface-Mounted Medical Gas Rail Systems. It is the intent that surface-mounted medical gas rail systems would be permitted in individual patient rooms but would not be allowed to go directly through room walls to adjacent patient rooms. However, it is the intent to allow surface-mounted medical gas rails to be used in a given critical care area where there can be a partition separating certain patient care functions, essentially leaving the system within the given critical care area. As an example, two adjacent patient rooms outside of a critical care unit would not be permitted to have a surface-mounted medical gas rail interconnect between the two rooms through the wall. However, in a nursery where there might be one or two segregated areas for isolation, a medical gas rail system supplying more than one isolation room, but within the nursery area, would be permitted to be interconnected with the nursery system.

A *surface-mounted medical gas rail system* (SMMGRS) is intended to service one given patient care area without penetrating any normal room wall enclosures. For example, two adjoining rooms could have rail systems connected in series from one source. The interconnection between the rooms is intended to be a section of the piping distribution system, not the rail itself.

Where two adjoining areas in a room are separated with a partition that is not floor-to-ceiling, the SMMGRS could be continuous within the room enclosure.

3.3.176 Task Illumination. Provisions for the minimum lighting required to carry out necessary tasks in the areas described in Chapter 4, including safe access to supplies and equipment and access to exits. (ELS)

3.3.177 Terminal. The end of a flexible hose or tubing used in a manufactured assembly where the user is intended to make connection and disconnection. (PIP)

3.3.178 Tube.

3.3.178.1* Endotracheal Tube. A tube for insertion through the mouth or nose into the upper portion of the trachea (windpipe). (GAS)

A.3.3.178.1 Endotracheal Tube. An endotracheal tube can be equipped with an inflatable cuff.

3.3.178.2* Tracheotomy Tube. A curved tube for insertion into the trachea (windpipe) below the larynx (voice box) during the performance of an appropriate operative procedure (tracheotomy). (GAS)

A.3.3.178.2 Tracheotomy Tube. A tracheotomy tube can be equipped with an inflatable cuff.

3.3.179* Unattended Laboratory Operation. A laboratory procedure or operation at which there is no person present who is knowledgeable regarding the operation and emergency shutdown procedures. [**45**, 2004] (LAB)

A.3.3.179 Unattended Laboratory Operation. Absence for even short periods without coverage by a knowledgeable person constitutes an unattended laboratory operation.

3.3.180 Use Point. A location with any number of station outlets and inlets arranged for access by a practitioner during treatment of a patient. (PIP)

3.3.181* Utility Center (J box). A type of terminal enclosure for utilities (e.g., gas power, vacuum, water, electrical power) used in office-based occupancies. (PIP)

A.3.3.181 Utility Center (J box). A utility center typically includes electrical receptacle(s), compressed air, nitrogen, vacuum, and water.

The definition of *utility center (J box) identifies the enclosure that is found in typical Level 3 systems.*

3.3.182 Vaporizer. A heat exchange unit designed to convert cryogenic liquid into the gaseous state. (PIP)

3.3.183* WAGD Interface. A device provided on the anesthesia gas machine that connects the WAGD network to the patient breathing circuit. (PIP)

A.3.3.183 WAGD Interface. Interfaces are provided with overpressure, underpressure, overflow, and underflow compensation to ensure the breathing circuit is isolated from the WAGD system.

3.3.184 Waste Anesthetic Gas Disposal (WAGD). The process of capturing and carrying away gases vented from the patient breathing circuit during the normal operation of gas anesthesia or analgesia equipment. (PIP)

WAGD is often termed *scavenging* or *evacuation.* The term *WAGD,* however, is technically correct, more descriptive, and less susceptible to misinterpretation. Scavenging and evacuation have other medical uses and are sometimes confused with WAGD. For further information on WAGD, see the commentary following 5.1.3.7.

The WAGD system has formerly been called evacuation, scavenging, exhaust, and in Europe is known as AGSS. Note that the 2000 edition of the CGA V-5 DISS standard [8] still denotes the connector "Evacuation" or "Evac," and thus the old name persists.

3.3.185* Wet Locations. The area in a patient care area where a procedure is performed that is normally subject to wet conditions while patients are present including standing fluids on the floor or drenching of the work area, either of which condition is intimate to the patient or staff. (ADM)

A.3.3.185 Wet Locations. Routine housekeeping procedures and incidental spillage of liquids do not define a wet location.

Wet locations are limited to areas where there are long-term significant amounts of water. Many patient areas become wet due to such things as washing, incontinence, or hot packs, but these areas are not considered wet locations for the purpose of this document.

◀ **FAQ**
Is the patient care vicinity considered a wet location?

The term *wet locations* appears in Chapter 3 because the definition, originally developed for hospitals, was deemed applicable to all health care facilities.

REFERENCES CITED IN COMMENTARY

1. Bruner, J. and Leonard, P., "Electricity, Safety and the Patient." Year Book Medical Publishers, Chicago, 1989, pp. 249–251. (Reprinted 1996, by authors, c/o Box 617, Groton, MA 01450.)
2. NFPA *101*®, *Life Safety Code*®, 2006 edition.
3. NFPA 70, *National Electrical Code*®, 2005 edition.
4. NFPA 30, *Flammable and Combustible Liquids Code,* 2003 edition.
5. Schmidt, T. C., Dorr, V. A., and Hamilton, Jr., R. W., Technical Memorandum UCRI-721, *Chamber Fire Safety,* Ocean Systems, Inc., Research and Development Laboratory, Tarrytown, NY 10591.
6. DiNenno, P. J., ed., *The SFPE Handbook of Fire Protection Engineering,* 3rd edition, NFPA, Quincy, MA, and SFPE, Baltimore, MD, 2002.
7. Cote, A. E., ed., *Fire Protection Handbook,* 19th edition, NFPA, Quincy, MA, 2003.
8. *V-5 Diameter-Index Safety System (Noninterchangeable Low Pressure Connections for Medical Gas Applications),* Compressed Gas Association, Arlington, VA, August 4, 2000.
9. NFPA 326, *Standard for the Safeguarding of Tanks and Containers for Entry, Cleaning, or Repair,* 2005 edition.
10. NFPA 1600, *Standard on Disaster/Emergency Management and Business Continuity Programs,* 2004 edition.
11. NFPA 45, *Standard on Fire Protection for Laboratories Using Chemicals,* 2004 edition.
12. NFPA 259, *Standard Test Method for Potential Heat of Building Materials,* 2003 edition.
13. "Compressed Air," USPXXII-NF17, U.S.-Pharmacopeia, Rockville, MD, January 1, 1990.
14. NFPA 53, *Recommended Practice on Materials, Equipment, and Systems Used in Oxygen-Enriched Atmospheres,* 2004 edition.

CHAPTER 4

Electrical Systems

Chapter 4 deals with hazards associated with electrical systems in health care facilities. The material has been developed over many years by experts concerned with the reliability and continuity of the power supply to crucial equipment and systems and the risk of fires, explosions, electrical shock, and electrocution that might be caused by faults in the electrical system.

All requirements and recommendations on *flammable* inhalation anesthetics were moved to Annex E, Flammable Anesthetizing Locations, in 2002. References in Chapters 1 through 21, and in Annexes A, C, and F, are to *nonflammable* inhalation anesthetics and anesthetizing locations.

Chapter 4 includes commentary on the development of the scope of Article 517 of NFPA 70, *National Electrical Code*® [1]. That article includes much of the text of Chapter 4 of NFPA 99. The Health Care Facilities technical committees are responsible for establishing the criteria for performance, maintenance, and testing of, among other things, electrical systems and electrical appliances. Panel 17 of the National Electrical Code Committee, responsible for Article 517 of NFPA 70, establishes the requirements for electrical construction and installation based on such performance criteria.

4.1* Applicability

This chapter applies to health care facilities as referenced in other chapters.

A.4.1 The application of requirements contained in Chapter 4 for specific types of health care facilities can be found in Chapters 13, 14, 17, 18, and 21.

Although complete compliance with this chapter is desirable, variations in existing health care facilities should be considered acceptable in instances where wiring arrangements are in accordance with prior editions of this document or afford an equivalent degree of performance and reliability. Such variations could occur, particularly with certain wiring in separate or common raceways, with certain functions connected to one or another system or branch, or with certain provisions for automatically or manually delayed restoration of power from the alternate (emergency) source of power.

4.2 Nature of Hazards

See Section B.1.

The hazards addressed in this chapter and in Chapter 8 relate primarily to electrical shock, power continuity, and fire. Although these are important in any occupancy, the unique circumstances that are encountered in hospitals and other health care facilities require special consideration. Consequently, this chapter goes into considerable detail regarding compliance with the electrical requirements particular to health care facilities.

4.2.1* Fire and Explosions.

A.4.2.1 Electrical systems can be subject to the occurrence of electrical fires. Grounding systems, overcurrent protective devices, and other subjects discussed in this standard could be intended for fire prevention as well as other purposes. This aspect of electrical systems is the primary focus of other NFPA standards and will not be emphasized herein.

4.2.2 Shock.

4.2.2.1 General.

4.2.2.2 Control. See B.1.2.2.2.

4.2.3 Thermal. (Reserved)

4.2.4 Interruption of Power.

See B.1.4.1.

4.3 Electrical System Requirements

4.3.1 Sources.

Each appliance of a hospital requiring electrical line power for operation shall be supported by power sources and distribution systems that provide power adequate for each service.

4.3.1.1 Power/Utility Company. (Reserved)

4.3.1.2 On-Site Generator Set. (Reserved)

4.3.2 Distribution.

4.3.2.1 Electrical Installation. Installation shall be in accordance with NFPA 70, *National Electrical Code*.

4.3.2.2* All Patient Care Areas.

A.4.3.2.2 For additional wiring requirements for anesthetizing locations, see 13.4.1.

4.3.2.2.1* Regular voltage wiring shall comply with the requirements in 4.3.2.2.1.1 through 4.3.2.2.1.3.

A.4.3.2.2.1 At the time of installation of regular voltage wiring, steps should be taken to ensure that the insulation on each conductor intended to be energized, or on quiet grounds, has not been damaged in the process of installation. When disconnected and unenergized, the resistance should be at least 20 megohms when measured with an ohmmeter having an open-circuit test voltage of at least 500 V dc.

Consideration should be given to providing reasonable accessibility to branch-circuit switching and overcurrent protection devices by the hospital staff in the patient care area. Consideration should also be given to providing labels at each receptacle and on installed equipment as to the location and identity of the distribution panel serving that power outlet or equipment, especially where the location or identity might not be readily apparent.

4.3.2.2.1.1* Circuits. Branch circuits serving a given patient bed location shall be fed from not more than one normal branch circuit distribution panel. When required, branch circuits serving a given patient bed location shall be permitted to be fed from more than one emergency branch circuit distribution panel.

Circuits from more than one critical branch panel are allowed for those facilities that desire increased reliability at patient bed locations. Also see the commentary following 4.3.2.2.1.2 and 3.3.137, *Patient Bed Location*. Exhibit 4.1 shows a typical method of wiring a receptacle.

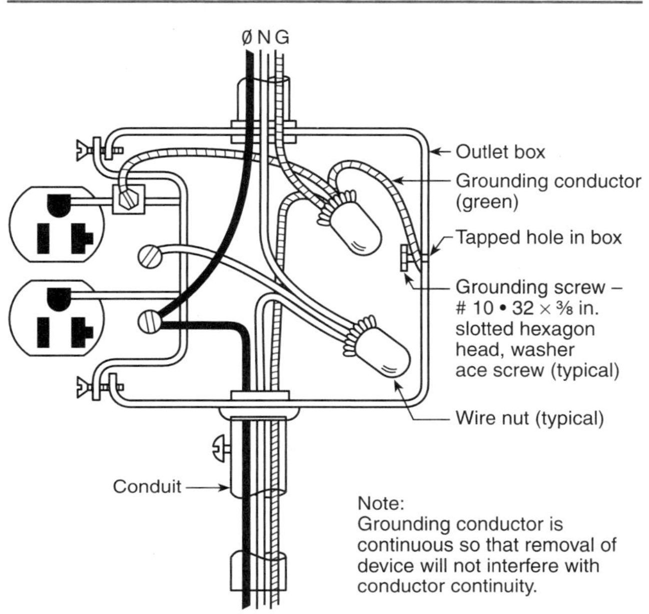

EXHIBIT 4.1 Wiring of a receptacle.

A.4.3.2.2.1.1 The requirement that branch circuits be fed from not more than one distribution panel was introduced for several reasons. A general principle is to minimize possible potential differences between the grounding pins of receptacles in one area by bringing the grounding conductors to a common point. A specific reason is to simplify maintenance by making it easier to find the source for the receptacles in a room. This is particularly a problem in hospitals where emergency conditions might require rapid restoration of power. 

4.3.2.2.1.2 Critical Care Areas. These areas shall be served by circuits from critical branch panel(s) served from a single automatic transfer switch and a minimum of one circuit served by the normal power distribution system or by a system originating from a second critical branch transfer switch.

The intent of 4.3.2.2.1.2 is to provide power to critical care areas in the event of a catastrophic failure of a distribution system or transfer switch at a time when utility power is still available. Serving the "normal" receptacle(s) from a second critical branch transfer switch satisfies this intent. This method can be particularly useful when the hospital has multiple stand-alone generators and the "second (or additional) critical branch transfer switch" is served from a (second or additional) standby generator.

4.3.2.2.1.3 Special Purpose Outlets. Branch circuits serving only special-purpose outlets or receptacles (e.g., portable X-ray receptacles) shall not be required to conform to the requirements of 4.3.2.2.1.2.

4.3.2.2.2 Grounding requirements shall comply with the requirements in 4.3.2.2.2.1 through 4.3.2.2.2.4.

4.3.2.2.2.1 Grounding Circuitry Integrity. Grounding circuits and conductors in patient care areas shall be installed in such a way that the continuity of other parts of those circuits cannot be interrupted nor the resistance raised above an acceptable level by the installation, removal, and replacement of any installed equipment, including power receptacles.

A requirement to have only one phase of power in a patient vicinity was used for a short period by some designers, based on the false premise that it would prevent faults involving 208 V from occurring. This practice was not widely adopted for several of the following reasons:

1. Occurrence of a fault involving 208 V is extremely unlikely. It would require a double fault (loss of ground in the appliance plus 110 V coming in contact with the chassis) on two different appliances, in addition to the patient touching both appliances simultaneously.
2. If one phase of power dropped out, most of the power to that patient vicinity could be lost.
3. Because at least one circuit to a patient vicinity has to be on an emergency circuit, single phasing a room would be more difficult and costly because of the correlation and extra wiring that would be necessary.

This chapter does not contain criteria requiring this wiring configuration.

4.3.2.2.2.2* Reliability of Grounding. Where used, the reliability of installed grounding circuits to a power receptacle in all patient care areas shall be at least equivalent to that provided by an electrically continuous copper conductor of appropriate ampacity run from the receptacle to a grounding bus in the distribution panel. The grounding conductor shall conform to NFPA 70, *National Electrical Code*.

A.4.3.2.2.2.2 This requirement is usually met by appropriate mounting hardware and not by wire jumpers.

Paragraph A.4.3.2.2.2.2 is included to avoid misinterpretation concerning the use of wire jumpers, as well as to avoid specifying a particular method to meet requirements for grounding.

4.3.2.2.2.3 Separate Grounding Conductor. When existing construction does not use a separate grounding conductor, the continued use of the system shall be permitted to be used, provided it meets the performance requirements in 4.3.3.1, Grounding System in Patient Care Areas.

4.3.2.2.2.4 Metal Receptacle Boxes. Where metal receptacle boxes are used, the performance of the connection between the receptacle grounding terminal and the metal box shall be equivalent to the performance provided by copper wire no smaller than 12 AWG.

Acceptable grounding limits are listed in 4.3.3.1.

4.3.2.2.3* Grounding Interconnects. In patient care areas supplied by the normal distribution system and any branch of the essential electrical system, the grounding system of the normal distribution system and that of the essential electrical system shall be interconnected.

A.4.3.2.2.3 The requirement for grounding interconnection between the normal and essential power systems follows the principle of minimizing possible potential differences between the grounding pins of receptacles in one area by bringing the grounding conductors to a common point.

Because the wiring for the normal electric power system and the essential electric power system are installed in separate conduits, it may be possible to have widely separated grounds. Paragraph A.4.3.2.2.3 emphasizes that the grounding of both systems needs to be connected together locally to avoid potential differences between local grounds.

4.3.2.2.4 Circuit Protection.

4.3.2.2.4.1* The main and downstream ground-fault protective devices (where required) shall be coordinated as required in 4.3.2.5.

A.4.3.2.2.4.1 Within the constraints of the equipment provided, consideration should be given to coordinating circuit breakers, fuses, and other overcurrent protective devices so that power interruption in that part of the circuit that precedes the interrupting device closest to a fault is not likely to occur.

It is difficult, if not impossible, to provide coordination (selectivity) for circuit breakers for high-level fault currents within the instantaneous trip ranges of two circuit breakers connected in series. Likewise, it is not always possible to achieve 100 percent coordination between two fuses or a fuse and circuit breaker. Still, as suggested in A.4.3.2.2.4.1, designers should strive to achieve coordination where overcurrent protective devices serve emergency system loads and where nonselective tripping will needlessly interrupt circuits to critical care areas and life support.

4.3.2.2.4.2* If used, ground-fault circuit interrupters (GFCIs) shall be listed and approved for the purpose.

A.4.3.2.2.4.2 Listed Class A ground-fault circuit interrupters trip when a fault current to ground is 6 mA or more.

4.3.2.2.5 Low-voltage wiring shall comply with either of the following:

(1) Fixed systems of 30 V (dc or ac rms) or less shall be ungrounded, provided the insulation between each ungrounded conductor and the primary circuit, which is supplied from a conventionally grounded distribution system, is the same protection as required for the primary voltage.
(2) A grounded low-voltage system shall be permitted provided that load currents are not carried in the grounding conductors.

It should not be inferred from 4.3.2.2.5 that low-voltage wiring must be insulated in the same way as 120 V wiring. Only insulation of low-voltage wiring on the transformer is required to be provided, with protection equivalent to that of higher-voltage wiring.

4.3.2.2.5.1 Wiring for low-voltage control systems and nonemergency communications and signaling systems shall not be required to be installed in metal raceways in anesthetizing locations.

Paragraph 4.3.2.2.5.1 is intended to eliminate confusion about whether low-voltage systems are required to be installed in metal raceways in anesthetizing locations.

4.3.2.2.6* Receptacles.

A.4.3.2.2.6 For additional requirements for receptacles in anesthetizing locations, see 13.4.1.2.6.

4.3.2.2.6.1* Types of Receptacles. Each power receptacle shall provide at least one separate, highly dependable grounding pole capable of maintaining low-contact resistance with its mating plug despite electrical and mechanical abuse. Special receptacles such as the following shall be permitted:

(1) Four-pole units providing an extra pole for redundant grounding or ground continuity monitoring
(2) Locking-type receptacles
(3) Where required for reduction of electrical noise on the grounding circuit, receptacles in which the grounding terminals are purposely insulated from the receptacle yoke

A.4.3.2.2.6.1 It is best, if possible, to employ only one type of receptacle (standard three-prong type) for as many receptacles being served by the same line voltage to avoid the inability to connect life-support equipment in emergencies. The straight-blade, three-prong receptacle is now permitted in all locations in a hospital. Previously, special receptacles were specified in operating room locations and have caused compatibility problems.

4.3.2.2.6.2 Minimum Number of Receptacles. The number of receptacles shall be determined by the intended use of the patient care areas in accordance with 4.3.2.2.6.2(A) through 4.3.2.2.6.2(D).

(A) Receptacles for Patient Bed Locations in General Care Areas. Each patient bed location shall be provided with a minimum of four receptacles (or two duplex receptacles).

(B) Receptacles for Patient Bed Locations in Critical Care Areas. Each patient bed location shall be provided with a minimum of six receptacles (or three duplex receptacles).

(C) Receptacles for Bathrooms or Toilets. Receptacles shall not be required in bathrooms or toilet rooms.

(D) Receptacles for Special Areas. Receptacles shall not be required in areas where medical requirements mandate otherwise (e.g., certain psychiatric, pediatric, or hydrotherapy areas).

It is stressed that each number of receptacles specified in 4.3.2.2.6.2(A) through (D) is a minimum number.

4.3.2.2.6.3 Polarity of Receptacles. Each receptacle shall be wired in accordance with NFPA 70, *National Electrical Code*, to ensure correct polarity.

4.3.2.2.6.4 Receptacles and Amperage. Receptacles for use with 250 V, 50 A, and 60 A ac service shall be designed for use in anesthetizing locations and shall be so designed that the 60 A receptacle will accept either the 50 A or the 60 A plug. Fifty-ampere receptacles shall be designed so as not to accept the 60 A attachment plug. These receptacles shall be of the two-pole, three-wire design with the third contact connecting to the grounding wire (green or green with yellow stripe) of the electrical system.

The usual type of receptacle installed in a health care facility, one that accepts a plug with two flat, straight blades and a U-shaped pin, would be acceptable anywhere in nonflammable anesthetizing locations if the receptacle were listed.

FAQ ▶
Is it permissible to have both isolated and grounded power circuits in an area where isolated power is not required?

It is not prohibited to have both isolated and grounded power circuits in an area that is not required to have isolated power. Properly labeling receptacles will at least tell staff and maintenance personnel which receptacles are on isolated power and which are not. If isolated and grounded power circuits are present in an operating room, equipment should preferably be plugged into all the ungrounded power circuits first.

4.3.2.2.6.5 Other Services Receptacles. Receptacles provided for other services having different voltages, frequencies, or types on the same premises shall be of such design that attachment plugs and caps used in such receptacles cannot be connected to circuits of a different voltage, frequency, or type, but shall be interchangeable within each classification and rating required for two-wire, 125 V, single-phase ac service.

4.3.2.2.7 Special Grounding.

4.3.2.2.7.1* Use of Quiet Grounds. A quiet ground, if used, shall not defeat the purposes of the safety features of the grounding systems detailed herein.

A.4.3.2.2.7.1 Care should be taken in specifying such a quiet grounding system because the grounding impedance is controlled only by the grounding wires and does not benefit from any conduit or building structure in parallel with it.

Isolated ground receptacles are often used to reduce noise when serving physiological monitors and other electronic equipment. In addition, manufacturers of diagnostic and treatment equipment may require a dedicated (or quiet) ground. These accommodations must not, however, violate the grounding requirements of Article 250 of NFPA 70, *National Electrical Code* [1].

4.3.2.2.7.2 Patient Equipment Grounding Point. A patient equipment grounding point comprising one or more grounding terminals or jacks shall be permitted in an accessible location in the patient care vicinity.

4.3.2.2.7.3* Special Grounding in Patient Care Areas. In addition to the grounding required to meet the performance requirements of 4.3.3.1, additional grounding shall be permitted where special circumstances so dictate.

A.4.3.2.2.7.3 Special grounding methods could be required in patient vicinities immediately adjacent to rooms containing high-power or high-frequency equipment that causes electrical interference with monitors or other electromedical devices. In extreme cases, electromagnetic induction can cause the voltage limits of 4.3.3.1 to be exceeded.

Electromagnetic interference problems can be due to a variety of causes, some simple, others complex. Such problems are best solved one at a time. In some locations, grounding of stretchers, examining tables, or bed frames will be helpful. Where necessary, a patient equipment grounding point should be installed. This can usually be accomplished even after completion of construction by installing a receptacle faceplate fitted with grounding posts. Special grounding wires should not be used unless they are found to be essential for a particular location because they can interfere with patient care procedures or present trip hazards.

As noted in A.4.3.2.2.7.3, eliminating electrical interference can be difficult because interference can be generated by various mechanisms: conducted (or power line), radiated, or coupled (via magnetic fields). It is often easier to locate and remove the source of interference than it is to protect the appliance being disturbed. In any event, simple solutions, such as relocating the appliance, should be tried before expensive ones, such as the installing of special grounding or shielding.

4.3.2.2.8 Wet Locations.

4.3.2.2.8.1* Wet location patient care areas shall be provided with special protection against electric shock. This special protection shall be provided as follows:

(1) A power distribution system that inherently limits the possible ground-fault current due to a first fault to a low value, without interrupting the power supply
(2) A power distribution system in which the power supply is interrupted if the ground-fault current does, in fact, exceed a value of 6 mA

A.4.3.2.2.8.1 Moisture can reduce the contact resistance of the body, and electrical insulation is more subject to failure.

4.3.2.2.8.2 Patient beds, toilets, bidets, and wash basins shall not be required to be considered wet locations.

4.3.2.2.8.3 In existing construction, the requirements of 4.3.2.2.8.1 are not required when written inspection procedure, acceptable to the authority having jurisdiction, is continuously enforced by a designated individual at the hospital, to indicate that equipment-grounding conductors for 120 V, single-phase, 15 A and 20 A receptacles, equipment connected by cord and plug, and fixed electrical equipment are installed and maintained in accordance with NFPA 70, *National Electrical Code*, and applicable performance requirements of this chapter.

(A) The procedure shall include electrical continuity tests of all required equipment, grounding conductors, and their connections.

(B) Fixed receptacles, equipment connected by cord and plug, and fixed electrical equipment shall be tested as follows:

(1) When first installed
(2) Where there is evidence of damage
(3) After any repairs
(4) At intervals not exceeding 6 months

FAQ ▶ Is an operating room considered a wet location?

Although 4.3.2.2.8 does not state where isolated power systems (IPSs) or GFCIs are required, this requirement can be applied to operating rooms, many of which meet the definition of *wet location* in Chapter 3. It thus becomes necessary for a facility to determine which types of procedures will normally take place in each operating room and what types of special protection against electric shock must be provided if wet procedures are likely to be performed. (See also related commentary under the definitions of *isolated power system* and *wet location* in Chapter 3.) Note that it is left to the user to determine the method of protection used in a particular location.

Paragraph 4.3.2.2.8.3 is included in the standard in the event a local jurisdiction enforces new construction requirements on existing construction as well. Requirements in each edition of NFPA 99 apply only to new construction, equipment, systems, and so forth, built or approved *after the effective date* of that edition, unless specifically noted otherwise. (See Section 1.3.)

4.3.2.2.8.4 The use of an isolated power system (IPS) shall be permitted as a protective means capable of limiting ground fault current without power interruption. When installed, such a power system shall conform to the requirements of 4.3.2.6.

4.3.2.2.8.5 Where power interruption under first fault condition (line-to-ground fault) is tolerable, the use of a ground-fault circuit interrupter (GFCI) shall be permitted as the protective means that monitors the actual ground-fault current and interrupts the power when that current exceeds 6 mA.

The phrase *first fault condition* refers to a high-impedance fault to ground. GFCI breakers are intended to interrupt high-impedance ground faults. It is important to note that the line isolation monitors provided with an isolated power system (IPS) will generally alarm under first fault conditions, before conventional circuit breakers (without GFCI) trip. If faults continue, these "first fault conditions" can develop into low-impedance faults, which can produce currents of sufficient magnitude to trip conventional (non-GFCI) circuit breakers.

4.3.2.2.9 Isolated Power. An isolated power system shall not be required to be installed in any patient care area except as specified in 4.3.2.2.8. The system shall be permitted to be installed where it conforms to the performance requirements specified in 4.3.2.6.

See the commentary following A.3.3.85, *Isolated Power System,* for an explanation of the need for isolated power.

4.3.2.3 Laboratories. Outlets with two to four receptacles, or an equivalent power strip, shall be installed every 0.5 m to 1.0 m (1.6 ft to 3.3 ft) in instrument usage areas, and either installation is to be at least 8 cm (3.15 in.) above the countertop.

4.3.2.4 Other Nonpatient Areas. (Reserved)

4.3.2.5 Ground-Fault Protection.

4.3.2.5.1 Applicability. The requirements of 4.3.2.5.2 shall apply to hospitals and other buildings housing critical care areas or utilizing life support equipment, and buildings that provide essential utilities or services for the operation of critical care areas or electrical life support equipment.

4.3.2.5.2 When ground-fault protection is provided for operation of the service or feeder disconnecting means, an additional step of ground-fault protection shall be provided in the next level of feeder downstream toward the load. Ground-fault protection for operation of the service and feeder disconnecting means shall be fully selective such that the downstream device and not the upstream device shall open for downstream ground faults.

Paragraph 4.3.2.5.2 provides performance criteria for ground-fault protection. It reflects the standard's intent that ground-fault protection be installed in health care facilities to prevent tripping of the main or feeder ground-fault protection where tripping might needlessly interrupt power to patient care areas or to life support equipment. New paragraph 4.3.2.5.1, Applicability, clarifies the intent with regard to the facility types that must comply with 4.3.2.5.2. Central plants, for example, that do not have critical care areas or life support equipment and do not provide essential utilities or services (e.g., medical vacuum pumps) for the operation of critical care areas or electrical life support equipment are not required to comply with 4.3.2.5.2. In addition, the new section clarifies that it is incumbent upon owners of office buildings, malls, and other buildings that house these health care facilities to provide ground-fault protection for all tenants where necessary to comply with 4.3.2.5.2.

4.3.2.6* Isolated Power Systems.

The performance, maintenance, and testing criteria for isolated power systems are listed in 4.3.2.6. For the use of isolated power systems in wet locations, see 4.3.2.2.8.

A.4.3.2.6 Patient protection is provided primarily by an adequate grounding system. The ungrounded secondary of the isolation transformer reduces the cross-sectional area of grounding conductors necessary to protect the patient against voltage resulting from fault current by reducing the maximum current in case of a single probable fault in the grounding system. The line isolation monitor is used to provide warning when a single fault occurs. Excessive current in the grounding conductors will not result in a hazard to the patient unless a second fault occurs. If the current in the grounding system does not exceed 10 mA, even under fault conditions, the voltage across 9.84 ft (3 m) of No. 12 AWG wire will not exceed 0.2 mV, and the voltage across 9.84 ft (3 m) of No. 18 AWG grounding conductor in a flexible cord will not exceed 0.8 mV. Allowing 0.1 mV across each connector, the voltage between two pieces of patient-connected equipment will not exceed 2 mV.

The reference grounding point is intended to ensure that all electrically conductive surfaces of the building structure, which could receive heavy fault currents from ordinary (grounded) circuits, are grounded in a manner to bypass these heavy currents from the operating room.

4.3.2.6.1 Isolation Transformer.

4.3.2.6.1.1 The isolation transformer shall be listed and approved for the purpose.

4.3.2.6.1.2 The primary winding shall be connected to a power source so that it is not energized with more than 600 V (nominal). The neutral of the primary winding shall be grounded in an approved manner. If an electrostatic shield is present, it shall be connected to the reference grounding point.

This value of 600 V as required by 4.3.2.6.1.2 allows 3-phase transformers to supply single-phase power to the same anesthetizing location. There is no requirement for two transformers to isolate circuits in those rooms where 3-phase power is needed.

4.3.2.6.1.3 Wiring of isolated power systems shall be in accordance with Section 517.62 of NFPA 70, *National Electrical Code*.

Since the 1984 edition of NFPA 70, *National Electrical Code* [1], Article 517 has allowed 3-phase, 3-wire systems, with up to 600 V across the secondary of the transformer.

4.3.2.6.2 Impedance of Isolated Wiring.

4.3.2.6.2.1* The impedance (capacitive and resistive) to ground of either conductor of an isolated system shall exceed 200,000 ohms when installed. The installation at this point shall include receptacles but is not required to include lighting fixtures or components of fixtures. This value shall be determined by energizing the system and connecting a low-impedance ac milliammeter (0 mA to 1 mA scale) between the reference grounding point and either conductor in sequence. This test shall be permitted to be performed with the line isolation monitor *(see 4.3.2.6.3)* connected, provided the connection between the line isolation monitor and the reference grounding point is open at the time of the test. After the test is made, the milliammeter shall be removed and the grounding connection of the line isolation monitor shall be restored. When the installation is completed, including permanently connected fixtures, the reading of the meter on the line isolation monitor, which corresponds to the unloaded line condition, shall be made. This meter reading shall be recorded as a reference for subsequent line-impedance evaluation. This test shall be conducted with no phase conductors grounded.

The test addressed in 4.3.2.6.2.1 is not to be conducted unless the connection between the line isolation monitor and the reference ground point is open at the time of the test. Note that to determine impedance of isolated power wiring, it is necessary to convert the meter reading (in milliamperes) to line impedance (in ohms).

A.4.3.2.6.2.1 It is desirable to limit the size of the isolation transformer to 10 kVA or less and to use conductor insulation with low leakage to meet the impedance requirements. Keeping branch circuits short and using insulation with a dielectric constant less than 3.5 and insulation resistance constant greater than 6100 megohmmeters (20,000 megohm-ft) at 60°F (16°C) reduces leakage from line to ground.

To correct milliammeter reading to line impedance use the following equation:

$$\text{Line impedance (in ohms)} = \frac{V \times 100}{I}$$

where:

V = isolated power system voltage

I = milliammeter reading made during impedance test

4.3.2.6.2.2 An approved capacitance suppressor shall be permitted to be used to improve the impedance of the permanently installed isolated system; however, the resistive impedance to ground of each isolated conductor of the system shall be at least 1 megohm prior to the connection of the suppression equipment. Capacitance suppressors shall be installed so as to prevent inadvertent disconnection during normal use.

4.3.2.6.3 Line Isolation Monitor.

Exhibit 4.2 illustrates a line isolation monitor in an operating room that has an analog display. Digital displays are in widespread use as well.

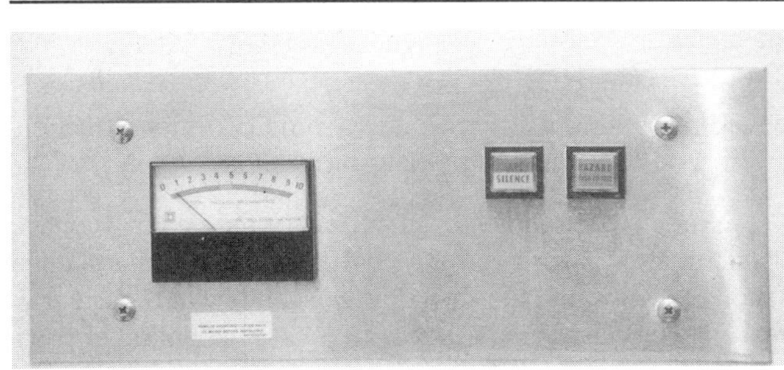

***EXHIBIT** 4.2 Line isolation monitor with an analog display.*

4.3.2.6.3.1* In addition to the usual control and protective devices, each isolated power system shall be provided with an approved continually operating line isolation monitor that indicates possible leakage or fault currents from either isolated conductor to ground.

A.4.3.2.6.3.1 Protection for the patient is provided primarily by a grounding system. The ungrounded secondary of the isolation transformer reduces the maximum current in the grounding system in case of a single fault between either isolated power conductor and ground. The line isolation monitor provides warning when a single fault occurs, or when excessively low impedance to ground develops, which might expose the patient to an unsafe condition should an additional fault occur. Excessive current in the grounding conductors will not result from a first fault. A hazard exists if a second fault occurs before the first fault is cleared.

4.3.2.6.3.2 The monitor shall be designed such that a green signal lamp, conspicuously visible in the area where the line isolation monitor is utilized, remains lighted when the system is adequately isolated from ground; and an adjacent red signal lamp and an audible warning signal (remote if desired) shall be energized when the total hazard current (consisting of possible resistive and capacitive leakage currents) from either isolated conductor to ground reaches a threshold value of 5.0 mA under normal line voltage conditions. The line isolation monitor shall not alarm for a fault hazard current of less than 3.7 mA.

The alarm threshold value was raised from 2.0 mA to 5.0 mA in 1978 to account for the increased number of appliances that were being used during operations. It is now common in major procedures to have more than 20 electrically powered devices functioning. Note that 5.0 mA, as required by 4.3.2.6.3.2, is a maximum threshold value.

Although 5.0 mA will produce tingling, it is still well below the 100 mA to 150 mA required to induce ventricular fibrillation from external, arm-to-arm contact with a power source. Note that the hazard current value (5.0 mA) is the important factor and is not to be exceeded, regardless of the voltage, impedance, and so forth, of the system.

4.3.2.6.3.3* The line isolation monitor shall comply with either of the following:

(1) It shall have sufficient internal impedance such that, when properly connected to the isolated system, the maximum internal current that will flow through the line isolation monitor, when any point of the isolated system is grounded, shall be 1 mA.
(2) It shall be permitted to be of the low-impedance type such that the current through the line isolation monitor, when any point of the isolated system is grounded, will not exceed twice the alarm threshold value for a period not exceeding 5 msec.

High-impedance technology uses line isolation monitors (LIMs) that are in parallel with any fault impedance contributing to hazard current. Low-impedance technology uses LIMs that are in series with any fault impedance. However, the time that the low-impedance LIMs are actually in series is very short (one cycle or less; 0.0167 second or less).

A.4.3.2.6.3.3 It is desirable to reduce this monitor hazard current provided this reduction results in an increased "not alarm" threshold value for the fault hazard current.

4.3.2.6.3.4* An ammeter connected to indicate the total hazard current of the system (contribution of the fault hazard current plus monitor hazard current) shall be mounted in a plainly visible place on the line isolation monitor with the "alarm on" zone (total hazard current = 5.0 mA) at approximately the center of the scale. It is desirable to locate the ammeter such that it is conspicuously visible to persons in the anesthetizing location.

The phrase "at approximately the center of the scale" in 4.3.2.6.3.4 should not be construed to exclude the digital-type meters that are available today. It can be argued that the midpoint of a 0-to-9-unit scale of a digital meter is between 4 and 5. Because the alarm threshold is now up to 5.0 mA, this meets the intent of alarming at approximately the center of the scale.

A.4.3.2.6.3.4 The line isolation monitor can be a composite unit, with a sensing section cabled to a separate display panel section, on which the alarm and test functions are located, if the two sections are within the same electric enclosure.

4.3.2.6.3.5 Means shall be provided for shutting off the audible alarm while leaving the red warning lamp activated. When the fault is corrected and the green signal lamp is reactivated, the audible alarm silencing circuit shall reset automatically, or an audible or distinctive visual signal shall indicate that the audible alarm is silenced.

4.3.2.6.3.6 A reliable test switch shall be mounted on the line isolation monitor to test its capability to operate (i.e., cause the alarms to operate and the meter to indicate in the "alarm on" zone). This switch shall transfer the grounding connection of the line isolation monitor from the reference grounding point to a test impedance arrangement connected across the isolated line; the test impedance(s) shall be of the appropriate magnitude to produce a meter reading corresponding to the rated total hazard current at the nominal line voltage, or to a lesser alarm hazard current if the line isolation monitor is so rated. The operation of this switch shall break the grounding connection of the line isolation monitor to the reference grounding point before transferring this grounding connector to the test impedance(s), so that making this test will not add to the hazard of a system in actual use, nor will the test include the effect of the line to ground stray impedance of the system. The test switch shall be of a self-restoring type.

Paragraph 4.3.2.6.3.6 applies only to a switch used for testing. The actual values of alarming are set by 4.3.2.6.3.2 and 4.3.2.6.3.4.

4.3.2.6.3.7 The line isolation monitor shall not generate energy of sufficient amplitude or frequency, as measured by a physiological monitor with a gain of at least 10^4 with a source impedance of 1000 ohms connected to the balanced differential input of the monitor, to create interference or artifact on human physiological signals. The output voltage from the amplifier shall not exceed 30 mV when the gain is 10^4. The 1000 ohms impedance shall be connected to the ends of typical unshielded electrode leads that are a normal part of the cable assembly furnished with physiological monitors. A 60 Hz notch filter shall be used to reduce ambient interference as is typical in physiological monitor design.

Interference on physiological monitors can result from a variety of reasons, including dried-out patient electrodes or a faulty patient cable; the location of the building with respect to transmitting antennas; or the LIM. Interference is particularly possible on some older models of LIMs due to their switching circuitry design. The performance test is required by 4.3.2.6.3.7 because of reports received over the years of interference from LIMs.

4.3.2.6.4 Identification of Conductors for Isolated (Ungrounded) Systems. The isolated conductors shall be identified in accordance with Section 517.160(a)(5) of NFPA 70, *National Electrical Code*.

4.3.3 Performance Criteria and Testing.

4.3.3.1 Grounding System in Patient Care Areas.

4.3.3.1.1* Grounding System Testing. The effectiveness of the grounding system shall be determined by voltage measurements and impedance measurements.

Both voltage and impedance measurements are required by 4.3.3.1.1 because they check two different possible hazards. Voltage measurement determines whether there is inadvertent connection or coupling that would raise the potential of the object being tested with respect to other parts of the grounding system. A problem would exist if conductive parts of the building structure became connected to ground but at points remote from the local power system grounds. Impedance measurement verifies that there is indeed a common grounding path for the power system within a patient vicinity.

A.4.3.3.1.1 In a conventional grounded power distribution system, one of the line conductors is deliberately grounded, usually at some distribution panel or the service entrance. This grounded conductor is identified as the neutral conductor. The other line conductor (or conductors) is (are) the high side of the line. The loads to be served by this distribution system are fed by the high and neutral conductors.

In addition to the high and neutral conductors, a grounding conductor is provided. One end is connected to the neutral at the point where the neutral is grounded, and the other end leads out to the connected loads. For purposes here, the load connection point will be considered to be a convenience receptacle, with the grounding conductor terminating at the grounding terminal of that receptacle.

This grounding conductor can be a separate wire running from the receptacle back to the remote grounding connection (where it joins the neutral conductor). If that separate conductor does not make any intermediate ground contacts between the receptacle and the remote ground, then the impedance of the connection between the receptacle and the remote ground is primarily the resistance of the grounding conductor itself and is, therefore, predictable.

If, however, the receptacle is also interconnected with the remote ground point by metallic conduit or other metallic building structures, the impedance of the circuit between receptacle and remote ground is not easily predictable, nor is it easy to measure accurately, although one can be sure that the impedance will be less than that of the grounding wire itself because of the additional parallel paths.

Fortunately, as will become apparent in the following paragraphs, the absolute value of the apparent impedance between the grounding contact of an outlet and the remote ground point need not be known or measured with great accuracy.

Ideally, and under no-fault conditions, the grounding system described earlier is supposed to be carrying no current at all. If that were true, then no voltage differences would be found between exposed conductive surfaces of any electrical appliances that were grounded to the grounding contacts of the receptacles that powered them. Similarly, there would be no voltage differences between these appliances and any other exposed metal surface that was also interconnected with the grounding system, provided that no currents were flowing in that interconnection.

Ideal conditions, however, do not prevail, and even when there are no "faults" within an appliance, residual "leakage" current does flow in the grounding conductor of each of the appliances, producing a voltage difference between the chassis of that appliance and the grounding contact of the receptacle that feeds it. Furthermore, this current can produce voltage differences among other appliances plugged into various receptacles on the system.

Fortunately, these leakage currents are small, and for reasonably low grounding-circuit impedances, the resulting voltage differences are entirely negligible.

If, however, a breakdown of insulation between the high side of the line and the chassis of an appliance should occur, the leakage condition becomes a fault condition, the magnitude of which is limited by the nature of the breakdown or, in the case of a dead short circuit in the appliance, the magnitude of the fault current is limited only by the residual resistance of the appliance power cord conductors and that of the power distribution system.

In the event of such a short circuit, the impedance of the grounding circuit, as measured between the grounding contact of the receptacle that feeds the defective appliance and the remote ground point where the neutral and grounding conductors are joined, should be so small that a large enough fault current will flow to ensure a rapid breaking of the circuit by the overcurrent protective device that serves that receptacle.

For a 20-A branch circuit, a fault current of 40 or more amperes would be required to ensure a rapid opening of the branch-circuit overcurrent-protective device. This corresponds to a circuit impedance of 3 ohms or less, of which the grounding system should contribute 1 ohm or less.

During the time this large fault current flows in the grounding system, the chassis of the defective appliance is raised many volts above other grounded surfaces in the same vicinity. The hazard represented by this condition is minimized by the fact that it exists for only a short time, and unless a patient simultaneously contacts both the defective appliance and some other grounded surface during this short time interval, there is no hazard. Furthermore, the magnitude of an applied voltage required to produce a serious shock hazard increases as its duration decreases, so the rapidity with which the circuit is interrupted helps reduce shock hazard even if such a patient contact should occur.

If, however, the defect in the appliance is not such as to cause an immediate circuit interruption, then the effect of this intermediate level of fault current on the voltages appearing on various exposed conductive surfaces in the patient care vicinity should be considered.

Because all of this fault current flows in the grounding conductor of the defective appliance's power cord, the first effect is to raise the potential of this appliance above that of the receptacle that feeds it by an amount proportional to the power cord grounding conductor resistance. This resistance is required to be less than 0.15 ohm, so fault currents of 20 A or less, which will not trip the branch-circuit overcurrent-protective device, will raise the potential of the defective appliance above the grounding contact of its supply receptacle by only 3 V or less. This value is not hazardous for casual contacts.

The fault current that enters the grounding system at the grounding contact of any receptacle in the patient care vicinity could affect the potential at the grounding contacts of all the other receptacles, and, more importantly, it could produce significant voltage differences between them and other grounded surfaces, such as exposed piping and building structures.

If one grounded point is picked as a reference (a plumbing fixture in or near the patient care vicinity, for example), and then the voltage difference is measured between that reference and the grounding contact of a receptacle, produced by driving some known current into that contact, a direct measure of the effectiveness of the grounding system within the patient care vicinity is obtained. The "figure of merit" can be stated as so many volts per ampere of fault current. The ratio volts per ampere is, of course, impedance; but because the exact path taken by the fault current is not known, and because the way in which the reference point is interconnected with the grounding system is not known, it cannot be stated that this value is the impedance between the receptacle and some specific point, such as the joining of the neutral and grounding conductors. But it can be stated that this measured value of "effective impedance" is indicative of the effectiveness with which the grounding system minimizes voltage differences between supposedly grounded objects in the patient care vicinity that are produced by ground faults in appliances used in that vicinity. This impedance, which characterizes the ability of the grounding system to maintain nearly equipotential conditions within the patient care vicinity, is of prime importance in assessing shock hazard; but this impedance is not necessarily the same as the impedance between receptacle and remote ground point, which controls the magnitude of the short-circuit current involved in tripping the branch-circuit overcurrent-protective device.

Fault currents on the grounding system can also come from neutral-to-ground faults, which permit some current to flow in the neutral and some in the ground. This type of fault is often the cause of interference on EEG and ECG equipment. It is often not recognized easily because, except for 60-Hz interference, the equipment works perfectly properly. It is most easily found by causing a substantial change in the line-to-line load and noting changes in the ground-to-reference voltage.

A neutral-to-ground fault, as noted in the last paragraph of A.4.3.3.1.1, is not a common occurrence. When it does occur, it can be difficult to locate (it might not even be in the patient care area). The only visible manifestation is 60-Hz interference on ECG and EEG equipment. A shock hazard is possible but very improbable. A neutral-to-ground fault is more a diagnostic safety problem.

4.3.3.1.1.1 For new construction, the effectiveness of the grounding system shall be evaluated before acceptance.

4.3.3.1.1.2 Small, wall-mounted conductive surfaces, not likely to become energized, such as surface-mounted towel and soap dispensers, mirrors, and so forth, shall not be required to be intentionally grounded or tested.

4.3.3.1.1.3 Large, metal conductive surfaces not likely to become energized, such as windows, door frames, and drains, shall not be required to be intentionally grounded or periodically tested.

The fine distinction between 4.3.3.1.1.2 and 4.3.3.1.1.3 (*tested* vs. *periodically tested*) should be noted. Large metal conductive surfaces should be tested at least once to ensure that such surfaces are not inadvertently carrying excessive potentials. No further testing need be done after this initial check. However, if major changes are made and there is concern whether conditions have changed, it is wise to conduct another test.

4.3.3.1.1.4* Whenever the electrical system has been altered or replaced, that portion of the system shall be tested.

FAQ ▶
If an existing electrical system is modified, does it need to be tested again?

The distinction between new and existing construction is a practical one. It is not possible to test existing construction before acceptance. However, if significant modifications are made to an existing structure so that the electrical system under construction is essentially new, it is prudent to test that portion as if it were new.

The effectiveness of grounding does not significantly change with the aging of a system that has not been altered or repaired. Testing of parts of the grounding system that have been altered or replaced is still required.

A.4.3.3.1.1.4 The grounding system (reference ground and conduit) is to be tested as an integral system. Lifting of grounds from receptacles and fixed equipment is not required or recommended for the performance of this test.

Paragraph A.4.3.3.1.1.4 clarifies how the system is to be tested. It is also not intended that testing be performed only if an entire electrical system is replaced. Whatever portion is repaired, replaced, or altered should be tested. If only one receptacle is replaced, then only that one receptacle needs to be tested.

4.3.3.1.2 Reference Point. The voltage and impedance measurements shall be taken with respect to a reference point. The reference point shall be one of the following:

(1) A reference grounding point *(see Chapter 3, Definitions)*
(2) A grounding point, in or near the room under test, that is electrically remote from receptacles, for example, an all-metal cold-water pipe
(3) The grounding contact of a receptacle that is powered from a different branch circuit from the receptacle under test

The purpose of paragraph 4.3.3.1.2 is to ensure that more consistent voltage and impedance measurements will be taken. For 4.3.3.1.2(2), plastic piping, although electrically remote, would not be acceptable.

4.3.3.1.3* Voltage Measurements. The voltage measurements shall be made under no-fault conditions between a reference point and exposed fixed electrical equipment with conductive surfaces in a patient care vicinity. The voltage measurements shall be made with an accuracy of ± 20 percent. Voltage measurements for faceplates of wiring devices shall not be required.

Paragraph 4.3.3.1.3 requires performance criteria only. The wiring methodology used to achieve the performance levels in the next several sections is left to the discretion of designers. The method used to install the wiring, however, must be in accordance with NFPA 70, *National Electrical Code* [1]. Other authorities (governmental and nongovernmental) might have other requirements that also must be met.

The 20 mV value in 4.3.3.1.6.1 was derived from various sources. This limit is reasonably attainable and provides a reasonable margin of safety. Experiments on human reaction to electrical stimulus have shown that it was the amount of current that flowed that was critical (i.e., it was the current that induced the ventricular fibrillation). Thus, although the measurement in 4.3.3.1.6.1 is given in terms of a maximum voltage (20 mV) across a specified resistance (1000 ohms), the concern is the amount of current ($I = V/R$) that will flow under this condition. This fact is particularly important when measuring in the microampere range.

A.4.3.3.1.3 Effective grounding to safely handle both fault and leakage currents requires following the requirements of both Chapter 4 of NFPA 99 and Article 250 of NFPA 70,

National Electrical Code, having good workmanship, and using some techniques that are not in these documents.

The performance of the grounding system is made effective through the existence of the green grounding wire, the metal raceway, and all of the other building metal. Measurements have shown that it is the metal raceway and building steel that provide most of the effective grounding path of less than 10 milliohms at the receptacle, including plug-to-receptacle impedance. The green grounding wire becomes a backup, not a primary grounding path performer.

Good practice calls for each receptacle to have a good jumper grounding connection to the metal raceway at the receptacle location in addition to having the green grounding wire connecting these points to the grounding bus in the distribution panel. Good workmanship includes seeing that these grounding connections are tight at each receptacle and that all metal raceway joints are secure and tight.

The voltage difference measurements listed in 4.3.3.1.3 in connection with power distribution grounding systems should ideally be made with an oscilloscope or spectrum analyzer in order to observe and measure components of leakage current and voltage differences at all frequencies.

For routine testing, such instruments could be inconvenient. An alternative is to use a metering system that weighs the contribution to the meter reading of the various components of the signal being measured in accordance with their probable physiological effect.

A meter specifically designed for this purpose would have an impedance of approximately 1000 ohms, and a frequency characteristic that was flat to 1 kHz, dropped at the rate of 20 decibels per decade to 100 kHz, and then remained flat to 1 MHz or higher. This frequency response characteristic could be achieved by proper design of the internal circuits of the amplifier that probably precedes the indicating instrument or by appropriate choice of a feedback network around the amplifier. These details are, of course, left to the instrument designer.

If a meter specifically designed for these measurements is not available, a general-purpose laboratory millivoltmeter can be adapted for the purpose by adding a frequency response–shaping network ahead of the meter. One such suggested network is shown in Figure A.4.3.3.1.3(a).

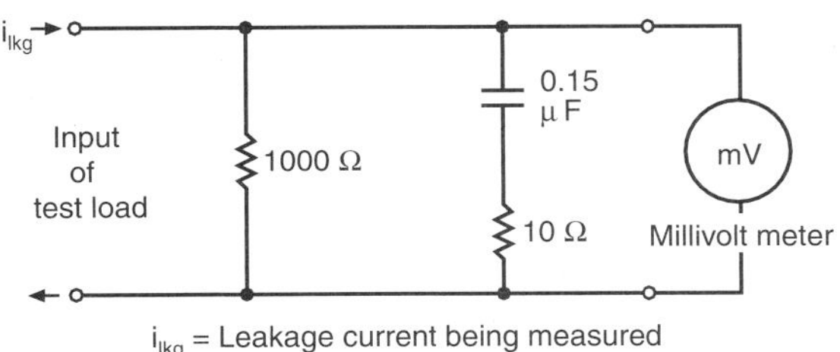

FIGURE A.4.3.3.1.3(a) *Circuit Used to Measure Leakage Current with High Source Impedance.*

The circuit shown in Figure A.4.3.3.1.3(a) is especially applicable to measurements of leakage current, where the current being measured is derived from a circuit whose source impedance is high compared to 1000 ohms. Under these conditions, the voltage developed across the millivoltmeter will be proportional to the impedance of the network. The network impedance will be 1000 ohms at low frequencies and 10 ohms at high frequencies, and the transition between these two values will occur in the frequency range between 1 kHz and 100 kHz.

The basic low-frequency sensitivity will be 1 millivolt (mV) of meter reading for each 1 milliampere (mA) of leakage current.

The millivoltmeter's own input impedance needs to be very large compared to 1000 ohms (100 kilohms), and the meter should have a flat frequency response to well beyond 100 kHz. (If the meter impedance is lower than 100 kilohms, then the 1000-ohm resistor can be raised to a higher value, such that the impedance of that resistor in parallel with the meter will still be 1000 ohms.)

The circuit in Figure A.4.3.3.1.3(a) can be used for the voltage difference measurements required in Section 4.5, but, because the source impedance will be very low compared to 1000 ohms, the frequency response of the measurement system will remain flat. If any high-frequency components, produced, for example, by pickup from nearby radio frequency transmitters, appear on the circuit being measured, then they will not be attenuated and the meter reading will be higher than it should be.

For meter readings below any prescribed limits, this possible error is of no consequence. For borderline cases it could be significant. To avoid this uncertainty when making voltage-difference measurements, a slightly more elaborate version of a frequency response–shaping network is given in Figure A.4.3.3.1.3(b).

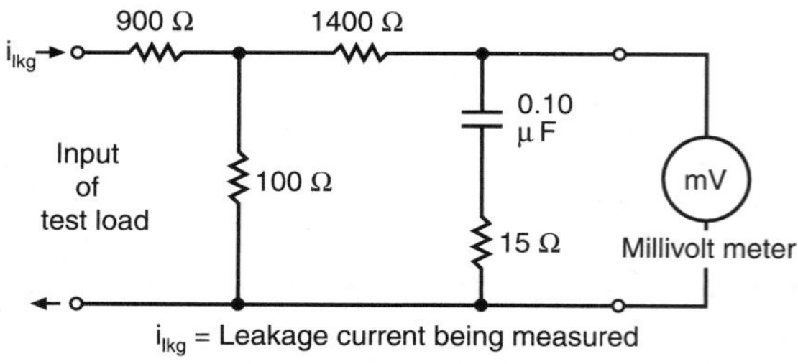

FIGURE A.4.3.3.1.3(b) *Circuit Used to Measure Leakage Current with Low Source Impedance.*

Here the source being measured is separated from the frequency response–shaping network by the combination of the 900-ohm and 100-ohm resistors. The frequency response characteristic is now independent of the circuit being tested.

This independence is achieved, however, at a loss in signal delivered to the millivoltmeter. The basic low-frequency sensitivity of this metering circuit is 1 millivolt of meter reading for 10 µA of leakage current or, on a voltage basis, 1 mV of meter reading for 10 mV at the input terminals of the network.

The millivoltmeter should have an input impedance of 150 kilohms and a frequency response flat to well beyond 100 kHz.

For either of the suggested networks, the resistors and capacitors should be mounted in a metal container close to the millivoltmeter to avoid stray pickup by the leads going to the meter.

4.3.3.1.4* Impedance Measurements. The impedance measurement shall be made with an accuracy of ±20 percent. For new construction, the impedance measurement shall be made between the reference point and the grounding contact of 10 percent of all receptacles in each patient care vicinity. The impedance measurement shall be the ratio of voltage developed (either 60 Hz or dc) between the point under test and the reference point to the current applied between these two points.

A.4.3.3.1.4 It is not the intent that each receptacle be tested. It is intended that compliance be demonstrated through random testing. The 10 percent random testing should include a mixture of both normal and emergency receptacles.

Only 10 percent of the receptacles located in the patient care vicinity are tested for impedance testing. *Patient care vicinity* requirements are specified in 4.3.3.1.4. Paragraph 4.3.3.2 covers other testing of all receptacles in the patient care area that extends beyond the patient care vicinity.

This previous change correlates with the NFPA 70, *National Electrical Code* [1] requirement for multiple pathways to ground (grounding conductor and metallic conduit), which reduces the probability of ineffective grounding systems.

◀ **FAQ**
Why are only 10 percent of the receptacles in the patient care vicinity required to be tested?

The intent is to have at least one receptacle be tested in each patient care vicinity that is roughly 6 ft (1.8 m) in all directions around the normal location of the bed, chair, table, treadmill, or other device that supports the patient during examination and treatment. Paragraph A.4.3.3.1.4 includes a recommendation that, in the process of random testing of patient vicinities, both normal and emergency receptacles be tested. This does not imply that within each patient care vicinity it is necessary to test both a normal and an emergency receptacle. For example, during random testing, an emergency receptacle might be tested at one patient care vicinity and a normal receptacle tested at another.

4.3.3.1.5 Test Equipment. Electrical safety test instruments shall be tested periodically, but not less than annually, for acceptable performance.

4.3.3.1.5.1 Voltage measurements specified in 4.3.3.1.3 shall be made with an instrument having an input resistance of 1000 ohms ± 10 percent at frequencies of 1000 Hz or less.

4.3.3.1.5.2 The voltage across the terminals (or between any terminal and ground) of resistance-measuring instruments used in occupied patient care areas shall not exceed 500 mV rms or 1.4 dc or peak to peak.

Research is ongoing on the question of how best to measure and verify the integrity of building wiring systems. The high-current test has been found to temporarily weld poor connections together. The low-current test will not detect a connection point that is only barely making a connection.

Rather than include any recommendations on tester configuration, only instrument input resistance and maximum rms, dc, or peak-to-peak voltage across terminals for resistance-measuring instruments have been specified in 4.3.3.1.5.2.

Whichever test instrument(s) are used, it is essential for accuracy of measurements that these instruments be checked to verify that they are functioning within their listed specifications. They should also be periodically checked to ensure they are operating safely.

4.3.3.1.6 Criteria for Acceptability for New Construction.

4.3.3.1.6.1 Voltage limit shall be 20 mV.

4.3.3.1.6.2 Impedance limit shall be 0.2 ohms for quiet ground systems, and 0.1 ohms for all others.

4.3.3.2 Receptacle Testing in Patient Care Areas.

This testing is to be performed on all new receptacles in patient care areas. Subsection 4.3.3 covers performance criteria and testing for new systems and equipment.

The continuity of all the grounding circuits can be verified by the impedance test of 4.3.3.1.4. However, physical integrity and polarity tests should be performed before the continuity test.

4.3.3.2.1 The physical integrity of each receptacle shall be confirmed by visual inspection.

4.3.3.2.2 The continuity of the grounding circuit in each electrical receptacle shall be verified.

4.3.3.2.3 Correct polarity of the hot and neutral connections in each electrical receptacle shall be confirmed.

4.3.3.2.4 The retention force of the grounding blade of each electrical receptacle (except locking-type receptacles) shall be not less than 115 g (4 oz).

FAQ ▶ Why is it important to have at least 4 oz of retention force on the grounding blade?

A low tension value means the ground pin of the attachment plug of the appliance is not making good contact with the grounding blade in the receptacle, thereby defeating the purpose of providing a low-impedance path to ground for the green ground wire of the appliance.

4.3.3.3 Isolated Power Systems.

See 4.3.2.6 and the related commentary regarding where isolated power systems are to be installed.

4.3.3.3.1 Patient Care Areas. If installed, the isolated power system shall be tested in accordance with 4.3.3.3.2.

4.3.3.3.2 Line Isolation Monitor Tests.

4.3.3.3.2.1 The Line Isolation Monitor (LIM) circuit shall be tested after installation, and prior to being placed in service, by successively grounding each line of the energized distribution system through a resistor of 200 × V ohms, where V equals measured line voltage. The visual and audible alarms *(see 4.3.2.6.3.2)* shall be activated.

4.3.3.4 Ground-Fault Protection Testing. When equipment ground-fault protection is first installed, each level shall be performance-tested to ensure compliance with 4.3.2.5.

4.3.4* Administration of Electrical System.

A.4.3.4 Administration is in conjunction with 4.3.4.1, Maintenance and Testing of Electrical System.

4.3.4.1 Maintenance and Testing of Electrical System.

4.3.4.1.1 Testing for hospital grade receptacles required at patient bed locations and in anesthetizing locations shall be performed after initial installation, replacement, or servicing of the device.

4.3.4.1.2 Additional testing of receptacles in patient care areas shall be performed at intervals defined by documented performance data.

4.3.4.1.3 Receptacles at patient bed locations and in anesthetizing locations not listed as hospital-grade shall be tested at intervals not exceeding 12 months.

Previous editions of NFPA 99 have specified intervals for testing hospital-grade receptacles. These test intervals no longer exist. Hospital facility managers are permitted to determine appropriate test intervals for hospital-grade receptacles based on "documented performance data." The 2005 edition clarifies that not all non-hospital-grade receptacles are required to be tested at 12-month intervals; just those non-hospital-grade receptacles installed where hospital-grade receptacles are required for new construction are to be tested annually.

4.3.4.1.4 The LIM circuit shall be tested at intervals of not more than 1 month by actuating the LIM test switch *(see 4.3.2.6.3.6)*. For a LIM circuit with automated self-test and self-calibration capabilities, this test shall be performed at intervals of not more than 12 months. Actuation of the test switch shall activate both visual and audible alarm indicators.

4.3.4.1.5 After any repair or renovation to an electrical distribution system, the LIM circuit shall be tested in accordance with 4.3.3.3.2.1.

4.3.4.2 Recordkeeping.

4.3.4.2.1* General. A record shall be maintained of the tests required by this chapter and associated repairs or modification. At a minimum, this record shall contain the date, the rooms or areas tested, and an indication of which items have met or have failed to meet the performance requirements of this chapter.

A.4.3.4.2.1 Although several approaches to documentation exist in hospitals, the minimum acceptable documentation should convey what was tested, when it was tested, and whether it performed successfully. Adopting a system of exception reporting can be the most efficient form of recordkeeping for routine rechecks of equipment or systems and thereby minimize technicians' time in recording the value of each measurement taken. For example, once a test protocol is established, which simply means testing the equipment or system consistent with Chapter 4, the only item (value) that needs to be recorded is what failure or what deviation from the requirements of the chapter was detected when a corrective action (repair) was undertaken. This approach can serve to eliminate, for example, the need to keep individual room sheets to record measured results on each receptacle or to record measurement values of all types of leakage current tests.

The format of the documentation noted in A.4.3.4.2.1 is left to the discretion and thus the responsibility of the facility. However, it is advisable to consult with inspection agencies, insurance companies, and other authorities for any recommended formats.

4.3.4.2.2 Isolated Power System (Where Installed). A permanent record shall be kept of the results of each of the tests.

If an IPS alarms, the source of the alarm must be investigated and corrected. For IPSs in operating rooms, immediate correction may be difficult if an operation is in progress. Immediately following the procedure, an investigation should be conducted and the results recorded with other tests.

4.4 Essential Electrical System Requirements — Type 1

4.4.1 Sources (Type 1 EES).

Section 4.4 applies to situations in which the normal power source is a public utility and the alternate source is on-site generation. Other requirements apply to situations in which normal power is provided by on-site generation. It should be clearly noted that there must always be at least two independent power sources, and at least one of them must be located on-site. In certain situations, the power source(s) defined as "normal" and "alternate" could change, and even be reversed, under different modes of operation.

The normal source should be made as reliable as possible, as dictated by local conditions. When the normal source is a public utility, a properly protected network fed by multiple independent services provides the greatest reliability and continuity. The next highest reliability level comes from multiple independent services with local automatic switching. This chapter does not require multiple services or network or switching arrangements owing to widely varying local conditions and the limited availability of multiple services at certain locations.

With the low but probable occurrence of occasional blackouts from accidents, failures, or natural causes, multiple public utility services cannot be considered absolutely reliable and thus cannot be used as the alternate source in lieu of on-site generation. When the normal source is on-site generation, it is suggested that its reliability be designed and maintained to be at least equal to that of any available public utility.

4.4.1.1 On-Site Generator Set.

Nothing in 4.4.1.1 precludes the use of coolants for heat recovery purposes. See Exhibit 4.3.

EXHIBIT 4.3 An example of an emergency generator for a large medical facility. Note batteries at base of engine.

4.4.1.1.1* Design Considerations. Dual sources of normal power shall be considered but shall not constitute an alternate source of power as described in this chapter.

A.4.4.1.1.1 *Connection to Dual Source of Normal Power.* For the greatest assurance of continuity of electrical service, the normal source should consist of two separate full-capacity services, each independent of the other. Such services should be selected and installed with full recognition of local hazards of interruption, such as icing and flooding.

Where more than one full-capacity service is installed, they should be connected in such a manner that one will pick up the load automatically upon loss of the other, and so arranged that the load of the emergency and equipment systems will be transferred to the alternate source (generator set) only when both utility services are deenergized, unless this arrangement is impractical and waived by the authority having jurisdiction. Such services should be interlocked in such a manner as to prevent paralleling of utility services on either primary or secondary voltage levels.

Note that in any installation where it is possible to parallel utility supply circuits, for example, to prevent interruption of service when switching from one utility source to another, it is imperative to consult the power companies affected as to problems of synchronization.

Facilities whose normal source of power is supplied by two or more separate central-station–fed services (dual sources of normal power) experience greater reliability than those with only a single feed.

Installation of Generator Sets. For additional material on diesel engines, see *Diesel Engines for Use with Generators to Supply Emergency and Short Term Electric Power*, National Research Council Publication 1132 *(see Annex G).*

Dual sources of power cannot completely eliminate power interruptions within a facility. A facility can be affected by external incidents or failures beyond its control.

Essential electrical systems must be designed as complete systems. They are not simply generators and transfer switches appended to normal distribution wiring. Engine horsepower; transient voltage response (i.e., motor starting); the number, rating, and type of transfer switch(es); the location of the generator; and the placement and setting of overcurrent protective devices are just some of the design factors that must be considered when designing the essential electrical system. The overall goal when designing the system should be to provide reliable power for fire protection, life safety, and medical functions.

This chapter does not require the application of all available technology and techniques that can be used for essential electrical systems. The optimum combination of reliability, economics, and allowance for human factors is stressed in the design of an essential electrical system. Additional technology and techniques not mentioned in this chapter can and should be applied to individual facilities.

4.4.1.1.1.1 Distribution system arrangements shall be designed to minimize interruptions to the electrical systems due to internal failures by the use of adequately rated equipment.

4.4.1.1.1.2 The following factors shall be considered in the design of the distribution system:

(1) Abnormal voltages such as single phasing of three-phase utilization equipment, switching and/or lightning surges, voltage reductions, and so forth
(2) Capability of achieving the fastest possible restoration of any given circuit(s) after clearing a fault
(3) Effects of future changes, such as increased loading and/or supply capacity
(4) Stability and power capability of the prime mover during and after abnormal conditions
(5)* Sequence reconnection of loads to avoid large current inrushes that trip overcurrent devices or overload the generator(s)

A.4.4.1.1.1.2(5) Careful consideration should be given to the location of the spaces housing the components of the essential electrical system to minimize interruptions caused by natural forces common to the area (e.g., storms, floods, or earthquakes, or hazards created by adjoining structures or activities). Consideration should also be given to the possible interruption of normal electrical services resulting from similar causes as well as possible disruption of normal electrical service due to internal wiring and equipment failures.

Consideration should be given to the physical separation of the main feeders of the essential electrical system from the normal wiring of the facility to prevent possible simultaneous destruction as a result of a local catastrophe.

In selecting electrical distribution arrangements and components for the essential electrical system, high priority should be given to achieving maximum continuity of the electrical supply to the load. Higher consideration should be given to achieving maximum reliability of the alternate power source and its feeders rather than protection of such equipment, provided the protection is not required to prevent a greater threat to human life such as fire, explosion, electrocution, and so forth, than would be caused by the lack of essential electrical supply.

(6) Bypass arrangements to permit testing and maintenance of system components that could not otherwise be maintained without disruption of important hospital functions

◀ **FAQ**
Are bypass-isolation switches for automatic transfer switches required?

The issue of making mandatory the use of bypass-isolation switches for automatic transfer switches has been addressed repeatedly over the years. The use of these switches has never been made a requirement because of their significant cost. Facilities considering installing this type of transfer switch need to carefully evaluate the cost/benefit ratio.

Bypass-isolation switches are, however, very useful for properly maintaining automatic transfer switches. Information describing their installation (if they are used) is included in 4.4.2.1.7.

(7) Effects of any harmonic currents on neutral conductors and equipment

Harmonic currents specified in 4.4.1.1.1.2(7) are not necessarily abnormal currents, but they can overheat conductors and equipment. This tendency to overheat is particularly great in "shared" neutral conductors.

4.4.1.1.2 Current-sensing devices, phase and ground, shall be selected to minimize the extent of interruption to the electrical system due to abnormal current caused by overload and/or short circuits.

A single incoming power line, a single generator set, or a single transfer switch is allowed under certain conditions (see A.4.4.2.2.1, 4.4.2.2.1.1 through 4.4.2.2.1.4, and 4.5.2.2.1). However, this setup requires that everything must function when needed. A greater safety margin than this exists for a system supplying essential electricity when the normal power source is interrupted. Factors such as redundancy and separation of circuits need to be considered when designing the essential electrical system.

4.4.1.1.3 Generator load-shed circuits designed for the purpose of load reduction or for load priority systems shall not shed life safety branch loads, critical branch loads serving critical care areas, medical air compressors, medical–surgical vacuum pumps, pressure maintenance (jockey) pump(s) for water-based fire protection systems, generator fuel pumps, or other generator accessories.

Generators operating in parallel on a common synchronizing bus often have load priority/load shed circuits that shed load upon loss of one or more generators. It is a common practice to shed the equipment system load first upon loss of one or more generators. Generally, this reduction in load will keep the remaining generators from "cascading" so that generators remain on-line in order to support the remaining emergency system loads. The designer must be sure that highly critical loads, such as medical air compressors and medical-surgical vacuum pumps, are not shed when shedding the equipment system loads.

It is advisable to place medical air compressors, medical-surgical vacuum pumps, fuel pumps, jockey pumps, and generator accessories on a separate equipment branch transfer switch that is not shed upon the loss of one or more generators. It should also be noted that 4.4.2.2.3.3 permits central suction and compressed air systems serving medical and surgical functions to be placed on the critical branch.

With regard to multiple generator systems, shedding of highly critical loads upon loss of one or more of the generators is prohibited. It is sometimes necessary, however, to shed some emergency system loads in general patient care areas in order to maintain emergency system service in critical patient care areas. For this reason, the words *emergency system loads* were replaced with the words *critical branch loads serving critical care areas.* For example, a system with three generators on a common synchronizing bus might shed some equipment system loads upon loss of one generator and shed critical branch loads serving general patient care areas upon loss of the second generator. The system could not, however, shed the loads listed in 4.4.1.1.3 under any circumstances. In our example, the remaining on-line generator would serve these loads. See also 4.4.1.1.7 regarding load shedding when multiple generator sets are installed.

4.4.1.1.4 Essential electrical systems shall have a minimum of two independent sources of power: a normal source generally supplying the entire electrical system and one or more alternate sources for use when the normal source is interrupted.

It is not the intention for this chapter that dual sources of normal power be used in lieu of an alternate power source. At least one source of power has to be on-site.

4.4.1.1.5 Where the normal source consists of generating units on the premises, the alternate source shall be either another generating set or an external utility service.

It should be noted that at least one source of power (normal or alternate) must be on-site. Located "on the premises," as required by 4.4.1.1.5, refers to property encompassing the facility, not to several noncontiguous pieces of property.

◀ **FAQ**
Where should emergency generators be located?

There are no restrictions in NFPA 99 regarding where a generator set can be located on the premises. Location depends on the number of buildings involved, climatic conditions, the noise levels that can be tolerated, ease of maintenance, ease of accessibility under adverse conditions, safety from flooding, and numerous other factors. In light of several recent fires in a large teaching hospital that disrupted emergency generators and emergency wiring, it is clear that the protection of generators, transfer switching, and the running of power lines in the vicinity of the generator must be carefully studied. Reasonable scenarios, including smoky conditions, sabotage, and accidental or deliberate explosions (e.g., the 1993 World Trade Center explosion), should be examined.

4.4.1.1.6 General. Generator sets installed as an alternate source of power for essential electrical systems shall be designed to meet the requirements of such service.

4.4.1.1.6.1 Type 1 and Type 2 essential electrical system power sources shall be classified as Type 10, Class X, Level 1 generator sets per NFPA 110, *Standard for Emergency and Standby Power Systems*.

4.4.1.1.6.2 Type 3 essential electrical system power sources shall be classified as Type 10, Class X, Level 2 generator sets per NFPA 110, *Standard for Emergency and Standby Power Systems*.

Although many of the requirements for general-purpose generator sets are set forth in NFPA 110, *Standard for Emergency and Standby Power Systems* [2], utility or general-purpose generators are not acceptable in health care facilities if they do not also meet the requirements listed in this chapter. These criteria (in NFPA 99) were originally developed for the generator portion of the essential electrical system to ensure the generators are reliable enough for the special needs of health care facilities.

Type 1, Type 2, and Type 3 "essential electrical systems" are referenced for applicability in Chapters 12 through 17 (e.g., see 13.3.4.2, 14.3.4.2, etc.). Type 10, as well as Class X and Level 1, "generator sets," have meaning in NFPA 110. Note that the terms *type, class,* and *level* are designators only and do not have definitions.

4.4.1.1.7 Uses for Essential Electrical System.

4.4.1.1.7.1 The generating equipment used shall be either reserved exclusively for such service or normally used for other purposes of peak demand control, internal voltage control, load relief for the external utility, or cogeneration. If normally used for the other purposes listed above, two or more sets shall be installed, such that the maximum actual demand likely to be produced by the connected load of the emergency system as well as medical air compressors, medical–surgical vacuum pumps, electrically operated fire pumps, jockey pumps, fuel pumps, and generator accessories shall be met with the largest single generator set out-of-service. The alternate source of emergency power for illumination and identification of means of egress shall be the essential electrical system. The alternate power source for fire protection signaling systems shall be the essential electrical systems.

Paragraph 4.4.1.1.7.1 ensures that highly critical equipment (i.e., medical-surgical vacuum pumps) would remain on-line with a single generator out of service.

4.4.1.1.7.2 A single generator set that operates the essential electrical system shall be permitted to be part of the system supplying the other purposes as listed in 4.4.1.1.7.1, provided any such use will not decrease the mean period between service overhauls to less than three years.

Users should carefully consider the risks involved when using a single generator installation for peak shaving, load control, cogeneration, or other uses not specifically related to providing standby power. Even though there may be three years between overhauls, facilities with only one standby generator will require a temporary generator during the overhaul period.

4.4.1.1.7.3* Optional loads shall be permitted to be served by the essential electrical system generating equipment. Optional loads shall be served by their own transfer means, such that these loads shall not be transferred onto the generating equipment if the transfer will overload the generating equipment and shall be shed upon a generating equipment overload. Use of the generating equipment to serve optional loads shall not constitute "other purposes" as described in 4.4.1.1.7.1 and therefore shall not require multiple generator sets.

The term *optional* was added in the 2002 edition of NFPA 99 to differentiate between the "selected loads" and "selected power circuit" loads that are permitted in 4.4.2.2 to be connected to the critical branch and/or equipment system and larger blocks of load that might be served by the generating equipment at the user's discretion. For example, 4.4.2.2 permits selected circuits and equipment intended for patient care or for effective operation of the facility to be served by the critical branch and/or the equipment system. Selected offices, conference rooms, or public areas might have lighting and receptacles connected to the critical branch or equipment system to assist in emergencies or simply to better operate the facility during emergencies (i.e., triage or command center during natural disasters). Likewise, these selected circuits might serve microwave ovens, refrigerators, blanket warmers, and other equipment.

On the other hand, 4.4.1.1.7.3 permits an entire nonessential wing, gymnasium, or day care center to be connected to the generating equipment using a separate "nonessential" transfer switch. The new wording makes it clear that the loads described in 4.4.1.1.7.3 are not to be confused with the loads listed in 4.4.1.1.7.1 (i.e., cogeneration). Because there has been much confusion concerning the different types of loads that can be served by the standby generator(s), additional explanatory material is included in the annex.

It is important to note that contiguous and same-site health care facilities are permitted by 13.3.4.3 to be served by the hospital standby generator(s) without the load-shed provisions of 4.4.1.1.7.3. Authorities having jurisdiction have required load-shed for contiguous or same-site clinics or medical office buildings covered under Chapter 14. This was not and is not the intent of 4.4.1.1.7.3. It is also important to note that buildings and facilities served by the generating equipment as permitted in 4.4.1.1.7.3 must meet the egress lighting requirements of NFPA *101, Life Safety Code,* (i.e., batteries per Article 700 of NFPA 70, *National Electrical Code*), under load-shed conditions [3,1].

A.4.4.1.1.7.3 The intent of this subparagraph is as follows:

(1) Contiguous or same site nonhospital buildings can be served by the generating equipment. However, such loads should not compromise the integrity of the system serving the hospital. Thus, any such contiguous or same site nonhospital buildings can be served by the generating equipment only if the transfer means operates in accordance with this subparagraph.
(2) Within a hospital building, 4.4.2.2.2.3(9) allows "additional" loads on the critical branch and 4.4.2.2.3.5(9) allows "other equipment" on the equipment system in order to provide limited flexibility to a facility to add one or two loads not otherwise listed in 4.4.2.2.2.3(1)

through 4.4.2.2.2.3(8), or 4.4.2.2.3.4, or 4.4.2.2.3.5(1) through 4.4.2.2.3.5(9) to a critical branch panel or an equipment system panel. This allowance is to prevent the need for an additional panel to serve a small number of selected circuits in a particular area. These sections are not intended to allow large blocks of loads not listed in these sections to be on the critical branch or equipment system. The intent of the division of the essential system loads into systems and branches is to ensure maximum reliability of service to loads considered essential. Every additional load placed onto a system somewhat increases the probability of a failure on the system that threatens the integrity of service to the balance of loads served by the system. Therefore, while "additional" loads and "other equipment" can be placed onto the critical branch and equipment system in very limited situations, where a facility wants to put large blocks of loads not listed in 4.4.2.2.2.3(1) through 4.4.2.2.2.3(8), or 4.4.2.2.3.4, or 4.4.2.2.3.5(1) through 4.4.2.2.3.5(9) onto the generating equipment, the facility can do so, but only by designating these large blocks of loads as "optional loads" and by complying with 4.4.1.1.7.3.

4.4.1.1.7.4 Where optional loads include contiguous or same-site facilities not covered in Chapters 12 through 20, provisions shall be made to meet the requirements of NFPA *101, Life Safety Code*, Article 700 of NFPA 70, *National Electrical Code*, and other applicable NFPA requirements for emergency egress under load-shed conditions.

Where same-site or contiguous non–health care facilities are served from the hospital generator, and where these facilities are subject to the load-shed provisions of 4.4.1.1.7.3, these facilities must comply with the requirements of NFPA *101, Life Safety Code* [3], and Article 700 of NFPA 70, *National Electrical Code* [1], under load-shed conditions. A day care center, for example, must have exit and egress lighting powered (by batteries) in accordance with the requirements of the applicable NFPA codes.

4.4.1.1.8 Work Space or Room.

The specific size of the space or room for the generator has been deliberately left undefined in 4.4.1.1.8 because of the unique nature of each facility. However, NFPA 110, *Standard for Emergency and Standby Power Systems* [2], addresses several issues that affect the clearance around the generator (EPS) and limitations upon the types of equipment that can be housed in the same space as the generator (EPS) and the other essential electrical system equipment (EPSS). Refer to NFPA 110, Chapter 7, for installation and environmental considerations.

◀ **FAQ**
How big of a room is needed for generators?

4.4.1.1.8.1 The EPS shall be installed in a separate room for Level 1 installations. EPSS equipment shall be permitted to be installed in this room. [**110:**7.2.1]

(A) The room shall have a minimum 2-hour fire rating or be located in an adequate enclosure located outside the building capable of resisting the entrance of snow or rain at a maximum wind velocity required by local building codes. [**110:**7.2.1.1]

4.4.1.1.8.2 The rooms, shelters, or separate buildings housing Level 1 or Level 2 EPSS equipment shall be designed and located to minimize the damage from flooding, including that caused by the following:

(1) Flooding resulting from fire fighting
(2) Sewer water backup
(3) Similar disasters or occurrences [**110:**7.2.3]

4.4.1.1.8.3 The EPS equipment shall be installed in a location that permits ready accessibility and a minimum of 76 cm (30 in.) from the skid rails' outermost point in the direction of access for inspection, repair, maintenance, cleaning, or replacement. This requirement shall not apply to units in outdoor housings. [**110:**7.2.5]

4.4.1.1.9* Capacity and Rating. The generator set(s) shall have sufficient capacity and proper rating to meet the maximum actual demand likely to be produced by the connected load of the essential electrical system(s) at any one time.

Paragraph 4.4.1.1.9 has been modified on several occasions to emphasize the standard's intent that generators should be sized for the actual demand rather than the connected load. If the design engineer does not have experience with health care facilities or access to health care facility load data, 517.30(D) of NFPA 70, *National Electrical Code* [1], permits sizing for connected load or by means of the calculations described in Article 220 of NFPA 70. It is important to point out that sizing generators for connected load (or using the Article 220 calculations) can result in grossly oversizing generators, in which case actual demands are so small that the generator cannot be exercised with sufficient building load to ensure reliable operation. (Refer to NFPA 110, *Standard for Emergency and Standby Power Systems* [2], for testing requirements for Level 1 generators.)

NFPA 110 is consistent with Article 517 of NFPA 70 and with NFPA 99. NFPA 110 simply says, "The energy converters shall have the required capacity and response to pick up and carry the load within the time specified in Table 4.1(b) after loss of primary power."

Wording in NFPA 70 has been interpreted to mean that the emergency system is to be sized for all connected, but noncoincident, loads. The language in NFPA 110, NFPA 99, and NFPA 70, Article 517, should take precedence over NFPA 70, Article 700, because the former specifically address health care facilities. It should also be noted that standby generators in health care facilities serve both the equipment system and the emergency system and that the emergency system consists of the life safety branch and the critical branch. While the life safety branch is similar to the emergency system of a non–health care facility (consisting of egress lighting, exit lights, life safety circuits, etc.), the equipment system and the critical branch are quite different. A considerable amount of diversity can be exercised in sizing the generator for equipment system and the critical branch loads.

Paragraph 4.4.1.1.3 clearly permits load-shed circuits for multiple generator systems. These circuits are permitted to shed loads as required upon loss of one or more generators to prevent "cascading" (the loss of additional generators as the result of overloading). With single and multiple generator installations, load-shed circuits, lockout circuits, and noncoincident loads (i.e., summer/winter) can and should be considered when determining the maximum expected system demand.

A.4.4.1.1.9 It is the intent of this subparagraph to mandate generator sizing based upon actual demand likely to be produced by the connected load of the essential electrical system(s) at any one time. It is not the intent that generator sizing be based upon connected load or feeder calculation procedures described in NFPA 70, *National Electrical Code*. Demand calculations should be based upon prudent demand factors and historical data.

4.4.1.1.10 Load Pickup. The energy converters shall have the required capacity and response to pick up and carry the load within the time specified in Table 4.1(b) of NFPA 110, *Standard for Emergency and Standby Power Systems*, after loss of primary power.

Voltage and frequency stability of the alternate power source, as required by 4.4.1.1.10, is necessary before connection to the load (i.e., the wiring system) in order to prevent damage to such items as voltage-sensitive equipment and fluorescent lighting. The operation of transfer switches is usually delayed until the voltage and frequency from the generator system are within specified limits. Although this standard calls for such stability in a maximum of 10 seconds (for the emergency system) from the time normal power is lost, transfer to an alternate power source can be accomplished whenever stability of the alternate power source is achieved (even if less than 10 seconds).

4.4.1.1.11 Maintenance of Temperature. The EPS shall be heated as necessary to maintain the water jacket temperature determined by the EPS manufacturer for cold start and load acceptance for the type of EPSS. [**110:**5.3.1]

4.4.1.1.12 Heating, Cooling, and Ventilating.

4.4.1.1.12.1* With the EPS running at rated load, ventilation airflow shall be provided to limit the maximum air temperature in the EPS room to the maximum ambient air temperature required by the EPS manufacturer. [**110:**7.7.1]

A.4.4.1.1.12.1 During operation, EPS and related equipment reject considerable heat that needs to be removed by proper ventilation or air-cooling. In some cases, outdoor installations rely on natural air circulation, but enclosed installations need properly sized, properly positioned ventilation facilities, to prevent recirculation of cooling air. The optimum position of air-supply louvers and radiator air discharge is on opposite walls, both to the outdoors. [**110:** A.7.7.1]

(A) Consideration shall be given to all the heat rejected to the EPS equipment room by the energy converter, uninsulated or insulated exhaust pipes, and other heat-producing equipment. [**110:**7.7.1.1]

4.4.1.1.12.2 Air shall be supplied to the EPS equipment for combustion. [**110:**7.7.2]

Exhibit 4.4 shows how ventilation air is supplied directly from a source outside of a building through an opening in an exterior wall.

EXHIBIT 4.4 *Louvered ventilation through outside wall.*

(A) For EPS supplying Level 1 EPSS, ventilation air shall be supplied directly from a source outside of the building by an exterior wall opening or from a source outside the building by a 2-hour fire-rated air transfer system. [**110:**7.7.2.1]

(B) For EPS supplying Level 1 EPSS, discharge air shall be directed outside of the building by an exterior wall opening or to an exterior opening by a 2-hour fire-rated air transfer system. [**110:**7.7.2.2]

(C) Fire dampers, shutters, or other self-closing devices shall not be permitted in ventilation openings or ductwork for supply or return/discharge air to EPS equipment for Level 1 EPSS. [**110:**7.7.2.3]

4.4.1.1.12.3 Ventilation air supply shall be from outdoors or from a source outside of the building by an exterior wall opening or from a source outside the building by a 2-hour fire-rated air transfer system. [**110:**7.7.3]

4.4.1.1.12.4 Ventilation air shall be provided to supply and discharge cooling air for radiator cooling of the EPS when running at rated load. [**110:**7.7.4]

(A) Ventilation air supply and discharge for radiator cooled EPS shall have a maximum static restriction of 125 Pa (0.5 in.) of water column in the discharge duct at the radiator outlet. [**110:**7.7.4.1]

(B) Radiator air discharge shall be ducted outdoors or to an exterior opening by a 2-hour fire-rated air transfer switch. [**110:**7.7.4.2]

4.4.1.1.12.5 Motor operated dampers, when used, shall be spring-operated to open and motor-closed. Fire dampers, shutters, or other self-closing devices shall not be permitted in ventilation openings or ductwork for supply or return/discharge air to EPS equipment for Level 1 EPSS. [**110:**7.7.5]

4.4.1.1.12.6 The ambient air temperature in the EPS equipment room or outdoor housing containing Level 1 rotating equipment shall be not less than 4.5°C (40°F). [**110:**7.7.6]

4.4.1.1.12.7 Units housed outdoors shall be heated as specified in 5.3.3 of NFPA 110, *Standard for Emergency and Standby Power Systems*. [**110:**7.7.7]

4.4.1.1.12.8 Design of the heating, cooling, and ventilation system for the EPS equipment room shall include provision for factors including, but not limited to, the following:

(1) Heat
(2) Cold
(3) Dust
(4) Humidity
(5) Snow and ice accumulations around housings
(6) Louvers
(7) Remote radiator fans
(8) Prevailing winds blowing against radiator fan discharge air [**110:**7.7.8]

4.4.1.1.13 Cranking Batteries. Internal combustion engine cranking batteries shall be in accordance with the battery requirements of NFPA 110, *Standard for Emergency and Standby Power Systems*.

4.4.1.1.14 Compressed Air Starting Devices. Other types of stored energy starting systems (except pyrotechnic) shall be permitted to be used where recommended by the manufacturer of the prime mover and subject to approval of the authority having jurisdiction, under the following conditions:

(1) Where two complete periods of cranking cycles are completed without replacement of the stored energy
(2) Where a means for automatic restoration from the emergency source of the stored energy is provided

(3) Where the stored energy system has the cranking capacity specified in 5.6.4.2.1 of NFPA 110, *Standard for Emergency and Standby Power Systems*
(4) Where the stored energy system has a "black start" capability in addition to normal discharge capability [**110:**5.6.4.1.2]

4.4.1.1.15 Fuel Supply. The fuel supply for the generator set shall comply with Sections 5.5 and 7.9 of NFPA 110, *Standard for Emergency and Standby Power Systems.*

If the preceding requirements are met by a generator system, as opposed to a battery system, the requirements for the battery system must be factored into the fuel supply decision. Whatever supply is maintained, consideration should be given to the logistical requirements of replenishing the fuel supply before it is exhausted. If, for example, the fuel supply is sufficient for three days, consideration should be given to ordering fuel 24 hours or even 48 hours before it is needed. During a tropical storm, for example, downed trees and power lines could delay fuel supply trucks.

Another example would be a temporary governmental prohibition against the transport of combustible materials at a time when downed power lines present the risk of fire or explosion. Where NFPA 110, *Standard for Emergency and Standby Power Systems,* refers to the "low probability" of interruption (e.g. natural gas), this judgment should be made by technical personnel in consultation with such groups as local utility companies and state energy authorities. Documentation should be prepared for the authority having jurisdiction in order to utilize the interruptible source of energy. As much as any other requirements of NFPA 99 and NFPA 110 [2], fuel supply requirements will be determined by local authorities having jurisdiction, state regulatory authorities, and other codes and standards. While the low-fuel alarms specified in NFPA 110 pertain to the main tank, consideration should be given to low-fuel alarms on both the day tank and main tank (where applicable). In determining fuel supply, other considerations are the type of facility, the possibility of fuel aging, the presence of other equipment that might use or "turn over" the fuel supply (e.g., boilers), the types and lengths of medical procedures, and licensing considerations (e.g., statutory "patient stays" of less than 24 hours).

4.4.1.1.16 Requirements for Safety Devices.

NFPA 99 and NFPA 110, *Standard for Emergency and Standby Power Systems* [2], do not specify fuel capacity and generator run-time for essential electrical systems in health care facilities. Paragraph 4.4.1.1.17(2)(d) of NFPA 99 does, however, require an alarm notification when any main liquid fuel supply contains less than a 4-hour operating supply.

Reference to fuel capacity and generator run-time in general can be found in the following NFPA publications:

1. NFPA *101, Life Safety Code* [3], which requires a minimum of 1 hour for lights used for illuminating exits and exit signs
2. Section 700.12(B)(2) in NFPA 70, *National Electrical Code* [1], which requires a minimum fuel supply of 2 hours for legally required standby emergency generators
3. *NFPA 72, National Fire Alarm Code* [4], which requires emergency power systems to supply power to fire alarm systems for 24 hours to 60 hours, depending on the type of fire alarm signaling system

Other authorities (e.g., local, state) might have requirements that impact the fuel supply and replenishment requirements noted herein.

If the preceding requirements are met by a generator system, as opposed to a battery system, these requirements must then be factored into fuel supplies for the generator. Whatever supply is maintained, consideration should be given to its capability to replenish the fuel supply before it is exhausted. (An essential electrical system might have to function for an extended period in some emergencies.) As an example, if a facility maintains an on-site fuel supply capable of running the generator for 3 days, replenishment procedures should not exceed 2 days.

Determination of low probability, as noted in NFPA 110 [2], should be made by technical personnel in consultation with such groups as local utility companies and state energy authorities. Documentation must be prepared for the authority having jurisdiction in order to utilize this requirement.

4.4.1.1.16.1 Internal Combustion Engines. Internal combustion engines serving generator sets shall be equipped with the following:

(1) A sensor device plus visual warning device to indicate a water-jacket temperature below those required in 4.4.1.1.11
(2) Sensor devices plus visual prealarm warning device to indicate the following:
    (a) High engine temperature (above manufacturer's recommended safe operating temperature range)
    (b) Low lubricating oil pressure (below manufacturer's recommended safe operating range)
    (c) Low water coolant level
(3) An automatic engine shutdown device plus visual device to indicate that a shutdown took place due to the following:
    (a) Overcrank (failed to start)
    (b) Overspeed
    (c) Low lubricating oil pressure
    (d) Excessive engine temperature
(4) A common audible alarm device to warn that any one or more of the prealarm or alarm conditions exist

4.4.1.1.16.2 Safety indications and shutdowns shall be in accordance with Table 4.4.1.1.16.2.

Table 4.4.1.1.16.2 is extracted in part from NFPA 110, *Standard for Emergency and Standby Power Systems* [2]. Only the portion of the table showing the requirements for Level 1 systems is included. Level 2 systems are not generally used in health care facilities.

The safety devices listed in 4.4.1.1.16.2 are specifically for health care facility essential electrical systems. They are required in addition to any general requirements for internal combustion engines contained in NFPA 37, *Standard for the Installation and Use of Stationary Combustion Engines and Gas Turbines* [5], and NFPA 110 [2]. Audible, as well as visual, indicators are considered necessary to help ensure that malfunctions are identified and investigated in a timely manner.

4.4.1.1.17 Alarm Annunciator. A remote annunciator, storage battery–powered, shall be provided to operate outside of the generating room in a location readily observed by operating personnel at a regular work station *(see Section 700.12 of* NFPA 70, *National Electrical Code).* The annunciator shall be hard-wired to indicate alarm conditions of the emergency or auxiliary power source as follows:

(1) Individual visual signals shall indicate the following:
    (a) When the emergency or auxiliary power source is operating to supply power to load
    (b) When the battery charger is malfunctioning

TABLE 4.4.1.1.16.2 *Safety Indications and Shutdowns*

Indicator Function (at Battery Voltage)	***Level 1***		
	C.V.	***S.***	***R.A.***
(a) Overcrank	X	X	X
(b) Low water temperature	X		X
(c) High engine temperature prealarm	X		X
(d) High engine temperature	X	X	X
(e) Low lube oil pressure prealarm	X		X
(f) Low lube oil pressure	X	X	X
(g) Overspeed	X	X	X
(h) Low fuel main tank	X		X
(i) Low coolant level	X	O	X
(j) EPS supplying load	X		
(k) Control switch not in automatic position	X		X
(l) High battery voltage	X		
(m) Low cranking voltage	X		X
(n) Low voltage in battery	X		
(o) Battery charger ac failure	X		
(p) Lamp test	X		
(q) Contacts for local and remote common alarm	X		X
(r) Audible alarm silencing switch			X
(s) Low starting air pressure	X		
(t) Low starting hydraulic pressure	X		
(u) Air shutdown damper when used	X	X	X
(v) Remote emergency stop		X	

C.V.: Control panel–mounted visual. S.: Shutdown of EPS indication. R.A.: Remote audible. X: Required. O: Optional.

Notes:

1. Item (p) shall be provided, but a separate remote audible signal shall not be required when the regular work site in 5.6.6 of NFPA 110 is staffed 24 hours a day.
2. Item (b) is not required for combustion turbines.
3. Item (r) or (s) shall apply only where used as a starting method.
4. Item (j): EPS ac ammeter shall be permitted for this function.
5. All required C.V. functions shall be visually annunciated by a remote, common visual indicator.
6. All required functions indicated in the R.A. column shall be annunciated by a remote, common audible alarm as required in 5.6.5.2(4) of NFPA 110.
7. Item (i) on gaseous systems shall require a low gas pressure alarm.
8. Item (b) shall be set at 11°C (20°F) below the regulated temperature determined by the EPS manufacturer as required in 5.3.1 of NFPA 110.

(2) Individual visual signals plus a common audible signal to warn of an engine-generator alarm condition shall indicate the following:

(a) Low lubricating oil pressure
(b) Low water temperature (below those required in 4.4.1.1.11)
(c) Excessive water temperature
(d) Low fuel — when the main fuel storage tank contains less than a 4-hour operating supply
(e) Overcrank (failed to start)
(f) Overspeed

For 4.4.1.1.17(1)(a), the usual practice is to provide a visual signal indicating that the generator is producing voltage. For 4.4.1.1.17(2)(a) and 4.4.1.1.17(2)(c), the audible/visual signal is generally a pre-shutdown type, providing a warning before shutdown actually occurs. It is not intended that two lights be provided at the alarm annunciator, one for warning (pre-shutdown) and one at shutdown. An annunciator remote from the generating room is useful only if it indicates impending problems.

An annunciator is normally located in one location near the generator(s). A derangement signal, if necessary, is in another location where continuous monitoring (i.e., 24 hours a day) is possible.

4.4.1.1.17.1* A remote, common audible alarm shall be provided as specified in 4.4.1.1.17.4 that is powered by the storage battery and located outside of the EPS service room at a work site observable by personnel. [**110:**5.6.6]

A.4.4.1.1.17.1 As a supplement to hard-wired alarm annunciations, it is permissible to have Level 1 and Level 2 EPS and ATS functions monitored offsite. Monitoring stations can include pagers, cell phones, and internet-connected devices.

4.4.1.1.17.2 An alarm-silencing means shall be provided, and the panel shall include repetitive alarm circuitry so that, after the audible alarm has been silenced, it reactivates after the fault condition has been cleared and has to be restored to its normal position to be silenced again. [**110:**5.6.6.1]

4.4.1.1.17.3 In lieu of the requirement of 5.6.6.1 of NFPA 110, a manual alarm-silencing means shall be permitted that silences the audible alarm after the occurrence of the alarm condition, provided such means do not inhibit any subsequent alarms from sounding the audible alarm again without further manual action. [**110:**5.6.6.2]

4.4.1.1.17.4 Individual alarm indication to annunciate any of the conditions listed in Table 4.4.1.1.16.2 shall have the following characteristics:

(1) Battery-powered
(2) Visually indicated
(3) Have additional contacts or circuits for a common audible alarm that signals locally and remotely when any of the itemized conditions occurs
(4) Have a lamp test switch(es) to test the operation of all alarm lamps

4.4.1.2 Battery. Battery systems shall meet all requirements of Article 700 of NFPA 70, *National Electrical Code*.

FAQ ▶ Is a battery system allowed as an alternate source of power for the essential electrical system?

It is generally agreed that battery systems are permitted for Type 1 systems. If battery systems are used, however, the battery time must be equivalent to the fuel requirement for on-site generators. Using battery systems is generally impractical for Type 1 systems in hospitals. Battery systems are more practical when used on Type 1 systems in outpatient facilities, where the duration of the procedure and the duration of the patient stay is limited. It is important to consult with local authorities having jurisdiction and state licensing authorities before using batteries for Type 1 systems.

It is also agreed that the reference should be to NFPA 111, *Standard on Stored Electrical Energy Emergency and Standby Power Systems* [6], and not Article 700 of NFPA 70, *National Electrical Code* [1]. It is expected that these issues will be resolved in the next edition of NFPA 99.

4.4.2* Distribution (Type 1 EES).

The requirements of 4.4.2 cover the type of essential electrical system that should be installed, taking into consideration the medical procedures that will be carried out in the facility. It was not the intent of the committee that developed the requirements for essential electrical systems that the entire facility have power restored if normal power were lost. Only specific portions are to be connected to the essential electrical system.

A.4.4.2 It should be emphasized that the type of system selected and its area and type of coverage should be appropriate to the medical procedures being performed in the facility. For example, a battery-operated emergency light that switches "on" when normal power is interrupted and an alternate source of power for suction equipment, along with the immediate availability of some portable hand-held lighting, would be advisable where oral and maxillofacial surgery (e.g., extraction of impacted teeth) is performed. On the other hand, in dental offices where simple extraction, restorative, prosthetic, or hygienic procedures are performed, only remote corridor lighting for purposes of egress would be sufficient. Emergency power for equipment would not be necessary. As with oral surgery locations, a surgical clinic requiring use of life support or emergency devices such as suction machines, ventilators, cauterizers, or defibrillators would require both emergency light and power.

4.4.2.1 General Requirements.

4.4.2.1.1 Electrical characteristics of the transfer switches shall be suitable for the operation of all functions and equipment they are intended to supply.

See Exhibit 4.5 for a detail of a transfer switch cabinet for the life safety and critical branches of the essential electrical system.

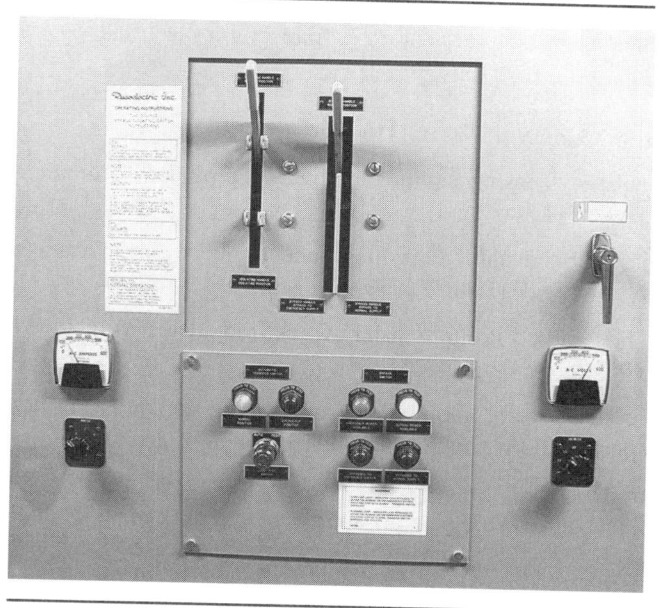

EXHIBIT 4.5 *Detail of transfer switch cabinet.*

4.4.2.1.2 Switch Rating. The rating of the transfer switches shall be adequate for switching all classes of loads to be served and for withstanding the effects of available fault currents without contact welding.

For requirements on the capacity of switches, refer to Article 517 of NFPA 70, *National Electrical Code* [1].

4.4.2.1.3 Automatic Transfer Switch Classification. Transfer of all loads shall be accomplished using automatic transfer switch(es). Each automatic transfer switch 600 volts or below shall be listed for the purpose and approved for emergency electrical service *(see Section 700.3 of* NFPA 70, *National Electrical Code)* as a complete assembly.

FAQ ▶
Can a method other than transfer switches be used to switch to an alternate power source?

NFPA 99 goes to great length to describe automatic transfer switches and their application to health care facilities. It is generally agreed that automatic transfer switches are required. It is expected that the standard will be clarified in the next edition of NFPA 99.

4.4.2.1.4 Automatic Transfer Switch Features.

4.4.2.1.4.1 Source Monitoring.

(A)* Undervoltage-sensing devices shall be provided to monitor all ungrounded lines of the primary source of power as follows:

A.4.4.2.1.4.1(A) Where special loads require more rapid detection of power loss, underfrequency monitoring also might be provided. Upon frequency decay below the lower limit necessary for proper operation of the loads, the transfer switch should automatically initiate transfer to the alternate source. *(See A.6.2.15 of NFPA 110.)* [**110:** A.6.2.2.1]

(1) When the voltage on any phase falls below the minimum operating voltage of any load to be served, the transfer switch shall automatically initiate engine start and the process of transfer to the emergency power supply (EPS).
(2)* When the voltage on all phases of the primary source returns to within specified limits for a designated period of time, the process of transfer back to primary power shall be initiated. [**110:**6.2.2.1]

Monitoring only the ungrounded lines is considered satisfactory for essential electrical system purposes.

A.4.4.2.1.4.1(A)(2) See 6.2.5 and 6.2.7 of NFPA 110. [**110:** A.6.2.2.1(2)]

(B) Both voltage-sensing and frequency-sensing equipment shall be provided to monitor one ungrounded line of the EPS power. [**110:**6.2.2.2]

(C) Transfer to the EPS shall be inhibited until the voltage and frequency are within a specified range to handle loads to be served. [**110:**6.2.2.3]

(D) Sensing equipment shall not be required in the transfer switch, provided it is included with the engine control panel. [**110:**6.2.2.3(A)]

(E) Frequency-sensing equipment shall not be required for monitoring the public utility source where used as an EPS, as permitted by 5.1.4 of NFPA 110, *Standard for Emergency and Standby Power Systems*. [**110:**6.2.2.3(B)]

4.4.2.1.4.2 Interlocking. Mechanical interlocking or an approved alternate method shall prevent the inadvertent interconnection of the primary power supply and the EPS, or any two separate sources of power. [**110:**6.2.3]

The inadvertent interconnection of the normal and alternate sources of power, or of any two separate sources of power, is likely to cause major damage to an electrical system, as well as place personnel in danger. Components will probably be destroyed and require replacement or major repair, resulting in great expense and disruption to the facility.

The interlocking feature of the transfer switch must be reliable and fail-safe. Available interlocking schemes vary from simple mechanical means to complex combinations of mechanical, electrical, and electronic means. It is recommended that all interlocking include a reliable stand-alone mechanical means that is completely independent of all electrical and electronic means. Those considering alternate methods are advised to give due recognition to the NFPA definition of *approved.* It should also be noted that 4.4.2.1.4.15 requires nonautomatic transfer switches to be either direct manual or electrically remote controlled and mechanically held.

Closed transition transfer is not prohibited. However, the requirements for reliable interlocking included in 4.4.2.1.4.2 must be met.

4.4.2.1.4.3* Manual Operation.

A.4.4.2.1.4.3 Authorized personnel should be available and familiar with manual operation of the transfer switch and should be capable of determining the adequacy of the alternate source of power prior to manual transfer. [**110:** A.6.2.4]

(A) Instruction and equipment shall be provided for safe manual nonelectric transfer in the event the transfer switch malfunctions. [**110:**6.2.4.1]

Manual operation is required by 4.4.2.1.4.3(A) so that operational problems of automatic transfer switches can be resolved or corrected. Manual operation can be accomplished by direct manual means, electrical remote manual means, or both. Many operating personnel prefer the positive advantages of direct manual means.

This requirement has been included to safeguard those operating personnel who might place themselves at risk of injury or worse in attempting to troubleshoot malfunctions that have left patients in a facility without electrical power.

No guidelines have been included with respect to how switching might be accomplished. No guidelines could be suggested without impinging on the design of some manufacturer's products. The transfer switch manufacturer should be consulted before operating an automatic transfer switch manually under load.

(B) An automatic transfer switch shall visually annunciate when "not-in-automatic." [**110:**6.2.4.2]

4.4.2.1.4.4* Time Delay on Starting of EPS. A time-delay device shall be provided to delay starting of the EPS. The timer shall prevent nuisance starting of the EPS and possible subsequent load transfer in the event of harmless momentary power dips and interruptions of the primary source. [**110:**6.2.5]

It is the intent of this chapter that essential electrical systems be powered by the alternate source within the time specified for the type classification after the failure of the normal source. ("Failure" can be thought of as a drop in voltage below a pre-established minimum for a specified length of time.)

The time limit value takes into consideration the following intervals:

1. A time delay on commanding the starting of the emergency power supply, considered to be an on-site generator set; plus
2. The time for the generator set to start, attain operating voltage and frequency, and be capable of generating the required power; plus
3. The time for operation of the transfer switches; plus
4. A design-safety interval factor.

Interval 1 is considered to be about 2 seconds, with a range from about 1 second to 3 seconds. The actual time is the result of setting a field-adjustable timer to meet local needs. The timer starts when normal supply voltage is sensed to have dropped to less than the predetermined value, which is also selected to meet local needs.

Interval 2 is considered to be about 5 seconds, with a range from about 3 seconds to 7 seconds. It is a function of the generator set, its controls, and its loading. The interval is actually 0 second when the alternate source is an external utility service. (See 4.4.1.1.4 for instances in which an external utility may be an approved alternate source.)

Interval 3 is considered to be a fraction of a second. It is a function of the characteristics of the transfer switches. Time delays can be imposed upon interval 3 as part of an individual design (i.e., to prevent loading the generator too rapidly).

Interval 4, used in establishing the 10-second value of the chapter, is discretionary. The 10-second value is reasonably attainable on a national and facility-wide basis. It is not based on the established needs of any fire protection, life safety, or medical function.

For equipment that cannot tolerate a loss of even a cycle of power (e.g., computer-driven equipment) or for procedures where a 10-second power outage cannot be tolerated, the use of uninterrupted power supplies (UPS) have to be considered. (For further discussion on this issue, see the commentary under B.1.4.2.)

A.4.4.2.1.4.4 For most applications, a nominal delay of 1 second is adequate. The time delay should be short enough so that the generator can start and be on the line within the time specified for the type classification. [**110:** A.6.2.5]

4.4.2.1.4.5 Time Delay at Engine Control Panel. Time delays shall be permitted to be located at the engine control panel in lieu of in the transfer switches. [**110:**6.2.6]

4.4.2.1.4.6 Time Delay on Transfer to EPS. An adjustable time-delay device shall be provided to delay transfer and sequence load transfer to the EPS to avoid excessive voltage drop when the transfer switch is installed for Level 1 use. [**110:**6.2.7]

(A) Time Delay Commencement. The time delay shall commence when proper EPS voltage and frequency are achieved. [**110:**6.2.7.1]

(B) Time Delay at Engine Control Panel. Time delays shall be permitted to be located at the engine control panel in lieu of in the transfer switches. [**110:**6.2.7.2]

4.4.2.1.4.7* Time Delay on Retransfer to Primary Source. An adjustable time-delay device with automatic bypass shall be provided to delay retransfer from the EPS to the primary source of power, and allow the primary source to stabilize before retransfer of the load. [**110:**6.2.8]

A.4.4.2.1.4.7 It is recommended that the timer for delay on retransfer to the primary source be set for 30 minutes. The 30-minute recommendation is to establish a "normalized" engine temperature, when it is beneficial for the engine. NFPA 70, *National Electrical Code*, establishes a minimum time requirement of 15 minutes. [**110:** A.6.2.8]

4.4.2.1.4.8 Time Delay Bypass If EPS Fails. The time delay shall be automatically bypassed if the EPS fails. [**110:**6.2.9]

(A) The transfer switch shall be permitted to be programmed for a manually initiated retransfer to the primary source to provide for a planned momentary interruption of the load. [**110:**6.2.9.1]

(B) If used, the arrangement in 6.2.9.1 of NFPA 110, *Standard for Emergency and Standby Power Systems*, shall be provided with a bypass feature to allow automatic retransfer in the event that the EPS fails and the primary source is available. [**110:**6.2.9.2]

4.4.2.1.4.9 Time Delay on Engine Shutdown. A minimum time delay of 5 minutes shall be provided for unloaded running of the EPS prior to shutdown to allow for engine cooldown. [**110:**6.2.10]

(A) The minimum 5-minute delay shall not be required on small (15 kW or less) air-cooled prime movers. [**110:**6.2.10.1]

(B) A time-delay device shall not be required, provided it is included with the engine control panel, or if a utility feeder is used as an EPS. [**110:**6.2.10.2]

4.4.2.1.4.10 Engine Generator Exercising Timer. A program timing device shall be provided to exercise the EPS as described in Chapter 8 of NFPA 110, *Standard for Emergency and Standby Power Systems.* [**110:**6.2.11]

(A) Transfer switches for Level 1 and Level 2 shall transfer the connected load to the EPS and immediately return to primary power automatically in case of the EPS failure. [**110:**6.2.11.1]

(B) Exercising timers shall be permitted to be located at the engine control panel in lieu of in the transfer switches. [**110:**6.2.11.2]

(C) A program timing device shall not be required in health care facilities that provide scheduled testing in accordance with NFPA 99, *Standard for Health Care Facilities.* [**110:**6.2.11.3]

4.4.2.1.4.11 Test Switch. A test means shall be provided on each automatic transfer switch (ATS) that simulates failure of the primary power source and then transfers the load to the EPS. [**110:**6.2.12]

Test switches permit appropriate testing of individual components and the entire essential electrical system without requiring interruption of the normal source. Test switches ensure that the switch will automatically return to the source should the standby unit fail during the test.

Test switches generally utilize the "time delay on retransfer to normal" timer. This timer is generally adjustable from 0 to 30 minutes. If the test switch is to be used for testing and exercising the on-site generator (as it should be) and the test interval is required to be longer than 30 minutes, a transfer switch accessory should be specified. The test switch can be arranged to initiate the longer time interval. With this accessory, the "time delay on retransfer to normal" and the "test interval" will require different settings. For example, the "time delay on retransfer to normal" might be set at 30 minutes and the "test interval" might be set at 4 hours to meet the test requirements of NFPA 110, *Standard for Emergency and Standby Power Systems,* paragraph 8.4.9 [2].

4.4.2.1.4.12* Indication of Switch Position. Two pilot lights with identification nameplates or other approved position indicators shall be provided to indicate the transfer switch position. [**110:**6.2.13]

A.4.4.2.1.4.12 For maintenance purposes, consideration should be given to a transfer switch counter. [**110:** A.6.2.13]

One pilot light indicates that the switch is in the normal power position, and the other pilot light indicates that the switch is in the alternate power position. Indicating lights not only indicate the transfer switch position to the system operator, but they can be useful in troubleshooting operational problems. The commentary following 4.4.2.1.4.11 is appropriate here as well.

4.4.2.1.4.13 Motor Load Transfer. Provisions shall be included to reduce currents resulting from motor load transfer if such currents could damage EPSS equipment or cause nuisance tripping of EPSS overcurrent protective devices. [**110:**6.2.14]

4.4.2.1.4.14* Isolation of Neutral Conductors. Provisions shall be included for ensuring continuity, transfer, and isolation of the primary and the EPS neutral conductors wherever they are separately grounded to achieve ground-fault sensing. [**110:**6.2.15]

A.4.4.2.1.4.14 Automatic transfer switches (ATS) can be provided with accessory controls that provide a signal to operate remote motor controls that disconnect motors prior to transfer,

and to reconnect them after transfer when the residual voltage has been substantially reduced. Another method is to provide inphase monitors within the ATS in order to prevent retransfer to the primary source until both sources are nearly synchronized. A third method is to use a programmed neutral position transfer switch. See Section 230.95(b) of NFPA 70, *National Electrical Code*. [**110:** A.6.2.15]

4.4.2.1.4.15* Nonautomatic Transfer Switch Features. Switching devices shall be mechanically held and shall be operated by direct manual or electrical remote manual control. [**110:**6.2.16]

A.4.4.2.1.4.15 Standards for nonautomatic transfer switches are similar to those for automatic transfer switches, as defined in 3.3.7.1 and 3.3.7.3 of NFPA 110, *Standard for Emergency and Standby Power Systems*, with the omission of automatic controls. [**110:** A.6.2.16]

(A) Interlocking. Reliable mechanical interlocking, or an approved alternate method, shall prevent the inadvertent interconnection of the primary power source and the EPS. [**110:**6.2.16.1]

(B) Indication of Switch Position. Two pilot lights with identification nameplates, or other approved position indicators, shall be provided to indicate the switch position. [**110:**6.2.16.2]

4.4.2.1.5 Nonautomatic Transfer Device Classification. Nonautomatic transfer devices 600 volts or below shall be listed for the purpose and approved.

4.4.2.1.6 Nonautomatic Transfer Device Features.

4.4.2.1.6.1 General. Switching devices shall be mechanically held and shall be operated by direct manual or electrical remote manual control. [**110:**6.2.16]

4.4.2.1.6.2 Interlocking. Reliable mechanical interlocking, or an approved alternate method, shall prevent the inadvertent interconnection of the primary power source and the EPS. [**110:**6.2.16.1]

4.4.2.1.6.3 Indication of Switch Position. Two pilot lights with identification nameplates, or other approved position indicators, shall be provided to indicate the switch position. [**110:**6.2.16.2]

4.4.2.1.7 Bypass-Isolation Switches. Bypass-isolation switches shall be permitted for bypassing and isolating the transfer switch and installed in accordance with 4.4.2.1.7.1 through 4.4.2.1.7.4. [**110:**6.4.1]

Note that bypass-isolation switching is not mandated. Bypass-isolation switches do eliminate system downtime when normal transfer switches need maintenance, as well as provide an alternate method of transfer in the event normal transfer switches are damaged.

4.4.2.1.7.1 Bypass-Isolation Switch Rating. The bypass-isolation switch shall have a continuous current rating and a current rating compatible with that of the associated transfer switch. [**110:**6.4.2]

4.4.2.1.7.2 Bypass-Isolation Switch Classification. Each bypass-isolation switch shall be listed for emergency electrical service as a completely factory-assembled and factory-tested apparatus. [**110:**6.4.3]

4.4.2.1.7.3* Operation. With the transfer switch isolated or disconnected, the bypass-isolation switch shall be designed so it can function as an independent nonautomatic transfer switch and allow the load to be connected to either power source. [**110:**6.4.4]

A.4.4.2.1.7.3 Consideration should be given to the effect that load interruption could have on the load during maintenance and service of the transfer switch.

4.4.2.1.7.4 Reconnection of Transfer Switch. Reconnection of the transfer switch shall be possible without a load interruption greater than the maximum time, in seconds, specified by the type of system. [**110:**6.4.5]

4.4.2.2 Specific Requirements.

◀ **FAQ**
How is a Type 1, 2, or 3 essential electrical system defined?

Use of the term *Type 1* is simply for identification purposes. The type of essential electrical system (1, 2, or 3) for a particular health care facility (hospital, nursing home, etc.) is stipulated in Chapters 12 through 17. See Chapter 1, text and commentary, for a complete explanation of how NFPA 99 is structured and how it is to be used. NFPA 99 does not define Type 1, 2, or 3 essential electrical systems. Exhibit 4.6 is a graphical representation of the different types of essential electrical systems. This is useful in determining the similarities and differences between the types.

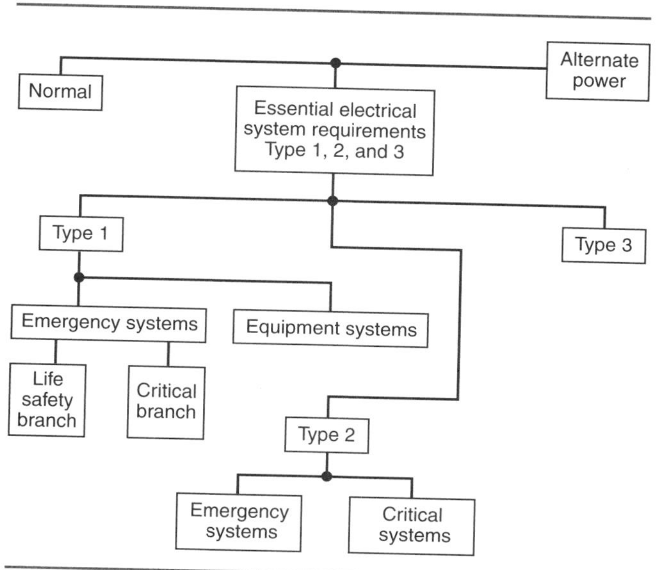

EXHIBIT 4.6 NFPA 99 essential electrical system types.

4.4.2.2.1* General.

A.4.4.2.2.1 Type 1 essential electrical systems are comprised of two separate systems capable of supplying a limited amount of lighting and power service that is considered essential for life safety and effective facility operation during the time the normal electrical service is interrupted for any reason. These two systems are the emergency system and the equipment system. 

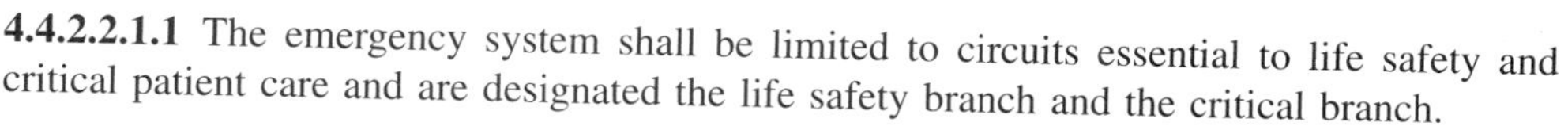

4.4.2.2.1.1 The emergency system shall be limited to circuits essential to life safety and critical patient care and are designated the life safety branch and the critical branch.

4.4.2.2.1.2 The equipment system shall supply major electrical equipment necessary for patient care and basic Type 1 operation.

4.4.2.2.1.3 Both systems shall be arranged for connection, within time limits specified in this chapter, to an alternate source of power following a loss of the normal source.

4.4.2.2.1.4 The number of transfer switches to be used shall be based upon reliability, design, and load considerations. Each branch of the emergency system and each equipment system shall have one or more transfer switches. One transfer switch shall be permitted to serve one or more branches or systems in a facility with a continuous load on the switch of 150 kVA (120 kW) or less.

The 150 kVA (120 kW) load is on the "switch" rather than the "essential electrical system." Although a small hospital is permitted to have a single switch, the possibility also exists that the facility might have two switches (i.e., combining critical and life safety). However, the intent of 4.4.2.2.1.4 is that the load on the essential electrical system not exceed 150 kVA (120 kW) for small facilities. It is assumed that the load power factor is 80 percent, thus the reference to 150 kVA (120 kW). Because the power factor will likely be higher than 80 percent, the actual load could be, for example, 150 kVA and 130 kW. Thus, the values given should be taken as nominal values, and authorities having jurisdiction will not split hairs on the exact values of kVA and kW. Although the standard is silent on the number of essential system branches for a single-switch "small facility," it is recommended that separate branches and systems be installed for small facilities. This will facilitate the addition of transfer switches as the facility expands.

Sometimes the question arises about whether a single overcurrent protective device (OPD) on the generator to the distribution board is permissible or whether a minimum of two OPDs is necessary: one for the emergency system and one for the equipment system. The interpretation is that one feeder (and thus one OPD at the generator) is permitted to serve a distribution board, which in turn distributes power via transfer switches, and so on. It was noted that a single feeder is often used when the generator is remote from the distribution board. A parallel set of feeders is considered unnecessary and costly. No significant differences in safety or reliability are noted in using just one feeder.

4.4.2.2.2 Emergency System.

The division of the emergency system (for Type 1 essential electrical systems) into two branches is for identification purposes. The life safety branch (see 4.4.2.2.2.2) provides power only to those functions or warning systems, such as alarm systems, exit signs, lighting of means of egress, and communication systems, necessary for safely leaving any building in an emergency. The critical branch (see 4.4.2.2.2.3) includes those functions that maintain essential patient services, because health care facility fire response is designed around a defend-in-place concept. Evacuation of the building occurs only when absolutely necessary. Paragraph 4.4.2.2.2.3 includes those functions that do not have to be restored within 10 seconds because their rapid restoration is not critical. In addition, they might overload the alternate power source if they were to come on-line within the 10 seconds specified for the emergency system.

Task illumination does not necessarily mean that all lighting in a location need be connected to the essential electrical system. The lights that are connected depend on the activities in the particular area.

4.4.2.2.2.1 General. Those functions of patient care depending on lighting or appliances that shall be permitted to be connected to the emergency system are divided into two mandatory branches, described in 4.4.2.2.2.2 and 4.4.2.2.2.3.

The location of 4.4.2.2.2.1 makes it clear that if patient care–related appliances and lighting are served by a transfer switch, they are to be connected to an emergency system transfer switch that restores power in 10 seconds. This text gives the hospital design engineer some latitude in making this connection. Accessories can be supplied from a life safety branch transfer switch, a critical branch transfer switch, or, in some cases, directly off the standby generator. For example, a remote radiator can be fed directly from the standby generator by means of a relay that "picks up" when the generator output reaches nominal voltage.

4.4.2.2.2.2 Life Safety Branch. The life safety branch of the emergency system shall supply power for the following lighting, receptacles, and equipment:

(1) Illumination of means of egress as required in NFPA *101*, *Life Safety Code*

NFPA *101, Life Safety Code* [3], lists where and how much illumination is required for means of egress. Given the critical and urgent need for electricity in a fire emergency — for example, lighting when exiting and emergency instructions — the issue of whether there should be a backup to the backup is now debated. Is emergency power from a generator enough of a guarantee that lighting and power to other critical items will be restored, or should there be redundancy, such as automatic battery-charged lighting, in addition to a power generator? (The bombing of the World Trade Center in New York City in 1993, where stairwells went dark when the emergency generators shut down from lack of cooling water, unfortunately brought this point to the forefront.) Given the maintenance associated with individual battery units, plus the number that would be required for some buildings (such as a 15-story hospital complex), there is one situation involving lighting in NFPA 99 where a "backup to the backup" is required [see 4.4.2.2.2.2(5)], but there are no prohibitions against doing it either.

(2) Exit signs and exit direction signs required in NFPA *101*, *Life Safety Code*
(3) Alarm and alerting systems including the following:

   (a) Fire alarms

This includes any type of fire alarm, whether for one area, one function, or the entire facility. These alarm and alerting systems can include, under certain conditions, interfaces with an engineered smoke-control system.

Exhibit 4.7 is an example of a typical fire alarm panel with a detail of the controls.

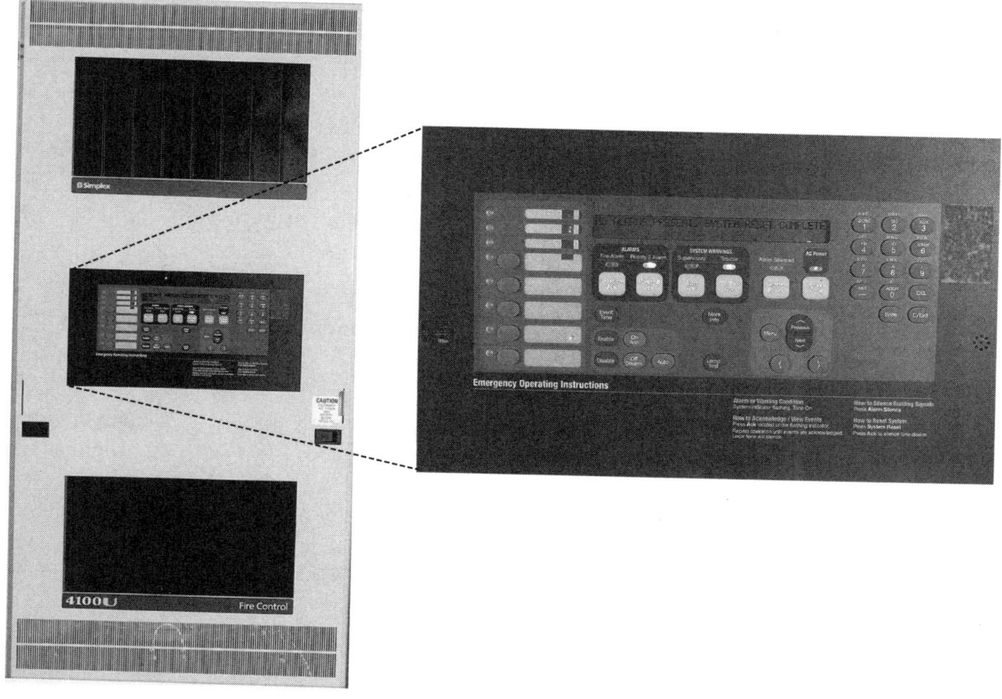

EXHIBIT 4.7 *Fire alarm panel.*

(b) Alarms required for systems used for the piping of nonflammable medical gases as specified in Chapter 5, Gas and Vacuum Systems

(4)* Hospital communication systems, where used for issuing instruction during emergency conditions

A.4.4.2.2.2.2(4) Departmental installations such as digital dialing systems used for intradepartmental communications could have impaired use during a failure of electrical service to the area. In the event of such failure, those systems that have lighted selector buttons in the base of the telephone instrument or in the desk units known as "director sets" will be out of service to the extent that the lights will not function and that the buzzer used to indicate incoming calls will be silenced. The lack of electrical energy will not prevent the use of telephones for outgoing calls, but incoming calls will not be signaled, nor will intercommunicating calls be signaled. This communication failure should be taken into consideration in planning essential electrical systems.

(5) Generator set location: Task illumination, battery charger for emergency battery-powered lighting unit(s), and selected receptacles at the generator set location and essential electrical system transfer switch locations

FAQ ▶
Why does the generator set location need to be illuminated?

This requirement was changed in the 2002 edition to include spaces housing essential electrical system transfer switches. Emergency lighting is necessary to troubleshoot the generator(s) or transfer switch(es) under real emergency conditions.

(6) Elevator cab lighting, control, communication, and signal systems

Item 6 was added to the life safety branch because of concern for persons who might be in elevators when normal power was interrupted and because these functions, in a real sense, provide a means of egress for these persons. Although power for elevator movement might be restored on a delayed or manual basis, it could be a very stressful wait for those in the elevators. Restoring lights and communication within 10 seconds would reduce the possibility of panic.

(7) Automatically operated doors used for building egress

This text, concerning automatically operated doors, was removed from the equipment system and added to the life safety branch because the requirement is related to life safety and service needs to be restored in 10 seconds. The general public is not usually familiar with the manual operation of automatic doors under emergency conditions.

(8) The auxiliary functions of fire alarm combination systems complying with *NFPA 72, National Fire Alarm Code*

In a fire or other emergency, electricity is automatically interrupted to any hold-open devices (generally via any fire alarm signal) so that smoke and fire doors that are being held open will close and stay closed until manually reset. However, if a smoke or fire door requires an electrical motor in order to close, that motor needs to be connected to the most reliable branch of the essential electrical system, that is, to the life safety branch. In this way, the door will close if normal power is lost and a fire alarm signal will indicate an emergency (e.g., a smoke detector activates).

See Exhibit 4.8 for an example of a corridor door being held open by electric magnets. Magnets will de-energize upon interruption of electricity (e.g., from fire alarm activation,

EXHIBIT 4.8 A corridor door being held open by electric magnets.

from loss of normal electric power), and doors will close. Doors must be manually reset open when the fire alarm is reset or power is restored.

If electromechanical locks for security (egress) doors of psychiatric wards unlock on loss of power, the 120 V to the locks can be placed on the critical branch. However, if such doors require power to unlock and the locks are not connected to a battery system, the 120 V to the locks would have to be placed on the life safety branch.

No function other than those listed in items 4.4.2.2.2.2(1) through 4.4.2.2.2.2(8) shall be connected to the life safety branch.

4.4.2.2.2.3* Critical Branch. The critical branch shall be permitted to be subdivided into two or more branches. The critical branch of the emergency system shall supply power for task illumination, fixed equipment, selected receptacles, and selected power circuits serving the following areas and functions related to patient care:

A.4.4.2.2.2.3 It is recommended that facility authorities give consideration to providing and properly maintaining automatic battery-powered lighting units or systems to provide minimal task illumination in operating rooms, delivery rooms, and certain special-procedure radiology rooms where the loss of lighting due to failure of the essential electrical system could cause severe and immediate danger to a patient undergoing surgery or an invasive radiographic procedure.

◀ **FAQ**
Do all areas of the operating room, delivery room, and other critical care areas need to be illuminated?

Task illumination, as specified by 4.4.2.2.2.3, will vary depending on the activity in a given area in an operating room. Sufficient lighting to maintain patient care would mean that all surgical lights are to be connected to the essential electrical system. In a general ward, it might be sufficient to connect just one overhead light in the room to the essential electrical system. A pediatric ward would require lighting to be restored everywhere youngsters are allowed to go. Task illumination does not mean restoring power to lighting used for nonessential purposes or for activities that can be temporarily postponed.

(1) Critical care areas that utilize anesthetizing gases, task illumination, selected receptacles, and fixed equipment

These requirements reflect changes in the requirements for IPSs in anesthetizing locations. Receptacles, task illumination, and fixed equipment in anesthetizing locations must be on the essential electrical system whether IPSs are present or not.

FAQ ▶
Should all of the electrical circuits in an anesthetizing location be on the critical branch circuit?

Debate has been considerable on whether *all* circuits in anesthetizing locations should be on the critical branch or whether, like other patient care areas, only *selected* or *special* circuits should be on the critical branch of the essential electrical system, with the rest connected to the normal electrical distribution system. Proponents of having both normal and essential circuits in an operating room argue that this requirement will increase reliability and that having all circuits on the essential electrical system subjects anesthetizing locations to a 100 percent loss of power if a transfer switch fails.

The term *selected receptacles* in 4.4.2.2.2.3(1) permits the installation of a minimum of one normal circuit [and receptacle(s)] as required by 4.3.2.2.1.1 and 4.3.2.2.1.2. Remember that the definition of *patient bed location* (3.3.137) includes procedure tables in critical care areas.

Because selected receptacles in operating rooms might be on normal circuits (like other patient care areas), it is important that emergency-powered receptacles in operating rooms be clearly marked and/or readily distinguishable (e.g., color-coded) from those on the normal system. In the event of a failure of one of these systems (normal or emergency), personnel might have to quickly switch equipment to different receptacles.

(2) The isolated power systems in special environments

Reference to isolated power systems is not to be interpreted as meaning that this chapter requires the provision of such systems. Rather, it means that the electrical receptacles on isolated power systems in special environments must be served from the critical branch, enabling power to be restored in 10 seconds to all receptacles on the isolated power system.

Special environments are those areas, determined by the facility, where restoration of electricity (via the facility's essential electrical system) is critical for quality patient care.

(3) Task illumination and selected receptacles in the following:

  (a) Patient care areas, including infant nurseries, selected acute nursing areas, psychiatric bed areas (omit receptacles), and ward treatment rooms
  (b) Medication preparation areas
  (c) Pharmacy dispensing areas

Pharmacy dispensing areas, such as the one shown in Exhibit 4.9, need illumination to properly dispense medication. The lighting and circuits that power equipment in this area must be connected to the critical branch of the emergency system for accurate and timely dispensing of medication.

  (d) Nurses' stations (unless adequately lighted by corridor luminaires)

(4) Additional specialized patient care task illumination and receptacles, where needed
(5) Nurse call systems
(6) Blood, bone, and tissue banks

See Exhibit 4.10 for an example of blood bank refrigerators, which have alarms that sound if the temperature inside any refrigerator changes more than −15.5°C (−4°F) (whether from power loss or equipment failure or door being left ajar).

(7)* Telephone equipment rooms and closets

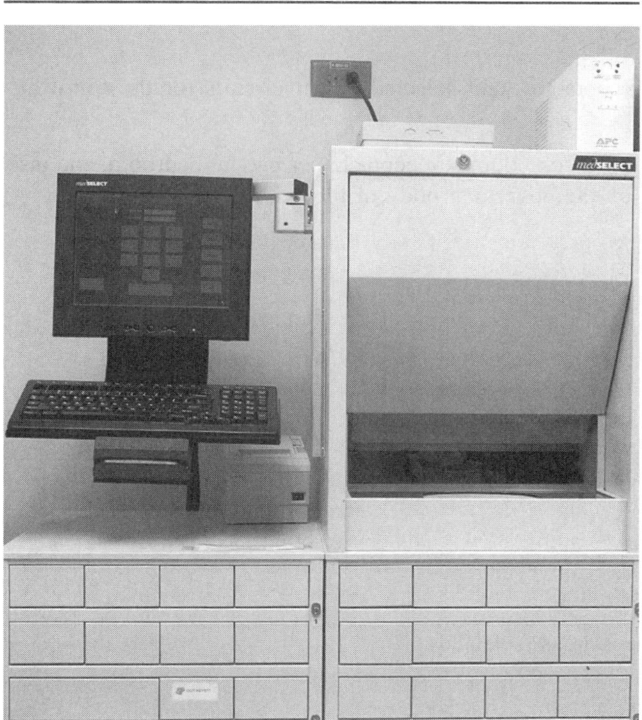

EXHIBIT 4.9 *Pharmacy dispensing equipment.*

EXHIBIT 4.10 *Blood bank refrigerators.*

A.4.4.2.2.2.3(7) Departmental installations such as digital dialing systems used for intradepartmental communications could have impaired use during a failure of electrical service to the area. In the event of such failure, those systems that have lighted selector buttons in the base of the telephone instrument or in the desk units known as "director sets" will be out of service to the extent that the lights will not function and that the buzzer used to indicate incoming calls will be silenced. The lack of electrical energy will not prevent the use of telephones for outgoing calls, but incoming calls will not be signaled, nor will intercommunicating calls be signaled. This communication failure should be taken into consideration in planning essential electrical systems.

(8) Task illumination, selected receptacles, and selected power circuits for the following areas:

  (a) General care beds with at least one duplex receptacle per patient bedroom, and task illumination as required by the governing body of the health care facility
  (b) Angiographic labs
  (c) Cardiac catheterization labs

See the commentary after 4.4.2.2.2.3(9) on mobile cardiac catheterization labs.

  (d) Coronary care units
  (e) Hemodialysis rooms or areas

Hemodialysis rooms or areas are included on the emergency system of Type 1 essential electrical systems because of the condition of patients generally seen in the facilities that require Type 1 systems. In freestanding clinics, patients are usually not in immediate danger and can be handcranked off this device without ac power.

  (f) Emergency room treatment areas (selected)
  (g) Human physiology labs
  (h) Intensive care units
  (i) Postoperative recovery rooms (selected)

(9) Additional task illumination, receptacles, and selected power circuits needed for effective facility operation. Single-phase fractional horsepower motors shall be permitted to be connected to the critical branch.

Item 9 should not be construed as an open-ended option to include anything on the critical branch. Only essential items should be included. However, whatever is determined to be "needed for effective facility operation" must be known and included during the design of the essential electrical system so that the generator is not overloaded. (See 4.4.4.1.1.2.) In addition to lighting, receptacles, and certain pieces of equipment needed for effective hospital operation, selected areas, such as administrative offices, conference rooms, waiting rooms, and public areas, are permitted to be connected to the critical branch to ensure effective hospital operation and to provide for patient care (i.e., triage) during emergencies and natural disasters. It is not the intent of the standard that large administrative suites, gymnasiums, day care centers, and the like be permitted to be connected to the critical branch under this section. For large nonessential areas, see 4.4.1.1.7.

For a discussion of task illumination, see commentary under 4.4.2.2.2.

Exhaust fan motors are included in the critical branch for practicality. These motors are sometimes located at the end of a wing, making it costly to link up with three-phase motors of the equipment system, which could be on the roof. These small exhaust motors do not add significantly to the critical branch load. Other single-phase motors can be connected to the critical system if they are required for effective facility operation.

NFPA 99 does not currently address "mobile" patient labs, such as mobile cardiac catheterization labs, mobile MRI units, and mobile CT units. These labs are "housed" in tractor trailers and "connected" to a facility's utility supply (electricity, water, medical gases, etc.) by an umbilical cord. In light of no explicit requirements concerning mobile patient labs, one should consult with the authority having jurisdiction. In the absence of specific guidance from the authority having jurisdiction, it would be safe to assume that mobile units should be treated like any other patient care area within the confines of the facility. For example, the electric power for task illumination and selected power circuits of mobile cardiac catheterization labs connected to the facility are to be connected to the essential electrical system in accordance with 4.4.2.2.2.3(8)(c).

4.4.2.2.3 Equipment System.

Some of the equipment in 4.4.2.2.3 can initially draw heavy currents or be a large electrical load for the generator set (e.g., chillers, air-conditioning systems). This does not mean that a second generator set is required. It does mean that the timing of restoring power to such loads needs to be considered when the essential electrical system is being designed.

4.4.2.2.3.1 General. The equipment system shall be connected to equipment described in 4.4.2.2.3.3 through 4.4.2.2.3.5.

4.4.2.2.3.2 Connection to Alternate Power Source. The equipment system shall be installed and connected to the alternate power source, such that equipment described in 4.4.2.2.3.4 is automatically restored to operation at appropriate time-lag intervals following the energizing of the emergency system. Its arrangement shall also provide for the subsequent connection of equipment described in 4.4.2.2.3.5.

4.4.2.2.3.3 AC Equipment for Nondelayed Automatic Connection. Generator accessories, including, but not limited to, the transfer fuel pump, electrically operated louvers, and other generator accessories essential for generator operation, shall be arranged for automatic connection to the alternate power source.

If everything on the essential electrical system were restored at the same time, the generator could be overloaded, even though it might be capable of carrying the total load if it were restored over a period of time.

4.4.2.2.3.4* Equipment for Delayed-Automatic Connection. The following equipment shall be permitted to be arranged for delayed-automatic connection to the alternate power source:

A.4.4.2.2.3.4 The equipment in 4.4.2.2.3.4(1) through 4.4.2.2.3.4(3) can be arranged for sequential delayed-automatic connection to the alternate power source to prevent overloading the generator where engineering studies indicate that it is necessary.

(1) Central suction systems serving medical and surgical functions, including controls. It shall be permitted to place such suction systems on the critical branch.

The actual time lag for delayed automatic transfer is left unspecified. This is left to the discretion of the user and engineer. The ability of the standby generator to accept load increments and other factors (i.e., the clinical air compressor's reserve capacity) should determine the appropriate time delay. The words *permitted to be* accommodate small facilities with a single automatic transfer switch as permitted by 4.4.2.2.1.4. A facility with a single switch would not be able to provide 10-second restoration of power and delayed automatic transfer.

Central suction systems are permitted to be connected to the critical branch for two reasons. First, power might be required to be restored within 10 seconds, depending on the medical/surgery application, the load on the compressor, the storage capability of the compressor's receiver, and other considerations. Second, standby systems utilizing multiple generators often have load shed circuits, and the equipment system is often shed upon loss of one or more generators. Because of the highly critical nature of some central suction systems, the facility designer might prefer to place these systems on the critical branch or to provide a separate equipment branch transfer switch that is not affected by the load shed circuit.

(2) Sump pumps and other equipment required to operate for the safety of major apparatus, including associated control systems and alarms.
(3) Compressed air systems serving medical and surgical functions, including controls. It shall be permitted to place such air systems on the critical branch.

Medical and surgical compressed air systems are permitted to be served by the critical branch instead of the equipment system. The reasons for this allowance are the same as those given in the commentary following 4.4.2.2.3.4(1) for central suction (vacuum) systems serving medical and surgical functions.

(4) Smoke control and stair pressurization systems.
(5) Kitchen hood supply and/or exhaust systems, if required to operate during a fire in or under the hood.

Fans are generally shut down in an emergency to prevent the spread of smoke. Kitchen hood fans can be used to provide smoke control.

(6) Supply, return, and exhaust ventilating systems for airborne infectious/isolation rooms, protective environment rooms, exhaust fans for laboratory fume hoods, nuclear medicine areas where radioactive material is used, ethylene oxide evacuation, and anesthetic evacuation. Where delayed automatic connection is not appropriate, such ventilation systems shall be permitted to be placed on the critical branch.

4.4.2.2.3.5* Equipment for Delayed-Automatic or Manual Connection. The following equipment shall be permitted to be arranged for either delayed-automatic or manual connection to the alternate power source *(also see A.4.4.2.2.3.4)*:

A.4.4.2.2.3.5 For elevator cab lighting control, and signal system requirements, see 4.4.2.2.2.2(6).

In instances where interruption of normal power would result in other elevators stopping between floors, throw-over facilities shall be provided to allow the temporary operation of any elevator for the release of patients or other persons who are confined between floors.

(1) Heating equipment to provide heating for operating, delivery, labor, recovery, intensive care, coronary care, nurseries, infection/isolation rooms, emergency treatment spaces, and general patient rooms; and pressure maintenance (jockey or make-up) pump(s) for water-based fire protection systems.

The actual time lag for delayed automatic transfer, unspecified in 4.4.2.2.3.5, is left to the discretion of the user and engineer. The ability of the standby generator to accept load increments and other factors should determine the appropriate time delay. The words *permitted to be* accommodate small facilities with a single automatic transfer switch as permitted by 4.4.2.2.1.4. A facility with a single switch would not be able to provide 10-second restoration of power and delayed automatic transfer.

This requirement dates from the early 1960s, during the development of an emergency power standard. It was added strictly for economic reasons — to save costs on the system. In the early 1970s, it became, by coincidence, an energy conservation measure. It is also an aid to facilities that use electric heat throughout, because, in an emergency, only selected rooms would have to be heated if the facility met this requirement.

(2)* Heating of general patient rooms during disruption of the normal source shall not be required under any of the following conditions:

(a) The outside design temperature is higher than −6.7°C (+20°F).
(b) The outside design temperature is lower than −6.7°C (+20°F) and a selected room(s) is provided for the needs of all confined patients [then only such room(s) need be heated].
(c) The facility is served by a dual source of normal power as described in 4.3.2.1.

A.4.4.2.2.3.5(2) The outside design temperature is based on the 97½ percent design value as shown in Chapter 24 of the ASHRAE *Handbook of Fundamentals*.

(3) Elevator(s) selected to provide service to patient, surgical, obstetrical, and ground floors during interruption of normal power.
(4) Supply, return, and exhaust ventilating systems for surgical and obstetrical delivery suites, intensive care, coronary care, nurseries, and emergency treatment spaces.

It should be observed that no distinction is made in 4.4.2.2.3.5(4) between clinical and nonclinical exhaust fans for laboratory fume hoods. All such exhaust fans are to be connected to the equipment system of the essential electrical system. The purpose of this requirement is to prevent backfeeding of air between those laboratories that were connected and those that were not.

(5) Hyperbaric facilities.
(6) Hypobaric facilities.

With the types of infectious diseases being treated in acute care environments, and the need to maintain an environment as free of indoor air quality problems as possible, the mechanical ventilation systems serving these areas noted in 4.4.2.2.3.4(5) and 4.4.2.2.3.4(6) cannot be on a manual connection to the emergency power supply system. A significant delay of service cannot be tolerated without potentially disastrous results. Facilities should have the flexibility to add these ventilation systems to the critical branch if they deem it necessary.

(7) Autoclaving equipment shall be permitted to be arranged for either automatic or manual connection to the alternate source.
(8) Controls for equipment listed in 4.4.2.2.3.
(9)* Other selected equipment shall be permitted to be served by the equipment system.

As previously noted, 4.4.2.2.3.5(9) should not be construed as a carte blanche allowance for anything to be connected to the equipment system. Each item should be reviewed for its effect on patient safety when power to the item might be interrupted for an extended period of time.

A.4.4.2.2.3.5(9) Consideration should be given to selected equipment in kitchens, laundries, and radiology rooms and to selected central refrigeration.

It is desirable that, where heavy interruption currents can be anticipated, the transfer load be reduced by the use of multiple transfer devices. Elevator feeders, for instance, might be less hazardous to electrical continuity if they are fed through an individual transfer device.

4.4.2.2.4 Wiring Requirements.

4.4.2.2.4.1* Separation from Other Circuits. The life safety branch and critical branch of the emergency system shall be kept entirely independent of all other wiring and equipment.

A.4.4.2.2.4.1 See NFPA 70, *National Electrical Code*, for installation requirements.

Wiring for the normal power and the essential electrical system must be separated, as required by 4.4.2.2.4.1. Separating the installations is the only way to ensure against simultaneous damage to both systems. For requirements on the installation of wires, see 517.44 and 700.9(B) in NFPA 70, *National Electrical Code* [1].

4.4.2.2.4.2 Receptacles. The requirements for receptacles shall comply with 4.4.2.2.4.2(A) and 4.4.2.2.4.2(B).

(A) The number of receptacles on a single branch circuit for areas described in 4.4.2.2.2.3(8) shall be minimized to limit the effects of a branch circuit outage. Branch circuit overcurrent devices shall be readily accessible to authorized personnel.

The intention of 4.4.2.2.4.2(A) is to limit the number of receptacles on a branch circuit (in this instance, essential electrical systems' circuits) to minimize power outages of these circuits caused by overloading. It is considered poor practice to design systems in a manner such that a faulty piece of equipment connected to a circuit could, by opening its branch circuit protective device, cause other essential equipment to become inoperative. Outages of these circuits can be life-threatening because of the condition of patients and their dependency on the electrical equipment being used for their care (these electrical devices are functioning in a life-support capacity). Nursing personnel are specifically identified because they are always in a patient care area and must be able to reset circuit breakers if assistance is not readily available.

(B)* The electrical receptacles or the cover plates for the electrical receptacles supplied from the emergency system shall have a distinctive color or marking so as to be readily identifiable.

A.4.4.2.2.4.2(B) If color is used to identify these receptacles, the same color should be used throughout the facility.

It is very important that *all* facility personnel know what the different colors specified by 4.4.2.2.4.2(B) signify so that in an emergency they will know which necessary (essential) devices to plug into those outlets on the essential electrical system. Additionally, life-support devices must be plugged into receptacles on essential electrical circuits so that these devices will be repowered automatically within 10 seconds when normal power is interrupted.

FAQ ▶ What is considered a distinctive color or marking for the cover plates of receptacles in the emergency system?

It should be noted that the use of a distinctive color or marking is acceptable. The color chosen should be very obvious and not similar to any other color used. A marking (such as an *E* or the letters *EMER*) should not be easily removable by such things as cleaning fluids. If it is necessary to remove receptacles during repairs or renovations, extra care needs to be exercised not to mix up cover plates.

4.4.2.2.4.3 Switches. Switches installed in the lighting circuits connected to the essential electrical system shall comply with Article 700, Section V, of NFPA 70, *National Electrical Code*.

4.4.2.2.4.4 Mechanical Protection of the Emergency System. The wiring of the emergency system shall be mechanically protected by raceways, as defined in NFPA 70, *National Electrical Code*.

4.4.2.2.4.5 Flexible power cords of appliances or other utilization equipment connected to the emergency system shall not be required to be enclosed in raceways.

4.4.2.2.4.6 Secondary circuits of transformer-powered communication or signaling systems shall not be required to be enclosed in raceways unless otherwise specified by Chapters 7 or 8 of NFPA 70, *National Electrical Code*.

Wiring for Type 1 essential electrical systems is required in raceways by 4.4.2.2.4.4 through 4.4.2.2.4.6 because of the high percentage of nonambulatory patients found in facilities requiring this type of system. (See 13.3.4.2 in Chapter 13, Hospital Requirements.) Patients in these facilities can or might be anesthetized, comatose, in traction, or connected to electrical life-support equipment. As such, these facilities need the greatest mechanical protection for electrical wiring because evacuation (or even movement) is the action least desired. Accordingly, the essential electrical systems in these facilities are provided with the most protection.

It should not be construed that the patients in facilities with Type 2 or Type 3 essential electrical systems are considered any less important. It means only that it is easier, in general, to move these patients in an emergency, if only horizontally to another portion of the building.

For the definition of *Raceway* and the type allowed, see NFPA 70, *National Electrical Code* [1]. For reader reference, Type AC cable is listed as a cable, not as a raceway.

4.4.3 Performance Criteria and Testing (Type 1 EES).

4.4.3.1 Source. The branches of the emergency system shall be installed and connected to the alternate power source specified in 4.4.1.1.4 and 4.4.1.1.5 so that all functions specified herein for the emergency system shall be automatically restored to operation within 10 seconds after interruption of the normal source.

See the commentary on 4.4.2.1.4.4 regarding how the 10-second criteria specified in 4.4.3.1 were selected. The 10-second clock does not simply note, for example, that there has been a drop in voltage from 120 V ac to 118 V ac. The clock starts when the normal source has dropped to a pre-established level and has remained there for a specified period of time. After 10 seconds have elapsed, the generator is required to accept the electrical load. (See 4.4.3.2.1 or 4.4.3.2.2.)

This chapter requires one level of redundancy for sources of power but does not require redundancy for transfer switches or distribution wiring. (The battery-powered light now required in anesthetizing locations is considered a "backup to the backup" just for that area but is not part of the essential electrical "system.") It is left to each facility to make its own determinations concerning the possible simultaneous failure of the normal and alternate source of power and possible failures of transfer switches or distribution wiring and what to do in this event. This chapter, however, does not require such determinations.

4.4.3.2 Transfer Switches.

4.4.3.2.1 All ac-powered support and accessory equipment necessary to the operation of the EPS shall be supplied from the load side of the automatic transfer switch(es), or the output terminals of the EPS, ahead of the main EPS overcurrent protection, as necessary, to ensure continuity of the EPSS operation and performance. [**110:**7.12.5]

4.4.3.2.2 The essential electrical system shall be served by the normal power source except when the normal power source is interrupted or drops below a predetermined voltage level. Settings of the sensors shall be determined by careful study of the voltage requirements of the load.

4.4.3.2.3 Failure of the normal source shall automatically start the alternate source generator after a short delay as described in 4.4.2.1.4.4. When the alternate power source has attained a voltage and frequency that satisfies minimum operating requirements of the essential electrical system, the load shall be connected automatically to the alternate power source.

Paragraph 4.4.3.2.2 defines what constitutes a loss of normal power. When this failure occurs, the generator starts. However, transfer of loads does not occur until after the alternate power source has attained minimum operating requirements for loads, as specified in 4.4.3.2.3. This is ensured through requirements covering the transfer switch. [See 4.4.2.1.4.1.]

4.4.3.2.4 Upon connection of the alternate power source, the loads comprising the emergency system shall be automatically re-energized. The load comprising the equipment system shall be connected either automatically after a time delay as described in 4.4.2.1.4.6 or nonautomatically and in such a sequential manner as not to overload the generator.

4.4.3.2.5 When the normal power source is restored, and after a time delay as described in 4.4.2.1.4.7, the automatic transfer switches shall disconnect the alternate source of power and connect the loads to the normal power source. The alternate power source generator set shall continue to run unloaded for a preset time delay as described in 4.4.2.1.4.9.

Paragraph 4.4.2.1.4.9 sets criteria for time delay on engine shutdown, as specified in 4.4.3.2.5.

4.4.3.2.6 If the emergency power source fails and the normal power source has been restored, retransfer to the normal source of power shall be immediate, bypassing the retransfer delay timer.

4.4.3.2.7 If the emergency power source fails during a test, provisions shall be made to immediately retransfer to the normal source.

In most testing schemes, a failure, such as a loss of normal power, has to be simulated. If the alternate power source fails during the test, however, nothing will happen to restore the normal power source, because normal power was shut down to simulate the failure. Paragraph 4.4.3.2.7 requires that a facility be able to retransfer to normal power if this situation develops.

4.4.3.2.8 Nonautomatic transfer switching devices shall be restored to the normal power source as soon as possible after the return of the normal source or at the discretion of the operator.

4.4.4 Administration (Type 1 EES).

4.4.4.1 Maintenance and Testing of Essential Electrical System.

4.4.4.1.1 Maintenance and Testing of Alternate Power Source and Transfer Switches.

4.4.4.1.1.1 Maintenance of Alternate Power Source. The generator set or other alternate power source and associated equipment, including all appurtenant parts, shall be so maintained as to be capable of supplying service within the shortest time practicable and within the 10-second interval specified in 4.4.1.1.10 and 4.4.3.1. Maintenance shall be performed in accordance with NFPA 110, *Standard for Emergency and Standby Power Systems*, Chapter 8.

Paragraph 4.4.4.1.1.1 sets the performance goal that the maintenance program for the alternate power source should be designed to achieve. The alternate power source is expected to provide power within 10 seconds of interruption of the normal source. (Again, the 10-second restoration criterion is for the *emergency system* of the essential electrical system. The *equipment system* of the essential electrical system can have power restored subsequent to that for the emergency system.) The specific test and maintenance activities for the alternate power source are those of 4.4.4.1.1. These activities are not to be considered as a complete maintenance program, however. They are only minimum elements. Each facility is expected to prepare a maintenance program that will meet the performance goal of 4.4.4.1.1. Annex C.4.2 contains suggested elements for consideration in preparing such a program, and 4.4.4.2 requires documentation of the implementation of the program.

4.4.4.1.1.2 Inspection and Testing. Criteria, conditions, and personnel requirements shall be in accordance with 4.4.4.1.1.2(A) through 4.4.4.1.1.2(C).

FAQ ▶ Is there a set time when the facility manager should conduct testing?

In recognition of the hospital facility manager's need to schedule testing around the medical needs of the facility, some latitude is permitted in terms of the timing of the test. The wording of 4.4.4.1.1.2 allows the facility manager to schedule the testing to provide minimum disruption of facility operation.

(A)* Test Criteria. Generator sets shall be tested 12 times a year with testing intervals between not less than 20 days or exceeding 40 days. Generator sets serving emergency and equipment systems shall be tested in accordance with NFPA 110, *Standard for Emergency and Standby Power Systems*, Chapter 8.

The requirements of 4.4.4.1.1.2 have been reviewed and debated extensively over the past decade. Energy conservation, optimum generator equipment test intervals, actual loading versus simulated loading, and the effect on patient safety and equipment have been among the major topics under scrutiny. There is universal agreement that the generator set and the essential electrical system need to be tested periodically to be reasonably certain that they will function in an actual emergency. Differences exist, however, on how often and under what conditions this testing should be conducted. The actual running time of the engine must be long enough to ensure that engine parts are properly lubricated; however, this must be balanced by a test load large enough to ensure acids and carbon are purged by the operating temperature of the engine. Thus, two basic parameters, load and operating temperature, are listed in 8.4.2 of NFPA 110, *Standard for Emergency and Standby Power Systems* [2], with 30 minutes an absolute minimum running time.

Extensive debate has arisen regarding the amount of testing necessary to provide reasonable assurance that the engine (prime mover) would operate when needed in an emergency. Monthly testing was seen as necessary, as was the minimum of 30 minutes. It was the *load* on the engine that created the most debate. A major indicator that insufficient loading is occurring is *wetstacking,* a condition that can cause serious engine problems. Additional load testing of an engine that has exhibited wetstacking was included in previous editions of NFPA 110. NFPA 110 is referenced here, rather than showing extracted text, in order to ensure that the two documents will never be in conflict on the issue, even when NFPA 110 revises requirements.

If, as is the case in many instances, a large generator in relation to the load is installed (e.g., to account for the largest motor connected to the essential electrical system), the operating temperature of the generator might not be reached in 30 minutes. This factor should be considered when testing the generator.

A.4.4.4.1.1.2(A) When indications such as the issuance of storm warnings indicate that power outages might be likely, good practice recommends the warming up of generator sets by a regular exercise period. Operation of generator sets for short intervals should be avoided, particularly with compression ignition engines, since it is harmful to the engines.

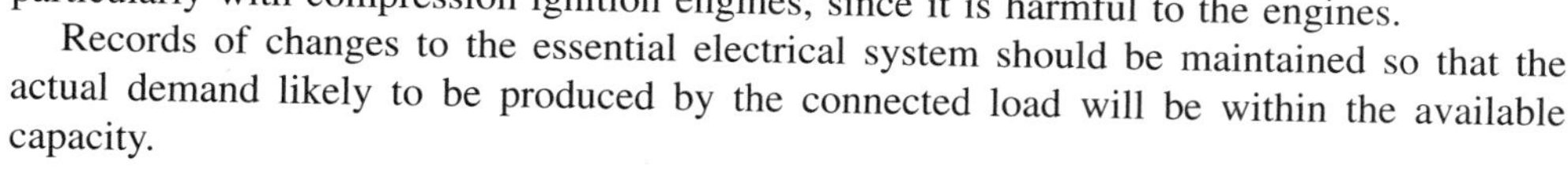

Records of changes to the essential electrical system should be maintained so that the actual demand likely to be produced by the connected load will be within the available capacity.

(B) Test Conditions. The scheduled test under load conditions shall include a complete simulated cold start and appropriate automatic and manual transfer of all essential electrical system loads.

◀ **FAQ**
What procedures should be employed when testing the essential electrical system?

Testing criteria in 4.4.4.1.1.2(B) might range from manually disconnecting power to the power sensors on transfer switches to manually opening the main incoming feeder breakers. It is very important that each test method be fully understood by all staff through appropriate notification and that the consequences of each method (if something fails to function) be weighed carefully. A procedure for returning to the normal power source should also be established in the event a failure occurs during testing.

There is a false assumption that disconnecting a facility's mains is the best method of testing the standby generator(s) and essential electrical system. One must always consider the possibility that failure of the disconnecting means or some other unexpected contingency might make it difficult or impossible to restore normal power. It is probably better to initiate engine start by interrupting power just ahead of the transfer switch(es) on an alternating or rotating basis in order to make sure each transfer switch has an intact engine start circuit.

(C) Test Personnel. The scheduled tests shall be conducted by competent personnel. The tests are needed to keep the machines ready to function and, in addition, serve to detect causes of malfunction and to train personnel in operating procedures.

Training programs for test personnel in 4.4.4.1.1.2(C) should take into consideration the requirements of local, state, and federal authorities. Some authorities having jurisdiction might have regulations or have certification criteria for "generator mechanics." The Occupational Safety and Health Administration (OSHA) mandates training in such areas as electrical safety, personal protective equipment, and hazard communication. Relevance to emergency generators should be determined.

4.4.4.1.2 Maintenance and Testing of Circuitry.

Power failures are generally associated with failures on the electric utility system. However, many power failures, especially in large facilities, are known to occur within the health care facility. A significant number of these internal power failures occur because of circuit breaker failure. Therefore, as required by 4.4.4.1.1.2, circuit breakers should be inspected regularly and tested periodically.

Annual inspection is required, but annual operation of the breaker is no longer mandatory. Some facilities might want to operate breakers periodically, based on a facility's particular needs. Other useful maintenance techniques include the following testing.

Infrared Testing. Some facilities choose to conduct infrared testing only if there is evidence of heating. Others prefer to conduct infrared testing every three years to five years.

High-Current Testing. Generally this test is done with varying levels of current while recording trip times. This calibration exercise verifies that the breaker is tripping in reasonable accordance with the manufacturer's time–current curve. If the test set is capable of producing sufficiently high current levels, the breaker's interrupting rating can also be verified. This type of test and calibration can be expensive, so the user could prefer to test only selected main and distribution breakers on an as-needed basis.

Another time-marker in the life-cycle maintenance schedule should occur following retransfer back to normal power source. An inspection of circuit breakers feeding each transfer switch should be made to ascertain that circuit breakers did not open after the alternate power source was removed from the breaker and normal power.

4.4.4.1.2.1* Circuit Breakers. Main and feeder circuit breakers shall be inspected annually and a program for periodically exercising the components shall be established according to manufacturer's recommendations.

A.4.4.4.1.2.1 Main and feeder circuit breakers should be periodically tested under simulated overload trip conditions to ensure reliability *(see C.4.2)*.

4.4.4.1.2.2 Insulation Resistance. The resistance readings of main feeder insulation shall be taken prior to acceptance and whenever damage is suspected.

Taking resistance measurements on a periodic basis has been found to be unnecessary and disruptive of facility activities (it can require shutdown of the entire system). Thus, resistance testing is required by 4.4.4.1.2.2 only at the times listed.

Knowledge of initial resistance readings or of past resistance readings when feeders not tested initially were functioning normally is necessary to diagnose certain actual failures or detect certain incipient failures of electrical feeders. The readings are to be recorded and available in the maintenance record. (See 4.4.4.2.)

4.4.4.1.3 Maintenance of Batteries. Batteries for on-site generators shall be maintained in accordance with NFPA 110, *Standard for Emergency and Standby Power Systems*.

Nonfunctioning starting batteries and malfunction of the starting/charging system itself are the most common reasons for the emergency power source to fail to come on-line. The lack of proper maintenance is usually the cause for these failures.

Spare charged starting batteries for engine generator sets are a prudent investment to provide flexibility to maintenance personnel in taking emergency starting actions when generators do not start. These batteries should be connected to the charger and isolated from the main set. This chapter, however, does not require such spare batteries. For further guidance on maintenance of batteries, see NFPA 110, *Standard for Emergency and Standby Power Systems* [2].

◀ **FAQ**
Are spare starting batteries for the generator required?

Battery-powered lights are required in selected areas, such as anesthetizing locations and rooms housing generator sets. When installed, they are intended to provide lighting (1) during the maximum 10-second interval permitted between loss of normal power and the switch to emergency power and (2) in the event of simultaneous failure of the alternate source and normal source. When installed, it is suggested that adequate attention be given to the proper maintenance of these required battery systems and any other battery systems. See Exhibit 4.11, and note the clean contacts. Authorities having jurisdiction cite poor battery maintenance as the major reason for generators failing to start.

EXHIBIT 4.11 *Detail of batteries used for starting an engine used for emergency power purposes.*

4.4.4.2 Recordkeeping. A written record of inspection, performance, exercising period, and repairs shall be regularly maintained and available for inspection by the authority having jurisdiction.

Use of computers to store records of inspections, maintenance, and other information should be acceptable if such data can be made readily available to inspectors, as required by 4.4.4.2. If this method is used, a backup hard copy of data is highly recommended.

The practice of "trending" (i.e., reviewing data gathered over a period of time) is a valuable tool in the science of preventive maintenance. It should be used throughout this process. Computer spreadsheets can aid significantly in this endeavor.

4.5 Essential Electrical System Requirements — Type 2

4.5.1 Sources (Type 2 EES).

The requirements for sources for Type 2 essential electrical systems shall conform to those listed in 4.4.1.

4.5.2 Distribution (Type 2 EES).

4.5.2.1 General. The distribution requirements for Type 2 essential electrical systems shall conform to those listed in 4.4.2.1.

4.5.2.2 Specific Requirements.

4.5.2.2.1* General. The number of transfer switches to be used shall be based upon reliability, design, and load considerations. Each branch of the emergency system and each critical system shall have one or more transfer switches. One transfer switch shall be permitted to serve one or more branches or systems in a facility with a continuous load on the switch of 150 kVA (120 kW) or less.

The intent of 4.5.2.2.1 is that the load on the essential electrical systems not exceed 150 kVA (120 kW) for small facilities. It is assumed that the load power factor is 80 percent, thus the reference to 150 kVA (120 kW). Because the power factor will likely be higher than 80 percent, the actual load could, for example, be 150 kVA and 130 kW. Thus, the values given should be taken as nominal values, and authorities having jurisdiction will not split hairs on the exact values of kVA and kW. Although the standard is silent on the number of essential system branches for a single-switch "small facility," it is recommended that separate systems be installed for small facilities. This will facilitate the addition of a second (or additional) transfer switch(es) as the facility expands.

A.4.5.2.2.1 Type 2 essential electrical systems are comprised of two separate systems capable of supplying a limited amount of lighting and power service that is considered essential for the protection of life and safety and effective operation of the institution during the time normal electrical service is interrupted for any reason. These two separate systems are the emergency system and the critical system.

The number of transfer switches to be used shall be based upon reliability, design, and load considerations. Each branch of the emergency system and each critical system shall have one or more transfer switches. One transfer switch shall be permitted to serve one or more branches or systems in a facility with a maximum demand on the essential electrical system of 150 kVA (120 kW).

4.5.2.2.2 Emergency System. The emergency system shall supply power for lighting, receptacles, and equipment as follows:

(1) Illumination of means of egress in accordance with NFPA *101, Life Safety Code*
(2) Exit signs and exit directional signs in accordance with NFPA *101, Life Safety Code*
(3) Alarm and alerting systems, including the following:

(a) Fire alarms

All fire alarms are to be connected to the essential electrical system.

(b) Alarms required for systems used for the piping of nonflammable medical gases as specified in Chapter 5, Gas and Vacuum Systems

(4)* Communication systems, where used for issuing instructions during emergency conditions

See the commentary following 4.4.2.2.2 for an explanation of why only those functions listed for the life safety branch of Type 1 essential electrical systems, equivalent to the emergency system of Type 2 essential electrical systems, are to be placed on such circuits.

A.4.5.2.2.2(4) Departmental installations such as digital dialing systems used for intradepartmental communications could have impaired use during a failure of electrical service to the area. In the event of such failure, those systems that have lighted selector buttons in the base of the telephone instrument or in the desk units known as "director sets" will be out of service to the extent that the lights will not function and that the buzzer used to indicate incoming calls will be silenced. The lack of electrical energy will not prevent the use of telephones for outgoing calls, but incoming calls will not be signaled, nor will intercommunicating calls be signaled. This communication failure should be taken into consideration in planning essential electrical systems.

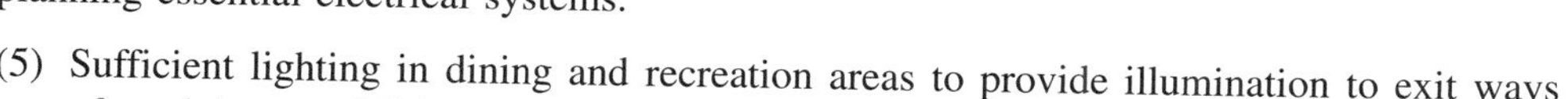

(5) Sufficient lighting in dining and recreation areas to provide illumination to exit ways of a minimum of 5 ft-candles
(6) Task illumination and selected receptacles at the generator set location
(7) Elevator cab lighting, control, communication, and signal systems

See the commentary following 4.4.2.2.2.2(6); the reason for inclusion of elevators in 4.5.2.2.2(7) is the same.

See the commentary following 4.4.2.2.2 for an explanation of why only those functions listed for the life safety branch of Type 1 essential electrical systems, equivalent to the emergency system of Type 2 essential electrical systems, are to be placed on such circuits.

No function other than those listed in 4.5.2.2.2(1) through 4.5.2.2.2(7) shall be connected to the emergency system.

4.5.2.2.3 Critical System.

4.5.2.2.3.1 General. The critical system shall be so installed and connected to the alternate power source that equipment listed in 4.5.2.2.3.2 shall be automatically restored to operation at appropriate time-lag intervals following the restoration of the emergency system to operation. Its arrangement shall also provide for the additional connection of equipment listed in 4.5.2.2.3.3.

4.5.2.2.3.2 AC Equipment for Nondelayed Automatic Connection. Generator accessories, including but not limited to, the transfer fuel pump, electrically operated louvers, and other generator accessories essential for generator operation, shall be arranged for automatic connection to the alternative power source.

4.5.2.2.3.3 Delayed-Automatic Connections to Critical System. The following equipment shall be permitted to be connected to the critical system and be arranged for delayed-automatic connection to the alternate power source:

(1) Task illumination and selected receptacles in the following:

(a) Patient care areas
(b) Medication preparation areas
(c) Pharmacy dispensing areas
(d) Nurses' stations (unless adequately lighted by corridor luminaires)

(2) Supply, return, and exhaust ventilating systems for airborne infectious isolation rooms
(3) Sump pumps and other equipment required to operate for the safety of major apparatus and associated control systems and alarms
(4) Smoke control and stair pressurization systems

The actual time lag for delayed automatic transfer, unspecified by 4.5.2.2.3.3, is left to the discretion of the user and engineer. The ability of the standby generator to accept load increments and other factors should determine the appropriate time delay. The words *permitted to be* accommodate small facilities with a single automatic transfer switch as permitted by 4.5.2.2.1. A facility with a single switch would not be able to provide 10-second restoration of power and delayed automatic transfer. See the commentary following 4.4.2.2.3.4(1).

(5) Kitchen hood supply and/or exhaust systems, if required to operate during a fire in or under the hood

4.5.2.2.3.4* Delayed-Automatic or Manual Connections to Critical System. The equipment in 4.5.2.2.3.4(A) and 4.5.2.2.3.4(B) shall be permitted to be connected to the critical system and be arranged for either delayed-automatic or manual connection to the alternate power source.

A.4.5.2.2.3.4 Other selected equipment can be served by the critical system.

Note that consideration should be given to selected equipment in kitchens and laundries, and to selected central refrigeration.

It is desirable that, where heavy interruption currents can be anticipated, the transfer load be reduced by the use of multiple transfer devices. Elevator feeders, for instance, might be less hazardous to electrical continuity if they are fed through an individual transfer device.

(A) Heating Equipment to Provide Heating for General Patient Rooms. Heating of general patient rooms during disruption of the normal source shall not be required under any of the following conditions:

(1)* The outside design temperature is higher than −6.7°C (+20°F).

A.4.5.2.2.3.4(A)(1) The outside design temperature is based on the 97½ percent design value as shown in Chapter 24 of the ASHRAE *Handbook of Fundamentals*.

(2) The outside design temperature is lower than −6.7°C (+20°F) and, where a selected room(s) is provided for the needs of all confined patients, then only such room(s) need be heated.
(3) The facility is served by a dual source of normal power as described in A.4.4.1.1.1.

The actual time lag for delayed automatic transfer is unspecified and is left to the discretion of the user and engineer. The ability of the standby generator to accept load increments and other factors should determine the appropriate time delay. The term *permitted to be* was added to accommodate small facilities with a single automatic transfer switch as permitted by 4.5.2.2.1. A facility with a single switch would not be able to provide 10-second restoration of power and delayed automatic transfer. The same rationale given in the commentary to 4.4.2.2.3.5(1), on the heating of general patient rooms, applies here as well — to reduce energy needs by the moving and grouping of patients as is practical.

(B)* Elevator Service. In instances where interruptions of power would result in elevators stopping between floors, throw-over facilities shall be provided to allow the temporary operation of any elevator for the release of passengers.

A.4.5.2.2.3.4(B) For elevator cab lighting, control, and signal system requirements, see 4.5.2.2.2(6).

(C) Optional Connections to the Critical System. Additional illumination, receptacles, and equipment shall be permitted to be connected only to the critical system.

(D) Multiple Systems. Where one switch serves multiple systems as permitted under 4.5.2.2, transfer for all loads shall be nondelayed automatic.

4.5.2.2.4 Wiring Requirements.

4.5.2.2.4.1* Separation from Other Circuits. The emergency system shall be kept entirely independent of all other wiring and equipment.

A.4.5.2.2.4.1 See NFPA 70, *National Electrical Code*, for installation requirements.

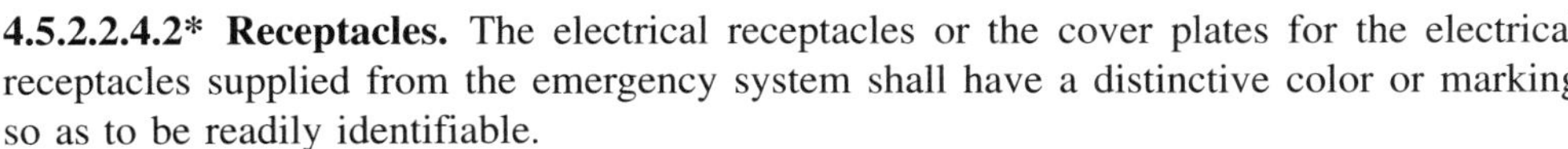

4.5.2.2.4.2* Receptacles. The electrical receptacles or the cover plates for the electrical receptacles supplied from the emergency system shall have a distinctive color or marking so as to be readily identifiable.

A.4.5.2.2.4.2 If color is used to identify these receptacles, the same color should be used throughout the facility.

4.5.3 Performance Criteria and Testing (Type 2 EES).

4.5.3.1 Source. The emergency system shall be installed and connected to the alternate source of power specified in 4.4.1.1.4 and 4.4.1.1.5 so that all functions specified herein for the emergency system will be automatically restored to operation within 10 seconds after interruption of the normal source.

The commentary following 4.4.3.1 applies to 4.5.3.1 as well.

4.5.3.2 Transfer Switches.

4.5.3.2.1 The essential electrical system shall be served by the normal power source until the normal power source is interrupted or drops below a predetermined voltage level. Settings of the sensors shall be determined by careful study of the voltage requirements of the load.

4.5.3.2.2 Failure of the normal source shall automatically start the alternate source generator, after a short delay as described in 4.4.2.1.4.4. When the alternate power source has attained a voltage and frequency that satisfies minimum operating requirements of the essential electrical system, the load shall be connected automatically to the alternate power source.

4.5.3.2.2.1 All ac-powered support and accessory equipment necessary to the operation of the EPS shall be supplied from the load side of the automatic transfer switch(es), or the output terminals of the EPS, ahead of the main EPS overcurrent protection to ensure continuity of the EPSS operation and performance.

Previously, NFPA 99 was unclear regarding the method for serving generator accessories. This text gives the hospital design engineer some latitude in making this connection. Accessories can be supplied from a transfer switch or, in some cases, directly off the standby generator. For example, a remote radiator can be supplied directly from the standby generator by means of a relay that "picks up" when the generator output reaches nominal voltage.

4.5.3.2.3 Upon connection of the alternate power source, the loads comprising the emergency system shall be automatically reenergized. The loads comprising the critical system shall be connected either automatically after a time delay as described in 4.4.2.1.4.6 or nonautomatically and in such a sequential manner as not to overload the generator.

4.5.3.2.4 When the normal power source is restored, and after a time delay as described in 4.4.2.1.4.7, the automatic transfer switches shall disconnect the alternate source of power and connect the loads to the normal power source. The alternate power source generator set shall continue to run unloaded for a preset time delay as described in 4.4.2.1.4.9.

Paragraph 4.4.2.1.4.9 sets criteria for time delay on engine shutdown.

4.5.3.2.5 If the emergency power source fails and the normal power source has been restored, retransfer to the normal source of power shall be immediate, bypassing the retransfer delay timer.

4.5.3.2.6 If the emergency power source fails during a test, provisions shall be made to immediately retransfer to the normal source.

4.5.3.2.7 Nonautomatic transfer switching devices shall be restored to the normal power source as soon as possible after the return of the normal source or at the discretion of the operator.

4.5.4 Administration (Type 2 EES).

4.5.4.1 Maintenance and Testing of Essential Electrical System.

4.5.4.1.1 Maintenance and Testing of Alternate Power Source and Transfer Switches.

4.5.4.1.1.1 Maintenance of Alternate Power Source. The generator set or other alternate power source and associated equipment, including all appurtenant parts, shall be so maintained as to be capable of supplying service within the shortest time practicable and within the 10-second interval specified in 4.4.1.1.7 and 4.4.3.1.

4.5.4.1.1.2 Inspection and Testing. Generator sets shall be inspected and tested in accordance with 4.4.4.1.1.2.

4.5.4.1.2 Maintenance and Testing of Circuitry. Circuitry shall be maintained and tested in accordance with 4.4.4.1.2.

4.5.4.1.3 Maintenance of Batteries. Batteries shall be maintained in accordance with 4.4.4.1.3.

4.5.4.2 Recordkeeping. A written record of inspection, performance, exercising period, and repairs shall be regularly maintained and available for inspection by the authority having jurisdiction.

4.6 Essential Electrical System Requirements — Type 3

4.6.1 Sources (Type 3 EES).

The alternate source of power for the system shall be specifically designed for this purpose and shall be either a generator, battery system, or self-contained battery integral with the equipment.

4.6.1.1 Generators shall conform to 4.4.1.1 and 4.4.1.1.6.2.

4.6.1.2 Battery systems shall conform to 4.4.1.2.

4.6.2 Distribution (Type 3 EES).

4.6.2.1 General. The distribution requirements for Type 3 essential electrical systems shall conform to those listed in 4.4.2.1.

4.6.2.2 Specific Requirements.

4.6.2.2.1* General.

A.4.6.2.2.1 Type 3 essential electrical systems are comprised of a system capable of supplying a limited amount of lighting and power service that is considered essential for life safety and orderly cessation of procedure during the time normal electrical service is interrupted for any reason.

4.6.2.2.2 Connection to the Essential Electrical System. The system shall supply power for task illumination that is related to the safety of life and that is necessary for the safe cessation of procedures in progress.

4.6.2.2.3 Wiring Requirements.

4.6.2.2.3.1 General. The design, arrangement, and installation of the system shall be in accordance with NFPA 70, *National Electrical Code*.

4.6.2.2.3.2* Receptacles. The cover plates for the electrical receptacles or the electrical receptacles themselves supplied from the emergency system shall have a distinctive color or marking so as to be readily identifiable.

A.4.6.2.2.3.2 If color is used to identify these receptacles, the same color should be used throughout the facility.

4.6.3 Performance Criteria and Testing (Type 3 EES).

4.6.3.1 Source.

4.6.3.1.1 The emergency system shall have an alternate source of power separate and independent from the normal source that will be effective for a minimum of 1½ hours after loss of the normal source.

The 1½-hour requirement in 4.6.3.1.1 is consistent with the minimum requirements of NFPA *101, Life Safety Code* [3]. However, readers are reminded that 1½ hours might not be sufficient for some medical procedures.

4.6.3.1.2 The emergency system shall be so arranged that, in the event of failure of normal power source, the alternate source of power shall be automatically connected to the load within 10 seconds.

See the commentary following 4.4.2.1.4.4 for an explanation of how the 10-second criterion in 4.6.3.1.2 was selected.

4.6.3.2 Transfer Switches with Engine Generator Sets.

The number of transfer switches for a Type 3 essential electrical system is not suggested in 4.6.3.2 because the number is dependent on the load and so forth. (For the number of transfer switches in Type 1 or Type 2 systems with the maximum demand on the essential electrical system, see 4.4.2.2.1.4 or 4.5.2.2.1, respectively.)

4.6.3.2.1 The operation of the equipment shall be arranged such that the load will be served by the normal source until the normal source is interrupted, or when the voltage drops below the setting of the voltage-sensing device. The settings of the voltage-sensing relays shall be determined by careful study of the voltage requirements of the load.

4.6.3.2.2 When the normal source is restored, and after a time delay as described in 4.4.2.1.4.7, the automatic transfer switch shall disconnect the alternate source of power and connect the loads to the normal power source.

4.6.3.2.3 If the alternate power source fails and the normal power source has been restored, retransfer to the normal source of power shall be immediate.

4.6.3.3 Transfer Switches with Battery System.

4.6.3.3.1 Failure of the normal source shall automatically transfer the load to the battery system.

4.6.3.3.2 Retransfer to the normal source shall be automatic upon restoration of the normal source.

4.6.4 Administration (Type 3 EES).

4.6.4.1 Maintenance and Testing.

4.6.4.1.1 Maintenance and Testing of Alternate Power Source and Transfer Switches.

4.6.4.1.1.1 Maintenance of Alternate Power Source. The generator set or other alternate power source and associated equipment, including all appurtenant parts, shall be so maintained as to be capable of supplying service within the shortest time practicable and within the 10-second interval specified in 4.4.1.1.10 and 4.6.3.1.2.

4.6.4.1.1.2 Inspection and Testing. Generator sets shall be inspected and tested in accordance with 4.4.4.1.1.2.

4.6.4.1.1.3 Stored Energy Power Source. Maintenance and testing of stored emergency power supply systems shall be in accordance with NFPA 111, *Standard on Stored Electrical Energy Emergency and Standby Power Systems*, Section 6.1 through 6.4.5.

4.6.4.1.2 Maintenance and Testing Circuitry. Circuitry shall be maintained and tested in accordance with 4.4.4.1.2.

4.6.4.1.3 Maintenance of Batteries. Batteries shall be maintained in accordance with 4.4.4.1.3.

4.6.4.2 Recordkeeping. A written record of inspection, performance, exercising period, and repairs shall be regularly maintained and available for inspection by the authority having jurisdiction.

REFERENCES CITED IN COMMENTARY

1. NFPA 70, *National Electrical Code®*, 2005 edition.
2. NFPA 110, *Standard for Emergency and Standby Power Systems,* 2005 edition.
3. NFPA *101®*, *Life Safety Code®*, 2006 edition.
4. *NFPA 72®*, *National Fire Alarm Code®*, 2002 edition.
5. NFPA 37, *Standard for the Installation and Use of Stationary Combustion Engines and Gas Turbines,* 2002 edition.
6. NFPA 111, *Standard on Stored Electrical Energy Emergency and Standby Power Systems,* 2005 edition.

CHAPTER 5

Gas and Vacuum Systems

The subject of piped gas systems and their hazards was first brought before the then NFPA Committee on Gases in 1932. The concerns raised then remain cogent today. These include the ability of piped oxygen and nitrous oxide to violently enhance fires, patient safety concerns which arise from pressurized gas, simple debris in the pipe, restrictions to flow, the significance of vacuum in medical treatments, and a host of other challenges arising from the increasing complexity and variety of applications for gases in medicine.

The ubiquitous presence and inherent reliability of piped gas and vacuum systems in medical facilities has in turn crowded out alternatives. The medical facility of today is much less able to do without these systems or to deal with their sudden loss than was their analogue of 1932. This elevates concerns over patient safety and system reliability, and therefore the standard has become more complex and prescriptive over the years.

The organization of NFPA 99 is essentially unchanged from the 2002 edition. Requirements for gas and vacuum systems are first categorized as Levels 1, 2, and 3 on the basis of the level of risk to patients from a failure of the supply. Level 1 systems are the most reliable and complex because patients being served by this system will be at the greatest risk if the system fails (i.e., patients being served by this system are the most dependent on this system's functioning properly). Level 2 systems are a step down from Level 1 systems; Level 3 systems are another step down. This does not mean that Level 3 systems are marginal systems; rather, the needs of patients and procedures for medical gas or vacuum support (if any) are simply not as critical as the other two levels.

Chapter 5 is organized by Level 1 requirements (Section 5.1), Level 2 requirements (Section 5.2), and Level 3 requirements (Section 5.3). Generally speaking, similar requirements are numbered the same; thus you will find requirements for labeling under 5.1.11.1 for Level 1, 5.2.11.1 for Level 2, and 5.3.11.1 for Level 3. Although not exact, this organization has been maintained generally across the levels. The criteria to determine which level to use in any given facility are found in the occupancy chapters: Chapters 13, 14, 17, and 18, under Section ____.5. Additionally the requirements that pertained to cylinder maintenance, inspection, and special handling procedures were moved to Chapter 9, Gas Equipment.

All requirements for gas systems in laboratories are found in Chapter 11 with other laboratory requirements.

Figures are drawn not for engineering precision but rather for wide comprehension. They are drawn in a semirealistic fashion, showing devices that resemble those on the actual equipment and resorting to schematic representations where no obvious semirealistic representation was appropriate. These semirealistic representations are in no way restrictive; merely because a device in a real installation does not look like a device shown here does not mean it is not compliant in every way. Most of these figures formerly resided in Chapter 5, and their relocation to Annex A is intentional, reflecting the fact that they are not and never have been required parts of the standard but are here only as a means of illustrating the text. Figure A.5.1.3 is a legend for all the drawings in the Annex A text for Chapter 5.

Note that Figure A.5.1.3.4.9 and Figure A.5.1.3.4 are subcomponents used in Figure A.5.1.3.4.10 through Figure A.5.1.3.4.12, except that Figure A.5.1.3.4.9(a) can also have a life of its own in a few cases where "headers" are used by themselves.

5.1 Level 1 Piped Gas and Vacuum Systems

5.1.1* Applicability.

A.5.1.1 Section 5.1 covers requirements for Level 1 piped gas and vacuum systems; Section 5.2 covers Level 2 piped gas and vacuum systems; Section 5.3 covers Level 3 piped gas and vacuum systems. Laboratory systems are no longer covered by Chapter 5 (2002 edition).

5.1.1.1 These requirements shall apply to health care facilities that require Level 1 systems as referenced in Chapters 13 through 21.

5.1.1.2* Wherever the terms *medical gas* or *vacuum* occur, the provisions shall apply to all piped systems for oxygen, nitrous oxide, medical air, carbon dioxide, helium, medical–surgical vacuum, waste anesthetic gas disposal, and mixtures thereof. Wherever the name of a specific gas or vacuum service occurs, the provision shall apply only to that gas.

A.5.1.1.2 These requirements do not restrict the distribution of other inert gases through piping systems.

FAQ ▶ Are flammable gases covered by this chapter?

Natural gas, hydrogen, and acetylene are flammable gases, so they are not included under the requirements for piped nonflammable medical gases for Level 1, Level 2, or Level 3 systems. However, they are permitted in laboratory systems, so they are covered under Chapter 11. Readers should be aware that requirements for piped gas systems are in some respects different from requirements for piped vacuum systems.

5.1.1.3 Wherever the term *medical–surgical vacuum* occurs, the provisions shall apply to systems for piped medical–surgical vacuum and piped waste anesthetic gas disposal (WAGD). Wherever the name of a specific vacuum service occurs, the provision shall apply only to that vacuum service.

5.1.1.4 An existing system that is not in strict compliance with the provisions of this standard shall be permitted to be continued in use as long as the authority having jurisdiction has determined that such use does not constitute a distinct hazard to life.

What can be considered to constitute a "distinct hazard to life" is largely in the eye of the beholder. As a recent example, consider that although CGA V-1/ANSI B57.1, *Compressed Gas Association Standard for Compressed Gas Cylinder Valve Outlet and Inlet Connections* [1] (noninterchangeable cylinder connection standard), has been in use for decades, the best known cause of medical gas–related deaths during the life of the 1999 edition was due to abuse of those very connections (see FDA, "Guidance to Hospitals, Nursing Homes and other Health Care Facilities," March 2000 [2]). It is clear from the discussions that surrounded the writing of Chapter 5 that "distinct hazards to life" continue to appear with surprising frequency in the life cycle of medical gas and vacuum systems, despite their long history. Therefore, it is prudent to construe the definition broadly and to ensure that wherever possible, systems are brought into compliance.

Notwithstanding, where a risk analysis concludes that hazards are remote, 5.1.1.4 does permit the facility to leave older systems untouched and to continue their use. This paragraph places existing systems for the most part outside the scope of this chapter, with the exception of those provisions that mandate certain maintenance operations necessary to keep a system (otherwise designed and installed to the standard) safely operating.

5.1.2 Nature of Hazards of Gas and Vacuum Systems.

Potential fire and explosion hazards associated with positive pressure gas central piping systems and medical–surgical vacuum systems shall be considered in the design, installation, testing, operation, and maintenance of these systems.

Readers should review Chapter 9, Gas Equipment, for requirements for freestanding cylinders that are not associated with piped gas systems, including their storage and transfilling.

5.1.3* Level 1 Sources.

A.5.1.3 See Figure A.5.1.3. Level 1 source drawings in this annex are representational, demonstrating a possible arrangement of components required by the text. The diagrams are not intended to imply method, materials of construction, or more than one of many possible and equally compliant arrangements. Alternative arrangements are permitted if they meet the intent of the text. Listed paragraphs may not be the only paragraphs that apply.

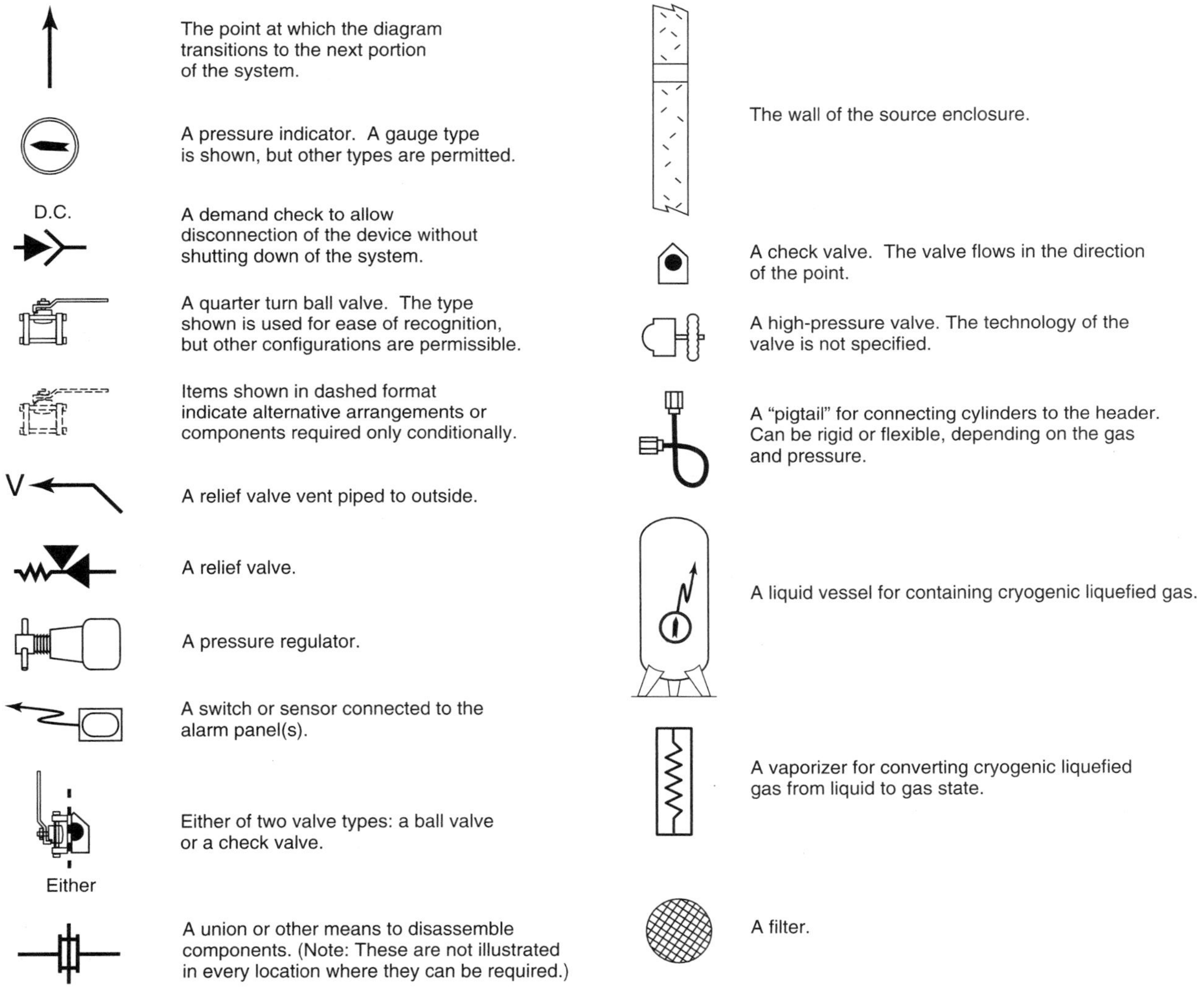

The point at which the diagram transitions to the next portion of the system.

A pressure indicator. A gauge type is shown, but other types are permitted.

D.C.

A demand check to allow disconnection of the device without shutting down of the system.

A quarter turn ball valve. The type shown is used for ease of recognition, but other configurations are permissible.

Items shown in dashed format indicate alternative arrangements or components required only conditionally.

V

A relief valve vent piped to outside.

A relief valve.

A pressure regulator.

A switch or sensor connected to the alarm panel(s).

Either

Either of two valve types: a ball valve or a check valve.

A union or other means to disassemble components. (Note: These are not illustrated in every location where they can be required.)

The wall of the source enclosure.

A check valve. The valve flows in the direction of the point.

A high-pressure valve. The technology of the valve is not specified.

A “pigtail” for connecting cylinders to the header. Can be rigid or flexible, depending on the gas and pressure.

A liquid vessel for containing cryogenic liquefied gas.

A vaporizer for converting cryogenic liquefied gas from liquid to gas state.

A filter.

FIGURE A.5.1.3 *Legend for Typical Level 1 Source Drawings.*

5.1.3.1 Central Supply System Identification and Labeling.

5.1.3.1.1* Only cylinders and containers constructed, tested, and maintained in accordance with U.S. Department of Transportation specifications and regulations shall be permitted to be used.

A.5.1.3.1.1 Regulations of the U.S. Department of Transportation (formerly U.S. Interstate Commerce Commission) outline specifications for transportation of explosives and dangerous articles (49 CFR 171–190). In Canada, the regulations of the Canadian Transport Commission, Union Station, Ottawa, Ontario, apply.

The U.S. Department of Transportation (DOT) regulations, 49 CFR, 171–190, "Specifications for Transportation of Explosives and Dangerous Articles" [3], for the manufacture and requalification of compressed gas cylinders provide for reasonably safe and economical cylinders. These regulations are thus referenced to avoid redundancy. Cylinders complying with DOT regulations are also considered safe for the storage of gases in health care facilities.

5.1.3.1.2 Cylinder contents shall be identified by attached labels or stencils naming the contents in accordance with CGA C-7, *Guide to the Preparation of Precautionary Labeling and Marking of Compressed Gas Containers.*

The exchanging of cylinders on a manifold is the most common interface facility staff have with the medical gas pipelines. It was lack of attention to 5.1.3.1.2, 5.1.3.1.3, and 5.1.3.1.6 that caused a multiple-death incident and prompted the U.S. Food and Drug Administration (FDA) to issue its only medical gas–related alert in recent memory.

Although cylinders are "keyed" by the gas contained therein, and the manifolds are fitted with the matching "key" in the form of the gas-specific connector attached, it is always possible for someone unaware of the system and clever with a wrench to defeat these measures. In addition, gases have been delivered mislabeled and miskeyed. Although it is not practical in most facilities to test the gas contents of each cylinder, it is very easy to confirm that the labels are in place, are legible, and match the gas-specific connector. A simple go/no go tester can be made of a known CGA connector from an old cylinder lead or purchased from any reputable supplier. Cylinders that are missing their labels or have cylinder connections that do not match the labels should be assumed to contain something other than the gas they are expected to contain. Such cylinders should be quarantined and returned to the supplier immediately. Such cylinders must NEVER be used.

5.1.3.1.3 Liquid containers shall have additional product identification visible from all directions with a minimum of 51 mm (2 in.) high letters such as a 360 degree wraparound tape for medical liquid containers.

5.1.3.1.4 Cryogenic liquid containers shall be provided with gas-specific outlet connections in accordance with CGA V-5, *Diameter-Index Safety System (Noninterchangeable Low Pressure Connections for Medical Gas Applications)*, or CGA V-1, *Compressed Gas Association Standard for Compressed Gas Cylinder Valve Inlet and Outlet Connections.*

5.1.3.1.5 Cylinder and cryogenic liquid container outlet connections shall be affixed in such a manner as to be integral to the valve(s), unremovable with ordinary tools or so designed as to render the attachment point unusable when removed.

Manufacturers have gone to great lengths to refit containers that had easily removable valves and outlet connections, thus increasing the potential for the wrong gases being connected. No medical facility in the United States that buys its gases from a reputable supplier should experience this problem now. However, in many other parts of the world, this retrofit has not been done and facilities in those areas must rely on training and procedures to prevent cross connection.

5.1.3.1.6 Contents of cylinders and cryogenic liquid containers shall be verified prior to use.

5.1.3.1.7 Labels shall not be defaced, altered, or removed, and connecting fittings shall not be modified.

5.1.3.1.8 Locations containing positive pressure gases other than oxygen and medical air shall have their door(s) labeled substantially as follows:

CAUTION
Positive Pressure Gases
NO Smoking or Open Flame
Room May Have Insufficient Oxygen
Open Door and Allow Room to Ventilate Before Entering

With any gas source, it must be accepted as inevitable that the gas will leak. Although the greatest hazard arises with a massive discharge of gas (e.g., after a relief valve failure), the more commonplace problems include the cylinder lead that was not tightened properly, the connector that was nicked and does not quite seal, the pigtail that has a small break, and the connector that has lost its sealing O-ring. Large-scale discharges are very rare, but little leaks are almost universal.

◀ **FAQ**
Are leaks very common with source equipment?

Two hazards exist whereby gases might accumulate in a closed space. One of course is fire, which is the reason smoking is prohibited around oxygen and nitrous oxide (both strong oxidizers). A second is simple displacement of breathable air — for instance by nitrogen — and the third is the presence of nonflammable gases that can themselves be toxic, such as nitrous oxide and carbon dioxide. The case of the maintenance person who fell unconscious because he or she walked into an airless manifold room is all too common, and the speed at which unconsciousness and death occur is frightening.

5.1.3.1.9 Locations containing central supply systems or cylinders containing only oxygen or medical air shall have their door(s) labeled as follows:

CAUTION
Medical Gases
NO Smoking or Open Flame

5.1.3.2 Central Supply System Operations.

5.1.3.2.1 The use of adapters or conversion fittings to adapt one gas-specific fitting to another shall be prohibited.

The "cheater" fittings noted in 5.1.3.2.1 are easily made but are absolutely inappropriate. There is no legitimate reason to run the risks in making such a fitting.

5.1.3.2.2 Cylinders and containers shall be handled in strict accordance with 5.1.13.

Not all of the requirements for handling cylinders are found in this chapter. It is also strongly recommended that readers refer to Chapter 9 for additional advice on handling gases.

5.1.3.2.3 Only gas cylinders, reusable shipping containers, and their accessories shall be permitted to be stored in rooms containing central supply systems or gas cylinders.

Exhibit 5.1 shows medical gas cylinders stored in the manner described in 5.1.3.2.3.

EXHIBIT 5.1 *Medical gas cylinders stored in a wire mesh enclosure in a loading dock area.*

5.1.3.2.4 No flammable materials, cylinders containing flammable gases, or containers containing flammable liquids shall be stored in rooms with gas cylinders.

Although nonflammable compressed gases are to be kept separated from volatile liquids and flammable gases, oxygen and nitrous oxide gas cylinders and containers are allowed to be stored together.

5.1.3.2.5 Wooden racks for cylinder storage shall be permitted.

FAQ ▶ Paragraph 5.1.3.3.2 requires racks to be of noncombustible or limited-combustible material. Isn't this in conflict with 5.1.3.2.5?

Wooden storage racks are permitted; such racks are economical, convenient, and not proven to be a hazard over the test of time. (Note: This is the only exception with respect to combustible materials within gas cylinder storage rooms.)

5.1.3.2.6 If cylinders are wrapped when received, the wrappers shall be removed prior to storage.

5.1.3.2.7 Cylinders not in use shall have their valve protection caps secured tightly in place.

If a cylinder that does not have a cylinder valve protection cap as required by 5.1.3.2.7 falls over, the cylinder valve could snap off. Depending on cylinder size, quantity of gas within the cylinder, and the orifice size at the break, the cylinder could be propelled rapidly and/or violently about after it is damaged.

5.1.3.2.8 Cylinders without correct markings or whose markings and gas-specific fittings do not match shall not be used.

See the commentary following 5.1.3.1.2.

5.1.3.2.9 Cryogenic liquid storage units intended to supply gas to the facility shall not be used to transfill other liquid storage vessels.

To transfill liquid vessels (so-called "walkers" or other vessels) from the main oxygen supply is very tempting, is regrettably not uncommon, and is extremely dangerous. Cryogenic liquids in general pose a whole series of hazards to life and limb that can be appreciated only by a trained individual. These hazards are difficult to guard against. Cryogenic oxygen poses two additional hazards: that of spontaneous combustion (encountered with certain flooring materials), and "soaking" with oxygen the very protective safety clothing used to handle the liquid so that it then burns violently. Transfilling oxygen is believed be so hazardous that it is simply wisest to prohibit it entirely.

◀ **FAQ**
What are the hazards of transfilling liquid oxygen?

5.1.3.2.10 Care shall be exercised when handling cylinders that have been exposed to freezing temperatures or containers that contain cryogenic liquids to prevent injury to the skin.

5.1.3.2.11 Cylinders containing compressed gases and containers for volatile liquids shall be kept away from radiators, steam piping, and like sources of heat.

5.1.3.2.12 When cylinder valve protection caps are supplied, they shall be secured tightly in place unless the cylinder is connected for use.

5.1.3.2.13 Containers shall not be stored in a tightly closed space.

5.1.3.3* Central Supply System Locations.

Paragraphs 5.1.3.3.1.1 through 5.1.3.3.1.4 clarify the allowable locations for various sources and are intended to minimize the dangerous practice of placing various medical gas sources together in the same room or enclosure. The hazards are particularly acute where motor driven equipment is located in the same room with strong oxidizing gases (oxygen and nitrous oxide). The one exception — the placing of instrument air headers with instrument air compressors (see 5.1.3.3.1.4) — is permitted only because of the relatively inert characteristics of air, the unique configuration allowed for instrument air sources (compressor with cylinder reserve), and the provisions for venting both the cylinder header and the enclosure contained in this standard. (See Exhibit 5.2.)

A.5.1.3.3 The bulk supply system should be installed on a site that has been prepared to meet the requirements of NFPA 50, *Standard for Bulk Oxygen Systems at Consumer Sites*, or CGA G-8.1, *Standard for Nitrous Oxide Systems at Consumer Sites*. Storage unit(s), reserve, pressure regulation, and signal actuating switch(es) are components of the supply system. Shutoff valves, piping from the site, and electric wiring from a signal switch(es) to the master signal panels are components of the piping system.

The bulk supply system is normally installed on the site by the owner of this equipment. It is the responsibility of the owner or the organization responsible for the operation and maintenance of the bulk supply system to ensure that all components of the supply system — main supply, reserve supply, supply system signal actuating switch(es), and delivery pressure regulation equipment — function properly before the system is put in service.

5.1.3.3.1 Central supply systems shall be located to meet the criteria in 5.1.3.3.1.1 through 5.1.3.3.1.12.

5.1.3.3.1.1 Any of the following systems shall be permitted to be located together in the same outdoor enclosure:

(1) Manifolds for gas cylinders without reserve supply *(See 5.1.3.4.10.)*
(2) Manifolds for gas cylinders with reserve supply
(3) Manifolds for cryogenic liquid containers *(See 5.1.3.4.12.)*
(4) Bulk cryogenic liquid systems *(See 5.1.3.4.13.)*

5.1.3.3.1.2 Any of the following systems shall be permitted to be located together in the same indoor enclosure:

***EXHIBIT** 5.2 Storage tanks, holding bulk supplies of liquid oxygen, which are usually found in health care facilities. The smaller tank acts as a reserve supply. Note the security fencing and the signs prohibiting smoking.*

(1) Manifolds for gas cylinders without reserve supply *(See 5.1.3.4.10.)*
(2) Manifolds for gas cylinders with reserve supply
(3) Manifolds for cryogenic liquid containers *(See 5.1.3.4.12.)*
(4) In-building emergency reserves *(See 5.1.3.4.15.)*
(5) Instrument air standby headers *(See 5.1.3.8.5.)*

Indoor locations, as stated in this paragraph and elsewhere, should not be interpreted as necessarily meaning within the confines of the building. It is meant to ensure that this kind of equipment will not be located where it will be exposed to the elements. It is not uncommon, for example, to locate this equipment in a remote power plant or boiler plant building, which also could satisfy these requirements. A shed or outbuilding, provided that the interior conditions and ventilation are in other respects suitable, could fulfill this requirement equally well.

5.1.3.3.1.3 Any of the following systems shall be permitted to be located together in the same room:

(1) Medical air compressor supply sources *(See 5.1.3.5.3.)*
(2) Medical–surgical vacuum sources *(See 5.1.3.6.)*
(3) Waste anesthetic gas disposal (WAGD) sources *(See 5.1.3.7.)*
(4) Instrument air compressor sources *(See 5.1.3.8.)*
(5) Any other compressor, vacuum pump, or electrically powered machinery

FAQ ▶
Can air compressors and vacuum pumps be in the same room as other equipment?

NFPA 99 does not prohibit medical air compressors and vacuum pumps from being in the same room as air handlers, chillers, or gas hot water heaters. The reason this arrangement is acceptable is, in part, that air compressor intakes and vacuum pump exhausts are required by NFPA 99 to be located outdoors.

5.1.3.3.1.4 Any system listed under 5.1.3.3.1.3 shall not be located in the same room with any system listed under 5.1.3.3.1.1 or 5.1.3.3.1.2, except instrument air reserve headers complying with 5.1.3.3.1.7 and 5.1.3.8.5 shall be allowed to be in the same room as an instrument air compressor.

5.1.3.3.1.5 Locations shall be chosen to permit access by delivery vehicles and management of cylinders (e.g., proximity to loading docks, access to elevators, passage of cylinders through public areas).

5.1.3.3.1.6 Indoor locations for oxygen, nitrous oxide, and mixtures of these gases shall not communicate with the following:

(1) Areas involved in critical patient care
(2) Anesthetizing locations
(3) Locations storing flammables
(4) Rooms containing open electrical contacts or transformers
(5) Storage tanks for flammable or combustible liquids
(6) Engines
(7) Kitchens
(8) Areas with open flames

5.1.3.3.1.7 Cylinders in use and in storage shall be prevented from reaching temperatures in excess of 54°C (130°F).

The temperature at which a full cylinder might approach the popoff pressure for the burst disk on the cylinder is 54°C (130°F). Some authorities consider even this temperature too high, and certainly it is advisable never to allow cylinders to reach elevated temperatures. A common way cylinders could reach these temperatures is to be placed in full sun on a hot summer day.

5.1.3.3.1.8 Central supply systems for nitrous oxide and carbon dioxide using cylinders or portable containers shall be prevented from reaching temperatures lower than the recommendations of the central supply system's manufacturer, but shall never be lower than −7°C (20°F) or greater than 54°C (130°F).

The minimum temperatures for nitrous oxide and carbon dioxide result from the fact that these gases are actually above their triple point in a standard cylinder and are thus in liquid form inside the cylinder. Their pressure–temperature curves are steep, so they lose pressure rapidly as temperatures fall, reaching a point where the liquid simply cannot vaporize and the gas cannot be drawn off.

5.1.3.3.1.9 Central supply systems for oxygen with a total capacity connected and in storage of 566,335 L (20,000 ft^3) or more at standard temperature and pressure (STP) shall comply with NFPA 50, *Standard for Bulk Oxygen Systems at Consumer Sites.*

At the time the 2005 edition of NFPA 99 was being processed, NFPA 50, *Standard for Bulk Oxygen Systems at Consumer Sites,* had not yet been incorporated into NFPA 55. The subsequent integration of NFPA 50 into NFPA 55 is reflected in this handbook commentary. NFPA 55, *Standard for the Storage, Use, and Handling of Compressed Gases and Cryogenic Fluids in Portable and Stationary Containers, Cylinders, and Tanks* [4], requires that bulk systems be located either outdoors or in a building used only for that purpose. Because 5.1.3.3.1.9 requires that locations storing more than 566,335 L (20,000 ft^3) of oxygen comply with NFPA 55, the maximum amount of oxygen that can be stored inside a health care facility is 566,335 L (20,000 ft^3).

There is a tendency to use this number as the sole test of a bulk gas installation, which is not really the intent. To protect the operator, any installation provided with a stationary tank of liquefied gases should be installed following these rules insofar as possible. The hazards are common to any stationary liquid installation and are not unique to those above 566,335 L (20,000 ft^3).

5.1.3.3.1.10 Central supply systems for nitrous oxide with a total capacity connected and in storage of 1451 kg (3200 lb) or more shall comply with CGA G-8.1, *Standard for Nitrous Oxide Systems at Consumer Sites*.

5.1.3.3.1.11 Central supply systems for carbon dioxide using permanently installed containers with product capacities greater than 454 kg (1000 lb) shall comply with CGA G-6.1, *Standard for Insulated Carbon Dioxide Systems at Consumer Sites*.

5.1.3.3.1.12 Central supply systems for carbon dioxide using permanently installed containers with product capacities of 454 kg (1000 lb) or less shall comply with CGA G-6.5, *Standard for Small, Stationary, Insulated Carbon Dioxide Supply Systems*.

5.1.3.3.2* Design and Construction. Locations for central supply systems and the storage of positive pressure gases shall meet the following requirements:

(1) Be constructed with access to move cylinders, equipment, and so forth, in and out of the location on hand trucks complying with 9.5.3.1.1
(2) Be secured with lockable doors or gates or otherwise secured

Although NFPA 99 does not require that storage rooms for gases be locked, it does require that they be "secured" if the public has access. In light of reported thefts of nitrous oxide cylinders for substance-abuse purposes, and to prevent unauthorized persons from creating a hazard or harming themselves, some means of limiting access to storage rooms is prudent.

(3) If outdoors, be provided with an enclosure (wall or fencing) constructed of noncombustible materials
(4) If indoors, be constructed and use interior finishes of noncombustible or limited-combustible materials such that all walls, floors, ceilings and doors are of a minimum 1-hour fire resistance rating

(5) Be compliant with NFPA 70, *National Electrical Code*, for ordinary locations, with electrical devices located at or above 1520 mm (5 ft) above finished floor to avoid physical damage
(6) Be heated by indirect means (e.g., steam, hot water), if heat is required

Indirect heating in 5.1.3.3.2(6) means that the source of the heat itself is outside the room. Only the medium (warm air, hot water, steam) will pass into the room.

(7) Be provided with racks, chains, or other fastenings to secure all cylinders, whether connected, unconnected, full, or empty, from falling

FAQ ▶ Does "secure all cylinders" mean a single chain can be used to secure multiple cylinders?

Paragraph 5.1.3.3.2(7) is a change to the 2002 requirement for individual securing of the cylinders. Here in the 2005 edition, the standard returns to the more relaxed "secure all cylinders," which permits again, for instance, the single chain around multiple cylinders, which was common practice prior to the 2002 edition.

(8) Be supplied with electrical power compliant with the requirements for essential electrical systems as described in Chapter 4 of this document
(9) Have racks, shelves, and supports, where provided, constructed of noncombustible materials or limited-combustible materials

A.5.1.3.3.2 Electric wiring and equipment in storage rooms for oxygen and nitrous oxide are not required to be explosionproof.

5.1.3.3.3 Ventilation.

With any gas source, the gas inevitably will leak. Although the greatest hazard arises with a mass discharge of gas (e.g., after a relief valve failure), the more commonplace problems are the cylinder lead that was not tightened properly, the connector that was nicked and does not quite seal, the pigtail with a small break, or the connector that lost its sealing O-ring. Large-scale discharges are very rare, but little leaks are almost universal.

With containers holding cryogenic gases, venting from the containers is normal. These containers are designed to vent the overpressure created by heat leakage through the container wall. Ventilation has traditionally been left to the designer, and little was required. Previous editions have greatly strengthened the requirements and added a mandate for active ventilation for all but the smallest systems.

5.1.3.3.3.1 Ventilation of Locations for Manifolds. Locations containing central supply systems or used for storing medical gas containers shall be ventilated to prevent the accumulation of medical gases from leaks and operation of cylinder or manifold overpressure safety devices in accordance with 5.1.3.3.3.1(A) through 5.1.3.3.3.1(G).

(A) Indoor supply systems shall have all relief valves vented per 5.1.3.4.6.1(4) through 5.1.3.4.6.1(9).

Since the 2002 edition, all relief valves are required to be vented to the outside. Previous editions required only that the final line relief valves be vented.

(B) Where the total volume of medical gases connected and in storage is greater than 84,950 L (3000 ft^3) at STP, indoor supply locations shall be provided with dedicated mechanical ventilation systems that draw air from within 300 mm (1 ft) of the floor and operate continuously. A means of makeup air shall be provided.

The requirement in 5.1.3.3.3.1(B) for the ventilation to be located at the floor is a recognition that the most dangerous gases in common use are also heavier than air. In the stillness of a closed manifold room, these gases tend to settle at the floor level. Note that this provision is meant to include all gases and all cylinders — both those connected to the source and those standing idle. A manifold room containing four "H" cylinders of oxygen and four "H" cylinders of nitrous oxide is over this limit — those eight cylinders contain 91,578 L (3,236 ft^3).

Venting systems for gas storage locations should not be interconnected with other facility air-handling systems.

(C) The power supply for mechanical ventilation fans shall conform to the requirements of an essential electrical system as described in Chapter 4 of this document.

(D) Where the total volume of medical gases connected and in storage is less than 84,950 L (3000 ft^3) at STP or the only compressed gas in the room is medical air, natural ventilation shall be permitted to be employed.

(E) Where natural ventilation is permitted, it shall consist of two louvered openings, each having a minimum free area of 46,500 mm^2 (72 $in.^2$), with one located within 300 mm (1 ft) of the floor and one located within 300 mm (1 ft) of the ceiling.

Paragraph 5.1.3.3.3.1(E) requires two vents, one at the floor and one at the ceiling. This requirement and the requirement for makeup air with mechanical ventilation were added in an effort to ensure some cross-ventilation in these cases, instead of the simple diffusion that earlier versions of the standard permitted.

(F) Louvered natural ventilation openings shall not be located in an exit access corridor.

When a manifold or other bulk storage room opens onto an exit access corridor, it could be dangerous to have excess nonflammable gases dumping into this corridor when it is being used as an exit from a fire or other emergency. Paragraph 5.1.3.3.3.1(F), in those cases, mandates the use of dedicated mechanical ventilation. This ventilation would be in operation 24 hours a day and would remove any gases vented from the tanks or other storage containers directly to the outside of the facility. Previously, the standard allowed louvered vents in the doors under other circumstances. These louvered vents would occasionally exist in doors that led into exit access corridors.

The requirements for storage locations that have openings onto exit access corridors correlate with NFPA *101®*, *Life Safety Code®* [5].

(G) Mechanical ventilation shall be provided if the requirements of 5.1.3.3.3.1(F) cannot be met.

5.1.3.3.3.2 Ventilation for Motor Driven Equipment. The following source locations shall be adequately ventilated to prevent accumulation of heat:

(1) Medical air sources *(See 5.1.3.5.)*
(2) Medical–surgical vacuum sources *(See 5.1.3.6.)*
(3) Waste anesthetic gas disposal (WAGD) sources *(See 5.1.3.7.1.)*
(4) Instrument air sources *(See 5.1.3.8.)*

All motor-driven equipment will of necessity create heat, which the equipment is designed to discharge into the enclosure. Such heat is unlikely to create a fire hazard, but in extremes it can cause the tripping of motor overloads, thermal malfunction devices, and so on. Moreover, the stress on the equipment is greatly increased when it is not held within the temperature limits recommended by its manufacturer.

There are two elements to ventilation as it is conceived here: (1) the ambient temperature, which may itself become higher than the manufacturer recommends; and (2) prevention of accumulated heat from raising the room temperature above the recommended maximum. In climates with low ambient temperatures year round, simple natural ventilation might be sufficient. In warmer climates, mechanical ventilation up to or including air conditioning of mechanical spaces might be required. Because it is essential to the reliability of the equipment, this ventilation is a life safety concern.

5.1.3.3.3.3 Ventilation for Outdoor Locations. Outdoor locations surrounded by impermeable walls shall have protected ventilation openings located at the base of each wall to allow free circulation of air within the enclosure. Walls that are shared with other enclosures or with buildings shall be permitted to not have openings.

This requirement is aimed at preventing a cryogenic liquid system from being placed in a vault or surrounded by a solid wall (such as a wall of concrete blocks or brick). In such situations, the gate might be the only opening where vented gas might escape. The provision in 5.1.3.3.3.3 is intended to ensure a minimal cross-ventilation. The size of these openings will have to be determined by consultation with the bulk system supplier because it will vary with the system size and configuration. Because the air might contain elevated levels of the gas in the enclosure, it is inappropriate to allow it into a building, which would be the result of opening a common wall for ventilation.

5.1.3.3.4 Storage.

5.1.3.3.4.1 Full or empty medical gas cylinders, when not connected, shall be stored in locations complying with 5.1.3.3.2 through 5.1.3.3.3 and shall be permitted to be in the same rooms or enclosures as their respective central supply systems.

5.1.3.3.4.2 Cylinders, whether full or empty, shall not be stored in enclosures containing medical air compressor sources, medical vacuum supply systems, or WAGD supply systems. Only cylinders intended for instrument air reserve headers complying with 5.1.3.8.5 shall be permitted to be stored in enclosures containing instrument air compressors.

5.1.3.4* Central Supply Systems. Central supply systems shall be permitted to consist of the following:

(1) Cylinder manifolds for gas cylinders per 5.1.3.4.10
(2) Manifolds for cryogenic liquid containers per 5.1.3.4.12
(3) Bulk cryogenic liquid systems per 5.1.3.4.13
(4) Medical air compressor systems per 5.1.3.5
(5) Medical–surgical vacuum producers per 5.1.3.6
(6) WAGD producers per 5.1.3.7
(7) Instrument air compressor systems per 5.1.3.8

A.5.1.3.4 See Figure A.5.1.3.4. A four-valve bypass arrangement is illustrated. Three-way valves are permitted in lieu of the four valves shown. 

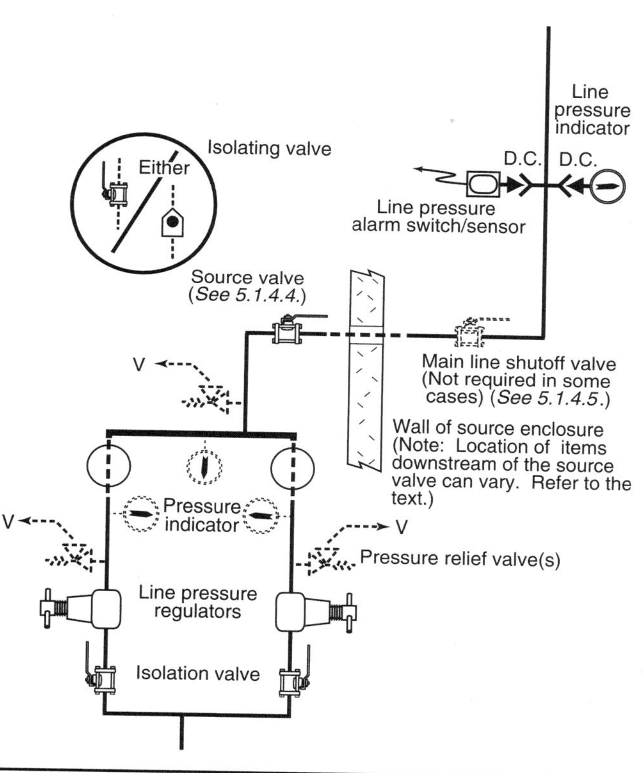

***FIGURE A.5.1.3.4** Typical Arrangement for Line Controls at Pressure Sources.*

The subsystem illustrated in Figure A.5.1.3.4 is critical to any medical gas source of supply, and the same or very similar arrangements of components will be seen in any medical gas system. A relief valve is required downstream of any pressure regulator and where gas may become trapped. The two alternate locations reflect the text and the options for valving illustrated in Figure A.5.1.3.4, but good engineering practice should be observed here. The text would also permit use of a three-way valve under some circumstances, which is not illustrated.

5.1.3.4.1 Central supply systems shall be obtained from a supplier or manufacturer familiar with their proper construction and use and installed in accordance with the manufacturer's instructions.

5.1.3.4.2* Central supply systems for oxygen, medical air, nitrous oxide, carbon dioxide, and all other patient medical gases shall not be piped to, or used for, any purpose except patient care application. Medical air shall be used only in the application of human respiration, and calibration of medical devices for respiratory application.

FAQ ▶
Can medical gases be used for other purposes?

Paragraph 5.1.3.4.2 reflects a long-term concern that medical gases are piped to areas that are outside of the control of medical personnel and where the gas is intended for uses other than patient care. Common examples of this misuse include piping medical oxygen into a laboratory for instrumentation, piping medical air into central supply to run sterilizers or blow down tools, or using medical nitrogen to operate door openers.

The intent of this provision is to prevent these abuses and thus to ensure that the systems do not fail and are not contaminated as a result of inappropriate use. Medical gas systems are meant to be treated with the respect due to the pharmaceuticals they convey and are not to be thought of or treated as simple utilities.

A.5.1.3.4.2 Prohibited uses of medical gases include fueling torches, blowing down or drying any equipment such as lab equipment, endoscopy or other scopes, or any other purposes. Also prohibited is using the oxygen or medical air to raise, lower, or otherwise operate booms or other devices in operating rooms (ORs) or other areas.

5.1.3.4.3 Central supply systems for support gases shall not be piped to, or used for, any purpose except medical support application.

Paragraph 5.1.3.4.3 and the concept of medical support gas is the first time the standard has recognized that there is a distinct difference in the nature of a medical gas that patients depend on for life and the medical support gases that are used to conduct procedures but are not in fact respired. Medical support gas may nevertheless be critical to patient outcome. Imagine, for instance, if the bone saw simply failed in the middle of a procedure! At this time, the standard only envisions two medical support gases: nitrogen and instrument air, both of which are primarily used for tools.

5.1.3.4.4* Materials used in central supply systems shall meet the following requirements:

(1) In those portions of systems intended to handle oxygen at gauge pressures greater than 2070 kPa (300 psi), interconnecting hose shall contain no polymeric materials.

Paragraph 5.1.3.4.4(1) arises from reports received of ignitions in the linings of these so-called "flexible pigtails." It appears that under some circumstances, including the presence of pure oxygen at cylinder pressures, the linings can ignite and blow out or explode. Although there are always potential issues with placing polymeric materials in pure oxygen, these flexible pigtails have accumulated a particularly problematic history and thus were prohibited in the 2002 edition. Note that this prohibition is limited to oxygen at high pressures and therefore does not preclude pigtails when used with other gases or with oxygen at gauge pressures less than 2070 kPa (300 psi).

(2) In those portions of systems intended to handle oxygen or nitrous oxide at gauge pressures of less than 2070 kPa (300 psi), material construction shall be compatible with oxygen under the temperatures and pressures to which the components can be exposed in the containment and use of oxygen, nitrous oxide, mixtures of these gases, or mixtures containing more than 23.5 percent oxygen.

(3) If potentially exposed to cryogenic temperatures, materials shall be designed for low temperature service.
(4) If intended for outdoor installation, materials shall be installed per the manufacturer's requirements.

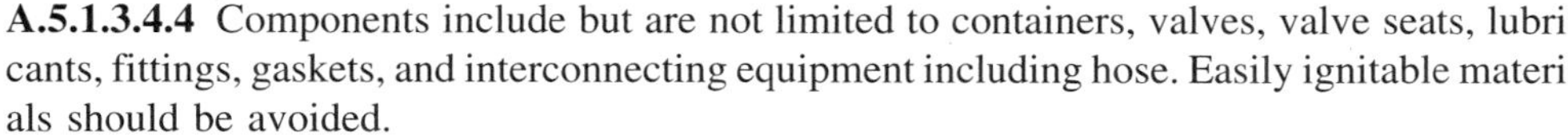

A.5.1.3.4.4 Components include but are not limited to containers, valves, valve seats, lubricants, fittings, gaskets, and interconnecting equipment including hose. Easily ignitable materials should be avoided.

Compatibility involves both combustibility and ease of ignition. Materials that burn in air will burn violently in pure oxygen at normal pressure and explosively in pressurized oxygen. Also, many materials that do not burn in air will do so in pure oxygen, particularly under pressure. Metals for containers and piping have to be carefully selected, depending on service conditions. The various steels are acceptable for many applications, but some service conditions can call for other materials (usually copper or its alloys) because of their greater resistance to ignition and lower rate of combustion.

Similarly, materials that can be ignited in air have lower ignition energies in oxygen. Many such materials can be ignited by friction at a valve seat or stem packing or by adiabatic compression produced when oxygen at high pressure is rapidly introduced into a system initially at low pressure.

5.1.3.4.5 Final Line Pressure Regulators.

5.1.3.4.5.1 All positive pressure central supply systems shall be provided with duplex final line pressure regulators, installed in parallel with isolation valves before each regulator, and an isolation or check valve after each regulator permitting service to either regulator without interruption of supply.

Paragraph 5.1.3.4.5.1 originally allowed regulators for all new central supply systems to be either duplexed or placed in a three-valve bypass arrangement. This requirement was altered in 1996 to require a full bypass arrangement to prevent gauge pressures of possibly 1034 kPa to 2069 kPa (150 psi to 300 psi) or more from entering the distribution pipeline. These pressures could readily damage pressure switches, station outlets, and so forth not designed for such pressures.

Bypasses are intended to facilitate serviceability while a system remains in operation and can be arranged in a variety of ways to facilitate this objective. The committee considers regulators particularly likely to require service, the reason for mandating bypass requirements. Check valves would be an unusual but perfectly acceptable method of providing this serviceability.

5.1.3.4.5.2 The line pressure regulators required under 5.1.3.4.5.1 when used for bulk cryogenic liquid systems shall be of a balanced design.

5.1.3.4.5.3 A pressure indicator(s) shall be located downstream (patient or use side) of each regulator or immediately downstream of the isolating valves for the regulators.

5.1.3.4.6 Relief Valves.

5.1.3.4.6.1 All pressure relief valves shall meet the following requirements:

(1) Be of brass, bronze, or stainless steel construction
(2) Be designed for the specific gas service
(3) Have a relief pressure setting not higher than the maximum allowable working pressure (MAWP) of the component with lowest working pressure rating in the portion of the system being protected
(4) Be vented to the outside of the building, except that relief valves for compressed air systems having less than 84,950 L (3000 ft^3) at STP shall be permitted to be diffused locally by means that will not restrict the flow

(5) Have a vent discharge line that is not smaller than the size of the relief valve outlet
(6) Where two or more relief valves discharge into a common vent line, its internal cross-sectional area shall be not less than the aggregate cross-sectional area of all relief valve vent discharge lines served
(7) Shall not discharge into locations creating potential hazards
(8) Have the discharge terminal turned down and screened to prevent the entry of rain, snow, or vermin

(9) Shall be designed in accordance with ASME B31.3, *Pressure Process Piping*

Three requirements are new in this section of the 2005 edition:

1. The relief valve must relieve at or below the maximum working pressure.
2. The relief vent line must not be smaller than the relief valve outlet.
3. The relief valve must comply with ASME B31.3, *Pressure Process Piping* [6].

These are all primarily related to bulk gas installations, but they apply to all relief valves used with medical gases.

The location of the pressure relief valve in relation to shutoff valves is important. No shutoff valve should be positioned in a location that would allow pressure to build up in the supply portion of a system if the shutoff valve were closed.

Although the hazards vary, any release of gas(es) in an enclosed area could be hazardous to persons inside or around the immediate area. All gases, except medical air, should be vented to the outside and into a safe location, as required by 5.1.3.4.6.1(4) and (7).

Vent lines are intended to be short, to discharge outdoors, and to discharge where they will not be a hazard either to the building or to anyone who might be nearby. Specific hazards of concern are the gas (e.g., nitrous oxide could be hazardous if discharged into any occupied space or drawn into the building), aggravation of a fire hazard (e.g., oxygen could cause a severe fire if discharged anywhere near an ignition source), and the pressure (e.g., a sudden discharge of high pressure gas could be noisy and very frightening to passersby and might physically blow dirt, stones, or other items near the discharge toward people).

Relief valve vent lines are permitted to be tied together (e.g., to allow a single penetration of the wall). In this case, line size is determined by calculating the areas of each of the individual vent connections (e.g., a valve with a ½ in. NPT outlet will have an area of 0.196 in.^{2}) and summing them (e.g., four ½ in. valves will have an aggregate area of 0.785 in.^{2}, indicating a line size of 1 in.).

Relief valve lines (the actual piping) need to be labeled, as there has been at least one report of a person tying into a relief line under the assumption that it was the system pipeline, which is an easy mistake to make since the pipe material is the same and it connects to the same equipment.

5.1.3.4.6.2 When vented to outdoors, materials and construction for relief valve discharge lines shall be the same as required for positive pressure gas distribution *(see 5.1.10.1)*.

5.1.3.4.6.3 Central supply systems for positive pressure gases shall include one or more relief valves, all meeting the following requirements:

(1) Be located between each final line regulator and the source valve
(2) Have a relief setting that is 50 percent above the normal system operating pressure, as indicated in Table 5.1.11

5.1.3.4.6.4 When vented outside, relief valve vent lines shall be labeled in accordance with 5.1.11.1, in any manner that will distinguish them from the medical gas pipeline.

5.1.3.4.7 Multiple Pressures. Where a single central supply system supplies separate piped distribution networks operating at different pressures, each piped distribution network shall comply with the following:

(1) Medical air compressor systems: 5.1.3.5.9 (pressure regulators) and 5.1.9.2.4(7) (master alarm)
(2) All central supply systems: 5.1.3.4.5 (pressure regulators), 5.1.3.4.6 (relief valves), 5.1.4.4 (source valve), 5.1.9.2.4(7) (master alarm)

Paragraph 5.1.3.4.7 recognizes that some piped gas systems use the same gas sources or manifolds but distribute the gas at more than one pressure. Overall safety of a system operating at several different pressures should be equal to that of a system at a single operating pressure. A degree of redundancy in the components is thus required as described in 5.1.3.4.7(2).

EXHIBIT 5.3 Cylinder manifold source for a nitrous oxide piped gas system.

5.1.3.4.8 Local Signals.

5.1.3.4.8.1 The following systems shall have local signals located at the source equipment:

(1) Manifolds for gas cylinders without reserve supply *(See 5.1.3.4.10.)*
(2) Manifolds for gas cylinders with reserve supply
(3) Manifolds for cryogenic liquid containers *(See 5.1.3.4.12.)*
(4) Bulk cryogenic liquid systems *(See 5.1.3.4.13.)*
(5) In-building emergency reserves *(See 5.1.3.4.15.)*
(6) Instrument air headers *(See 5.1.3.4.9.)*

5.1.3.4.8.2 The local signals shall meet the following requirements:

(1) Provide visual indication only
(2) Be labeled for the service and condition being monitored
(3) If intended for outdoor installation, be installed per manufacturer's requirements

Local signal requirements arise from the simple need of a maintenance person to know what is going on with any given piece of source equipment. Note that a local signal is not an alarm in the sense of a local or master alarm. It is simply an indicator — which might be a gauge, a flag, a light, or some other possible manifestation — that allows a maintenance person to stand at the equipment and know what conditions are present (e.g., which header of cylinders is in service, if the reserve is full, if the main or secondary tank on the bulk system is in service). The elements to be displayed are typically those that are also monitored at the master alarm, but the local signal is visible at the equipment rather than remotely. See 3.3.101, *Local Signal.*

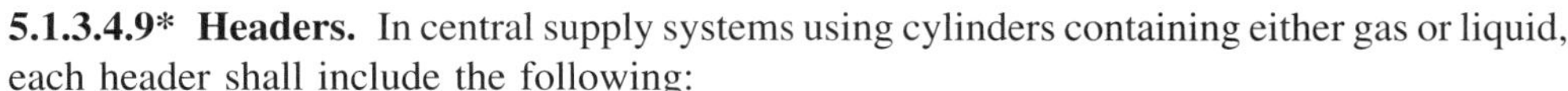

5.1.3.4.9* Headers. In central supply systems using cylinders containing either gas or liquid, each header shall include the following:

A.5.1.3.4.9 See Figure A.5.1.3.4.9(a) and Figure A.5.1.3.4.9(b). Connection to the gas outlet connection is illustrated. If the liquid outlet connection were used, an external vaporizer could be required.

The concept of the header is presented in 5.1.3.4.9 as an element of a source system that can be applied in various ways as appropriate to the configuration of source desired. There are two variants — a header with cylinders and a header with containers — that are identical in most requirements. (See Exhibit 5.3.)

An inline filter upstream of the main line regulator is required per 5.1.3.4.9(3). The requirement was added to prevent debris from entering the regulator itself, one of the more common reasons for regulator failure. The filter is typically inside the regulator and therefore might not be visible. It ordinarily requires no maintenance and therefore does not need to be accessible.

Figure A.5.1.3.4.9(a) and Figure A.5.1.3.4.9(b) are primarily subcomponents used in Figures A.5.1.3.4.10, A.5.1.3.4.12, and A.5.1.3.4.13. However, a header as illustrated in

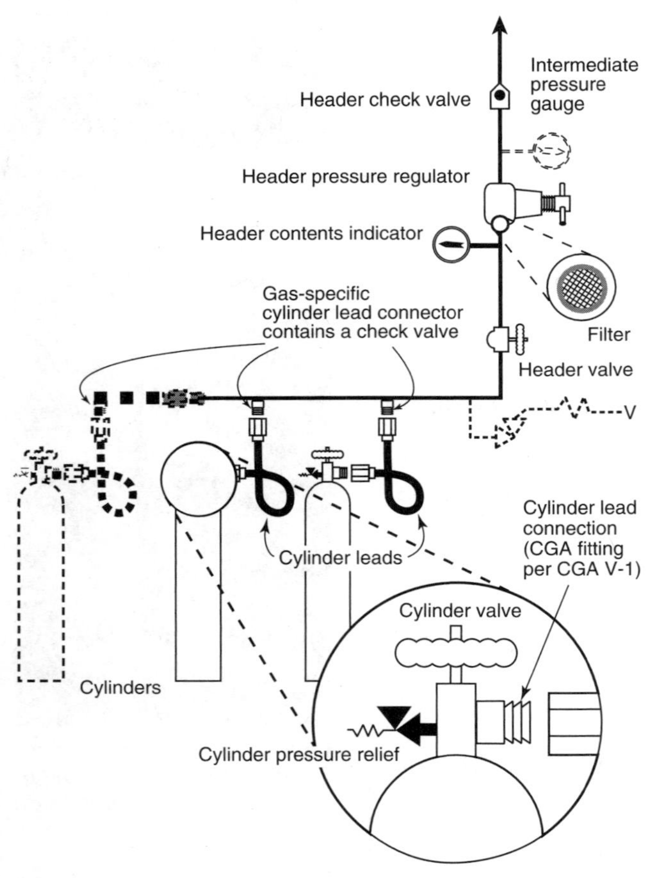

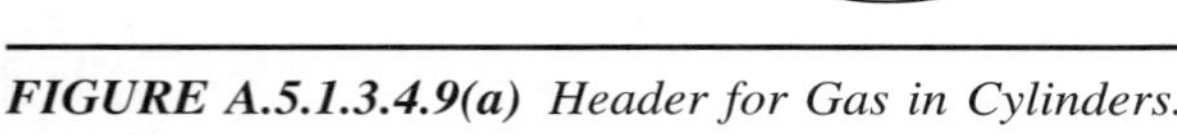

FIGURE A.5.1.3.4.9(a) Header for Gas in Cylinders.

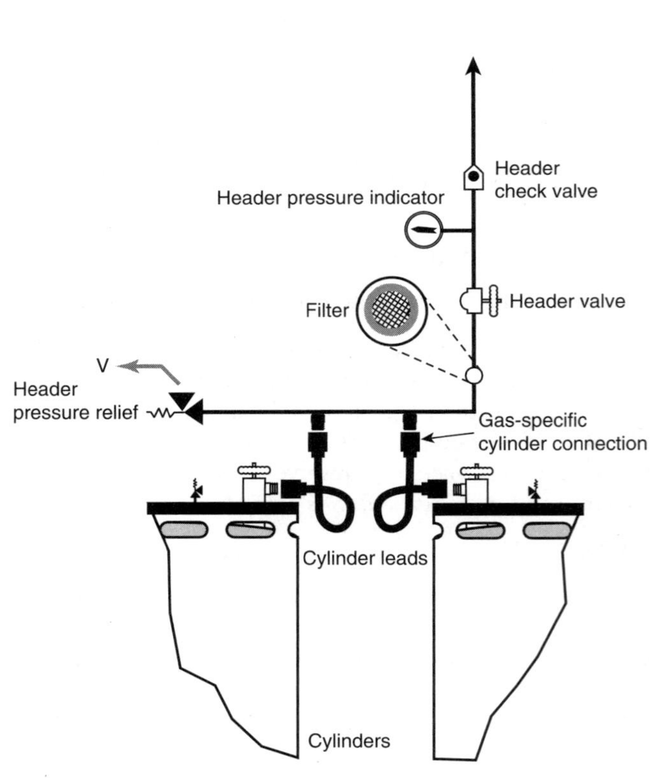

FIGURE A.5.1.3.4.9(b) Header for Cryogenic Gas in Containers.

Figure A.5.1.3.4.9(a) might also exist by itself in a few cases where "headers" are used. A careful reading of the text will demonstrate that a header similar to the one shown in Figure A.5.1.3.4.9(b) should never be used by itself, except perhaps in some temporary application under close and continuous supervision.

(1)* Cylinder connections in the number required for the header's application

A.5.1.3.4.9(1) The appropriate number of cylinders should be determined after consideration of delivery schedules, proximity of the facility to alternate supplies, and the emergency plan.

(2) A cylinder lead for each cylinder constructed of materials complying with 5.1.3.4.4 and provided with end fittings permanently attached to the cylinder lead complying with CGA V-1, *Standard for Compressed Gas Cylinder Valve Outlet and Inlet Connections* (ANSI B57.1)
(3) A filter of a material complying with 5.1.3.4.4 to prevent the intrusion of debris into the manifold controls
(4) A header shutoff valve downstream of the nearest cylinder connection, but upstream of the point at which the header connects to the central supply system
(5) A pressure indicator indicating the pressure of header contents
(6) A check valve to prevent backflow into the header and to permit service to the header

(7) If intended for gas cylinder service, a check valve at each connection for the cylinder lead in 5.1.3.4.9(2) to prevent loss of gas in the event of damage to the cylinder lead or operation of an individual cylinder relief valve
(8) If intended for gas cylinder service, a pressure regulator to reduce the cylinder pressure to an intermediate pressure to permit the proper operation of the primary and secondary headers
(9) If intended for service with cryogenic liquid containers, a pressure relief valve
(10) Vent valves, if fitted on a header, shall be vented outside of the building per 5.1.3.4.6.1(5) through 5.1.3.4.6.1(9) and 5.1.3.4.6.2.

5.1.3.4.10* Manifolds for Gas Cylinders without Reserve Supply.

A.5.1.3.4.10. See Figure A.5.1.3.4.10.

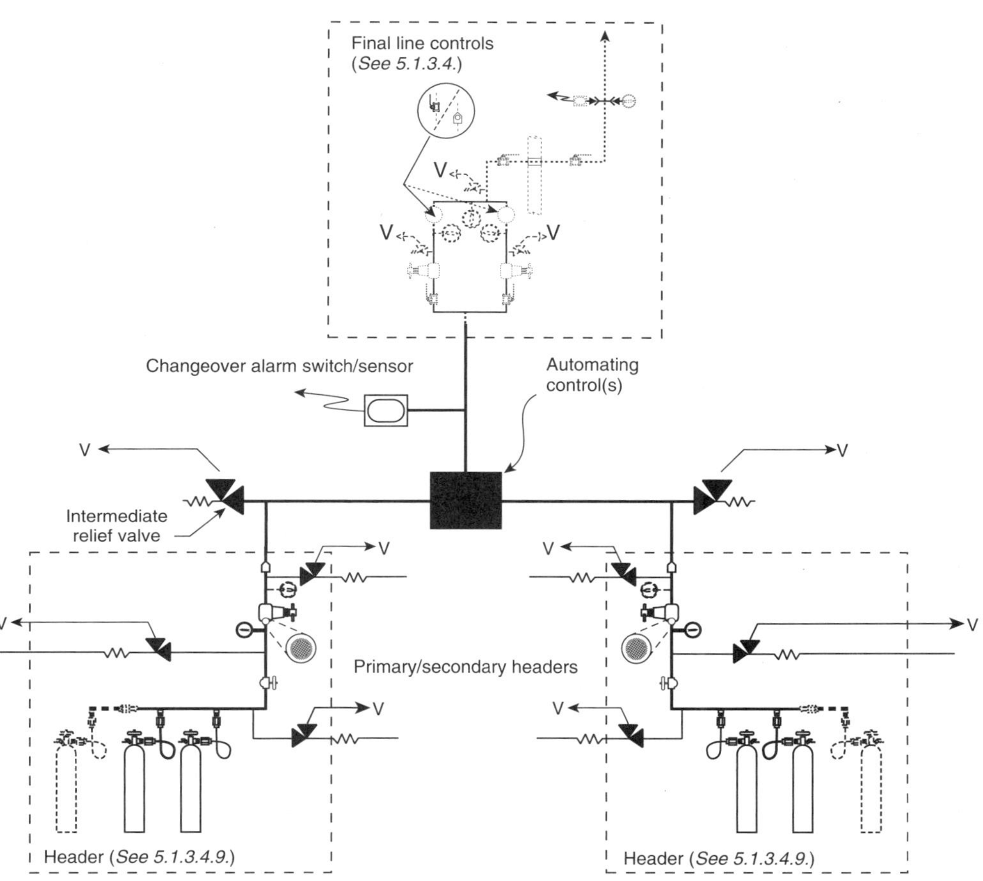

FIGURE A.5.1.3.4.10 Manifold for Gas Cylinders.

The use of a "black box" to illustrate the controls in Figure A.5.1.3.4.10 is a departure from earlier usage in this figure, reflecting the fact that many alternative control sequences are possible and could all equally meet the intent of this standard. It is not intended that the standard define how this mechanism must work, only that it define what the mechanism must achieve.

5.1.3.4.10.1 The manifolds in this category shall be located in accordance with 5.1.3.3.1 and the following:

(1) If located outdoors, be installed in an enclosure used only for this purpose and sited to comply with minimum distance requirements in Figure 5.1.3.4.10.1

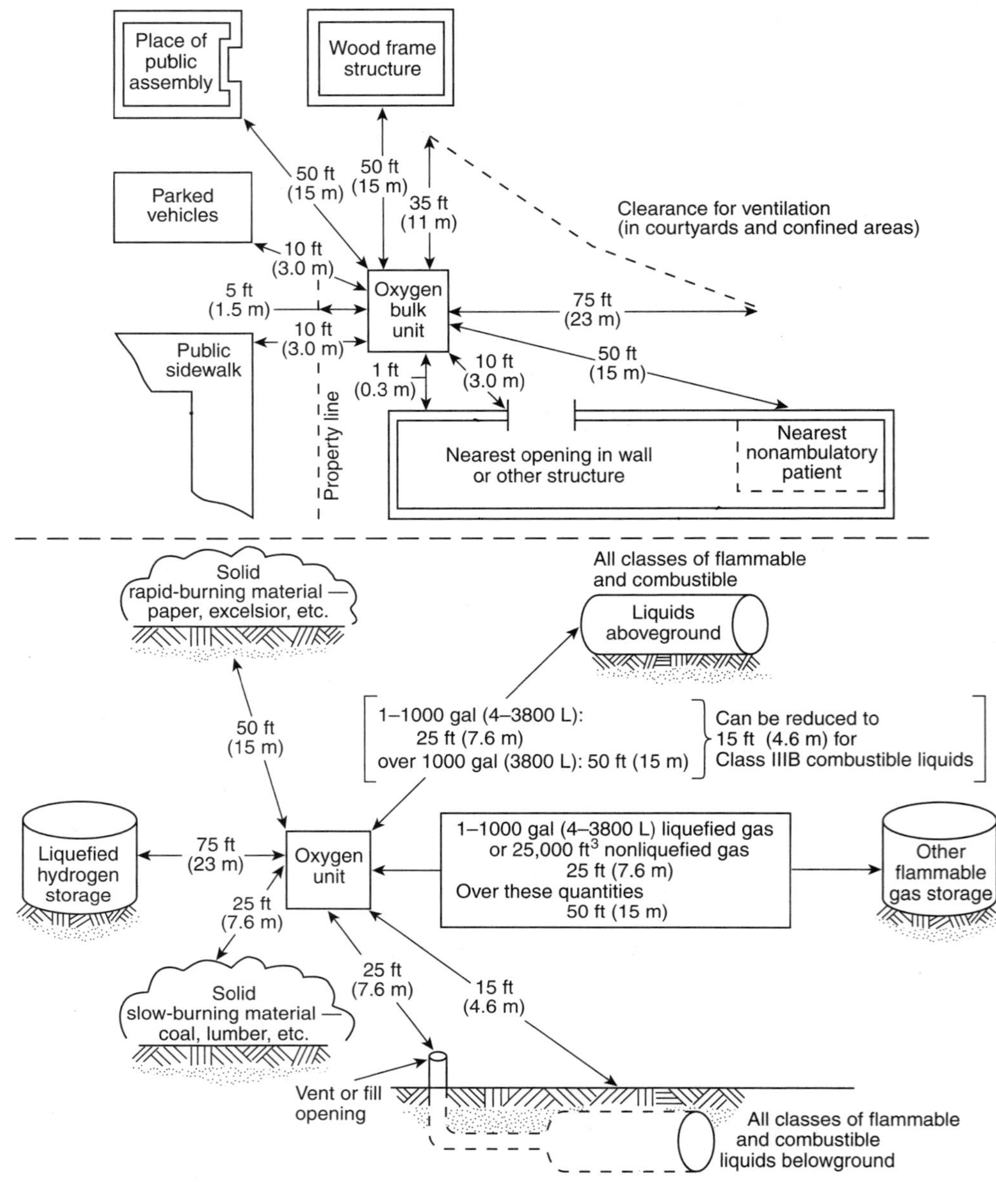

FIGURE 5.1.3.4.10.1 *Distance Between Bulk Oxygen Systems and Exposures.*

(2) If located indoors, be installed within a room used only for this purpose

5.1.3.4.10.2 The manifold locations in this category shall be constructed in accordance with 5.1.3.3.2.

5.1.3.4.10.3 The manifold locations in this category shall be ventilated in accordance with 5.1.3.3.3.

5.1.3.4.10.4 The manifolds in this category shall consist of the following:

(1) Two equal headers in accordance with 5.1.3.4.9, each with a sufficient number of gas cylinder connections for an average day's supply, but not fewer than two connections, and with the headers connected to the final line pressure regulator assembly in such a manner that either header may supply the system

(2) Vent valves, if fitted on a header, vented outside of the building per 5.1.3.4.6.1(5) through 5.1.3.4.6.1(9) and 5.1.3.4.6.2
(3) An intermediate relief valve(s), piped to the outside in accordance with 5.1.3.4.6.1(5) through 5.1.3.4.6.1(9), that protects the piping between the header pressure regulator and the line pressure regulator assembly, and protects the line pressure regulators from overpressure in the event of a header regulator failure

See Exhibit 5.4 for an example of a typical manifold.

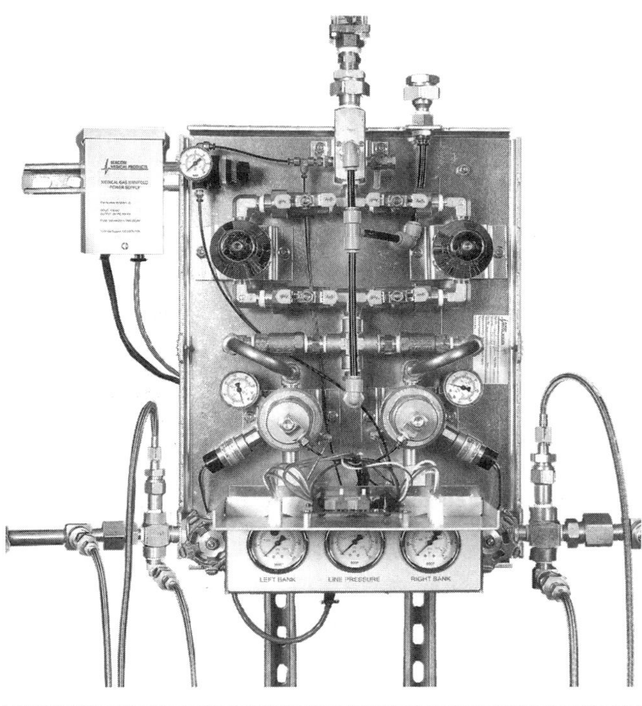

EXHIBIT 5.4 *Typical manifold for cylinder gases. (Courtesy of Beacon Medical)*

5.1.3.4.10.5 The manifolds in this category shall include an automatic means of alternating the two headers to accomplish the following in normal operation:

(1) One header is the primary and the other is the secondary, with either being capable of either role.
(2) When the primary header is supplying the system, the secondary header is prevented from supplying the system.
(3) When the primary header is depleted, the secondary header automatically begins to supply the system.

The twofold intent behind the construction requirements for all medical gas sources is most clearly visible in 5.1.3.4.10.5:

◀ **FAQ**
What is the purpose of the secondary source?

1. To provide redundancy so that one source of gas is always backed up by another
2. To provide cascade, so that the system automatically draws from that secondary source in the event of failure of the first and, where there is a reserve source, it automatically feeds the system in the event of failure of the primary and secondary sources

5.1.3.4.10.6 The manifolds in this category shall actuate a local signal and shall activate an indicator at all master alarm panels when or at a predetermined set point before the secondary header begins to supply the system, indicating changeover has occurred or is about to occur.

5.1.3.4.10.7 If manifolds are located out of doors, they shall be installed per the manufacturer's requirements.

All manifolds are not suitable for outdoor use. Many have electrical components that may present a hazard to persons nearby if they get wet. Some manifolds are not designed for the thermal stresses encountered outdoors.

5.1.3.4.11 Manifolds for Gas Cylinders with Reserve Supply. See Figure 5.1.3.4.10.1.

The manifold configuration illustrated in Figure 5.1.3.4.10.1 for gas cylinders with reserve supply is rarely, but occasionally, seen in the United States. A similar configuration is considered "standard" under the international ISO standard. This standard configuration shows a primary, a secondary, and a reserve bank of cylinders, providing a double redundancy.

5.1.3.4.11.1 The manifolds in this category shall be located in accordance with 5.1.3.3.1 and the following:

(1) If located outdoors, be installed in an enclosure used only for this purpose and sited to comply with minimum distance requirements in Figure 5.1.3.4.10.1
(2) If located indoors, be installed within a room used only for this purpose

5.1.3.4.11.2 The manifolds in this category shall have their primary and secondary headers located in the same enclosure.

5.1.3.4.11.3 The reserve header shall be permitted to be located in the same enclosure as the primary and secondary headers or in another enclosure compliant with 5.1.3.4.11.1.

This allowance in 5.1.3.4.11.3 of separating the headers could be problematic, because it might be assumed that there is no third header as required. When taking advantage of this allowance, it is wise to clearly label the manifolds and the reserve header to note that the "Reserve Header Is Located in Room _____" and "This Is the Reserve Header for Manifold in Room _____."

5.1.3.4.11.4 The manifold locations in this category shall be constructed in accordance with 5.1.3.3.2.

5.1.3.4.11.5 The manifold locations in this category shall be ventilated in accordance with 5.1.3.3.3.

5.1.3.4.11.6 The manifolds in this category shall consist of the following:

(1) Two equal headers per 5.1.3.4.9 each having sufficient number of gas cylinder connections for an average day's supply, but not fewer than two connections, and with the headers connected to the final line pressure regulator assembly in such a manner that either header may supply the system
(2) A reserve header per 5.1.3.4.9 having sufficient number of gas cylinder connections for an average day's supply, but not fewer than three connections, and connected downstream of the primary/secondary headers and upstream of the final line pressure regulators
(3) An intermediate relief valve(s), piped to the outside in accordance with 5.1.3.4.6.1(5) through 5.1.3.4.6.1(9), that protects the line pressure regulators from overpressure in the event of a header regulator failure

5.1.3.4.11.7 The manifolds in this category shall include an automatic means of controlling the three headers to accomplish the following during normal operation:

(1) One gas cylinder header is the primary and the other is the secondary, with either capable of either role.
(2) When the primary header is supplying the system, the secondary header is prevented from supplying the system.
(3) When the primary header is depleted, the secondary header automatically begins to serve the system.

The standard does not state here, but clearly indicates in 5.1.3.4.11.9, that there are two additional stages that are outside of "normal" operation. The reserve header is prevented from supplying the system when either the primary nor secondary header is supplying the system, and when neither the primary nor secondary can supply the system, the reserve must come on to do so.

5.1.3.4.11.8 The manifolds in this category shall include a manual or automatic means to place either header into the role as primary header and the other in the role of secondary header.

5.1.3.4.11.9 The manifolds in this category shall include a means to automatically activate the reserve header if for any reason the primary and secondary headers cannot supply the system.

5.1.3.4.11.10 The manifolds in this category shall actuate a local signal and shall activate an indicator at all master alarms under the following conditions:

(1) When or at a predetermined set point before the secondary header begins to supply the system, indicating changeover
(2) When or at a predetermined set point before the reserve header begins to supply the system, indicating reserve is in use
(3) When or at a predetermined set point before the reserve header contents fall to one day's supply, indicating reserve low

5.1.3.4.11.11 If manifolds in this category are located outdoors, they shall be installed per manufacturer's requirements.

5.1.3.4.12* Manifolds for Cryogenic Liquid Containers.

In the 2002 edition, a manifold with two or more containers on the primary and the secondary backed with a cylinder on the reserve was the only configuration explicitly permitted for manifolds for cryogenic liquid containers. The 2005 edition has allowance for two further variants of these manifolds:

1. A manifold with one container as primary, one container as secondary, and a cylinder reserve
2. A manifold with one or more containers as primary, cylinders on the secondary, and cylinders on the reserve

This type of manifold can be extremely cost effective and can save the operator a great deal of money. However, it has various limitations and requires its operator to supervise it carefully to achieve top performance. The standard has undertaken to provide a minimum suite of alarms to assist with this monitoring, and a three-step cascade to ensure the system will not run short of gas even if operated less than ideally. It is important to understand the underlying technology of these manifolds to ensure completely satisfactory operation.

A.5.1.3.4.12 See Figure A.5.1.3.4.12.

The use of a "black box" to illustrate the controls in Figure A.5.1.3.4.12 is a departure from earlier usage in this figure, reflecting the fact that many alternative control sequences are possible and could all equally meet the intent of this standard. It is not intended that the

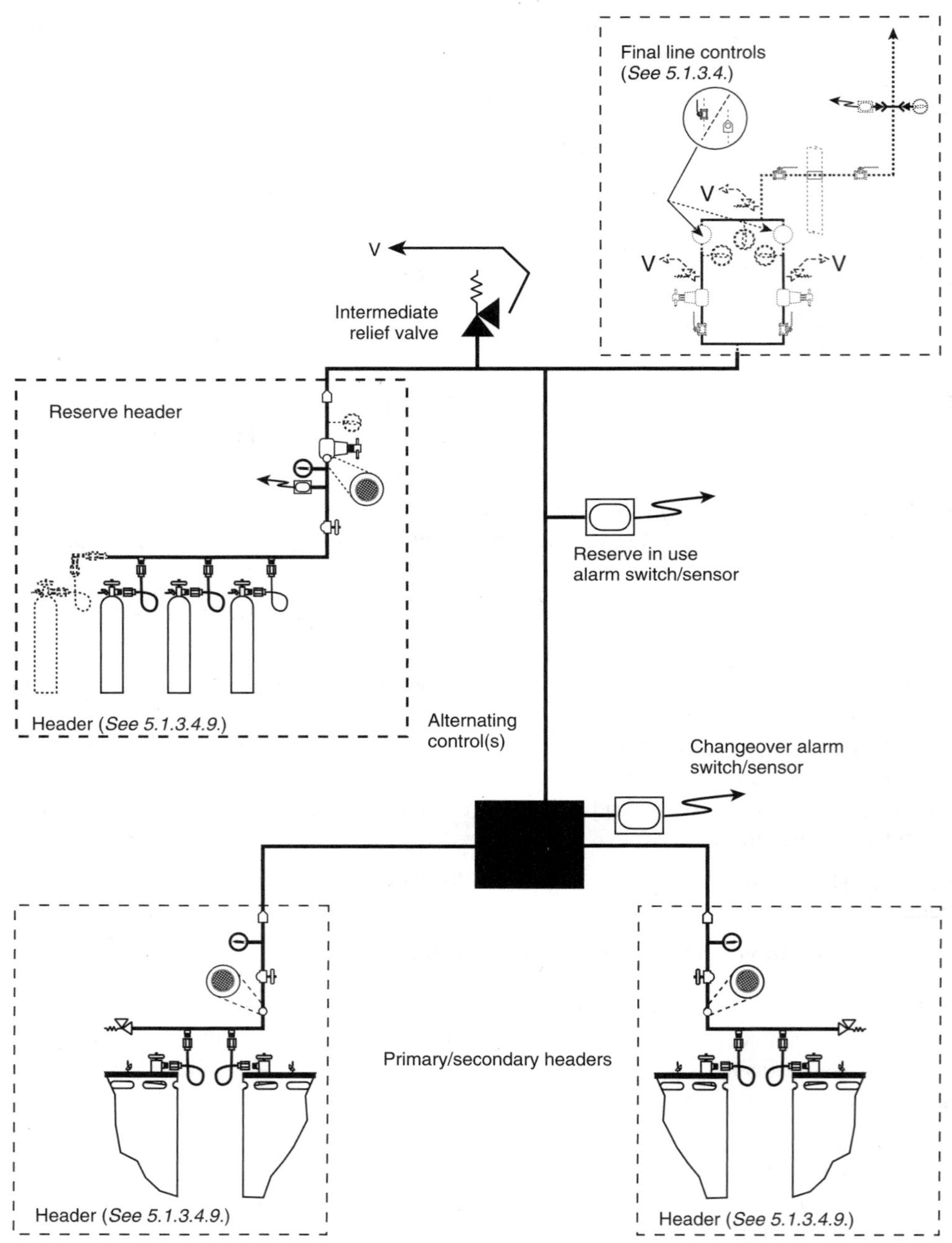

FIGURE A.5.1.3.4.12 *Typical Source of Supply for Cryogenic Gas in Containers.*

standard define how this mechanism must work, only that it define what the mechanism must achieve.

5.1.3.4.12.1 The manifolds in this category shall be located in accordance with 5.1.3.3.1 and the following:

(1) If located outdoors, be installed in an enclosure used only for this purpose and sited to comply with minimum distance requirements in Figure 5.1.3.4.10.1
(2) If located indoors, be installed within a room used only for this purpose

5.1.3.4.12.2 The manifolds in this category shall have their primary and secondary headers located in the same enclosure.

5.1.3.4.12.3 The reserve header shall be permitted to be located in the same enclosure as the primary and secondary headers or in another enclosure compliant with 5.1.3.4.12.1.

5.1.3.4.12.4 The manifolds in this category shall consist of the following:

(1) Two equal headers, per 5.1.3.4.9, each having sufficient number of liquid container connections for an average day's supply, and with the headers connected to the final line pressure regulator assembly in such a manner that either header may supply the system

(2) A reserve header, per 5.1.3.4.9, having sufficient number of gas cylinder connections for an average day's supply, but not fewer than three connections, and connected downstream of the primary/secondary headers and upstream of the final line pressure regulators

The reserve header required by 5.1.3.4.12.4(2) consists of high-pressure gas cylinders, as opposed to low-pressure cryogenic containers. Containers are not used as reserve supplies in these types of systems because they can lose 3 percent of their contents per day in boil-off and might not contain enough, or any, gas when needed (i.e., when the main or primary supply is depleted).

◀ **FAQ**
Why can't the cryogenic container be used as the reserve supply?

(3) A pressure relief installed downstream of the connection of the reserve header and upstream of the final line pressure regulating assembly and set at 50 percent above the nominal inlet pressure

5.1.3.4.12.5 The manifolds in this category shall include an automatic means of controlling the three headers to accomplish the following during normal operation:

(1) If provided with two liquid container headers, one cryogenic liquid header is the primary and the other is the secondary, with either being capable of either role.
(2) If provided with one liquid container header and one gas cylinder header (a hybrid arrangement), the liquid header is the primary and the gas cylinder header is the secondary.
(3) When the primary header is supplying the system, the secondary header is prevented from supplying the system.
(4) When the primary header is depleted, the secondary header automatically begins to supply the system.

5.1.3.4.12.6 The manifolds in this category shall be equipped with a means to conserve the gas produced by evaporation of the cryogenic liquid in the secondary header (when so provided). This mechanism shall discharge the conserved gas into the system upstream of the final line regulator assembly.

The means to conserve the gas as required by 5.1.3.4.12.6 is commonly termed an *economizer.*

5.1.3.4.12.7 The manifolds in this category shall include a manual or automatic means to place either header into the role as primary header and the other in the role of secondary header, except where a liquid/gas hybrid manifold is employed.

5.1.3.4.12.8 The manifolds in this category shall include a means to automatically activate the reserve header if for any reason the primary and secondary headers cannot supply the system.

5.1.3.4.12.9 The manifolds in this category shall actuate a local signal and shall activate an indicator at all master alarms under the following conditions:

(1) When or at a predetermined set point before the secondary header begins to supply the system, indicating changeover

(2) Where a hybrid arrangement is employed, when or at a predetermined set point before the secondary (cylinder) header contents fall to one day's average supply, indicating secondary low
(3) When or at a predetermined set point before the reserve header begins to supply the system, indicating reserve is in use
(4) When or at a predetermined set point before the reserve header contents fall to one day's average supply, indicating reserve low

5.1.3.4.12.10 A variant on the cryogenic liquid container manifold shall be permitted having three headers of cylinders. Such a variant shall comply with all requirements of 5.1.3.4.12, except:

(1) The minimum number of cylinder connections required for each header under 5.1.3.4.12.4(1) shall be two.
(2) Paragraph 5.1.3.4.12.6 shall not apply.

5.1.3.4.13* Bulk Cryogenic Liquid Systems.

The requirements for bulk gas systems were entirely revised for the 2005 edition. Numerous new requirements are included, and many others were clarified and made more complete. Above all, the requirements are now far more comprehensive. The supplier of bulk gas is a crucial partner in complying with these requirements.

When suppliers are changed, it is vital that the facility reexamine the sizing of bulk cryogenic liquid sources. The greatest issue with planning a bulk gas source is the time required to get a tanker to the site to refill the vessel(s) once the low-level alarm is triggered. In this planning, one should consider not only the time required under normal circumstances but also the time required when predictable emergencies arise. As an example, where a facility is located in an active seismic zone or in the likely path of violent storms, it might be necessary to consider how much oxygen the facility will use during a period when no tanker can be dispatched from the usual gas production facility and one must come from a more distant facility over roads compromised by the disaster. This planning will influence and be influenced by the facility's disaster plan, which may in fact not yet be drafted when design and construction is underway. See also Chapter 12 on Health Care Emergency Management.

A.5.1.3.4.13 For bulk oxygen systems, see NFPA 50, *Standard for Bulk Oxygen Systems at Consumer Sites*. See Figure A.5.1.3.4.13. Two possible choices of reserves are illustrated. Both are not required.

5.1.3.4.13.1 Bulk cryogenic liquid systems shall have the following protections:

(1) Oxygen systems compliant with NFPA 50, *Standard for Bulk Oxygen Systems at Consumer Sites*; NFPA 55, *Standard for the Storage, Use, and Handling of Compressed Gases and Cryogenic Fluids in Portable and Stationary Containers, Cylinders, and Tanks*; or Chapter 9, Bulk Oxygen Systems, of NFPA 50, 1996 edition
(2) Location in an enclosure constructed per 5.1.3.3.2(1) through 5.1.3.3.2(3) and 5.1.3.3.2(5), 5.1.3.3.2(8), and 5.1.3.3.2(9)
(3) Location in an enclosure ventilated per 5.1.3.3.3.3

(4) Location in compliance with CGA M-1, *Guide for Medical Gas Installations at Consumer Sites*

CGA M-1, *Guide for Medical Gas Installations at Consumer Sites,* is a new publication and appears for the first time in this edition [7]. Compressed Gas Association publications that are referenced in the standard are listed in 2.3.7.

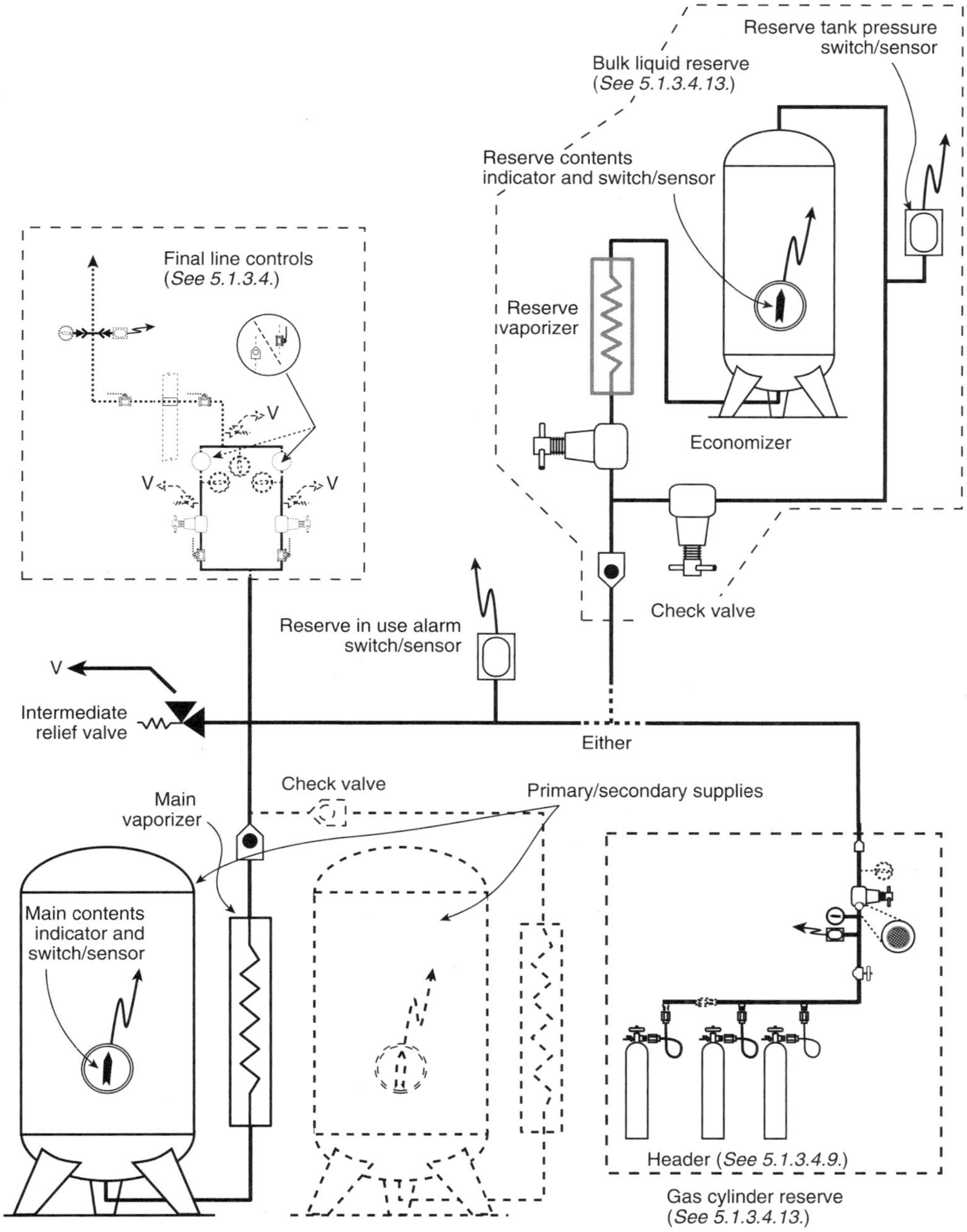

FIGURE A.5.1.3.4.13 *Typical Source of Supply for Cryogenic Gas in Bulk.*

(5) Design such that the items noted in 5.1.3.4.13.2 and items located in trailer unloading area are readily visible to delivery personal during filling operations
(6) Protection against overpressurization of the pressure vessel during filling operations
(7) Installation per 5.1.10.1 through 5.1.10.5.7
(8) Installation by personnel qualified to meet CGA M-1, *Guide for Medical Gas Installations at Consumer Sites* 
(9) Installation in compliance with Food and Drug Administration (FDA) Current Good Manufacturing Practices as found in 21 CFR 210 and 21 CFR 211 

5.1.3.4.13.2 The following components of the bulk system shall be readily accessible to delivery personnel:

(1) Fill connection
(2) Top and bottom fill valves
(3) Hose purge valve
(4) Vent valve
(5) Full try/cock
(6) Liquid level gauge
(7) Tank pressure gauge

5.1.3.4.13.3 Bulk cryogenic liquid system sites shall include the following:

(1) A poured concrete pad, designed for the weight, dynamic loads, wind loads, and surface loading, and complying with local seismic requirements
(2) Permanent anchors holding the components to the pad in accordance with the design requirements
(3) A complete enclosure as per 5.1.3.3.2(3)
(4) Concrete or crushed stone completely filling the enclosed space.

(5) A vehicle pad for the delivery vehicle that is compliant with NFPA 50, *Standard for Bulk Oxygen Systems at Consumer Sites*, and readily accessible for refilling supply as stated in CGA M-1, *Guide for Medical Gas Installations at Consumer Sites*
(6) Allowance for at least 1 m (3 ft) of clearance around storage container, vaporizer(s), and pressure-regulating manifold for system maintenance and operation

5.1.3.4.13.4 The equipment pad and vehicle pad shall:

(1) Be sloped to provide that all drainage run away from any building, parked vehicles, or combustible materials.
(2) Have no drain located within the pad or closer than 2450 mm (8 ft) from the edge of the pad.

5.1.3.4.13.5 Bulk cryogenic liquid sources shall consist of the following:

(1) One or more main supply vessel(s), whose capacity shall be determined after consideration of the customer usage requirements, delivery schedules, proximity of the facility to alternate supplies, and the emergency plan
(2) A contents gauge on each of the main vessel(s)
(3) A reserve supply sized for greater than an average day's supply, with the appropriate size of vessel or number of cylinders being determined after consideration of delivery schedules, proximity of the facility to alternate supplies, and the facility's emergency plan
(4) At least two main vessel relief valves and rupture discs installed downstream of a three-way (three-port) valve
(5) A check valve located in the primary supply piping upstream of the intersection with a secondary supply or reserve supply

5.1.3.4.13.6 Bulk cryogenic liquid sources shall include a reserve supply, as follows:

(1) A second cryogenic liquid vessel or a cylinder header per 5.1.3.4.9 having sufficient gas cylinder connections for an average day's supply, but not fewer than three

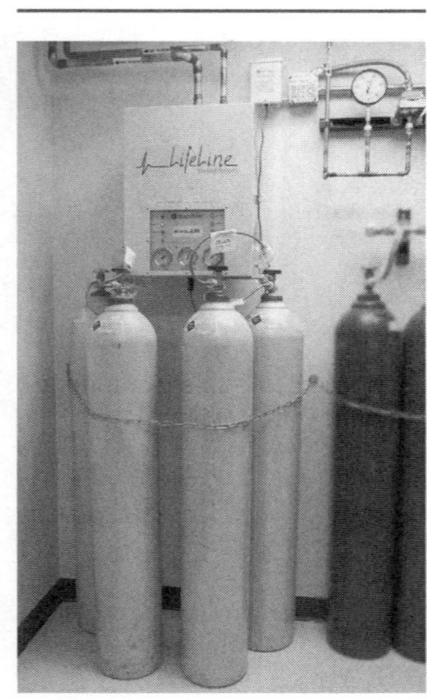

***Exhibit 5.5** Additional oxygen reserve feeding an ICU.*

For bulk cryogenic liquid sources, NFPA 99 requires a reserve in the form of another cryogenic liquid vessel or gas cylinders. These reserves are to be connected before the final line controls. The standard does not require another reserve beyond the final line controls.

Exhibit 5.5 shows an additional reserve feeding an ICU, which is an extra measure of redundancy. This system will be called into service if the primary system, secondary system, and reserve all fail.

(2) An actuating switch/sensor monitoring internal pressure of the reserve cryogenic liquid vessel (if provided)
(3) A contents gauge monitoring liquid level in the reserve cryogenic liquid vessel (if provided)
(4) A check valve to prevent backflow into the reserve system
(5) A pressure switch monitoring the pressure in the cylinder header (if provided)

5.1.3.4.13.7 Bulk cryogenic liquid sources shall include a fill circuit consisting of the following components:

(1) A nonremovable product-specific fill connection in compliance with CGA V-6, *Standard Cryogenic Liquid Transfer Connection*
(2) A means to cap and secure the fill connection inlet
(3) A minimum 100 mesh strainer of Monel® or brass construction
(4) A check valve to prevent product backflow from the fill inlet
(5) A fill hose purge valve
(6) Supports that hold the fill piping off the ground
(7) A secure connection between the bulk tank and the fill piping
(8) Supports as necessary to hold the fill line in position during all operations associated with the filling procedure

5.1.3.4.13.8 Bulk cryogenic liquid sources shall include automatic means to provide the following functions:

(1) When the main supply is supplying the system, the reserve supply shall be prevented from supplying the system until the main supply is reduced to a level at or below the reserve activation pressure.
(2) When the main supply cannot supply the system, the reserve supply shall automatically begin to supply the system.
(3) Where there is more than one main supply vessel, the system shall operate as described in 5.1.3.4.12 for primary, secondary, and reserve operation.
(4) Where there are two or more cryogenic vessels, they shall be permitted to alternate (e.g., on a timed basis) in the roles of primary, secondary, and reserve, providing an operating cascade (primary–secondary–reserve) as required in 5.1.3.4.12.4 is maintained at all times.
(5) Where a cryogenic vessel is used as the reserve, the reserve vessel shall include a means to conserve the gas produced by evaporation of the cryogenic liquid in the reserve vessel and to discharge the gas into the line upstream of the final line regulator assembly as required by 5.1.3.4.12.6.

A cryogenic system is allowed as a reserve supply only if it is connected to the master alarm panel as indicated in 5.1.3.4.13.9. Cryogenic systems continually boil off gas, so it is critical that their status be monitored. Although evaporating gas can be channeled into the piping system, its loss means that much less gas will remain in the container for use when the primary supply is depleted.

5.1.3.4.13.9 The bulk systems shall actuate a local signal and an indicator at all master alarms under the following conditions:

(1) When or at a predetermined set point before the main supply reaches an average day's supply, indicating low contents
(2) When or at a predetermined set point before the reserve supply begins to supply the system, indicating reserve is in use
(3) When or at a predetermined set point before the reserve supply contents fall to one day's average supply, indicating reserve low

(4) If the reserve is a cryogenic vessel, when or at a predetermined set point before the reserve internal pressure falls too low for the reserve to operate properly, indicating reserve failure
(5) Where there is more than one main supply vessel, when or at a predetermined set point before the secondary vessel begins to supply the system, indicating changeover

5.1.3.4.13.10 Where vaporizers are required to convert cryogenic liquid to the gaseous state, the vaporizer units shall conform to the following:

(1) Be permitted to operate by either ambient heat transfer or external thermal source (e.g., electric heater, hot water, steam)
(2) Be designed to provide adequate capacity for the customer's peak and average flowrates under local conditions, seasonal conditions for weather and humidity, and structures that obstruct air circulation flow and sunlight
(3) Have piping and manual/automatic valving configured in such a manner that operating vaporizer(s) or sections of the vaporizer can be switched to nonoperating vaporizer or section of the vaporizer to de-ice through a valving configuration that assures continuous flow to the facility through either or both vaporizers and/or sections of the vaporizer if valving switchover partially hangs up or fails

5.1.3.4.13.11 Where a vaporizer requires an external thermal source, the flow from the source of supply shall be unaffected by the loss of the external thermal source through either of the following:

(1) Reserve ambient heat transfer vaporizers of sufficient capacity for at least one day's average supply and piped so as to be unaffected by flow stoppage through the main vaporizer
(2) A reserve noncryogenic source capable of providing at least one day's average supply

5.1.3.4.14* Emergency Oxygen Supply Connection (EOSC). EOSCs shall be installed to permit connection of a temporary auxiliary source of supply for emergency or maintenance situations under the following conditions:

(1) Where the bulk cryogenic liquid central supply system is outside of and remote from the building that the oxygen supply serves
(2) Where there is not in the building a connected oxygen reserve sufficient for an average day's supply *(See 5.1.3.4.15 for requirements for such reserves.)*
(3) Where multiple freestanding buildings are served from a single oxygen source such that damage to the interconnecting oxygen line could result in one or more buildings losing oxygen supply. In this situation, each building shall be provided with a separate emergency connection.

A.5.1.3.4.14 See Figure A.5.1.3.4.14.

If the relief valve on the emergency oxygen connection is moved to downstream from the check valve in the emergency oxygen line, connect it to the system with a demand check fitting.

FAQ ▶ What is the purpose of the emergency oxygen supply connection?

The purpose of the emergency oxygen supply connection (EOSC) as required by 5.1.3.4.14 is to allow the facility to be supplied from a temporary source of oxygen, for instance, while repairs to or the replacement of an outdoor oxygen supply source is completed. The connection should be sufficiently remote from the supply source to allow this temporary connection without impeding the work that is being done on the bulk system. It would be inappropriate, therefore, to locate the connection within the enclosure around the source supply or in any area where access to the supply source would be compromised while using the connection.

The EOSC should be located in the building served and in an area that will remain accessible in any weather. It would be unsuitable, for example, to require a temporary source vehicle to have to traverse a lawn or snow drifts to supply the facility in an emergency.

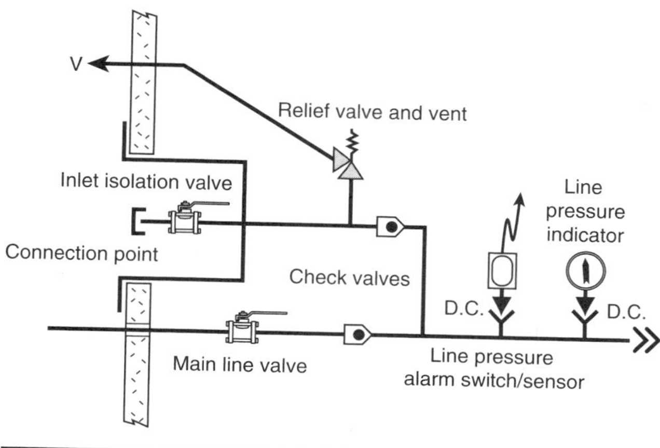

FIGURE A.5.1.3.4.14 *Emergency Oxygen Supply Connection.*

5.1.3.4.14.1 EOSCs shall be located as follows:

(1) On the exterior of the building being served in a location accessible by emergency supply vehicles at all times in all weather conditions
(2) Connected to the main supply line immediately downstream of the main shutoff valve

5.1.3.4.14.2 EOSCs shall consist of the following:

(1) Physical protection to prevent unauthorized tampering
(2) A female DN (NPS) inlet for connection of the emergency oxygen source that is sized for 100 percent of the system demand at the emergency source gas pressure
(3) A manual shutoff valve to isolate the EOSC when not in use

Paragraph 5.1.3.4.14.2 exists to eliminate an issue unique to multibuilding campuses served from a single source. If there is a danger to the main line from the source to the first building, is there not an equal danger to the line from the first to the second building, and from the second to the third and so on? (See Exhibit 5.6.)

(4) Two check valves, one downstream of the EOSC and one downstream of the main line shutoff valve, with both upstream from the tee connection for the two pipelines
(5) A relief valve sized to protect the downstream piping system and related equipment from exposure to pressures in excess of 50 percent higher than normal line pressure

Placing the relief valve downstream instead of upstream of the check valve on the emergency fill line as required by 5.1.3.4.14.2(5) better protects the patient if someone overpressurizes the emergency low-pressure oxygen connection. If the relief valve is placed upstream and someone realizes the error of overpressuring the patient side of the check valve, this pressure would be greater than the pressure between the emergency connection at the box and the check valve located on the emergency low-pressure oxygen connection. The relief valve would no longer protect the patient.

(6) Any valves necessary to allow connection of an emergency supply of oxygen and isolation of the piping to the normal source of supply

5.1.3.4.15 In-Building Emergency Reserves.

NFPA 99 recognizes and permits a rare but useful variation on the basic theme of providing supply for gases whose source is located remotely and is therefore subject to damage or inadvertent disconnection (i.e., digging up the pipe with a backhoe during construction). Although the typical method for covering this event is the emergency oxygen supply connec-

EXHIBIT 5.6 *An emergency oxygen supply inlet used in case of failure of the normal source.*

tion described in 5.1.3.4.14, it was agreed that another and generally superior method (albeit typically more expensive) would be a permanent small source inside the building. This concept as seen in the field and under these provisions might be implemented either as an emergency source for an entire building or as a specific local source for specific areas of very high criticality such as neonatal intensive care units (NICUs), intensive care units (ICUs), and so on.

5.1.3.4.15.1 In-building emergency reserves shall not be used as substitutes for the bulk gas reserves that are required in 5.1.3.4.13.4.

5.1.3.4.15.2 If a reserve is provided inside the building as a substitute for the EOSC, it shall be located in accordance with 5.1.3.3 as follows:

(1) In a room or enclosure constructed per 5.1.3.3.2
(2) In a room or enclosure ventilated per 5.1.3.3.3

5.1.3.4.15.3 In-building emergency reserves shall consist of either of the following:

(1) A gas cylinder header per 5.1.3.4.9 with sufficient cylinder connections to provide for at least an average day's supply
(2) A manifold for gas cylinders complying with 5.1.3.4.10

5.1.3.4.15.4 In-building emergency reserves shall include a check valve in the main line placed on the distribution system side of the ordinary source's main line valve to prevent flow of gas from the emergency reserve to the ordinary source.

5.1.3.4.15.5 In-building emergency reserves shall actuate a local signal and an alarm at all master alarms when or just before it begins to serve the system.

5.1.3.5* Level 1 Medical Air Supply Systems.

Paragraph 5.1.3.5 applies to medical air systems used to distribute medical air throughout a facility and intended or expected to provide air for direct patient purposes. Special, limited systems would not necessarily fall within this intent. However, any such limited application system should be totally separate and noninterconnectable with the medical air system. (See also provisions for instrument air supply systems in 5.1.3.8.) Design criteria for equipment components of the medical air compressor system are addressed as they relate to the safety of the system.

The number of individual devices and the accompanying risk of a single device failing and rendering the entire medical air supply system unusable has been a concern. This problem has been addressed through provisions for duplexing or bypassing each important element (device) in the system. Should any device fail, the system could be kept in operation while that element is serviced or replaced. The decision to duplex or use a bypass arrangement should be based on the degree of importance of the device to the effective operation of the system. For example, if the receiver were removed from the system, the compressor might short-cycle, causing some compressors to be damaged.

The defining characteristics of medical air appear here [5.1.3.5.1(1) through 5.1.3.5.1(5)]. In this, NFPA is in line with other major international standards in requiring a medical air system to produce air to a pharmacopoeia grade, in this case Medical Air, USP.

Medical air is permitted to be used for any purpose related to human respiration (see 5.1.3.5.2). Although the language is perhaps somewhat obscure, the standard intends that medical air be allowed, for instance, to be used for supplied air respirators for the medical staff. This allowance is sensible and a relief to facilities where the staff uses such devices during patient care in such settings as decontamination, infectious disease isolation, care of immunosuppressed patients, or high-risk operating rooms. Medical air is therefore now usable for an occupational safety application and, as such, overlaps with the requirements promulgated by the Occupational Safety and Health Administration (OSHA) in 29 CFR

1910.134(i)(1)(ii) [8], which are in some ways more specific and stringent than NFPA 99 requirements for medical air.

The net effect of the NFPA requirements and the OSHA requirements is that medical air must be viewed as the oxygen would be viewed — a gas whose purity must be assured.

Fortunately, for most of the United States, most of the time [per the Environmental Protection Agency (EPA)], ambient air meets or exceeds the requirements set forth by USP and OSHA, and a medical air system provided in accordance with this standard with an intake, dryers, and filters will be able to provide air of this quality without additional apparatus. However, it is important that this quality not be taken for granted. Especially where the air is to be used for occupational support, a quality maintenance regimen acceptable to OSHA should be implemented. As a minimum, appropriate monitoring and periodic sampling should be undertaken. Where the quality of local ambient air is suspect, known, or suspected to vary outside USP limits or otherwise not be perfectly reliable, additional purifiers might be advised.

A.5.1.3.5 Air supplied from on-site compressor and associated air treatment systems (as opposed to medical air USP supplied in cylinders) that complies with the specified limits is considered medical air. Hydrocarbon carryover from the compressor into the pipeline distribution system could be detrimental to the safety of the end user and to the integrity of the piping system. Mixing of air and oxygen is a common clinical practice, and the hazards of fire are increased if the air is contaminated. Compliance with these limits is thus considered important to fire and patient safety. The quality of local ambient air should be determined prior to its selection for compressors and air treatment equipment. See Figure A.5.1.3.5.

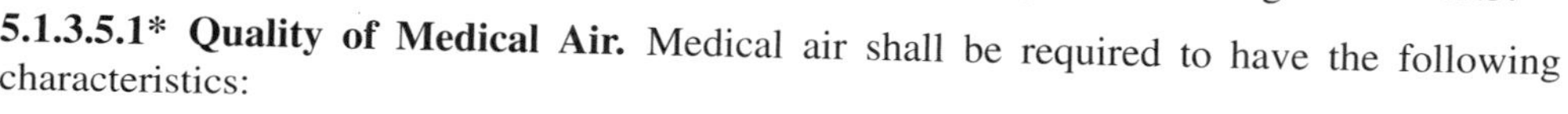

5.1.3.5.1* Quality of Medical Air. Medical air shall be required to have the following characteristics:

(1) Be supplied from cylinders, bulk containers, medical air compressor sources, or be reconstituted from oxygen USP and oil-free, dry Nitrogen NF
(2) Meet the requirements of medical air USP
(3) Have no detectable liquid hydrocarbons
(4) Have less than 25 ppm gaseous hydrocarbons
(5) Have equal to or less than 5 mg/m^3 of permanent particulates sized 1 micron or larger in the air at normal atmospheric pressure

A.5.1.3.5.1 Supply systems for medical air using compressors draw air of the best available quality from a source of clean local ambient air; add no contaminants in the form of particulate matter, odor, or other gases; dry, filter, regulate, and supply that air only via the medical air piping distribution system for use exclusively in the application of human respiration.

The utilization of an air treatment system is the joint responsibility of the system designer, hospital clinical and engineering staffs, and the authority having jurisdiction. Different types of compressors have characteristics that affect the selection of the type of air treatment system. Some air treatment systems impose an additional load upon the compressors that has to be accounted for in the sizing of the system (usable capacity). The compressor duty cycle has to be chosen in accordance with the manufacturer's recommendation.

The type of air compressor and air condition at the intake will govern the type of filter provided for the air compressor supply system. All filters should be examined quarterly for the presence of liquids or excessive particulates and replaced according to the manufacturer's instructions.

One procedure for reaching a decision on the quality of the medical air is the following:

(1) Test at the intake and at the sample connection valve.
(2) If the two purities agree within the limits of accuracy of the test, the compressor system can be accepted.
(3) If the air is found to exceed the values for medical compressed air as defined in 5.1.3.5.1, the facility can elect to install purification apparatus for the contaminants in question.

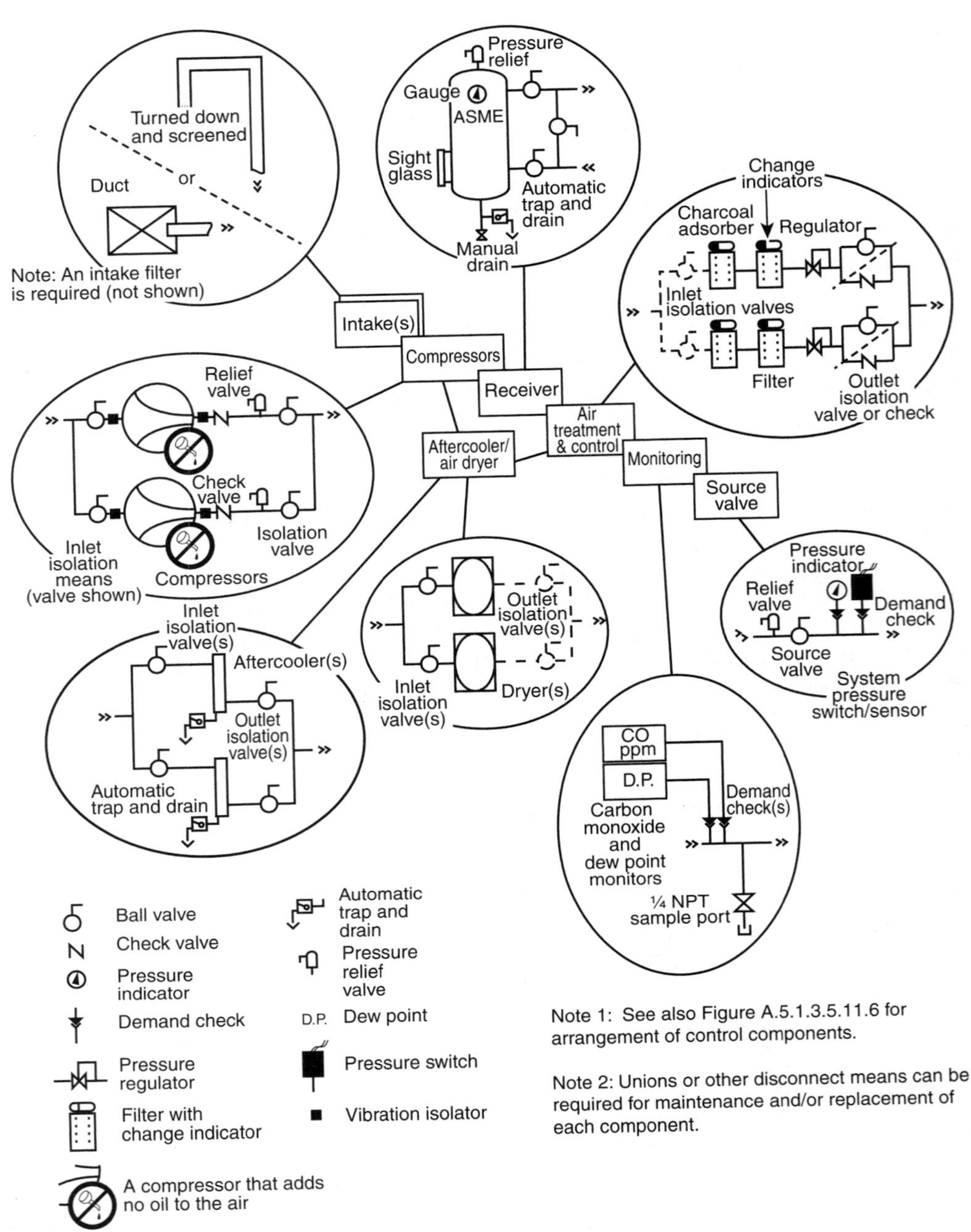

FIGURE A.5.1.3.5 Elements of a Typical Duplex Medical Air Compressor Source System (Level 1 Gas Systems).

5.1.3.5.2* Medical air sources shall be connected to the medical air distribution system only and shall be used only for air in the application of human respiration, and calibration of medical devices for respiratory application.

FAQ ▶
Can medical air be used for non-patient applications?

The choice of words in 5.1.3.5.2 is intentional and specific. Although medical air is now permitted for use by medical staff through supplied air respirators, the medical air compressor is not to be used for other air-driven patient therapy devices such as air cushion mattresses, for cleaning or blowing down scopes either before or after use of sterilizers, for laboratory or pneumatic temperature controllers, or for other nonpatient functions. The use of the medical air compressor to power pneumatically driven arms, booms, pendants, or columns is also inappropriate (for these applications, see 5.1.3.8, *Instrument Air Supply Systems*). See Exhibit 5.7 through Exhibit 5.9.

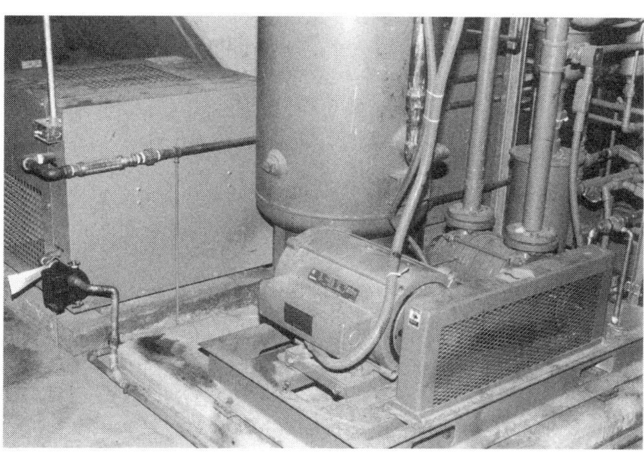

EXHIBIT 5.7 *A medical compressed air source. Compressors are in the foreground of this unit, the receiver is in the middle, and dryers are in the background.*

EXHIBIT 5.8 *Twin-tower desiccant dryer and refrigerated noncycling dryer installed near medical air compressor. The desiccant unit is the facility's primary dryer, with the refrigerated unit used when the desiccant is being serviced.*

EXHIBIT 5.9 *Main shutoff valves and filters for a medical compressed air system.*

A.5.1.3.5.2 It is the intent that the medical air piping distribution system support only the intended need for breathable air for such items as intermittent positive pressure breathing (IPPB) and long-term respiratory assistance needs, anesthesia machines, and so forth. The system is not intended to be used to provide engineering, maintenance, and equipment needs for general hospital support use. It is the intent that the life safety nature of the medical air be protected by a system dedicated solely for its specific use.

As a compressed air supply source, a medical air compressor should not be used to supply air for other purposes because such use could increase service interruptions, reduce service life, and introduce additional opportunities for contamination.

5.1.3.5.3* Medical Air Compressor Sources.

A.5.1.3.5.3 See Figure A.5.1.3.5.

5.1.3.5.3.1 Medical air compressor systems shall be located per 5.1.3.3 as follows:

(1) Indoors in a dedicated mechanical equipment area, adequately ventilated and with any required utilities (e.g., electricity, drains, lighting, etc.)
(2) In a room constructed per 5.1.3.3.2
(3) In a room ventilated per 5.1.3.3.3.2
(4) For air-cooled equipment, in a room designed to maintain the ambient temperature range as recommended by the manufacturer

For some medical air treatment systems, the temperature of the inlet air is critical. Recommended ambient temperatures for equipment need to consider the compressors, aftercooling capability, maximum acceptable temperature at the dryer/air treatment system inlet, and maximum ambient temperature for the dryer/air treatment system itself.

5.1.3.5.3.2 Medical air compressor systems shall consist of the following:

(1) Components complying with 5.1.3.5.4 through 5.1.3.5.10, arranged per 5.1.3.5.11
(2) An automatic means to prevent backflow from all on-cycle compressors through all off-cycle compressors
(3) A manual shutoff valve to isolate each compressor from the centrally piped system and from other compressors for maintenance or repair without loss of pressure in the system
(4) Intake filter–muffler(s) of the dry type
(5) Pressure relief valve(s) set at 50 percent above line pressure
(6) Piping and components between the compressor and the source shutoff valve, that do not contribute to contaminant levels
(7) Except as defined in 5.1.3.5.3.2(1) through 5.1.3.5.3.2(6), materials and devices used between the medical air intake and the medical air source valve shall be permitted to be of any design or construction appropriate for the service as determined by the manufacturer.

The materials for individual components and the interconnecting piping of the medical air compressor system are permitted to be of materials the manufacturer considers suitable. This exception does allow for considerable variation in materials and methods of construction and recognizes that making components from the same materials as the pipeline can be prohibitively expensive and, in some cases, impractical. Therefore, the manufacturer is allowed to select any appropriate materials for components such as the compressor, aftercoolers, receiver, regulators, filters, and dryers.

5.1.3.5.3.3 Medical air compressor systems shall preclude the condensation of water vapor in the piping distribution system by the selection of the air drying equipment.

On the surface, 5.1.3.5.3.3 might seem unnecessary, given that a maximum and design dew point are specified. However, because there are circumstances where the stipulated dew points are not low enough, this provision remains in the standard. See Exhibit 5.10 for a medical air compressor system showing control panel, sight glass for receiver tank, two twin-tower desiccant dryer packages, dual filter banks, and dew point analyzer. These more compact desiccant dryers have been well received by facilities because of their smaller size and ability to be prepiped by the manufacturer.

EXHIBIT 5.10 *Medical air compressor system.*

See Exhibit 5.11 for an example of a portion of the piping around a medical air compressor system. Note the dual airline regulators with valves and unions permitting repairs. Also note the dew point analyzer, the carbon monoxide analyzer, the test port, the sensor chamber for the analyzers, and the source valve.

EXHIBIT 5.11 *A portion of the piping around a medical air compressor system.*

5.1.3.5.4 Compressors for Medical Air.

It is sometimes asserted that the provisions of 5.1.3.5.4.1 were written around a certain compressor type and therefore some other types are not covered by the standard and can thus be used or not used. Various technologies were considered as the model for these provisions, but the provisions themselves are carefully written to apply broadly to any technology. These provisions have been successfully applied to a number of technologies over the years. The only named technology is liquid ring, which will be analyzed against the requirements of 5.1.3.5.4.1(1) and 5.1.3.5.4.2.

Application of other compressor technologies requires determination of the basic character of the compressor. If the compressor contains oil or grease in the compression chamber or air end, it fits none of the categories and is excluded. If it contains oil in the running gear but not in the compression chamber or air end, it must be analyzed against the requirements of 5.1.3.5.4.1(2) or (3). If the machine contains no free oil or grease at all, it might be appropriate to evaluate the compressor against 5.1.3.5.4.1(1).

5.1.3.5.4.1* Compressors for medical air shall be designed to prevent the introduction of contaminants or liquid into the pipeline by any of the following methods:

(1) Elimination of oil anywhere in the compressor (e.g., liquid ring and permanently sealed bearing compressors)
(2) Reciprocating compressors provided with a separation of the oil-containing section from the compression chamber by at least two seals creating an area open to atmosphere that allows the following:
 (a) Direct and unobstructed visual inspection of the interconnecting shaft through vent and inspection openings no smaller than 1.5 shaft diameters in size

FAQ ▶ What is the purpose of having an inspection hole 1.5 times the shaft diameter, in size?

Reciprocating compressors can provide a visual indication of the failure of the critical seals between the oil-lubricated crankcase and the compression chamber, but the seal must be easily seen. The provision for an opening of 1.5 shaft diameters is intended to ensure that the visual inspection required can be effectively performed.

 (b) The facility operators to confirm proper seal operation by direct visual inspection through the above-shaft opening, without disassembly of the compressor (e.g., extended head compressors with an atmospheric vent between the compression chamber and the crankcase)
(3) Rotating element compressors provided with a compression chamber free of oil that provides the following:
 (a) Separation of each oil-containing section from the compression chamber by at least one seal having atmospheric vents on each side with the vent closest to the oil-containing section supplied with a gravity drain to atmosphere
 (b) Unobstructed visualization of the atmospheric vent(s), closest to each oil-containing section, that is accessible for inspection without disassembling the compressor
 (c) Entry of the rotating shaft into each compression chamber at a point that is above atmospheric pressure
 (d) The facility operators to confirm proper seal operation by direct visual inspection of the atmospheric vents

FAQ ▶ Is oil allowed in a rotating element compressor?

In the 2005 edition, the standard for the first time permits "rotating element compressors" (i.e., oil-free screw compressors) with their own specific requirements. One can readily see that they closely follow the requirements for oil-containing compressors in 5.1.3.5.4.1(2), as is appropriate given that they do contain oil. Rotating element compressors must be designed to exclude oil from the compression chamber; be provided with a method to directly check, without disassembly of the compressor, for oil migration from failure of the seals; and be provided with the same safeguards (e.g., filters and oil indicators) required of any oil-containing compressor.

In fact, the only difference between a compressor under 5.1.3.5.4.1(2) and one under (3) is the technical method permitted for inspection of the seals. Under (2) it is a physical hole, 1.5 shaft diameters. Under (3) it is a physical hole through which oil will emerge by the action of gravity. Essential in both cases is the provision for not requiring disassembly to visualize the hole, which is intended to ensure that the inspection, being easy, will be performed often.

A.5.1.3.5.4.1 Examples of 5.1.3.5.4.1(1) are liquid ring and permanently sealed bearing compressors.

An example of 5.1.3.5.4.1(2) is an extended head reciprocating compressor with an atmospheric vent between the compression chamber and the crankcase.

An example of 5.1.3.5.4.1(3) is a rotating element compressor with the compression chamber being nonlubricated and separated from the lubricated gears by at least one shaft seal with an atmospheric vent on both sides. The vent on the lubricated side is provided with a gravity drain to atmosphere.

5.1.3.5.4.2 For liquid ring compressors, service water and seal water of a quality recommended by the compressor manufacturer shall be used.

5.1.3.5.4.3 Compressors shall be constructed of materials deemed suitable by the manufacturer.

5.1.3.5.4.4 Anti-vibration mountings shall be installed for compressors as required by equipment dynamics or location and in accordance with the manufacturer's recommendations.

Anti-vibration mountings and flex connectors are important not only to the operation of the equipment, but to prevent noise transmission into the building. Consideration needs to be given to seismic requirements as well.

5.1.3.5.4.5 Flexible connectors shall connect the air compressors with their intake and outlet piping.

5.1.3.5.5 Aftercoolers. Aftercoolers, where required, shall be provided with individual condensate traps. The receiver shall not be used as an aftercooler or aftercooler trap.

Provision for and proper design of an aftercooler are among the most crucial elements in assuring that medical air remains dry. It is in the aftercooler, not in the dryer, that the overwhelming bulk of water will be removed. In addition, dryers are designed to accept a certain maximum inlet temperature (typically 100°F), and for most compressor types, an aftercooler is the only reliable way to ensure that the inlet air does not exceed this temperature.

Provision for traps and drains for an aftercooler is good engineering practice, based on the fact that water will re-evaporate into the air if allowed to stand in the system. Immediate removal of any liquid is vital.

5.1.3.5.5.1 Aftercoolers shall be constructed of materials deemed suitable by the manufacturer.

5.1.3.5.5.2 Anti-vibration mountings shall be installed for aftercoolers as required by equipment dynamics or location and in accordance with the manufacturer's recommendations.

5.1.3.5.6 Medical Air Receivers. Receivers for medical air shall meet the following requirements:

(1) Be made of corrosion-resistant materials or otherwise be made corrosion-resistant

(2) Comply with Section VIII, Unfired Pressure Vessels, of the ASME *Boiler and Pressure Vessel Code*

(3) Be equipped with a pressure relief valve, automatic drain, manual drain, sight glass, and pressure indicator

A sight glass, as required by 5.1.3.5.6(3), enables visual inspection of automatic drains to see whether they are operating properly.

(4) Be of a capacity sufficient to prevent the compressors from short-cycling

5.1.3.5.7 Medical Air Dryers. Medical air dryers shall meet the following requirements:

(1) Be designed to provide air at a maximum dew point that is below the frost point [0°C (32°F)] at any level of demand

Water accumulation has for many years been the most common problem reported with medical gas systems. Preventing the formation of liquid water in a medical air system is of the greatest importance. In the 2002 edition, a significant change was made as a result of continuing reports of this problem. First, the design dew point was changed to "below the frost point [0°C (32°F)] at any level of demand" instead of "35°F (1.7°C) pressure dew point at peak calculated demand." This more stringent requirement still permits all the earlier dryer technologies but places on the designer an additional burden to ensure that dryers are selected and applied with appropriate care. It also reflects the finding that the most problematic dryers in medical service are not typically those operated at their full load, but rather those operated at fractional or highly variable loads. A designer must plan for this load variability, which is inherent to medical application.

Dryers have optimum operating characteristics, and providing the dryer with air meeting these criteria is dependent on the type of medical air compressor used, the operating pressure range of the medical compressors, and the discharge temperature of the compressors. Selection for optimum efficiency will thus vary from system to system.

See also the commentary following 5.1.3.5.15.

(2) Be sized for 100 percent of the system peak calculated demand at design conditions

(3) Be constructed of materials deemed suitable by the manufacturer

(4) Be provided with anti-vibration mountings installed as required by equipment dynamics or location and in accordance with the manufacturer's recommendations

5.1.3.5.8 Medical Air Filters. Medical air filters shall meet the following requirements:

(1) Be appropriate for the intake air conditions

(2) Be located upstream (source side) of the final line regulators

(3) Be sized for 100 percent of the system peak calculated demand at design conditions and be rated for a minimum of 98 percent efficiency at 1 micron or greater

(4) Be equipped with a continuous visual indicator showing the status of the filter element life

(5) Be constructed of materials deemed suitable by the manufacturer

Duplexed air filters (98 percent efficient at 1 micron or greater) are required as part of the piped air system. This quality of filter and filters of even better quality are readily available. Selection of filters should be based on the characteristics of the compressor, probable intake conditions, and other considerations that affect the quality of the air leaving the source equipment.

Filters of any type require periodic replacement, maintenance, or both. To facilitate these tasks, filters must be duplexed. Final line filters require a visual indicator to ensure proper maintenance of these filters.

5.1.3.5.8.1 Compressors complying with 5.1.3.5.4.1(2) and 5.1.3.5.4.1(3) shall be provided with the following:

(1) Coalescing filters with element change indicators
(2) Charcoal absorbers with colorimetric hydrocarbon indicators

The additional coalescing filters required by 5.1.3.5.8.1 recognize that even with all other safety provisions in place, oil vapor is a possibility in these machines and could pass unnoticed into the system. Coalescing filters provide a last defense against the oil vapors entering the pipeline.

5.1.3.5.9 Medical Air Regulators. Medical air regulators shall meet the following requirements:

(1) Be sized for 100 percent of the system peak calculated demand at design condition
(2) Be constructed of materials deemed suitable by the manufacturer
(3) Be equipped with a pressure indicator indicating delivery pressure

The practice of operating the pipeline system at higher pressures with remote airline regulators (distributed pressure systems) is not permitted for any medical gas pipeline. The medical air is to be piped throughout the facility at a gauge pressure of 345 kPa (50 psi) (+5/–0). The piping network needs to be designed adequately to accommodate this pressure at the far reaches of the facility.

5.1.3.5.10* Medical Air Local Alarm. A local alarm complying with 5.1.9.5 shall be provided for the medical air compressor source.

A.5.1.3.5.10 Other functions can be added at the request of the facility, such as low water pressure, and so forth. A

5.1.3.5.11 Piping Arrangement and Redundancies.

5.1.3.5.11.1 Component arrangement shall be as follows:

(1) Components shall be arranged to permit service and a continuous supply of medical air in the event of a single fault failure.
(2) Component arrangement shall be permitted to vary as required by the technology(ies) employed, provided an equal level of operating redundancy and medical air quality is maintained.

NFPA 99 does not govern how a system is arranged (i.e., the order of components), with a few noted exceptions. The ordering of components is largely determined by how they are designed to work and what they are intended to accomplish. For example, the standard would not prevent locating an aftercooler after the receiver, but in practice such an arrangement would defeat the whole purpose of an aftercooler.

The most important practical example of this allowance is in the location of dryers. One school of thought holds that a dryer should be located downstream of the receiver. The other school holds it should be upstream. Irrespective of the technical merit or lack of merit in either argument, NFPA 99 allows either arrangement, provided simply that the dew point design requirement in 5.1.3.5.7 is met.

5.1.3.5.11.2 Medical air compressors shall be sufficient to serve the peak calculated demand with the largest single compressor out of service. In no case shall there be fewer than 2 (two) compressors.

Clearly, there is no upper limit on the number of compressors as long as there are at least two, as required by 5.1.3.5.11.2.

5.1.3.5.11.3 When aftercoolers are provided, they shall be either one of the following:

(1) Arranged as a duplex or multiplex set, sized to serve the peak calculated demand with the largest single aftercooler out of service and provided with valves adequate to isolate any single aftercooler from the system without shutting down supply of medical air
(2) Arranged one per compressor, sized to handle the output of that compressor, and valved as appropriate to permit repair or replacement with that compressor out of service but without shutting down supply of medical air

The allowance for aftercoolers coupled with their air compressors as a set is a new allowance in the 2005 edition. Although the practice is very common and debatably superior to any other design, the standard in earlier years could be construed to prohibit such an arrangement. Here in the 2005 edition that oversight has been corrected.

5.1.3.5.11.4* Medical air receiver(s) shall be provided with proper valves to allow the flow of compressed air to enter and exit out of separate receiver ports during normal operation and allow the receiver to be bypassed during service without shutting down the supply of medical air.

A

A.5.1.3.5.11.4 A typical example of valving the receiver is shown in Figure A.5.1.3.5.11.4.

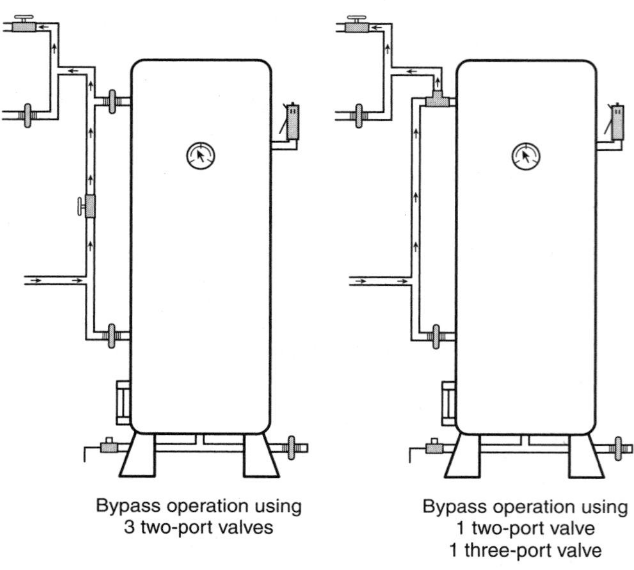

FIGURE A.5.1.3.5.11.4 *Receiver Valving Arrangement.*

5.1.3.5.11.5 Dryers, filters, and regulators shall be at least duplexed with each component sized to serve the peak calculated demand with the largest of each component out of service.

As with compressors, two is the typical number of dryers, filters, and regulators, but more than two would be allowed.

5.1.3.5.11.6* Dryers, filters, and regulators shall be provided with manual valves upstream and manual valves or check valves downstream to allow service to the components without shutting down the system in either one of the following ways:

(1) Be installed for each component, upstream and downstream of each component, allowing each to be individually isolated

(2) Be installed upstream (source side) and downstream of components in series so as to create redundant parallel branches of components

A.5.1.3.5.11.6 The two configurations are equally acceptable. The components can be arranged in either of the arrangements shown in Figure A.5.1.3.5.11.6.

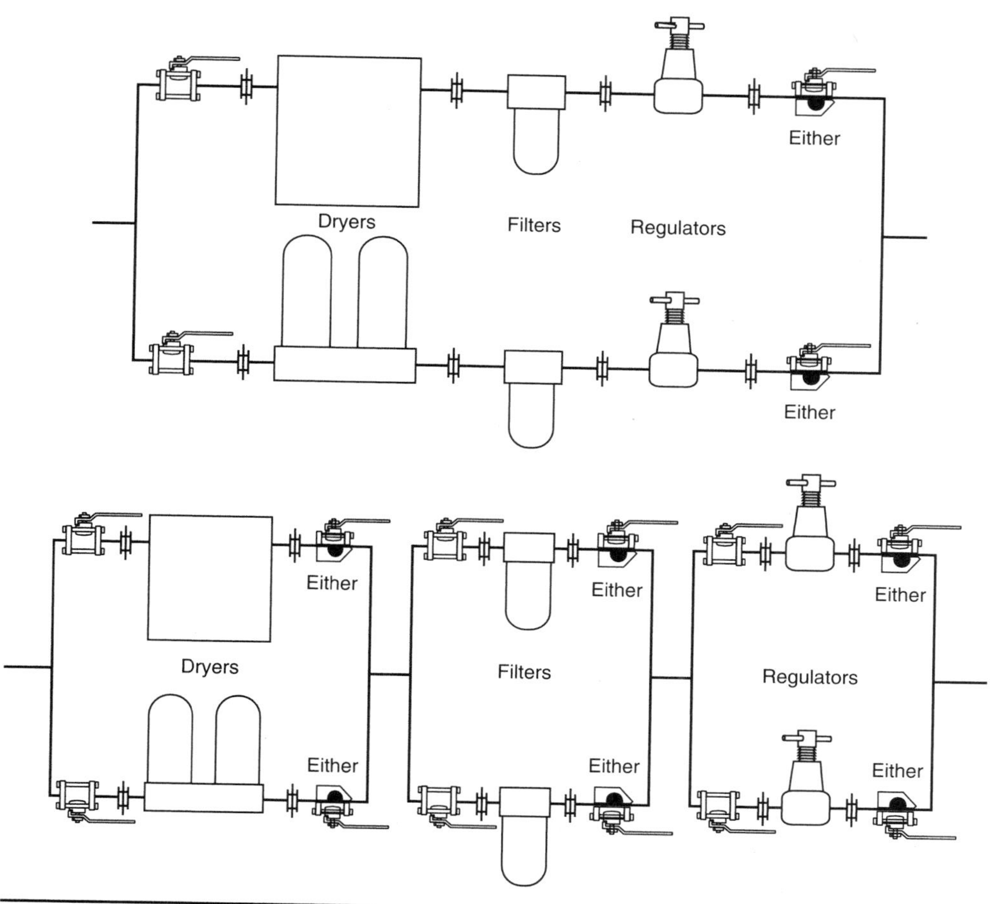

FIGURE A.5.1.3.5.11.6 *Alternate Valving Sequences for Line Controls in Medical Air.*

In addition to the valves around dryers, regulators, and filters required by 5.1.3.5.11.6 to permit their servicing, piping unions or other means should also be used to permit easier removal of these items should they need replacement.

Redundancy of critical components to compensate for potential failure has always been an important underlying principle in medical gas and vacuum systems designed to comply with NFPA 99. Successive revisions have expanded the principle of redundancy to include components that could require service in the ordinary course of operation and would require shutting down the system. Through all these revisions, a single principle has emerged — single fault. The single fault principle provides that no single failure should be able to render the system inoperable.

◀ **FAQ**
Does NFPA 99 consider multiple fault failures?

The single fault principle is significant. Without it, NFPA 99 could quickly begin to stack redundancy on top of redundancy, attempting to compensate for any combination of failures (if A fails and B fails . . .), which is beyond the intent of a minimum safe standard.

Such an eventuality had emerged in the duplex valving arrangement for air system components, where previous editions of NFPA 99 illustrated separate four-valve bypasses for each component. Although undoubtedly a convenient arrangement, it far exceeded the single fault principle. Paragraph 5.1.3.5.11.6 and Figure A.5.1.3.5.11.6 explicitly allow a single-fault arrangement or the more elaborate multiple-valve arrangement.

5.1.3.5.11.7 A three-way valve (three-port), indexed to flow, full port shall be permitted to be used to isolate one branch or component for the purposes of 5.1.3.5.11.3, 5.1.3.5.11.4, 5.1.3.5.11.5, and 5.1.3.5.11.6.

Generally, where there are duplex sets of components, only one set will be in operation and the other will be in standby (see 5.1.3.5.11.8 through 5.1.3.5.11.10). In this situation, a three-way valve is an acceptable choice.

5.1.3.5.11.8 Under normal operation, only one aftercooler shall be open to airflow with the other aftercooler valved off.

5.1.3.5.11.9 Under normal operation, only one dryer–filter(s)–regulator sequence shall be open to airflow with the other sequence valved off.

5.1.3.5.11.10 If the relief valve required in 5.1.3.5.3.2(5) and 5.1.3.5.6(3) can be isolated from the system by the valve arrangement used to comply with 5.1.3.5.11.6, then redundant relief valve(s) shall be installed in the parallel sequence.

5.1.3.5.11.11 A DN8 (NPS ¼) valved sample port shall be provided downstream of the final line pressure regulators, dew point monitor, and carbon monoxide monitor and upstream of the source shutoff valve to allow for sampling of the medical air.

5.1.3.5.11.12 Medical air source systems shall be provided with a source valve per 5.1.4.4.

5.1.3.5.11.13 Where medical air piping systems at different operating pressures are required, the piping shall separate after the filters, but shall be provided with separate line regulators, dew point monitors, relief valves, and source shutoff valves.

5.1.3.5.12 Electrical Power and Control.

5.1.3.5.12.1 Additional compressor(s) shall automatically activate when the compressor(s) in operation is incapable of maintaining the required pressure.

5.1.3.5.12.2 Automatic or manual alternation of compressors shall allow division of operating time. If automatic alternation of compressors is not provided, the facility staff shall arrange a schedule for manual alternation.

5.1.3.5.12.3 Each compressor motor shall be provided with electrical components including, but not limited to, the following:

(1) A dedicated disconnect switch installed in the electrical circuit ahead of each motor starter
(2) Motor starting device
(3) Overload protection
(4) Where compressor systems having two or more compressors employ a control transformer or other voltage control power device, at least two such devices shall be installed
(5) Control circuits arranged in such a manner that the shutdown of one compressor does not interrupt the operation of another compressor
(6) Automatic restart function such that compressor(s) will restart after power interruption without manual intervention

FAQ ▶ Why is it important to have the compressors restart after a power interuption?

The requirement for an automatic restart function, new to the 2005 edition, represents a reaction to a problem that is particularly common to rotating element compressors, especially very large machines. These machines are not designed for start-stop operation but are designed to run continuously, loading and unloading as needed. If forced to restart too soon after stopping, they can eject oil, damage their rotating elements, or suffer other damage. With such a compressor, in the event of a power failure or even during their generator test, the voltage dropout is often enough to cause the compressor to shut down and possibly cause the medical air system to crash. Such machines are unsuitable for use in a medical air system.

5.1.3.5.12.4 Electrical installation and wiring shall conform to the requirements of NFPA 70, *National Electrical Code*.

5.1.3.5.12.5 Emergency electrical service for the compressors shall conform to the requirements of the essential electrical system as described in Chapter 4 of this document.

5.1.3.5.13 Compressor Intake.

No decision will have greater impact on the ongoing quality of medical air than the location of the intake. Location is a decision unique to each site, and the dimensions cited should be considered as the starting point in a detailed site investigation. The occurrences of contaminated air are frequently found to be associated with intake placement close to, or downwind of, vacuum exhausts, WAGD exhausts, laboratory or sanitary vents, HVAC exhausts, loading docks, and other sources of polluted air.

If a building has a series of stepped (staggered) roofs, the best location for the intake becomes more complicated to determine. Meeting all the requirements of this section does not necessarily mean locating the intake above the highest roof. Factors such as the size of each roof, the nearest doors and windows, and other equipment on the roof all influence the final location(s).

5.1.3.5.13.1 The medical air compressors shall draw their air from a source of clean air located where no contamination is anticipated from engine exhausts, fuel storage vents, medical–surgical vacuum system discharges, particulate matter, or odor of any type.

5.1.3.5.13.2 The compressor air intake shall be located outdoors above roof level, at a minimum distance of 3.05 m (10 ft) from any door, window, exhaust, other intake, or opening in the building and a minimum distance of 6.1 m (20 ft) above the ground.

5.1.3.5.13.3 If an air source equal to or better than outside air (e.g., air already filtered for use in operating room ventilating systems) is available, it shall be permitted to be used for the medical air compressors with the following provisions:

(1) This alternate source of supply air shall be available on a continuous 24-hour-per-day, 7-day-per-week basis.
(2) Ventilating systems having fans with motors or drive belts located in the air stream shall not be used as a source of medical air intake.

It is advisable to conduct periodic tests to verify that the alternative source is equal to or better than the ambient source and that it remains that way. Conditions can change, causing the source of air to become unacceptable for medical air use. The air characteristics to be tested can be determined by reference to 5.1.3.5.1.

The standard now requires that alternative sources of air be available 24 hours per day. This means such sources need to be maintained at all times. Many air-handling systems that might be used as a source of air are shut off during nonpeak times, thus lowering the quality and quantity of air within the system.

Concerns exist about air taken from air ventilating systems that have motors and bearing systems in the air duct. On failure, these systems can generate noxious vapors that would be taken in by the compressor, and thus they are not allowed to be used as air sources.

5.1.3.5.13.4 Compressor intake piping shall be hard-drawn seamless copper, and one of the following:

(1) ASTM B 819, *Standard Specification for Seamless Copper Tube for Medical Gas Systems*, medical gas tube

(2) ASTM B 88, *Standard Specification for Seamless Copper Water Tube*, water tube (Type K or L)
(3) ASTM B 280, *Standard Specification for Seamless Copper Tubing for Air Conditioning and Refrigeration Field Service*, 280 ACR tube

The 2005 edition firmly clarifies from which materials the air system intake may be constructed. Earlier allowances for intakes to be made of materials suitable for vacuum have been replaced with this simple list.

5.1.3.5.13.5 Air intakes for separate compressors shall be permitted to be joined together to one common intake where the following conditions are met:

(1) The common intake is sized to minimize back pressure in accordance with the manufacturer's recommendations.
(2) Each compressor can be isolated by manual or check valve, blind flange, or tube cap to prevent open inlet piping when compressor(s) are removed for service and consequent backflow of room air into the other compressor(s).

Running a common intake for several compressors as permitted by 5.1.3.5.13.5 is often done when intakes would have to be piped considerable distances. When joining several air intakes, care must be taken to size the intake piping and intake filter(s) appropriately. In addition, isolation means are necessary to prevent room air from being drawn into the operating compressor(s) when other compressors are removed from service. If proper isolation or valving at compressors is not installed, equipment can be damaged and pipelines contaminated.

Where intakes are joined in this manner, one compressor can react on the other and damage the inlet valves in the compressor itself. Intake sizing, always important, can become critical in these cases.

The fundamental design principle for medical air compressors is that any single compressor must be able to be removed from service for maintenance or replacement, without compromising the ability of the remaining compressor(s) to meet the demand. The actual sizing of the medical compressed air system requires a detailed engineering review, along with knowledge of this standard.

Because repair and maintenance are a normal part of system operation, each compressor must be valved with a manual shutoff valve.

5.1.3.5.13.6 The end of the intake shall be turned down and screened or otherwise be protected against the entry of vermin, debris, or precipitation by screening, fabricated or composed of a noncorroding material.

FAQ ▶ What kind of materials can be used for the screening of the intake?

Note that screening of the end of the intake should be on noncorroding material, such as galvanized steel, plastic, stainless steel, or other similar materials.

5.1.3.5.14 Operating Alarms and Local Signals. Medical air systems shall be monitored for conditions that may affect air quality during use or in the event of failure, based on the type of compressor(s) used in the system.

To ensure the continued maintenance of medical compressed air, the appropriate monitors for each type of compressor are defined, consistent with the single component failure and the available monitoring technology.

Required local alarms must be individually displayed locally (e.g., at the compressor site) but can be drawn to the master alarms as a group. Typically, this grouped signal might read "Medical Air System Fault" and would cause a technician to examine the compressor to determine which of the several advisory alarms had been activated. Only certain signals, such as dew point, require their own signal connected to each master alarm panel. See also the requirements for local alarms in 5.1.9.5.

5.1.3.5.14.1 Where liquid ring air compressors, compressors having water-cooled heads, or water-cooled aftercoolers are used, air receivers shall be equipped with a high water level sensor that shuts down the compressor system and activates a local alarm indicator. *[See 5.1.9.5.4(7).]*

5.1.3.5.14.2 Where liquid ring compressors are used, each compressor shall have a liquid level sensor in each air–water separator, which, when the liquid level is above the design level, shuts down its compressor and activates a local alarm indicator. *[See 5.1.9.5.4(8).]*

Liquid ring compressors introduce a unique hazard: failure of the water/air separation mechanism(s) and consequent filling of the system with liquid water. This hazard is unique to the liquid ring compressors technology and thus is specifically named in the standard. Any compressor system using water as a cooling medium (e.g., in the compressor head, an aftercooler, the dryers) could also suffer infiltration of water into the system, which is the origin of the requirement for a high-water switch in the receiver.

◀ **FAQ**
Do liquid ring compressors have any unique hazards?

A more insidious hazard exists with any compressor if the receiver simply fails to drain. In such a case, water can accumulate over time and ultimately fill the receiver. This possibility led to an interpretation of the provision in 5.1.3.5.14.1 that all compressors needed to be fit with the float switch in the receiver. Although the language was improved in the 2002 edition, some systems are provided with this alarm even though they are served by compressor types without water.

5.1.3.5.14.3 Where nonliquid ring compressors compliant with 5.1.3.5.4.1(1) are used, the air temperature at the immediate outlet of each compressor cylinder shall be monitored by a high-temperature sensor that shuts down that compressor and activates a local alarm indicator. *[See 5.1.9.5.4(9).]* The temperature setting shall be as recommended by the compressor manufacturer.

Paragraph 5.1.3.5.14.3 is intended to be applied as written. Each compressor cylinder is meant to have an individual switch/sensor (e.g., if the compressor has three cylinders, three switches are to be provided). Although this may seem to be an overdesign if the entire machine is monitored, there is perceived to be a contamination hazard that can result from failure of a single cylinder where there is more than one. That hazard is not believed to be adequately addressed by a single switch, which could detect only the combined output of the many cylinders.

5.1.3.5.14.4 Where compressors compliant with 5.1.3.5.4.1(2) and 5.1.3.5.4.1(3) are used, the following requirements shall apply:

(1) The air temperature at the immediate outlet of each compressor chamber shall be monitored by a high-temperature sensor that shuts down that compressor and activates a local alarm indicator. *[See 5.1.9.5.4(9).]* The temperature setting shall be as recommended by the compressor manufacturer.

See the commentary following 5.1.3.5.14.3.

(2) Coalescing filters with element change indicator shall be provided.
(3) Charcoal filters with colorimetric hydrocarbon indicator shall be provided.
(4) Liquid hydrocarbons shall be monitored on a continuous basis by pigment indicator or other type of instrument permanently installed downstream of each compressor and shall be inspected and documented daily.
(5) Gaseous hydrocarbons shall be monitored on a quarterly basis.

5.1.3.5.14.5 When the backup or lag compressor is running, a local alarm shall activate. *[See 5.1.9.5.4(1).]* This signal shall be manually reset.

The reserve compressor alarm (sometimes referred to as a "lag in use" alarm) required by 5.1.3.5.14.5 warns of the activation of the off-duty compressor. This condition could indicate the following:

1. Failure of the on-duty compressor
2. Inadequate capacity in the on-duty compressor
3. A controls failure or some other unusual event

All of these conditions are important and need to be checked. However, they can be checked only at the compressor site, which is why this alarm is not mandated to signal at the master alarms as such.

5.1.3.5.15 Medical Air Quality Monitoring. Medical air quality shall be monitored downstream of the medical air regulators and upstream of the piping system as follows:

(1) Dew point shall be monitored and shall activate a local alarm and all master alarms when the dew point at system pressure exceeds +4°C (+39°F).

The local alarm specified in 5.1.3.5.15(1) will apply to the dew point monitor for all systems and to any air-treatment system where installed. This alarm must be echoed at the master alarm panel (see 5.1.9.2).

Where a facility uses desiccant-type dryers, some of which provide dew points in the −40°C to −73°C (−40°F to −100°F) range, it is important to remember that the dew point alarm system provided with these systems will need to be capable of monitoring a value that low. Dew point monitors that read out "below range" are not appropriate.

The dew point alarm set point represents the nominal performance of a refrigerated dryer [1.7°C (35°F)], with 4 Fahrenheit degrees added to allow for individual variation in systems. The standard recognizes that to consistently attain this dew point, the system should be designed for better performance. Therefore, the design dew point (see 5.1.3.5.7) must be "below the frost point."

The question of the pressure at which dew point is to be expressed is decided by reference to the preferred location of the sensor, which is immediately downstream of the pressure regulators and filters. This location should experience only system pressure, so dew point is expressed at system gauge pressure (39°F at 50 psi is equivalent to 4°F at 0 psi).

The term *pressure dew point* provides one criterion for dew point readings. Although it is relatively easy to convert Celsius to Fahrenheit, it is more difficult to convert atmospheric dew point readings to pressure dew point readings. It is the intent of the standard to set a maximum for the dew point of the medical air within the pipeline at pressure, not after it is expanded and expelled into the room (i.e., atmospheric dew point).

The pressure dew point at compressor operating pressures will rise and fall with operation of the compressor. For instance, some compressors energize at a gauge pressure as low as 517 kPa (75 psi) and turn off at 695 kPa (95 psi). Pressure dew points at these gauge pressures would be higher than the dew point of the medical air downstream of the regulator at 345 kPa (50 psi). The designer of an air system must consider this phenomenon. Incidentally, this is how a refrigerant dryer can be brought to comply with this standard, and it is how the "below frost point" criteria were chosen.

The basic intent of setting a dew point is the preclusion of liquid water forming in the pipes. Users are advised that the minimum dew point that will prevent water from forming in pipes varies from system to system. Under some conditions, the dew points set in this standard might not be sufficiently low.

Chapter 5 uses the term *dew point* frequently. The following is offered for those readers not familiar with the term.

In a compressed air system, the temperature at which water vapor begins to condense into liquid is called the dew point. As an example, air with a dew point of −6.7°C (20°F) will form dew on the outside of a glass of ice. The dew point of the air does not necessarily have any relationship to the actual temperature of the air [e.g., air at 37.8°C (100°F) can still have a dew point of −17.8°C (0°F)].

Whether water forms, however, is very closely related to the temperature of the air. Air cooled below its dew point will form water; air cooled below its frost point will form ice. For example, if air dried to a dew point of −1.6°C (35°F) pressure dew point (PDP) is blown into a room where the temperature of the ambient air is 21°C (70°F), the expelled air will not give up any moisture. However, if the same treated air is expelled into a room where the ambient air is only −6.6°C (20°F), water will be expelled because the ambient temperature is below the dew point to which the air has been treated.

For another example, consider a dryer drying the air only to a dew point of 15.5°C (60°F) PDP. The pipeline distributing this air has been installed inside the facility, but on an exterior wall that has not been adequately insulated. The pipeline is exposed to temperatures of 1.6°C to 4.4°C (35°F to 40°F). It is quite possible that water will form as the air passes through this colder area and be expelled out patient outlets as liquid.

Refrigerated dryers are common in many health care facilities in the United States. These dryers are subject to reentrainment of water after it leaves the refrigerated portion of the dryer, and thus often cannot perform as required under low flow conditions. For this reason, the standard now states "under all conditions of flow."

Regenerative dryers employ an adsorptive desiccant that attracts and holds moisture on its surface. These units have two towers: one that collects moisture while the other is dried of moisture that it has collected. A timing circuit reverses the roles of the towers after a preset time, and dry air is used to drive collected moisture off of the desiccant.

These regenerative dryers are capable of discharging air at much lower dew points than the standard requires [as low as −73.3°C (−100°F)], and they are not subject to a low-flow performance penalty, but they do use air for internal regeneration, which can be objectionable, particularly on systems with highly variable usage.

Technologies exist to reduce the objectionable aspects of both types of dryers.

There are other dryer technologies in use, but they are rare enough not to merit further consideration at this time.

(2) Carbon monoxide shall be monitored and shall activate a local alarm when the CO level exceeds 10 ppm. *[See 5.1.9.5.4(2).]*

Air-treatment systems for medical air compressor systems are not mandated by this standard, because ambient air, taken from a location free from auto exhausts or other sources of pollution, can be well within the purity limits in this standard. Compressors that comply with the requirements of a medical air compressor are designed not to add contamination to the air stream and thus might not require separate air treatment. [However, please note that medical air systems employed for occupational uses (as permitted herein) are also subject to OSHA regulation, which may require additional apparatus.]

Although other gases of concern are listed in 5.1.3.5.1, carbon monoxide (CO) is the only one that is continuously monitored — for two reasons: Monitors are widely available and not excessively expensive or complex, and CO is a good indicator gas, meaning that its presence often is the best indicator of air quality problems in general. Air quality can vary from place to place and day to day. Local air quality can be determined only through knowledge of local conditions and testing at the intake. Testing could be necessary on a regular basis. Where the quality of the intake air is unreliable, specific air-treatment devices can be desirable. Where installed, these devices must be monitored and alarmed. Such devices do increase the frequency and complexity of maintenance, so their use should be reviewed in light of ambient air quality.

EXHIBIT 5.12 A triplex vacuum pump setup for a piped medical vacuum system, including control panel.

EXHIBIT 5.13 A vertical mount duplex vacuum pump system with control panel and receiver. The pump is an oil-flooded rotary vane unit.

It is sometimes contended that CO monitors are needed only for oil-containing compressors and that they function to detect oil burning in the machine. Whether or not this is a valid use of a CO monitor is irrelevant, because it is not the reason such monitors are required by this standard.

See Exhibit 5.12 and Exhibit 5.13. They illustrate the different types of vacuum pumps and their controllers.

(3) Dew point and carbon monoxide monitors shall activate the individual monitor's signal at all master alarm panels if the monitor loses power.

5.1.3.6* Medical–Surgical Vacuum Supply Systems.

A.5.1.3.6 See Figure A.5.1.3.6.

5.1.3.6.1 Medical–Surgical Vacuum Sources.

5.1.3.6.1.1 Medical–surgical vacuum sources shall be located per 5.1.3.3 as follows:

(1) Indoors in a dedicated mechanical equipment area, adequately ventilated and with any required utilities
(2) In a room constructed per 5.1.3.3.2
(3) In a room ventilated per 5.1.3.3.3.2
(4) For air-cooled equipment, in a room designed to maintain the ambient temperature range as recommended by the equipment manufacturer

5.1.3.6.1.2 Medical–surgical vacuum sources shall consist of the following:

(1) Two or more vacuum pumps sufficient to serve the peak calculated demand with the largest single vacuum pump out of service

FAQ ▶
Is vacuum treated to the same high standards as a medical gas?

The standard recognizes that vacuum systems in health care facilities (in particular those systems that are used in surgery and for respiratory therapy) are true life-saving, life-support systems. (See Exhibit 5.14.) Therefore, failure or shutdown of a vacuum pump(s) (causing reduction or loss of vacuum) can be injurious or fatal to patients, and vacuum is a true "medical gas" in that sense. Medical gases are generally thought of as a positive pressure gas, but a negative pressure gas (vacuum) is also a "medical gas."

(2) An automatic means to prevent backflow from any on-cycle vacuum pumps through any off-cycle vacuum pumps

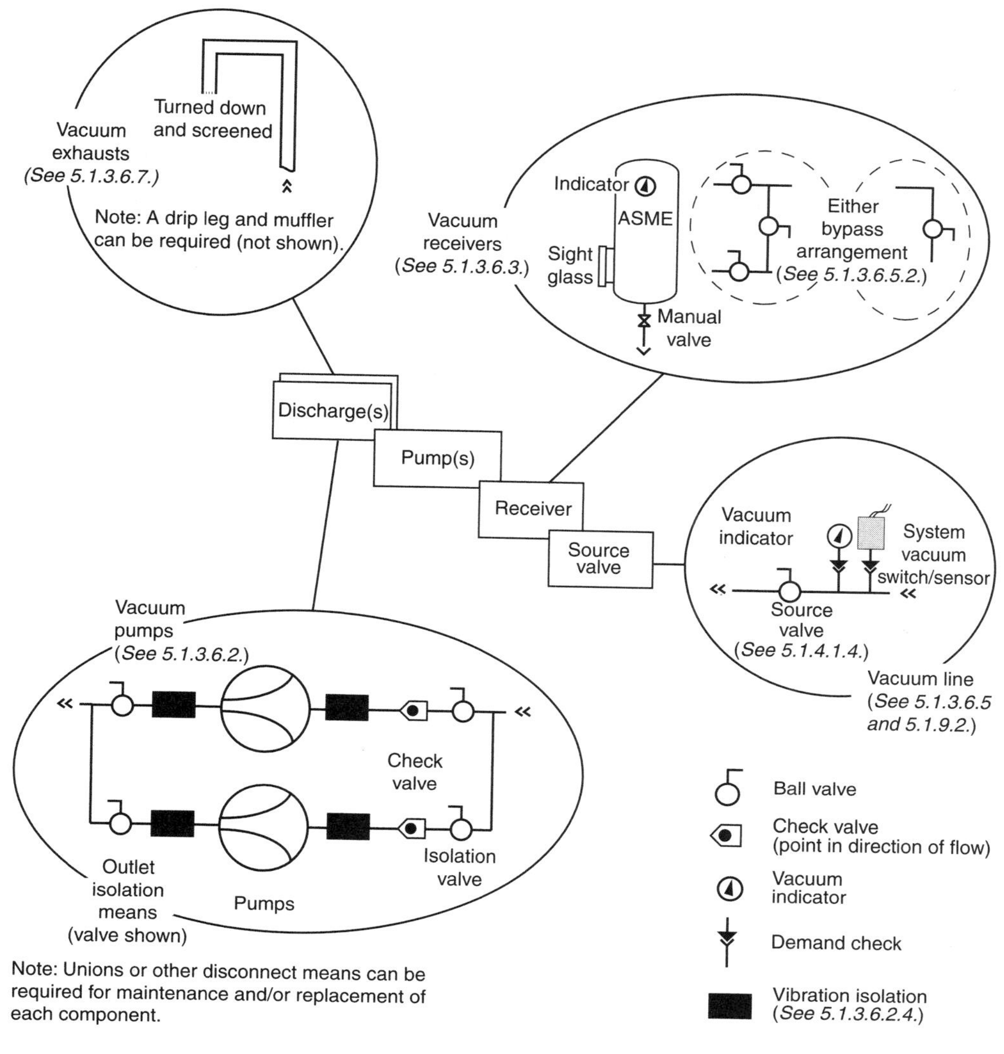

FIGURE A.5.1.3.6 *Elements of a Typical Duplex Vacuum Source System (Level 1 Vacuum Systems).*

(3) A shutoff valve or other isolation means to isolate each vacuum pump from the centrally piped system and other vacuum pumps for maintenance or repair without loss of vacuum in the system
(4) A vacuum receiver
(5) Piping between the vacuum pump(s), discharge(s), receiver(s), and the vacuum source shutoff valve shall be in accordance with 5.1.10.2 except that stainless, galvanized, or black steel pipe shall be permitted to be used.
(6) Except as defined in 5.1.3.6.1.2(1) through 5.1.3.6.1.2(5), materials and devices used between the medical vacuum exhaust and the medical vacuum source shall be permitted to be of any design or construction appropriate for the service as determined by the manufacturer.

5.1.3.6.2 Vacuum Pumps.

5.1.3.6.2.1 Vacuum pumps shall be constructed of materials deemed suitable by the manufacturer.

EXHIBIT 5.14 Typical medical vacuum system. (Courtesy of Beacon Medical)

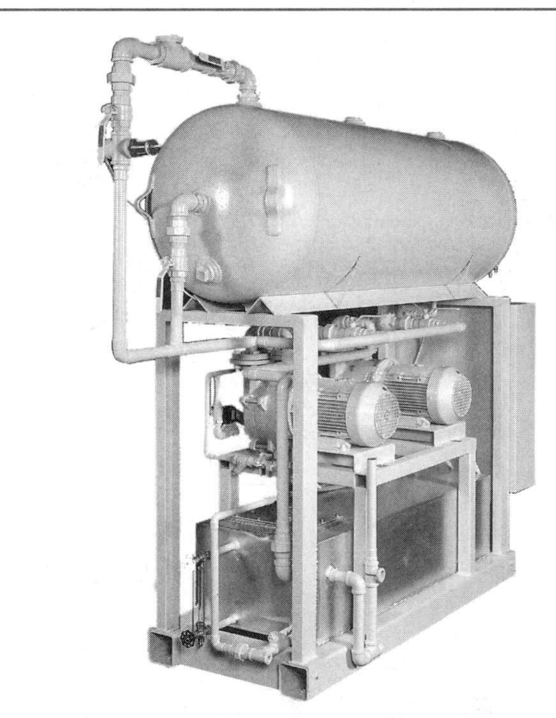

5.1.3.6.2.2 Anti-vibration mountings shall be installed for vacuum pumps as required by equipment dynamics or location and in accordance with the manufacturer's recommendations.

It is important that anti-vibration mountings as required by 5.1.3.6.2.2 actually perform as intended and that they have not simply been added to a system for "show." Seismic requirements of the local building code should be considered when selecting any anti-vibration system.

5.1.3.6.2.3 Flexible connectors shall connect the vacuum pumps with their intake and outlet piping.

5.1.3.6.2.4 For liquid ring vacuum pumps, seal water shall be of a quality recommended by the vacuum pump manufacturer.

5.1.3.6.3 Vacuum Receivers. Receivers for vacuum shall meet the following requirements:

(1) Be made of ferrous and/or nonferrous materials

(2) Comply with Section VIII, Unfired Pressure Vessels, of the ASME *Boiler and Pressure Vessel Code*

(3) Be capable of withstanding a gauge pressure of 415 kPa (60 psi) and 760 mm (29.9 in.) gauge HgV

The use of receivers with vacuum systems reflects current practice but is somewhat problematic. In an air system, a receiver can be shown to actually store air and thus can perform a useful function in the system. Vacuum, however, cannot be stored, so the value of a receiver is thus not obvious. Many pump technologies are now in use that do not require any receiver and will in fact operate perfectly well without one. One significant reason they remain in the standard is that they act as a "knockout," providing a place for liquids and other debris that might pass down the pipe to settle. Ideally, this debris will not then enter the pump.

The question of sizing the receiver has been removed from the standard and is now left to be determined on the basis of good engineering and the requirements of the specific pump technology employed.

Because the receiver is part of the vacuum piping system, it too must be metallic. The standard considers the ASME *Boiler and Pressure Vessel Code* [9] to be appropriate for the subject of vacuum receivers.

(4) Be equipped with a manual drain
(5) Be of a capacity based on the technology of the pumps

5.1.3.6.4 Vacuum Local Alarm. A local alarm complying with 5.1.9.5 shall be provided for the vacuum source.

5.1.3.6.5 Piping Arrangement and Redundancies.

5.1.3.6.5.1 Piping arrangement shall be as follows:

(1) Piping shall be arranged to permit service and a continuous supply of medical–surgical vacuum in the event of a single fault failure.
(2) Piping arrangement shall be permitted to vary based on the technology(ies) employed, provided an equal level of operating redundancy is maintained.
(3) Where only one set of vacuum pumps is available for a combined medical–surgical vacuum system and an analysis, research, or teaching laboratory vacuum system, such laboratories shall be connected separate from the medical–surgical system directly to the receiver tank through its own isolation valve and fluid trap located at the receiver. Between the isolation valve and fluid trap, a scrubber shall be permitted to be installed.

5.1.3.6.5.2 The medical–surgical vacuum receiver(s) shall be serviceable without shutting down the medical–surgical vacuum system by any of the following methods:

(1) By providing an isolation valve where the receiver is tee'd into the main line
(2) By piping the receiver at the end of a valved isolation line
(3) By providing a three-valve bypass

5.1.3.6.5.3 Medical–surgical vacuum source systems shall be provided with a source shutoff valve per 5.1.4.4.

5.1.3.6.6 Electrical Power and Control.

5.1.3.6.6.1 Additional pumps shall automatically activate when the pump(s) in operation is incapable of adequately maintaining the required vacuum.

5.1.3.6.6.2 Automatic or manual alternation of pumps shall allow division of operating time. If automatic alternation of pumps is not provided, the facility staff shall arrange a schedule for manual alternation.

Alternation of pumps (automatically or manually) is required by 5.1.3.6.6.2 because it allows even wear on both pumps, thereby extending the life of the pumps and reducing the probability of system failure at any given time. Whether pump alternation is automatic or manual, activation of the nonoperating pump must be automatic in the event of operating pump failure or overload. Where pumps that require off-time for proper operation are used, the pump(s) should be sized at the top of the operating range so the stop setting can be reached on intermittent operation.

5.1.3.6.6.3 Each pump motor shall be provided with electrical components including, but not limited to, the following:

(1) A dedicated disconnect switch installed in the electrical circuit ahead of each motor starter

(2) Motor starting device
(3) Overload protection
(4) Where pump systems having two or more pumps employ a control transformer or other voltage control power device, at least two such devices are required
(5) Control circuits arranged in such a manner that the shutdown of one pump does not interrupt the operation of another pump
(6) Automatic restart function such that pump(s) will restart after power interruption without manual intervention

The requirement for automatic restart, new to the 2005 edition, represents a reaction to a problem that is particularly common to rotating element pumps, especially very large machines. These machines are not designed for start-stop operation but are designed to run continuously, loading and unloading as needed. If forced to restart too soon after stopping, they can eject oil, damage their rotating elements, or suffer other damage. With such a pump, in the event of a power failure or even during their generator test, the voltage dropout is often enough to cause the pump to shut down and possibly cause the vacuum system to crash. Such machines are unsuitable for use in a medical vacuum system.

5.1.3.6.6.4 Electrical installation and wiring shall conform to the requirements of NFPA 70, *National Electrical Code.*

5.1.3.6.6.5 Emergency electrical service for the pumps shall conform to the requirements of the essential electrical system as described in Chapter 4 of this document.

5.1.3.6.7 Medical–Surgical Vacuum Source Exhaust.

5.1.3.6.7.1 The medical–surgical vacuum pumps shall exhaust in a manner and location that will minimize the hazards of noise and contamination to the facility and its environment.

FAQ ▶ Is the vacuum discharge dangerous?

The discharging of exhausts to the outside is required by 5.1.3.6.7.1 because the discharge from patient drainage must always be considered contaminated. Such discharge can carry infectious material that should never be discharged within a building. Filtration of this discharge can also be considered if the patients served are highly infectious.

5.1.3.6.7.2 The exhaust shall be located as follows:

(1) Outdoors
(2) At least 3.05 m (10 ft) from any door, window, air intake, or other openings in buildings
(3) At a level different from air intakes
(4) Where prevailing winds, adjacent buildings, topography, or other influences that would not divert the exhaust into occupied areas or prevent dispersion of the exhaust

5.1.3.6.7.3 The end of the exhaust shall be turned down and screened or otherwise be protected against the entry of vermin, debris, or precipitation by screening fabricated or composed of a noncorroding material.

5.1.3.6.7.4 The exhaust shall be piped of materials approved for medical–surgical vacuum piping under 5.1.10.2.

5.1.3.6.7.5 The exhaust shall be free of dips and loops that might trap condensate or oil. Where such low points are unavoidable, a drip leg and valved drain shall be installed.

5.1.3.6.7.6 Vacuum exhausts from multiple pumps shall be permitted to be joined together to one common exhaust where the following conditions are met:

(1) The common exhaust is sized to minimize back pressure in accordance with the pump manufacturer's recommendations.

(2) Each pump can be isolated by manual or check valve, blind flange, or tube cap to prevent open exhaust piping when pump(s) is removed for service and consequent flow of exhaust air into the room.

Manifolding of exhausts represents considerable savings if the distances of pipe runs are great. However, adequate ability to isolate each pump is necessary when manifolding exhausts, as required by 5.1.3.6.7.6(2). This requires a method to isolate both the inlet side of each pump and the exhaust side.

Provision for these elements must consider the pump technology and the potential problems this technology might present. Many pumps do poorly when the backpressure in the discharge is great, and most will suffer declines in their efficiency. Manual valves in the discharge line are particularly problematic because turning off a discharge valve can utterly ruin a pump in a very short time. These valves should always be locked open to prevent accidental closure. Automatic valves might be preferred for this reason.

EXHIBIT 5.15 Scavenging device mounted on the side of an anesthesia setup that connects to the waste anesthetic gas disposal system in an operating room.

5.1.3.6.8 Operating Alarms. Medical–surgical vacuum systems shall activate a local alarm when the backup or lag pump is running per 5.1.9.5. This signal shall be manually reset.

The signal required by 5.1.3.6.8 is intended to notify maintenance personnel that a piece of normally standby equipment is operating. This signal usually indicates a system malfunction that should be investigated.

5.1.3.7* Waste Anesthetic Gas Disposal (WAGD).

WAGD is sometimes called *scavenging* or *evacuation*. It is preferable, however, to use the term *scavenging* in connection with the equipment used between the anesthesia machine and inlet of a disposal system, rather than with the pipeline itself. (See Exhibit 5.15.)

A medical–surgical vacuum system functions for suction therapies directly applied to patient care. WAGD is primarily an environmental system with occupational safety implications. However, because WAGD directly connects with the patient breathing circuit, its proper design, installation, and functioning are a matter of importance to patient safety.

The standard explicitly includes requirements for three different WAGD methods. Which method to use is best decided on the basis of clinical preferences and practice, economics, and safety. Along with the inclusion of three alternative methods, the standard requires a certain minimum level of operating safety, including alarms and redundant WAGD producers. Here in the 2005 edition, the basic options remain unchanged, but the methods for implementation have increased.

Significantly in this edition, particular emphasis has been placed on fire safety in WAGD producers following a number of reports of fires in pumps used for dual use (WAGD and medical–surgical vacuum) service. Several of these reports appear to have a possible WAGD component, thus the more stringent requirement seen in 5.1.3.7.1.2(2).

Significant changes are occurring in WAGD at the anesthesia machine. Research in the 1970s by the former Committee on Medical–Surgical Vacuum and ANSI Z79.11, *Standard for Anesthetic Equipment-Scavenging Systems for Excess Anesthetic Gases* [10] found that the maximum volume flowing into WAGD terminal from a single patient was less than 15.3 SLPM (0.54 SCFM), during a worst-case displacement/momentary demand [maximum 5 seconds or 0.045 standard ft^3 (1.27 L)] during oxygen flush or because of occluded scavenging equipment (as noted in Table A1 in ANSI Z79.11). Normal operational displacement was held to be less than 9.9 SLPM (0.35 SCFM). Design of WAGD systems in the United States has generally assumed these would be typical inflows at the terminals. As a result, WAGD systems in the United States have tended to become little more than appendages of the vacuum system, often no more than an extra vacuum terminal with a different color.

However, the data are now outdated. WAGD interfaces that flow a continuous 51 SLPM (1.8 SCFM) into the wall inlet are now in use, and others have been demonstrated to flow even more under some circumstances. These high inflows have a positive impact on anesthesia machine operation and patient and staff safety, but they greatly change the way WAGD needs to be dealt with at the producer.

NFPA 99 has long included the following list of references and reasons for separating the WAGD and vacuum systems to which we would now add high flows:

1. ANSI Z79.11 [10] states that the maximum safe negative pressure for the patient "shall not exceed 0.5 cm H_2O (0.014 in. Hg)." This vacuum level is very low compared to the minimum 300 mm (12 in.) Hg of vacuum in the medical–surgical vacuum system (MSVS).
2. The standard alarm systems and monitoring gauges required for MSVS cannot be used in a WAGD system. WAGD requires switches, sensors, and gauges appropriate for the very low vacuum levels encountered and, in some implementations, can require the use of flow in place of pressure as an operating indicator.
3. Nonrecirculating ventilation systems, dedicated blower systems, and passive systems (ambient differential) have all been demonstrated to be effective for WAGD. The intent of ANSI Z79.11 [10] that the pressure of a scavenging system approximate ambient pressure in normal use can be met by these systems but not by an MSVS system.
4. Some of the valving and piping material acceptable for use in an MSVS is not acceptable for WAGD. This material includes components made of some elastomers (many anesthetic agents can cause O-rings made of these materials to swell) and aluminum, brass, magnesium, tin, and lead (halothane and other fluorinated agents can attack these unalloyed metals in the presence of water vapor).
5. The International Standards Organization (ISO) and the British Standards Institute oppose using an MSVS for WAGD. Both organizations concur with 0.5 cm H_2O (0.014 in. Hg) as the maximum safe negative pressure for patients.
6. High air flows between WAGD and vacuum may not be compatible.

A.5.1.3.7 A functioning WAGD system will permit the facility to comply with occupational safety requirements by preventing the accumulation of waste anesthetic gases in the work environment.

WAGD using an HVAC (i.e., heating, ventilation, and air conditioning) system are not within the scope of Chapter 5.

Flammable and nonflammable gases are known to be incompatible with some seals and piping used in medical–surgical vacuum systems. If waste anesthetic gas disposal is to be included as part of the medical–surgical vacuum system, it should be recognized that this activity might cause deterioration of the vacuum system. The station inlet performance tests outlined in 5.1.12.3.10 are extremely important in maintaining the integrity of the medical–surgical vacuum system, and they should be made at more frequent intervals if waste anesthetic gas disposal is included in the vacuum system.

5.1.3.7.1* Sources. WAGD sources shall be chosen in consultation with the medical staff having knowledge of the requirements to determine the type of system, number and placement of terminals, and other required safety and operating devices.

A.5.1.3.7.1 Interfaces are provided with overpressure, underpressure, overflow, and underflow compensation to ensure the breathing circuit is isolated from the WAGD system.

5.1.3.7.1.1 WAGD shall be permitted to be produced by a dedicated producer, through the medical–surgical vacuum source or by venturi.

5.1.3.7.1.2 If WAGD is produced by the medical–surgical vacuum source, the following shall apply:

(1) The medical–surgical vacuum source shall comply with 5.1.3.6.

(2) Flammable anesthetics or other flammable vapors shall be diluted below the lower flammable limit prior to disposal into the medical–surgical vacuum system or the vacuum pumps shall comply with 5.1.3.7.2.1(2).
(3) The medical–surgical vacuum source shall be sized to accommodate the additional volume.

It is inappropriate to label WAGD terminals "suction" or to use a suction terminal for WAGD, even when using a dual-use piped system. Each occupancy considered an anesthetizing location should have at least one dedicated and labeled WAGD terminal.

5.1.3.7.1.3 If WAGD is produced by a dedicated WAGD producer with a total power greater than 1 horsepower in total (both producers), the following shall apply:

(1) The WAGD source shall be located in accordance with 5.1.3.3.
(2) The WAGD source shall be indoors in a dedicated mechanical equipment area with any required utilities.
(3) The WAGD source shall be in a room constructed per 5.1.3.3.2.
(4) The WAGD source shall be ventilated per 5.1.3.3.3.2.
(5) For air-cooled equipment, the WAGD source shall be located to maintain the ambient temperature range as recommended by the manufacturer.
(6) The WAGD producers shall comply with 5.1.3.7.2.

The division between "greater than 1 Hp" and "less than 1 Hp" herein recognizes a division in the operating parameters of these two different styles of systems wherein one is a large central system and the other is a smaller producer mounted locally. The hazards associated with each are different, and burdening the small system with the same requirements as the large makes it impractical.

5.1.3.7.1.4 If WAGD is produced by a dedicated WAGD producer with a total power less than 1 horsepower in total (both producers), the following shall be permitted to apply:

(1) The WAGD source shall be permitted to be located near the inlet(s) served.
(2) For air-cooled equipment, the WAGD source shall be located to maintain the ambient temperature range as recommended by the manufacturer.

5.1.3.7.1.5 For liquid ring pumps in WAGD service, seal water shall be of a quality as recommended by the pump manufacturer.

5.1.3.7.1.6 The WAGD source shall consist of the following:

(1) Two or more WAGD producers sufficient to serve the peak calculated demand with the largest single WAGD producer out of service
(2) An automatic means to prevent backflow from any on-cycle WAGD producers through any off-cycle WAGD producers
(3) A shutoff valve to isolate each WAGD producer from the centrally piped system and other WAGD producers for maintenance or repair without loss of medical–surgical vacuum in the system
(4) Piping between the WAGD producers and the source shutoff valve compliant with 5.1.10.2, except that stainless steel shall be permitted to be used as a piping material
(5) Anti-vibration mountings shall be installed for WAGD producers as required by equipment dynamics or location and in accordance with the manufacturer's recommendations
(6) Flexible connectors interconnecting the producers with their intake and outlet piping as required by equipment dynamics or location, in accordance with the WAGD producer manufacturer's recommendations

5.1.3.7.1.7 If WAGD is produced by a venturi, the following shall apply:

(1) The venturi shall not be user-adjustable (i.e., shall require the use of special tools).
(2) The venturi shall be driven using water, inert gas, instrument air, or other dedicated air source.
(3) Medical air shall not be used to power the venturi.

5.1.3.7.2 WAGD Producers.

5.1.3.7.2.1 Vacuum pumps used for WAGD service shall be as follows:

(1) Compliant with 5.1.3.6.2
(2) Designed of materials and using lubricants and sealants that are inert in the presence of oxygen, nitrous oxide, and halogenated anesthetics

FAQ ▶ Why is it important that the lubricants and sealants be inert in the presence of oxidizers?

Because of the possible presence of gases that are strong oxidizers in a WAGD system, it is imperative that a vacuum producer use a sealant, such as water (in liquid ring pumps), or halogenated lubricants in pumps requiring oil or grease, that will not react with explosive force when the sealant or lubricant comes in contact with oxidizers.

The use of flammable anesthetics in the United States has essentially ceased. However, the emergency use of flammable anesthetics can contribute additional and unnecessary hazards if a medical–surgical vacuum system is used for WAGD. Paragraph 5.1.3.7.2 has remained to draw attention to the potential hazard of a medical–surgical vacuum system used for WAGD when flammable anesthetics are used.

5.1.3.7.2.2 Vacuum producers (e.g., fans or blowers) designed for operation at vacuums below 130 mm (5 in.) HgV shall be as follows:

(1) Permitted to be made of any materials determined by the manufacturer as suitable for the service
(2) Provided with anti-vibration mountings as required by equipment dynamics or location and in accordance with the manufacturer's recommendation
(3) Connected with their intake and outlet piping through flexible connections
(4) Used only for WAGD service and not employed for other services
(5) Interconnected via piping, ductwork, and so on made of materials determined by the manufacturer as suitable to the service

5.1.3.7.3 If WAGD is joined to vacuum piping, it shall be connected a minimum distance of 1.5 m (5 ft) from any vacuum inlet.

5.1.3.7.4 WAGD Alarms. When the WAGD system is served by a central source(s), a local alarm complying with 5.1.9.5 shall be provided for the WAGD source.

5.1.3.7.4.1 A WAGD source system shall activate a local alarm when the backup or lag producer is running.

5.1.3.7.5 Electrical Power and Control.

5.1.3.7.5.1 Additional producers shall automatically activate when the producer(s) in operation is incapable of maintaining the required vacuum.

5.1.3.7.5.2 Automatic or manual alternation of producers shall allow division of operating time. If automatic alternation of producers is not provided, the facility staff shall arrange a schedule for manual alternation.

5.1.3.7.5.3 Each producer motor shall be provided with electrical components including, but not limited to, the following:

(1) A dedicated disconnect switch installed in the electrical circuit ahead of each motor starter
(2) Motor starting device
(3) Overload protection
(4) Where WAGD systems having two or more producers employ a control transformer or other voltage control power device, at least two such devices
(5) Control circuits arranged in such a manner that the shutdown of one producer does not interrupt the operation of another producer
(6) Automatic restart function such that pump(s) will restart after power interruption without manual intervention

5.1.3.7.5.4 Electrical installation and wiring shall conform to the requirements of NFPA 70, *National Electrical Code*.

5.1.3.7.5.5 Emergency electrical service for the producers shall conform to the requirements of the essential electrical system as described in Chapter 4 of this document.

5.1.3.7.6 WAGD Exhaust. The WAGD pumps shall exhaust in compliance with 5.1.3.6.7.

The location of the exhaust of a WAGD producer is particularly critical with regard to intakes, for example, for air conditioning or medical air.

5.1.3.8* Instrument Air Supply Systems.

Instrument air is being installed in some facilities and is viewed in NFPA 99 as an alternative to piped high-pressure nitrogen. It operates at similar pressures, is filtered and dried to similar levels, and is intended to perform the same functions. Instrument air is naturally less hazardous than nitrogen, and so is more suited to applications where the gas might be released into the workspace, such as blowing out instruments or running tools. Instrument air is not to be confused with medical air, being of a very different quality, running at a very different pressure, and possibly containing contaminants unacceptable for patient treatment.

◀ **FAQ**
Is instrument air an alternative to nitrogen to power equipment or tools?

The choice of an instrument air system versus a nitrogen system will usually be made on the basis of economics and staff convenience.

A.5.1.3.8 See Figure A.5.1.3.8.

5.1.3.8.1 The quality of instrument air shall be as follows:

(1) Compliant with Instrument Air section in ANSI/ISA S-7.0.01, *Quality Standard for Instrument Air*
(2) Filtered to 0.01 micron
(3) Free of liquids (e.g., water, hydrocarbons, solvents, etc.)
(4) Free of hydrocarbon vapors
(5) Dry to a dew point of −40°C (−40°F)

5.1.3.8.2 General.

5.1.3.8.2.1 Instrument air shall be permitted to be used for any medical support purpose (e.g., to operate tools, air driven booms, pendants, or similar applications) and (if appropriate to the procedures) to be used in laboratories.

Instrument air cannot be used as medical air. Other than this restriction, it can be used for a wide range of applications such as moving booms and pedestals or moving other types of medical equipment. In this respect it is complementary to medical air, which is very limited in acceptable uses.

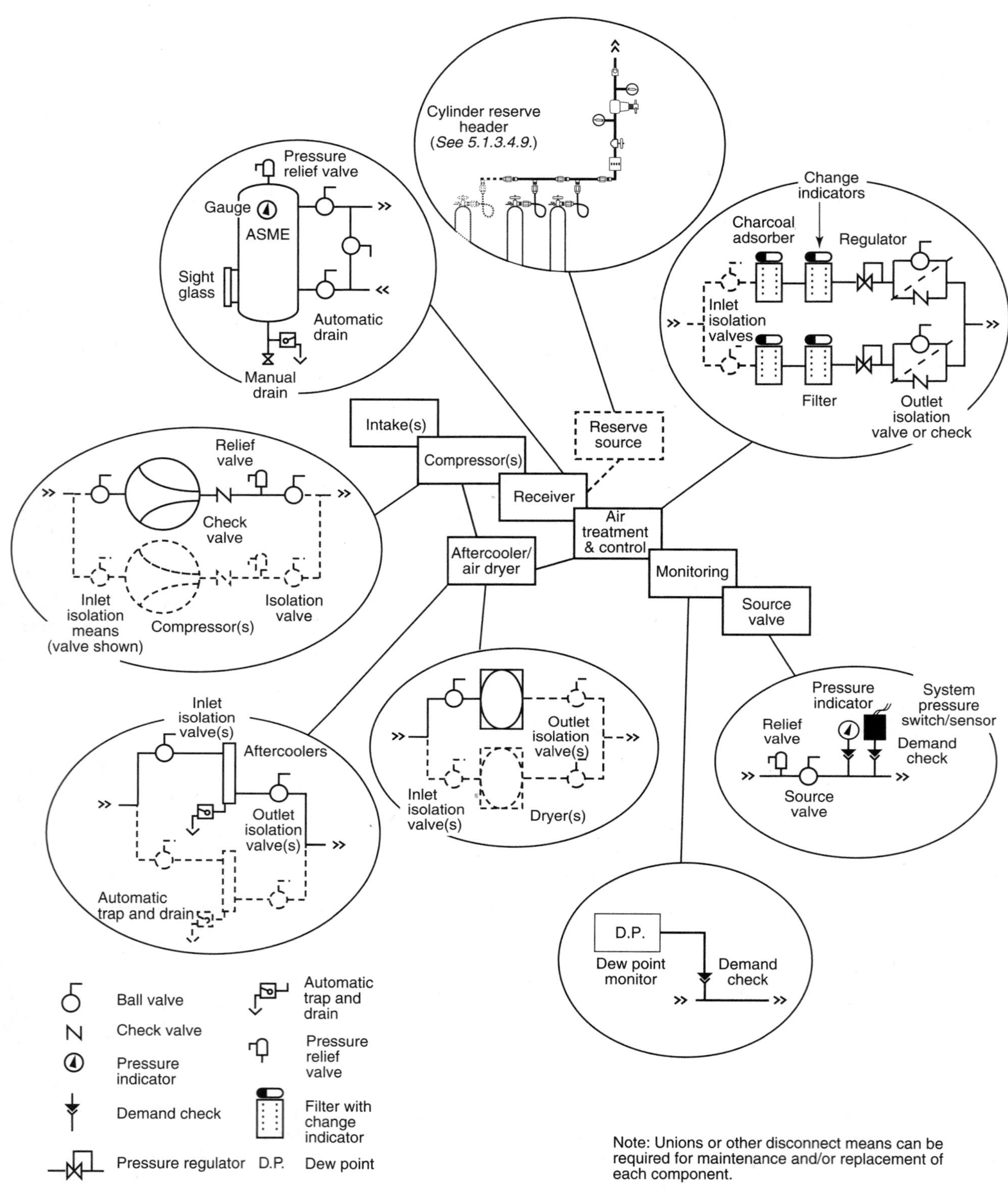

FIGURE A.5.1.3.8 *Elements of Typical Instrument Air Source.*

5.1.3.8.2.2 Instrument air supply systems shall be located per 5.1.3.3 as follows:

(1) Indoors, in a dedicated mechanical equipment area, adequately ventilated and with any required utilities
(2) In a room constructed per 5.1.3.3.2
(3) In a room ventilated per 5.1.3.3.3.2
(4) For air-cooled equipment, in a room designed to maintain the ambient temperature range as recommended by the equipment manufacturer

5.1.3.8.2.3 Instrument air systems shall be prohibited from the following:

(1) Interconnection with medical air systems
(2) Usage for any purpose where the air will be intentionally respired by patients or staff

5.1.3.8.3 Instrument Air Source.

5.1.3.8.3.1 Instrument air sources shall produce air at not less than a gauge pressure of 1380 kPa (200 psi) output pressure.

5.1.3.8.3.2 Instrument air sources shall provide air meeting the definition of Instrument Air in Chapter 3.

5.1.3.8.3.3 Instrument air sources shall be permitted to include at least two compressors or one compressor and a standby header complying with 5.1.3.4.8.

This allowance in 5.1.3.8.3.3 reflects the much less critical application of instrument air when compared with medical air. If the compressor fails, the cylinders allow enough time for some action to be taken to terminate any procedure requiring the use of the air or to provide a temporary source. It is understood that it might not be possible to maintain the system indefinitely with a standby header, which itself is a reflection of the less critical nature of instrument air.

5.1.3.8.3.4 Instrument air sources shall comply with 5.1.3.5.3 with exceptions as specified in 5.1.3.8.

5.1.3.8.4 Instrument Air Compressors. Instrument air compressors shall be permitted to be of any type capable of not less than a gauge pressure of 1380 kPa (200 psi) output pressure and of providing air meeting the definition of Instrument Air in Chapter 3.

5.1.3.8.5* Instrument Air Standby Headers.

A.5.1.3.8.5 Drawing intake air from outside in compliance with 5.1.3.5.13 is recommended. A

5.1.3.8.5.1 Where instrument air systems are provided with a standby header, the header shall meet the following requirements:

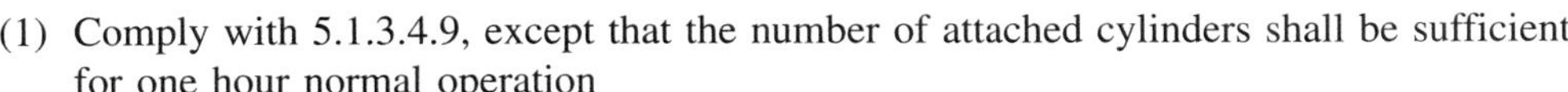

(1) Comply with 5.1.3.4.9, except that the number of attached cylinders shall be sufficient for one hour normal operation

The reserve supply in the cylinders will be medical air. It is not necessary or desirable to buy a specific instrument grade air for this purpose.

(2) Use connectors as for medical air in CGA V-1, *Standard for Compressed Gas Cylinder Valve Outlet and Inlet Connections* (ANSI B57.1)

(3) Enter the system upstream (source side) of the final line filters *(See Figure A.5.1.3.8.)*
(4) Automatically serve the system in the event of a failure of the compressor

5.1.3.8.6 Intake Air. Intake air for instrument air compressors shall be permitted to be drawn from the equipment location.

Unlike medical air, instrument air does not have to be drawn from an outside location. An outside source might be desirable for other reasons, such as general cleanliness and reduction of odors.

5.1.3.8.7 Instrument Air Filters.

5.1.3.8.7.1 Instrument air sources shall be filtered with activated carbon filters that meet the following requirements:

(1) Be located upstream (source side) of the final line filters
(2) Be sized for 100 percent of the system peak calculated demand at design conditions
(3) Be constructed of materials deemed suitable by the manufacturer

5.1.3.8.7.2 Final line filters shall meet the following requirements:

(1) Be located upstream (source side) of the final line regulators and downstream of the carbon filters
(2) Be sized for 100 percent of the system peak calculated demand at design conditions
(3) Be rated for a minimum of 98 percent efficiency at 0.01 micron
(4) Be equipped with a continuous visual indicator showing the status of the filter element life
(5) Be constructed of materials deemed suitable by the manufacturer

5.1.3.8.7.3 Filters combining the function of 5.1.3.8.7.1 and 5.1.3.8.7.2 shall be permitted to be used.

5.1.3.8.8 Instrument Air Accessories. Accessories used for instrument air sources shall comply with the following subparagraphs:

(1) 5.1.3.5.5 for aftercoolers
(2) 5.1.3.5.6 for air receivers
(3) 5.1.3.5.7 for air dryers

Although an instrument air dryer must comply with general requirements for a medical air dryer, note that it must achieve a substantially lower dew point. In this respect, the requirements in 5.1.3.8.1(5) supersede those in 5.1.3.5.7.

(4) 5.1.3.5.9 for air regulators

5.1.3.8.9 Instrument Air Piping Arrangement and Redundancies. Instrument air sources shall comply with 5.1.3.5.11 except for the following:

(1) Systems employing a standby header shall be permitted to have simplex aftercoolers and dryers.
(2) Systems employing a standby header shall not require a three-valve receiver bypass.
(3) Standby headers, where provided, shall be isolated from the compressor by a check valve to prevent backflow through the compressor.

5.1.3.8.10 Instrument Air Monitoring and Alarms.

5.1.3.8.10.1 Instrument air sources shall include the following alarms:

(1) A local alarm that activates when or just before the backup compressor (if provided) activates, indicating that the lag compressor is in operation. This signal shall be manually reset.
(2) A local alarm and alarms at all master alarm panels that activate when the dew point at system pressure exceeds −30°C (−22°F), indicating high dew point.

The dew point for instrument air is significantly lower than for medical air. This seeming anomaly stems from instrument air being used to drive tools, where the adiabatic cooling caused by rapid release of large volumes of gas can chill the air and wring moisture out unless the air has a very low dew point.

5.1.3.8.10.2 For sources with standby headers, the following additional conditions shall activate a local alarm at the compressor site, a local signal at the header location, and alarms at all master alarm panels:

(1) An alarm that activates when or just before the reserve begins to supply the system, indicating reserve in use
(2) An alarm that activates when or just before the reserve falls below an average hour's supply, indicating reserve low

5.1.3.8.11 Electrical Power and Control.

5.1.3.8.11.1 When multiple compressors are used, additional compressor(s) shall automatically activate when the compressor(s) in operation is incapable of maintaining the required pressure.

5.1.3.8.11.2 When multiple compressors are used, automatic or manual alternation of compressors shall allow division of operating time. If automatic alternation of compressors is not provided, the facility staff shall arrange a schedule for manual alternation.

5.1.3.8.11.3 Each compressor motor shall be provided with electrical components including, but not limited to, the following:

(1) A dedicated disconnect switch installed in the electrical circuit ahead of each motor starter
(2) Motor starting device
(3) Overload protection
(4) Where compressor systems having two or more compressors employ a control transformer or other voltage control power device, at least two such devices shall be installed
(5) Control circuits arranged in such a manner that the shutdown of one compressor does not interrupt the operation of another compressor
(6) Automatic restart function such that compressor(s) will restart after power interruption without manual intervention

5.1.3.8.11.4 Electrical installation and wiring shall conform to the requirements of NFPA 70, *National Electrical Code.*

5.1.3.8.11.5 Emergency electrical service for the compressors shall conform to the requirements of the essential electrical system as described in Chapter 4 of this document.

5.1.4* Valves.

A.5.1.4 See Figure A.5.1.4.

Area alarms are required in critical care locations (examples include intensive care units, coronary care units, angiography laboratories, cardiac catherization laboratories, postanesthesia recovery rooms, and emergency rooms) and anesthetizing locations (examples include operating rooms and delivery rooms). Refer to definitions for these areas.

The symbol illustrating "a valve which must be secured" is shown as a key in Figure A.5.1.4. The key image does not imply a lock, although that could be one way of securing the valve. The text simply requires that the valve be secure.

5.1.4.1 Gas and Vacuum Shutoff Valves. Shutoff valves shall be provided to isolate sections or portions of the piped distribution system for maintenance, repair, or planned future expansion need, and to facilitate periodic testing.

Good design places valves where necessary to break the system into discrete, logical sections. (See Exhibit 5.16.)

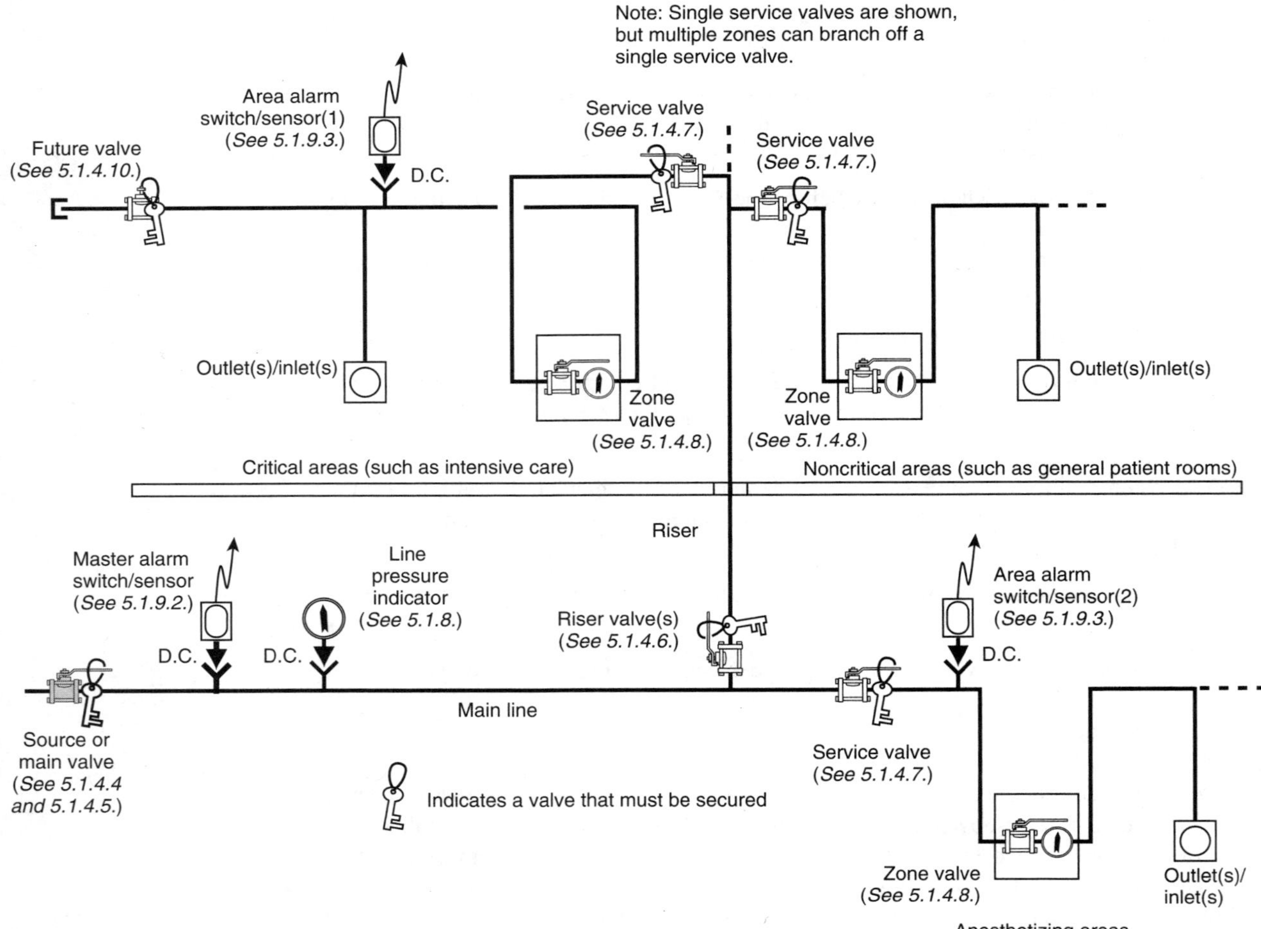

FIGURE A.5.1.4 Arrangement of Pipeline Components.

5.1.4.2 Accessibility. All valves except valves in zone valve box assemblies shall be located in secured areas such as locked piped chases, or be locked or latched in their operating position, and be labeled as to gas supplied and the area(s) controlled.

FAQ ▶
Is the space above a drop ceiling considered a secure area?

The question is often asked: Is the space above a drop ceiling considered a secured area? Although it might be useful or even necessary to lock valves open or closed, the basic intent of 5.1.4.2 is to separate those valves that are intended for fire or other emergency use (i.e., the zone valves) from those that are intended to be operated only by staff in a controlled, planned way for maintenance or construction. A valve above the ceiling clearly is invisible and inaccessible to the casual passerby or to staff during an evacuation, and it cannot be

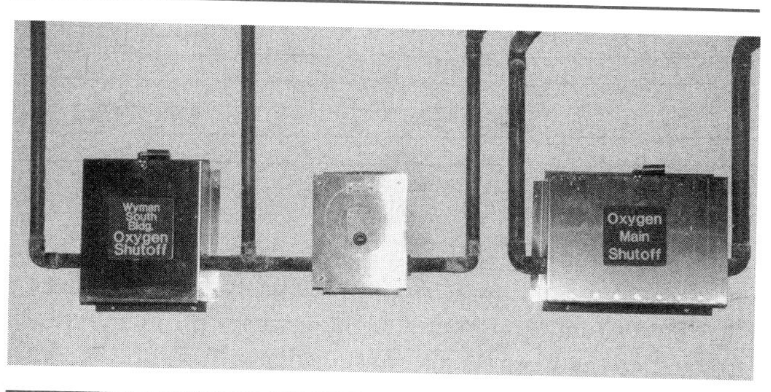

EXHIBIT 5.16 The main oxygen shutoff valve in a hospital.

accessed without a ladder or other extraordinary effort. The area above a drop ceiling therefore can be considered secure for most purposes.

5.1.4.2.1 Shutoff valves accessible to other than authorized personnel shall be installed in valve boxes with frangible or removable windows large enough to permit manual operation of valves.

Only zone valves are meant to be accessible to staff during an emergency, especially a fire. Although there is sometimes anxiety about these valves being closed maliciously, the risk of an uncontrolled release of medical gases in an emergency or fire is sufficient to continue requiring these valves.

5.1.4.2.2 Shutoff valves for use in certain areas, such as psychiatric or pediatric, shall be permitted to be secured with the approval of the authority having jurisdiction to prevent inappropriate access.

◄ **FAQ**
What are some examples of securing the shutoff valves in these certain areas?

Zone valve box assemblies have for years been required to be readily accessible in an emergency. This may not be practical, however, in areas such as pediatric or psychiatric wards.

Typical modifications to secure zone valves in these locations can include a lockable valve box door with only staff having the key, removable handles that are kept at the nurses' station, and the zone valves installed inside a locked area such as the nurses' station or the drug storage area in the unit.

Zone valves placed in a locked room must be relocated if the type of patients in that area changes. Therefore, consideration should be given to using a standard location for the valves, and removing handles or installing a lockable door as the security feature.

5.1.4.2.3 Valves for nonflammable medical gases shall not be installed in the same zone valve box assembly with flammable gases.

5.1.4.3 Valve Types. New or replacement shutoff valves shall be as follows:

(1) Quarter turn, full ported, ball type
(2) Brass or bronze construction
(3) Have extensions for brazing
(4) Have a handle indicating open or closed
(5) Consist of three-pieces permitting inline serviceability

The quarter turn ball valve required by 5.1.4.3(1) has become the standard type of valve used in medical gas systems. It allows for the quick shutoff of gas, which is highly desirable in an emergency such as a fire. The requirement that new valves be of three-piece construction facilitates maintenance.

The standard is silent on the question of "double-port" or "single-port" valves, so either can be used at the convenience of the client.

5.1.4.3.1 Valves for positive pressure gases shall be cleaned for oxygen service by the manufacturer.

5.1.4.3.2 Valves for vacuum or WAGD service shall be permitted to be ball or butterfly type and shall not be required to be cleaned for oxygen service.

5.1.4.4 Source Valve. A shutoff valve shall be placed at the immediate connection of each source system to the piped distribution system to permit the entire source, including all accessory devices (e.g., air dryers, final line regulators, etc.), to be isolated from the facility.

The 5.1.4.4 provision for a source valve was made to eliminate an anomaly created in the requirements for piped gas systems when the leak testing in 5.1.12.2.6 was done with the main line shutoff valve closed. This situation allowed a system to be tested without testing the piping between the valve and the source equipment. Because this line could run substantial distances, a distinct hazard existed. The provision for a source valve is intended to eliminate this anomaly.

5.1.4.4.1 The source valve shall be located in the immediate vicinity of the source equipment.

5.1.4.4.2 The source valve shall be labeled in accordance with 5.1.11.2.

5.1.4.5* Main Line Valve. A shutoff valve shall be provided in the main supply line inside of the building, except where one or more of the following conditions exist:

(1) The source and source valve are located inside the building served.

FAQ ▶ Are main line valves always required?

The source valve is allowed to substitute for the main line shutoff valve if both would normally be located inside the building. This is commonly the case with a medical air compressor system or can happen with a manifold room in the basement. This eliminates the wasteful installation of a source valve and a main line valve inches apart.

(2) The source system is physically mounted to the wall of the building served and the pipeline enters the building in the immediate vicinity of the source valve.

The main line valve required by 5.1.4.5 is often misconstrued as a valve intended for the fire department to shut off the supply to the building in an emergency. It is not and has never been intended for this purpose. Under a "defend in place" fire protection strategy (for facilities that cannot easily be evacuated, such as hospitals and nursing homes), shutting off the main valve could have the most disastrous consequences. The primary function of the main valve is to isolate the source from the building, as might be required when changing the bulk system or if the main line is damaged. The one time a main line shutoff valve is ever likely to be used is when a new source is being installed or the source is relocated.

New to the 2005 edition is the allowance for omitting the main line shutoff valve when the source equipment (and by extension, the source valve) are located on an exterior wall. This is commonly seen with manifolds, which might literally be mounted to the outside of the building with the source valve right next to the point where the line enters the building. Previously, the test was for the main line valve simply being outdoors, which led to some anomalous situations and virtually redundant valves. Now the test is one of separation from the building, which means that if the piping is not at risk, the main line valve can be omitted in many cases.

A **A.5.1.4.5** The presence of a main line shutoff valve is optional where the source valve can equally or more effectively perform the same function. An example is a case where the source is within the building or just on the outside of the building and therefore there would be no great distance separating the two valves. A source that was physically separate from the building would require both valves to assure the intervening piping could be controlled.

5.1.4.5.1 The main line valve shall be located to permit access by authorized personnel only (i.e., by locating above a ceiling or behind a locked access door).

5.1.4.5.2 The main line valve shall be located on the facility side of the source valve and outside of the source room, enclosure, or where the main line first enters the building.

5.1.4.5.3 The main line valve shall be labeled in accordance with 5.1.11.2.

5.1.4.6 Riser Valve. Each riser supplied from the main line shall be provided with a shutoff valve in the riser adjacent to the main line.

The valve required by 5.1.4.6 allows one riser to be shut down without having to shut down the entire piped gas distribution system (e.g., for repairs or modifications). In addition, during new construction, a shutoff valve at the base of each riser will allow isolation and testing of the system in increments.

With single-story facilities, the term *riser* is not relevant, but the concept of isolation by larger sections might still be important. The prudent designer seeks to apply (within reason) the old hospital engineer's saying: "There is no such thing as too many valves."

5.1.4.6.1 Riser valves shall be permitted to be located above ceilings, but shall remain accessible and not be obstructed.

Although ball valves at the base of risers are required, these valves must not be blocked from access. It is frequently observed that riser valves are visually obscured or blocked by other service ducts or piping. Because the riser valves allow a facility more flexibility with future work or additions to the medical gas pipeline systems, these valves should always be accessible, albeit only to service personnel.

5.1.4.6.2 The riser valve shall be labeled in accordance with 5.1.11.2.

5.1.4.7 Service Valves. Service valves shall be installed to allow servicing or modification of lateral branch piping from a main or riser without shutting down the entire main, riser, or facility.

Service shutoff valves as required by 5.1.4.7 reduce the number of valves and areas affected when only one floor of a multistory building requires shutdown for maintenance or other reasons. In the simplest terms, there must never be a zone valve without a preceding service valve, although multiple zone valves can come off one service valve.

Service shutoff valves are to be located immediately off the riser prior to any zone valves installed on that lateral. With such valves installed at the origin of the lateral branch, even if that lateral branch leads to four or five separate zone valve sets, it is easier to plan the temporary shutdown of those four or five zones rather than an entire facility. These valves are to be held in the open position and either in a locked chase or locked open at all times.

Service valves do need to be locked open or locked in a secure area, unlike riser and main line valves, which must merely be secured.

All service shutoff valves should have labels indicating gas and area controlled.

5.1.4.7.1 Only one service valve shall be required for each branch off of a riser regardless of how many zone valve boxes are installed on that lateral.

5.1.4.7.2 Service valves shall be placed in the branch piping prior to any zone valve box assembly on that branch.

5.1.4.7.3 Service valves shall be located according to any one of the following:

(1) Behind a locked access door
(2) Locked open above a ceiling
(3) Locked open in a secure area

5.1.4.7.4 Service valves shall be labeled in accordance with 5.1.11.2.

5.1.4.7.5 Sensors for area alarm panels as required in 5.1.9.3.4 shall be permitted to be placed in any relationship to service valves (if installed).

Paragraph 5.1.4.7.5 makes it clear that the location of the service valve can be ignored when locating the alarm switch or sensor. This allowance reflects the fact that the service valve will always be open (and typically locked open) and thus does not impact the operation of the alarm.

5.1.4.8 Zone Valve. All station outlets/inlets shall be supplied through a zone valve as follows:

(1) The zone valve shall be placed such that a wall intervenes between the valve and outlets/inlets that it controls.
(2) The zone valve shall serve only outlets/inlets located on that same story.

The purpose of requiring a "wall" between the valves and outlets is to allow someone to shut off the flow of gas to a fire site without being directly exposed to the fire and any products of combustion.

FAQ ▶
Is a door also required in the "wall" between the valves and outlets?

A zone valve box assembly is permitted to be installed at the nurses' station of a patient area as long as patient rooms have walls and doors, as might be seen in an intensive care unit. An emergency suite, however, might only have curtains separating cubicles from the nurses' station. In this case, the nurses' station is not an acceptable location for the valve box.

Piped gas and vacuum systems must have a gauge in, or near, the alarm panel location (see 5.1.8.2.2) and gauges on the patient side of zone valve box assemblies. This standard does not mandate installing new gauges, valves, zone valve box assemblies with gauges, or alarm panels in existing systems. A renovation project could make their installation possible, depending on the extent of the project. (See Exhibit 5.17.)

EXHIBIT 5.17 A typical zone valve box assembly in a unit of the facility. Note that it shows what rooms are controlled by these valves.

5.1.4.8.1 Zone valves shall be readily operable from a standing position in the corridor on the same floor they serve.

5.1.4.8.2 Zone valves shall be so arranged that shutting off the supply of medical gas or vacuum to one zone will not affect the supply of medical gas or vacuum to another zone or the rest of the system.

A simple rule of valve placement is that zone valves must never be placed in series. Some examples of how valves can be placed in series might include the following:

1. Tie-ins are made downstream from an existing zone valve with a second set of zone valves installed, creating a condition whereby zone valves are installed in series.
2. Zone valves and piping are installed in such a manner that a zone valve controls piping in more than one zone.
3. A zone valve controlling station terminals is placed on more than one floor.

Because closure of a single set of valves would create undesirable and unexpected effects, the preceding conditions would compromise both fire safety and patient care.

5.1.4.8.3 A pressure/vacuum indicator shall be provided on the station outlet/inlet side of each zone valve.

5.1.4.8.4 Zone valve boxes shall be installed where they are visible and accessible at all times.

It has always been the intent of the standard that zone valve box assemblies be readily accessible and visible at all times, as required by 5.1.4.8.4. These valve boxes, for example, should not be installed behind doors that normally will be open or held open or next to doors that will be opened in an emergency, because such valve boxes might be hidden as patients are removed from a fire scene. Further, if floor actuators are used for automatic doors, the doors will not close if someone is standing on the switch. This could make it difficult to shut off the gases in the affected area if the valve box is behind the opened door.

5.1.4.8.5 Zone valve boxes shall not be installed behind normally open or normally closed doors, or otherwise hidden from plain view.

5.1.4.8.6 Zone valve boxes shall not be located in closed or locked rooms, areas, or closets.

5.1.4.8.7 A zone valve shall be located immediately outside each vital life-support, critical care, and anesthetizing location in each medical gas and/or vacuum line, and located so as to be readily accessible in an emergency.

Zone valves are required by 5.1.4.8.7 to be located outside the areas listed, because in the event of a fire, the staff would not have to enter the fire site to shut off the gas. Also, staff outside an operating room, in addition to those inside, would be able to shut off the gas supplies if required or necessary.

"Outside" in an operating room means near the door that would be used to exit in the event of a fire. Typically, the door of choice is the same one through which the patients will be brought in and out. It does not usually mean a rear door through which equipment might be brought, or a side door where a common scrub room might be located.

If there is more than one operating room in the anesthetizing location, each room must have an independent shutoff valve, which does not preclude a facility from installing an additional shutoff valve inside an operating room.

See also the commentary on medical gas alarms following 5.1.9.

5.1.4.8.7.1 All gas-delivery columns, hose reels, ceiling tracks, control panels, pendants, booms, or other special installations shall be located downstream of the zone valve.

5.1.4.8.7.2 Zone valves shall be so arranged that shutting off the supply of gas to any one operating room or anesthetizing location will not affect the others.

5.1.4.8.8 Zone valves shall be labeled in accordance with 5.1.11.2.

5.1.4.9 In-Line Valves. Optional in-line valves shall be permitted to be installed to isolate or shut off piping for servicing of individual rooms or areas.

For example, in an intensive care unit with 20 beds arranged in a U-shaped pattern, the normal practice is to have one set of valves in a box with the gas feeding from one end of the U to the other. This arrangement is a problem if one oxygen outlet at a bedside in the middle of the unit has to be replaced — oxygen for the entire unit would have to be shut down. An alternate solution would be to pipe the gas in a complete loop and to install a few in-line valves in the piping in the ceiling. When one bed has to be worked on, two valves could be closed, isolating a bed or two only.

Another example of an area where in-line shutoff valves would be helpful is the intensive care nursery. In most arrangements, the isolettes are grouped in pods or along walls. In-line shutoff valves to isolate groups of these beds would prevent disruption of the flow of gases to all of the beds.

It should also be noted that these service valves need not be readily accessible in an emergency — they are not intended for that purpose. Typically they would be located above ceiling tiles or inside casework.

5.1.4.9.1 In-line shutoff valves intended for use to isolate piping for maintenance or modification shall meet the following requirements:

(1) Be located in a restricted area
(2) Be locked or latched open
(3) Be identified in accordance with 5.1.11.2

5.1.4.9.2 Sensors for area alarm panels as required in 5.1.9.3.4 shall be permitted to be placed in any relationship to in-line valves (if installed).

5.1.4.10 Valves for Future Connections. Shutoff valves provided for the connection of future piping shall meet the following requirements:

(1) Be located in a restricted area
(2) Be locked or latched closed
(3) Be identified in accordance with 5.1.11.2

Valves for future connections are optional and placed at the discretion of the facility. They are never mandatory.

5.1.4.10.1 Future connection valves shall be labeled as to gas content.

5.1.4.10.2 Downstream piping shall be closed with a brazed cap with tubing allowance for cutting and rebrazing.

5.1.5* Station Outlet/Inlets.

A.5.1.5 Station outlets/inlets should be located at an appropriate height above the floor to prevent physical damage to equipment attached to the outlet.

See Exhibits 5.18 and 5.19. Note that the oxygen outlet in Exhibit 5.19 is mechanically different from the medical air outlet, to prevent mix-up in gases when hoses are connected to outlets.

***EXHIBIT 5.18** Typical gas outlet/vacuum inlet configuration in an operating room.*

5.1.5.1 Each station outlet/inlet for medical gases or vacuum shall be gas-specific, whether the outlet/inlet is threaded, or is a noninterchangeable quick-coupler.

5.1.5.2 Each station outlet shall consist of a primary and a secondary valve (or assembly).

5.1.5.3 Each station inlet shall consist of a primary valve (or assembly) and shall be permitted to include a secondary valve (or assembly).

5.1.5.4 The secondary valve (or assembly) shall close automatically to stop the flow of gas (or vacuum, if provided) when the primary valve (or assembly) is removed.

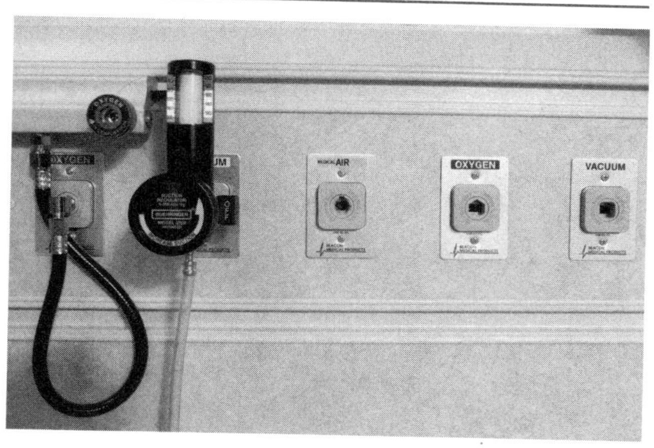

EXHIBIT 5.19 *Station outlets at the head end of a patient bed in a manufactured assembly.*

5.1.5.5 Each outlet/inlet shall be legibly identified in accordance with 5.1.11.3.

5.1.5.6 Threaded outlets/inlets shall be non-interchangeable connections complying with CGA V-5, *Diameter-Index Safety System (Noninterchangeable Low Pressure Connections for Medical Gas Applications).* 

5.1.5.7 Each station outlet/inlet, including those mounted in columns, hose reels, ceiling tracks, or other special installations, shall be designed so that parts or components that are required to be gas-specific for compliance with 5.1.5.1 and 5.1.5.9 cannot be interchanged between station outlet/inlet for different gases.

5.1.5.8 The use of common parts in outlets/inlets, such as springs, O-rings, fasteners, seals, and shutoff poppets, shall be permitted.

5.1.5.9 Components of a vacuum station inlet necessary for the maintenance of vacuum specificity shall be legibly marked to identify them as components or parts of a vacuum or suction system.

5.1.5.10 Components of inlets not specific to vacuum shall not be required to be marked.

5.1.5.11 Factory-installed copper inlet tubes on station outlets extending no further than 205 mm (8 in.) from the body of the terminal shall be not less than DN8 (NPS ¼) (⅜ in. O.D.) size, with 8 mm (0.3 in.) minimum inside diameter.

5.1.5.12 Factory-installed copper inlet tubes on station inlets extending no further than 205 mm (8 in.) from the body of the terminal shall be not less than DN10 (NPS ⅜) (½ in. O.D.) size, with 10 mm (0.4 in.) minimum inside diameter.

5.1.5.13 Station outlets/inlets shall be permitted to be recessed or otherwise protected from damage.

5.1.5.14 When multiple wall outlets/inlets are installed, they shall be spaced to permit the simultaneous use of adjacent outlets/inlets with any of the various types of therapy equipment.

5.1.5.15 Station outlets in systems having non-standard operating pressures shall meet the following additional requirements:

(1) Be gas-specific
(2) Be pressure-specific where a single gas is piped at more than one operating pressure [e.g., a station outlet for oxygen, 550 kPa (80 psi) shall not accept an adapter for oxygen, 345 kPa (50 psi)]
(3) If operated at a pressure in excess of 550 kPa (80 psi), be either D.I.S.S. connectors or comply with 5.1.5.15(4)

(4) If operated at a gauge pressure between 1380 kPa (200 psi) and 2070 kPa (300 psi), the station outlet shall be so designed as to prevent the removal of the adapter until the pressure has been relieved, to prevent the adapter injuring the user or others when removed from the outlet.

The use of station outlets for purposes other than medical gas should not be allowed. Station outlets for medical air, for example, should not be used on pipelines intended for equipment blowdown, cleaning, and so forth.

FAQ ▶ Do the minimum flow characteristics also apply to existing installations?

Minimum flow characteristics for station outlets (see 5.1.12.3.10) apply to the installation of new piped gas systems only. The standard does not include retroactive requirements for existing station outlets.

When installing gas station outlets, it is good practice to consider the space directly over the outlets as well as the distance between them. Because oxygen and vacuum therapy equipment frequently have a height of 0.18 m (7 in.) or more, installing outlets directly under overbed lights or under cabinets could cause the outlets to be inaccessible.

Similarly, many suction canisters in use today are at least 0.18 m (7 in.) or more in diameter. Thus, if oxygen, vacuum, and air are specified at a patient bed location, the best installation sequence would be oxygen–air–vacuum. This arrangement would allow the vacuum outlet and equipment to be located on the end, not cramped between other equipment.

Another point to consider is the number of outlets installed at each patient bed location. For instance, it is usually better, and less expensive, to provide two separate oxygen outlets rather than to install a "twinning" device that plugs into one outlet and provides two connections.

The reuse of old medical gas outlets in renovation projects should be avoided because used outlets generally require extensive cleaning and refurbishing, with new O-rings and other seals, so the cost of a new outlet will most likely be comparable.

5.1.5.16 WAGD networks shall provide a WAGD inlet in all locations where nitrous oxide or halogenated anesthetic gas is intended to be administered.

The location in which WAGD inlets must be installed is a very complex issue in a health care environment, where the nature of anesthesia is changing rapidly. At one time, most general anesthesia involved gaseous anesthetics; now much general anesthesia is performed by injection. As a result, almost any site in the hospital could now be an anesthetizing location, thereby greatly complicating the question of where to place WAGD inlets.

The designer should at least define an anesthetizing location for the purpose of WAGD as any site where nitrous oxide or halogenated anesthetic will be administered. It should also be taken into consideration that there are other instances for installing a WAGD inlet (e.g., use of portable supplies of nitric oxide).

5.1.5.16.1 Station inlets for WAGD service shall have the following additional characteristics:

(1) They shall not be interchangeable with any other systems, including medical–surgical vacuum.
(2) Components necessary for the maintenance of WAGD specificity shall be legibly marked to identify them as components of a WAGD inlet.
(3) They shall be of a type appropriate for the flow and vacuum level required by the facility's gas anesthetic machines.
(4) They shall be located to avoid physical damage to the inlet.

5.1.6* Manufactured Assemblies.

A **A.5.1.6** Manufactured assembly examples include headwalls, columns, ceiling columns, ceiling hung pendants, movable track systems, and so forth. See Figure A.5.1.6.

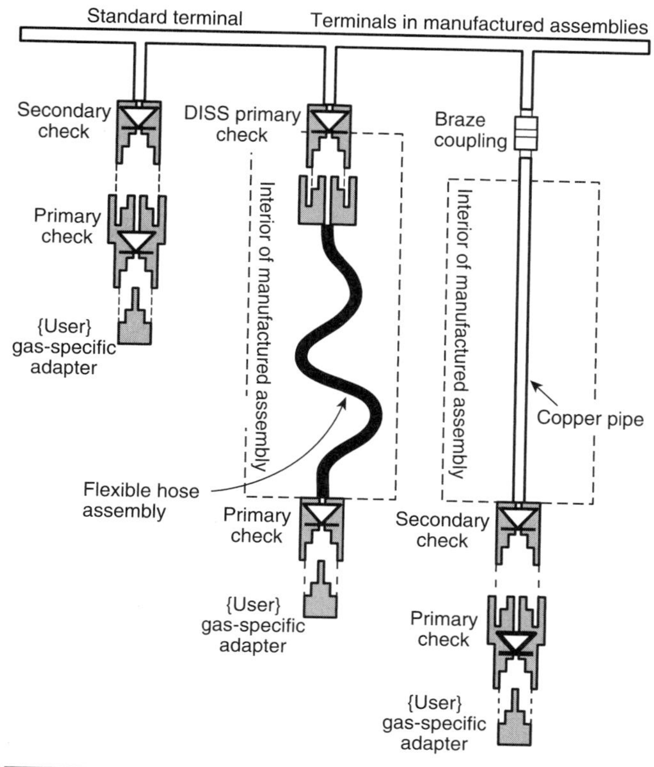

FIGURE A.5.1.6 *Terminals in Manufactured Assemblies.*

The entire question of manufactured assemblies — modular headwalls, ceiling columns, booms, pedestals, and horizontal trunking systems — was previously left to the discretion of users and manufacturers with only general guidance in NFPA 99. A variety of problems, however, were reported as a result of the way these manufactured assemblies were installed and applied. The standard now recognizes these issues and includes safety requirements for these "subcomponents" of a medical gas system.

Traditionally, the pipeline would be considered to end at the station outlet where the copper tubing terminated. However, in manufactured assemblies, several station outlets could be placed along the length of the assembly, ostensibly for "future convenience." The manufactured assembly is then placed over the station outlets, usually with a panel that can be removed for access to the outlets. Attached to some of the station outlets are flexible connectors (usually rubber hoses) connected to a remote terminal point where the user will actually make connections and disconnections. This user outlet forms an extension of the pipeline, which in practice is permanent. Hoses and station outlets are hidden behind or within the manufactured assembly.

Hiding the station outlets and using flexible hoses present hazards relative to the operation of a safe medical gas and vacuum system. Some of these hazards are outlined here:

1. Hidden station outlets are problematic for testing and certification. Unless the verifier is made aware of their presence and these items are left accessible, it is easy to overlook them during the testing process.
2. Flexible connectors and particularly rubber hoses are far less fire resistant than copper pipe. Use of these items significantly increases risks to patients and staff if a fire occurs within or near the assembly. Hiding them behind a panel, where their physical condition cannot be readily inspected, greatly increases the risk of a rupture. In addition, these hoses require periodic replacement because they age over time.

3. The number of connections and outlets from the pipeline that are enclosed inside the manufactured assembly greatly increases the risk of small leaks that can occur with any connection or seal. There is significant risk of developing an oxygen-enriched atmosphere behind the panel, which would greatly increase the speed with which a fire would spread.
4. The use of standard station outlets in series with the terminal is known to create a significant flow restriction. This in turn risks inadequate flow of gas in some clinical situations.
5. Outlets served through small bore flexible tubing will flow less gas and could represent a serious restriction in vacuum.

Although these risks are very real and of great concern, manufactured assemblies have been used with success for decades. The standard attempts to address these concerns without reducing the operational effectiveness of the assemblies.

See 3.3.104, *Manufactured Assembly.*

5.1.6.1 Manufactured assemblies shall be pre-tested by the manufacturer prior to arrival at the installation site as follows:

(1) Initial blowdown test per 5.1.12.2.2
(2) Initial pressure test per 5.1.12.2.3
(3) Piping purge test per 5.1.12.2.5
(4) Standing pressure test per 5.1.12.2.6 or 5.1.12.2.7, except as permitted under 5.1.6.2

Piping internal to manufactured assemblies is deemed to require the same system integrity as the remainder of the piped system.

5.1.6.2 The standing pressure test under 5.1.6.1(4) shall be permitted to be performed by any testing method that will assure a pressure decay of less than 1 percent in 24 hours.

5.1.6.3 The manufacturer of the assembly shall provide documentation certifying the performance and successful completion of the tests required in 5.1.6.1.

5.1.6.4 Manufactured assemblies employing flexible hose shall use hose and flexible connectors with a minimum burst gauge pressure of 6895 kPa (1000 psi).

5.1.6.5 Manufactured assemblies shall have a flame spread rating of not greater than 200 when tested in accordance with NFPA 255, *Standard Method of Test of Surface Burning Characteristics of Building Materials.*

Tubing and flexible hoses used in manufactured assemblies must also have the rating required by 5.1.6.5.

5.1.6.6 Manufactured assemblies employing flexible hose or tubing shall be attached to the pipelines using station outlets /inlets.

5.1.6.7 Manufactured assemblies employing hose or flexible connectors, where the station outlet/inlet attached to the piping is not fully and immediately accessible (i.e., cannot be manipulated without the removal of panels, doors, etc.), shall have station outlets/inlets with the following additional characteristics:

(1) Be D.I.S.S. connectors
(2) In pressure gases, be permitted to omit the secondary valve (or assembly) required in 5.1.5.2
(3) In vacuum and WAGD, be permitted to omit both primary and secondary valves (or assemblies) for minimum restriction to flow
(4) Be provided with a second terminal at which the user connects and disconnects complying with 5.1.5

5.1.6.8 Manufactured assemblies connected to the pipeline by brazing shall have station outlets/inlets that comply with 5.1.5 in all respects.

5.1.6.9 The installation of manufactured assemblies shall be tested in accordance with 5.1.12.

5.1.7* Surface-Mounted Medical Gas Rails (MGR).

Paragraph 5.1.7 codifies the technology of a surface-mounted extension of the traditional piped system, which was introduced in the mid-1980s. The technology does have several limitations and restrictions.

Caution is necessary when determining the number of additional station outlets to be added to a system by the installation of a surface-mounted medical gas rail system. It is akin to the use of electrical extension cords where, if too many appliances are connected, the fuse or circuit breaker for the branch circuit will trip. In this situation, the gas flow rate could be appreciably affected.

A.5.1.7 It is the intent that surface-mounted medical gas rail systems would be permitted in individual patient rooms but would not be allowed to go directly through room walls to adjacent patient rooms. However, it is the intent to allow surface-mounted medical gas rails to be used in a given critical care area where there can be a partition separating certain patient care functions, essentially leaving the system within the given critical care area. As an example, two adjacent patient rooms outside of a critical care unit would not be permitted to have a surface-mounted medical gas rail interconnect between the two rooms through the wall. However, in a nursery where there might be one or two segregated areas for isolation, a medical gas rail system supplying more than one isolation room, but within the nursery area, would be permitted to be interconnected with the nursery system. 

5.1.7.1 MGR assemblies shall be permitted to be installed where multiple uses of medical gases and vacuum at a single patient location are required or anticipated.

Use of the term *patient location* in 5.1.7.1 is very deliberate so as not to exclude any new type of patient treatment configuration that might be developed and eventually lend itself to this type of system.

It should also be noted that a rail system can serve only one (single) patient location. A separate rail system must be installed for each patient location. The rail system cannot penetrate a wall (floor to ceiling).

5.1.7.2 MGR assemblies shall be entirely visible in the room, not passing into or through walls, partitions, and so forth.

5.1.7.3 MGR assemblies shall be made of materials with a melting point at least 538°C (1000°F).

It should be noted that 5.1.7.3 makes no reference to a specific type of metal that can be used for MGR assemblies. Material that is equivalent in mechanical, thermal, and sealing integrity to that of a brazed joint can be used. Note that this equivalency must be determined under actual operating conditions because the melting point of some materials — for example, for basic aluminum — is below 538°C (1000°F). However, with appropriate design consideration, aluminum alloys can be selected with melting points above 538°C (1000°F). Some authorities are restricting aluminum medical gas rails from installations on the basis of the melting point of pure aluminum and are not considering the melting point of the specific aluminum alloy being used.

It is general health care industry practice to use fittings compatible with both metals if the metal used for the medical gas rail system is dissimilar to that of the piping system to which it is connected.

The use of performance criteria (in lieu of specifications) was a deliberate action. The criterion was made as performance-oriented as possible to allow suppliers freedom of design. Compliance will thus have to be determined by a testing laboratory acceptable to the authority having jurisdiction.

5.1.7.4 MGR assemblies shall be cleaned per 5.1.10.1.1.

5.1.7.5 Station outlets or inlets shall not be placed on the ends of MGR assemblies.

5.1.7.6 Openings for station outlets/inlets in the MGR shall be gas-specific.

5.1.7.7 Openings in the MGR not occupied by station outlets/inlets (e.g., for future use) shall be capped or plugged so that a special tool is required for removal (i.e., cannot be removed by a wrench, pliers, screwdriver, or other common tools).

5.1.7.8 MGR assemblies shall connect to the pipeline through fittings that are brazed to the pipeline.

5.1.7.9* Where the pipeline and the MGR assembly are of dissimilar metals, the connections shall be plated or otherwise protected from interaction between the metals.

A.5.1.7.9 Typical plating would be nickel plating over copper or brass per Federal Specification QQ-N290, Class I, Type 7.

5.1.7.10 The installation of the MGR shall be tested in accordance with 5.1.12 and 5.1.13.

5.1.8 Pressure and Vacuum Indicators.

5.1.8.1 General.

5.1.8.1.1 Pressure indicators and manometers for medical gas piping systems shall be cleaned for oxygen service.

5.1.8.1.2 Gauges shall comply with ANSI/ASME B40.100, *Pressure Gauges and Gauge Attachments*.

5.1.8.1.3 The scale range of positive pressure analog indicators shall be such that the normal reading falls within the middle 50 percent of the scale.

5.1.8.1.4 The scale range of digital indicators shall be not more than two times the working pressure of the piping system.

5.1.8.1.5 The scale range of vacuum indicators shall be 0 mm to 760 mm (0 in. to 29.9 in.) gauge HgV, except that indicators with a normal range display shall indicate normal only above 300 mm (12 in.) gauge HgV.

5.1.8.1.6 Indicators adjacent to master alarm actuators and area alarms shall be labeled to identify the name of or chemical symbol for the particular piping system that they monitor.

5.1.8.1.7 The rated accuracy of indicators used for testing shall be 1 percent (full scale) or better at the point of reading.

5.1.8.2 Locations.

5.1.8.2.1 Pressure and vacuum indicators shall be readable from a standing position.

5.1.8.2.2 Pressure/vacuum indicators shall be provided at the following locations, as a minimum:

(1) Adjacent to the alarm-initiating device for source main line pressure and vacuum alarms in the master alarm system

(2) At or in area alarm panels to indicate the pressure/vacuum at the alarm activating device for each system that is monitored by the panel
(3) On the station outlet/inlet side of zone valves

5.1.8.2.3 All pressure-sensing devices and mainline pressure gauges downstream of the source valves shall be provided with a gas-specific demand check fitting to facilitate service testing or replacement.

The requirement of 5.1.8.2.4 for demand check fittings in 5.18.2.3 is not intended to apply to the gauges that are typically found in valve boxes. (See Exhibit 5.20.)

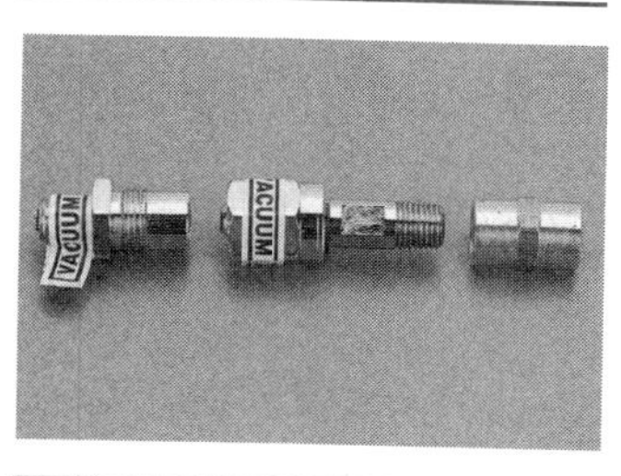

EXHIBIT 5.20 Parts of a typical demand check. (Courtesy of Beacon Medical)

5.1.8.2.3.1 Gas-specific demand check fittings shall not be required on zone valve pressure indicators.

5.1.8.2.4 Demand check fittings shall be provided for all monitors.

Demand check fittings allow sensors, gauges, and other devices to be conveniently detached from the pipeline for servicing, testing, or replacement. Without these checks, many tests required by NFPA 99 would be impractical.

Demand check fittings are required to be gas specific. The need for gas-specific demand check fittings stems from the requirement that alarms be tested on a routine basis (a prime reason for the original demand check requirement). Because the sensors are detached from the lines periodically, it was possible to reinstall the sensors on the wrong lines when reattaching them. Gas-specific connectors reduce this risk.

◀ **FAQ**
Why do demand check fittings need to be gas specific?

5.1.9* Level 1 Warning Systems.

The largest recurring issue with warning systems — that is, alarms — and indeed with valves is the question of where they are required. NFPA 99 calls for alarms for any "critical care or vital life support area," but the definition for such an area is fuzzy, especially given the way health care is delivered in many facilities today.

An instructive case is an endoscopy suite. In the past, a procedure like endoscopy would have been carried out in an operating room (OR), and the question of placing a valve or not, or placing an alarm or not, would have been relatively straightforward. Today, however, an endoscopy suite resides in a gray area. Is an endoscopy suite critical care?

The traditional tests for critical care include answering the following questions:

- Is anesthesia administered there?
- Is the patient rendered incapable of self-preservation?
- Is the patient ever dependent on the gases for life?

In the case of endoscopy, the answer to all three will typically be "no," however great the challenge to a patient obliged to get up and walk out in the middle of a procedure. Therefore, we might seem to conclude that such an area is not critical care and thus does not need an alarm or a dedicated valve. Still, it is uncomfortable that such an occupancy is not considered critical care, and alarms and dedicated valves are very common in such areas. Some regulatory bodies will insist on having them installed there.

It is clear that a better, more relevant test is needed, one that is more germane to the way health care is delivered. That question might best be answered by hospitals, using the same criteria they use for themselves, including the following questions:

- If gases were to fail in that area or room during a procedure, would the procedure have to terminate prematurely? Is it possible that patient outcomes would be negatively impacted?

If the facility answers "yes," then for the purposes of the medical gas and vacuum systems, the area could be treated as critical care, at least for the purpose of locating alarms.

- If a fire were to occur in this area or room, could the adjacent areas be immediately evacuated without negative impact on patient outcomes, or would the adjacent rooms or areas require time to prepare their patients for evacuation?

If the facility were to answer "yes" to this question, the area or room should be considered critical care for the purposes of installing valves. Remember that the most important reason to install valves (albeit the least used) is to help isolate an area in the event of fire. The valves do not help much in the room itself, because the fire is already in there, but they buy time for stabilizing the adjacent patients for evacuation and they act to allow a "defend in place" fire attack to take effect.

A second common case involves the anesthetizing location, where NFPA 99 allows an alarm for a "suite" of rooms but does not require an alarm for each room. Paradoxically, this is due to the fact that the OR is typically able to deal with loss of gas better than any other location in the facility, and the desirability of an alarm in the OR itself is questionable.

Nevertheless, when a facility does put an alarm in each OR, does it also need the "suite" alarm? There are two schools of thought. The first contends that the facility is at liberty to exceed the requirements of NFPA 99 but must still meet the standard; consequently, yes, a "suite" alarm is still required. The second school of thought contends that an alarm in each OR exceeds NFPA 99 and therefore no "suite" alarm is necessary. The document itself only purports to be a minimum safe standard and offers no guidance whatever in cases where the facility elects to exceed the minimum.

In such cases, the only guidance must derive from intent, and owners must make decisions based on their own procedures. Clearly, the intent of alarms in the OR is to inform the staff so that they can act to preserve patients' lives and perhaps resolve the problem. An alarm in the OR clearly best achieves the first goal but in fact might do little to address the second. In a typical OR, it is undesirable and sometimes impossible to have anyone leave the room. Because no one can leave, the options for informing others of the problem in hopes of correcting it could be very limited. Therefore, an alarm at a central location might be desirable in addition. However, particularly with newer technology alarms, other options might exist that are equally good at achieving that objective, and the owner might in that case reasonably elect to eliminate the "suite" alarm.

A.5.1.9 See Figure A.5.1.4.

5.1.9.1 General. All master, area, and local alarm systems used for medical gas and vacuum systems shall include the following:

(1) Separate visual indicators for each condition monitored, except as permitted in 5.1.9.5.2 for local alarms that are displayed on master alarm panels
(2) Visual indicators that remain in alarm until the situation that has caused the alarm is resolved
(3) A cancelable audible indication of each alarm condition that produces a sound with a minimum level of 80 dBA at .92 m (3 ft)
(4) A means to visually indicate a lamp or LED failure
(5) Visual and audible indication that the wiring to an alarm initiating device is disconnected
(6) Labeling of each indicator, indicating the condition monitored
(7) Labeling of each alarm panel for its area of surveillance
(8) Re-initiation of the audible signal if another alarm condition occurs while the audible alarm is silenced
(9) Power for master and area alarms from the life safety branch of the emergency electrical system as described in Chapter 4, Electrical Systems

(10) Power for local alarms, dew point sensors, and carbon monoxide sensors permitted to be from the same essential electrical branch as is used to power the air compressor system

(11) Wiring from switches or sensors that is supervised or protected as required by Section 517.30(c)(3) of NFPA 70, *National Electrical Code*, for emergency system circuits

(12) Assurance by the responsible authority of the facility that the labeling of alarms, where room numbers or designations are used, is accurate and up-to-date

(13) Provisions for automatic restart after a power loss of 10 seconds (e.g., during generator startup) without giving false signals or requiring manual reset

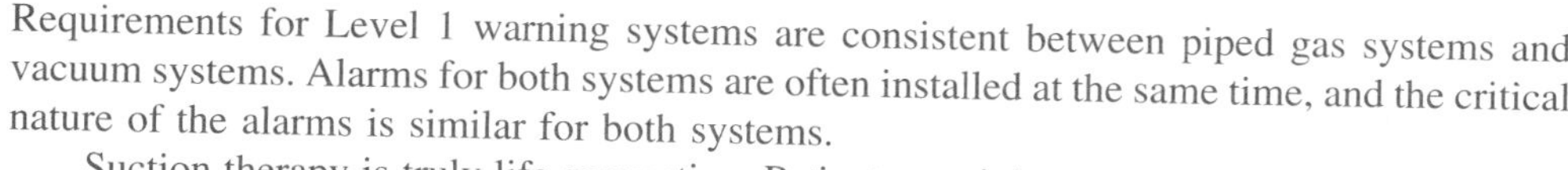

Requirements for Level 1 warning systems are consistent between piped gas systems and vacuum systems. Alarms for both systems are often installed at the same time, and the critical nature of the alarms is similar for both systems.

Suction therapy is truly life supporting. Patients receiving suction therapy are generally in serious condition. Although not generally understood, failure of suction can be injurious and life threatening. Thus, the proper functioning of alarms to indicate a failure or shutdown of a Level 1 vacuum system is most essential.

Warning systems were nonexistent or conflicting in some of the design guidelines prior to the development of the vacuum alarm system requirements beginning in the late 1970s.

5.1.9.2* Master Alarms. A master alarm system shall be provided to monitor the operation and condition of the source of supply, the reserve source (if any), and the pressure in the main lines of each medical gas and vacuum piping system.

A.5.1.9.2 See Table A.5.1.9.2.

TABLE A.5.1.9.2 *Requirements for Level 1 Master Alarms for Gas and Vacuum Systems*

Alarm Condition	***Manifold for Gas Cylinders w/o Reserve (5.1.3.4.10)***	***Manifold for Cryogenic Liquid Cylinders w/ Reserve (5.1.3.4.12)***	***Cryogenic Bulk w/ Cryogenic Reserve (5.1.3.4.13)***	***Cryogenic Bulk w/ Cylinder Reserve (5.1.3.4.13)***	***Medical Air Compressors (5.1.3.5)***	***Instrument Air Compressors (5.1.3.8)***	***Medical–Surgical Vacuum Pumps (5.1.3.6)***	***WAGD Producers (5.1.3.7)***
Nitrogen main line pressure high	5.1.9.2.4(7)							
Nitrogen main line pressure low	5.1.9.2.4(7)							
Nitrogen changeover to secondary supply	5.1.3.4.10.6 5.1.9.2.4(1)							
Carbon dioxide main line pressure high	5.1.9.2.4(7)							
Carbon dioxide main line pressure low	5.1.9.2.4(7)							
Carbon dioxide changeover to secondary supply	5.1.3.4.10.6 5.1.9.2.4(1)							
Medical air main line pressure high	5.1.9.2.4(7)				5.1.9.2.4(7)			
Medical air main line pressure low	5.1.9.2.4(7)				5.1.9.2.4(7)			
Medical air changeover to secondary supply	5.1.3.4.10.6 5.1.9.2.4(1)							
Medical air dew point high					5.1.3.5.15(1) 5.1.9.2.4(10)			

(continues)

TABLE A.5.1.9.2 Continued

Alarm Condition	*Manifold for Gas Cylinders w/o Reserve (5.1.3.4.10)*	*Manifold for Cryogenic Liquid Cylinders w/ Reserve (5.1.3.4.12)*	*Cryogenic Bulk w/ Cryogenic Reserve (5.1.3.4.13)*	*Cryogenic Bulk w/ Cylinder Reserve (5.1.3.4.13)*	*Medical Air Compressors (5.1.3.5)*	*Instrument Air Compressors (5.1.3.8)*	*Medical–Surgical Vacuum Pumps (5.1.3.6)*	*WAGD Producers (5.1.3.7)*
Oxygen main line pressure high	5.1.9.2.4(7)	5.1.9.2.4(7)	5.1.9.2.4(7)	5.1.9.2.4(7)				
Oxygen main line pressure low	5.1.9.2.4(7)	5.1.9.2.4(7)	5.1.9.2.4(7)	5.1.9.2.4(7)				
Oxygen changeover to secondary supply	5.1.3.4.10.6 5.1.9.2.4(1)	5.1.3.4.12.9(1) 5.1.9.2.4(1)	5.1.3.4.13.6(5) 5.1.9.2.4(1)	5.1.3.4.13.6(5) 5.1.9.2.4(1)				
Oxygen main supply less than one day (low contents)			5.1.3.4.13.6(1) 5.1.9.2.4(2)	5.1.3.4.13.6(1) 5.1.9.2.4(2)				
Oxygen reserve in use		5.1.3.4.12.9(3) 5.1.3.4.15.5 5.1.9.2.4(3)	5.1.3.4.13.6(2) 5.1.9.2.4(3)	5.1.3.4.13.6(2) 5.1.3.4.15.5 5.1.9.2.4(3)				
Oxygen reserve supply less than one day (low contents)		5.1.3.4.12.9(4) 5.1.9.2.4(5)	5.1.3.4.13.6(3) 5.1.9.2.4(5)					
Oxygen reserve pressure low (not functional)			5.1.3.4.11.6(4) 5.1.9.2.4(6)					
Nitrous oxide main line pressure high	5.1.9.2.4(7)	5.1.9.2.4(7)	5.1.9.2.4(7)	5.1.9.2.4(7)				
Nitrous oxide main line pressure low	5.1.9.2.4(7)	5.1.9.2.4(7)	5.1.9.2.4(7)	5.1.9.2.4(7)				
Nitrous oxide changeover to secondary supply	5.1.3.4.10.6 5.1.9.2.4(1)	5.1.3.4.12.9(1) 5.1.9.2.4(1)	5.1.3.4.13.6(5) 5.1.9.2.4(1)	5.1.3.4.13.6(5) 5.1.9.2.4(1)				
Nitrous oxide main supply less than one day (low contents)			5.1.3.4.13.6(1) 5.1.9.2.4(2)	5.1.3.4.13.6(1) 5.1.9.2.4(2)				
Nitrous oxide reserve in use		5.1.3.4.12.9(3) 5.1.3.4.15.5 5.1.9.2.4(3)	5.1.3.4.13.6(2) 5.1.9.2.4(3)	5.1.3.4.13.6(2) 5.1.3.4.15.5 5.1.9.2.4(3)				
Nitrous oxide reserve supply less than one day (low contents)		5.1.3.4.12.9(4) 5.1.9.2.4(5)	5.1.3.4.13.6(3) 5.1.9.2.4(5)					
Nitrous oxide reserve pressure low (not functional)			5.1.3.4.13.6(4) 5.1.9.2.4(6)					
Medical–surgical main line vacuum low							5.1.9.2.4(8)	
WAGD main line vacuum low								5.1.9.2.4(8)
Local alarm					5.1.3.5.14 5.1.9.2.4(9) 5.1.9.5.2	5.1.3.8.10 5.1.9.2.4(9) 5.1.9.5.2	5.1.3.6.8 5.1.9.2.4(9) 5.1.9.5.2	5.1.3.7.4 5.1.9.2.4(9) 5.1.9.5.2
Instrument air main line pressure high						5.1.9.2.4(7)		
Instrument air main line pressure low						5.1.9.2.4(7)		
Instrument air dew point high						5.1.3.8.10.1 5.1.9.2.4(12)		

TABLE A.5.1.9.2 Continued

Alarm Condition	*Manifold for Gas Cylinders w/o Reserve (5.1.3.4.10)*	*Manifold for Cryogenic Liquid Cylinders w/ Reserve (5.1.3.4.12)*	*Cryogenic Bulk w/ Cryogenic Reserve (5.1.3.4.13)*	*Cryogenic Bulk w/ Cylinder Reserve (5.1.3.4.13)*	*Medical Air Compressors (5.1.3.5)*	*Instrument Air Compressors (5.1.3.8)*	*Medical–Surgical Vacuum Pumps (5.1.3.6)*	*WAGD Producers (5.1.3.7)*
Instrument air cylinder reserve in use (if provided)						5.1.3.8.10.2(1)		
Instrument air cylinder reserve less than one hour supply						5.1.3.8.10.2(2)		

5.1.9.2.1 The master alarm system shall consist of two or more alarm panels located in at least two separate locations, as follows:

(1) One master alarm panel shall be located in the office or work space of the on-site individual responsible for the maintenance of the medical gas and vacuum piping systems.
(2) In order to assure continuous surveillance of the medical gas and vacuum systems while the facility is in operation, the second master alarm panel shall be located in an area of continuous observation (e.g., the telephone switchboard, security office, or other continuously staffed location).

The basic intent of 5.1.9.2.1 is to provide continuous observation of the master alarm signal panel by personnel who, upon hearing the alarm, know what to do. It is assumed that one alarm signal panel would be typically located in an engineering department. (See Exhibit 5.21.)

◀ **FAQ**
Why are two master panels needed in two locations?

EXHIBIT 5.21 *Master alarm panel mounted in the engineering offices of a hospital.*

5.1.9.2.2 A centralized computer system shall be permitted to be substituted for one of the master alarms required in 5.1.9.2.1, if the computer system complies with 5.1.9.4.

The allowance in 5.1.9.2.2 for computers to substitute for master alarms in some circumstances is new to the 2005 edition. The change is a major reversal from previous editions. The standard has resisted allowing computers to act in this role from fear of the kinds of abuses of the intent already often seen with computers. The primary concern is that computers naturally treat every input the same. Thus, a life-threatening medical gas alarm is treated on a par with the ordinary activation of a heater. The notification that the oxygen supply is critically low scrolls across the screen in a train of data as the fire sensors are polled. The operator, seeking to troubleshoot a problem with the A/C chiller, has the screen busy with the HVAC diagram when the dew point alarm activates, and thus never sees the alarm has triggered. The facility engineer, in a bout of cyber enthusiasm, has the desktop computer in his office set up as the medical gas alarm, then goes home for the weekend, locking his door behind him.

However, it is recognized that the problem in these cases is not with the computer per se, but with the programming and the protocols the facility establishes. In fact, because many facilities now man the computer virtually full time, and computers are often set up to activate pagers and the like, the computer might in fact be the best route to alert the facility to problems. Therefore, computers are now permitted as a substitute for the traditional alarm as long as certain strict requirements are met. See 5.1.9.4 for these requirements.

5.1.9.2.3 The master alarm panels required in 5.1.9.2.1 shall connect directly to the alarm initiating devices that they monitor.

It is not necessary to have two separate switches or sensors unless the alarm requires them. One sensor is adequate as long as the output signal is connected to two separately located warning panels. This requirement seems problematic because the power supply from the two panels might "buck" one another, and from the electrical perspective two panels to a single switch is therefore often argued to be undesirable. However, medical gas alarms are designed to accommodate this anomalous wiring. It must be admitted that a single switch creates an opportunity for single fault failure, but the practical issues involved with providing redundant switches/sensors are many and thus a single switch is permitted.

The wiring to each panel does need to be completely independent, running from switch/sensor to each panel. Although certain alarms might permit a single signal wire and a common ground, this is also not permitted because it would allow the failure of a single wire to take down a whole panel.

5.1.9.2.3.1 Master alarm signals shall not be relayed from one master alarm panel to another.

5.1.9.2.3.2 Where multi-pole alarm relays are used to isolate the alarm initiating signals to master alarm panels, the control power source for the relays shall be independent of any of the master alarm panels.

5.1.9.2.3.3 Multiple master alarms shall be permitted to monitor a single initiating device.

5.1.9.2.4 Master alarm panels for medical gas and vacuum systems shall each include the following signals:

(1) An alarm indication when, or just before, changeover occurs in a medical gas system that is supplied by a manifold or other alternating-type bulk system that has as a part of its normal operation a changeover from one portion of the operating supply to another
(2) An alarm indication for a bulk cryogenic liquid system when the main supply reaches an average day's supply, indicating low contents
(3) An alarm indication when, or just before, the changeover to the reserve supply occurs in a medical gas system that consists of one or more units that continuously supply the piping system while another unit remains as the reserve supply and operates only in the case of an emergency

(4) An alarm indication for cylinder reserve pressure low when the content of a cylinder reserve header is reduced below one average day's supply
(5) For bulk cryogenic liquid systems, an alarm when or at a predetermined set point before the reserve supply contents fall to one day's average supply, indicating reserve low
(6) Where a cryogenic liquid storage unit is used as a reserve for a bulk supply system, an alarm indication when the gas pressure available in the reserve unit is below that required for the medical gas system to function
(7) An alarm indication when the pressure in the main line of each separate medical gas system increases 20 percent or decreases 20 percent from the normal operating pressure
(8) An alarm indication when the medical–surgical vacuum pressure in the main line of each vacuum system drops to or below 300 mm (12 in.) gauge HgV

Only low-vacuum alarming is stipulated. The upper limit is not relevant because the facility should be regulating all vacuum prior to the patient connection. Unregulated vacuum, even at 300 mm (12 in.) HgV, can be dangerous.

It should also be noted that the high alarm setting and vacuum are not related to the operating level of pumps, which typically operate at much higher pressures (475 mm–725 mm [19 in.–29 in.] HgV is common).

(9) An alarm indication(s) from the local alarm panel(s) as described in 5.1.9.5.2 to indicate when one or more of the conditions being monitored at a site is in alarm
(10) A medical air dew point high alarm from each compressor site to indicate when the line pressure dew point is greater than +2°C (+35°F)
(11) A WAGD low alarm when the WAGD vacuum level or flow is below effective operating limits
(12) An instrument air dew point high alarm from each compressor site to indicate when the line pressure dew point is greater than −30°C (−22°F)

5.1.9.2.5 The alarm indications required in 5.1.9.2.4(7) and 5.1.9.2.4(8) shall originate from sensors installed in the main lines immediately downstream (on the patient or use side) of the source valves. Where it is necessary to install a main line valve in addition to a source valve *(see 5.1.4.5)*, the sensors shall be located downstream (on the patient or use side) of the main valve.

The main line shutoff valve can be eliminated if the source of equipment is within the facility. If the main line valve is eliminated, the actuating switch for these signals must be installed immediately downstream (on the piping distribution side) of the source shutoff valve. Supply systems remote from the facility (such as oxygen bulk supplies) would still require both a source valve and a main valve just inside the facility. The pressure switch in this instance would be just downstream of the main valve where it first enters the facility or building. The requirements are constructed so no switch should ever need to be placed outdoors.

5.1.9.3* Area Alarms. Area alarm panels shall be provided to monitor all medical gas, medical–surgical vacuum, and piped WAGD systems supplying anesthetizing locations, and other vital life support and critical areas (e.g., post anesthesia recovery, intensive care units, emergency departments, etc.).

An area alarm panel for a piped Level 1 gas system is not required at all nurses' stations. The very limited list in 5.1.9.3 is also not an infallible guide, because the presence of an alarm should be based on application and the importance of monitoring the gases in this area. The decision to alarm or not alarm an area should not be based primarily on the name of that area. (See the discussion on critical care in A.5.1.9.3.4(1).)

The intent is: Any occupancy where loss of the supply of gas or vacuum will adversely affect patient outcomes without immediate intervention by staff should be provided with an alarm. The purpose of the alarm is to inform the staff that immediate action is required. For example, a unit where patients can be expected to be on mechanical ventilators would clearly qualify, irrespective of whether the name of the unit is Recovery, PACU, Neonatal Intensive Care, or Extra Love Nursery. In contrast, patients on nasal cannulas for oxygen support probably would not suffer undue risk if the oxygen system went out, so a medical care unit for patients who are only receiving this low-intensity treatment could reasonably be excused an alarm panel. In today's health care environment, the infinite number of names being used and technologies being developed makes the name almost irrelevant. The objective — positive patient outcomes even when the medical gas system fails — is a medical criterion that can apply to any occupancy.

An exception is made for anesthetizing locations. On the surface, this will seem contradictory to the basic principle, because there are few locations where outcomes could be worse in the event of system failure than in the OR. The exception has its origin in the old "central sterile core" design used for ORs back when all ORs were in one location in the hospital and any surgery was done there. A single alarm made sense because there would always be someone in that central location. In addition, the anesthesia gas machines are provided with their own alarms and with enough gas on-board to complete a procedure. Because there are now designs that do not follow this pattern, it may be necessary to install alarms for each room or cluster of rooms instead.

A.5.1.9.3 See Table A.5.1.9.3.

TABLE A.5.1.9.3 *Requirements for Level 1 Area Alarms*

Alarm Condition	***Paragraph Number of Requirement***
High line pressure (for each gas piped to the area)	5.1.9.3 5.1.9.3.1 5.1.9.3.2 5.1.9.3.4
Low line pressure (for each gas piped to the area)	5.1.9.3 5.1.9.3.1 5.1.9.3.2 5.1.9.3.4
Low medical–surgical vacuum (if piped to the area)	5.1.9.3 5.1.9.3.1 5.1.9.3.3 5.1.9.3.4
Low WAGD vacuum (if piped to the area)	5.1.9.3 5.1.9.3.1 5.1.9.3.3 5.1.9.3.4

5.1.9.3.1 Area alarms shall be located at a nurse's station or other similar location that will provide for surveillance.

As required by 5.1.9.3.1, the proper location for an area alarm is inside the room or area being monitored by the alarm panel, near the nurses' station, or other location that is most likely to be staffed whenever patients are present. The area alarm should not be mounted in the hall near the zone valve box assembly, because it cannot be continuously monitored there.

The proper location for area alarms in occupancies that do not have a classic nurses' station might be on a common wall visible to several nurses at all times. It is also permitted to install more than one alarm panel or relay signals. This might be necessary in occupancies that have only one large zone for an entire area, or floor plans that are divided into several "pods." This would ensure that staff are warned about gas delivery problems even if no one is near a particular alarm panel.

◀ **FAQ**
Where should the area alarm be mounted if there is no nurses' station?

Alarms are sometimes placed in each anesthetizing location. This arrangement exceeds the requirements of NFPA 99 and is thus permitted (see also commentary for A.5.1.9.3.4(1)).

The placement of an alarm panel inside each operating room does not remove the requirement for an area alarm panel at the OR nurses' control desk (presuming there is such a location). The purpose of this panel at the OR control desk is to allow staff to alert all the operating rooms if a supply problem arises with the medical gases. Alarms inside operating rooms can be silenced without further corrective action taken and the staff cannot simply run out to inform other rooms.

When multiple alarms are installed at a common nurses' station and the alarms monitor separate areas controlled by distinct zone valves, the alarms should be clearly labeled for the specific areas they monitor. (See Exhibit 5.22.)

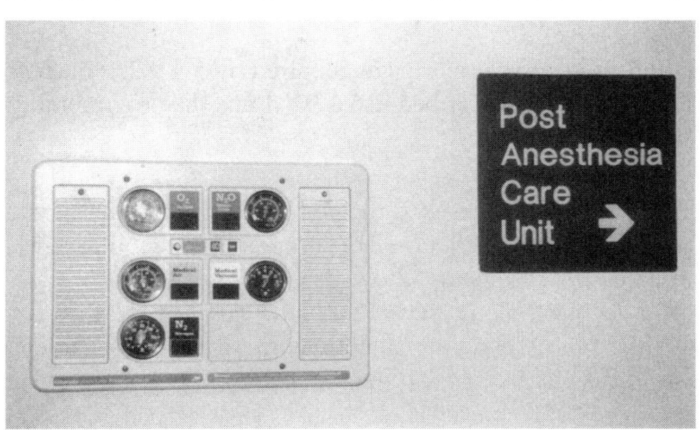

EXHIBIT 5.22 An area alarm panel for the operating room and signage to the post-anesthesia recovery unit.

5.1.9.3.2 Area alarm panels for medical gas systems shall indicate if the pressure in the lines in the area being monitored increases or decreases by 20 percent from the normal line pressure.

5.1.9.3.3 Area alarm panels for medical–surgical vacuum systems shall indicate if the vacuum in the area drops to or below 300 mm (12 in.) gauge HgV.

5.1.9.3.4 Sensors for area alarms shall be located as follows:

(1)* Vital life support and critical areas shall have the alarm sensors installed on the patient or use side of any of the individual zone valve box assemblies.

A.5.1.9.3.4(1) This signal is intended to provide immediate warning for loss of, or increase in, system pressure for each individual vital life support and critical care area. 

(2)* Areas for anesthetizing gas delivery shall have the sensors installed either on the source side of any of the individual room zone valve box assemblies or on the patient or use side of each of the individual zone valve assemblies.

New in the 2005 edition is a specific allowance permitting the sensors/switches for an anesthetizing area to be on the source side of all zone valves (one switch/sensor) or on the patient side (one switch/sensor for each zone). Placing the sensor/switch on the patient side requires more switches but ensures that closure of a valve will in fact cause an alarm.

A.5.1.9.3.4(2) This signal is intended to provide immediate warning for loss of, or increase in, system pressure for all anesthetizing locations supplied from a single branch line — not for each individual operating or delivery room.

(3) The placement of the sensors shall not be affected by valves located in areas accessible to authorized personnel only, such as service valves *(see 5.1.4.7)* or in-line valves *(see 5.1.4.9)*.

The requirements for locating actuating switches in anesthetizing locations differ from those for vital life support and critical care units. Figure A.5.1.4 illustrates the different applications.

The service shutoff valve (see 5.1.4.7) does not have to be considered in the placement of the switch/sensors for the alarms. The service valve is a maintenance valve only and is located immediately where the lateral line(s) branches off the riser. Given that the switches/sensors are all placed on demand checks, they can be serviced without reference to any valve. Placing them on the patient side of the service valve might be preferred only because it then would indicate if the service valve is closed.

5.1.9.4 Computer systems used as substitute master alarms as required by 5.1.9.2.1(2) shall have the mechanical and electrical characteristics described in 5.1.9.4.1 and the programming characteristics described in 5.1.9.4.2.

The requirements of 5.1.9.4 govern a computer when used to substitute for a master alarm. They are divided into the physical requirements (5.1.9.4.1) and the programming requirements (5.1.9.4.2). A reading of the requirements will quickly show that the intent is to make a computer behave in most respects as a stand-alone panel, with the addition of features such as pagers, autodialers, and the like. These computer functions must be verified under 5.1.12.3.5.1(A), which might require the assistance of a programmer.

5.1.9.4.1 Computer systems used to substitute for alarms shall have the following mechanical and electrical characteristics:

(1) The computer system shall be in continuous uninterrupted operation and provided with power supplies as needed to ensure such reliability.
(2) The computer system shall be continuously attended by responsible individuals or shall provide remote signaling of responsible parties (e.g., through pagers, telephone autodialers, or other such means).
(3) Where computer systems rely on signal interface devices (e.g., electronic interfaces, other alarm panels, 4-20 mA cards, etc.), such interfaces shall be supervised such that failure of the device(s) shall initiate (an) alarm(s).
(4) If the computer system does not power the signaling switches/sensors from the same power supply required in 5.1.9.4.1(1), the power supply for the signaling switches/sensors shall be powered from the life safety branch of the emergency electrical system as described in Chapter 4, Electrical Systems.
(5) Computer systems shall be permitted to connect directly to the sensors/switches in 5.1.9.2.3 in the same manner as an alarm panel if operation of other alarm panel(s) is not impaired.
(6) Wiring from the computer system to the signaling switches or sensors shall comply with 5.1.9.1(11).

(7) Computer systems shall be provided with an audio alert per 5.1.9.1(3) except the audio alert shall be permitted to be only as loud as needed to alert the system operator.
(8) The facility shall assure compliance with 5.1.9.1(12)

5.1.9.4.2 The operating program(s) for computer systems used to substitute for alarms shall include the following:

(1) Medical gas alarms shall be allocated the priority of a life safety signal.
(2) A medical gas alarm signal shall interrupt any other activity of a lesser priority to run the alarm algorithm(s).
(3) The alarm algorithm shall include activation of an audible alert, activation of any remote signaling protocol, and display of the specific condition in alarm.
(4) The alarm algorithm shall provide for compliance with 5.1.9.1(1), 5.1.9.1(2), 5.1.9.1(3), 5.1.9.1(5), 5.1.9.1(6), and 5.1.9.1(8).

5.1.9.5* Local Alarms. Local alarms shall be installed to monitor the function of the air compressor system(s), medical–surgical vacuum pump system(s), WAGD systems, and instrument air systems.

A.5.1.9.5 Activation of any of the warning signals should immediately be reported to the department of the facility responsible for the medical gas piping system involved. If the medical gas is supplied from a bulk supply system, the owner or the organization responsible for the operation and maintenance of that system, usually the supplier, should also be notified. As much detail as possible should be provided. See Table A.5.1.9.5.

TABLE A.5.1.9.5 *Requirements for Level 1 Local Alarms*

	Medical Air Compressors					
Alarm Condition	***Oil-less (Sealed bearing) 5.1.3.5.4.1(1)***	***Oil-Free (separated) 5.1.3.5.4.1(2)***	***Liquid Ring (water-sealed) 5.1.3.5.4.1(1)***	***Instrument Air Compressors***	***Medical–Surgical Vacuum Pumps***	***WAGD Producers***
Backup (lag) compressor in operation	5.1.3.5.14.5 5.1.9.5.4(1)	5.1.3.5.14.5 5.1.9.5.4(1)	5.1.3.5.14.5 5.1.9.5.4(1)			
Backup (lag) medical–surgical vacuum pump in operation					5.1.3.6.8 5.1.9.5.4(4)	
Backup (lag) WAGD producer in operation						5.1.3.7.4.1 5.1.3.7.4.4 5.1.9.5.4(5)
Backup (lag) instrument air compressor in operation				5.1.3.8.10.1(1) 5.1.9.5.4(1)		
Carbon monoxide high	5.1.3.5.15(2) 5.1.9.5(2)	5.1.3.5.15(2) 5.1.9.5(2)	5.1.3.5.15(2) 5.1.9.5(2)			
High discharge air temperature	5.1.3.5.14.3 5.1.9.5.4(9)	5.1.3.5.14.4(1) 5.1.9.5.4(9)				
High water in receiver	5.1.3.5.14.1 5.1.9.5.4(7)	5.1.3.5.14.1 5.1.9.5.4(7)	5.1.3.5.14.1 5.1.9.5.4(7)			
High water in separator			5.1.3.5.14.2 5.1.9.5.4(8)			
Medical air dew point high	5.1.3.5.15(1) 5.1.9.5.4(3)	5.1.3.5.15(1) 5.1.9.5.4(3)	5.1.3.5.15(1) 5.1.9.5.4(3)			
Instrument air dew point high				5.1.3.8.10.1(2) 5.1.9.5.4(6)		

5.1.9.5.1 The signals referenced in 5.1.9.5.4 shall be permitted to be located as follows:

(1) On or in the control panel(s) for the machinery being monitored
(2) Within a monitoring device (e.g., dew point monitor or carbon monoxide monitor)
(3) On a separate alarm panel(s)

A common implementation is to build the signals referenced in 5.1.9.4.1 into the control enclosure, which is perfectly acceptable as long as the basic principles of any alarm are considered: (1) continuous visual signal for each condition and (2) audible signal with silence (see 5.1.9.1).

5.1.9.5.2 The master alarm shall include at least one signal from the source equipment to indicate a problem with the source equipment at this location. This master alarm signal shall activate when any of the required local alarm signals for this source equipment activates.

Paragraph 5.1.9.4.2 is somewhat misleading if taken in isolation. This single signal allowance is most relevant for medical air, which can have six (and sometimes more) signals on the local alarm. In that case, a single signal marked "Medical Air Fault" or something similar can be used for all but the dew point alarm, which must always have a separate signal. However, to find that requirement, see 5.1.9.2.4, which is the governing paragraph for master signals and takes precedence.

5.1.9.5.3 If there is more than one medical air compressor system, instrument air compressor system, WAGD system, and/or more than one medical–surgical vacuum pump system at different locations in the facility, or if the compressors and/or vacuum sources are in different locations in the facility, then it shall be necessary for each location to have separate alarms at the master panels.

5.1.9.5.4 The following functions shall be monitored at each local alarm site:

(1) Backup or lag compressor in operation to indicate when the primary or lead air compressor is incapable of satisfying the demand of the requirements of the system, except when the medical air system consists of three or more compressors, then the backup or lag signal shall be permitted to energize when the last compressor has been signaled to start.
(2) High carbon monoxide level to indicate when the carbon monoxide level in the medical air system is 10 ppm or higher.
(3) Medical air dew point high to indicate when the line pressure dew point is greater than +4°C (+39°F).
(4) Backup or lag vacuum pump in operation to indicate when the primary or lead vacuum pump is incapable of satisfying the demand of the requirements of the system, except when the vacuum pump system consists of three or more pumps, then the backup or lag signal shall be permitted to energize when the last pump has been signaled to start.
(5) When a central dedicated WAGD producer is provided per 5.1.3.7.1.3, WAGD lag in use. The signal shall be manually reset.
(6) Instrument air dew point high to indicate when the line pressure dew point is greater than −30°C (−22°F).
(7) For compressor systems using liquid ring compressors or compressors with water-cooled components, high water in the receiver tank to indicate when the water level in the receiver tank has reached a level determined to be detrimental to the operation of the system.
(8) For compressor systems using liquid ring compressors, high water in the separators.
(9) For compressor systems using other than liquid ring compressors, high discharge air temperature.

5.1.10 Level 1 Distribution.

Readers are reminded that 5.1.10 applies to distribution requirements for Level 1 and by reference Level 2 systems. Distribution requirements for Level 3 systems can be found in 5.3.10.

5.1.10.1 Piping Materials for Field-Installed Positive Pressure Medical Gas Systems.

◀ **FAQ**
Can new piping for oxygen service be cleaned on-site?

All on-site cleaning of new piping construction was banned in the 1993 edition, with the exception of cleaning necessary to prepare the immediate joint area for brazing. Suppliers and contractors need to protect material that has previously been cleaned for oxygen service during delivery to, and storage on, the job site (e.g., caps should not be removed from the ends of pipes until the piping is ready for installation and brazing; caps should be removed one at a time).

The publication of ASTM B 819, *Standard Specification for Seamless Copper Tube for Medical Gas Systems,* was a major advance in the ability of NFPA 99 to specify tubing of an appropriate cleanliness [11]. Since ASTM B 819 became available, medical gas tubing can be purchased to that standard and received clean, which made on-site cleaning unnecessary. The referencing and use of tubing permits on-site recleaning only in certain instances as noted. No other cleaning is allowed on-site.

Piping that has been cleaned and labeled "oxy" or "oxygen" indicates that it has been cleaned in such a manner as to be suitable for the piping of oxygen. It also means that the piping is suitable for use with any other nonflammable medical gas. The requirement for manufacturer-cleaned piping for all nonflammable medical piped gas systems to be suitable for oxygen eliminates the possibility that some manufacturer-cleaned piping will be suitable for some nonflammable gases but not others and helps to ensure the correct piping is installed.

5.1.10.1.1 Tubes, valves, fittings, station outlets, and other piping components in medical gas systems shall have been cleaned for oxygen service by the manufacturer prior to installation in accordance with CGA G-4.1, *Cleaning Equipment for Oxygen Service*, except that fittings shall be permitted to be cleaned by a supplier or agency other than the manufacturer.

On-site cleaning of new piping prior to installation is prohibited by 5.1.10.1.1 because of the inability to properly prepare piping for oxygen service at the installation site. A second reason for withdrawal of the allowances for on-site cleaning is the environmental hazards of using phosphates and other chemicals in an unregulated setting. The allowance for the cleaning of fittings is a recognition that most cleaning is done by parties other than the actual fitting manufacturer. It is not meant to be an allowance for on-site cleaning of fittings by the contractor.

5.1.10.1.2 Each length of tube shall be delivered plugged or capped by the manufacturer and kept sealed until prepared for installation.

NFPA 99 allows "plugged or capped" pipe. However, there have been numerous instances where plugs have remained in the line during assembly. Plugs that are left in the line usually end up forcing all piping downstream to be replaced due to residual smoke and so on. Plugs are internal, and fittings are installed on the tube with the plug still in the line. Caps are preferred for this reason — it is not possible to leave a cap on and get the next fitting in place. Where plugs are used, great care must be taken to ensure they are removed as each section is installed.

5.1.10.1.3 Fittings, valves, and other components shall be delivered sealed, labeled, and kept sealed until prepared for installation.

5.1.10.1.4* Tubes shall be hard-drawn seamless copper ASTM B 819, *Standard Specification for Seamless Copper Tube for Medical Gas Systems*, medical gas tube, Type L, except that where operating pressures are above a gauge pressure of 1275 kPa (185 psi) Type K shall be used for sizes larger than DN80 (NPS 3) (3⅛ in. O.D.).

FAQ ▶ Why can't soft-tempered copper be used with medical air systems?

It should be noted that any of the piping listed in 5.1.10.1.4 is acceptable for Level 1 piped gas systems and that piping for Level 1 piped gas systems has to be "hard-drawn." Part of the reason for requiring hard-drawn piping is that soft tubing kinks very easily, and kinking causes restriction of flow. All tubing must be ½ in. or greater, and because the standard in the industry is already ½ in. drops for positive-pressure gases such as oxygen, air, nitrogen, and nitrous oxide, and ¾ in. drops for vacuum and evacuation, this requirement should not be a problem.

A.5.1.10.1.4 Operation of piped medical gas systems at gauge pressures in excess of 1280 kPa (185 psi) involves certain restrictions because of the limitations in materials.

5.1.10.1.5 ASTM B 819, *Standard Specification for Seamless Copper Tube for Medical Gas Systems*, medical gas tube shall be identified by the manufacturer's markings "OXY," "MED," "OXY/MED," "OXY/ACR," or "ACR/MED" in blue (Type L) or green (Type K).

5.1.10.1.6 The installer shall furnish documentation certifying that all installed piping materials comply with the requirements of 5.1.10.1.1.

5.1.10.2 Piping Materials for Field-Installed Medical–Surgical Vacuum and WAGD Systems.

A comparison of the vacuum material requirements of 5.1.10.2.1 to the pressure gas specifications (see 5.1.10.1) will quickly show that the vacuum requirements have been eased considerably in this edition.

5.1.10.2.1 Piping for vacuum systems shall be constructed of any of the following:

(1) Hard-drawn seamless copper tube:
   (a) ASTM B 88, *Standard Specification for Seamless Copper Water Tube*, copper tube (Types K, L, M)
   (b) ASTM B 280, *Standard Specification for Seamless Copper Tubing for Air Conditioning and Refrigeration Field Service*, copper ACR tube
   (c) ASTM B 819, *Standard Specification for Seamless Copper Tube for Medical Gas Systems*, copper medical gas tubing (Type K or L)
(2) Stainless steel tube

5.1.10.2.2 Vacuum Tubing Marking.

5.1.10.2.2.1 If copper vacuum tubing is installed along with any medical gas tubing, the vacuum tubing shall, prior to installation, be prominently labeled or otherwise identified to preclude using materials or installation procedures in the medical gas system that are not suitable for oxygen service.

5.1.10.2.2.2 If medical gas tube (ASTM B 819, *Standard Specification for Seamless Copper Tube for Medical Gas Systems*) is used for vacuum piping, such special marking shall not be required, provided that the vacuum piping installation meets all other requirements for medical gas piping, including the prohibition of flux on copper-to-copper joints and the use of a nitrogen purge while brazing.

5.1.10.2.3 WAGD systems shall be piped as follows:

(1) Using materials compliant with 5.1.10.2.1 or 5.1.10.2.2
(2) In systems operated under 130 mm (5 in.) HgV maximum vacuum only, using any noncorroding tube or ductwork

This allowance is particularly aimed to allow low-vacuum WAGD systems to be installed at the lowest possible cost, reflecting their inherent simplicity.

5.1.10.3 Fittings.

5.1.10.3.1* Turns, offsets, and other changes in direction in welded or brazed medical gas and vacuum piping shall be made with wrought copper capillary fittings complying with ASME B16.22, *Wrought Copper and Copper Alloy Solder-Joint Pressure Fittings*, or brazed fittings complying with ASME B16.50, *Wrought Copper and Copper Alloy Braze-Joint Pressure Fittings*.

Paragraph 5.1.10.3.1 is an excellent example of why one needs to read the entire standard before beginning work. This paragraph taken alone implies that only these fittings are permitted, but throughout 5.1.10.5 and 5.1.10.6, references to other jointing methods are found and it is only when one reads 5.1.10.7 that other methods, which will not use these fittings, are seen to be permitted.

◀ **FAQ**
Are the fittings specified in 5.1.10.3.1 the only ones that are allowed?

A.5.1.10.3.1 A distinction is made between deep-socket solder-joint fittings (ASME B16.22) and those having shallow sockets for brazing (ASME B16.50). The use of shallow-socket brazing fittings improves the quality of the brazement without decreasing its strength, particularly in larger sizes, which are difficult to heat. See Table A.5.1.10.3.1 for socket depths conforming to ASME B16.50. The installer can use ASME B16.50 fittings (if available) or have the sockets on ASME B16.22 fittings cut down to ASME B16.50 depths. Where shallow-socket fittings are used for the medical gas piping, care should be taken to avoid their use in other piping systems where joints could be soldered instead of brazed.

TABLE A.5.1.10.3.1 *Socket Depths for ASME B16.50 Brazing Fittings*

Tube Size (in.)	*Socket Depth (in.)*
¼ (⅜ O.D.)	0.17
⅜ (½ O.D.)	0.2
½ (⅝ O.D.)	0.22
¾ (⅞ O.D.)	0.25
1 (1⅛ O.D.)	0.28
1¼ (1⅜ O.D.)	0.31
1½ (1⅝ O.D.)	0.34
2 (2⅛ O.D.)	0.40
2½ (2⅝ O.D.)	0.47
3 (3⅛ O.D.)	0.53
4 (4⅛ O.D.)	0.64
5 (5⅛ O.D.)	0.73
6 (6⅛ O.D.)	0.83

5.1.10.3.2 Cast copper alloy fittings shall not be permitted.

5.1.10.3.3 Branch connections in vacuum piping systems shall be permitted to be made using mechanically formed, drilled, and extruded tee-branch connections that are formed in accordance with the tool manufacturer's instructions, and brazed.

The extruded tee-branch connection or "tee drill" technique in 5.1.10.3.3 is permitted on vacuum and WAGD systems only. It is sometimes seen as a time-saver, but there are issues with its use. For instance, if improperly applied, it might block flow, and it has the probability of leaving significant amounts of cutting oil in the piping. It therefore requires close attention to the tool manufacturer's instructions, careful application, and some discretion in its use.

5.1.10.4 Threaded Joints. Threaded joints in medical gas and vacuum distribution piping shall meet the following requirements:

(1) Be limited to connections to pressure/vacuum indicators, alarm devices, check valves, and source equipment

(2) Be tapered pipe threads complying with ASME B1.20.1, *Pipe Threads, General Purpose, Inch*

(3) Be made up with polytetrafluoroethylene (such as Teflon™) tape or other thread sealant recommended for oxygen service, with the sealant applied to the male threads only

5.1.10.5 Brazed Joints.

The way pipes are joined reflects concerns that piping remain intact during a fire and withstand some degree of physical shaking and impact. Problems over the years have included mechanically weak joints and overheated piping and fittings. Changes in NFPA 99 to address such problems have included all of the following:

1. Reference to a specific American Welding Society (AWS) standard
2. Reference to the inclusion of a phosphorus element in the brazing alloy
3. Continuous purging of the pipe with an inert gas (e.g., nitrogen) while brazing
4. Permission to use other jointing techniques that have been demonstrated to be equivalent to a brazed joint

The change to ANSI/AWS A5.8, *Specification for Filler Metals for Brazing and Braze Welding,* was made to reference a national standard requiring the melting point of the brazing alloy to be a minimum of 1000°F (538°C) [12]. (This temperature criterion has always been required in the standard.) Reference to a specific type of brazing alloy prevents any specific supplier from being preferred.

5.1.10.5.1 General Requirements.

5.1.10.5.1.1 Brazed joints shall be made using a brazing alloy that exhibits a melting temperature in excess of 538°C (1000°F) to retain the integrity of the piping system in the event of fire exposure.

5.1.10.5.1.2 Brazed tube joints shall be the socket type.

5.1.10.5.1.3 Filler metals shall bond with and be metallurgically compatible with the base metals being joined.

5.1.10.5.1.4 Filler metals shall comply with ANSI/AWS A5.8, *Specification for Filler Metals for Brazing and Braze Welding*.

5.1.10.5.1.5 Copper-to-copper joints shall be brazed using a copper–phosphorus or copper–phosphorus–silver brazing filler metal (BCuP series) without flux.

The copper–phosphorus and copper–phosphorus–silver (BCuP series) brazing filler metal is designed to be used with like metals only. The phosphorus within the (BCuP series) brazing rod acts as the flux. On dissimilar metals, a flux must be applied to wet the tube and fitting, as well as to stop oxidation caused by the heat of the torch.

5.1.10.5.1.6 Brazing performed between bulk cryogenic liquid vessels and their vaporizers (i.e., subject to cryogenic exposure) shall be permitted to be brazed using BAg brazing alloy with flux by a brazer qualified to CGA M-1, *Guide for Medical Gas Installations at Consumer Sites*.

5.1.10.5.1.7 Joints to be brazed in place shall be accessible for necessary preparation, assembly, heating, filler application, cooling, cleaning, and inspection.

5.1.10.5.1.8 Braze joints shall be continuously purged with Nitrogen NF.

5.1.10.5.2 Cutting Tube Ends.

5.1.10.5.2.1 Tube ends shall be cut square using a sharp tubing cutter to avoid deforming the tube.

5.1.10.5.2.2 The cutting wheels on tubing cutters shall be free from grease, oil, or other lubricant not suitable for oxygen service.

5.1.10.5.2.3 The cut ends of the tube shall be deburred with a sharp, clean deburring tool, taking care to prevent chips from entering the tube.

5.1.10.5.3 Cleaning Joints for Brazing.

5.1.10.5.3.1 The interior surfaces of tubes, fittings, and other components that are cleaned for oxygen service shall be stored and handled to avoid contamination prior to assembly and brazing.

5.1.10.5.3.2 The exterior surfaces of tube ends shall be cleaned prior to brazing to remove any surface oxides.

5.1.10.5.3.3 When cleaning the exterior surfaces of tube ends, no matter shall be permitted to enter the tube.

5.1.10.5.3.4 If the interior surfaces of fitting sockets become contaminated prior to brazing, they shall be recleaned for oxygen in accordance with 5.1.10.5.3.10 and be cleaned for brazing with a clean, oil-free wire brush.

5.1.10.5.3.5 Clean, nonshedding, abrasive pads shall be used to clean the exterior surfaces of the tube ends.

5.1.10.5.3.6 The use of steel wool or sand cloth shall be prohibited.

Steel wool and sand cloth can send debris into the pipe.

◀ **FAQ**
Why is steel wool or sand cloth prohibited from cleaning the ends of tubing?

5.1.10.5.3.7 The cleaning process shall not result in grooving of the surfaces to be joined.

5.1.10.5.3.8 After being abraded, the surfaces shall be wiped using a clean, lint-free white cloth.

5.1.10.5.3.9 Tubes, fittings, valves, and other components shall be visually examined internally before being joined to verify that they have not become contaminated for oxygen service and that they are free of obstructions or debris.

5.1.10.5.3.10 The interior surfaces of tube ends, fittings, and other components that were cleaned for oxygen service by the manufacturer, but became contaminated prior to being installed, shall be permitted to be recleaned on-site by the installer by thoroughly scrubbing the interior surfaces with a clean, hot water–alkaline solution, such as sodium carbonate or trisodium phosphate 450 g to 11 L (1 lb to 3 gal) of potable water and thoroughly rinsing them with clean, hot, potable water.

The allowance in 5.1.10.5.3.10 is not intended to stretch to cleaning fittings and pipe on-site, but rather to allow a very limited on-site recleaning of items already cleaned but inadvertently contaminated during installation. The allowance is meant to prevent hardships when complying with 5.1.10.5.3.12.

5.1.10.5.3.11 Other aqueous cleaning solutions shall be permitted to be used for on-site recleaning permitted in 5.1.10.5.3.10 provided that they are as recommended in CGA G-4.1, *Cleaning Equipment for Oxygen Service*, and are listed in CGA O2-DIR, *Directory of Cleaning Agents for Oxygen Service*.

5.1.10.5.3.12 Material that has become contaminated internally and is not clean for oxygen service shall not be installed.

5.1.10.5.3.13 Joints shall be brazed within eight hours after the surfaces are cleaned for brazing.

The time allowance has changed over the various editions of the standard and is now the most liberal allowance the standard has required.

5.1.10.5.4 Brazing Dissimilar Metals.

5.1.10.5.4.1 Flux shall only be used when brazing dissimilar metals such as copper and bronze or brass, using a silver (BAg series) brazing filler metal.

5.1.10.5.4.2 Surfaces shall be cleaned for brazing in accordance with 5.1.10.5.3.

5.1.10.5.4.3 Flux shall be applied sparingly to minimize contamination of the inside of the tube with flux.

5.1.10.5.4.4 The flux shall be applied and worked over the cleaned surfaces to be brazed using a stiff bristle brush to ensure complete coverage and wetting of the surfaces with flux.

5.1.10.5.4.5 Where possible, short sections of copper tube shall be brazed onto the noncopper component and the interior of the subassembly shall be cleaned of flux prior to installation in the piping system.

A common application of 5.1.10.5.4.5 is in the valves, where brazing in place might ruin the internal seals. However, it is generally valuable in any case where dissimilar metals are to be brazed, because it ensures a very clean final result. The procedure is more relevant for a factory or shop installation under controlled conditions because it is very difficult to do properly in the field (see also 5.1.4.3).

5.1.10.5.4.6 On joints DN20 (NPS ¾) (⅞ in. O.D.) size and smaller, flux-coated brazing rods shall be permitted to be used in lieu of applying flux to the surfaces being joined.

5.1.10.5.5* Nitrogen Purge.

The purging methods covered in 5.1.10.5.5 are those under which an installer should qualify for the purposes of 5.1.10.10.11 and 5.1.10.10.12.

A.5.1.10.5.5 The intent is to provide an oxygen-free atmosphere within the tubing and to prevent the formation of copper oxide scale during brazing. This is accomplished by filling the piping with a low-volume flow of low-pressure inert gas.

5.1.10.5.5.1 When brazing, joints shall be continuously purged with oil-free, dry Nitrogen NF to prevent the formation of copper oxide on the inside surfaces of the joint.

Note that oil-free dry air, carbon dioxide, and argon are not permitted as purge gas. Industrial-grade carbon dioxide, in particular, might have oil contaminants that cannot be cleaned out after brazing pipes. There is also the risk associated with the release of carbon dioxide in large quantities. The user is cautioned that a risk exists with nitrogen as well if the nitrogen is released into an enclosed space. Sufficient ventilation is absolutely mandatory during all purging operations.

◀ **FAQ**
Why is oil-free dry nitrogen the only gas allowed for purging?

5.1.10.5.5.2 The source of the purge gas shall be monitored and the installer shall be audibly alerted when the source content is low.

The requirement in 5.1.10.5.5.2 to monitor the source of purge reflects an obvious problem: If the nitrogen runs out during the brazing operations, there will be no way for the installer to know until it is too late and the quality of the braze is already compromised. The requirement could be met with an automatic device or by having an observer monitor the cylinder(s).

5.1.10.5.5.3 The purge gas flow rate shall be controlled by the use of a pressure regulator and flow meter or combination thereof.

Purging is meant to exclude oxygen from the piping, and this requires neither high rates of flow nor any more pressure than will waft the nitrogen out of the end of the line and prevent air entering. High flow rates or high pressures are wasteful and actually make the brazing more difficult.

A flowmeter is also usually installed in the purge rig.

5.1.10.5.5.4 Pressure regulators alone shall not be used to control purge gas flow rates.

5.1.10.5.5.5 In order to assure that all ambient air has been removed from the pipeline prior to brazing, an oxygen analyzer shall be used to verify the effectiveness of the purge. The oxygen analyzer shall read below 1 percent oxygen concentration before brazing is to begin.

This new requirement in the 2005 edition reflects the simple problem that the installer had no way to know whether the purge was effective. The analyzer is a simple and relatively inexpensive device, and since the standard excludes oxygen, a reading of 0 indicates the oxygen is gone.

5.1.10.5.5.6 During and after installation, openings in the piping system shall be kept sealed to maintain a nitrogen atmosphere within the piping to prevent debris or other contaminants from entering the system.

To comply with 5.1.10.5.5.6, plugs are often used; in fact, many suppliers deliver the cleaned tube already fitted with plugs. These plugs are sometimes not removed from the tube ends before the next section is installed. This leaves the plug in the line, and often that plug is burned or melted during the brazing of the joint. Usually the plug is discovered during flow or odor testing (to the great embarrassment of the installer), but it can represent a very great hazard if not detected.

Good practice is to use only external caps to seal openings in the piping system, which must be removed before the next fitting can be attached. As an additional complication, many suppliers of clean pipe supply internal plugs at each end, which must be removed and discarded before use.

5.1.10.5.5.7 While a joint is being brazed, a discharge opening shall be provided on the opposite side of the joint from where the purge gas is being introduced.

5.1.10.5.5.8 The flow of purge gas shall be maintained until the joint is cool to the touch.

5.1.10.5.5.9 After the joint has cooled, the purge discharge opening shall be sealed to prevent contamination of the inside of the tube and maintain the nitrogen atmosphere within the piping system.

5.1.10.5.5.10 The final connection of new piping to an existing, in-use pipeline shall be permitted to be made without the use of a nitrogen purge.

New piped gas systems have to be purged with nitrogen during installation. The primary reason for a nitrogen purge is to prevent the formation of copper oxide scale. If only the final connection is made without nitrogen, as permitted by 5.1.10.5.5.10, the small amount of scale that forms can easily be blown out during final purging and analysis.

A typical reason not to use nitrogen for a final connection to an existing system is that if a valve is not present for isolation, it is possible to fill up an entire pipeline with nitrogen during the tie-in. It would then be necessary to blow down all outlets in a facility to be sure that the nitrogen is removed from the system. If a valve is present but has a defective seal, it is also possible to contaminate the existing piping system with nitrogen.

This requirement also serves as a reminder that the affected portion of the pipeline needs to be tested just like any new or modified portion of a system.

5.1.10.5.5.11 After a final connection in a positive pressure medical gas pipeline is made without a nitrogen purge, an outlet in the immediate downstream zone of the affected portion(s) of both the new and existing in-use piping shall be tested in accordance with 5.1.12.3.9, Final Tie-In Test.

5.1.10.5.5.12* When using the autogenous orbital welding process, joints shall be continuously purged inside and outside with inert gas(es) in accordance with the qualified welding procedure.

A.5.1.10.5.5.12 This is to assure a quality joint and to prevent the formation of copper oxide on the inside and outside surfaces of the joint.

5.1.10.5.6 Assembly and Heating Joints.

5.1.10.5.6.1 Tube ends shall be inserted fully into the socket of the fitting.

5.1.10.5.6.2 Where flux is permitted, the joint shall be heated slowly until the flux has liquefied.

5.1.10.5.6.3 After flux is liquefied, or where flux is not permitted to be used, the joint shall be heated quickly to the brazing temperature, taking care not to overheat the joint.

5.1.10.5.6.4 Techniques for heating the joint, applying the brazing filler metal, and making horizontal, vertical, and large-diameter joints shall be as stated in sections on "Applying Heat and Brazing" and "Horizontal and Vertical Joints" in Chapter VII, "Brazed Joints," in the CDA *Copper Tube Handbook.*

5.1.10.5.7 Inspection of Brazed Joints.

5.1.10.5.7.1 After brazing, the outside of all joints shall be cleaned by washing with water and a wire brush to remove any residue and permit clear visual inspection of the joint.

FAQ ▶
How do I conduct a visual inspection of the brazed joint?

Visual inspection is required after brazing, using only a cloth to wipe the brazed joint clean. The purpose of visual inspection is to see whether braze metal has flowed properly. If the metal has not flowed properly or there is a bridge brazement at the joint, it is indicative that penetration is questionable and workmanship is shoddy.

Visual inspection cannot establish the exact degree of penetration. Penetration is established by the procedures used in the brazing process and intended to achieve adequate penetration. The visual inspection is by "sight only."

The subsequent leak and pressure tests demonstrate, among other things, that the degree of penetration is adequate for the installation. Actual quantitative degree of penetration is not defined.

5.1.10.5.7.2 Where flux has been used, the wash water shall be hot.

5.1.10.5.7.3 Each brazed joint shall be visually inspected after cleaning the outside surfaces.

5.1.10.5.7.4 Joints exhibiting the following conditions shall not be permitted:

(1) Flux or flux residue (when flux or flux-coated BAg series rods are used with dissimilar metals)
(2) Base metal melting or erosion
(3) Unmelted filler metal
(4) Failure of the filler metal to be clearly visible all the way around the joint at the interface between the socket and the tube
(5) Cracks in the tube or component
(6) Cracks in the braze filler metal
(7) Failure of the joint to hold the test pressure under the installer-performed initial pressure test (5.1.12.2.3) and standing pressure test (5.1.12.2.6 or 5.1.12.2.7)

5.1.10.5.7.5 Brazed joints that are identified as defective under conditions 5.1.10.5.7.4(2) or 5.1.10.5.7.4(5) shall be replaced.

5.1.10.5.7.6 Brazed joints that are identified as defective under conditions 5.1.10.5.7.4(1), 5.1.10.5.7.4(3), 5.1.10.5.7.4(4), 5.1.10.5.7.4(6), or 5.1.10.5.7.4(7) shall be permitted to be repaired, except that no joint shall be reheated more than once before being replaced.

◀ **FAQ**
Why are there restrictions to heating and reheating a joint?

Normally, the failure of a brazed joint is caused by either underheating or overheating a joint. The alloy of silver and copper separates within the joint when overheated. The temperature needed to remelt the alloy is approximately 968°C (1800°F), which is much higher than the original melting temperature of the alloy of 649°C–815°C (1200°F–1500°F). The melting temperature of copper is approximately 1065°C (1975°F). The temperature needed to repair the bad joint is therefore close to the melting temperature of the copper tubing. As a result, the copper tubing could melt when a brazed joint is being repaired or has become soft (annealed). If the repaired joint is moved, raised, or stepped on during additional work in the area, for example, the repaired joint has a high probability of leaking. Consequently, the repair compromises the integrity of the medical gas system.

This requirement addresses the issue of how much repair of a joint is reasonable and possible. Repeated repair of a joint would increase the probability of contaminating the pipe. Also, the probability of achieving an acceptable joint deteriorates with each attempted repair. Further attempted repair could, in fact, compromise the integrity of the medical gas system.

5.1.10.6 Welded Joints.

The requirements of 5.1.10.6 are new in the 2005 edition. They permit for the first time the use of a new technology, the gas tungsten arc welding (GTAW) autogenous procedure. This technique for joining piping has been used for many years on high-purity piping in stainless steel and recently has been adapted for copper. It produces a very smooth, almost invisible joint that approaches the strength of the tubing itself.

The procedure requires a very skilled operator properly trained in the use of the equipment (see 5.1.10.6.2 through 5.1.10.6.4) and a unique purge gas (nitrogen will *not* work; see 5.1.10.6.5), and it is subject to failure if quality control is not strict (see 5.1.10.6.7 through

5.1.10.6.10). It is not a technique the average brazer can use or should attempt but can be effective, for instance, in a shop where volume prefabrication is the rule.

5.1.10.6.1 Welded joints for medical gas and medical–surgical vacuum systems shall be permitted to be made using a gas tungsten arc welding (GTAW) autogenous orbital procedure.

5.1.10.6.2 The GTAW autogenous orbital procedure and the welder qualification procedure shall be qualified in accordance with ASME Section IX, Welding and Brazing Qualifications of the ASME *Boiler and Pressure Vessel Code.*

5.1.10.6.3 Welder qualification procedures shall include a "bend test" and a "tensile test" per ASME Section IX on each tube size diameter.

5.1.10.6.4 Each welder shall qualify to a welding procedure specification (WPS) for each tube diameter.

5.1.10.6.5* GTAW autogenous orbital welded joints shall be purged during welding with a commercially available mixture (± 5 percent) of 75 percent helium and 25 percent argon.

A.5.1.10.6.5 Gas mixtures are commonly used in GTAW autogenous fusion welding. The identification of a gas mixture as "75He 25Ar" is a common industry term to define a commercially available grade from gas suppliers. Should test welding results lead to questions about the mixture percentage or gas quality, another bottle should be substituted and test welds performed.

5.1.10.6.6 The shield gas shall be as required in 5.1.10.6.5.

5.1.10.6.7 Test coupons shall be welded and inspected, as a minimum, at start of work and every 4 hours thereafter, or when the machine is idle for more than 30 minutes, and at the end of the work period.

5.1.10.6.8 Test coupons shall be inspected on the I.D. and O.D. by a qualified quality control inspector.

5.1.10.6.9 Test coupons shall also be welded at change of operator, weld head, welding power supply or gas source.

5.1.10.6.10 All production welds shall be visually inspected on the O.D. by the operator and any obvious weld failures shall be cut out and re-welded.

5.1.10.7 Special Fittings. The following special fittings shall be permitted to be used in lieu of brazed joints:

(1) Memory-metal couplings having temperature and pressure ratings joints not less than that of a brazed joint

Memory-metal fittings are radically different from those requiring the use of a hot flame and brazing metal to form a seal at each end of a fitting joining two pipes. They are made of a special alloy that contracts upon heating (e.g., if kept very cold, contraction occurs upon exposure to ambient temperatures). Thus, fittings must be stored in liquid nitrogen until ready for use.

When fittings are removed from the super-cold nitrogen, the installer has about 30 seconds to slip half the fitting over the end of one of the pipes and place the other pipe into the other half of the fitting. The fitting, because it is now exposed to a warmer temperature, will contract, creating a permanent and very tight seal. No flame or solder is required. They require some skill to use, and could be more expensive than a brazed joint.

Recently, another variety of this fitting has appeared that does not have the same thermal resistance as the original design. This newer design is proof only to approximately 315.6°C

(600°F) [versus the 537.8°C (1000°F) insisted upon for a brazed joint]. The user must be careful when procuring the fittings to ensure a sufficiently robust coupling is obtained.

(2) Listed or approved metallic gas tube fittings that, when made up, provide a permanent joint having the mechanical, thermal, and sealing integrity of a brazed joint
(3) Dielectric fittings where required by the manufacturer of special medical equipment to electrically isolate the equipment from the piping distribution system

The allowance in 5.1.10.7(3) for the insertion of a dielectric coupling addresses the necessity, practicality, and risk of allowing such a fitting. It must be understood that these fittings will compromise the fire resistance of any system in which they are placed. However, some manufacturers of magnetic resonance imaging (MRI) equipment require absolute radio frequency shielding for their enclosures, and there had to be an allowance to prevent the medical gas lines from acting as antennae in the MRI rooms.

The user is urged to use these fittings only where absolutely required, and to ensure that they are of a type and so installed as to prevent inadvertent disassembly (i.e., the union is pinned or otherwise prevented from "working" apart). Many of these fittings have elastomeric components internally that could require replacement over time, so where the fitting must be used, it should be placed so as to be readily accessible for this rare but necessary service.

(4) Axially swaged, elastic strain preload fittings providing metal to metal seal having pressure and temperature ratings not less than that of a brazed joint and when complete are permanent and nonseparable

◀ **FAQ**
What is an axially swaged, elastic strain preload fitting?

This style of coupling, which is assembled using a hydraulic press, is new in the 2005 edition. The fitting does not have any elastomeric components (the major objection to earlier designs) but creates a metal-to-metal seal by virtue of the force exerted by the installation tool. The installation is relatively simple but does require several steps not needed with a braze fitting, so an operator would be well advised to practice before actually attempting permanent installations. The fitting is more expensive than a simple braze fitting, but the fact that no purging is required could make this a particularly popular choice for quick installations and work where using a torch involves complications.

5.1.10.8 Prohibited Joints. The following joints shall be prohibited throughout medical gas and vacuum distribution pipeline systems:

(1) Flared and compression-type connections, including connections to station outlets and inlets, alarm devices, and other components
(2) Other straight-threaded connections, including unions
(3) The use of pipe-crimping tools to permanently stop the flow of medical gas and vacuum piping shall be prohibited.

5.1.10.9 Joints in WAGD networks.

5.1.10.9.1 WAGD networks designed for operation at vacuum in excess of 130 mm (5 in.) HgV shall be permitted to be joined by any method usable for medical vacuum under 5.1.10.5.

5.1.10.9.2 WAGD networks designed for operation at vacuum below 130 mm (5 in.) HgV shall be joined by any method usable for medical vacuum under 5.1.10.5 or by any method that will result in a leak-free network when tested per 5.1.12.3.2.

This requirement is a companion to 5.1.10.2.3 and is another section where the two styles of WAGD systems have been given separate requirements to reflect their different hazards and to ensure that the least expensive option is available when appropriate.

5.1.10.10 Installation of Piping and Equipment.

5.1.10.10.1 Pipe Sizing.

5.1.10.10.1.1 Piping systems shall be designed and sized to deliver the required flow rates at the utilization pressures.

5.1.10.10.1.2 Mains and branches in medical gas piping systems shall be not less than DN15 (NPS ½) (⅝ in. O.D.) size.

5.1.10.10.1.3 Mains and branches in medical–surgical vacuum systems shall be not less than DN20 (NPS ¾) (⅞ in. O.D.) size.

5.1.10.10.1.4 Drops to individual station outlets and inlets shall be not less than DN15 (NPS ½) (⅝ in. O.D.) size.

5.1.10.10.1.5 Runouts to alarm panels and connecting tubing for gauges and alarm devices shall be permitted to be DN8 (NPS ¼) (⅜ in. O.D.) size.

5.1.10.10.2 Protection of Piping. Piping shall be protected against freezing, corrosion, and physical damage.

5.1.10.10.2.1 Piping exposed in corridors and other areas where subject to physical damage from the movement of carts, stretchers, portable equipment, or vehicles shall be protected.

5.1.10.10.2.2 Piping underground within buildings or embedded in concrete floors or walls shall be installed in a continuous conduit.

5.1.10.10.3 Location of Piping.

5.1.10.10.3.1 Piping risers shall be permitted to be installed in pipe shafts if protected from physical damage, effects of excessive heat, corrosion, or contact with oil.

5.1.10.10.3.2 Piping shall not be installed in kitchens, elevator shafts, elevator machine rooms, areas with open flames, electrical service equipment over 600 volts, and areas prohibited under NFPA 70, *National Electrical Code*, except for the following locations:

(1) Room locations for medical air compressor supply systems and medical–surgical vacuum pump supply systems
(2) Room locations for secondary distribution circuit panels and breakers having a maximum voltage rating of 600 volts.

Earlier versions of the standard stated that medical gases were not to be run in "switchgear rooms," which was a widely used term but one that did not have any official definition in NFPA documents. It therefore became a matter of dispute as to what was implied. Under one definition, the medical air and vacuum lines could not be run to their sources, because to do so meant that pipes had to run in the same room as the controls, which contained high-voltage electrical switches and were thus "switchgear."

This absurdity was finally addressed by setting a voltage limit (600 volts), which is a dividing line used in the NFPA 70, *National Electrical Code* [13]. To ensure the issue just described was truly eliminated, mechanical rooms where air and vacuum systems are placed are explicitly excluded.

5.1.10.10.3.3 Medical gas piping shall be permitted to be installed in the same service trench or tunnel with fuel gas lines, fuel oil lines, electrical lines, steam lines, and similar utilities provided that the space is ventilated (naturally or mechanically) and the ambient temperature around the medical gas piping is limited to 54°C (130°F) maximum.

There should be no problems when gas piping is placed in the same riser shafts with other utilities, such as water and electricity, as long as protection, such as from damage, heat, corrosion, and oil, is provided.

5.1.10.10.3.4 Medical gas piping shall not be located where subject to contact with oil, including a possible flooding area in the case of a major oil leak.

Paragraphs 5.1.10.10.3.3 and 5.1.10.10.3.4 are somewhat at odds. The principle involved is to prevent oil and medical gases from coming into contact under any circumstances, including serious problems like a simultaneous oil and medical gas leak. The best way to reconcile the two requirements is to avoid running medical gases and oil together whenever possible (5.1.10.10.3.4), and only when absolutely unavoidable to run them as stipulated in 5.1.10.10.3.3.

5.1.10.10.4 Pipe Support.

5.1.10.10.4.1 Piping shall be supported from the building structure in accordance with MSS SP-69, *Pipe Hangers and Supports — Selection and Application.*

The requirement in 5.1.10.10.4.1 that piping be supported directly from the building structure is meant to preclude the use of ductwork or other piping for support.

◀ FAQ
Is ductwork or other piping considered building structure?

5.1.10.10.4.2 Hangers and supports shall comply with MSS SP-58, *Pipe Hangers and Supports — Materials, Design, and Manufacture.*

5.1.10.10.4.3 Hangers for copper tube shall have a copper finish and be sized for copper tube.

5.1.10.10.4.4 In potentially damp locations, copper tube hangers or supports that are in contact with the tube shall be plastic-coated or otherwise be insulated from the tube.

5.1.10.10.4.5 Maximum support spacing shall be in accordance with Table 5.1.10.10.4.5.

TABLE 5.1.10.10.4.5 *Maximum Pipe Support Spacing*

	Hanger Spacing	
Pipe Size	*m*	*ft*
DN8 (NPS ¼) (⅜ in. O.D.)	1520	5
DN10 (NPS ⅜) (½ in. O.D.)	1830	6
DN15 (NPS ½) (⅝ in. O.D)	1830	6
DN20 (NPS ¾) (⅞ in. O.D.)	2130	7
DN25 (NPS 1) (1⅛ in. O.D.)	2440	8
DN32 (NPS 1¼) (1⅜ in. O.D.)	2740	9
DN40 (NPS 1½) (1⅝ in. O.D.) and larger	3050	10
Vertical risers, all sizes		
Every floor but not to exceed:	4570	15

5.1.10.10.4.6 Where required, medical gas and vacuum piping shall be seismically restrained against earthquakes in accordance with the applicable building code.

With health care facilities needing to operate in adverse conditions such as an earthquake, it is imperative that medical gas piping be properly braced for seismic incidents. This paragraph highlights the need to apply the many requirements for seismic bracing found in the applicable building code.

5.1.10.10.5 Underground Piping Outside of Buildings.

Buried piping cannot be placed directly into poured concrete. It must be installed within a conduit so that it will not be affected by the weight, the settling of the concrete, or chemical interaction with the concrete.

5.1.10.10.5.1 Buried piping outside of buildings shall be installed below the local level of frost penetration.

The depth of buried pipe depends on such factors as the climatic conditions of the region, the type of traffic anticipated, and the routing of the piping.

The installation of buried piping outside of buildings is covered by 5.1.10.10.5.1, whereas the installation of piping within or under slabs within the building is covered in 5.3.10.10.7.

5.1.10.10.5.2 The installation procedure for underground piping shall protect the piping from physical damage while being backfilled.

5.1.10.10.5.3 If underground piping is protected by a conduit, cover, or other enclosure, the following requirements shall be met:

(1) Access shall be provided at the joints for visual inspection and leak testing.
(2) The conduit, cover, or enclosure shall be self-draining and not retain groundwater in prolonged contact with the pipe.

FAQ ▶ Can "continuous split enclosures" still be used to protect buried pipe?

The 2005 edition removes the requirement for a "continuous split enclosure" previously mandated. Instead, it recognizes that other methods might be satisfactory and offers this more general guidance.

5.1.10.10.5.4 Buried piping that will be subject to surface loads shall be buried at a depth that will protect the piping or its enclosure from excessive stresses.

5.1.10.10.5.5 The minimum backfilled cover above the top of the pipe or its enclosure for buried piping outside of buildings shall be 900 mm (36 in.), except that the minimum cover shall be permitted to be reduced to 450 mm (18 in.) where physical damage is otherwise prevented.

5.1.10.10.5.6 Trenches shall be excavated so that the pipe or its enclosure has firm, substantially continuous bearing on the bottom of the trench.

5.1.10.10.5.7 Backfill shall be clean and compacted so as to protect and uniformly support the pipe or its enclosure.

5.1.10.10.5.8 A continuous tape or marker placed immediately above the pipe or its enclosure shall clearly identify the pipeline by specific name.

5.1.10.10.5.9 A continuous warning means shall also be provided above the pipeline at approximately one-half the depth of bury.

5.1.10.10.5.10 Where underground piping is installed through a wall sleeve, the ends of the sleeve shall be sealed to prevent the entrance of ground water into the building.

5.1.10.10.6 Branch Takeoffs. Runouts from horizontal piping shall be taken off above the centerline of the main or branch pipe and rise vertically or at an angle of not more than 45 degrees from vertical.

Paragraph 5.1.10.6.6 is aimed at preventing any debris in the line from passing out of the main line and into the branch. (See Exhibit 5.23.)

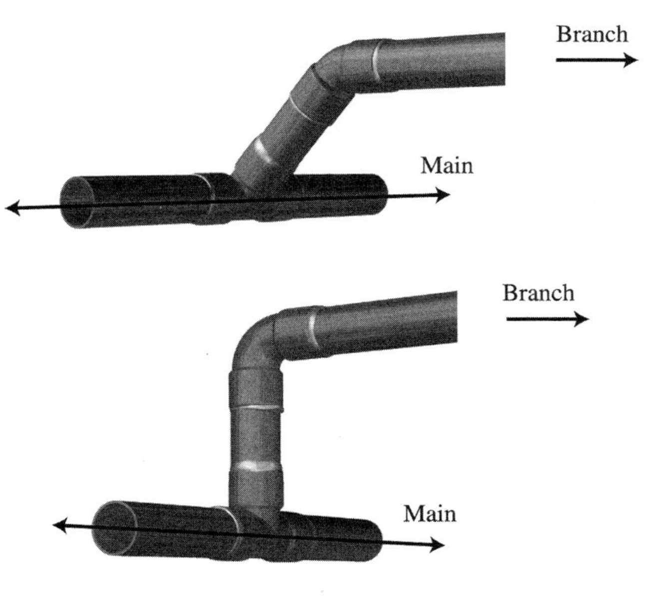

Exhibit 5.23 *Takeoffs.*

5.1.10.10.7 Hose and Flexible Connectors.

5.1.10.10.7.1 Hose and flexible connectors, both metallic and nonmetallic, shall be no longer than necessary and shall not penetrate or be concealed in walls, floors, ceilings, or partitions.

Paragraph 5.1.10.10.7.1 applies only to those implementations that use a hose to extend a pipeline in a semi-permanent way. This paragraph does not apply to the use of hose as a means to connect patient care equipment downstream of an outlet (e.g., after the pipeline has terminated). The key distinction is that patient care hoses themselves, and their connectors, are in plain view.

In most respects, the pipeline is considered to terminate in a station outlet or inlet that is brazed to the piping, as discussed in 5.1.5. However, where manufactured assemblies are installed, the function of these assemblies might require the flexibility of permanent hoses, which are more or less concealed. Such hosing, because it is intended to be permanent and because access is limited, must be considered an integral part of the piped gas distribution system. See 5.1.6 for information on manufactured assemblies.

Because any hoses are subject to movement and wear, some means of visually inspecting and/or changing the hoses on a periodic basis is appropriate. Thus, hoses cannot be concealed inside walls.

Requirements for piping penetrating walls inside a building can be found in Chapter 8 of NFPA *101, Life Safety Code* [5]. 

5.1.10.10.7.2 Flexible connectors, metallic or nonmetallic, shall have a minimum burst pressure, with a gauge pressure of 6895 kPa (1000 psi).

5.1.10.10.8 Prohibited System Interconnections.

5.1.10.10.8.1 Two or more medical gas or vacuum piping systems shall not be interconnected for installation, testing, or any other reason.

Paragraph 5.1.10.10.8.1 addresses the problem created if a temporary connection for pressure testing or purging is not removed. The intent of this paragraph is to prohibit this interconnection even on a temporary basis. Each piping system is to be tested separately.

5.1.10.10.8.2 Leak testing shall be accomplished by separately charging and testing each individual piping system.

5.1.10.10.9 Manufacturer's Instructions.

5.1.10.10.9.1 The installation of individual components shall be made in accordance with the instructions of the manufacturer.

5.1.10.10.9.2 Such instructions shall include directions and information deemed by the manufacturer to be adequate for attaining proper operation, testing, and maintenance of the medical gas and vacuum systems.

5.1.10.10.9.3 Copies of manufacturer's instructions shall be left with the system owner.

5.1.10.10.10 Changes in System Use.

5.1.10.10.10.1 Where a positive pressure medical gas piping distribution system originally used or constructed for the use at one pressure and for one gas is converted for operation at another pressure or for another gas, all provisions of 5.1.10 shall apply as if the system were new.

5.1.10.10.10.2 A vacuum system shall not be permitted to be converted for use as a gas system.

The need for prohibiting the conversion of a vacuum pipeline into a gas pipeline might seem obvious, but the standard wishes to stress that the contamination to which a pipeline is exposed when it is used for vacuum precludes it from ever being used for carrying gas.

5.1.10.10.11 Qualification of Installers.

The standard originally required that only qualified persons install medical gas but did not give any further guidance on what qualified a person for the work. In many jurisdictions over the intervening years, this vague statement expanded into a broader qualification and covered more than the basic brazing operation. These jurisdictions are now required to comply with ASSE 6010, *Professional Qualifications Standard for Medical Gas Systems Installers* [14].

5.1.10.10.11.1 The installation of medical gas and vacuum systems shall be made by qualified, competent technicians who are experienced in making such installations.

5.1.10.10.11.2 Installers of medical gas and vacuum systems shall meet the requirements of ASSE 6010, *Professional Qualification Standard for Medical Gas Systems Installers.*

5.1.10.10.11.3 Brazing shall be performed by individuals who are qualified under the provisions of 5.1.10.10.12.

5.1.10.10.11.4 Prior to any installation work, the installer of medical gas and vacuum piping shall provide and maintain documentation on the job site for the qualification of brazing procedures and individual brazers that is required under 5.1.10.10.12.

5.1.10.10.11.5 Health care organization personnel shall be permitted to install piping systems if all of the requirements of 5.1.10.10.11 are met during the installation.

The allowance here for health care facility personnel should not be taken to exclude them from meeting the same requirements governing any medical gas installer, but is rather to prevent anyone from asserting that installations cannot be performed by in-house personnel.

5.1.10.10.12 Qualification of Brazing Procedures and Brazing.

Paragraph 5.1.10.10.12 covers requirements for qualifying a brazer. It is not the field test for determining the integrity of brazed joints in a piped gas or vacuum system, which is covered under 5.1.12, Performance Criteria and Testing — Level 1 (Gases, Medical–Surgical Vacuum, and WAGD).

These requirements are complementary to those in the ASSE 6010, *Professional Qualifications Standard for Medical Gas Systems Installers* [14], these being the quality controls that the brazer qualified under the ASSE 6010 will operate.

5.1.10.10.12.1 Brazing procedures and brazer performance for the installation of medical gas and vacuum piping shall be qualified in accordance with either Section IX, Welding and Brazing Qualifications, of the ASME *Boiler and Pressure Vessel Code*, or AWS B2.2, *Standard for Brazing Procedure and Performance Qualification*, both as modified by 5.1.10.10.12.2 through 5.1.10.10.12.5.

5.1.10.10.12.2 Brazers shall be qualified by visual examination of the test coupon followed by sectioning.

5.1.10.10.12.3 The brazing procedure specification shall address cleaning, joint clearance, overlap, internal purge gas, purge gas flow rate, and filler metal.

5.1.10.10.12.4 The brazing procedure qualification record and the record of brazer performance qualification shall document filler metal used, cleaning, joint clearance, overlap, internal purge gas and flow rate during brazing of coupon, and the absence of internal oxidation in the completed coupon.

5.1.10.10.12.5 Brazing procedures qualified by a technically competent group or agency shall be permitted under the following conditions:

(1) The brazing procedure specification and the procedure qualification record meets the requirements of this standard.
(2) The employer obtains a copy of both the brazing procedure specification and the supporting qualification records from the group or agency and signs and dates these records, thereby accepting responsibility for the qualifications that were performed by the group or agency.
(3) The employer qualifies at least one brazer following each brazing procedure specification used.

5.1.10.10.12.6 An employer shall be permitted to accept brazer qualification records of a previous employer under the following conditions:

(1) The brazer has been qualified following the same or an equivalent procedure that the new employer uses.
(2) The new employer obtains a copy of the record of brazer performance qualification tests from the previous employer and signs and dates these records, thereby accepting responsibility for the qualifications performed by the previous employer.

5.1.10.10.12.7 Performance qualifications of brazers shall remain in effect indefinitely unless the brazer does not braze with the qualified procedure for a period exceeding 6 months, or there is a specific reason to question the ability of the brazer.

5.1.11 Labeling and Identification.

See Table 5.1.11.

5.1.11.1 Pipe Labeling.

***TABLE 5.1.11** Standard Designation Colors and Operating Pressures for Gas and Vacuum Systems*

Gas Service	*Abbreviated Name*	*Colors (Background/ Text)*	*Standard Gauge Pressure*
Medical air	Med Air	Yellow/black	345–380 kPa (50–55 psi)
Carbon dioxide	CO_2	Gray/black or gray/white	345–380 kPa (50–55 psi)
Helium	He	Brown/white	345–380 kPa (50–55 psi)
Nitrogen	N_2	Black/white	1100–1275 kPa (160–185 psi)
Nitrous oxide	N_2O	Blue/white	345–380 kPa (50–55 psi)
Oxygen	O_2	Green/white or white/green	345–380 kPa (50–55 psi)
Oxygen/carbon dioxide mixtures	O_2/CO_2 *n*% (*n* is % of CO_2)	Green/white	345–380 kPa (50–55 psi)
Medical–surgical vacuum	Med Vac	White/black	380 mm to 760 mm (15 in. to 30 in.) HgV
Waste anesthetic gas disposal	WAGD	Violet/white	Varies with system type
Other mixtures	Gas A%/Gas B%	Colors as above Major gas for background/ minor gas for text	None
Nonmedical air (Level 3 gas-powered device)		Yellow and white diagonal stripe/ black	None
Nonmedical and level 3 vacuum		White and black diagonal stripe/ black boxed	None
Laboratory air		Yellow and white checkerboard/ black	None
Laboratory vacuum		White and black checkerboard/ black boxed	None
Instrument air		Red/white	1100–1275 kPa (160–185 psi)

A bewildering variety of labels are made. Some wrap completely around the pipe, some are of a fixed width, and some come with different adhesives and different preparation requirements. NFPA 99 does not stipulate what kind of label is to be used as long as the basic features in this section are included. Specifics of labels are left to the installer's discretion.

Exhibits 5.24 and 5.25 show examples of piping labels.

5.1.11.1.1 Piping shall be labeled by stenciling or adhesive markers that identify the patient medical gas, the support gas, or vacuum system, and include:

(1) The name of the gas/vacuum system or the chemical symbol per Table 5.1.11
(2) The gas or vacuum system color code per Table 5.1.11
(3) Where positive pressure gas piping systems operate at pressures other than the standard gauge pressure in Table 5.1.11, the pipe labeling shall include the operating pressure in addition to the name of the gas

EXHIBIT 5.24 *Typical pressure gauge and sensor for monitoring pressure inside piped gas system. Gas-specific demand checks are now required.*

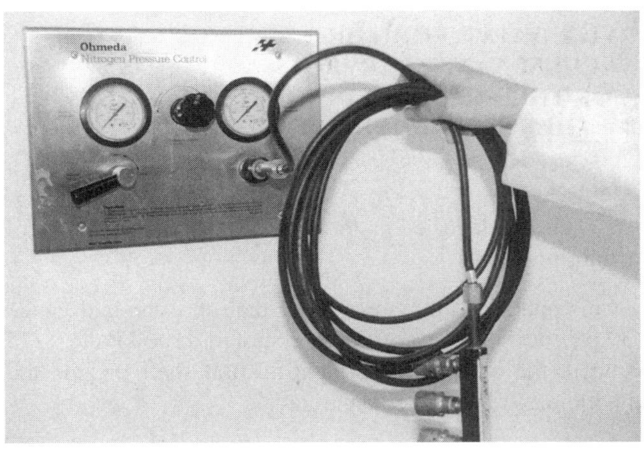

EXHIBIT 5.25 *Control panel in an operating room for a piped nitrogen system used to power pneumatic devices, such as high-speed drills.*

5.1.11.1.2 Pipe labels shall be located as follows:

(1) At intervals of not more than 6.1 m (20 ft)
(2) At least once in or above every room
(3) On both sides of walls or partitions penetrated by the piping
(4) At least once in every story height traversed by risers

5.1.11.1.3 Medical gas pipeline shall not be painted.

5.1.11.2 Shutoff Valves.

5.1.11.2.1 Shutoff valves shall be identified as follows:

(1) The name or chemical symbol for the specific medical gas or vacuum system
(2) The room or areas served
(3) A caution to not close or open the valve except in emergency

5.1.11.2.2 Where positive pressure gas piping systems operate at pressures other than the standard gauge pressure of 345 kPa to 380 kPa (50 psi to 55 psi) or a gauge pressure of 1100 kPa to 1275 kPa (160 psi to 185 psi) for nitrogen or instrument air, the valve identification shall also include the nonstandard operating pressure.

5.1.11.2.3 Source valves shall be labeled in substance as follows:

SOURCE VALVE
FOR THE (SOURCE NAME).

5.1.11.2.4 Main line valves shall be labeled in substance as follows:

MAIN LINE VALVE FOR THE
(GAS/VACUUM NAME) SERVING THE
(NAME OF THE BUILDING).

5.1.11.2.5 Riser valve(s) shall be labeled in substance as follows:

RISER FOR THE (GAS/VACUUM NAME)
SERVING (NAME OF THE AREA/BUILDING
SERVED BY THE PARTICULAR RISER).

5.1.11.2.6 Service valve(s) shall be labeled in substance as follows:

SERVICE VALVE FOR THE
(GAS/VACUUM NAME) SERVING
(NAME OF THE AREA/BUILDING
SERVED BY THE PARTICULAR VALVE).

5.1.11.3 Station Outlets and Inlets.

5.1.11.3.1 Station outlets and inlets shall be identified as to the name or chemical symbol for the specific medical gas or vacuum provided.

5.1.11.3.2 Where medical gas systems operate at pressures other than the standard gauge pressure of 345 kPa to 380 kPa (50 psi to 55 psi) or a gauge pressure of 1100 kPa to 1275 kPa (160 psi to 185 psi) for nitrogen, the station outlet identification shall include the nonstandard operating pressure in addition to the name of the gas.

5.1.11.4 Alarm Panels. Labeling of alarm panels shall comply with the requirements of 5.1.9.1(6) and 5.1.9.1(7).

5.1.12* Performance Criteria and Testing — Level 1 (Gases, Medical–Surgical Vacuum, and WAGD).

A.5.1.12 All testing should be completed before putting a new piping system, or an addition to an existing system, into service. Test procedures and the results of all tests should be made part of the permanent records of the facility of which the piping system forms a part. They should show the room and area designations, dates of the tests, and name(s) of persons conducting the tests.

5.1.12.1 General.

5.1.12.1.1 Inspection and testing shall be performed on all new piped gas systems, additions, renovations, temporary installations, or repaired systems, to assure the facility, by a documented procedure, that all applicable provisions of this document have been adhered to and system integrity has been achieved or maintained.

5.1.12.1.2 Inspection and testing shall include all components of the system or portions thereof, including, but not limited to, gas bulk source(s), manifolds, compressed air source systems (e.g., compressors, dryers, filters, regulators), source alarms and monitoring safeguards, master alarms, pipelines, isolation valves, area alarms, zone valves, and station inlets (vacuum) and outlets (pressure gases).

5.1.12.1.3 All systems that are breached and components that are subject to additions, renovations, or replacement (e.g., new gas sources: bulk, manifolds, compressors, dryers, alarms) shall be inspected and tested.

5.1.12.1.4 Systems shall be deemed breached at the point of pipeline intrusion by physical separation or by system component removal, replacement, or addition.

5.1.12.1.5 Breached portions of the systems subject to inspection and testing shall be confined to only the specific altered zone and components in the immediate zone or area that is located upstream for vacuum systems and downstream for pressure gases at the point or area of intrusion.

Determining which portions of a system must be tested and what tests must be conducted for any given project are frequently in question. Paragraph 5.1.12.1.12 defines what might be required after maintenance work. Some additional examples are provided as guidance in making those determinations:

- If a single oxygen outlet were added to a 50-room zone, and the entire zone was drained of oxygen and refilled with nitrogen for the work, the entire zone would need to be retested prior to returning the system to normal operation and the connection of patients.
- If a five-story riser were shut down for a tie-in on the second floor, and nitrogen was not used for the tie-in, it should be necessary only to check the closest outlets upstream and downstream of the tie-in for particulate and concentration and to check on the furthermost outlet for concentration. (These steps are in addition to whatever tests are necessary for the new section itself prior to tie-in.)
- If a section of the piping could be isolated (e.g., using valves already in place) and the system kept pressurized from an alternate source (e.g., by back-feeding from somewhere else), it would be acceptable to test the section in isolation. Tests would be performed on the new or modified section at each end. The isolated sections would be undisturbed, and a simple spot check would confirm that they had remained isolated.

5.1.12.1.6 The inspection and testing reports shall be submitted directly to the party that contracted for the testing, who shall submit the report through channels to the responsible facility authority and any others that are required.

Test reports are now to be sent directly to the party contracting for the testing; that party will, in turn, distribute copies to the necessary authorities, insurers, and other parties requiring a copy of the report. This procedure reflects the difficulty at times of determining who the authority(ies) having jurisdiction (AHJ) is for a particular installation and the additional parties that need to receive a copy of the report. The installing contractor should be in a better position to know this than the verifier.

5.1.12.1.7 Reports shall contain detailed listings of all findings and results.

5.1.12.1.8 The responsible facility authority shall review these inspection and testing records prior to the use of all systems to assure that all findings and results of the inspection and testing have been successfully completed.

5.1.12.1.9 All documentation pertaining to inspections and testing shall be maintained on-site within the facility.

5.1.12.1.10 Before piping systems are initially put into use, the facility authority shall be responsible for ascertaining that the gas/vacuum delivered at the outlet/inlet is that shown on the outlet/inlet label and that the proper connecting fittings are installed for the specific gas/vacuum service.

5.1.12.1.11 Acceptance of the verifier's report shall be permitted to satisfy the requirements in 5.1.12.1.10.

5.1.12.1.12 The removal of components within a source system for repair and re-installation, or the replacement of components like for like shall be treated as new work for the purposes of testing whenever such work involves cutting and/or brazing new piping.

FAQ ▶
If some source equipment needs replacing, what type of testing is required?

Paragraph 5.1.12.1.12 is intended to prevent an unnecessarily burdensome testing regimen where a facility was simply replacing like for like, as might happen with an air compressor that had worn out. Although it is inappropriate to perform such work with no testing, clearly the testing that would be performed on a new source was also excessive.

The underlying principles are that the replaced equipment should be tested as appropriate to that piece of equipment (i.e., functional tests) and that this allowance should cease when pipe is cut or brazed, passing then out of the realm of simple replacement and into the realm of the more extensive tests required of new work. This section should be applied with an eye to the intent — it is not, for instance, meant to permit an entirely new source to be installed without testing simply because there happened to be a convenient union available.

5.1.12.1.12.1 Where no piping is changed, functional testing shall be performed as follows:

(1) To verify the function of the replaced device
(2) To assure no other equipment in the system has been adversely impacted

5.1.12.1.12.2 Where no piping is changed, in addition to tests of general function required by 5.1.12.1.12.1, testing shall be performed as follows:

(1) Pressure gas sources shall be tested for compliance with 5.1.12.3.14.2 as applicable to the equipment type.
(2) Medical air and instrument air sources shall be tested to 5.1.12.3.14.3.
(3) Vacuum and WAGD systems shall be tested to 5.1.12.3.14.4.
(4) Alarm systems shall be tested to 5.1.12.3.5.2 and 5.1.12.3.5.3.
(5) All affected components shall be tested as appropriate to that specific component (e.g., a replaced dew point monitor would be tested to 5.1.3.5.15).

5.1.12.2 Installer Performed Tests.

System testing is divided into tests to be conducted by the installer prior to the final verification tests (5.1.12.2) and tests to be conducted by a technically qualified party experienced in testing piped gas systems and verifying the installation (5.1.12.3).

Fatalities have occurred due to cross-connection of gases. It is absolutely essential to verify that labeling of outlets and of the delivered gas are the same. The tests listed in this section have been developed, among other reasons, for that purpose. Other methods acceptable to the authority having jurisdiction can be used for testing for cross-connections.

The sequence of the tests shown here is not meant to be restrictive. It is felt to be the most logical and least likely to force repetition. However, individual circumstance may make alternate sequencing of the tests preferable. In any case, the test sequence must ensure that new and old work do not cross-contaminate, that there is no damage to the equipment, and that every test is performed.

5.1.12.2.1 General.

5.1.12.2.1.1 The tests required by 5.1.12.2 shall be performed and documented by the installer prior to the tests listed in 5.1.12.3, System Verification.

5.1.12.2.1.2 The test gas shall be oil-free, dry Nitrogen NF.

5.1.12.2.1.3 Where manufactured assemblies are to be installed, the tests required by 5.1.12.2 shall be performed as follows:

(1) After completion of the distribution piping but before the standing pressure test
(2) Prior to installation of manufactured assemblies supplied through flexible hose or flexible tubing
(3) At all station outlets/inlets on installed manufactured assemblies supplied through copper tubing

5.1.12.2.2 Initial Blow Down. Piping in medical gas and vacuum distribution systems shall be blown clear by means of oil-free, dry Nitrogen NF as follows:

(1) After installation of the distribution piping
(2) Before installation of station outlets/inlets and other system components (e.g., pressure/vacuum alarm devices, pressure/vacuum indicators, pressure relief valves, manifolds, source equipment)

5.1.12.2.3 Initial Pressure Test.

Pressure testing is conducted as a means to find leaks. Leaks not only represent a fire hazard, they are also considered by many to pose significant health risks. Excessive exposure of staff to gases such as nitrous oxide has reportedly been linked to diseases. Financially, leaks represent waste.

◀ **FAQ**
Why is the initial pressure test important?

It is also very important that the leak-testing solution be specifically approved for oxygen service (this holds true for all medical gases, whether conveying oxidizers or not). Solutions approved for "compressed gas" are not necessarily approved for "oxygen service."

5.1.12.2.3.1 Each section of the piping in medical gas and vacuum systems shall be pressure tested.

5.1.12.2.3.2 Initial pressure tests shall be conducted as follows:

(1) After installation of station outlets/inlets rough-in assemblies. Test caps shall be permitted to be used.
(2) Prior to the installation of components of the distribution piping system that would be damaged by the test pressure (e.g., pressure/vacuum alarm devices, pressure/vacuum indicators, line pressure relief valves, manufactured assemblies with flexible hose, hose, etc.).

5.1.12.2.3.3 The source shutoff valve shall remain closed during these tests.

5.1.12.2.3.4 The test pressure for pressure gases shall be 1.5 times the system working pressure but not less than a gauge pressure of 1035 kPa (150 psi).

5.1.12.2.3.5 The test pressure for vacuum shall be not less than a gauge pressure of 415 kPa (60 psi).

5.1.12.2.3.6 The test pressure shall be maintained until each joint has been examined for leakage by means of soapy water or other equally effective means of leak detection that is safe for use with oxygen.

5.1.12.2.3.7 Leaks, if any, shall be located, repaired (if permitted), replaced (if required), and retested.

See also the commentary following 5.1.10.5.7.6.

5.1.12.2.4 Cross-Connection Test. It shall be determined that no cross-connections exist between the various medical gas and vacuum piping systems.

5.1.12.2.4.1 All piping systems shall be reduced to atmospheric pressure.

5.1.12.2.4.2 Sources of test gas shall be disconnected from all piping systems except for the one system being tested.

5.1.12.2.4.3 The system under test shall be charged with oil-free, dry Nitrogen NF to a gauge pressure of 345 kPa (50 psi).

5.1.12.2.4.4 After the installation of the individual faceplates with appropriate adapters matching outlet/inlet labels, each individual outlet/inlet in each installed medical gas and vacuum piping system shall be checked to determine that the test gas is being dispensed only from the piping system being tested.

5.1.12.2.4.5 The cross-connection test referenced in 5.1.12.2.4 shall be repeated for each installed medical gas and vacuum piping system.

5.1.12.2.4.6 The proper labeling and identification of system outlets/inlets shall be confirmed during these tests.

5.1.12.2.5 Piping Purge Test. The outlets in each medical gas piping system shall be purged to remove any particulate matter from the distribution piping.

5.1.12.2.5.1 Using appropriate adapters, each outlet shall be purged with an intermittent high-volume flow of test gas until the purge produces no discoloration in a clean white cloth.

FAQ ▶ What is considered an appropriate adapter?

The pulse purge test has been found to effectively break up material in the pipeline, such as copper oxide scale and other by-products of fabrication, and transport it to the outlet being purged. This purge is to be conducted into a clean, white cloth loosely held over the adapter. For purposes of this test, the adapter used must be an adapter only and not have a flowmeter or other flow-restricting device. These types of adapters are generally available directly from the manufacturers.

An appropriate adapter is necessary to prevent damage to the O-rings from screwdrivers, pencils, nails, tubing, or other miscellaneous items used to open the outlet and let gas out. For example, when the proper adapter is used, the O-rings cannot unseat themselves under high purge. Plastic poppets and other outlet components can also be damaged if the appropriate adapter is not used.

5.1.12.2.5.2 This purging shall be started at the closest outlet/inlet to the zone valve and continue to the furthest outlet/inlet within the zone.

5.1.12.2.6 Standing Pressure Test for Positive Pressure Medical Gas Piping. After successful completion of the initial pressure tests under 5.1.12.2.3, medical gas distribution piping shall be subject to a standing pressure test.

5.1.12.2.6.1 Tests shall be conducted after the final installation of station outlet valve bodies, face plates, and other distribution system components (e.g., pressure alarm devices, pressure indicators, line pressure relief valves, manufactured assemblies, hose, etc.).

5.1.12.2.6.2 The source valve shall be closed during this test.

5.1.12.2.6.3 The piping systems shall be subjected to a 24-hour standing pressure test using oil-free, dry Nitrogen NF.

5.1.12.2.6.4 Test pressures shall be 20 percent above the normal system operating line pressure.

5.1.12.2.6.5 At the conclusion of the tests, there shall be no change in the test pressure other than that attributed to changes of ambient temperature, as permitted under 5.1.12.2.7.6.

5.1.12.2.6.6 Leaks, if any, shall be located, repaired (if permitted) or replaced (if required), and retested.

5.1.12.2.7 Standing Vacuum Test for Vacuum System. After successful completion of the initial pressure tests under 5.1.12.2.3, vacuum distribution piping shall be subjected to a standing vacuum test.

As required by 5.1.12.2.7, the final vacuum test, as part of a system verification procedure, is considered to be essential to ensure that all components of the system are functioning properly when connected together.

5.1.12.2.7.1 Tests shall be conducted after installation of all components of the vacuum system.

5.1.12.2.7.2 The piping systems shall be subjected to a 24-hour standing vacuum test.

5.1.12.2.7.3 Test pressure shall be between 300 mm (12 in.) HgV and full vacuum.

5.1.12.2.7.4 During the test, the source of test vacuum shall be disconnected from the piping system.

5.1.12.2.7.5 At the conclusion of the test, there shall be no change in the vacuum other than that attributed to changes of ambient temperature, as permitted under 5.1.12.2.7.6.

5.1.12.2.7.6 Test vacuum changes due to expansion or contraction shall be permitted to be determined by means of the following pressure–temperature relationship:

(1) The calculated final absolute pressure equals the initial absolute pressure times the final absolute temperature, divided by the initial absolute temperature.
(2) Absolute pressure is the gauge pressure reading plus 101.4 kPa (14.7 psi).
(3) Absolute temperature is the temperature reading plus 238°C (460°F).
(4) The final allowable gauge pressure reading equals the final allowable absolute pressure minus a gauge pressure of 101.4 kPa (14.7 psi).

5.1.12.2.7.7 Leaks, if any, shall be located, repaired (if permitted) or replaced (if required), and retested.

5.1.12.3 System Verification.

5.1.12.3.1 General.

5.1.12.3.1.1 Verification tests shall be performed only after all tests required in 5.1.12.2, Installer Performed Tests, have been completed.

5.1.12.3.1.2 The test gas shall be oil-free, dry Nitrogen NF or the system gas where permitted.

◀ **FAQ**
When is it appropriate to use the system gas for testing?

The system gas allowance acknowledges that it might not be practical to use nitrogen as the test gas in all instances. For example, if a small amount of oxygen, air, or vacuum outlets are added to an existing in-use zone, the existing zone valve might be of older design and might leak nitrogen back across the seals into the oxygen system during pressure testing procedures. Also it would be inappropriate to pressurize the existing zone to a gauge pressure of 1034 kPa (150 psi) for the leak test. Because the requirement in 5.1.12.3.1.8 already permits tie-in work to be made with source gas at a source gas gauge pressure of 345 kPa (50 psi) oxygen — for instance, for an oxygen tie-in — it was considered appropriate to permit project(s) to be installed and tested with source gases at source pressure. Obviously, it is still very important to perform the leak test at source gas pressure, the blowdown for particulate, and the concentration test. This regimen eliminates the need for the facility to do a major shutdown and risk lateral or main line contamination due to older valves.

For example, a facility could renovate several rooms in a zone, then use nitrogen to perform all the installer testing on the new work in isolation. The actual tie-in would not use nitrogen and the verifier could perform testing using the source gas (oxygen, air, etc.) or vacuum. This approach would minimize downtime and risk for the facility, as well as keep cost minimal for a small project.

5.1.12.3.1.3 Testing shall be conducted by a party technically competent and experienced in the field of medical gas and vacuum pipeline testing and meeting the requirements of ASSE 6030, *Professional Qualifications Standard for Medical Gas Systems Verifiers.*

A persistent problem in the field has been determining what qualifies a person for this work. The number of persons purporting to be verifiers has multiplied at dramatic rates over the last few years, and there has been no uniformity in procedures, equipment, qualification, or documentation. It has truly been a case of "I am a verifier because I say I am." In the absence of any objective qualification, only the rules of *caveat emptor* could apply, and there have been abuses and, moreover, outright fraud.

Now the requirement calls for a verifier to have the minimum credential specified in ASSE 6030, *Professional Qualifications Standard for Medical Gas System Verifiers* [15]. This requirement will enable a facility to at least impose a baseline, although it will not by itself eliminate the flaws in the industry or abuses of the intent by individuals. The situation today remains one where the facility and its construction team must police their contractors.

5.1.12.3.1.4 Testing shall be performed by a party other than the installing contractor.

It is glaringly obvious that if the same contractor provides the equipment, performs the installation, and verifies his or her own work, the opportunities for conflicts of interest are legion. It must also be stated that some installers are more capable than the verifiers who test their work. Paragraph 5.1.12.3.1.4 seeks to impose a separation between the installer and the verifier, in the hope that the verification will constitute a thorough and dispassionate check of the systems before they are put in operation.

Although separating the installing and testing will reduce the most obvious conflict of interest, the user should also consider that other potential conflicts can remain. Verifiers who sell equipment or manufacturers who perform verifications can be involved in conflicts of interest. All potential conflicts cannot be written out of the standard, because there can be a fine line between restraining conflict of interest and restraining trade. The owners must always be aware of and act on their responsibility for the choice of their suppliers.

5.1.12.3.1.5 When systems have not been installed by in-house personnel, testing shall be permitted by personnel of that organization who meet the requirements of 5.1.12.3.1.3.

FAQ ▶
Why can't the in-house personnel install and verify the system?

Because the conflicts of interest of outside parties are partially addressed in 5.1.12.3.1.4, it may seem inappropriate to permit the facility's own employees to do the very thing outsiders have been enjoined from doing — testing their fellow employee's work. This seeming anomaly stems from the reasonable assertion that a properly qualified employee gains nothing from cutting the same corners that might temptingly enhance the profits of an outside contractor. The employees' own conflicts of interest are likely trivial when set against the very personal cost of an oversight.

5.1.12.3.1.6 All tests required under 5.1.12.3 shall be performed after installation of any manufactured assemblies supplied through flexible hose or tubing.

5.1.12.3.1.7 Where there are multiple possible connection points for terminals, each possible position shall be tested independently.

Paragraph 5.1.12.3.1.7 recognizes that some manufactured assemblies are built with multiple connection points to enhance future flexibility in outlet location, and so on, but that each of these connectors must represent a separate termination of the medical gas piping. The user is warned that these connection points are frequently hidden behind dress panels or other finishing trim and the trim might need to be removed to accomplish this testing.

5.1.12.3.1.8 The gas of system designation shall be permitted to be used for all tests, regardless of the size of the system. This includes:

(1) Standing pressure (5.1.12.3.2)
(2) Cross-connection (5.1.12.3.3)
(3) Alarms (5.1.12.3.5)
(4) Piping purge (5.1.12.3.6)
(5) Piping particulates (5.1.12.3.7)

5.1.12.3.2* Standing Pressure Test. Piping systems shall be subjected to a 10-minute standing pressure test at operating line pressure using the following procedure:

(1) After the system is filled with nitrogen or source gas, the source valve and all zone valves shall be closed.
(2) The piping system shall show no decrease in pressure after 10 minutes.
(3) Any leaks found shall be located, repaired, and retested per 5.1.12.2.6.

A.5.1.12.3.2 This is the final pressure test of the completely installed system and is intended to locate any leaks that would be more likely to occur at lower pressure, for example, leaks in station outlet valve seals.

5.1.12.3.3 Cross-Connection Test. After closing of walls and completion of requirements of 5.1.12.2, Installer Performed Tests, it shall be determined that no cross-connection of piping systems exists by either of the methods detailed in 5.1.12.3.3.1 or 5.1.12.3.3.2.

5.1.12.3.3.1 Individual Pressurization.

(A) All medical gas and vacuum piping systems shall be reduced to atmospheric pressure.

(B) All sources of test gas from all of the medical gas and vacuum systems, with the exception of the one system to be checked, shall be disconnected.

(C) The system being checked shall be pressurized to a gauge pressure of 345 kPa (50 psi).

(D) With adapters matching outlet labels, each individual station outlet/inlet of all medical gas and vacuum systems installed shall be checked to determine that test gas is being dispensed only from the outlets/inlets of the piping system being tested.

(E) The source of test gas shall be disconnected and the system tested reduced to atmospheric pressure.

(F) Proceed to test each additional piping system until all medical gas and vacuum piping systems are free of cross-connections.

5.1.12.3.3.2 Pressure Differential.

The pressures listed in Table 5.1.12.3.3.2 are for testing purposes only and do not reflect operating pressures. The intent of the table is to create a consistent and significant pressure differential between systems. Sequences and pressures other than those listed can be substituted.

It is also necessary to use a gauge that can accurately differentiate pressure. For example, a gauge that reads only in 69 kPa (10 psi) markings would not be sufficient when the gauge pressure differential is only 35 kPa (5 psi).

(A) The pressure in all medical gas systems shall be reduced to Atmospheric.

(B) The test gas pressure in all medical gas piping systems shall be increased to the values indicated in Table 5.1.12.3.3.2, simultaneously maintaining these nominal pressures throughout the test.

TABLE 5.1.12.3.3.2 *Alternate Test Pressures*

Medical Gas	*Pressure (Gauge)*
Gas mixtures	140 kPa (20 psi)
Nitrogen/instrument air	210 kPa (30 psi)
Nitrous oxide	275 kPa (40 psi)
Oxygen	345 kPa (50 psi)
Medical air	415 kPa (60 psi)
Systems at nonstandard pressures	70 kPa (10 psi) greater or less than any other system HgV Vacuum
Vacuum	510 mm (20 in.) HgV
WAGD	380 mm (15 in.) HgV (if so designed)

(C) Systems with nonstandard operating pressures shall be tested at a gauge pressure of at least 70 kPa (10 psi) higher or lower than any other system being tested.

(D) Any vacuum systems shall be in operation so that these vacuum systems are tested at the same time the medical gas systems are tested.

(E) Following the adjustment of pressures in accordance with 5.1.12.3.3.2(B) and 5.1.12.3.3.2(C), each station outlet for each medical gas system shall be tested using the gas-specific connection for each system with test gauge attached to verify that the correct test pressure/vacuum is present at each outlet/inlet of each system as listed in Table 5.1.12.3.3.2.

(F) Each test gauge used in performing this test shall be calibrated with the pressure indicator used for the line pressure regulator used to provide the source pressure.

Paragraph 5.1.12.3.3.2(F) serves to verify the accuracy of the main line gauge if performed against a calibrated test gauge, but its purpose is primarily to ensure that an inaccuracy in the main line gauge does not create an anomalous result in the test.

(G) Each station outlet shall be identified by label (and color marking, if used), and the pressure indicated on the test gauge shall be that listed in Table 5.1.12.3.3.2 for the system being tested.

5.1.12.3.4 Valve Test. Valves installed in each medical gas and vacuum piping system shall be tested to verify proper operation and rooms or areas of control.

5.1.12.3.4.1 Records shall be made listing the rooms or areas controlled by each valve for each gas.

5.1.12.3.4.2 The information shall be utilized to assist and verify the proper labeling of the valves.

5.1.12.3.5 Alarm Test.

5.1.12.3.5.1 General.

(A) All warning systems for each medical gas and vacuum system(s) shall be tested to ensure that all components function properly prior to placing the system in service.

(B) Permanent records of these tests shall be maintained.

(C) Warning systems that are part of an addition to an existing piping system shall be tested prior to the connection of the new piping to the existing system.

(D) Tests of warning systems for new installations (initial tests) shall be performed after the cross-connection testing (5.1.12.3.3), but before purging the piping (5.1.12.3.6) and performing the remaining verification tests (5.1.12.3.7 through 5.1.12.3.14).

(E) Initial tests of warning systems that can be included in an addition or extension to an existing piping system shall be completed before connection of the addition to the existing system.

(F) Test gases for the initial tests shall be oil-free, dry Nitrogen NF, the gas of system designation, or operating vacuum.

(G) Where computer systems are used as substitutes for a required alarm panel as allowed under 5.1.9.2.2, the computer system shall be included in the alarm tests as modified in 5.1.9.4.

5.1.12.3.5.2 Master Alarms.

(A) The master alarm system tests shall be performed for each of the medical gas and vacuum piping systems.

(B) Permanent records of these tests shall be maintained with those required under 5.1.12.1.7.

(C) The audible and noncancelable visual signals of 5.1.9.1 shall indicate if the pressure in the main line increases or decreases 20 percent from the normal operating pressure.

(D) The operation of all master alarm signals referenced in 5.1.9.2.4 shall be verified.

5.1.12.3.5.3 Area Alarms. The warning signals for all medical gas piping systems supplying anesthetizing locations and other vital life-support and critical care areas, such as post-anesthesia recovery, intensive care units, coronary care units, emergency suites, and operating rooms shall be tested to verify an alarm condition if the pressure in the piping system increases or decreases 20 percent from the normal operating pressure for positive-pressure gases, or when the vacuum system(s) drop below a gauge pressure of 300 mm (12 in.) HgV.

5.1.12.3.6 Piping Purge Test. In order to remove any traces of particulate matter deposited in the pipelines as a result of construction, a heavy, intermittent purging of the pipeline shall be done.

5.1.12.3.6.1 The appropriate adapter shall be obtained from the facility or manufacturer, and high purge rates of at least 225 Nl/min (8 SCFM) shall be put on each outlet.

5.1.12.3.6.2 After the purge is started, it shall be rapidly interrupted several times until the purge produces no discoloration in a white cloth loosely held over the adapter during the purge.

5.1.12.3.6.3 In order to avoid possible damage to the outlet and its components, this test shall not be conducted using any implement other than the proper adapter.

5.1.12.3.7 Piping Particulate Test. For each positive-pressure gas system, the cleanliness of the piping system shall be verified.

5.1.12.3.7.1 A minimum of 1000 L (35 ft^3) of gas shall be filtered through a clean, white 0.45-micron filter at a minimum flow rate of 100 Nl/min (3.5 SCFM).

5.1.12.3.7.2 Twenty-five percent of the zones shall be tested at the outlet most remote from the source.

5.1.12.3.7.3 The filter shall accrue no more than 0.001 g (1 mg) of matter from any outlet tested.

5.1.12.3.7.4 If any outlet fails this test, the most remote outlet in every zone shall be tested.

5.1.12.3.7.5 The test shall be performed with the use of oil-free, dry Nitrogen NF.

5.1.12.3.8 Piping Purity Test. For each patient medical gas system, the purity of the piping system shall be verified.

FAQ ▶ What is the pipe purity test looking for?

Paragraph 5.1.12.3.8 does not require a test of the purity of the gas; rather, it requires a test for cleanliness of the piping system before it is put into service. It is intended to find pipe and fittings that were not properly cleaned, installation faults that could have introduced grease or oil into the piping, and pipe that was improperly cleaned with halogenated solvents (e.g., Freon, tetrachloroethylene). The test is most easily conducted with oil-free, dry nitrogen, but with appropriate apparatus and skill it can be conducted with any gas. The test is intended to be a comparison, with the requirement being the differential between the measurement at the source and most remote outlet.

A test for dew point variation is included because a differential value would indicate moisture exists in the pipeline and is being picked up into the test gas. The requirement for the dew point differential reflects the fact that water vapor is the least dangerous of the items being tested, and thus absolute absence of water is less significant. The decision to express the water vapor value in parts per million reflects the many different methods to test for this value, not all of which will express their results directly as a dew point.

The 2005 edition relaxed the limits for this test from 1 ppm of total hydrocarbon and 2 ppm of halogenated hydrocarbons to 5 ppm of each.

5.1.12.3.8.1 These tests shall be performed with oil-free, dry Nitrogen NF or the gas of system designation.

5.1.12.3.8.2 The tests shall be for total nonmethane hydrocarbons (as methane), and halogenated hydrocarbons, and compared with the source gas.

5.1.12.3.8.3 This test shall be performed at the outlet most remote from the source.

5.1.12.3.8.4 The difference between the two tests shall in no case exceed the following:

(1) Total hydrocarbons (excluding methane), 5 ppm
(2) Halogenated hydrocarbons, 5 ppm

5.1.12.3.8.5 A test for dew point shall be conducted at the outlet most remote from the source and the dew point shall not exceed 500 ppm or −12°C (10°F) at 345 kPa (50 psig).

5.1.12.3.9 Final Tie-In Test.

5.1.12.3.9.1 Prior to the connection of any work or any extension or addition to an existing piping system, the tests in 5.1.12.3.1 through 5.1.12.3.8 shall be successfully performed on the new work.

5.1.12.3.9.2 Each joint in the final connection between the new work and the existing system shall be leak-tested with the gas of system designation at the normal operating pressure by means of soapy water or other means safe for use with oxygen. Vacuum joints shall be tested using an ultrasonic leak detector or other means that will permit detection of leaks in an active vacuum system.

5.1.12.3.9.3 For pressure gases, immediately after the final connection is made and leak-tested, the specific altered zone and components in the immediate zone or area that is downstream from the point or area of intrusion shall be purged per 5.1.12.3.6.

5.1.12.3.9.4 Before the new work is used for patient care, positive-pressure gases shall be tested for operational pressure, and gas concentration in accordance with 5.1.12.3.10 and 5.1.12.3.11.

5.1.12.3.9.5 Permanent records of these tests shall be maintained in accordance with 9.8.1.

5.1.12.3.10 Operational Pressure Test. Operational pressure tests shall be performed at each station outlet/inlet or terminal where the user makes connections and disconnections.

Note that in headwalls, ceiling columns, booms, and other manufactured assemblies, the point where "the user makes connection" is probably not the termination of the pipeline. It is not uncommon for such assemblies to have great difficulty meeting these flow and pressure drop requirements due to the amount of interconnecting hose between the pipeline termination and the user connection. Caution is advised in keeping hose runs short, using properly sized hose, and preventing kinking, crimping, or other restriction in the hoses.

◀ **FAQ**
What cautions should be observed when testing manufactured assemblies?

5.1.12.3.10.1 Tests shall be performed with the gas of system designation or the operating vacuum.

5.1.12.3.10.2 All gas outlets with a gauge pressure of 345 kPa (50 psi), including, but not limited to, oxygen, nitrous oxide, medical air, and carbon dioxide, shall deliver 100 SLPM (3.5 SCFM) with a pressure drop of not more than 35 kPa (5 psi) and static pressure of 345 kPa to 380 kPa (50 psi to 55 psi).

5.1.12.3.10.3 Support gas outlets shall deliver 140 SLPM (5.0 SCFM) with a pressure drop of not more than 35 kPa (5 psi) gauge and static pressure of 1100 kPa to 1275 kPa (160 psi to 185 psi) gauge.

5.1.12.3.10.4 Medical–surgical vacuum inlets shall draw 85 SLPM (3 SCFM) without reducing the vacuum pressure below 300 mm (12 in.) gauge HgV at any adjacent station inlet.

The difference between the 5.1.12.3.10 tests as performed for vacuum and as performed for pressure gases deserves some comment. The procedure for vacuum is reasonably clear from the wording and involves placing the flow-metering device on one inlet and the test gauge on an adjacent inlet. In pressure outlets, the procedure is not clear from the wording, and therefore either of two procedures would appear to fulfill the requirement: a test using two outlets (per the vacuum model) or a test with the gauge and flow-metering device attached to the same outlet.

Note that what is being determined varies with how the test is performed. In the vacuum test, the result shows that the piping can deliver 85 SLPM (3 SCFM) from an inlet without drawing the vacuum in the piping down below 300 mm (12 in.) Hg. The vacuum at the inlet with the inflow is actually unknown. For an inlet to fail this test, the restriction or undersized pipe must be downstream (nearer the pump) of the junction feeding both. Depending on which adjacent inlet is available for the test, the junction point could be very distant.

In the alternate pressure test, the actual outflow of the outlet is being measured at the same point the pressure is being assessed. In that case, the line supplying the actual outlet under test is being examined, and the restriction can be anywhere in the line up to and including the terminal itself.

The vacuum test is done this way because it was seen to reflect the limits of vacuum in a clinical setting. The flow rate of 85 SLPM (3 SCFM) is about twice the maximum flow through a terminal connected to the normal ancillary equipment (i.e., vacuum regulator, suction trap bottle, connecting tubing, and suction tip). The actual vacuum level achieved during this flow was felt to be insignificant because vacuum level must always be regulated in any event. The use of a high vacuum (e.g., straight from the inlet) can result in barotraumas — tissue damage at the catheter tip.

The 300 mm (12 in.) Hg minimum vacuum level was selected in consultation with clinical staff and in coordination with the use of the ancillary vacuum equipment.

Normal bronchial or thoracic suction is performed under intermittent operation, requiring a low degree of vacuum. In general, as vacuum increases, the actual displacement curve for fluids (i.e., the rate at which the system can draw fluid) becomes flat. A 375 mm (15 in.) Hg vacuum is ideal; a 300 mm (12 in.) Hg vacuum is a minimal accepted value.

The need to go to higher vacuum levels to achieve this 300 mm (12 in.) Hg last-inlet vacuum is reflective of other users, poor suction practice, leaks, and other restrictions in the system. Designers of the piping often forget the basic rough equation: "If I double the vacuum level, my flow doubles, but if I double pipe size, my flow increases by six times."

5.1.12.3.10.5 Oxygen and medical air outlets serving critical care areas shall permit a transient flow rate of 170 SLPM (6 SCFM) for 3 seconds.

The transient flow test required in 5.1.12.3.10.5 is a way to ensure that any given outlet in an intensive care area could support the operation of a ventilator. Although few (if any) ventilators will ever need a continuous flow as huge as 170 SLPM (6 SCFM), in many cases instantaneous flow rates could reach to this volume, depending on the cycle of the ventilator. This test ensures that the outlet can deliver this flow rate for the brief period it is likely to be required, and thus ensures that the outlet will not starve the ventilator during peak flows.

5.1.12.3.11 Medical Gas Concentration Test. After purging each system with the gas of system designation, the following shall be performed:

(1) Each pressure gas source and outlet shall be analyzed for concentration of gas, by volume.

FAQ ▶ What is the purpose of the gas concentration test?

The analysis of medical gas concentration as required by 5.1.12.3.11(1) is intended to achieve two results: First, it is an additional cross-connection test, ensuring that the right gas goes to the right outlet. Second, it ensures that all the nitrogen used for system purging, brazing, and so on, is gone and that the gas being delivered is pure. Regrettably, because the analyzers are expensive, sometimes delicate, and finicky, there is a strong temptation to avoid performing this test properly.

For example, an oxygen analyzer should be used for oxygen and medical air, a nitrous oxide analyzer should be used for analysis of nitrous oxide, and a carbon dioxide analyzer should be used for analysis of carbon dioxide. It is probably irrelevant to analyze nitrogen concentration directly because it is not usually respired, but an oxygen analyzer can be argued to identify nitrogen by deduction (a reading of <1 percent oxygen). Equally obviously, it cannot be used to separate nitrogen from nitrous oxide. In conjunction, an oxygen and nitrous oxide analyzer could be reasonably assumed to identify nitrogen (assuming, of course, that no other gas, such as carbon dioxide, was present).

It is also possible to do all these analyses with a single instrument (e.g., a gas chromatograph, mass or Raman spectrometer), assuming the operator is knowledgeable in the operation of such instrumentation. The verifier performing this test must use such analyzers to positively determine the true concentration of the gases in the system.

(2) Analysis shall be conducted with instruments designed to measure the specific gas dispensed.
(3)* Allowable concentrations shall be as indicated in Table 5.1.12.3.11.

TABLE 5.1.12.3.11 *Gas Concentrations*

Medical Gas	*Concentration*
Oxygen	≥99% oxygen
Nitrous oxide	≥99% nitrous oxide
Nitrogen	≤1% oxygen or 99% nitrogen
Medical air	19.5–23.5% oxygen
Other gases	Concentration as specified by ±1% unless otherwise specified.

A.5.1.12.3.11(3) The committee recognizes that current clinical practice is to use analyzers that might not be able to analyze oxygen to current U.S.P. requirements of 99 percent, and that these analyzers frequently have an error of up to 3 percent.

A

5.1.12.3.12 Medical Air Purity Test (Compressor System).

The tests specified in 5.1.12.3.12 are tests of medical compressed air as delivered by the source for those parameters that are unique to medical air (the only medical gas being produced on site) and can affect the safety of the system. Note that these tests are related closely to those in 5.1.12.3.14.3.

5.1.12.3.12.1 The medical air source shall be analyzed for concentration of contaminants by volume prior to the source valve being opened.

5.1.12.3.12.2 Sample(s) shall be taken for the air system test at the system sample port.

5.1.12.3.12.3 The test results shall not exceed the parameters in Table 5.1.12.3.12.3.

TABLE 5.1.12.3.12.3 *Contaminant Parameters for Medical Air*

Parameter	*Limit Value*
Pressure dew point	4°C (39°F)
Carbon monoxide	10 ppm
Carbon dioxide	500 ppm
Gaseous hydrocarbons	25 ppm (as methane)
Halogenated hydrocarbons	2 ppm

5.1.12.3.13 Labeling. The presence and correctness of labeling required by this standard for all components (e.g., station outlets/inlets, shutoff valves, and alarm panels) shall be verified.

5.1.12.3.14 Source Equipment Verification.

5.1.12.3.14.1 General. Source equipment verification shall be performed following the installation of the interconnecting pipelines, accessories, and source equipment.

5.1.12.3.14.2 Gas Supply Sources.

(A) The system apparatus shall be tested for proper function, including the changeover from primary to secondary supply (with its changeover signal) and the operation of the reserve (with its reserve-in-use signal), before the system is put into service.

(B) If the system has an actuating switch and signal to monitor the contents of the reserve, its function shall be tested before the system is put into service.

(C) If the system has an actuating switch and signal to monitor the pressure of the reserve unit, its function shall be tested before the system is put into service.

(D) Testing of the bulk supply signal and the master signal panel installations shall be arranged with the owner or the organization responsible for the operation and maintenance of the supply system for the testing of the bulk supply signals to ensure proper identification and activation of the master signal panels to be sure the facility can monitor the status of that supply system.

(E) The tests required in 5.1.12.3.14.2(D) shall also be conducted when the storage units are changed or replaced.

5.1.12.3.14.3 Medical Air Compressor Systems.

(A) Tests of the medical air compressor system shall include the purity test for air quality, and the test of the alarm sensors after calibration and setup per the manufacturer's instructions, as well as lead-lag controls.

(B) Tests shall be conducted at the sample port of the medical air system.

(C) The operation of the system control sensors, such as dew point, air temperature, and all other air quality monitoring sensors and controls, shall be checked for proper operation and function before the system is put into service.

(D) The quality of medical air as delivered by the compressor air supply shall be verified after installation of new components prior to use by patients.

(E) The air quality tests in 5.1.12.3.14.3(D) shall be performed after a minimum of 24 hours of operation in accordance with 5.1.12.3.14.3(F) of the machinery.

(F) A demand of approximately 25 percent of the rated compressor capacity shall be created to cause the compressors to cycle on and off continuously and the dryers to operate for the 24-hour period.

Paragraph 5.1.12.3.14.3(F) establishes that the compressor must be run under at least a 25 percent load for 24 hours before testing. This test method will cause the equipment involved (e.g., compressors, dryers, regulators) to cycle for at least 24 hours and will permit the air treatment equipment to dry down and operate as designed.

5.1.12.3.14.4 Medical–Surgical Vacuum Systems. The proper functioning of the medical–surgical vacuum source system(s) shall be tested before it is put into service.

Refer to 5.1.3.6.6.1 and 5.1.3.6.8.

5.1.13* Level 1 Operation and Management.

A.5.1.13 All cylinders containing compressed gases, such as anesthetic gases, oxygen, or other gases used for medicinal purposes, whether these gases are flammable or not, should comply with the specifications and be maintained in accordance with regulations of the U.S. Department of Transportation.

Cylinder and container temperatures greater than 52°C (125°F) can result in excessive pressure increase. Pressure relief devices are sensitive to temperature and pressure. When relief devices actuate, contents are discharged.

5.1.13.1 Special Precautions — Piped Patient Gas/Vacuum Systems.

5.1.13.1.1 Piping systems shall not be used for the distribution of flammable anesthetic gases.

5.1.13.1.2 Nonflammable medical gas systems used to supply gases for respiratory therapy shall be installed in accordance with 5.1.1 through 5.1.11 of this chapter.

Training for the medical staff on basic medical gas safety mechanisms is also advisable.

5.1.13.1.3 Piping systems for gases shall not be used as a grounding electrode.

5.1.13.1.4* Liquid or debris shall not be introduced into the medical–surgical vacuum system for disposal.

A.5.1.13.1.4 Vacuum systems from station inlets to the exhaust discharge should be considered contaminated unless proven otherwise. Methods exist to disinfect the system or portions thereof. 

Clogging of regulators, for example, with lint, debris, or dried body fluids, reduces vacuum system performance.

5.1.13.1.5 The medical–surgical vacuum system shall not be used for vacuum steam condensate return or other nonmedical or nonsurgical applications.

5.1.13.2 Gas/Vacuum Systems Information and Warning Signs.

5.1.13.2.1 The gas content of medical gas and vacuum piping systems shall be labeled in accordance with 5.1.11.1.

5.1.13.2.2 Labels for shutoff valves shall be in accordance with 5.1.11.2, and updated when modifications are made changing the areas served.

See Exhibits 5.26 through 5.28 for examples of labeling pipes. Exhibit 5.26 shows labeling on existing piping. New systems will be required to have labels indicating the pressure level of gas in the pipe if other than standard pressure, as well as the gas name and flow direction.

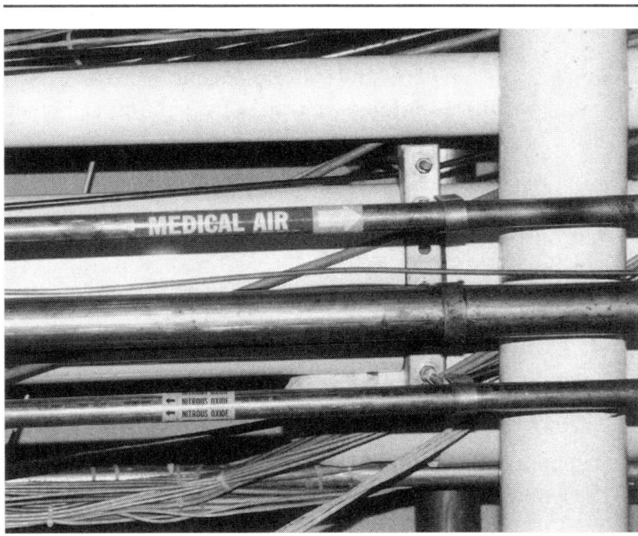

EXHIBIT 5.26 *Example of an existing gas piping system labeled with the name of the gas and the direction of its flow.*

EXHIBIT 5.27 *Labeled medical gas and vacuum piping above ceiling panel.*

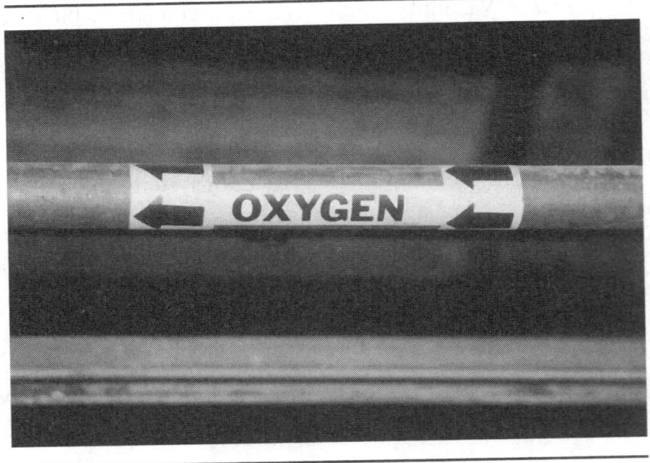

EXHIBIT 5.28 Labels on pipes that are part of a piped gas or vacuum system.

5.1.14 Level 1 Support Gases.

5.1.14.1 Applicability. Support gases (nitrogen and instrument air) shall be gases that are not used for respiration, but are used for powering pneumatic devices (medical–surgical tools, equipment booms, pendants) related to patient care.

5.1.14.2 Nature of Hazards. Support gas systems are subject to the same hazards as are present in any piped medical gas system with the additional hazard of operating at higher pressures.

5.1.14.3 Sources. Requirements for support gas sources shall be in accordance with the following:

(1) Paragraphs 5.1.3.1 through 5.1.3.4 for nitrogen
(2) Paragraph 5.1.3.8 for instrument air

5.1.14.4 Valves. Requirements for support gas shall be in accordance with 5.1.4.1 through 5.1.4.10.

5.1.14.5 Outlets.

5.1.14.5.1 Requirements for nitrogen support gas outlets shall be in accordance with 5.1.5.1, 5.1.5.2, 5.1.5.4 through 5.1.5.8, 5.1.5.11, and 5.1.5.13 through 5.1.5.15.

5.1.14.5.2 Requirements for other support gas outlets shall be in accordance with 5.1.5.1, 5.1.5.2, 5.1.5.4, 5.1.5.5, 5.1.5.7, 5.1.5.8, 5.1.5.11 and 5.1.5.13 through 5.1.5.15.

5.1.14.6 Manufactured Assemblies. Requirements for support gases in manufactured assemblies shall be in accordance with 5.1.6.1 through 5.1.6.9.

5.1.14.7 Pressure Indicators. Requirements for support gas pressure indicators shall be in accordance with 5.1.8.1.1 through 5.1.8.1.4, 5.1.8.1.6, 5.1.8.1.7, and 5.1.8.2.

5.1.14.8 Warning Systems.

5.1.14.8.1 General requirements for support gas warning systems shall be in accordance with 5.1.9.1.

5.1.14.8.2 Master alarm requirements for support gas shall be in accordance with 5.1.9.2.

5.1.14.8.3 Area alarm requirements for support gas shall be in accordance with 5.1.9.3.

5.1.14.8.4 Local alarm requirements for support gas shall be in accordance with 5.1.9.4.

5.1.14.9 Distribution. Requirements for support gas piping shall be in accordance with 5.1.10.1, 5.1.10.3, 5.1.10.4, 5.1.10.5.1 through 5.1.10.5.6, 5.1.10.7, 5.1.10.7(1), 5.1.10.7(2), 5.1.10.7(3), and 5.1.10.10.

5.1.14.10 Labeling and Identification. Requirements for support gas labeling shall be in accordance with 5.1.11.1 through 5.1.11.4.

5.1.14.11 Performance Testing. Requirements for support gas performance testing shall be in accordance with 5.1.12 with the following exceptions:

(1) The piping purity test (5.1.12.3.8) shall be permitted to be omitted.
(2) The medical gas concentration test (5.1.12.3.11) shall be permitted to be omitted.

5.2 Level 2 Piped Gas and Vacuum Systems

The designer/installer/user of these Level 2 requirements will benefit by reading all the commentary for Level 1 systems as well.

Level 2 is intended for application to facilities treating patients who might require the gases occasionally but ordinarily would not. When patients do require the gases, the need is short term. Examples of such facilities might include diagnostic facilities, clinics, "doc in a box" emergency centers, outpatient surgery centers performing low-intensity surgeries under local anesthesia, and so on. Patient lives are at minimal risk in these facilities if the gases fail, and the gases are used rarely enough or at a low enough intensity that the risk is minimal. Note that the existence of an "alternative" or a "plan" in the event of failure (e.g., a cylinder of oxygen kept at the nurses' station) is not sufficient grounds for permitting a facility to install Level 2 systems, although such alternatives are naturally in place in any well-run Level 2 facility and are mandated here where redundancy has been reduced. (See 5.2.3.5, 5.2.3.6, and 5.2.3.7.)

Do not attempt to apply Level 2 without prior reference to the decision "trees" in occupancy Chapters 13, 14, 17, and 18.

5.2.1* Applicability.

These requirements shall apply to health care facilities that qualify for Level 2 systems as referenced in Chapters 13 through 21.

A.5.2.1 Section 5.1 covers requirements for Level 1 piped gas and vacuum systems; Section 5.2 covers Level 2 piped gas and vacuum systems; Section 5.3 covers Level 3 piped gas and vacuum systems. Laboratory systems are no longer covered by Chapter 5 (2002 edition). 

5.2.2 Nature of Hazards of Gas and Vacuum Systems.

See Section B.2.

5.2.3 Level 2 Sources.

5.2.3.1 Central Supply System Identification and Labeling. Level 2 systems shall comply with 5.1.3.1.

5.2.3.2 Central Supply Operations. Level 2 systems shall comply with 5.1.3.2.

5.2.3.3 Central Supply System Locations. Level 2 systems shall comply with 5.1.3.3.

5.2.3.4 Central Supply Systems. Level 2 systems shall comply with 5.1.3.4.

5.2.3.5 Level 2 Medical Air Supply Systems. Level 2 systems shall comply with 5.1.3.5, except as follows:

(1) Medical air compressors, dryers, aftercoolers, filters, and regulators shall be permitted to be simplex.
(2) The facility staff shall develop their emergency plan to deal with the loss of medical air.

It is actually debatable whether a Level 2 facility can ever need medical air, given that medical air is generally associated with treatments that would exclude a facility from qualifying for installation of Level 2 systems. However, there is no hard rule that prohibits such an installation.

5.2.3.6 Level 2 Medical–Surgical Vacuum. Level 2 systems shall comply with 5.1.3.6, except as follows:

(1) Medical–surgical vacuum systems shall be permitted to be simplex.
(2) The facility staff shall develop their emergency plan to deal with the loss of medical–surgical vacuum.

5.2.3.7 Level 2 Waste Anesthetic Gas Disposal (WAGD). Level 2 systems shall comply with 5.1.3.7, except as follows:

(1) Medical WAGD pumps shall be permitted to be simplex.
(2) The facility staff shall develop their emergency plan to deal with the loss of WAGD.

5.2.3.8 Instrument Air Supply Systems. Level 2 systems shall comply with 5.1.3.8.

5.2.4 Valves.

Level 2 systems shall comply with 5.1.4.

5.2.5 Station Outlets/Inlets.

Level 2 systems shall comply with 5.1.5.

5.2.6 Manufactured Assemblies.

Level 2 systems shall comply with 5.1.6.

5.2.7 Surface-Mounted Medical Gas Rails.

Level 2 systems shall comply with 5.1.7.

5.2.8 Pressure and Vacuum Indicators.

Level 2 systems shall comply with 5.1.8.

5.2.9 Warning Systems (Level 2).

Warning systems associated with Level 2 systems shall provide the master, area, and local alarm functions of a Level 1 system as required in 5.1.8, except as follows:

(1) Warning systems shall be permitted to be a single alarm panel.

This "mixed function" alarm is not unique to Level 2 but is particularly useful in these systems.

(2) The alarm panel shall be located in an area of continuous surveillance while the facility is in operation.
(3) Pressure and vacuum switches/sensors shall be mounted at the source equipment with a pressure indicator at the master alarm panel.

5.2.10 Level 2 Distribution.

Level 2 systems shall comply with 5.1.10.

5.2.11 Labeling and Identification.

Level 2 systems shall comply with 5.1.11.

5.2.12 Performance Criteria and Testing — Level 2 (Gas, Medical–Surgical Vacuum, and WAGD).

Level 2 systems shall comply with 5.1.12.

5.2.13 Level 2 Operation and Management.

Level 2 systems shall comply with 5.1.13.

Section 5.3* Level 3 Piped Gas and Vacuum Systems

Level 3 is intended for office-based care. Gases are so used in Level 3 facilities that the life of the patient is never at issue in the event of failure of the gas. The natural example is a dental office, which uses the gas as a matter of course, but the need is not such that the loss of the gas is life threatening (although it would likely interrupt the procedure). Note that on this definition an oral surgeon would probably not qualify for Level 3, because oral surgeons could reasonably be expected to perform general anesthesia. However, a stand-alone sleep lab might qualify for treatment as Level 3.

Level 3 has two limitations. The first is the limit on medical procedure — procedures done in Level 3 facilities must never have patient lives dependent on the gases. The second is physical size. Level 3 is limited to facilities with two or fewer "treatment facilities" and systems with less than 84.950 L (3000 ft^3) of gas in total. Do not attempt to apply Level 3 without prior reference to the decision "trees" in occupancy Chapters 13, 14, 17, and 18.

A.5.3 A Level 3 vacuum system is not intended for Level 1 medical–surgical vacuum applications. A Level 3 wet piping system is designed to accommodate liquid, air–gas, and solids through the service inlet. A Level 3 dry piping system is designed to accommodate air–gas only through the service inlet, with liquids and solids being trapped before entering the system.

5.3.1* Applicability.

A.5.3.1 Section 5.1 covers requirements for Level 1 piped gas and vacuum systems; Section 5.2 covers Level 2 piped gas and vacuum systems; Section 5.3 covers Level 3 piped gas and vacuum systems. Laboratory systems are no longer covered by Chapter 5 (2002 edition).

5.3.1.1 These requirements shall apply to health care facilities that qualify to install Level 3 systems as referenced in Chapters 13 through 21.

5.3.1.2 Wherever the term *medical gas* occurs in Level 3, the term shall apply to all piped systems of nitrous oxide and oxygen only.

FAQ ▶
Is there a difference in level between medical gas and other piped gases?

The distinction between medical gas and piped systems for oxygen and nitrous oxide is very important. Level 3 systems can be conceptually divided into medical gases (usually only oxygen and nitrous oxide), which are treated virtually identically to the same systems in Level 2 with regard to installation, testing, and so on, and the other more utility-type gases such as vacuum, compressed air, or power gas (it could be nitrogen in some cases), which are treated much more casually and are therefore subject to considerably less stringent safeguards. Care must be taken to ensure that a given requirement is being appropriately applied; otherwise, the installer could spend more money than is necessary or install a system with greatly reduced safety. Watch for the term *medical gas* as the key criterion in many of the paragraphs where this is true.

5.3.1.3 Wherever the term *vacuum* occurs, the provisions shall apply to all piped systems for vacuum.

5.3.1.4 An existing Level 3 system that is not in strict compliance with the provisions of this standard shall be permitted to be continued in use as long as the authority having jurisdiction has determined that such use does not constitute a distinct hazard to life.

5.3.2 Nature of Hazards of Gas and Vacuum Systems.

Potential fire and explosion hazards associated with medical gas systems and vacuum systems shall be considered in the design, installation, testing, operation, and maintenance of these systems. *(See Annex B.2.)*

5.3.3 Level 3 Sources.

5.3.3.1 Medical Gas Supply System Identification and Labeling.

5.3.3.1.1 Only cylinders and containers constructed, tested, and maintained in accordance with U.S. Department of Transportation specifications and regulations shall be permitted to be used.

5.3.3.1.2 Cylinder contents shall be identified by attached labels or stencils naming the contents in accordance with CGA C-7, *Guide to the Preparation of Precautionary Labeling and Marking of Compressed Gas Containers*.

5.3.3.1.3 Contents of cylinders and containers shall be verified prior to use.

5.3.3.1.4 Labels shall not be defaced, altered, or removed, and connecting fittings shall not be modified.

5.3.3.1.5 Locations containing medical gases other than oxygen shall have their door(s) labeled substantially as follows:

CAUTION
Medical Gases
NO Smoking or Open Flame
Room May Have Insufficient Oxygen
Open Door and Allow Room to Ventilate before Entering

5.3.3.2* Supply System Operations.

A.5.3.3.2 When the storage/supply enclosure is remote from the single treatment facility, it should be locked for security reasons to prevent tampering. Access should be only via authorized staff or fire department. When the enclosure is within the single treatment facility, it is left to the discretion of the single treatment facility management as to whether greater benefit is achieved by immediate access or by security. An enclosure with direct access from a public hallway should be locked. If the door to the enclosure opens onto an exit access corridor, see 5.1.3.3.3.1(F). See Figure A.5.3.3.2.

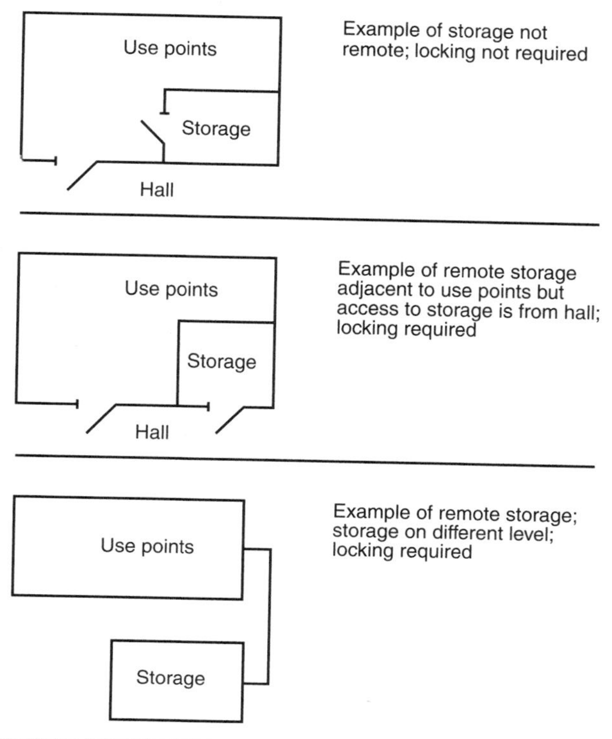

FIGURE A.5.3.3.2 *Examples of Storage/Supply Enclosures.*

5.3.3.2.1 The use of adapters or conversion fittings to adapt one gas-specific fitting to another shall be prohibited.

5.3.3.2.2 Only medical gas cylinders, reusable shipping containers, and their accessories shall be permitted to be stored in rooms containing medical gas supply systems or medical gas cylinders.

5.3.3.2.3 No flammable materials, cylinders containing flammable gases, or containers containing flammable liquids shall be stored in rooms with medical gas cylinders.

5.3.3.2.4 Wooden racks for cylinder storage shall be permitted.

5.3.3.2.5 If cylinders are wrapped when received, the wrappers shall be removed prior to storage.

5.3.3.2.6 Cylinders not in use shall have their valve protection caps secured tightly in place.

5.3.3.2.7 Cylinders without correct markings or whose markings and gas-specific fittings do not match shall not be used.

5.3.3.2.8 Cryogenic liquid storage units intended to supply gas to the facility shall not be used to transfill other liquid storage vessels.

5.3.3.2.9 Care shall be exercised when handling cylinders that have been exposed to freezing temperatures or containers that contain cryogenic liquids to prevent injury to the skin.

5.3.3.2.10 Cylinders containing compressed gases and containers for volatile liquids shall be kept away from radiators, steam piping, and like sources of heat.

5.3.3.2.11 When cylinder valve protection caps are supplied, they shall be secured tightly in place unless the cylinder is connected for use.

5.3.3.2.12 Containers shall not be stored in a tightly closed space such as a closet.

5.3.3.3 Source Systems — Level 3.

5.3.3.3.1 Cylinders in service and in storage shall be individually secured and located to prevent falling or being knocked over.

5.3.3.3.2 Locations for Medical Gas Supply Systems.

5.3.3.3.2.1 Medical gas supply systems shall be permitted to be located indoors or outdoors.

5.3.3.3.2.2 Air compressors and vacuum pumps shall be located separately from medical gas (i.e., oxygen and nitrous oxide) cylinder storage enclosures.

5.3.3.3.2.3 Locations for supply systems shall not be used for storage purposes other than for containers of nonflammable gases except that storage of full or empty containers shall be permitted.

5.3.3.3.2.4 Other nonflammable medical gas supply systems or storage locations shall be permitted to be in the same location with oxygen or nitrous oxide, or both, provided adequate ventilation to prevent the development of oxygen-deficient atmospheres in the event of functioning of cylinder or manifold pressure-relief devices is provided.

5.3.3.3.2.5 Enclosures shall not be located in close proximity to open electrical conductors and transformers.

5.3.3.3.2.6 Enclosures shall not be located adjacent to storage tanks for flammable or combustible liquids.

5.3.3.3.3 Indoor Locations.

5.3.3.3.3.1 Enclosures for medical gases shall serve no other purpose.

5.3.3.3.3.2 Enclosures shall be constructed of an assembly of building materials with a fire resistance rating of at least 1 hour.

5.3.3.3.3.3 Enclosures shall not communicate directly with anesthetizing or storage locations for flammable anesthetizing agents.

5.3.3.3.3.4 Other nonflammable (inert) medical gases shall be permitted to be stored in the enclosure.

5.3.3.3.3.5 Flammable gases shall not be stored with oxidizing agents.

5.3.3.3.3.6 Storage of full and/or empty cylinders is permitted in the same enclosure.

5.3.3.3.4 Outdoor Locations.

5.3.3.3.4.1 Storage facilities that are adjacent to a building wall shall be located such that the distance to any window of the adjacent building is greater than 7.62 m (25 ft).

5.3.3.3.5 Doors and Gates. Enclosures for medical gas supply systems shall be provided with doors or gates.

5.3.3.3.5.1 If the enclosure is outside and/or remote from the single treatment facility, it shall be kept locked.

5.3.3.3.5.2 If the storage area is within the single treatment facility (i.e., is not remote), it shall be permitted to be locked.

5.3.3.3.6 Ventilation. Enclosures for medical gas systems (i.e., oxygen and nitrous oxide) shall be ventilated.

5.3.3.3.6.1 Where the total volume of Level 3 medical gases (i.e., oxygen and nitrous oxide) connected and in storage is greater than 84,950 L (3000 ft^3) at STP, indoor supply locations shall be provided with dedicated mechanical ventilation systems that draw air from within .3 m (1 ft) of the floor and operate continuously.

5.3.3.3.6.2 The power supply for mechanical ventilation fans shall conform to the requirements of an essential electrical system as described in Chapter 4 of this document.

5.3.3.3.6.3 Where the total volume of Level 3 medical gases (i.e., oxygen and nitrous oxide) connected and in storage is less than 84,950 L (3000 ft^3) at STP, natural ventilation shall be permitted to be employed.

5.3.3.3.6.4 Where natural ventilation is permitted, it shall consist of two louvered openings, each having a minimum free area of 46,500 mm^2 (72 in.^{2}), with one located within .3 m (1 ft) of the floor and one located within .3 m (1 ft) of the ceiling.

5.3.3.3.6.5 Louvered natural ventilation openings shall not be located in an exit access corridor.

5.3.3.3.6.6 Mechanical ventilation shall be provided if the requirements of 5.3.3.3.6.5 cannot be met.

5.3.3.3.6.7 Heating (where required) shall be by steam, hot water, or other indirect means.

5.3.3.3.6.8 Where enclosures (interior or exterior) for medical gas supply systems are located near sources of heat, such as furnaces, incinerators, or boiler rooms, they shall be of construction that protects cylinders from reaching temperatures 54°C (130°F).

5.3.3.3.7 Locations for Air Compressors and Vacuum Pumps.

5.3.3.3.7.1 Air compressors and vacuum pumps shall be installed in a designated mechanical equipment area, ventilated and with required utilities (e.g., electricity, drains, lighting, etc.).

5.3.3.4 Medical Gas Supply Systems — Level 3.

5.3.3.4.1 Mechanical means shall be provided to ensure the connection of cylinders containing the correct gas to the piping system.

5.3.3.4.1.1 Cylinder valve outlets for nonflammable gases and gas mixtures for medical purposes shall comply with CGA V-1, *Compressed Gas Association Standard for Compressed Gas Cylinder Valve Outlet and Inlet Connections* (ANSI B57.1; CSA B96).

5.3.3.4.1.2 Threaded connections between the regulators and the piping system shall comply with CGA V-5, *Diameter-Index Safety System (Noninterchangeable Low Pressure Connections for Medical Gas Applications)*.

5.3.3.4.2 Level 3 medical gas supply systems shall include the components designated in 5.3.3.4.2.1 through 5.3.3.4.2.3.

5.3.3.4.2.1 A shutoff valve or check valve shall be installed downstream of each pressure regulator.

5.3.3.4.2.2 A pressure relief valve set at 50 percent above normal line pressure shall be installed downstream of the shutoff valve or check valve required in 5.3.3.4.2.1.

5.3.3.4.2.3 Pressure relief valves shall be of brass, bronze, or stainless steel and designed for oxygen service.

5.3.3.4.3 Flexible connectors of other than all-metal construction used to connect outlets of pressure regulators to fixed piping shall not exceed 1.52 m (5 ft) in length and shall not penetrate walls, floors, ceilings, or partitions.

5.3.3.4.3.1 Flexible connectors shall comply with the provisions of 5.3.3.4.1.2.

5.3.3.4.3.2 Flexible connectors shall have a pressure rating of at least a gauge pressure of 6895 kPa (1000 psi).

5.3.3.4.4* Supply systems supplying only a single treatment facility shall contain the following: a minimum of two banks of cylinders of oxygen and a minimum of two cylinders of nitrous oxide (if used), each containing the greater of either at least an average day's supply, or one of the following:

(1) When storage is not remote, two cylinders of oxygen and one cylinder of nitrous oxide (if used)
(2) When storage is remote, two cylinders of oxygen, minimum, and two cylinders of nitrous oxide, minimum (if used)

A.5.3.3.4.4 See Figure A.5.3.3.4.4 for an illustration of single treatment locations.

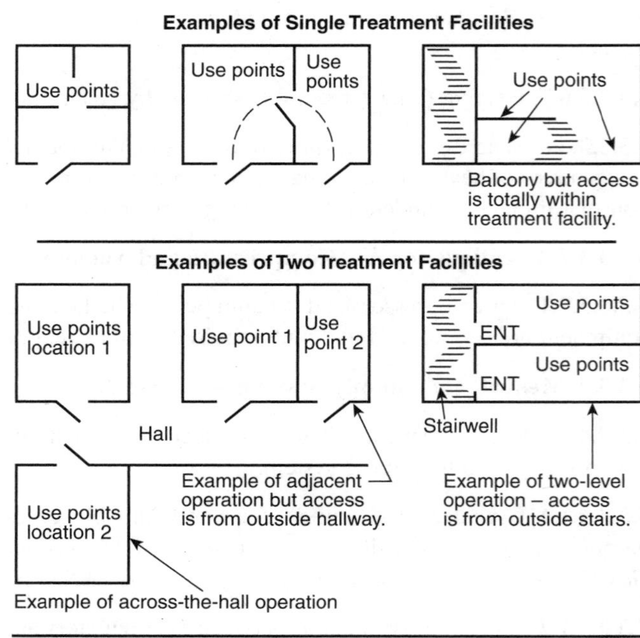

FIGURE A.5.3.3.4.4 *Examples of Single Treatment Locations.*

5.3.3.4.4.1 The cylinders for each gas service shall be manifolded so that the cylinders can alternately supply the piping system.

5.3.3.4.4.2* When the primary cylinder is unable to supply the system, the secondary cylinder shall be capable of being switched to supply the system.

A.5.3.3.4.4.2 If the supply system is within the confines of a single treatment facility, a simple manual transfer is permissible. Only high/low pressure alarms are required. The gases are to be manifolded so a quick manual transfer is possible without life-threatening consequences.

However, if the supply system is remote, a prompt transfer of gases becomes more difficult. It could require transcending one or more flights of stairs and/or going to a remote location on the same floor. Under these situations an automatic system is required.

5.3.3.4.4.3 When storage is not remote, either manual or automatic switchover shall be permitted to be used.

5.3.3.4.4.4* When the supply system is remote, automatic switchover shall be provided.

A.5.3.3.4.4.4 The installation of a supply serving more than one single treatment facility creates by its very nature a remote location relative to the other facility. Because more than one practice could be involved, the transfer of oxygen and nitrous oxide gases is to be automatically achieved.

5.3.3.4.5 Supply systems supplying multiple treatment facilities shall contain the following: two banks of cylinders each containing at least the greater of an average day's supply or at least two cylinders of oxygen and two cylinders of nitrous oxide (if used).

5.3.3.4.5.1 The cylinders for each gas service shall be manifolded so that the cylinders can alternately supply the piping system.

5.3.3.4.5.2 When the primary bank cylinder(s) is unable to supply the system, the secondary cylinder(s) shall automatically operate to supply the piping system.

5.3.3.5* Level 3 Gas-Powered Devices Supply Systems.

A.5.3.3.5 Level 3 compressed air and nitrogen gas systems are used primarily to drive gas-powered power devices. See Figure A.5.3.3.5 for an illustration of this type of system. Similar applications are in podiatry and plastic surgery. Examples of these are air used to drive turbine-powered drills and air used to dry teeth and gums. Some dental hand pieces have an internal self-contained air return system, while other hand pieces discharge air into the atmosphere. Some discharge a mixture of air and water. Nitrogen is often piped as an alternate or reserve supply to the compressor system.

The application of dental compressed air is not used for life-support purposes such as respirators, IPPB machines, analgesia, anesthesia, and so forth. Air discharged into the oral cavity is incidental and not a primary source of air to sustain life. However, if there is a coincident use of dental air for providing respiratory support, the requirements of dental air will be superseded by those of the respiratory support, and the compressed air system has to produce the higher quality, medical compressed air as defined in Chapter 3. This could affect the selection of a compressor.

A dental compressed air system should not be used to provide power for an air-powered evacuation system without specific attention paid to the discharge of the evacuated gases and liquids. An open discharge of evacuated gases into the general environment of an operatory could compromise the quality of breathing air in the treatment facility. Air discharge should be vented to the outside of the building through a dedicated vent.

An air-powered evacuation system might require significant quantities of air to operate. Manufacturer's recommendations should be followed regarding proper sizing of the air compressor. Inadequate sizing can result in overheating, premature compressor failures, and inadequate operating pressures and flows.

5.3.3.5.1 Level 3 gas-powered devices supply systems shall be used where compressed air is required to drive dynamic devices used for patient treatment.

5.3.3.5.1.1 A gas-powered devices supply system shall be permitted to be used to supply power to gas-driven devices for scavenging, but only where the exhaust of the scavenging device is a closed vent to the outside of the building.

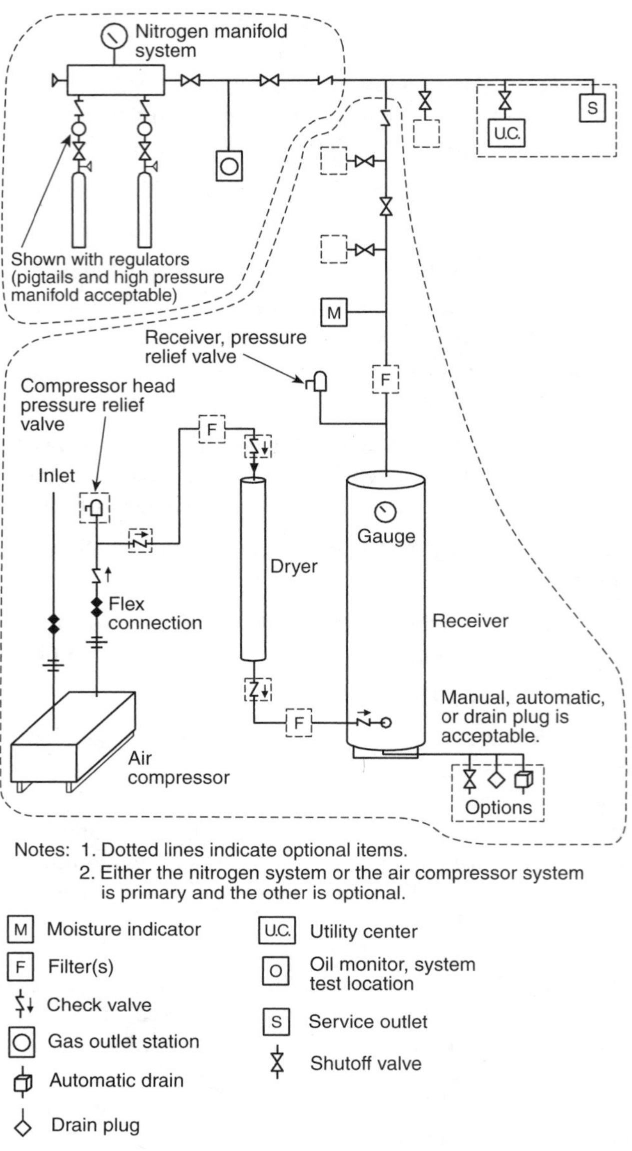

FIGURE A.5.3.3.5 Level 3 Gas-Powered Devices Supply System.

5.3.3.5.2* Level 3 gas-powered devices supply systems shall be obtained from and be installed under the supervision of a manufacturer(s) or supplier(s) familiar with proper practices for its construction and use.

A.5.3.3.5.2 Compressed-air quality can be compromised and expected life of system components can be shortened if an undersized system is installed. Manufacturer's recommendations should be followed regarding proper sizing of the air compressor(s).

5.3.3.5.3 Level 3 gas-powered devices supply systems shall include the following:

(1) Disconnect switch(es)
(2) Motor-starting device(s)

(3) Motor overload protection device(s)
(4) One or more compressors
(5) For single, duplex, or multiple compressor systems, a means for activation/deactivation of each individual compressor
(6) When multiple compressors are used, manual or automatic means to alternate individual compressors
(7) When multiple compressors are used, manual or automatic means to activate the additional unit(s) should the in-service unit(s) be incapable of maintaining adequate pressure
(8) Intake filter–muffler(s) of the dry type
(9) Receiver(s) with drain plug or a manual drain or an automatic drain
(10) Shutoff valves
(11) Air dryer(s) that maintain 40 percent relative humidity at operating pressure and temperature
(12) In-line final particulate filters rated at 5 microns, 98 percent efficiency, with filter status indicator to ensure the delivery of compressed air with a maximum allowable 0.05 ppm liquid oil
(13) Pressure regulator(s)
(14) Pressure relief valve
(15) Pressure indicator
(16) Moisture indicator
(17) Oil indicator

5.3.3.5.3.1 A reserve for cylinders shall be permitted to be used to supplement or act as a reserve for the compressor source.

5.3.3.5.4 Receiver.

5.3.3.5.4.1 Receiver(s) shall have the capacity to prevent short cycling of the compressor(s).

5.3.3.5.4.2 Receiver(s) shall comply with Section VIII, Unfired Pressure Vessels, of the ASME *Boiler and Pressure Vessel Code.*

5.3.3.5.5* Moisture Indicator.

A.5.3.3.5.5 A color dew point monitor downstream of the receiver indicating the quality of air coming into the receiver is desirable.

A color dew point monitor in the main treatment facility is appropriate to help the staff promptly identify when the system is being degraded with air of a dew point higher than is acceptable.

The design of the color monitor should be such that the normal tolerance of variations will limit the maximum moisture at 39°F at a gauge pressure of 100 psi (3.9°C at 690 kPa) at activation.

5.3.3.5.5.1 The moisture indicator shall be located in the active airstream prior to or after the receiver and upstream of any system pressure regulators.

5.3.3.5.5.2 The moisture indicator shall indicate (i.e., by color change, digital readout, or other method understood by the user) when the relative humidity of the compressed air exceeds 40 percent at line pressure and temperature.

5.3.3.5.6 Oil Indicator.

5.3.3.5.6.1 The oil indicator shall be located downstream of the receiver.

5.3.3.5.6.2 The oil indicator shall measure (i.e., by color change, digital readout, or other method understood by the user) an oil concentration of 0.05 ppm ± 0.03 ppm in air at a gauge pressure of 550 kPa to 690 kPa (80 psi to 100 psi).

5.3.3.5.7* Source of Intake Air.

A.5.3.3.5.7 The environmental air source for the compressor inlet should take into consideration possible contamination by particulates, concentrations of biological waste contaminants, ozone from nearby brush-type electric motors, and exhaust fumes from engines.

Air taken from an outside atmosphere could cause harmful condensation problems in the compressor. Long runs of inlet tube should also be avoided as it will degrade compressor performance. The compressor manufacturer's recommendations should be followed regarding appropriate pipe size to prevent possible degradation of system performance.

A dental air compressor and dental vacuum system can be in the same equipment room as long as the inlet for the dental air compressor does not draw air from a room or space containing an open discharge for the dental vacuum system.

Atmospheric air in an operatory can have traces of mercury vapor and other contaminants. A compressor inlet location that would draw its supply directly from an operatory should be avoided.

5.3.3.5.7.1 Air sources for a compressor(s) located inside the building shall meet the following requirements:

(1) Be located within a room where no chemical-based material is stored or used and that is not an operatory
(2) Not be taken from a room or space in which there is an open or semi-open discharge from a Level 3 vacuum or scavenging system

5.3.3.5.7.2 Air sources for a compressor(s) located outside the building shall be drawn from locations where no contamination from vacuum or scavenging system discharges or particulate matter is anticipated.

5.3.3.5.8* Cylinder Gas Reserves/Supplements to Compressor Sources.

A.5.3.3.5.8 If nitrogen is used as a backup supply to a compressed gas system, the nitrogen operating pressure should be regulated so as not to exceed the operating pressure of the Level 3 compressed air system.

5.3.3.5.8.1 When used, cylinder reserves/supplements for compressor sources shall be a system of cylinders and necessary supply equipment that will permit supplying the required supply gas as an alternative to the compressor supplied air.

5.3.3.5.8.2 When the content of one primary cylinder is unable to supply the normal operating pressures, the secondary cylinder(s) shall be activated manually or automatically.

5.3.3.5.8.3 When used, cylinder gas reserves/supplements to compressor sources shall be piped into the system through a check valve and shutoff valve located in each supply line prior to the tee connection to the main line.

5.3.3.5.8.4 The designed operating pressure shall be below a gauge pressure of 1100 kPa (160 psi).

5.3.3.5.8.5 Reserves/supplements to compressor source systems shall either have regulator(s) mounted on the individual cylinder(s) or the cylinder(s) may be connected to a manifold via pigtail with pressure regulated at the manifold.

5.3.3.5.8.6* When nitrogen is used as the gas in a reserves/supplement to a compressor source, the following shall be permitted to apply:

(1) The volume of nitrogen connected and in storage shall not be considered in the limit of 84,950 L (3000 ft^3) of medical gases (i.e., oxygen and nitrous oxide) for classification as Level 3 and the ventilation of enclosures.

(2) Nitrogen gas cylinders shall be permitted to be stored in compressor rooms.
(3) The gas used shall be oil-free, dry Nitrogen NF.

A.5.3.3.5.8.6 The cubic feet (or cubic meters) of stored nitrogen gas is not restricted.

5.3.3.6* Level 3 Vacuum Sources.

A.5.3.3.6 A Level 3 vacuum system is not intended for Level 1 vacuum applications. A wet piping system is designed to accommodate liquid, air–gas, and solids through the service inlet. A dry piping system is designed to accommodate air–gas only through the service inlet. [Liquid(s) and solid(s) are trapped before entering the service inlet.] See Figure A.5.3.3.6(a) through Figure A.5.3.3.6(d).

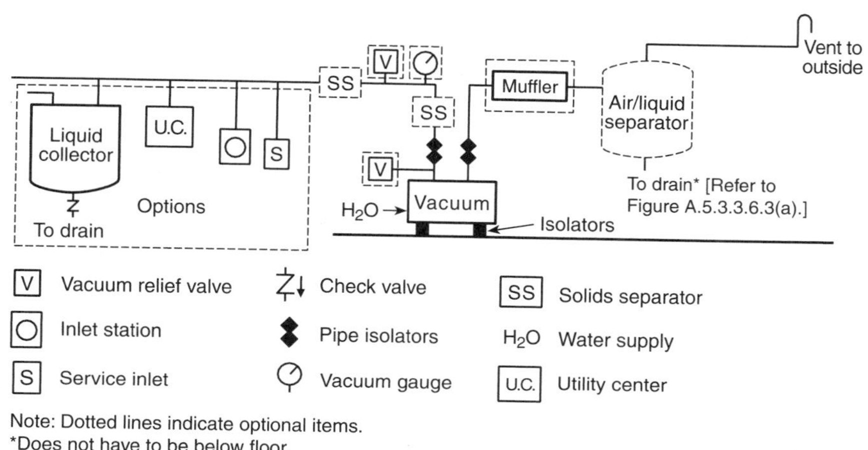

FIGURE A.5.3.3.6(a) *Typical Level 3 Wet or Dry Piping Systems with Single Vacuum Pump Source.*

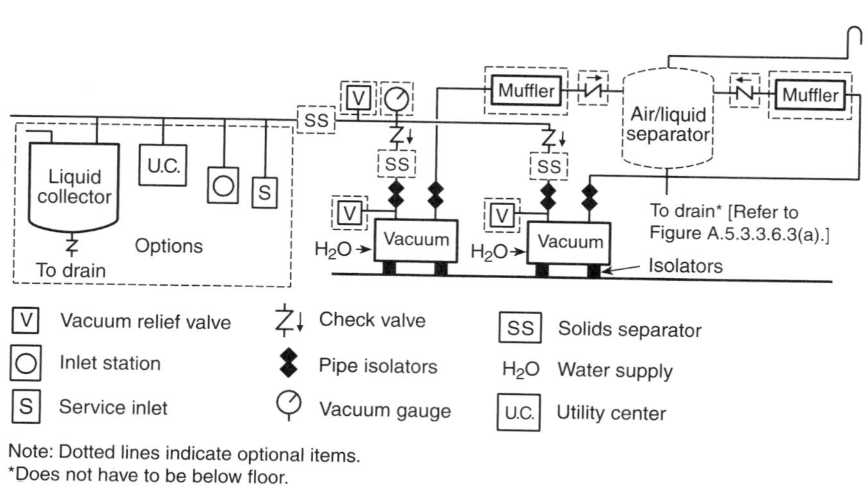

FIGURE A.5.3.3.6(b) *Typical Level 3 Wet or Dry Piping System with Duplex Vacuum Source with Air/Liquid Separator.*

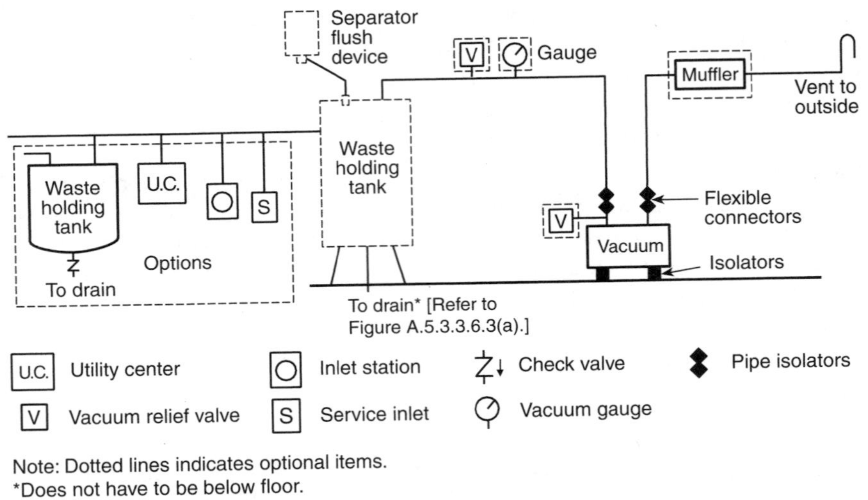

FIGURE A.5.3.3.6(c) Typical Level 3 Wet or Dry Piping System with Single Vacuum Source.

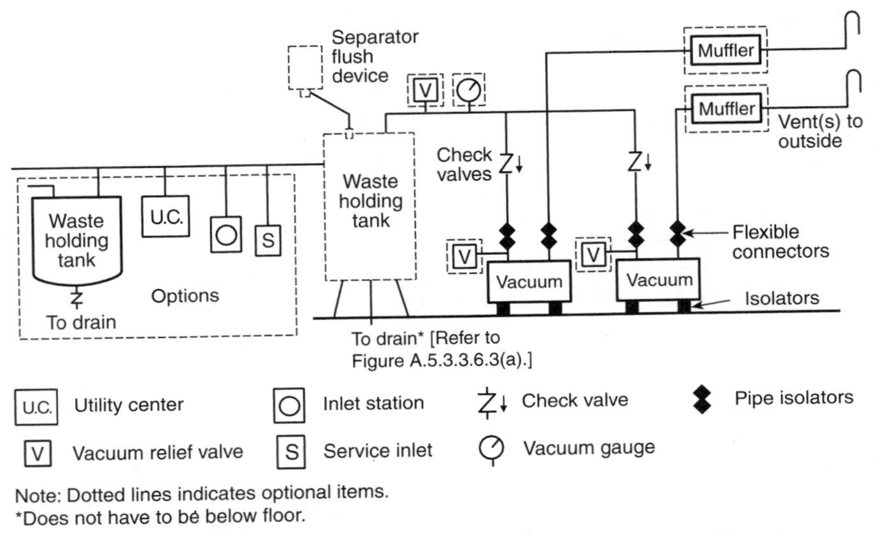

FIGURE A.5.3.3.6(d) Typical Level 3 Wet or Dry Piping System with Duplex Vacuum Source with Waste Holding Tank.

5.3.3.6.1 Level 3 vacuum sources shall be obtained from and be installed under the supervision of a manufacturer(s) or supplier(s) familiar with its installation and use.

5.3.3.6.2 Level 3 vacuum sources shall include the following:

(1) Pump or pumps suited for wet or dry service as intended in the design
(2) If intended for wet service, a liquid/air separator

5.3.3.6.3* Drains. None of the following provisions are intended to supersede provisions of local codes.

A **A.5.3.3.6.3** Improper design will permit gas pressure to build up in the ventilation system and might blow the trap on liquid seals. See Figure A.5.3.3.6.3(a) and Figure A.5.3.3.6.3(b).

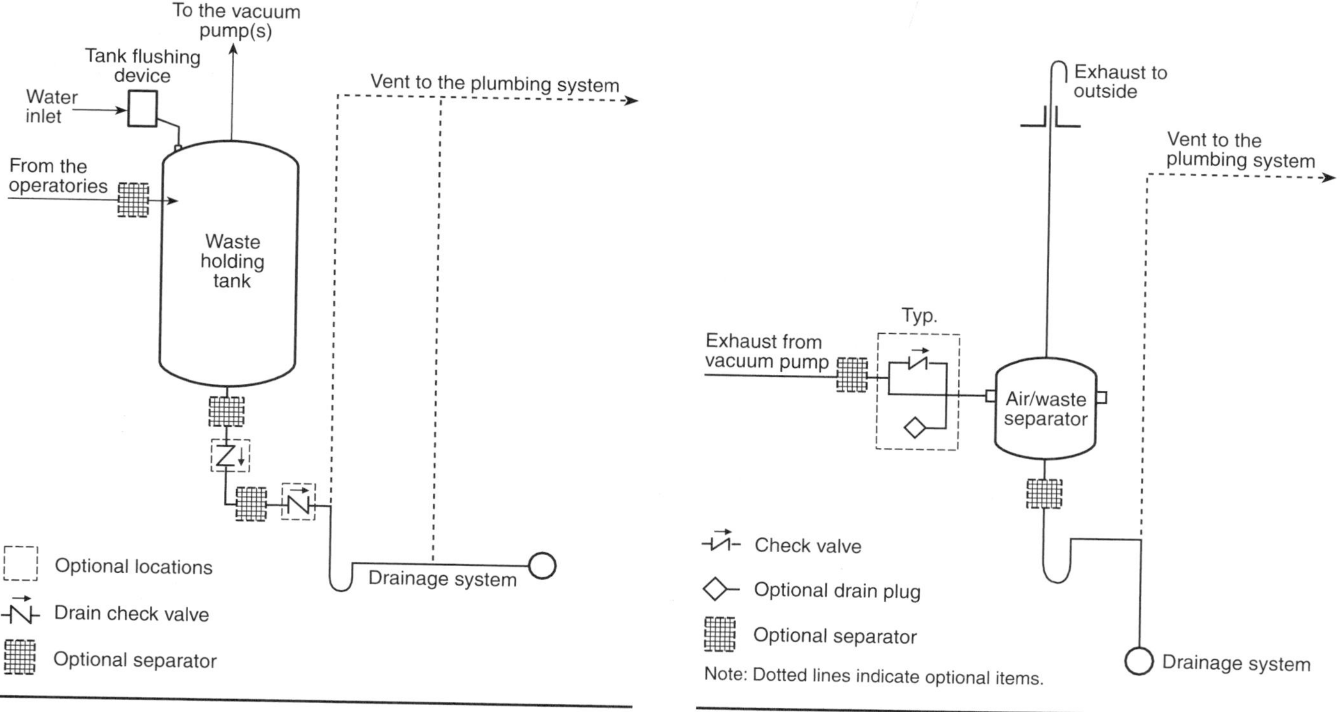

FIGURE A.5.3.3.6.3(a) *Drainage from a Gravity Drained Liquid Collector Tank.*

FIGURE A.5.3.3.6.3(b) *Drainage from a Positive Discharge Vacuum Pump through an Air/Liquid Separator.*

5.3.3.6.3.1 Liquids drained from a Level 3 vacuum source shall be directly connected to a sanitary drainage system through a trapped and vented drain.

5.3.3.6.3.2 Where the drainage is from a waste holding tank on the suction side of the vacuum source, the following requirements shall be met:

(1) A check valve shall be installed in the drain line from the holding tank.
(2) The trap in the building drainage system shall be the deep-seal type that is conventionally vented within the plumbing system.
(3) An additional vent shall be installed between the holding tank drain check valve and the drain trap, on the inlet side of the trap, to close and seal the check valve while the holding tank is operating under vacuum and collecting waste.
(4) The additional vent described in 5.3.3.6.3.2(3) shall be permitted to be connected to the plumbing system vents.
(5) Both of the vents in 5.3.3.6.3.2(3) and 5.3.3.6.3.2(4) shall extend vertically to not less than 152 mm (6 in.) above the top of the holding tank before turning horizontal.
(6) The trap and drain branch shall be not less than two pipe sizes larger than the waste pipe from the separator, but not less than DN50 (NPS 2).
(7) The trap seal shall be not less than 100 mm (4 in.) deep.
(8) The vent for the vacuum check valve shall be not less than the size of the check valve.
(9) The vent for the trap shall be not less than one-half the size of the trap and drain branch.

5.3.3.6.3.3 Where the drainage is at a positive pressure from an air/waste separator on the discharge side of the vacuum source, the following requirements shall be met:

(1) The trap in the building drainage system shall be the deep-seal type that is conventionally vented within the plumbing system.

(2) The trap vent shall extend vertically to not less than 152 mm (6 in.) above the top of the separator before turning horizontal.
(3) The trap and drain branch shall be not less than two pipe sizes larger than the waste pipe from the separator, but not less than DN40 (NPS 1½).
(4) The vent shall be the full size of the trap and drain.
(5) The trap seal shall be at least two times the exhaust back pressure in the separator, but not less than 100 mm (4 in.) deep.

5.3.3.6.4 Exhausts.

5.3.3.6.4.1 The gas discharge from a Level 3 vacuum source shall be piped to the outside.

5.3.3.6.4.2 The discharge point shall be chosen to minimize the hazards of noise.

5.3.3.6.4.3 The discharge point shall be located remote from any door, window, or other opening in the building.

5.3.3.6.4.4 The discharge point shall be located at a different level than air intakes.

5.3.3.6.4.5 The discharge point shall not be located where affected by prevailing winds, adjacent buildings, topography, or other obstacles to the rapid dispersion of the exhaust gases.

5.3.3.6.4.6 The discharge point shall be protected against the entry of insects, vermin, debris, and precipitation.

5.3.3.6.4.7 The discharge piping shall be sized to prevent back pressure greater than the pump manufacturer's recommendations.

5.3.3.6.4.8* Where multiple pumps discharge through a common pipe, each pump shall be fitted with a check valve, a manual isolation valve, or shall be arranged to permit capping the individual pump exhausts when a pump is removed for service.

A.5.3.3.6.4.8 Care should be taken to ensure the dual exhaust systems do not develop excessive back pressure when using a common exhaust line.

5.3.3.6.4.9 Where multiple pumps discharge through a common pipe, piping shall be arranged following the pump manufacturer's recommendations.

5.3.4* Level 3 Valves.

A.5.3.4 See Figure A.5.3.4 for diagrams showing emergency shutoff valve locations. Should a fire occur at night or when the facility is not in use, fire fighters should not be confronted with a potential pressurized gas source that could feed the fire and cause extensive damage and risk of life. Good economics also dictate that when the system is not in use, the leakage of gas through hose, couplings, and so forth, can be minimized if the system is shut off and portable equipment disconnected.

5.3.4.1 Emergency Shutoff Valves.

5.3.4.1.1 Where the central supply is remote from the medical gas system use points, the main supply line shall be provided with a shutoff valve so located in the single treatment facility as to be accessible from use-point locations in an emergency.

5.3.4.1.2 Where the supply is remote from a single treatment facility, the main supply line shall be provided with a shutoff valve so located in the single treatment facility as to be accessible from use-point locations in an emergency. Such valves shall be labeled to indicate the gas controlled and shall shut off only the gas to that single treatment facility. A remotely activated shutoff at the supply cylinder shall not be used for emergency shutoff. For clinical purposes, such a remote actuator shall not fail-close in the event of a loss of electric power.

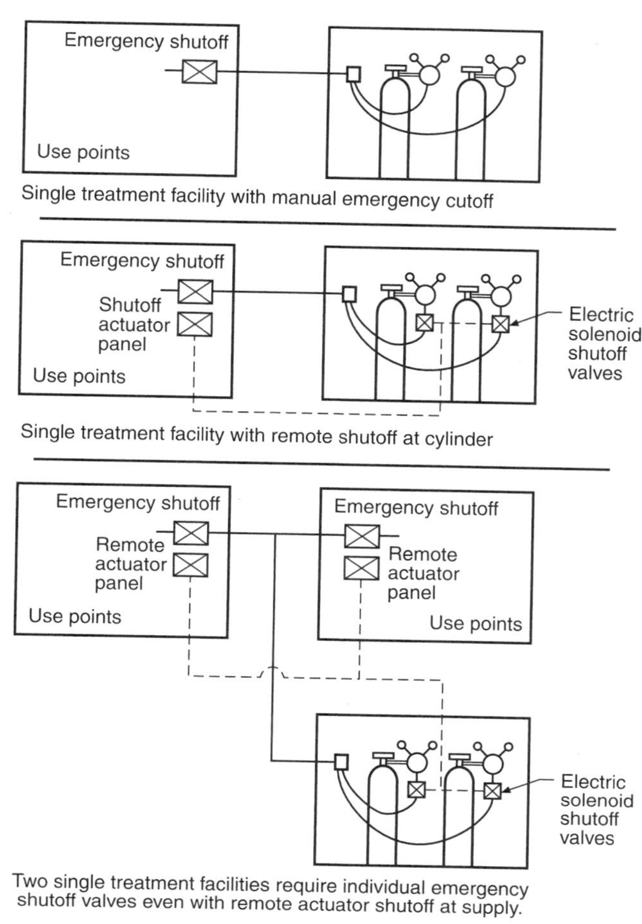

FIGURE A.5.3.4 Valves in Level 3 Facilities.

If remote actuators are the type that fail-open, it shall be mandatory that cylinder shutoff valves be closed whenever the system is not in use.

5.3.4.1.3 Where the central supply system supplies two single treatment facilities, each facility shall be provided with a shutoff valve so located in each treatment facility as to be accessible from the use-point locations in an emergency. Such valves shall be labeled to indicate the gas controlled and shall shut off only the gas to that single treatment facility. A remotely activated shutoff at the supply manifold shall not be used for emergency shutoff valves for dual treatment facility installations. For clinical purposes, such a remote actuator shall not fail-close in the event of a loss of electric power. If remote actuators are the type that fail-open, it shall be mandatory that cylinder shutoff valves be closed whenever the system is not in use.

5.3.4.1.4 Each riser supplied from the main line shall be provided with a shutoff valve adjacent to the riser connection. Riser valves shall remain accessible and shall not be obstructed.

5.3.5* Station and Service Inlets and Outlets.

A.5.3.5 Service outlets can be recessed or otherwise protected from damage.

5.3.5.1 Factory installed tubes on station outlets used for medical gases (i.e., oxygen and nitrous oxide) extending no more than 205 mm (8 in.) from the body of the terminal shall be not less than DN8 (NPS ¼) (⅜ in. O.D.) size with 8 mm (0.3 in.) minimum inside diameter.

5.3.5.2* The service outlet/inlet for Level 3 medical gas (i.e., oxygen and nitrous oxide) shall not be interchangeable with other service outlets/inlets [e.g., source for gas-powered devices (i.e., air or nitrogen), vacuum, or water].

A.5.3.5.2 This configuration will ensure that the required pressure and flow meet the secondary equipment manufacturer's requirements.

5.3.5.3 The service inlet for Level 3 vacuum shall be permitted to be either a shutoff valve with a threaded female pipe connector or a quick-connect fitting with a single check valve.

5.3.6 Level 3 Manufactured Assemblies. (Reserved)

5.3.7 Level 3 Surface Mounted Medical Gas Rails. (Reserved)

5.3.8 Level 3 Pressure and Vacuum Indicators. (Reserved)

5.3.9 Level 3 Warning Systems.

5.3.9.1 Warning systems for medical gases (i.e., oxygen and nitrous oxide) in Level 3 facilities shall conform to the alarm functions of a Level 1 facility as required in 5.1.9, except as follows:

(1) Area and local alarms shall not be required.
(2) Warning systems shall be permitted to have a single alarm panel.
(3) The alarm panel shall be located in an area of continuous surveillance while the facility is in operation.
(4) Pressure switches/sensors that monitor main line pressure shall be mounted at the source equipment with a pressure indicator(s) (lamp or LED) at the alarm panel. The audible and noncancelable alarm visual signals shall indicate if the pressure in the main line increases or decreases 20 percent from the normal operating pressure. Visual indicators shall remain until the situation that caused the alarm is resolved.
(5) When automatic changeover of source gases is required, the changeover alarm shall have a secondary indicator to suit the arrangement of the source equipment.
(6) A cancelable audible indication of each alarm condition that produces a sound at the alarm panel shall re-initiate the audible signal if another alarm condition occurs while the audible is silenced.
(7) Pressure switches/senses shall be installed downstream from any emergency shutoff valves required by 5.3.4.1 and shall comply with 5.3.9.1(4) and 5.3.9.1(5)

5.3.9.2 Systems for gases such as compressed air or nitrogen used to power devices, as well as Level 3 vacuum systems, shall not be required to have warning systems.

5.3.10 Level 3 Distribution.

5.3.10.1 Piping Materials for Field-Installed Level 3 Positive-Pressure Gas Systems.

5.3.10.1.1 Piping for Medical Gases. Piping for Level 3 positive-pressure nonflammable medical gases (i.e., oxygen and nitrous oxide) shall meet the requirements in 5.3.10.1.1.1 through 5.3.10.1.1.5.

5.3.10.1.1.1 Tubes, valves, fittings, station outlets, and other piping components in medical gas systems shall have been cleaned for oxygen service by the manufacturer prior to installation in accordance with CGA G-4.1 *Cleaning Equipment for Oxygen Service*.

5.3.10.1.1.2 Each length of tube shall be delivered plugged or capped by the manufacturer and kept sealed until prepared for installation.

5.3.10.1.1.3 Fittings, valves, and other components shall be delivered sealed and labeled by the manufacturer and kept sealed until prepared for installation.

5.3.10.1.1.4 Tubes shall be hard-drawn seamless copper ASTM B 819, *Standard Specification for Seamless Copper Tube for Medical Gas Systems*, medical gas tube, Type L or K.

5.3.10.1.1.5 ASTM B 819, *Standard Specification for Seamless Copper Tube for Medical Gas Systems*, medical gas tube shall be identified by the manufacturer's markings "OXY," "MED," "OXY/MED," "OXY/ACR," or "ACR/MED" in blue (Type L) or green (Type K).

5.3.10.1.2 Piping for Level 3 Gas-Powered Devices. Tubes shall be hard-drawn seamless copper and one of the following:

(1) ASTM B 819, *Standard Specification for Seamless Copper Tube for Medical Gas Systems*, medical gas tube (Type K or L)
(2) ASTM B 88, *Standard Specification for Seamless Copper Water Tube*, water tube (Type K or L)
(3) ASTM B 280, *Standard Specification for Seamless Copper Tubing for Air Conditioning and Refrigeration Field Service*, ACR tube (O.D. size), except that tube installed underground or within floor slabs shall be permitted to be soft annealed temper.

5.3.10.2 Piping Materials for Field-Installed Level 3 Vacuum Systems.

5.3.10.2.1 In copper piping systems, the tubes shall be hard-drawn seamless copper and one of the following:

(1) ASTM B 819, *Standard Specification for Seamless Copper Tube for Medical Gas Systems*, medical gas tube (Type K or L)
(2) ASTM B 88, *Standard Specification for Seamless Copper Water Tube*, water tube (Type K, L, or M)
(3) ASTM B 280, *Standard Specification for Seamless Copper Tubing for Air Conditioning and Refrigeration Field Service*, ACR tube (O.D. size), except that tube installed underground or within floor slabs shall be permitted to be soft annealed temper.

5.3.10.2.2 Copper tube installed underground or within floor slabs shall be permitted to be soft annealed temper.

5.3.10.2.3 In plastic piping systems, the pipe shall be polyvinylchoride (PVC) plastic, Schedule 40 minimum.

5.3.10.3 Fittings.

5.3.10.3.1 Turns, offsets, and other changes in direction in medical gas piping, copper Level 3 vacuum piping, and piping for gas-powered devices shall be made with brazed wrought copper capillary fittings complying with ASME B16.22, *Wrought Copper and Copper Alloy Solder-Joint Pressure Fittings*, or brazing fittings complying with ASME B16.50, *Wrought Copper and Copper Alloy Braze-Joint Pressure Fittings*.

5.3.10.3.2 Cast copper alloy fittings shall not be used where joints are brazed.

5.3.10.3.3 Branch connections in copper vacuum piping systems shall be permitted to be made using mechanically formed, drilled, and extruded tee-branch connections that are formed in accordance with the tool manufacturer's instructions, and brazed.

5.3.10.3.4 Turns, offsets, and other changes in direction in plastic Level 3 vacuum piping shall be made with solvent-cemented PVC plastic pressure fittings, Schedule 40 minimum.

5.3.10.4 Threaded Joints. Threaded joints in Level 3 gas-powered systems and vacuum distribution piping shall meet the following requirements:

(1) Be limited to connections to pressure/vacuum indicators, alarm devices, and source equipment

(2) Have tapered threads complying with ASME B1.20.1, *Pipe Threads, General Purpose, Inch*

(3) Be made up with polytetrafluoroethylene (such as Teflon™) tape or other thread sealant recommended for oxygen service, with the sealant applied to the male threads only

5.3.10.5 Soldered Joints. Soldered joints in copper Level 3 vacuum and Level 3 gas-powered systems piping shall be made in accordance with ASTM B 828, *Standard Practice for Making Capillary Joints by Soldering of Copper and Copper Alloy Tube and Fittings*, using a "lead-free" solder filler metal containing not more than 0.2 percent lead by volume.

5.3.10.6 Solvent-Cemented Joints. Solvent-cemented joints in plastic Level 3 vacuum piping shall be in accordance with ASTM D 2855, *Standard Practice for Making Solvent-Cemented Joints with Poly(Vinyl Chloride) (PVC) Pipe and Fittings.*

5.3.10.7 Brazed Joints.

5.3.10.7.1 General Requirements.

5.3.10.7.1.1 Brazed joints shall be made using a brazing alloy that exhibits a melting temperature in excess of 538°C (1000°F) to retain the integrity of the piping system in the event of fire exposure.

5.3.10.7.1.2 Brazed tube joints shall be the socket type.

5.3.10.7.1.3 Filler metals shall bond with and be metallurgically compatible with the base metals being joined.

5.3.10.7.1.4 Filler metals shall comply with ANSI/AWS A5.8, *Specification for Filler Metals for Brazing and Braze Welding.*

5.3.10.7.1.5 Copper-to-copper joints shall be brazed using a copper–phosphorus or copper–phosphorus–silver brazing filler metal (BCuP series) without flux.

5.3.10.7.1.6 Joints to be brazed in place shall be accessible for necessary preparation, assembly, heating, filler application, cooling, cleaning, and inspection.

5.3.10.7.2 Cutting Tube Ends.

5.3.10.7.2.1 Tube ends shall be cut square using a sharp tubing cutter to avoid deforming the tube.

5.3.10.7.2.2 The cutting wheels on tubing cutters shall be free from grease, oil, or other lubricant not recommended for oxygen service.

5.3.10.7.2.3 The cut ends of the tube shall be deburred with a sharp, clean deburring tool, taking care to prevent chips from entering the tube.

5.3.10.7.3 Cleaning Joints for Brazing.

5.3.10.7.3.1 The interior surfaces of tubes, fittings, and other components that are cleaned for oxygen service shall be stored and handled to avoid contamination prior to assembly and brazing.

5.3.10.7.3.2 The exterior surfaces of tube ends shall be cleaned prior to brazing to remove any oxides and surface dirt and to roughen the surfaces to prepare them for brazing.

5.3.10.7.3.3 If the interior surfaces of fitting sockets that were cleaned for oxygen become contaminated prior to brazing, they shall be re-cleaned for oxygen in accordance with 5.3.10.7.3.9 and be cleaned for brazing with a clean, oil-free wire brush.

5.3.10.7.3.4 Nonabrasive pads shall be used to clean the exterior surfaces of tube ends.

5.3.10.7.3.5 The use of steel wool or sand cloth shall be prohibited.

5.3.10.7.3.6 The cleaning process shall not result in grooving of the surfaces to be joined.

5.3.10.7.3.7 After being abraded, the surfaces shall be wiped using a clean, lint-free white cloth.

5.3.10.7.3.8 Tubes, fittings, valves, and other components shall be visually examined internally before being joined to verify that they have not become contaminated for oxygen service (if so required) and that they are free of obstructions or debris.

5.3.10.7.3.9 The interior surfaces of tube ends, fittings, and other components that were cleaned for oxygen service by the manufacturer, but become contaminated prior to being installed, shall be permitted to be re-cleaned on-site by the installer by thoroughly scrubbing the interior surfaces with a clean, hot water/alkaline solution, such as sodium carbonate or trisodium phosphate, mixed 450 g to 11 L (1 lb to 3 gal) of potable water and thoroughly rinsing them with clean, hot potable water.

5.3.10.7.3.10 Other aqueous cleaning solutions shall be permitted to be used for the on-site re-cleaning permitted in 5.3.10.7.3.9, provided that they are as recommended in CGA G-4.1, *Cleaning Equipment for Oxygen Service*, and are listed in CGA O2-DIR, *Directory of Cleaning Agents for Oxygen Service*.

5.3.10.7.3.11 Material that has become contaminated internally and is not clean for oxygen service (if so required) shall not be installed.

5.3.10.7.3.12 Joints shall be brazed within 1 hour after the surfaces are cleaned for brazing.

5.3.10.7.4 Brazing Dissimilar Metals.

5.3.10.7.4.1 Flux shall only be used when brazing dissimilar metals, such as copper and bronze or brass, using a silver (BAg series) brazing filler metal.

5.3.10.7.4.2 Surfaces shall be cleaned for brazing in accordance with 5.3.10.7.3.

5.3.10.7.4.3 Flux shall be applied sparingly to minimize contamination of the inside of the tube with flux.

5.3.10.7.4.4 The flux shall be applied and worked over the cleaned surfaces to be brazed using a stiff, stainless steel bristle brush to ensure complete coverage and wetting of the surfaces with flux.

5.3.10.7.4.5 Where possible, short sections of copper tube shall be brazed onto the noncopper component and the interior of the subassembly shall be cleaned of flux prior to installation in the piping system.

5.3.10.7.4.6 On joints DN20 (NPS ¾) (⅞ in. O.D.) size and smaller, flux-coated brazing rods shall be permitted to be used in lieu of applying flux to the surfaces being joined.

5.3.10.7.5* Nitrogen Purge.

A.5.3.10.7.5 The intent is to provide an oxygen-free atmosphere within the tubing and to prevent the formation of copper oxide scale during brazing. This is accomplished by filling the piping with a low-volume flow of low-pressure inert gas.

5.3.10.7.5.1 While being brazed, joints shall be continuously purged with oil-free, dry Nitrogen NF to prevent the formation of copper oxide on the inside surfaces of the joint.

5.3.10.7.5.2 The source of the purge gas shall be monitored and the installer shall be audibly alerted when the content is low.

5.3.10.7.5.3 The purge gas flow rate shall not produce a positive pressure in the piping system.

5.3.10.7.5.4 The purge gas flow rate shall be controlled by the use of a pressure regulator and flowmeter, or combination thereof.

5.3.10.7.5.5 Pressure regulators alone shall not be used to control purge gas flow rates.

5.3.10.7.5.6 During and after installation, openings in the piping system shall be kept capped or plugged to maintain a nitrogen atmosphere within the piping and to prevent debris or other contaminants from entering the system.

5.3.10.7.5.7 While a joint is being brazed, a discharge opening shall be provided on the opposite side of the joint from where the purge gas is being introduced.

5.3.10.7.5.8 The flow of purge gas shall be maintained until the joint is cool to the touch.

5.3.10.7.5.9 After the joint has cooled, the purge discharge opening shall be plugged or capped to prevent contamination of the inside of the tube and maintain the nitrogen atmosphere within the piping system.

5.3.10.7.5.10 The final connection of new piping to an existing in-use pipeline shall be permitted to be made without the use of a nitrogen purge.

5.3.10.7.5.11 After a final connection in a Level 3 positive-pressure gas pipeline is made without a nitrogen purge, an outlet in the immediate downstream zone of the affected portion(s) of both the new and existing in-use piping shall be tested in accordance with 5.3.12.3.8, Verifier Final Tie-In Test.

5.3.10.7.6 Assembling and Heating Joints.

5.3.10.7.6.1 Tube ends shall be inserted fully into the socket of the fitting.

5.3.10.7.6.2 Where flux is permitted, the joint shall be heated slowly until the flux has liquefied.

5.3.10.7.6.3 After flux is liquefied, or where flux is not permitted to be used, the joint shall be heated quickly to the brazing temperature, taking care not to overheat the joint.

5.3.10.7.6.4 Techniques for heating the joint; applying the brazing filler metal; and making horizontal, vertical, and large-diameter joints shall be as stated in sections on Applying Heat and Brazing and Horizontal and Vertical Joints in Chapter VII, Brazed Joints in the CDA *Copper Tube Handbook.*

5.3.10.7.7 Inspection of Brazed or Soldered Joints.

5.3.10.7.7.1 After brazing or soldering, the outside of all joints shall be cleaned by washing with water and a wire brush to remove any residue and permit clear visual inspection of the joint.

5.3.10.7.7.2 Where flux has been used, the wash water shall be hot.

5.3.10.7.7.3 Each joint shall be visually inspected after cleaning the outside surfaces.

5.3.10.7.7.4 Joints exhibiting the following conditions shall not be permitted:

(1) Flux or flux residue (when flux or flux-coated BAg rods are used with dissimilar metals)
(2) Base metal melting or erosion

(3) Unmelted filler metal
(4) Failure of the filler metal to be clearly visible all the way around the joint at the interface between the socket and the tube
(5) Cracks in the tube or component
(6) Cracks in the braze or solder filler metal
(7) Failure of the joint to hold the test pressure or vacuum under the installer-performed initial pressure or vacuum test (5.3.12.2.3 or 5.3.12.2.4) and standing pressure or vacuum test (5.3.12.2.7 or 5.3.12.2.8).

5.3.10.7.7.5 Joints that are identified as defective under conditions 5.3.10.7.7.4(2) or 5.3.10.7.7.4(5) shall be replaced.

5.3.10.7.7.6 Joints that are found to be defective under conditions 5.3.10.7.7.4(1), 5.3.10.7.7.4(3), 5.3.10.7.7.4(4), 5.3.10.7.7.4(6), or 5.3.10.7.7.4(7) shall be permitted to be repaired, except that no joint shall be reheated more than once before being replaced.

5.3.10.8 Special Joints.

5.3.10.8.1 The following joints shall be prohibited throughout Level 3 medical gas (i.e., oxygen and nitrous oxide) pipeline systems:

(1) Flared and compression connections, including connections to station outlets and inlets, alarm devices, and other components
(2) Other straight-threaded connections, including unions

5.3.10.8.2 Flared and compression connections shall be permitted in piping for Level 3 gas-powered devices and Level 3 vacuum in junction boxes, and where exposed at station outlets/inlets and source equipment.

5.3.10.9 Special Fittings. The following special fittings shall be permitted to be used in lieu of brazed joints:

(1) Memory-metal couplings having temperature and pressure ratings joints not less than that of a brazed joint
(2) Listed or approved metallic gas tube fittings that, when made up, provide a permanent joint having the mechanical, thermal, and sealing integrity of a brazed joint
(3) Axially swaged, elastic strain preload fittings providing metal to metal seal having pressure and temperature ratings not less than that of a brazed joint and when complete are permanent and nonseparable.

5.3.10.10 Installation of Level 3 Piping and Equipment.

In the paragraphs of 5.3.10.10, pay particular attention to the distinction between medical gases (typically only oxygen and nitrous oxide in Level 3 facilities) and all other systems. The requirements vary widely between the two.

5.3.10.10.1 Qualification of Installers.

5.3.10.10.1.1 The installation of Level 3 gas and vacuum systems shall be made by qualified, competent technicians who are experienced in making such installations.

5.3.10.10.1.2 The installers of Level 3 medical gas systems (i.e., oxygen and nitrous oxide) shall be qualified under the requirements of ASSE 6010, *Professional Qualifications Standard for Medical Gas Systems Installers.*

5.3.10.10.1.3 Brazing on medical gas system pipelines shall be performed by individuals who are qualified under the provisions of 5.3.10.10.15.

5.3.10.10.1.4 Prior to any installation work involving brazing, the installer of Level 3 medical gas piping shall provide documentation for the qualification of brazing procedures and individual brazers that is required under 5.3.10.10.15.

5.3.10.10.2 Pipe Sizing. Piping systems shall be designed and sized to deliver the required flow rates at the utilization pressures.

5.3.10.10.3* Minimum Pipe Sizes.

A.5.3.10.10.3 One of the major concerns is the cross-connection of piping systems of different gases. The reason for different sizes is to prevent cross-connections, not for capacity concerns.

5.3.10.10.3.1 Mains, branches, and drops to individual service outlets in Level 3 oxygen piping systems shall be not less than DN10 (NPS ⅜ in.) (½ in. O.D.) size, but at least one size larger than the piping for nitrous oxide.

5.3.10.10.3.2 Mains, branches, and drops to individual service outlets in Level 3 nitrous oxide and inlets in the following piping systems shall be not less than DN8 (NPS ¼ in.) (⅜ in. O.D.) size.

5.3.10.10.3.3 Mains, branches, and drops to individual service outlets/inlets in Level 3 piping systems for gas powered devices and vacuum shall not be the same as the sizes used for oxygen and nitrous oxide.

5.3.10.10.3.4 Runouts to alarm panels and connecting tubing for pressure/vacuum indicators and alarm devices shall be permitted to be DN8 (NPS ⅛) (¼ in. O.D.) size.

5.3.10.10.4 Protection of Piping. Piping shall be protected against freezing, corrosion, and physical damage.

5.3.10.10.4.1 Piping exposed in corridors and other areas where subject to physical damage from the movement of carts, stretchers, portable equipment, or vehicles shall be protected.

5.3.10.10.4.2 Tubing for Level 3 medical gas (i.e., oxygen and nitrous oxide) tubing that is underground within buildings or embedded in concrete floors or walls shall be installed in a continuous conduit.

5.3.10.10.5 Location of Piping.

5.3.10.10.5.1 Piping for Level 3 medical gases (i.e., oxygen and nitrous oxide) shall be located in accordance with 5.3.10.10.5.1(A) through 5.3.10.10.5.1(C):

(A) Piping shall be permitted to be installed overhead wherever possible.

(B) Piping shall not be installed in electrical switchgear rooms, elevator shafts, and areas having open flames.

(C) Medical gas piping (i.e., oxygen and nitrous oxide) shall not be located where subject to contact with oil.

5.3.10.10.5.2 Piping for Level 3 gas-powered devices, and Level 3 vacuum systems shall be located in accordance with 5.3.10.10.5.2(A) and 5.3.10.10.5.2(B):

(A) Piping shall be permitted to be installed at the following locations:

(1) Under floor or underground
(2) Underground within buildings
(3) Aboveground, within walls, within ceilings

(B) Piping shall not be installed in electrical switchgear rooms, elevator shafts, and areas having open flames, except for the following locations:

(1) Room locations for Level 3 gas-powered devices and Level 3 vacuum systems.
(2) Room locations for secondary distribution circuit panels and breakers having a maximum voltage rating of 600 volts.

5.3.10.10.6 Pipe Support.

5.3.10.10.6.1 Piping shall be supported from the building structure in accordance with MSS SP-69, *Pipe Hangers and Supports — Selection and Application.* 

5.3.10.10.6.2 Hangers and supports shall comply with MSS SP-58, *Pipe Hangers and Supports — Materials, Design, and Manufacture.* 

5.3.10.10.6.3 Hangers for copper tube shall be sized for copper tube and have a copper finish.

5.3.10.10.6.4 In potentially damp locations, copper tube hangers and supports that are in contact with the tube shall be plastic-coated or otherwise be electrically insulated from the tube.

5.3.10.10.6.5 Maximum support spacing for copper tubing shall be in accordance with Table 5.3.10.10.6.5.

TABLE 5.3.10.10.6.5 *Maximum Pipe Support Spacing*

	Hanger Spacing	
Pipe Size	***mm***	***ft***
DN8 (NPS ¼) (in. O.D.)	1520	5
DN10 (NPS) (½ in. O.D.)	1830	6
DN15 (NPS ½) (in. O.D.)	1830	6
DN20 (NPS ¾) (in. O.D.)	2130	7
DN25 (NPS 1) (1 in. O.D.)	2440	8
DN 32 (NPS 1¼) (1 in. O.D.)	2740	9
DN40 (NPS 1½) (1 in. O.D.) and larger	3050	10
Vertical risers, all sizes		
Every floor, but not to exceed:	4570	15

5.3.10.10.6.6 PVC plastic piping for Level 3 vacuum systems shall be supported at a maximum spacing of 1.22 m (4 ft), except that vertical piping shall be supported at every floor and with mid-story guides.

5.3.10.10.6.7 Where required, Level 3 gas and vacuum piping shall be seismically restrained against earthquakes in accordance with the applicable building code.

5.3.10.10.7 Piping Within Floor Slabs and Underground Within Buildings.

5.3.10.10.7.1 The tube(s) shall be installed in one (or more) continuous conduits that are of sufficient size to permit subsequent installation, removal, and replacement of the gas and/or vacuum lines.

5.3.10.10.7.2 Each tube pulled into the conduit shall be a continuous length having no joints within the conduit.

5.3.10.10.8 Underground Piping Outside of Buildings.

5.3.10.10.8.1 Buried piping outside of buildings shall be installed below the local level of frost penetration.

5.3.10.10.8.2 The installation procedure for underground piping shall protect the piping from physical damage while being backfilled.

5.3.10.10.8.3 If underground piping is protected by a conduit, cover, or other enclosure, the following requirements shall be met:

(1) Access during construction shall be provided at the joints for visual inspection and leak testing.
(2) The conduit, cover, or enclosure shall be self-draining and not retain groundwater in prolonged contact with the pipe.

5.3.10.10.8.4 Buried piping that will be subject to surface loads shall be buried at a depth that will protect the piping and or its enclosure from excessive stresses.

5.3.10.10.8.5 The minimum backfilled cover above the top of the pipe or its enclosure for buried piping outside of buildings shall be 900 mm (36 in.), except that the minimum cover shall be permitted to be reduced to 450 mm (18 in.) where physical damage is otherwise prevented.

5.3.10.10.8.6 Trenches shall be excavated so that the pipe or its enclosure has firm, substantially continuous bearing on the bottom of the trench.

5.3.10.10.8.7 Backfill shall be clean and compacted so as to protect and uniformly support the pipe or its enclosure.

5.3.10.10.8.8 A continuous tape or marker placed immediately above the pipe or its enclosure shall clearly identify the pipeline by specific name.

5.3.10.10.8.9 A continuous warning means shall also be provided above the pipeline at approximately one-half the depth of bury.

5.3.10.10.8.10 Where buried piping is installed through a wall sleeve, the ends of the sleeve shall be sealed to prevent the entrance of ground water into the building.

5.3.10.10.9 Branch Takeoffs. Runouts from horizontal piping for medical gas (i.e., oxygen and nitrous oxide) shall be taken off above the centerline of the main or branch pipe and rise vertically at an angle of not more than 45 degrees from vertical.

5.3.10.10.10 Special Requirements for Level 3 Vacuum Piping.

5.3.10.10.10.1 Horizontal piping in Level 3 vacuum systems shall be sloped a minimum of 7 mm per 3.05 m (¼ in. per 10 ft) toward the vacuum source equipment.

5.3.10.10.10.2 Horizontal piping shall include no sags or low points that will permit fluids or debris to accumulate.

5.3.10.10.10.3 Accessible cleanouts that are limited to vertical downflow shall be provided where necessary to clear the piping of obstructions.

5.3.10.10.11 Hose and Flexible Connectors.

5.3.10.10.11.1 Hose and flexible connectors, both metallic and nonmetallic, shall be no longer than necessary and shall not penetrate or be concealed in walls, floors, ceilings, or partitions.

5.3.10.10.11.2 Flexible connectors, metallic or nonmetallic, shall have a minimum burst pressure, with a gauge pressure of 6895 kPa (1000 psi).

5.3.10.10.12 Prohibited System Interconnections.

5.3.10.10.12.1 Two or more piping systems for medical gases, gas-powered devices, and Level 3 vacuum shall not be interconnected for testing or any other reason.

5.3.10.10.12.2 Leak testing shall be accomplished by separately charging and testing each individual piping system.

5.3.10.10.13 System Manufacturer's Instructions.

5.3.10.10.13.1 The installation of individual components shall be made in accordance with the instructions of the system manufacturer.

5.3.10.10.13.2 Such instructions shall include directions and information deemed by the system manufacturer to be necessary for attaining proper operation, testing, and maintenance of the system.

5.3.10.10.13.3 Copies of system manufacturer's instructions shall be left with the system owner.

5.3.10.10.14 Changes in System Use.

5.3.10.10.14.1 Where a Level 3 positive-pressure gas piping distribution system originally used or constructed for use at one pressure or for one gas is converted for operation at another pressure or for another gas, all provisions of 5.3.10 shall apply as if the system were new.

5.3.10.10.14.2 Piping for Level 3 gas-powered devices or Level 3 vacuum shall not be permitted to be converted for use as a medical gas piping system (i.e., oxygen or nitrous oxide).

5.3.10.10.15 Qualification of Brazing Procedures and Brazing.

5.3.10.10.15.1 Brazing procedures and brazer performance for the installation of Level 3 brazed piping shall be qualified the same as for Level 1 piping, in accordance with either Section IX, Welding and Brazing Qualifications, of the ASME *Boiler and Pressure Vessel Code*, or AWS B2.2, *Standard for Brazing Procedure and Performance Qualification*, both as modified by 5.3.10.10.15.2 through 5.3.10.10.15.5.

5.3.10.10.15.2 Brazers shall be qualified by visual examination of the test coupon followed by sectioning.

5.3.10.10.15.3 The brazing procedure specification shall address cleaning, joint clearance, overlap, internal purge gas, purge gas flow rate, and filler metal.

5.3.10.10.15.4 The brazing procedure qualification record and the record of brazer performance qualification shall document filler metal used, cleaning, joint clearance, overlap, internal purge gas and flow rate during brazing of coupon, and the absence of internal oxidation in the completed coupon.

5.3.10.10.15.5 Brazing procedures qualified by a technically competent group or agency shall be permitted under the following conditions:

(1) The brazing procedure specification and the procedure qualification record meet the requirements of this standard.
(2) The employer obtains a copy of both the brazing procedure specification and the supporting qualification records from the group or agency and signs and dates these records, thereby accepting responsibility for the qualifications that were performed by the group or agency.
(3) The employer qualifies at least one brazer following each brazing procedure specification used.

5.3.10.10.15.6 An employer shall be permitted to accept brazer qualification records of a previous employer under the following conditions:

(1) The brazer has been qualified following the same or an equivalent procedure that the new employer uses.
(2) The new employer obtains a copy of the record of brazer performance qualification tests from the previous employer and signs and dates these records, thereby accepting responsibility for the qualifications performed by the previous employer.

5.3.10.10.15.7 Performance qualifications of brazers shall remain in effect indefinitely unless the brazer does not braze with the qualified procedure for a period exceeding 6 months, or there is a specific reason to question the ability of the brazer.

5.3.11 Labeling and Identification.

5.3.11.1 Pipe Labeling.

5.3.11.1.1 Piping shall be labeled by stenciling or adhesive markers that identify the system.

5.3.11.1.2 Pipe labels shall show the name of the gas/vacuum system or the chemical symbol.

5.3.11.1.3 Where positive-pressure gas piping systems operate at pressures other than the standard gauge pressure of 345 kPa to 380 kPa (50 psi to 55 psi) or gauge pressure of 1100 kPa to 1275 kPa (160 psi to 185 psi) for nitrogen, the pipe labels shall include the nonstandard operating pressure in addition to the name or symbol of the gas.

5.3.11.1.4 Pipe labels shall be located as follows:

(1) At intervals of not more than 6.1 m (20 ft)
(2) At least once in or above every room
(3) On both sides of walls or partitions penetrated by the piping
(4) At least once in every story height traversed by risers

5.3.11.2 Shutoff Valves.

5.3.11.2.1 Shutoff valves shall be identified as to the following:

(1) The name or chemical symbol for the specific system
(2) The name of the room(s) or area(s) served
(3) A caution to not close (or open) the valve except in an emergency

5.3.11.2.2 Where positive-pressure gas systems operate at pressures other than the standard gauge pressure of 345 kPa to 380 kPa (50 psi to 55 psi) or gauge pressure of 1100 kPa to 1275 kPa (160 psi to 185 psi) for nitrogen, the valve identification shall also include the nonstandard operating pressure.

5.3.11.3 Service Outlets and Inlets.

5.3.11.3.1 Service outlets and inlets shall be identified as to the name or chemical symbol for the specific gas or vacuum provided.

5.3.11.3.2 Where positive-pressure gas systems operate at pressures other than the standard gauge pressure of 345 kPa to 380 kPa (50 psi to 55 psi) or gauge pressure of 1100 kPa to 1275 kPa (160 psi to 185 psi) for nitrogen, the station outlet identification shall include the nonstandard operating pressure.

5.3.12 Performance Criteria and Testing — Level 3 (Medical Gas, Gas-Powered Devices, Vacuum).

5.3.12.1 General.

5.3.12.1.1 Inspection and testing shall be performed on all new piped gas systems, additions, renovations, temporary installations, or repaired systems, to assure the facility, by a documented procedure, that all applicable provisions of this document have been adhered to and system integrity has been achieved or maintained.

5.3.12.1.2 Inspection and testing shall include all components of the system or portions thereof including, but not limited to, medical gas source(s), compressed air source systems (e.g., compressors, dryers, filters, regulators), alarms and monitoring safeguards, pipelines, isolation valves, and service outlets and inlets.

5.3.12.1.3 All systems that are breached and components that are subjected to additions, renovations, or replacement (e.g., new medical gas sources, compressors, dryers, alarms) shall be inspected and tested.

5.3.12.1.4 Systems shall be deemed breached at the point of pipeline intrusion by physical separation or by system component removal, replacement, or addition.

5.3.12.1.5 Breached portions of the systems subject to inspection and testing shall be confined to only the specific altered zone and components in the immediate zone or area that is located upstream for vacuum systems and downstream for pressure gases at the point or area of intrusion.

5.3.12.1.6 The inspection and testing reports shall be submitted directly to the party that contracted for the testing, who shall submit the report through channels to the responsible authority and any others that are required.

5.3.12.1.7 Reports shall contain detailed listings of all findings and results.

5.3.12.1.8 The responsible facility authority shall review these inspection and testing records prior to the use of any systems to assure that all findings and results of the inspection and testing have been successfully completed.

5.3.12.1.9 All documentation pertaining to inspections and testing shall be maintained on-site within the facility.

5.3.12.1.10 Before piping systems are initially put into use, the Level 3 health care facility authority shall be responsible for ascertaining that the gas/vacuum delivered at each outlet/inlet is that shown on the outlet/inlet label and that the proper connecting fittings are installed for the specific gas/vacuum. *(See 5.3.12.1.11.)*

5.3.12.1.11 Acceptance of the verifier's reports required under 5.3.12.3, System Verification, shall be permitted to satisfy the requirements of 5.3.12.1.10.

5.3.12.2 Initial Tests.

5.3.12.2.1 General.

5.3.12.2.1.1 The tests required by 5.3.12.3.1 through 5.3.12.3.12 shall be performed prior to the tests listed in 5.3.12.3, System Verification, by one or more of the following:

(1) The installer
(2) A representative of the system supplier
(3) A representative of the system manufacturer

5.3.12.2.1.2 The test gas for positive-pressure gas systems shall be oil-free, dry Nitrogen NF.

5.3.12.2.1.3 Where manufactured assemblies are to be installed, the tests required under 5.3.12.2 shall be performed as follows:

(1) After completion of the distribution piping
(2) Prior to installation or connection of manufactured assemblies supplied through flexible hoses or flexible tubing
(3) At all station outlets/inlets on manufactured assemblies supplied through copper tubing

5.3.12.2.2 Initial Blow Down. Piping in Level 3 positive-pressure gas distribution systems shall be blown clear by means of oil-free, dry Nitrogen NF as follows:

(1) After installation of the distribution piping
(2) Before installation of station outlets and other system components (i.e., pressure alarm devices, pressure indicators, pressure relief valves, manifolds, source equipment)

5.3.12.2.3 Initial Pressure Test for Positive-Pressure Gas Systems and Copper Level 3 Vacuum Piping.

5.3.12.2.3.1 Each section of the piping in Level 3 positive-pressure gas piping systems and copper Level 3 vacuum systems shall be pressure tested using oil-free, dry Nitrogen NF.

5.3.12.2.3.2 Initial pressure tests shall be conducted as follows:

(1) After installation of station outlets/inlets rough-in assemblies. Test caps shall be permitted to be used.
(2) Prior to the installation of components of the distribution piping system that would be damaged by the test pressure (i.e., pressure/vacuum alarm devices, pressure/vacuum indicators, line pressure relief valves).

5.3.12.2.3.3 Where Level 3 vacuum piping systems include plastic piping, they shall be inspected to assure that there are no visible cross-connections to positive-pressure gas piping systems prior to applying test pressures to the positive-pressure systems.

5.3.12.2.3.4 The source shutoff valves for all piping systems shall remain closed during these tests.

5.3.12.2.3.5 The test pressure for positive-pressure gas piping shall be 1.5 times the system working pressure, but not less than a gauge pressure of 1035 kPa (150 psi).

5.3.12.2.3.6 The test pressure for copper Level 3 vacuum piping shall be a gauge pressure of 105 kPa (15 psi).

5.3.12.2.3.7 The test pressure shall be maintained until each joint has been examined for leakage by means of soapy water or other equally effective means of leak detection.

5.3.12.2.3.8 Leaks, if any, shall be located, replaced (if permitted) or repaired (if required), and retested.

5.3.12.2.4 Initial Leak Tests — PVC Level 3 Vacuum Piping. Plastic Level 3 vacuum piping shall be leak-tested under vacuum conditions.

5.3.12.2.4.1 Plastic Level 3 vacuum piping shall not be tested with compressed gas.

5.3.12.2.4.2 Leak tests shall be conducted after installation of station inlets.

5.3.12.2.4.3 The piping being tested shall be subjected to a vacuum of not less than 485 mm (19 in.) gauge HgV, using either the vacuum source equipment or a vacuum test pump.

5.3.12.2.4.4 The test vacuum shall be maintained until each joint has been examined for leakage.

5.3.12.2.5 Initial Cross-Connection Test. The installer shall determine that no cross-connections exist between the various Level 3 gas and vacuum piping systems.

5.3.12.2.5.1 All Level 3 gas and vacuum piping systems shall be at atmospheric pressure.

5.3.12.2.5.2 Face plates for outlets/inlets shall be installed.

5.3.12.2.5.3 Level 3 vacuum piping systems shall be subjected to a vacuum of not less than 485 mm (19 in.) gauge HgV, using either the vacuum source equipment or a test pump.

5.3.12.2.5.4 Each individual system gas outlet and vacuum inlet in each piping system shall be checked to determine that the vacuum is present only at the inlets for the vacuum system being tested.

5.3.12.2.5.5 The vacuum piping system shall be relieved to atmospheric pressure.

5.3.12.2.5.6 The test gas for all positive-pressure gas piping systems shall be oil-free, dry Nitrogen NF.

5.3.12.2.5.7 Sources of test gas and vacuum shall be disconnected from all piping systems except for the one system being tested.

5.3.12.2.5.8 The positive-pressure gas system being tested shall be pressurized to a gauge pressure of 345 kPa (50 psi) with oil-free, dry Nitrogen NF.

5.3.12.2.5.9 Each individual system gas outlet and vacuum inlet in each installed piping system shall be checked to determine that the test gas is being dispensed only from the outlets in the piping system being tested.

5.3.12.2.5.10 The cross-connection test shall be repeated for each installed positive-pressure gas piping system.

5.3.12.2.5.11 The proper labeling and identification of system outlets/inlets shall be confirmed during these tests.

5.3.12.2.6 Initial Piping Purge Test. The outlets in each Level 3 positive-pressure gas piping system shall be purged to remove any particulate matter from the distribution piping.

5.3.12.2.6.1 The test gas shall be oil-free, dry Nitrogen NF.

5.3.12.2.6.2 Using appropriate adapters, each outlet shall be purged with an intermittent high-volume flow of test gas until the purge produces no discoloration in a clean white cloth.

5.3.12.2.6.3 The purging shall be started at the furthest outlet in the system and proceed towards the source equipment.

5.3.12.2.7 Initial Standing Pressure Test for Positive-Pressure Gas Piping. After successful completion of the initial pressure tests under 5.3.12.2.3, Level 3 positive-pressure gas distribution piping shall be subjected to a standing pressure test.

5.3.12.2.7.1 Tests shall be conducted after the installation of station outlet valve bodies and face plates, and other distribution system components (i.e., pressure alarm devices, pressure indicators, and line pressure relief valves).

5.3.12.2.7.2 The source valve shall be closed during this test.

5.3.12.2.7.3 The piping systems shall be subjected to a 24-hour standing pressure test using oil-free, dry Nitrogen NF.

5.3.12.2.7.4 Test pressures shall be 20 percent above the normal system operating line pressure.

5.3.12.2.7.5 At the conclusion of the tests, there shall be no change in the test pressure greater than a gauge pressure of 35 kPa (5 psi).

5.3.12.2.7.6 Leaks, if any, shall be located, repaired (if permitted), replaced (if required), and retested.

5.3.12.2.8 Initial Standing Vacuum Test for Vacuum Systems. Level 3 vacuum systems, with either plastic or copper piping, shall be subjected to a standing vacuum test.

5.3.12.2.8.1 The piping system shall be subjected to a vacuum of not less than 485 mm (19 in.) gauge HgV for 24 hours, using either the vacuum source equipment or a test source.

5.3.12.2.8.2 During the test, the source of test vacuum shall be disconnected from the piping system.

5.3.12.2.8.3 At the conclusion of the test, the vacuum shall not have reduced to less than 300 mm (12 in.) HgV.

5.3.12.2.8.4 Leaks, if any, shall be located, repaired (if permitted), replaced (if required), and retested.

5.3.12.3 System Verification.

5.3.12.3.1 General.

5.3.12.3.1.1 Verification tests shall be conducted on Level 3 medical gases (e.g., oxygen and nitrous oxide).

5.3.12.3.1.2 Verification tests shall be performed only after all tests required in 5.3.12.2, Initial Tests, have been completed on all positive-pressure and vacuum piping systems.

5.3.12.3.1.3 The test gas shall be oil-free, dry Nitrogen NF or the system gas where permitted.

5.3.12.3.1.4 Verification testing shall be conducted by a party technically competent and experienced in the field of medical gas and vacuum system verification and meeting the requirements of ASSE 6030, *Professional Qualifications Standard for Medical Gas Systems Verifiers*.

5.3.12.3.1.5 Verification testing shall be performed by a party other than the installing contractor.

5.3.12.3.1.6 All verification tests required under 5.3.12.3 shall be performed after installation of any manufactured assemblies supplied through flexible hose or tubing.

5.3.12.3.1.7 Where manufactured assemblies include multiple possible connection points for terminals, each possible position shall be tested independently.

5.3.12.3.1.8 For small projects affecting a limited number of areas where the use of nitrogen is impractical, the system gas shall be permitted to be used for the following tests:

(1) Standing pressure (5.3.12.3.2)
(2) Cross-connection (5.3.12.3.3)
(3) Warning system (5.3.12.3.4)
(4) Piping purge (5.3.12.3.5)
(5) Piping particulate (5.3.12.3.6)
(6) Piping purity (5.3.12.3.7)
(7) Operational pressure (5.3.12.3.9)

5.3.12.3.1.9 All verification test results shall be reported as required in 5.3.12.1.

5.3.12.3.2 Verifier Standing Pressure Test. Level 3 medical gas piping systems (i.e., oxygen and nitrous oxide) shall be subjected to a 10-minute standing pressure test at operating line pressure using the following procedures:

(1) After the system is filled with oil-free, dry Nitrogen NF or the system gas, the source valve and any zone valves shall be closed.
(2) The piping system downstream of the valves shall show no decrease in pressure after 10 minutes.
(3) Any leaks found shall be located, repaired (if permitted), replaced (if required), and retested.

5.3.12.3.3 Verifier Cross-Connection Test. After closing of walls and completion of the requirements of 5.3.12.2, Initial Tests, it shall be determined that no cross-connections exist between the Level 3 medical gas systems and any of the other positive-pressure and vacuum piping systems by use of the following method:

(1) Shut off the source of test gas for all positive-pressure gas piping systems and reduce systems to atmospheric pressure.
(2) Using oil-free, dry Nitrogen NF, or the system gas, pressurize one of the Level 3 medical gas piping systems to a gauge pressure of 345 kPa (50 psi).
(3) Test each positive-pressure gas outlet and Level 3 vacuum inlet using appropriate adapters to verify that the test gas pressure is present only at the outlets in the Level 3 medical gas piping system being tested.
(4) After it has been verified that a Level 3 medical gas piping system is free of cross-connections, disconnect the source of test gas and reduce the piping to atmospheric pressure.
(5) Proceed to test each Level 3 medical gas piping system until each is verified to be free of cross-connections.

5.3.12.3.4 Verifier Level 3 Warning System Tests.

5.3.12.3.4.1 All warning systems that are installed for Level 3 medical gases shall be verified to ensure that all components function correctly prior to placing the system into service.

5.3.12.3.4.2 Permanent records of these tests shall be maintained.

5.3.12.3.4.3 Warning systems that are part of an addition to an existing piping system shall be tested prior to connection of the new piping to the existing system.

5.3.12.3.4.4 Tests of warning systems for new installations shall be performed after the verifier's cross-connection testing (5.3.12.3.3), but before purging the piping (5.3.12.3.5) and performing the remaining verification tests (5.3.12.3.6 through 5.3.12.3.12).

5.3.12.3.4.5 Test gases shall be either oil-free, dry Nitrogen NF, or the gas of system designation.

5.3.12.3.4.6 The audible and noncancelable alarm signals in each single treatment facility shall be checked to verify that they are in a location that will be continuously attended while the facility is in operation.

5.3.12.3.4.7 The operation of the Level 3 line pressure alarms required by 5.3.9.1(4) shall be verified.

5.3.12.3.4.8 Audible and noncancelable visual signals in each single treatment facility shall indicate if the pressure in the Level 3 medical gas main line being monitored increases or decreases 20 percent from the normal operating pressure.

5.3.12.3.4.9 The operation of the Level 3 changeover alarms required by 5.3.9.1(5) shall be verified.

5.3.12.3.4.10 Audible and noncancelable visual signals shall indicate whenever automatic changeover occurs or is about to occur.

5.3.12.3.4.11 Where Level 3 medical gas systems include other alarm features that are not mandatory under 5.3.9, they shall be functionally tested in accordance with their intended purpose and the equipment manufacturer's recommendations.

5.3.12.3.5 Verifier Piping Purge Test. In order to remove any traces of particulate matter deposited in the pipelines as a result of construction, a heavy, intermittent purging of each Level 3 medical gas (i.e., oxygen and nitrous oxide) pipeline shall be done.

5.3.12.3.5.1 The appropriate adapter shall be obtained from the facility or manufacturer, and high purge rates of at least 230 SLPM (8 SCFM) shall be put on each outlet.

5.3.12.3.5.2 After the purge is started, it shall be rapidly interrupted several times until the purge produces no discoloration in a white cloth loosely held over the adapter during the purge.

5.3.12.3.5.3 In order to avoid possible damage to the outlet and its components, this test shall not be conducted using any implement other than the correct adapter.

5.3.12.3.6 Verifier Piping Particulate Test. The cleanliness of the piping in each Level 3 medical gas (i.e., oxygen and nitrous oxide) system shall be verified as follows:

(1) The test shall be performed using oil-free, dry Nitrogen NF or the system gas.
(2) A minimum of 1000 L (35 ft^3) of gas shall be filtered through a clean, white 0.45-micron filter at a minimum flow rate of 100 SLPM (3.5 SCFM).
(3) Each zone shall be tested at the outlet most remote from the source.
(4) The filter shall accrue no more than 0.001 g (1 mg) of matter from any outlet tested.

5.3.12.3.7 Verifier Piping Purity Test. For each Level 3 medical gas (i.e., oxygen and nitrous oxide) system, the purity of the piping system shall be verified as follows:

(1) These tests shall be performed with oil-free, dry Nitrogen NF or the system gas.
(2) The tests shall be for total hydrocarbons (as methane) and halogenated hydrocarbons, and compared with the source gas.
(3) This test shall be performed at the outlet most remote from the source.
(4) The difference between the two tests shall in no case exceed the following:
    (a) Total hydrocarbons, 1 ppm
    (b) Halogenated hydrocarbons, 2 ppm
(5) A test shall be conducted at the outlet most remote from the source and the moisture concentration shall not exceed 500 ppm or an equivalent pressure dew point of −12°C (10°F) at 345 kPa (50 psig).

5.3.12.3.8 Verifier Final Tie-In Test.

5.3.12.3.8.1 Prior to the connection of any new Level 3 medical gas piping to its source of supply, including extensions or additions to an existing piping system, the verification tests in 5.3.12.3.1 through 5.3.12.3.7 shall be successfully performed on the new work.

5.3.12.3.8.2 Each joint in the final connection between the new work and the existing system shall be leak-tested with the gas of system designation by means of soapy water or other means effective for use with oxygen.

5.3.12.3.8.3 For Level 3 medical gases, immediately after the final connection is made and leak-tested, the specific altered zone and components in the immediate zone or area that is downstream from the point or area of intrusion shall be purged per 5.3.12.3.5.

5.3.12.3.8.4 Before the new work is used for patient care, the following tests shall be performed for all Level 3 medical gas (i.e., oxygen and nitrous oxide) systems:

(1) Operational pressure (5.3.12.3.9)
(2) Gas concentration (5.3.12.3.10)

5.3.12.3.8.5 Permanent records of these tests shall be maintained in accordance with 5.3.13.7.1.

5.3.12.3.9 Verifier Operational Pressure Test. Operational pressure tests shall be performed at each station outlet in Level 3 medical gas piping systems (i.e., oxygen and nitrous oxide) where the user makes connections and disconnections.

5.3.12.3.9.1 Tests shall be performed using either oil-free, dry Nitrogen NF or the gas of system designation.

5.3.12.3.9.2 Medical gas outlets (i.e., oxygen and nitrous oxide) shall deliver 100 SLPM (3.5 SCFM) with a pressure drop of no more than 35 kPa (5 psi) and static pressure of 345 kPa to 380 kPa (50 psi to 55 psi).

5.3.12.3.10 Verifier Gas Concentration Test. After purging each Level 3 medical gas piping system with the gas of system designation, the following shall be performed:

(1) Each medical gas outlet (i.e., oxygen and nitrous oxide) shall be analyzed for concentration of gas, by volume.
(2) Analysis shall be conducted with instruments designed to measure the specific gas dispensed.
(3) Allowable concentrations shall be as follows:
 (a) Oxygen ≥ 99 percent oxygen
 (b)* Nitrous oxide ≥ 99 percent nitrous oxide

A.5.3.12.3.10(3)(b) The committee recognizes that current clinical practice is to use analyzers that might not be able to analyze oxygen to current U.S.P. requirements of 99 percent, and that these analyzers frequently have an error of up to 3 percent.

5.3.12.3.11 Labeling. The presence and correctness of labeling required by this standard for all Level 3 medical gas components (i.e., station outlets/inlets, shutoff valves, and alarm panels) shall be verified.

5.3.12.3.12 Source Equipment Verification.

5.3.12.3.12.1 General. Source equipment verification for Level 3 medical gases shall be performed following the installation of the interconnecting pipelines, accessories, and source equipment.

5.3.12.3.12.2 Use of Source Equipment for Pipeline Verification Tests. Where the source equipment and system gas is used for verification testing of the distribution piping, the source equipment shall be verified prior to verification of the distribution piping.

5.3.12.3.12.3 Source Equipment for Level 3 Medical Gases (Oxygen and Nitrous Oxide). The system apparatus shall be tested for proper function, including the changeover from primary to secondary supply (with its changeover signal), before the system is put into service.

5.3.12.4 Final Testing of Level 3 Systems for Gas-Powered Devices and Vacuum.

5.3.12.4.1 General.

5.3.12.4.1.1 Final testing of gas-powered device systems and vacuum systems shall be performed only after all tests required by 5.3.12.2, Initial Tests, have been performed.

5.3.12.4.1.2 The tests required by 5.3.12.4.2 through 5.3.12.4.8 shall be performed by one or more of the following:

(1) The installer
(2) A representative of the system supplier
(3) A representative of the system manufacturer
(4) A system verifier per 5.3.12.3.1.5

5.3.12.4.1.3 The test gas shall be oil-free, dry Nitrogen NF or the system gas where permitted.

5.3.12.4.2 Final Standing Pressure Test (Level 3 Gas-Powered Devices). Each gas-powered device piping system shall be subjected to a 10-minute standing pressure test at operating line pressure using the following procedures:

(1) After the system is filled with oil-free, dry Nitrogen NF or the system gas, the source valve and any zone valves shall be closed.

(2) The piping system downstream of the valves shall show no decrease in pressure after 10 minutes.
(3) Any leaks found shall be located, repaired (if permitted), replaced (if required), and retested.

5.3.12.4.3 Final Standing Vacuum Test (Level 3 Vacuum). Each Level 3 vacuum piping system shall be subjected to a 10-minute standing vacuum test at operating line vacuum using the following procedures:

(1) After the system has stabilized at the operating line vacuum, the source valve and any zone valves shall be closed.
(2) The piping system upstream of the valves shall show no decrease in vacuum after 10 minutes.
(3) Leaks, if any, shall be located, repaired (if permitted), replaced (if required), and retested.

5.3.12.4.4 Final Cross-Connection Test (Level 3 Gas-Powered Devices and Vacuum). After closing of walls and completion of the requirements of 5.3.12.2, Initial Tests, it shall be determined that no cross-connections exist between the piping systems for gas-powered devices and Level 3 vacuum using the following method:

(1) Where facilities have more than one gas or vacuum system, test each system separately.
(2) Shut off the source of test gas for all gas-powered device piping systems and reduce them to atmospheric pressure.
(3) Operate each Level 3 vacuum system at the normal system vacuum, using the source equipment.
(4) Each gas-powered device gas outlet and Level 3 vacuum inlet shall be tested with appropriate adapters to verify that vacuum is present only at the vacuum inlets in the system being tested and not at any gas-powered device gas outlets or inlets of other vacuum systems.
(5) Shut down the vacuum source equipment and slowly break the vacuum in the vacuum piping system, increasing its pressure to atmospheric.
(6) Test each Level 3 vacuum system until all are determined to be free of cross-connections.
(7) Using oil-free, dry Nitrogen NF or the system gas, pressurize the gas-powered device piping system to a gauge pressure of 345 kPa (50 psi).
(8) Test each gas-powered device gas outlet using appropriate adapters to verify that the test gas pressure is present only at the outlets in the gas-powered device system being tested.
(9) After it has been determined that a gas-powered device piping system is free of cross-connections, disconnect the source of test gas and reduce the piping to atmospheric pressure.
(10) Proceed to test each gas-powered device piping system until all are determined to be free of cross-connections.

5.3.12.4.5 Final Piping Purge Test (for Level 3 Gas-Powered Devices). In order to remove any traces of particulate matter deposited in the pipelines as a result of construction, a heavy, intermittent purging of each gas-powered device pipeline shall be done.

5.3.12.4.5.1 The appropriate adapter shall be obtained from the facility or manufacturer, and high purge rates shall be put on each outlet.

5.3.12.4.5.2 After the purge is started, it shall be rapidly interrupted several times until the purge produces no discoloration in a white cloth loosely held over the adapter during the purge.

5.3.12.4.5.3 In order to avoid possible damage to the outlet and its components, this test shall not be conducted using any implement other than the correct adapter.

5.3.12.4.6 Final Tie-In Test (Piping for Gas-Powered Devices and Level 3 Vacuum).

5.3.12.4.6.1 Prior to the connection of any new piping to its source of supply, including extensions or additions to an existing piping system, the final tests in 5.3.12.4.1 through 5.3.12.4.5 shall be successfully performed on the new work.

5.3.12.4.6.2 Each joint in the final connection between new work and an existing system shall be leak-tested with the gas of system designation or vacuum at the normal operating pressure by means of soapy water or other means effective for use with oxygen.

5.3.12.4.6.3 For gas-powered device piping, immediately after the final connection is made and leak-tested, the specific altered zone and components in the immediate zone or area that is downstream from the point or area of intrusion shall be purged per 5.3.12.4.5.

5.3.12.4.7 Labeling. The presence and correctness of labeling required by this standard for all Level 3 gas-powered device and vacuum system components (e.g., station outlets/inlets and shutoff valves) shall be checked.

5.3.12.4.8 Source Equipment Testing.

5.3.12.4.8.1 General. Source equipment checks for Level 3 gas-powered devices and Level 3 vacuum shall be performed following the installation of the interconnecting pipelines, accessories, and source equipment.

5.3.12.4.8.2 Use of Source Equipment for Pipeline Verification Tests. Where the source equipment and system gas or vacuum is used for final testing of the distribution piping, the source equipment shall be checked out and placed in operation prior to testing the distribution piping.

5.3.12.4.8.3 Level 3 Gas-Powered Devices Source Equipment. The source equipment for Level 3 gas-powered device system(s) shall be checked out and placed in operation according to the manufacturer's instructions.

5.3.12.4.8.4 Level 3 Vacuum Source Equipment. The source equipment for Level 3 vacuum systems shall be checked out and placed in operation according to the manufacturer's instructions.

5.3.13 Level 3 Operation and Management.

5.3.13.1 Special Precautions for Handling Oxygen Cylinders and Manifolds. Handling of oxygen cylinders and manifolds shall be based on CGA G-4, *Oxygen*.

5.3.13.1.1 Oxygen cylinders, containers, and associated equipment shall be protected from contact with oil or grease. Specific precautions shall include the following:

(1) Oil, grease, or readily flammable materials shall never be permitted to come in contact with oxygen cylinders, valves, regulators, gauges, or fittings.
(2) Regulators, fittings, or gauges shall never be lubricated with oil or any other flammable substance.
(3) Oxygen cylinders or apparatus shall never be handled with oily or greasy hands, gloves, or rags.

5.3.13.1.2 Equipment associated with oxygen shall be protected from contamination. Specific precautions shall include the following:

(1) Particles of dust and dirt shall be cleared from cylinder valve openings by slightly opening and closing the valve before applying any fitting to the cylinder.
(2) The high-pressure valve on the oxygen cylinder shall be opened before bringing the apparatus to the patient or the patient to the apparatus.

(3) An oxygen cylinder shall never be draped with any materials such as hospital gowns, masks, or caps.
(4) Cylinder-valve protection caps, where provided, shall be kept in place and be hand-tightened, except when cylinders are in use or connected for use.
(5) Valves shall be closed on all empty cylinders in storage.

5.3.13.1.3 Cylinders shall be protected from damage. Specific procedures shall include the following:

(1) Oxygen cylinders shall be protected from abnormal mechanical shock, which is liable to damage the cylinder, valve, or safety device.
(2) Oxygen cylinders shall not be stored near elevators, gangways, or in locations where heavy moving objects will strike them or fall on them.
(3) Cylinders shall be protected from the tampering of unauthorized individuals.
(4) Cylinders or cylinder valves shall not be repaired, painted, or altered.
(5) Safety relief devices in valves or cylinders shall never be tampered with.
(6) Valve outlets clogged with ice shall be thawed with warm — not boiling — water.
(7) A torch flame shall never be permitted under any circumstances to come in contact with cylinder valves or safety devices.
(8) Sparks and flame shall be kept away from cylinders.
(9) Even if they are considered to be empty, cylinders shall never be used as rollers, supports, or for any purpose other than that for which the supplier intended them.
(10) Large cylinders (exceeding size E) and containers larger than 45 kg (100 lb) weight shall be transported on a proper hand truck or cart complying with Chapter 9.
(11) Freestanding cylinders shall be properly chained or supported in a proper cylinder stand or cart.
(12) Cylinders shall not be supported by radiators, steam pipes, or heat ducts.

5.3.13.1.4 Cylinders and their contents shall be handled with care. Specific procedures shall include the following:

(1) Oxygen fittings, valves, regulators, or gauges shall never be used for any service other than that of oxygen.
(2) Gases of any type shall never be mixed in an oxygen cylinder or any other cylinder.
(3) Oxygen shall always be dispensed from a cylinder through a pressure regulator.
(4) The cylinder valve shall be opened slowly, with the face of the gauge on the regulator pointed away from all persons.
(5) Oxygen shall be referred to by its proper name, oxygen, not air, and liquid oxygen referred to by its proper name, not liquid air.
(6) Oxygen shall never be used as a substitute for compressed air.
(7) The markings stamped on cylinders shall not be tampered with because it is against federal statutes to change these markings without written authority from the Bureau of Explosives.
(8) Markings used for the identification of contents of cylinders shall not be defaced or removed, including decals, tags, stenciled marks, and the upper half of shipping tag.
(9) The owner of the cylinder shall be notified if any condition has occurred that might permit any foreign substance to enter a cylinder or valve, giving details and cylinder number.
(10) Neither cylinders nor containers shall be placed in proximity to radiators, steam pipes, heat ducts, or other sources of heat.
(11) Very cold cylinders or containers shall be handled with care to avoid injury.

5.3.13.1.5 Oxygen equipment that is defective shall not be used until one of the following has been performed:

(1) It has been repaired by competent in-house personnel.
(2) It has been repaired by the manufacturer or his or her authorized agent.
(3) It has been replaced.

5.3.13.1.6 Regulators that are in need of repair or cylinders having valves that do not operate properly shall never be used.

5.3.13.2 Special Precautions for Making Cylinder and Container Connections.

5.3.13.2.1 Wrenches and tools used to connect equipment shall be manufactured of material of adequate strength.

5.3.13.2.2 Cylinder valves shall be opened and connected in accordance with the following procedure:

(1) Make certain that apparatus and cylinder valve connections and cylinder wrenches are free of foreign materials.
(2) Turn the cylinder valve outlet away from personnel. Stand to the side — not in front and not in back. Before connecting the apparatus to cylinder valve, momentarily open cylinder valve to eliminate dust.
(3) Make connection of apparatus to cylinder valve. Tighten connection nut securely with a wrench.
(4) Release the low-pressure adjustment screw of the regulator completely.
(5) Slowly open cylinder valve to full open position.
(6) Slowly turn in the low-pressure adjustment screw on the regulator until the proper working pressure is obtained.
(7) Open the valve to the utilization apparatus.

5.3.13.2.3 Connections for containers shall be made in accordance with the container manufacturer's operating instructions.

5.3.13.3 Special Precautions for the Care of Safety Mechanisms.

5.3.13.3.1 Personnel using cylinders and containers and other equipment covered in this chapter shall be familiar with the Pin-Index Safety System *(see Chapter 9)* and the Diameter-Index Safety System *(see Chapter 9)*; both are designed to prevent utilization of the wrong gas.

5.3.13.3.2 Safety relief mechanisms, noninterchangeable connectors, and other safety features shall not be removed or altered.

5.3.13.4 Special Precautions — Storage of Cylinders and Containers.

5.3.13.4.1 Storage shall be planned so that cylinders can be used in the order in which they are received from the supplier.

5.3.13.4.2 If stored within the same enclosure, empty cylinders shall be segregated from full cylinders.

5.3.13.4.3 Empty cylinders shall be marked to avoid confusion and delay if a full cylinder is needed in a rapid manner.

5.3.13.4.4 Cylinders stored in the open shall be protected against the following conditions:

(1) Extremes of weather and from the ground beneath to prevent rusting
(2) Accumulations of ice or snow during winter
(3) Continuous exposure to direct rays of the sun in those localities where extreme temperatures prevail in summer

5.3.13.5 Special Precautions — Piped Patient Gas/Vacuum Systems.

5.3.13.5.1 Piping systems shall not be used for the distribution of flammable anesthetic gases.

5.3.13.5.2 Piping systems for gases shall not be used as a grounding electrode.

5.3.13.5.3 The vacuum system shall not be used for vacuum steam condensate return or other nonmedical applications.

5.3.13.5.4 Special Precautions.

5.3.13.5.4.1 Every facility shall establish a procedure for manually turning off the gas supply at the cylinder valves at the end of the work day, or when the facility is not in use.

5.3.13.5.4.2 No other method such as emergency shutoff valves or remote actuators (*see 5.3.4.1*) shall be used to turn off the gas supply.

5.3.13.6 Gas/Vacuum Systems Information and Warning Signs.

5.3.13.6.1 The gas content of medical gas piping systems shall be labeled according to 5.3.11.1.

5.3.13.7 Gas/Vacuum Systems Maintenance and Record Keeping.

5.3.13.7.1 Permanent records of all tests required by Section 5.3 shall be maintained in the organization's files.

5.3.13.7.2 A periodic testing procedure for nonflammable medical gas/vacuum and related alarm systems shall be implemented.

5.3.13.7.3 Whenever modifications are made or maintenance is performed that breaches the system, the tests specified in 5.3.12 shall be conducted on the downstream portions of the medical gas piping system.

5.3.13.7.4 A maintenance program shall be established for the following:

(1) Relief valves in accordance with applicable codes or manufacturer's recommendation
(2) The medical air compressor supply system in accordance with the manufacturer's recommendations
(3) The vacuum source and accessories in accordance with the manufacturer's recommendations
(4) Both the vacuum piping system and the secondary equipment attached to vacuum station inlets to ensure the continued good performance of the entire vacuum system
(5) The scavenger system to assure performance

5.3.13.7.5 Audible and visual alarm indicator(s) shall meet the following requirements:

(1) Be periodically tested to determine that they are functioning properly
(2) Have the records of the test maintained until the next test is performed

REFERENCES CITED IN COMMENTARY

1. CGA V-1/ANSI B57.1, *Standard for Compressed Gas Cylinder Valve Outlet and Inlet Connections,* 2003.
2. U.S. Food and Drug Administration, "Guidance to Hospitals, Nursing Homes and Other Health Care Facilities," U.S. Government Printing Office, Washington, DC, March 2000.
3. Title 49, Code of Federal Regulations, Parts 171–190, U.S. Department of Transportation (DOT) Regulations, "Specifications for Transportation of Explosives and Dangerous Articles," U.S. Government Printing Office, Washington, DC.

4. NFPA 55, *Standard for the Storage, Use, and Handling of Compressed Gases and Cryogenic Fluids in Portable and Stationary Containers, Cylinders, and Tanks,* 2005 edition.
5. NFPA *101®*, *Life Safety Code®*, 2006 edition.
6. ASME B31.3, *Pressure Process Piping,* 2002.
7. CGA M-1, *Guide for Medical Gas Installations at Consumer Sites,* 2003.
8. Title 29, Code of Federal Regulations, Part 1910.134(i)(1)(ii), Occupational Safety and Health Administration (OSHA), U.S. Government Printing Office, Washington, DC.
9. ASME *Boiler and Pressure Vessel Code,* 2001.
10. ANSI Z79.11, *Standard for Anesthetic Equipment-Scavenging Systems for Excess Anesthetic Gases,* 1982.
11. ASTM B 819, *Standard Specification for Seamless Copper Tube for Medical Gas Systems,* 2000.
12. ANSI/AWS A5.8, *Specification for Filler Metals for Brazing and Braze Welding,* 1992.
13. NFPA 70, *National Electrical Code®*, 2005 edition.
14. ANSI/ASSE 6010, *Professional Qualifications Standard for Medical Gas Systems Installers,* 2001.
15. ANSI/ASSE 6030, *Professional Qualifications Standard for Medical Gas Systems Verifiers,* 2001.

CHAPTER 6

Environmental Systems

Chapter 6 primarily covers ventilation in anesthetizing locations and laboratories. The laboratory air-conditioning systems it covers should be designed to conserve energy by recirculating the air. If a separate air-conditioning system serves the clinical laboratory, however, it might recirculate a reasonable percentage of the air removed instead of exhausting 100 percent to the outdoors. The system should be designed so it can be switched to 100 percent exhaust in the case of a large chemical spill or similar accident.

Most clinical laboratory tests are now done by machine processors using dry chemicals with reactions occurring in the solid phase. As a result, fewer solvents are used, and fewer hydrocarbon fuels are present. This technology has reduced the hazard level in laboratories, particularly the amount of products of combustion that would be released in a fire. This, in turn, reflects the amount of toxic air that would be subject to circulation.

In this commentary, *air conditioning* means conditioning the air by heating, cooling, or filtering.

6.1* Applicability

This chapter is applicable to health care facility laboratories and anesthetizing locations.

A.6.1 The application of requirements contained in this chapter for specific types of health care facilities can be found in Chapters 13 through 19.

6.2 Nature of Hazards

See B.4.2 and B.6.2.

6.3 Source

Air exhausted from laboratory areas shall not be recirculated to other parts of the facility.

6.4* Distribution

A.6.4 For additional distribution requirements, see NFPA 90A, *Standard for the Installation of Air-Conditioning and Ventilating Systems*, and NFPA 90B, *Standard for the Installation of Warm Air Heating and Air-Conditioning Systems*.

6.4.1 Ventilation — Anesthetizing Locations.

The anesthetizing locations referred to in 6.4.1 are only those using nonflammable inhalation anesthetics. (See Exhibit 6.1.) Ventilation requirements for flammable anesthetizing locations are found in Annex E.

EXHIBIT 6.1 An air handler unit for the anesthetizing location of a hospital. Note the duct-type smoke detector near the center of the photograph.

Subsection 6.4.1 addresses the management of smoke in anesthetizing locations, not smoke/fire control systems (fire protection). Fire protection measures are addressed in Chapters 4, 5, and 13, as well as in other documents such as NFPA *101*®, *Life Safety Code*® [1]. Activities such as surgery, the use of inhalation anesthetics, and the presence of an unconscious or immobile patient have added challenges to smoke management and fire response in anesthetizing locations. See also the commentary following 6.4.1.3.

6.4.1.1* The mechanical ventilation system supplying anesthetizing locations shall have the capability of controlling the relative humidity at a level of 35 percent or greater.

Maintaining a minimum level of humidity should be the major concern for nonflammable anesthetizing locations. Higher values of humidity can be used if desired.

A.6.4.1.1 Advantages claimed for humidity include avoidance of hypothermia in patients, especially during long operative procedures; the fact that floating particulate matter increases in conditions of low relative humidity; and the fact that the incidence of wound infections can be minimized following procedures performed in those operating rooms in which the relative humidity is maintained at the level of 50 to 55 percent.

6.4.1.2 Supply and exhaust systems for windowless anesthetizing locations shall be arranged to automatically vent smoke and products of combustion.

6.4.1.3 Ventilating systems for anesthetizing locations shall be provided that automatically (1) prevent recirculation of smoke originating within the surgical suite and (2) prevent the circulation of smoke entering the system intake, without in either case interfering with the exhaust function of the system.

Requirements for ventilation are now stated in 6.4.1.3 in terms of the desired performance rather than the particular type of damper or sensing mechanism to be used, in concert with the general move toward more performance-based codes and standards. See Chapter 5 of the 2002 edition of *NFPA 72®, National Fire Alarm Code®* [2], for types of detection for sensing smoke.

The stated performance criteria are applicable for most system configurations. However, there are situations, and system types such as a recirculating system, that could require a shutdown of the air-handling system for an anesthetizing location to avoid jeopardizing the safety of staff required to stay in the operating room during a fire. This procedure was necessary during a March 1989 fire in a Michigan hospital.

For this discussion, an anesthetizing location is a suite of operating rooms (ORs) that is part of a facility. It can occupy a portion of a floor or a whole floor. An OR's air-conditioning (AC) system is usually designed to be a separate and unique system for that suite. Properly maintained, the AC system, in turn, maintains a positive pressure in the entire suite with respect to other spaces adjacent to the suite on that floor. Within the OR suite, the AC system maintains individual operating rooms at a positive pressure to the spaces surrounding them.

Some AC systems are designed to provide 100 percent fresh air (i.e., none of the exhaust air is circulated back to the ORs). Other AC systems are designed to recirculate a large percentage of the exhaust air back into the ORs. If a fire occurs outside the OR suite, either of the two types of AC systems will keep smoke out of the OR suite. A more difficult situation arises when the fire is in the sterile core of the suite but still not in an operating room. In this situation, the noncirculating AC system will minimize the intrusion of smoke from the fire into the operating rooms themselves. AC systems designed to recirculate air can be designed to switch to 100 percent exhaust during this fire condition.

The most difficult fire condition is one in an individual OR. Design criteria require that the OR be positively pressurized with respect to all adjacent spaces. Unless the supply air to the involved OR is shut down, the smoke generated by the fire will most likely leak to adjacent spaces. If the supply air cannot be individually controlled for each OR, the entire supply air system might have to be shut down while the exhaust air system is kept running in order to keep the smoke from the fire inside the involved room from spreading into adjacent rooms.

◀ **FAQ**
What is the most difficult fire condition in an anesthetizing location?

Shutdown of the exhaust portion of an AC system or the entire AC system might be necessary to prevent smoke from being drawn into a particular room or rooms in an anesthetizing location [i.e., to comply with the first part of (2) in 6.4.1.3, "prevent the circulation of smoke entering the system intake," but not the criteria of "without . . . interfering with the exhaust function of the system"].

It should be noted that 6.4.1.3 does not mandate a completely separate smoke control system. That paragraph requires smoke management but leaves the method to the designers of such systems.

6.4.1.4 The electric supply to the ventilating system shall be served by the equipment system of the essential electrical system specified in Chapter 4, Electrical Systems.

6.4.1.5 Window-type temperature regulating units (air conditioners) are permitted to be installed in exterior windows or exterior walls of anesthetizing locations *(see also E.3.4 and E.3.5)*. Where such units are employed, the provisions of 6.4.1.1 shall be met.

6.4.1.6 Systems that capture or dispose of waste anesthetic gases, if installed, shall prevent their reentry into the facility. *(See 5.3.3.2 for further requirements on WAGD systems.)*

A variety of methods are permitted to be used for disposal of waste anesthetic gases to the outside of a facility, and the user is reminded about such requirements for alarm systems, ductwork, and labeling.

"Scavenging apparatus" (as they are commonly referred to) do not actually exhaust waste anesthetic gases to the outside of a facility. Instead, they collect and contain waste anesthetic gases as part of a waste anesthetic gas disposal (WAGD) system, which then exhausts the collected gases to the outside of the facility.

6.4.2 Ventilation — Laboratories.

General requirements for the design and construction of ventilation systems (ductwork and equipment) are covered in NFPA 90A, *Standard for the Installation of Air-Conditioning and Ventilating Systems* [3]. Requirements in 6.4.2 are specific for ventilation systems in laboratories.

At present, Chapter 6 does not address the preset or barometric damper or the subject of multiple fume hoods connected to a single exhaust.

Systems with multiple hoods on a single exhaust, with automatic, motorized dampers, or with both, should be monitored for proper ventilation at each hood immediately prior to its use. Hoods used more or less continuously can have an airflow indicator or a visual/audible alarm installed to warn operators and others in the area if the airflow drops below a safe level. Sensing equipment is now available that is not located in the exhaust stream and that provides an alarm. With the proper attention to details, this equipment can be properly maintained.

The use, inspection, and maintenance of ventilation systems in the laboratory should be coordinated among all areas involved. Whenever any cycling of fans or ventilation systems is instituted or energy management programs are employed, the impact of the positive/negative pressure differentials of laboratories and other sensitive areas needs to be accounted for in the system programming. Where pressure differentials are required, ventilation systems should be provided with overrides and imbalance alarms annunciated at an attended location. Direct measurement of pressure differential is seldom reliable, because the quality of general construction for most laboratories is simply not "tight" enough, or "leakproof" enough, to produce a reasonably measurable differential pressure between ventilation air supplied and exhausted. However, equipment is available to reliably measure and display the ventilation air quantities, supplied and exhausted, to demonstrate the correct "negativeness" (or "positiveness") of laboratory spaces.

6.4.2.1* Laboratories provided with mechanical ventilation throughout or employing fume hoods as a fixed part of the exhaust system shall have the air supply and exhaust balanced to provide a negative pressure with respect to surrounding hospital occupancies.

Exception: Laboratories for procedures requiring maximum protection against contamination and not involving infectious or noxious materials are permitted to be arranged for slight positive pressure when the safety of the arrangement is affirmed by a responsible laboratory official.

A.6.4.2.1 Prevalent practice when laboratories are provided with supply and exhaust ventilation is to design the fume hood exhaust as an integral part of the balanced ventilating system, so that the fume hood exhaust is in constant operation.

In general, the use of fume hoods for fixed parts of the exhaust system is a poor practice and should be avoided. For energy conservation, and if variable-volume fume hood exhaust controls are employed, the use of fume hoods as a fixed part of the ventilation system should also be avoided. Variable-volume control of the primary laboratory ventilating system to offset variable hood exhaust quantities, while simultaneously maintaining the required relative pressure between the laboratory and its adjacent areas, can introduce complexities that make controls difficult to set and maintain reliably. This is particularly true if pneumatic controls are used. Other means are available to maintain fume hood exhaust flows at variable, but desired, levels when hood sashes are moved. Electronic and direct digital control equipment is readily available to solve this problem.

6.4.2.2 Exit corridors shall not be used as plenums to supply or exhaust air from laboratory areas.

Paragraph 6.4.2.2 refers to exit access corridors. It does not apply to circulation corridors within the laboratory.

6.4.2.3* Exhaust systems for laboratory ventilation shall be arranged with motors and fans located at the discharge end of the systems, and with the exhaust air discharged above the roof in such a manner that it will not be drawn into any air intake or blown into windows.

A.6.4.2.3 The discharge side of fume hood exhaust fans is under positive pressure and often leaks toxic fumes into the surrounding environment; therefore, all fume hood exhaust fans should be installed outdoors, and not inside penthouses or other mechanical equipment enclosures that have to be frequented by maintenance and service personnel.

In essence, any location for discharge other than that described in 6.4.2.3 includes too many variables to reasonably ensure the safety of laboratory or other personnel (e.g., wind pressure on a side of a building would defeat side wall fans; erection of a new building adjacent to a laboratory could eliminate the clear area around the side of a building). Even with above-the-roof discharge, cases have been reported of exhaust fumes being drawn in through air intake ducts of nearby, higher buildings.

The annex information calls attention to the problem of the accumulation of fume hood exhausts from the discharge side of fume hood exhaust fans. Maintenance personnel, who may not be aware of the hazard, might ingest the toxic substances the fume hood removed from human contact in the first place.

6.4.3 Hood — Laboratories.

Other sources of information on fume hoods can be found in the 2004 edition of NFPA 45, *Standard on Fire Protection for Laboratories Using Chemicals* [4]; see Chapter 8, A.8.1 through A.8.13.5.1, G.1.2.3, and G.1.2.8 of NFPA 45.

Fume hoods are very susceptible to ventilation fluctuations that can lead to a range of hazards, depending on the process or activity taking place within the hood. The installation of hoods in areas of minimum traffic or air turbulence, the construction specifications for the hood and any associated utilities and shutoffs, warning signs and emergency directions and procedures, and periodic tests and inspections for performance need to be taken into account within the facility safety and/or hazard surveillance program. (See Exhibit 6.2.)

When hood operation involves hazardous or flammable materials, an alarm that is audible and visible should signal any lack of proper hood operation.

6.4.3.1* Fume hood and biological safety cabinet requirements shall comply with NFPA 45, *Standard on Fire Protection for Laboratories Using Chemicals.*

A.6.4.3.1 Biological safety cabinets (BSC) that are vented to the outside share some characteristics with chemical fume hoods. The interiors of each are at negative pressure with respect to the ambient environment. BSC are not intended to be used for protection from exothermic or potentially explosive chemical reactions. *[See HHS Publication No. (CDC) 93-8395, Biosafety in Microbiological and Biomedical Laboratories, for a description of BSC and their ventilating requirements.]*

For the reasons cited in A.6.4.3.1, the hazards of biological safety cabinets, such as the one shown in Exhibit 6.3, are included with those for fume hoods.

6.4.3.2 Fume hoods shall be located in areas of minimum air turbulence, away from doors and windows, and in a manner that will not impede access to egress.

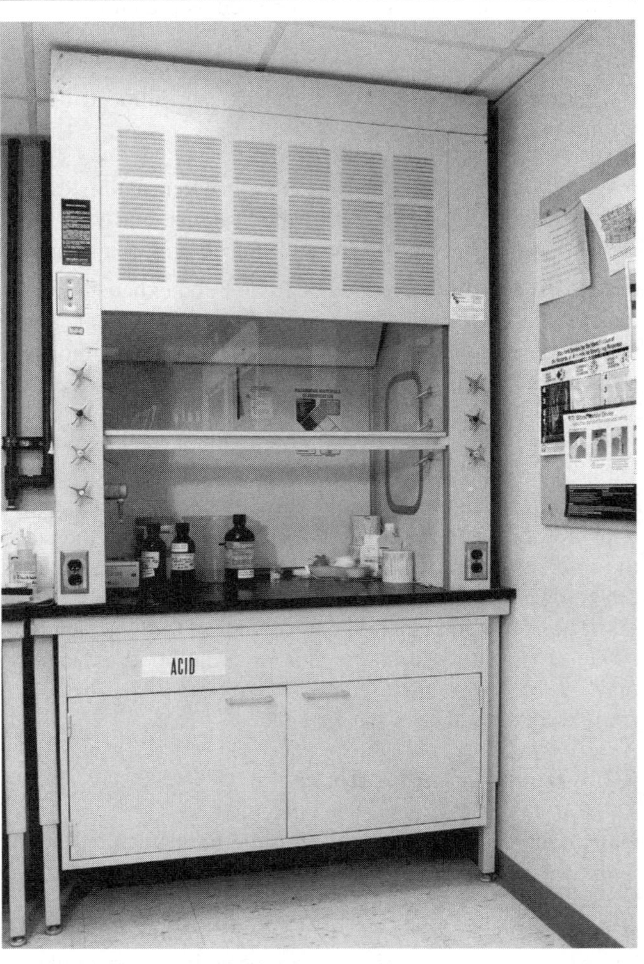

EXHIBIT 6.2 *Typical laboratory fume hood with the access window partially open.*

6.4.3.3* Fume hoods intended for use with radioactive isotopes shall be constructed of stainless steel or other material suitable for the particular exposure.

A.6.4.3.3 See NFPA 801, *Standard for Fire Protection for Facilities Handling Radioactive Materials*, for related information.

6.4.3.4 Fume Hood Ventilation.

6.4.3.4.1 Fume hood ventilating controls shall be so arranged that shutting off the ventilation of one fume hood will not reduce the exhaust capacity or create an imbalance between exhaust and supply for any other hood connected to the same system.

When fume hoods are shut off, their airflow reverses. This reversal is cause for concern about the air from the hood that is allowed to enter the room. The flow reversal from an individual hood with a fan that serves just that hood is not as serious a concern as the flow reversal that occurs when a fume hood is ganged with other fume hoods onto one fan. In this situation, when the fan is shut off, the contents of the exhaust from one hood can accidentally discharge into the laboratory space of another area through the fume hood located in that area.

Reliable sensors can detect this condition when the fume hood fan is turned on, but there are no sensors available to detect the condition when the fan is shut off. Serious thought

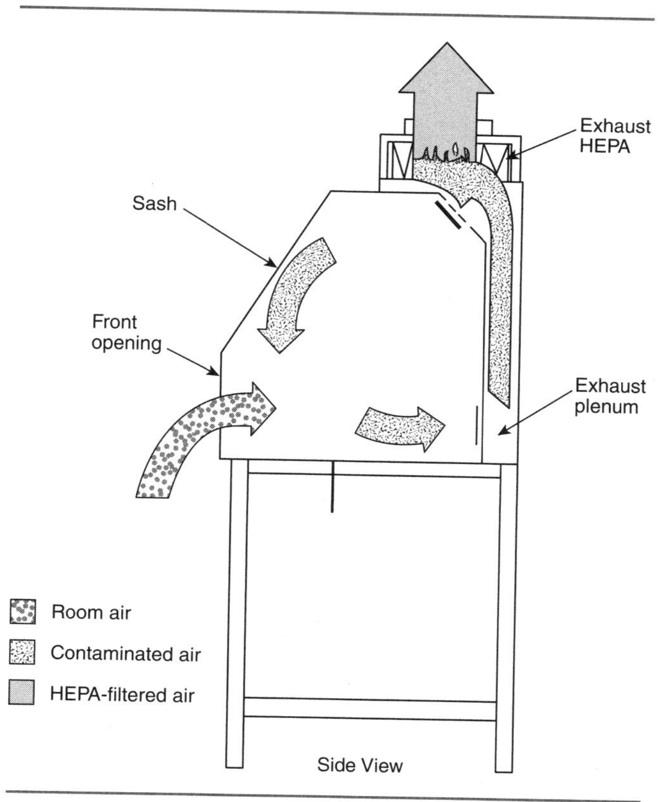

EXHIBIT 6.3 *Biological safety cabinet.*

should be given to the consequences of ganging fume hood exhausts together. In general, the practice of ganging fume hoods should be avoided.

6.4.3.4.2* The operation of fume hood ventilating controls shall be tested annually by a qualified person who shall certify the result of the test.

A.6.4.3.4.2 The qualified person can be a staff member of the facility. 

Fume hood ventilating controls today are complex and require an understanding of air movement to balance properly. Improper balance and operation of these controls can create hazardous fire conditions and endanger personnel. For example, inadequate exhaust can trap flammable gases and cause them to ignite in the presence of an ignition source such as a Bunsen burner, or it might create a back draft of toxic fumes. An annual check is a reasonable interval of time to ensure adequate operation and reveal any significant drifts in settings.

The stipulation that the person be "qualified" was considered necessary to ensure that only competent persons work on these systems. Because many health care facilities employ staff who are quite competent to inspect and test fume hood controls, 6.4.3.4.2 is intended to allow the utilization of these persons in lieu of contracting these services from an outside source.

6.4.3.5 Fume hoods shall be so designed that the face velocity ventilation is adequate to prevent the backflow of contaminants into the room, especially in the presence of cross drafts or the rapid movements of an operator working at the face of the hood.

6.4.3.6 Shutoff valves for services, including gas, air, vacuum, and electricity, shall be outside of the hood enclosure in a location where they will be readily accessible in the event of fire in the hood. The location of such shutoffs shall be legibly lettered in a related location on the exterior of the hood.

6.5 Performance Criteria and Testing (Reserved)

6.6 Administration

6.6.1 Anesthetizing Locations.

6.6.1.1 Ventilating and humidifying equipment for anesthetizing locations shall be kept in operable condition and be continually operating during surgical procedures *(see E.3.5).*

6.6.1.2 All gas storage locations or manifold enclosures shall be routinely inspected to ensure that the ventilation requirements stated in 5.1.3.3.3.1 are not obstructed.

6.6.2* Laboratories.

Warning signs describing the nature of any hazardous effluent content shall be posted at fume hoods' discharge points, access points, and filter locations.

A.6.6.2 Warning signs should include, or reference, information on hazards, and on the changing, handling, and disposal of filters.

REFERENCES CITED IN COMMENTARY

1. NFPA *101®*, *Life Safety Code®*, 2006 edition.
2. *NFPA 72®*, *National Fire Alarm Code®*, 2002 edition.
3. NFPA 90A, *Standard for the Installation of Air-Conditioning and Ventilating Systems,* 2006 edition.
4. NFPA 45, *Standard on Fire Protection for Laboratories Using Chemicals*, 2004 edition.

CHAPTER 7

Materials

This standard regulates materials because of past fires involving combustibles. Of most concern are those fires occurring inside operating rooms, because of the nature of the activities there and the limitations on the types of fire responses possible.

NFPA *101*®, *Life Safety Code*® [1], provides some criteria on furnishings, bedding, and decorations in health care facilities. Refer to 18.7.5 and 19.7.5 in the 2006 edition of that code and the commentary provided in the *Life Safety Code*® *Handbook* [2].

7.1* Applicability

This chapter is applicable to any health care facility using flammable and combustible materials.

A.7.1 The application of requirements contained in this chapter for specific types of health care facilities can be found in Chapters 13 through 19.

7.2 Nature of Hazards

7.2.1 Flammability. (Reserved)

7.2.2 Combustible Loading.

7.2.2.1 Flammable Agents. Facility administrative authorities, in consultation with the medical staff and others with training and expertise, shall determine the adequacy of storage space for disinfecting agents and medicaments and shall provide and enforce regulations for the storage and handling of containers of such agents. Said regulations also shall provide for the periodic inspection and maintenance of said storage locations.

This requirement is the beginning of an effort to address combustible loading in health care facilities. Developing guidance for this subject is difficult because the problem is not easy to identify or to quantify. The committees welcome any input from readers on this topic.

7.2.2.2 Flammable Materials.

Materials, such as surgical drapes, tracheal tubes, gauze sponges, and waste products, that can burn when exposed to ignition sources can be hazardous, especially in the presence of an oxygen-enriched atmosphere. (See Exhibit 7.1.)

EXHIBIT 7.1 A typical hospital supply closet containing many combustibles. (Courtesy of Rob Swift and Prince William Health System)

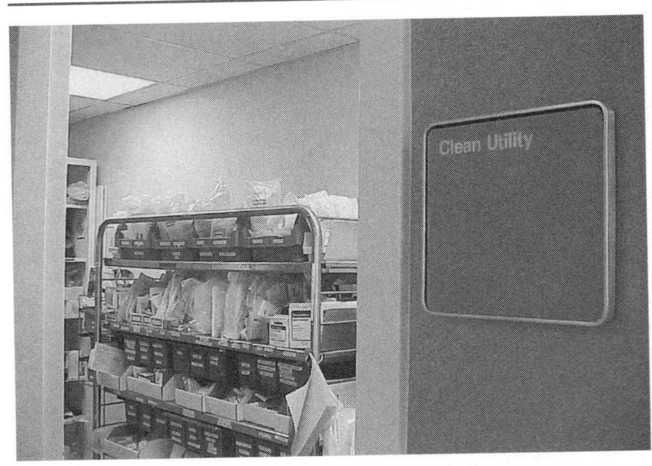

7.2.2.2.1 Flammable Hand Cleaning Materials.

7.2.2.2.1.1* Flammable liquids, gels, or other similar materials shall be limited to patient care rooms and other approved locations.

A.7.2.2.2.1.1 Hand cleaning dispensers or other flammable liquids should not be placed in corridors, means of egress, or other areas not located within the patient room. NFPA *101, Life Safety Code*, Chapter 18 and 19.7.5, prohibits combustible decorations and similar items from being in heath care occupancies.

7.2.2.2.1.2 The storage and handling of flammable liquids shall be in accordance with NFPA 30, *Flammable and Combustible Liquids Code.*

Paragraph 7.2.2.2.1.2 was added in this edition to address flammable hand cleaning materials, such as those shown in Exhibit 7.2, and where they can be used. NFPA *101, Life Safety Code* [1], and *NFPA 5000®, Building Construction and Safety Code®* [3], have greater detail on locations and limits in health care facilities.

NFPA 30, *Flammable and Combustible Liquids Code* [4], is a reference standard for the storage of hand cleaning materials.

Exhibit 7.2 Hand cleaning materials.

7.2.3 Toxicity of Products of Combustion.

See B.4.2.

7.2.4 Chemical Burns. (Reserved)

7.2.5 Safety. (Reserved)

7.2.6 Radioactivity. (Reserved)

7.3 Source (Reserved)

7.4 Distribution (Reserved)

7.5 Performance Criteria and Testing (Reserved)

7.6 Administration (Reserved)

REFERENCES CITED IN COMMENTARY

1. NFPA *101®*, *Life Safety Code®*, 2006 edition.
2. *Life Safety Code® Handbook,* 2006 edition.
3. *NFPA 5000®*, *Building Construction and Safety Code®*, 2006 edition.
4. NFPA 30, *Flammable and Combustible Liquids Code,* 2003 edition.

CHAPTER 8

Electrical Equipment

It has long been known that large electric currents through the body can be harmful, causing pain, involuntary muscle action, and death. Appropriate cautions and standards have been developed to reduce this hazard. However, the increasing application of technology to health care, at first in hospitals and now to many other health care facilities, has resulted in a great increase of electrical circuits and appliances closer and closer to the patient and into the patient's body. Smaller currents were seen to produce physiological effects and, in particular, when introduced into the heart at microampere levels, below a sensory stimulus, to cause cardiac malfunction and fatal fibrillation. It further came to be recognized that hospital patients are often less alert, can have less physical control than normal individuals, and can be at some level of sedation. They might therefore not be able to exercise the caution and self-protection that we assume normal individuals have and thus might require added protection.

An NFPA committee was established in the late 1960s to address this increased hazard and the subject of patient electrical safety. This resulted in a manual and later a standard that was incorporated as part of the present NFPA 99. Originally the electrical safety documents included considerations of power systems in hospitals as well as guidance for the manufacturer and the user of appliances. Since different audiences are concerned with the several facets of hazard reduction, the present NFPA 99 has split the total scope into three complementary parts: Chapter 4 addresses electrical power systems, Chapter 8 the use of appliances, and Chapter 10 manufacturer requirements.

Two other areas of concern in the early days were the use of electrical equipment in the flammable environment of an operating room and the use of electrical currents for surgery. These hazards have largely been reduced through changes in equipment and medical practice. However, the need for caution still remains, and advisory material is therefore appended to the present standard: Annex D for high-frequency equipment use and Annex E for flammable anesthetizing locations.

It must be remembered that safety is a system problem and that all the different aspects of electrical safety must be coordinated.

8.1* Applicability

This chapter is applicable to any health care facility as referenced in other chapters, and in consideration of the scope.

The scope of this chapter has been questioned many times because of its similarity to other NFPA and non-NFPA documents, particularly NFPA 70, *National Electrical Code®* [1]. In response, the NFPA Standards Council clarified the distinction between the two documents. NFPA 99 is responsible for the criteria for performance, maintenance, and testing of, among other things, the electrical systems and appliances peculiar to health care facilities, while NFPA 70 is responsible for construction and installation requirements based on such performance criteria.

The Standards Council chose to divide these responsibilities for two reasons. First, the division is a practical one. Electrical installation requirements are largely the same in all occupancies. Electrical inspectors, contractors, and so on, are familiar with the *National Electrical Code.* Although the *NEC* contains some special requirements peculiar to health care facilities, most requirements are similar to general provisions. A second compelling reason for this division of responsibilities is the problems that would exist in coordination and correlation if separate installation documents were developed for different occupancies. It has thus been a long-established policy that electrical installation requirements for all occupancies be contained in the *National Electrical Code.*

A.8.1 The application of requirements contained in this chapter for specific types of health care facilities can be found in Chapters 13, 14, 17, 18, 19, and 21.

This chapter originated from a concern about electrical safety in the hospital. It resulted in NFPA 76B-1980, *Safe Use of Electricity in Patient Care Areas of Hospitals* (incorporated into NFPA 99 in 1984).

This chapter states the basic electrical safety performance criteria for patient care areas to be followed by personnel. Chapter 10 provides performance criteria for manufacturers of appliances. Chapter 4 provides performance criteria for the installation implementation requirements contained in Article 517 of NFPA 70, *National Electrical Code*. The purpose of these chapters is the practical safeguarding of patients and staff from the hazards arising from the use of electricity in medical diagnosis and therapy.

The material in this annex, as it relates to electrical safety (see A.4.1 and A.8.1), interprets some of the basic criteria by presenting different methodologies and alternative procedures to achieve the level of safety defined by the criteria.

8.1.1 An appliance that yields erroneous data or functions poorly is potentially harmful. Quality and assurance of full appliance performance is not covered except as it relates to direct electrical or fire injury to patients or personnel.

8.1.2 Experimental or research apparatus built to order or under development shall be used under qualified supervision and shall have a degree of safety equivalent to that described herein or have a degree of safety that has been deemed acceptable by the facility.

8.2 Nature of Hazards

See B.5.2 for related electrical hazards.

Annex B contains informational material, not standard requirements. The reference here to B.5.2 is a guide to that information.

Training covering electrical hazards and safe practices should be conducted regularly to sensitize personnel to these problems. The training should occur during orientation and should be periodically reviewed thereafter.

8.2.1 Fire and Explosion.

See B.5.1.

8.2.2 Electrical Shock. Personnel shall be trained to recognize the shock hazards created by the use of defective or improperly used electrical equipment. See B.5.2.

8.2.3 Burns. See B.5.3.

8.2.4 Interruption of Power. (Reserved)

Even brief interruptions of power can cause some equipment to malfunction, particularly computer-based appliances such as physiological monitoring systems. Readers are referred to the Essential Electrical System requirements described in Sections 4.4, 4.5, and 4.6, which allow a switchover time of up to 10 seconds. If an appliance cannot tolerate even this brief interruption, special power provisions might be required.

Manufacturers are required to ensure that new patient-care-related appliances will not malfunction because of brief interruptions of power (see Chapter 10). Older equipment might not be designed to meet this criterion, and personnel should be aware of the potential hazards with these older appliances, particularly those with computer components. (See 10.2.6.5.)

8.2.5 RF Interference.

See B.5.5.

◀ **FAQ**
What are some sources of RFI and EMI?

Radio frequency interference (RFI) and *electromagnetic interference* (EMI) refer to the effects of electromagnetic radiation that comes from outside sources. This radiation can affect the proper operation of medical devices. Sources of RFI and EMI can be radio stations, portable telephones, electric power lines, electrical equipment, or even other medical devices. A related term, *electromagnetic compatibility* (EMC), denotes the ability of a device to function properly in the presence of disturbing electromagnetic fields while not acting to disturb other devices.

In the past, some cellular telephones, because of their operating characteristics, have been shown to activate the alarm signals of smoke detectors and to interfere with the operation of monitors and other medical equipment. This problem is still occasionally seen with some equipment. Facilities that experience these problems should contact the manufacturer of the suspect phones to learn how to mitigate the problem. Many institutions have prohibited the use of portable telephones in patient care areas.

The increasing proliferation of electrical devices in health care facilities, particularly devices with computer elements, along with their increasing sophistication (making them more susceptible to gross and subtle failures), demands heightened awareness of these potential hazards. Specific recommendations for ameliorating the problems of EMI and EMC are being studied by many agencies.

8.3 Electrical System

See Chapter 4, Electrical Systems.

8.4 Performance Criteria and Testing

8.4.1 Patient-Care-Related Electrical Appliances and Equipment.

Readers are reminded of the scope of NFPA 99 and that 8.4.1 *applies only to patient-care-related electrical appliances.* Exhibit 8.1, an emergency cart, is an example of a patient-care-related complex appliance. These carts are strategically placed throughout patient care areas in the event that a patient suddenly goes into cardiac arrest or fibrillation.

Special provisions for patient-care-related appliances used in flammable anesthetizing locations are in Annex E, which covers such locations. Although flammable anesthetics have essentially disappeared from medical practice in most countries, they could be used. The provisions of Annex E provide guidance to such an unlikely but possible event.

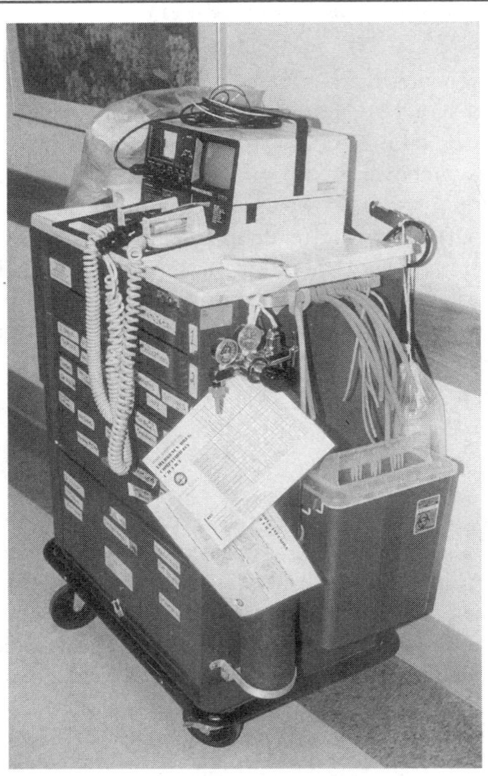

EXHIBIT 8.1 Typical emergency cart.

Requirements for low-voltage appliances can be found in 10.2.10. Installation requirements for such appliances can be found in NFPA 70, *National Electrical Code* [1].

8.4.1.1 Permanently Connected — Fixed Equipment. Patient-connected electric appliances shall be grounded to the equipment grounding bus in the distribution panel by an insulated grounding conductor run with the power conductors.

8.4.1.2 Cord- and Plug-Connected — Portable Equipment. All patient-care–related electrical equipment supplied by a flexible cord and plug, carrying 20 V or more, shall meet the requirements of 8.4.1.2.

8.4.1.2.1 Grounding of Appliances.

8.4.1.2.1.1 All cord-connected electrically powered appliances that are not double insulated and are used in the patient care vicinity shall be provided with a three-wire power cord and a three-pin grounding-type plug.

8.4.1.2.1.2 Double-insulated appliances shall be permitted to have two conductor cords.

FAQ ▶
What are the advantages of double-insulated appliances?

Double-insulated appliances are not merely appliances with nonconductive coating around a metal chassis. Double insulation involves deliberate design actions to prevent non-current-carrying conductive components from becoming energized and accessible to contact by persons using the appliance. One type of double-insulated appliance has normal insulation plus a second layer of insulation in case the normal one fails or is breached. Another type uses a single insulation that is much heavier than normal and is combined with other protective measures. Whatever method is used, appliances qualifying as double insulated require special testing or examination by qualified personnel. (See also the commentary following A.3.3.36 in Chapter 3.)

The problem of electromagnetic interference should be considered in relation to sensitive equipment that may be double insulated, because the double insulation might exacerbate possible EMC grounding problems.

8.4.1.2.2 Attachment Plugs. Attachment plugs installed by the facility shall meet the requirements of 10.2.2.1.

Paragraph 8.4.1.2.2 refers specifically to components made by the facility. They must have the same safety features as an attachment plug made by a manufacturer. Paragraph 8.4.1.2.3 makes the same requirement for power cords.

8.4.1.2.3 Power Cords. Power cords installed by the facility shall meet the requirements of 10.2.2.2.

Facilities should be aware that replacing, lengthening, or shortening a power cord supplied by the manufacturer could affect the appliance's warranty and any listing.

8.4.1.2.4 Line Voltage Equipment — Anesthetizing Locations. Flexible cord for portable lamps or portable electric appliances operating at more than 12 V between conductors, intended for use in anesthetizing locations, shall meet all of the following requirements:

(1) Cords shall be continuous.
(2) Cords shall be without switches from the appliance to the attachment plug.

The phrases *continuous* and *without switches from the appliance to the attachment plug* in 8.4.1.2.4(1) and 8.4.1.2.4(2) mean that extension cords are not permitted in any type of anesthetizing location (flammable or nonflammable). The following are reasons for the prohibition in all anesthetizing locations:

1. The possibility of damage to the cord connector from lying on the floor
2. The possibility of short circuits resulting from spilled liquids often found in operating rooms
3. The unreliability inherent in the introduction of additional connectors into a circuit
4. The probability of using a cord or connectors of inadequate ampacity
5. The probability of incorrect polarization
6. The probability of the introduction of increased grounding wire resistance

(3) Cords shall be of a type designated for extra-hard usage in accordance with NFPA 70, *National Electrical Code*.

(4) Cords shall be protected at the entrance to equipment by an insulating grommet.
(5) Cords shall be of sufficient length to reach any position in which the portable device is to be used.
(6) The attachment plug shall be inserted only in a fixed approved receptacle.
(7) Adapters shall be used and maintained in accordance with 8.5.2.1.7.

Permission is given in 8.4.1.2.4(7) to use adapters only in unusual circumstances. Regular use of adapters is not intended, as seen in 8.4.1.2.4.1 and 8.4.1.2.4.2. (See 8.5.2.1.7 for further requirements for adapter use in unusual circumstances.)

8.4.1.2.4.1 Foot-treadle–operated controllers shall be permitted in any anesthetizing location if appended to portable electric appliances in an approved manner. Foot-treadle–operated controllers and their connector shall be splashproof.

8.4.1.2.4.2 Two or more power receptacles supplied by a flexible cord shall be permitted to be used to supply power to plug-connected components of a movable equipment assembly that is rack-, table-, or pedestal-mounted, provided all of the following conditions are met:

(1) The receptacles are an integral part of the equipment assembly, permanently attached.
(2)* The sum of the ampacity of all appliances connected to the receptacles shall not exceed 75 percent of the ampacity of the flexible cord supplying the receptacles.

A.8.4.1.2.4.2(2) Whole-body hyperthermia/hypothermia units should be powered from a separate branch circuit.

(3) The ampacity of the flexible cord shall be in accordance with NFPA 70, *National Electrical Code*.
(4)* The electrical and mechanical integrity of the assembly shall be regularly verified and documented through an ongoing maintenance program.

A.8.4.1.2.4.2(4) See Chapter 4 for criteria of receptacles.

8.4.1.2.4.3 Overhead power receptacles shall be permitted to be supplied by a flexible cord with strain relief (ceiling drop) that is connected at a ceiling-mounted junction box in either of the following ways:

(1) Permanently
(2)* Utilizing a locking-type attachment plug cap and receptacle combination, or other method of retention

A.8.4.1.2.4.3(2) The disconnection means is permitted only to facilitate replacement; as such, ceiling drop cords can not be disconnected for alternative usage. See Chapter 4 for criteria of receptacles.

Overhead receptacles are one method of decreasing the number of electrical cords on the floor. Exhibit 8.2 is an example of an overhead receptacle. Note that the receptacles and plugs are of the twist-lock type because plugs hang vertically down, supporting the weight of the cord from the receptacle. Electrical cords on floors are subject to more abuse than those plugged into an overhead receptacle.

The requirement for a locking-type receptacle applies only at the ceiling-mounted junction box. The receptacles at the bottom of a drop cord can be normal straight blade types.

8.4.1.2.5 Adapters and Extension Cords. Adapters and extension cords shall meet the following requirements:

(1) Attachment plugs shall meet the requirements of 10.2.2.1.
(2)* Power cords shall meet the requirements of 10.2.2.2.

A.8.4.1.2.5(2) For policy on the use of extension cords, see 8.5.2.1.7.1.

Requirements for adapters are given in 8.5.2.1.7.

8.4.1.3 Testing Requirements — Fixed and Portable.

8.4.1.3.1 Physical Integrity. The physical integrity of the power cord assembly composed of the power cord, attachment plug, and cord-strain relief shall be confirmed by visual inspection or other applicable tests.

FAQ ▶ Why is a visual examination of the equipment important?

Verification of the physical integrity of the power cord, its conductors and insulation, and the power plug, as required in 8.4.1.3.1, and with particular attention to the condition of the grounding means, can prevent the possible introduction or utilization of an unsafe appliance

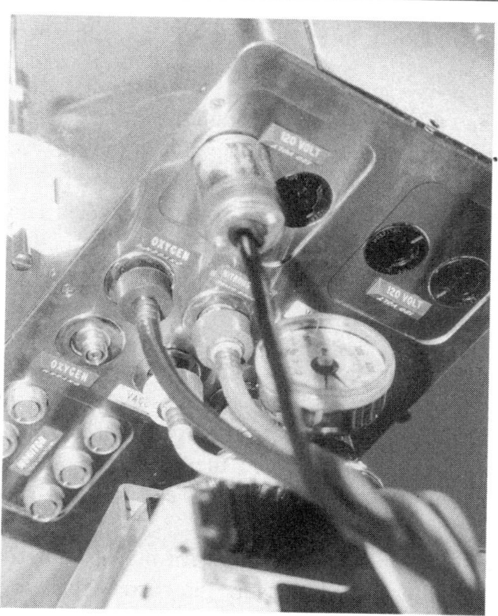

EXHIBIT 8.2 An overhead station that contains a vacuum outlet and electrical receptacles.

in the clinical area. A visual inspection before an appliance is used can often identify physical deteriorations.

8.4.1.3.2* Resistance. For appliances that are used in the patient care vicinity the resistance between the appliance chassis, or any exposed conductive surface of the appliance, and the ground pin of the attachment plug shall be less than 0.50 ohm under the following conditions:

(1) The cord shall be flexed at its connection to the attachment plug or connector.
(2) The cord shall be flexed at its connection to the strain relief on the chassis during the resistance measurement.

Exception: The requirement shall not apply to escutcheons or nameplates, small screws, and so forth, that are unlikely to become energized.

For appliances that use a battery charger, the measurement required in 8.4.1.3.2 should be made to the ground pin of the charger with the battery charger disconnected from the power supply. The maximum resistance allowed for an appliance used within a patient care area of a facility has been the subject of some debate. The value required of manufacturers has long been accepted as 0.15 ohm, based on the total resistance of 4.6 m (15 ft) of 18 AWG wire, the contact resistance at connectors, and a safety factor. The maximum value in testing at the health care facility is 0.50 ohm.

Reasons for the difference in requirements include the following:

◀ **FAQ**
Why is the maximum resistance allowed for appliances in anesthesia units more lenient than for manufacturers?

1. Health care facilities might not have measurement capabilities at the level of 0.15 ohm.
2. The appliance might have been subjected to some deterioration through use.
3. The value of 0.5 ohm is still within a safe limit.

A manufacturer's measurement above 0.15 ohm might indicate a fault in its quality control.

Although one measurement or a series of measurements below 0.50 ohm are acceptable, readings that increase each time measurements are made are a telltale sign of deterioration that could indicate incipient problems or failure. It should be remembered that power cords and connections could be subject to severe abuse.

A.8.4.1.3.2 There are several methods for measuring ground-wire resistance accurately. Three examples are described as follows and shown in Figure A.8.4.1.3.2(a) through Figure A.8.4.1.3.2(c):

(1) *Two-Wire Resistance Technique.* A known current is fed through the unknown resistance. A high-input-impedance voltmeter measures the voltage drop across the resistance and R is calculated as V/I. This technique measures the lead resistance in series with the unknown resistance. When the unknown resistance is a ground wire (less than 0.15 ohm), the lead resistance is appreciable. This is accounted for by shorting the lead wires together and "zeroing" the voltmeter. The actual resistance in effect subtracts out the lead wire resistance. In order for this technique to be reasonably accurate for measuring ground wires, an active high-impedance millivoltmeter has to be used.
(2) *Four-Wire Resistance Technique.* This technique is very similar to the two-wire resistance technique. The difference is that the known current is fed to the resistance to be measured through a pair of leads separate from the pair of leads to the voltmeter. The voltmeter is measuring the true voltage across the resistance to be measured regardless of the resistance of the measuring leads. This method eliminates the need for zeroing out the measuring lead resistance.
(3) *AC Current Method.* This technique utilizes a step-down transformer of known voltage output to feed current through the ground wire and measure the current that flows. The impedance of the ground wire is then calculated by Ohm's Law.

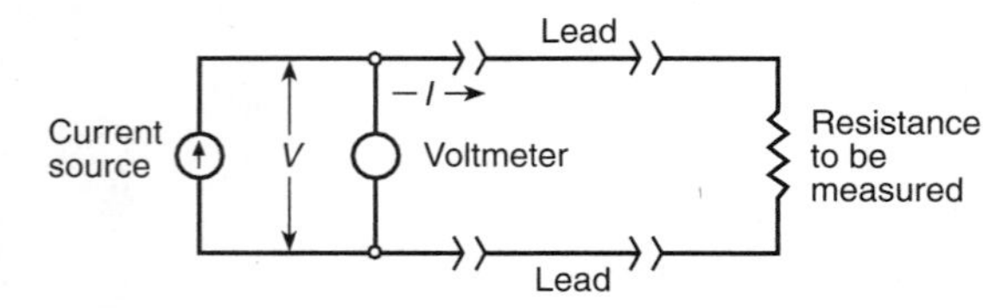

FIGURE A.8.4.1.3.2(a) *Two-Wire Resistance Technique.*

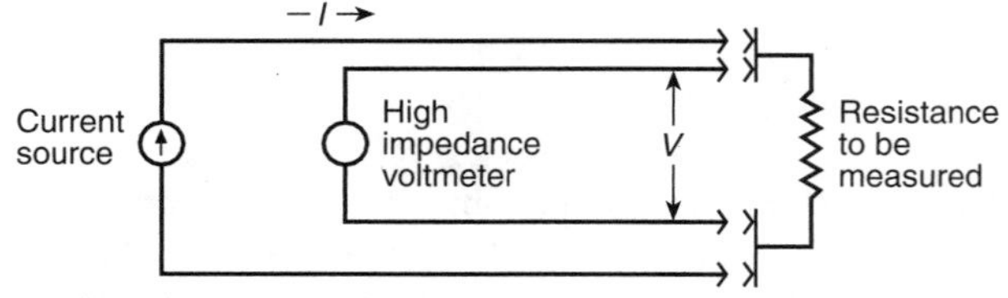

FIGURE A.8.4.1.3.2(b) *Four-Wire Resistance Technique.*

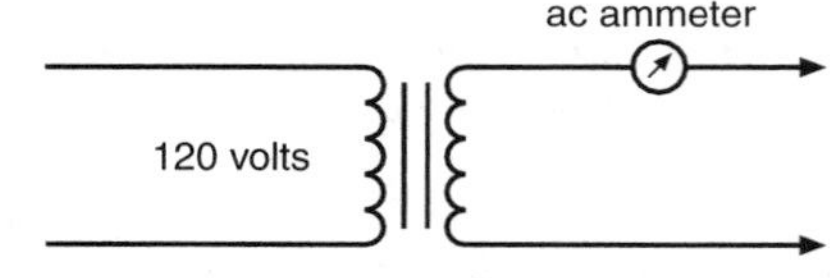

FIGURE A.8.4.1.3.2(c) *AC Current Method.*

Note that the internal impedance of the measuring circuit has to be established with the test leads shorted. This value needs to be subtracted from the test measurement.

8.4.1.3.3* Leakage Current Tests — General. The requirements in 8.4.1.3.3.1 through 8.4.1.3.3.4 shall apply to all tests. Power switch position shall be in accordance with Table 8.4.1.3.3.

The test equipment requirements outlined in 8.4.1.3.3 are intended to improve the equipment's ability to account for frequency weighting with low impedance sources. Paragraph A.8.4.1.3.3 explains how frequency weighting is achieved. The network shown in Figure A.8.4.1.3.3 is consistent with international documents on the subject.

The cited frequency range for testing is dc because direct current is the intended lower frequency limit.

TABLE 8.4.1.3.3 Leakage Current Tests — Power Switch Setting

Paragraph Number	Power Switch Setting	
	On and Off	On
8.4.1.3.4	X	
8.4.1.3.5	X	
8.4.1.3.6.1		X
8.4.1.3.6.2		X
8.4.1.3.6.3	X	
8.4.1.3.6.4		X
8.4.1.3.6.5		X

A.8.4.1.3.3 For complex leakage current waveforms, a single reading from an appropriate metering system can represent the physiologically effective value of the composite waveform, provided that the contribution of each component to the total reading is weighted in accordance with 8.4.1.3.3 or 10.2.13.3.

A

This "weighting" can be achieved by a frequency response–shaping network that precedes a flat-response meter, or by a meter whose own frequency response characteristic matches 8.4.1.3.3 or 10.2.13.3.

If the required performance is obtained by a meter with integral response shaping properties, then that meter should have a constant input resistance of 1000 ohms. (A high-input-impedance meter can be used by shunting a 1000-ohm resistor across the meter's input terminals.)

If, however, the required frequency response is obtained by a network that precedes an otherwise flat-response meter, then the input impedance of the network should be 1000 ohms ± 10 percent, over the frequency range from 0 to 1 MHz, and the frequency response of the network–meter combination should be substantially independent of the impedance of the signal source.

For maximum chassis leakage current allowed (i.e., 300 μA) below 1 kHz, this network will yield the limiting current of 10 mA above 30 kHz.

A suggested input network is shown in Figure A.8.4.1.3.3.

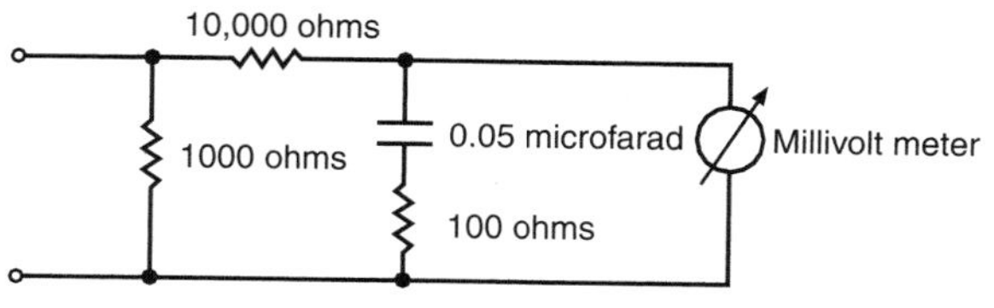

***FIGURE A.8.4.1.3.3** Leakage Current Measurements (1.0 millivolt meter reading corresponds to input current of 1.0 microampere).*

The suggested network in Figure A.8.1.4.3.3 approximates a proportional response up to 100 kHz. However, it is cautioned that the use of this network–meter combination was originally designed for an approximate proportional response up to 100 kHz when the chassis leakage limit was 100 μA, and now must conform to a maximum leakage current limit of 10 mA in accordance with 8.4.1.3.3.3. With the present chassis limit of 300 μA, this network–meter circuit is useable only to 30 kHz where it meets the 10 mA limitation. The 10 mA limitation addresses thermal safety, not shock hazard.

The following sequence of leakage testing is the same as that detailed for manufacturers in the commentary to A.10.2.13.3.

1. Chassis
   a. Permanently wired
   b. Cord-connected
2. Patient leads
   a. Lead to ground (nonisolated input)
   b. Lead to ground (isolated input)
   c. Isolated test (isolated input)
   d. Between leads (nonisolated input)
   e. Between leads (isolated input)

For further information, see A.10.2.13.4.3.

8.4.1.3.3.1 Resistance Test. The resistance tests of 8.4.1.3.2 shall be conducted before undertaking any leakage current measurements.

Before conducting the resistance test required in 8.4.1.3.3.1, it is important to first verify that the appliance is properly grounded, because operator safety and test results could otherwise be affected. Exhibit 8.3 is an example of an electrical safety tester that measures, among other things, leakage current of devices, wiring polarity, grounding resistance, and receptacle integrity.

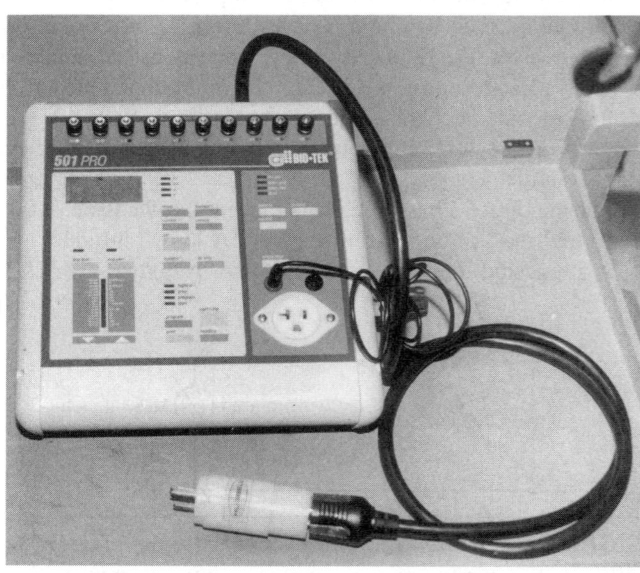

EXHIBIT 8.3 *A portable electric safety tester.*

8.4.1.3.3.2* Techniques of Measurement. Test shall not be made on the load side of an isolated power system or isolation transformer.

Leakage tests are to be made at the nominal voltage of the appliance.

A.8.4.1.3.3.2 This test is not valid when performed on the load side of an isolation transformer or an isolated power system because the values obtained will be falsely low.

8.4.1.3.3.3* Frequency of Leakage Current. The leakage current limits stated in 8.4.1.3.4, 8.4.1.3.5, and 8.4.1.3.6 shall be rms values for sinusoidal waveforms up to 1 kHz. For frequencies above 1 kHz, the leakage current limits shall be the values given in 8.4.1.3.4, 8.4.1.3.5, and 8.4.1.3.6 multiplied by the frequency, in kHz, up to a maximum of 10 mA.

A.8.4.1.3.3.3 The limits for nonsinusoidal periodic, modulated, and transient waveforms remain to be determined.

For complex leakage-current waveforms, a single reading from an appropriate metering system can represent the physiologically effective value of the composite waveform, provided that the contribution of each component to the total reading is weighted in accordance with 8.4.1.3.3.3. This weighting can be achieved by a frequency response–shaping network that precedes a flat-response meter, or by a meter whose own frequency-response characteristic matches 8.4.1.3.3.3.

8.4.1.3.3.4 Leakage Current in Relation to Polarity. Leakage current measurements shall be made as follows:

(1) With the polarity of the power line normal
(2) With the power switch of the appliance in the position shown in Table 8.4.1.3.3
(3) With all operating controls in the position to cause maximum leakage current readings

Leakage current must be measured using power that is supplied directly from the normal electrical distribution system, not from power supplied from an isolation transformer. Otherwise, incorrect values would result because neither power conductor would then be tied to ground.

8.4.1.3.4 Chassis Leakage Current — Fixed Equipment.

FAQ
Why are the tests conducted after installation different from those conducted during installation?

After installation, it might not be easy to disconnect ground(s) or temporarily insulate an appliance from ground. It is also very unlikely that the grounding will be disturbed after being permanently wired. Permanently wired appliances can thus be considered a part of the building's wiring system after installation. For this reason, the tests conducted after installation are different from those conducted during installation. (See 8.5.2.1.4.)

8.4.1.3.4.1 Permanently wired appliances in the patient care vicinity shall be tested prior to installation while the equipment is temporarily insulated from ground.

8.4.1.3.4.2 The leakage current from frame to ground of permanently wired appliances installed in general or critical patient care areas shall not exceed 5.0 mA with all grounds lifted.

8.4.1.3.5 Chassis Leakage Current — Portable Equipment.

8.4.1.3.5.1* Leakage Current Limits. The leakage current for cord-connected appliances shall not exceed 300 μA.

A.8.4.1.3.5.1 Where existing equipment exceeds 500 μA, methods to reduce leakage current, such as the addition of small isolation transformers to that device, or methods that provide equivalent safety by adding redundant equipment ground are permissible.

8.4.1.3.5.2 Chassis leakage current between 300 μA and 500 μA shall be permitted on existing or special equipment (such as mobile X-ray machines) under the following conditions:

(1) The grounding conductor is intact.
(2) A documented maintenance schedule is established to ensure the integrity of the grounding connection. The health care facility shall be permitted to establish a protocol with shortened or lengthened time intervals, depending on the intensity of the use of the appliance and prior test data.

8.4.1.3.5.3 If multiple devices are connected together and one power cord supplies power, the leakage current shall be measured as an assembly.

8.4.1.3.5.4 When multiple devices are connected together and more than one power cord supplies power, the devices shall be separated into groups according to their power supply cord and the leakage current shall be measured independently for each group as an assembly.

8.4.1.3.5.5 Chassis Leakage Test Procedure. Measurements shall be made using the circuit, as illustrated in Figure 8.4.1.3.5.5, with the appliance ground broken in two modes of appliance operation as follows:

(1) Power plug connected normally with the appliance on
(2) Power plug connected normally with the appliance off (if equipped with an on/off switch)

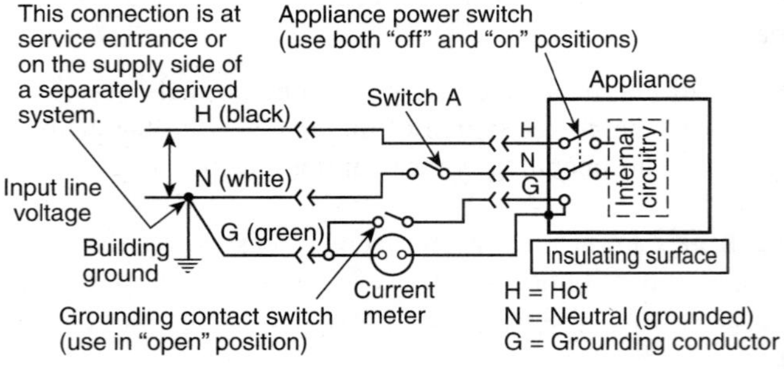

FIGURE 8.4.1.3.5.5 Test Circuit for Measuring Chassis Leakage Current.

(A) If the appliance has fixed redundant grounding (e.g., permanently fastened to the grounding system), the chassis leakage current test shall be conducted with the redundant grounding intact.

It may seem unproductive to measure the leakage current with the redundant ground intact, because redundant grounding presents a dead short across the meter input, causing the measured leakage current to read zero. However, the leakage current measurement should still be made to verify that the redundant grounding is indeed in place. Because redundant grounding is used only in potentially hazardous circumstances, it is worthwhile to check its presence.

The polarity reversal test is not required for users. Manufacturers are required to test appliances in both normal and reversed polarity modes. Because the probability of a problem occurring after testing by the manufacturer, when the end user receives an appliance, is perceived to be low, the testing requirement for the end user is relaxed.

(B) Test shall be made with Switch A in Figure 8.4.1.3.5.5 closed.

8.4.1.3.5.6 If there is no exposed conductive surface, measurement shall be made with a simulated surface, as described in 10.2.13.4.2, that is also temporarily grounded.

The simulated ground surface approximates placing a hand or a metal object on the appliance. The test serves as a check that the assumed insulation is actually functioning properly.

Note that this is a new requirement in this edition of the standard.

8.4.1.3.6 Lead Leakage Current Tests and Limits — Portable Equipment.

See 8.4.1.3.3 for general requirements governing the conducting of leakage current tests.

8.4.1.3.6.1* Lead to Ground — Nonisolated Input. The leakage current between all patient leads connected together and ground shall be measured with the power plug connected normally and the device on. An acceptable test configuration shall be as illustrated in Figure 8.4.1.3.6.1. The leakage current shall not exceed 100 μA for ground wire open and closed.

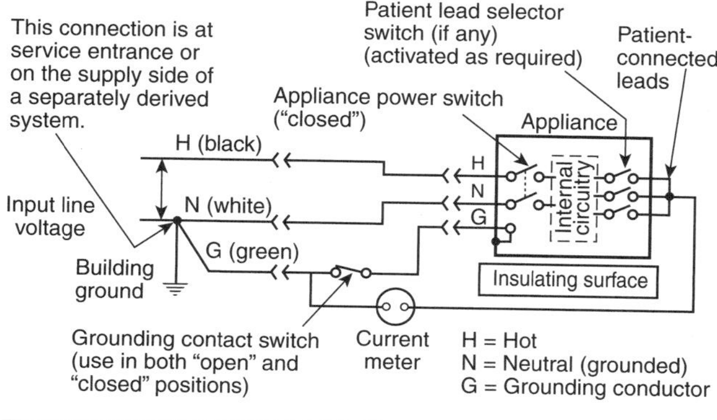

FIGURE 8.4.1.3.6.1 Test Circuit for Measuring Leakage Current Between Patient Leads and Ground — Nonisolated.

A.8.4.1.3.6.1 Although the chassis leakage current value is 300 μA, patient lead leakage current limit for non-isolated input has been intentionally limited to 100 μA. This decision is in recognition of the need for a greater level of electrical safety for those portions of devices that make direct electrical patient connection.

Paragraph A.8.4.1.3.6.1 clarifies questions on the apparent inconsistency between chassis leakage current limit and lead leakage limit values for nonisolated inputs.

8.4.1.3.6.2 Lead to Ground — Isolated Input. The leakage current between each patient lead and ground for an appliance with isolated leads shall be measured with the power plug connected normally and the device on. An acceptable test configuration shall be as illustrated in Figure 8.4.1.3.6.2. The leakage current shall not exceed 10 μA with the ground intact and 50 μA with the ground open.

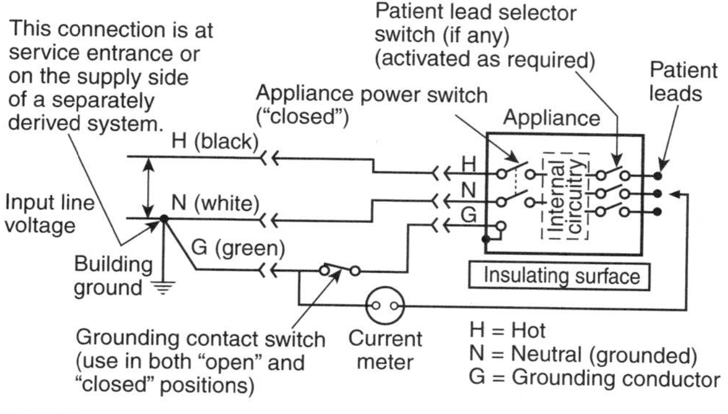

FIGURE 8.4.1.3.6.2 Test Circuit for Measuring Leakage Current Between Patient Leads and Ground — Isolated.

The limit for the lead leakage current in 8.1.4.3.6.2 was changed from 10 μA under all conditions to 50 μA with the ground open to be consistent with the International Electrotechnical Commission Standard IEC 60601-1, *Medical Electrical Equipment — Part 1: General Requirements for Safety* [2].

8.4.1.3.6.3 Isolation Test — Isolated Input. Only isolated patient leads shall be connected to intracardiac catheters or electrodes. The current driven into the leads of an appliance that has isolated leads, when an external power source at line voltage and frequency is applied between each lead and ground, shall be measured in accordance with Figure 8.4.1.3.6.3. The leakage current shall not exceed 50 μA in each case. The test shall be made with the appliance's normal patient cables.

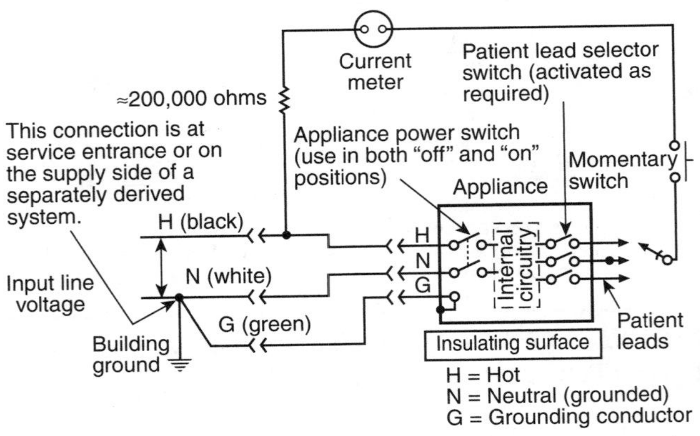

***FIGURE 8.4.1.3.6.3** Test Circuit for Measuring the Electrical Isolation of Isolated Patient Leads.*

FAQ ▶ Why was the leakage current limit increased?

The limit for this sink current — that is, the current driven by an external source into the isolated patient leads — was increased from 20 μA to 50 μA because experience has shown a limited hazard at the lower level. The limit is now in harmony with international standards.

(A) Safety precautions (such as including a resistance in series to limit the current, insulation of the meter, and a momentary switch) shall be taken to protect the operator.

The cautionary language of 8.1.4.3.6.3(A) serves to emphasize that the hazard associated with this test is present wherever the test is done. (The cautionary note was initially included only in manufacturer's requirements.)

(B) In appliances without a power cord with ungrounded, exposed conductive surfaces, measurements shall be made with the exposed conductive surfaces temporarily grounded.

(C) If there is no exposed conductive surface, measurement shall be made with a simulated surface, as described in 10.2.13.4.2, that is also temporarily grounded.

8.4.1.3.6.4 Between Leads — Nonisolated Input. The leakage current between any one lead (not ground) and each other lead shall be measured. An acceptable test configuration shall be as illustrated in Figure 8.4.1.3.6.4. The leakage current shall not exceed 50 μA for the ground wire open and closed.

8.4.1.3.6.5 Between Leads — Isolated Input. The leakage current between any one lead (not ground) and each other lead shall be measured. An acceptable test configuration shall be as illustrated in Figure 8.4.1.3.6.4. The leakage current shall not exceed 10 μA with the ground intact and 50 μA with the ground open.

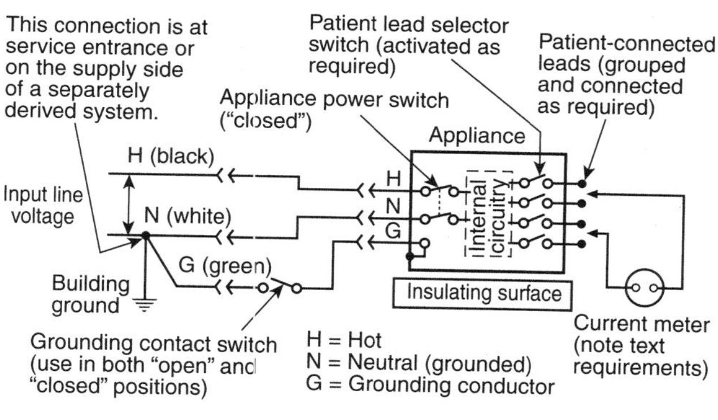

FIGURE 8.4.1.3.6.4 *Test Circuit for Measuring Leakage Current Between Patient Leads — Nonisolated and Isolated.*

8.4.2 Nonpatient Electrical Appliances and Equipment.

The only criteria developed for non-patient electrical appliances are for those non-patient appliances used in patient care areas and laboratories. These are areas in which problems have been reported or that present unusual risks to patients or staff. No criteria have been developed for equipment for offices, maintenance, or other uses. Such equipment is governed by other NFPA standards and other agencies.

Users should also be aware that manufacturers of non-medical devices that are used in patient care areas are within their rights to advise purchasers that their device is not a medical device if the manufacturer makes no claims, written or otherwise, about its device's acceptability for use as a medical device.

8.4.2.1 Permanently Connected — Fixed. (Reserved)

8.4.2.2 Cord- and Plug-Connected — Portable Equipment.

8.4.2.2.1 Patient Care Area.

8.4.2.2.1.1 The leakage current for facility-owned appliances (e.g., housekeeping or maintenance appliances) shall not exceed 500 μA in the following situations:

(1) When they are used in a patient care vicinity
(2) When they will, in normal use, contact patients

Tests shall be made with Switch A in Figure 8.4.1.3.5.5 in the open position for two-wire equipment that is not double-insulated.

8.4.2.2.1.2 Household or office appliances not commonly equipped with grounding conductors in their power cords shall be permitted provided they are not located within the patient care vicinity. Double-insulated appliances shall be permitted in the patient care vicinity.

Requirements, as well as commentary, relative to appliances not owned by a facility are covered in 8.5.2.1.13.

8.4.2.2.2* Laboratory.

All electrical equipment in laboratories needs to meet a minimum level of safety. NFPA 45, *Standard on Fire Protection for Laboratories Using Chemicals* [3], is the lead document on this subject.

A.8.4.2.2.2 As a guideline, 500 μA is recommended as the maximum allowable leakage current limit for laboratory equipment.

The annex material to 8.4.2.2.2 is for general guidance only. Laboratories might contain a wide variety of instruments, some cord-connected and some permanently wired. A single limit of 500 μA might be appropriate for most cord-connected instruments, but the limits of 8.4.1.3.4 might be more appropriate for fixed equipment.

8.4.2.2.2.1 Portable equipment intended for laboratory use shall be provided with an approved method to protect personnel against shock.

8.4.2.2.2.2 All electrical heating equipment to be used for laboratory procedures shall be equipped with overtemperature-limit controls so arranged that thermostatic failure will not result in hazardous temperatures.

8.4.2.2.2.3 When electrical heating equipment is intended for use with flammable or combustible liquids, its electrical components shall be at least one of the following:

(1) Explosionproof
(2) Intrinsically safe
(3) Ventilated

8.4.2.2.2.4 Electrical heating equipment equipped with fans shall be arranged with an interlock that will disconnect the heating elements when the fan is inoperative, unless the fan is not essential to safe operation.

8.4.2.2.2.5* Electrical equipment intended for use in laboratories shall meet the requirements of NFPA 45, *Standard on Fire Protection for Laboratories Using Chemicals.*

A.8.4.2.2.2.5 Electrical equipment has been a frequent source of ignition of flammable concentrations of gases and vapors when combustible and flammable liquids and gases have been used in or near equipment not designed or safe for such use. While general and special ventilation will usually prevent the accumulation of flammable concentrations of gases and vapors in health care laboratories, the hazards should be recognized. Recommended practice is to evaluate at least annually what combustible and flammable liquids and gases are being used in the laboratory, what electrical equipment is exposed to flammable vapors and gases routinely or under reasonably foreseeable circumstances, whether special listed and labeled electrical equipment is available and justified, or whether equivalent safety can be provided more economically and practically by ventilation or quantity limitations.

As an educational measure in laboratories that have many personnel and electrical devices and that handle combustible or flammable liquids in containers larger than 1.69 oz (50 ml), electrical equipment not listed or labeled for use in hazardous atmospheres should be marked with precautionary signs or labels with a legend such as the following:

May ignite flammable vapors or gases. Not safe for use with exposed organic liquids with flash point temperatures below 100°F (37.8°C) (or the temperature of the high-limit cutoff if the equipment is designed for heating, e.g., oil bath or hot plate).

8.5 Administration

8.5.1 Responsibilities of Governing Body. (Reserved)

8.5.2 Policies.

8.5.2.1 General.

8.5.2.1.1 Medical and surgical electrical instrumentation and monitoring devices, as well as all electric appliances used for the care and entertainment of the patient, acquired for use by the facility (e.g., purchased, leased, donated, constructed on-site, loaned, etc.), shall meet the safety performance criteria of Chapter 10.

The reference to Chapter 10, Manufacturer Requirements, is included for information on such requirements. User tests are those specified in this chapter. Guidance is given in Section 8.5 on ways to ensure that appliances are purchased from manufacturers who meet the requirements of Chapter 10.

8.5.2.1.2 Testing Intervals.

The establishment of testing intervals in 8.5.2.1.2 is intended to reduce the possibility of using an unsafe device in a patient care area. Justification for interval periods can be based on the device's design, manufacturers' guidelines, application, life support functions, age-performance history, institutional experience with similar devices, and risk level (that is, the type of hazard to be prevented).

8.5.2.1.2.1 The facility shall establish policies and protocols for the type of test and intervals of testing for each appliance.

8.5.2.1.2.2 All appliances used in patient care areas shall be tested in accordance with 8.4.1.3 or 8.4.2.2.1.1 before being put into service for the first time and after repair or modification. Patient-care–related electrical appliances shall be retested at intervals determined by their normal location or area of normal use, but not exceeding the intervals listed below:

(1) General care areas — 12 months
(2) Critical care areas — 6 months
(3) Wet locations — 6 months

Exception No. 1: The testing intervals listed are intended to be nominal values, and facilities shall be permitted to adopt a protocol using either longer or shorter intervals provided that there is a documented justification based on previous safety testing records for the equipment in question, unusually light or heavy utilization, or similar considerations.

Exception No. 2: Facility-owned household or other appliances that are used in the patient care vicinity, but that are not intended to contact the patient, shall be tested at intervals deemed appropriate by the facility. The facility shall be permitted to structure a testing protocol and frequency for some equipment that might be more limited than that prescribed in 8.4.1.3.

8.5.2.1.3 The tests specified in 8.4.1.3.6 shall be required only for incoming inspections and following repairs and modifications that might have compromised the patient lead leakage current.

Paragraph 8.5.2.1.3 clarifies that leakage current tests should not be done routinely. The isolation test, in fact, can be hazardous and can damage nonisolated patient equipment if not performed by knowledgeable persons. Experience has shown that the percentage of existing appliances failing the test, aside from those whose failure was readily apparent, was so low that requiring the test on a periodic basis was not considered productive.

8.5.2.1.4* After fixed equipment is installed, it shall be tested periodically in accordance with 4.3.3.1.3 and meet the following criteria:

(1) 500 mV for general care areas
(2) 40 mV for critical care areas

A.8.5.2.1.4 The 500-mV limit is based on physiological values. Since the actual voltages normally measured in modern construction are usually less than 10 mV with nominal construc-

tion, voltages exceeding 20 mV might indicate a deteriorating condition and should be investigated.

The 40-mV limit is based on physiological values. Since the actual voltages normally measured in modern construction are usually less than 10 mV with nominal construction, voltages exceeding 20 mV might indicate a deteriorating condition and should be investigated.

8.5.2.1.5 Protection of Patients with Direct Electrical Pathways to the Heart.

8.5.2.1.5.1 Only equipment that is specifically designed for the purpose, that is, provided with suitable isolated patient leads or connections, shall be connected directly to electrically conductive pathways to a patient's heart.

Electrical conductive pathways include intracardiac electrodes such as pacemakers and guide wires. They might also include insulated catheters containing conductive liquids.

8.5.2.1.5.2 The facility shall have a policy that prohibits the use of external cardiac pacemakers and pacing leads with external terminals that are not properly protected from potentially hazardous contact with conductive surfaces.

8.5.2.1.6 Controls. Electrical appliance controls (such as bed, pillow speakers, television, and nurse-call controls) that do not meet the minimum requirements of Section 10.2, Patient-Care–Related Electrical Appliances, shall be mounted so that they cannot be taken into the bed. Existing low-voltage controls used in general patient care areas shall be permitted.

8.5.2.1.7 Adapters and Extension Cords.

Conducting periodic performance verification of adapter and extension cords as part of the equipment control program is effective only if all adapters and extension cords are properly identified and labeled.

8.5.2.1.7.1 Adapters and extension cords meeting the requirements of 8.4.1.2.5 shall be permitted to be used.

FAQ ▶
When can extention cords be used and what are the limitations?

Caution is advised in the use of extension cords. They are intended to be temporary, not to substitute for an inadequate number of receptacles. In essence, extension cords extend the receptacle beyond the wall and invite the use of multiple terminals. Such use can subject the receptacle to more electrical loading than was originally intended, which can lead to overheating and fires. Adequate branches (and receptacles) should be added if necessary to meet unanticipated electrical loads in an area. Extension cords should not be used as a means of correcting this problem.

Note that 8.4.1.2.5 mandates high-quality construction for plugs and adapters.

8.5.2.1.7.2 Three-to-two-prong adapters shall not be permitted.

An earlier reference to distinctive plugs was eliminated from the standard.

8.5.2.1.7.3 The wiring shall be tested for all of the following:

(1) Physical integrity
(2) Polarity
(3) Continuity of grounding at the time of assembly and periodically thereafter

8.5.2.1.8* Appliances Intended to Deliver Electrical Energy. Electrical-energy–delivering appliances shall conform to the leakage, grounding, and other requirements of this chapter when powered but not delivering energy.

A.8.5.2.1.8 When delivering energy, such appliances can deviate from these requirements only to the extent essential for their intended clinical function.

Appliances that intentionally or that can inadvertently apply electrical energy to the patient or to components in contact with the patient require special safety considerations.

Since there is a wide range of power levels, output frequencies, and purposes of appliances that apply electricity directly to patients or to patient-connected devices, it is not feasible to cite them in detail.

The annex material to 8.5.2.1.8 is applicable to health care facility personnel conducting leakage current tests. Although it is primarily the responsibility of the manufacturer to design safe power-delivering equipment, facility personnel are responsible for ensuring that the equipment functions properly and is used correctly. This responsibility is particularly important when facility personnel make repairs.

8.5.2.1.9 Specification of Conditions of Purchase. The procurement authority shall include in its purchasing documents requirements or conditions specifically related to the facility's use of the appliance. These requirements and conditions shall include, but not be limited to, the following:

(1) The type of appliance listing or certification required, if any
(2) The delivery of manufacturer's test data, where pertinent
(3) Special conditions of use (such as in anesthetizing or other locations with special hazards)
(4) Unusual environmental conditions (such as high humidity, moisture, salt spray, etc.)
(5)* The type of electric power system (i.e., grounded or isolated) intended to energize the appliance

A.8.5.2.1.9(5) The facility might wish to reference compliance with this chapter and Chapter 10 on its purchasing document. 

(6) The nature of the overcurrent devices
(7) The use of auxiliary emergency power

Specific purchase documents addressing, among other issues, items (1) through (7) of 8.5.2.1.9 are used by some health care facilities. The documents are attached to the purchase requisitions issued for electrically powered patient care appliances. Over the years, this policy has helped control the introduction of items with compliance deficiencies and has ensured future access to replacement parts and product safety enhancements.

The requirements for 8.5.2.1.9 should include, where applicable, conformance with 10.2.6.4, *Electromagnetic Compatibility,* and 10.2.6.5.3, particularly in the case of programmable devices with computer properties that could be affected by signal noise and power interruption.

8.5.2.1.10* Manuals for Appliances. Purchase specifications shall require the vendor to supply the following manuals for operators or users upon delivery of the appliance:

(1) Installation and operating instructions
(2) Inspection and testing procedures
(3) Maintenance details *(see 10.2.8.1.1)*

The requirements of 8.5.2.1.10 for appliance manuals and the recommendations in A.8.5.2.1.10 can be incorporated into a conditions-of-purchase document. (See 8.5.2.1.9.) In addition, the purchaser can request that the vendor provide all safety-related enhancements for the duration of the life of the device.

A.8.5.2.1.10 Consideration should be given to requiring the vendor to sell parts to the individual or group designated by the hospital to service the equipment following the warranty period. 

8.5.2.1.11 System Demonstration.

8.5.2.1.11.1 Any system consisting of several electric appliances shall be demonstrated as a complete system, after installation, by the vendor designated to assume system responsibility, and prior to acceptance of the system by the facility. The vendor shall demonstrate the operation of the system and provide initial instruction to operators and maintenance personnel.

A facility should consider expanding the system demonstration into a training program if many staff members will be using the system or if the system is very complex. It might be necessary to periodically repeat the demonstration or the program.

8.5.2.1.11.2 Paragraph 8.5.2.1.11.1 shall not apply to facilities that assemble their own systems.

8.5.2.1.12 Electrical Equipment Systems. Purchase contracts for electrical equipment systems, such as nurse call and signaling, that consist of interconnected elements, shall require all of the following:

(1) That the elements be listed to function together
(2) That the manufacturers provide documentation for such interconnection
(3) That the systems be installed by personnel qualified to do such installations

Paragraph 8.5.2.1.12 was incorporated because of the increased use of medical electrical equipment in the form of interconnected elements. Such equipment can be obtained from a number of manufacturers and installed by anyone. For patient safety, these systems must function as a whole. If the entire system has not been coordinated, patient safety could be compromised.

8.5.2.1.13 Appliances Not Provided by the Facility. Policies shall be established for the control of appliances not supplied by the facility.

Specific policies depend on a facility's resources and staff, but some form of control over this group of appliances is essential for both patient and staff safety, as well as for legal liability purposes. The questions that should be asked when dealing with appliances not supplied by the facility include the following:

- Is the appliance a medical device, or does the manufacturer make no claims as to its design or use as a medical device?
- Is the device to be used by the facility staff on patients?
- Is the appliance owned by the patient and to be used only by the patient?

One possible policy is to subject all equipment that is brought into the facility to an incoming inspection, just as though the equipment were being purchased by the facility. These inspections should be made for all equipment (whether owned by a patient or a staff member) brought into the facility. Periodic checks should be made to ascertain that the equipment is still within the facility, that it continues to meet requirements, and that it has not been damaged. A record should be kept of each piece of equipment, again, just as if it were the property of the facility.

8.5.2.2 Servicing and Maintenance of Equipment.

8.5.2.2.1 Service manuals, instructions, and procedures provided by the manufacturer shall be used in the maintenance of equipment.

8.5.2.2.2 A scheduled preventive maintenance program shall be followed.

8.5.2.2.3 Areas designated for the servicing of oxygen equipment shall be clean, free of oil and grease, and not used for the repair of other equipment.

8.5.2.2.4 Defective electrical apparatus shall be tagged and repaired or discarded.

8.5.2.2.5 The health care facility shall monitor the use of appliances and portable electrical equipment, such as drills, that can cause electrical interference during operative procedures.

Paragraph 8.5.2.2.5 was inserted because of an increasing concern that some electrical devices might interfere with the proper operation of other electrical devices.

8.5.2.3 During Surgery.

8.5.2.3.1 Active electrodes or other applicators of electrosurgical, surgical laser, or fiber optic devices shall be secured as recommended by the manufacturer of the device, when not in active use.

The provisions of 8.5.2.3.1 are intended to reduce the risk of fire ignited by appliances that deliver high energy. It is recognized that appliances such as electrosurgical units and lasers intentionally deliver energy at levels high enough to ignite flammable materials in the operating field. This may be further exacerbated by oxygen or nitrous oxide concentrations leaking from the ventilation system or by the presence of flammable liquids such as isopropyl alcohol. Research into the development of nonflammable drapes has been ongoing for many years, but a solution has yet to be found that is economical, maintains appropriate levels of fire safety and sterility, is convenient, and is safe for the environment.

Fire safety in the operating room requires a continuing training program for all operating room staff on the hazards of high-energy surgical devices.

8.5.2.3.2 The cable that provides power from the electrosurgical generator to the active electrode shall be disconnected from the generator when contamination occurs.

The increasing use of multiple electrosurgical units during a surgical procedure, and the automatic action capabilities of these units, has heightened the danger of inadvertent activation of an electrosurgical unit. The common practice of dropping a contaminated electrode and allowing it to dangle in or beside the surgical drapes has been implicated in several operating room fires.

8.5.2.4 During Administration of Respiratory Therapy.

8.5.2.4.1* Electrical equipment used within the site of intentional expulsion shall have no hot surfaces.

A.8.5.2.4.1 For further information, see manufacturer requirements for equipment used within the site of intentional expulsion in 10.2.9.3. A

The term *site of intentional expulsion* has replaced an earlier term, *site of administration,* as a way of creating an easily identifiable and enforceable boundary [e.g., 30 cm (1 ft) around vents or expulsion points of oxygen-delivery equipment]. It is a place where no electrical equipment is to be brought unless the equipment is listed for use in an oxygen-enriched atmosphere. This 30 cm (1 ft) boundary is a conservative value. Controlled studies have confirmed that escaping oxygen is quickly diluted into the atmosphere and that oxygen concentrations return to normal levels at approximately 5 cm to 13 cm (2 in. to 5 in.).

The newer term, *site of intentional expulsion,* redefines the hazardous volume to just that volume where oxygen or an oxygen-enriched atmosphere was deliberately vented to the atmosphere. (See A.3.3.170.) While the hazardous volume is now smaller and more reflective of where higher-than-normal oxygen levels might occur, it does not negate all the other precautions that need to be observed when oxygen is being administered (e.g., no smoking in the room).

The requirements in this section are intended for users within health care facilities. Manufacturers' requirements, listed in 10.2.7, are more complex.

8.5.2.4.2 When only the remote control or signal leads of a device are to be used in the site of intentional expulsion, only the control or signal leads shall be required to comply with 8.5.2.4.1.

8.5.2.4.3 Subparagraphs 8.5.2.4.1 and 8.5.2.4.2 shall not apply to small (less than 2 W), hermetically sealed heating elements such as light bulbs.

8.5.2.4.4 Electrical equipment sold with the intent to be used in oxygen-enriched atmospheres shall be listed for use in oxygen-enriched atmospheres.

8.5.2.4.5* Electrical equipment used within oxygen delivery equipment shall be listed for use in oxygen-enriched atmospheres.

For manufacturers' criteria associated with electrical equipment used within oxygen-enriched atmospheres, see 10.2.9.3. For requirements for this equipment within hyperbaric facilities, see Chapter 20.

A.8.5.2.4.5 For further information, see manufacturer requirements for equipment used in oxygen delivery equipment in Section 10.2.

The use of electrical equipment in spaces where there is a high oxygen content is a matter of concern because of the fire hazard. It is particularly a problem where the oxygen is "pure," that is, 80–90 percent, because materials not very flammable in ordinary air become extremely flammable in pure oxygen.

In medical practice, particularly in surgery, patients are often given supplemental oxygen, via respirator, anesthesia machines, and so forth. Such supplements can range from room air to 100 percent oxygen. Clearly, different levels of protection are needed.

This standard addresses the problem by defining three elements of the situation:

(1) *Kind of Air.* An oxygen-enriched atmosphere (OEA) is air that ranges from slightly enriched (23.5 percent rather than 21 percent) to total oxygen (100 percent).
(2) *Kind of Apparatus.* Oxygen delivery equipment (ODE) is a device to deliver an OEA to a patient.
(3) *Kind of Space.* A site of intentional expulsion (SIE) is a small volume where oxygen that has been delivered to the patient is discharged to the ambient air.

When an OEA is within an ODE, it is much more likely to have a high concentration of oxygen. Paragraph 10.2.9.3 therefore advises manufacturers, and A.8.5.2.4.5 advises users, of precautions to take to reduce the fire hazard. Paragraph 10.2.9.3 lists four ways of attacking the problem. Note that an OEA can be created not only in a ventilator or oxygen tubing, but also in an oxygen tent or incubator. Special precautions should be taken.

At the other extreme of hazard is a space in the open air, the SIE. This space is defined as within 12 in. (30.5 cm) of the exhaust port, because, in most instances, dilution to ambient levels occurs within a few inches of the port; 12 in. (30.5 cm) provides an adequate safety factor. Paragraph 10.2.9.3 provides guidance to minimize this hazard by requiring that only those parts of the apparatus that are intended to be within the SIE are of concern. Even these, such as nurse call buttons, leads, and so forth, do not necessarily need to be listed for use in OEA because they usually conform to provisions of subparagraph (d), that is, they do not have hot surfaces and they meet the requirements of Figure 10.2.9.3(a) through Figure 10.2.9.3(f).

The intent of A.8.5.2.4.5 is to advise users to specify appliances that meet higher requirements where the hazard is higher, but not to overspecify where the hazard is minimal. Thus, as they are ordinarily used, nurse call buttons, pillow speakers, and so forth, do not need to be listed for use in oxygen-enriched atmospheres.

Note, however, that these requirements apply only to the intended use. The user should exercise vigilance to guard against an unintended use or an accidental failure, which can vastly increase the hazard.

◀ **FAQ**
Do nurse call buttons need to be listed for use in oxygen-enriched atmospheres?

The use and limitations of small device appendages, such as nurse call buttons and pillow speakers, in oxygen-enriched atmospheres has been a confusing area of patient safety. Because the use of such appendages is so widespread and the use of supplemental oxygen ever increasing, a reasonable compromise on their use is needed.

Although the text of 8.5.2.4.2 is technically correct, it is difficult for most users to fully comprehend. The lengthy annex guidance in A.8.5.2.4.5 is intended to clarify the issue. It should be read not as an explicit recommendation, but as an educational exercise to aid the user to better understand the problem and the intended use of these appendages

8.5.2.4.6* High-energy–delivering probes (such as defibrillator paddles) or other electrical devices that do not comply with 8.5.2.4.1 and 8.5.2.4.2 that are deemed essential to the care of an individual patient and must be used within an administration site or within oxygen-delivery equipment, shall be permitted.

Some of the types of devices described in 8.5.2.4.6 need to be used in emergencies such as patient cardiac arrest. As noted, extreme caution must be exercised if oxygen is also being used.

A.8.5.2.4.6 Where possible, combustible materials such as hair, fabric, and paper should be removed from the vicinity of where the energy is delivered. Water-soluble surgical jelly has been shown to dramatically reduce the combustibility of these materials.

8.5.2.5 Laboratory.

The use, inspection, and maintenance of electrical equipment and appliances used in laboratories must be coordinated among all areas responsible for the equipment and appliances. Typically, electrical safety, preventive maintenance, and hazard surveillance programs are all involved in laboratory electrical safety. It is good practice to include all aspects of electrical safety within the laboratory in the overall safety program, and to review them in conjunction with the facility-wide safety program, to determine whether they conform to the requirements of the authority having jurisdiction.

8.5.2.5.1* The laboratory shall establish policies and protocols for the type of test and intervals of testing for each appliance.

A.8.5.2.5.1 One reason for requiring testing of all electrical equipment used in the laboratory is to provide minimum assurance against electrical macroshock hazards.

Because a document covering laboratory electrical safety does not currently exist, it is considered reasonable as part of the overall facility program that laboratory electrical equipment is tested for electrical safety. As noted in A.8.5.2.5.2, a study of incidents showed which devices were most involved with laboratory fires.

A chassis leakage current limit of 500 μA is *recommended* in A.8.4.2.2.2.

8.5.2.5.2* The physical integrity of the power cord, attachment plug, and cord strain-relief shall be confirmed at least annually by visual inspection and other appropriate tests.

A.8.5.2.5.2 Most laboratory fires involve biomedical or other electronic equipment failures. The most common ignition factors are short circuits or ground faults. Electrical wire or cable insulation is the material most likely to first ignite in a clinical laboratory fire. *(See Hoeltge, G.A., Miller, A., Klein, B.R., Hamlin, W.B., "Accidental fires in clinical laboratories.")*

Laboratories often use combustible and flammable liquids and gases with or near electrical equipment that is not designed or safe for such use. Because electrical equipment has been a frequent source of ignition for such vapors and gases, a periodical assessment of the following is recommended:

1. The types of combustible and flammable liquids and gases being used
2. The types of electrical equipment being exposed to such liquids or gases (either routinely or likely)
3. Whether special listed or labeled electrical equipment is available or justified
4. Whether equivalent safety can be provided more economically by ventilation or quantity limitations

Precautionary signs and labels should be used as appropriate.

8.5.3 Record Keeping.

Section 8.5.3 discusses record keeping relating to the safe use of appliances in health care facilities. Because of the explosive expansion of the number of appliances used in health care and their intimate incorporation into the economics of health care practice, documentation and recordkeeping, for administrative as well as safety concerns, have become increasingly interrelated and regulated.

A number of regulatory agencies, federal and local, as well as certification agencies, such as the Joint Commission on the Certification of Health Organizations (JCAHO), have established requirements on recordkeeping. It is beyond the scope of this standard to discuss these interrelated areas of information technology except to note that proper recordkeeping is essential for maintaining an effective safety program.

8.5.3.1 Patient Care Appliances.

8.5.3.1.1 Instruction Manuals.

8.5.3.1.1.1 A permanent file of instruction and maintenance manuals as described in 10.2.8.1.1 shall be maintained and be accessible.

8.5.3.1.1.2 The file of manuals shall be in the custody of the engineering group responsible for the maintenance of the appliance.

8.5.3.1.1.3 Duplicate instruction and maintenance manuals shall be available to the user.

8.5.3.1.1.4 Any safety labels and condensed operating instructions on an appliance shall be maintained in legible condition.

8.5.3.1.2* Documentation.

A.8.5.3.1.2 Although several approaches to documentation exist in hospitals, the minimum acceptable documentation should convey what was tested, when it was tested, and whether it performed successfully. Adopting a system of exception reporting can be the most efficient form of recordkeeping for routine rechecks of equipment or systems and thereby minimize technicians' time in recording the value of each measurement taken. For example, once a test protocol is established, which simply means testing the equipment or system consistent with Chapter 8, the only item (value) that needs to be recorded is what failure or what deviation from the requirements of the chapter was detected when a corrective action (repair) was undertaken. This approach can serve to eliminate, for example, the need to keep individual room sheets to record measured results on each receptacle or to record measurement values of all types of leakage current tests.

8.5.3.1.2.1 A record shall be maintained of the tests required by this chapter and associated repairs or modifications.

8.5.3.1.2.2 At a minimum, this record shall contain all of the following:

(1) Date
(2) Unique identification of the equipment tested
(3) Indication of which items have met or have failed to meet the performance requirements of 8.5.3.1.2

8.5.3.1.3 Test Logs. A log of test results and repairs shall be maintained and kept for a period of time in accordance with a health care facility's record retention policy.

8.5.4 Use. (Reserved)

8.5.5 Qualification and Training of Personnel.

8.5.5.1* Personnel concerned for the application or maintenance of electric appliances shall be trained on the risks associated with their use.

A.8.5.5.1 "Personnel" includes physicians, nurses, nursing assistants, engineers, and technicians.

Continuing education programs are extremely important in hazard prevention. Although all personnel should be engaged in ongoing training, it is especially important for engineers and technicians who install, repair, maintain, and evaluate medical appliances and systems. Such programs not only should be part of the routine of the facility, but also should make use of information from professional societies and equipment manufacturers.

8.5.5.1.1 The health care facilities shall provide programs of continuing education for its personnel.

8.5.5.1.2 Continuing education programs shall include periodic review of manufacturers' safety guidelines and usage requirements for electrosurgical units and similar appliances.

8.5.5.2 Personnel involved in the use of energy-delivering devices including, but not limited to, electrosurgical, surgical laser, and fiberoptic devices, shall receive periodic training in fire suppression.

The provisions of 8.5.5.2 are the result of several serious fires in operating rooms. See the commentary following 8.5.2.3.1 for discussion of this topic, and Supplement 1 for an update on operating room fires.

8.5.5.3 Equipment shall be serviced by qualified personnel only.

Complying with the requirements of this standard through servicing and testing can mitigate the safety problems inherent in the use of medical appliances. Because of the complexity and hard usage of such devices, and the necessity for interaction with health care staff, it is essential that qualified professionals do the work. These professionals must have the appropriate background and have received proper interdisciplinary training.

REFERENCES CITED IN COMMENTARY

1. NFPA 70, *National Electrical Code®*, 2005 edition.
2. International Electrotechnical Commission Standard IEC 60601-1, *Medical Electrical Equipment — Part 1: General Requirements for Safety*, 2004 edition.
3. NFPA 45, *Standard on Fire Protection for Laboratories Using Chemicals*, 2004 edition.

CHAPTER 9

Gas Equipment

The hazards associated with gas equipment used in health care facilities are of two broad types (see Appendix B.6). The first is that of fire and explosions. Oxygen, the most common gas used in health care facilities (see 3.3.131 and A.3.3.131), and nitrous oxide, which is used frequently as an inhalation anesthetic (see 3.3.122 and 13.4.1), are oxidizers that, when present in sufficient quantity and concentration, form one leg of the "fire triangle." (See Exhibit 9.1.) When the other two sides of the triangle (ignition source and fuel) are added, fire and/or explosion can result. The hazard is intensified because many materials, commonly available in health care facilities that are not flammable in room air, become flammable (or extremely flammable) when the concentration of oxygen is raised above that in room air (see 9.6.1.2). Nitrous oxide is not an oxidizer at room temperature, but dissociates and forms oxygen under elevated temperatures that might be present during a fire.

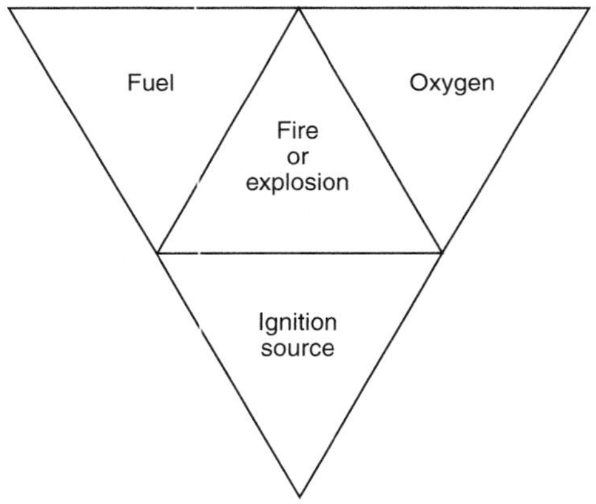

EXHIBIT 9.1 *Fire triangle.*

The second type of hazard is mechanical in nature and is associated with compressed gas cylinders (see 3.3.30, *cylinder*). Gases inside cylinders are generally under enormous pressures, and the cylinders often have significant weight. The cylinders can cause injuries directly because of their weight and inertia. Secondary damage can result from sufficient physical trauma to regulators/valves attached to a cylinder and can allow the escaping gas to violently propel the cylinder in a dangerous manner. The Pin-Index Safety System (see 9.5.1.2 and A.9.5.1.2) and gas regulators (see 9.3.6, 9.3.7, and 9.3.8) can also suffer physical damage and cause hazards to patients if the wrong gas is delivered.

These two types of hazards can come together. Compressed gas cylinders with oxygen or nitrous oxide can contain a large amount of gas. If the gases in these oxygen or nitrous oxide cylinders are abruptly released, there may be a sufficient concentration to initiate or exacerbate a fire (if the other two legs of the fire triangle are present).

Because of these hazards, personnel concerned with the application and maintenance of medical gases and others who handle medical gases and cylinders must be trained in their handling and use (see 9.6.2.1.1).

Exhibit 9.2 shows a burned face mask and breathing circuit, the result of a fire fueled by the flow of oxygen. Once the plastic is ignited, the fire is difficult to extinguish if oxygen is still flowing. The oxygen should be shut off immediately, then the fire extinguished.

EXHIBIT 9.2 Burned plastic face mask and breathing circuit.

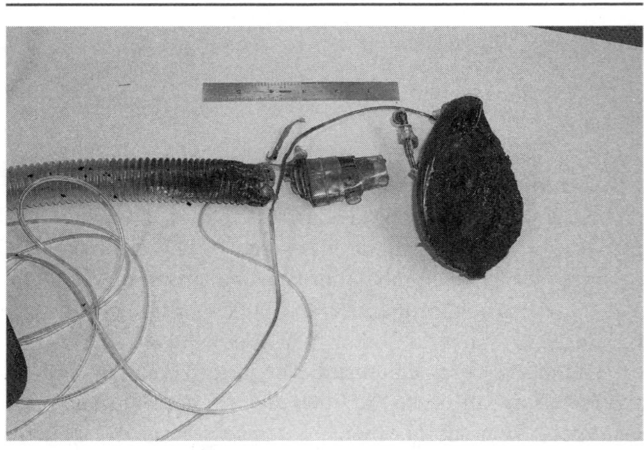

9.1* Applicability

A.9.1 The application of requirements contained in this chapter for specific types of health care facilities can be found in Chapters 6, 13, 14, 17, 18, 19, and 21.

9.1.1* This chapter applies to the use, at normal atmospheric pressure, of all of the following:

(1) Nonflammable medical gases
(2) Vapors and aerosols
(3) Equipment required for their administration

The phrase *at normal atmospheric pressure* can cause confusion. Although some equipment, such as intermittent positive pressure breathing (IPPB) machines, ventilators, and resuscitation equipment, functions internally at pressures above normal (room) atmospheric pressure, the devices themselves are employed in a normal atmospheric pressure environment. This environment differs from the inside of a hyperbaric chamber in which a total environment above normal atmospheric pressure is created. (See 9.1.3 and Chapter 20.)

A.9.1.1 Respiratory therapy is an allied health specialty employed with medical direction in the treatment, management, control, diagnostic evaluation, and care of patients with deficiencies and abnormalities of the cardiopulmonary system. (Courtesy of the American Association for Respiratory Therapy, 1720 Regal Row, Dallas, TX 75235.)

Respiratory therapy includes the therapeutic use of the following: medical gases and administration apparatus, environmental control systems, humidification, aerosols, medications, ventilatory support, broncho-pulmonary drainage, pulmonary rehabilitation, cardiopulmonary resuscitation, and airway management. (Courtesy of the American Association for Respiratory Therapy, 1720 Regal Row, Dallas, TX 75235.)

There is a continual need for human diligence in the establishment and maintenance of safe practices for respiratory therapy. It is essential for personnel having responsibility for respiratory therapy to establish and enforce appropriate programs to fulfill provisions of this chapter.

It is the responsibility of the administrative and professional staff of a hospital, or safety director if one is appointed, to adopt and enforce appropriate regulations for a hospital. In other health care facilities, responsibility could be assigned to a safety director or other responsible person, who is, in turn, responsible to the administration.

In institutions having a respiratory therapy service, it is recommended that this service be directly responsible for the administration of Chapter 9. Hazards can be mitigated only when there is continual recognition and understanding.

In 2000, the American Association for Respiratory Care (http://www.aarc.org/) estimated that there are approximately 112,000 respiratory therapy practitioners in the United States. These practitioners can be instrumental in applying the requirements established in this chapter for health care facilities. (See Exhibit 9.3.)

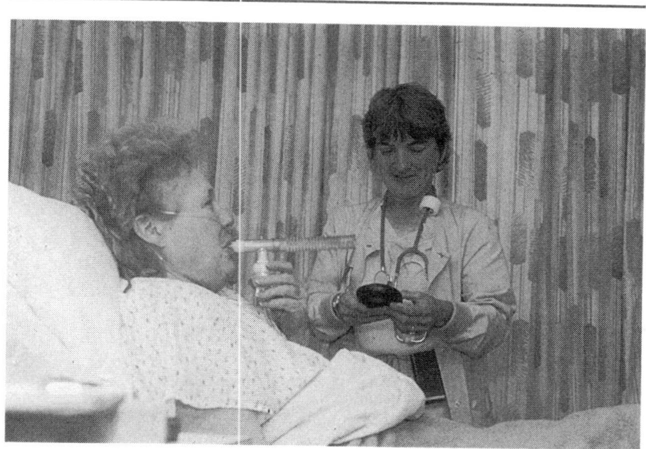

EXHIBIT 9.3 *A respiratory therapy practitioner implementing requirements for safe use of gas equipment. (Courtesy of American Association for Respiratory Care)*

In addition, there are approximately 30,000 nurse anesthetists according the American Association of Nurse Anesthetists (http://www.aana.org/) and approximately 30,000 anesthesiologists [according to American Society of Anesthesiologists (http://www.asahq.org/)] in the United States that routinely use gas equipment to deliver anesthesia. These clinical professionals need to be very cognizant of the requirements of this chapter.

9.1.2 When used in this chapter, the term *oxygen* is intended to mean 100 percent oxygen as well as mixtures of oxygen and air.

The term *oxygen,* as used in this chapter, does not apply to the air around us, which contains approximately 21 percent oxygen under normal conditions.

9.1.3* This chapter does not apply to special atmospheres, such as those encountered in hyperbaric chambers.

A.9.1.3 See Chapter 20.

A

9.2 Nature of Hazards

See Section B.6.

9.3 Cylinder and Container Source

For further information on gas cylinder safety, see 5.1.13.

9.3.1 Cylinders shall be permitted to be fitted with valves that include a means to slow the initial opening pressurization.

FAQ ▶
Why should the valves be opened slowly?

Paragraph 9.3.1 is new in the 2005 standard. It uses the term *shall be permitted to be* in order to be permissive: that is, not to require a slow opening valve, but to *allow* its use. At issue is the phenomenon of adiabatic heating (see 3.3.2). Adiabatic heating is defined as "the heating of a gas caused by its compression." This definition might seem counterintuitive because, when one opens a gas cylinder, the gas inside the cylinder is trying to go from a compressed to an uncompressed state. This seeming contradiction is resolved when you consider that, if a cylinder valve is opened rapidly, the escaping gas from the cylinder will be compressing the existing gas between what started out as a closed cylinder valve and the regulator. Especially if the gas is an oxidizer or combustible itself, the adiabatic heating can cause a fire. In the case of oxygen, the escaping gas is both the ignition source and the oxidizer.

In February 1999, the FDA and NIOSH jointly published a Public Health Advisory entitled "Explosions and Fires from Oxygen Regulators" (http://www.fda.gov/cdrh/oxyreg.html) [1]. That advisory states:

> Over the past 5 years, FDA has received 16 reports of aluminum regulators used with oxygen cylinders burning or exploding. These incidents caused severe burns to 11 health care workers and patients. Many of the incidents occurred during emergency medical use or during routine equipment checkout. FDA and the National Institute for Occupational Safety and Health (NIOSH) believe that the aluminum in these regulators was a major factor in both the ignition and severity of the fires, although there are likely other contributing factors.

The Public Health Advisory [1] contains the following recommendations:

> FDA is pursuing plans to work with manufacturers to improve the safety of oxygen regulators and restrict the use of aluminum exposed to high-pressure oxygen in regulators. In the meantime, FDA and NIOSH advise that the following precautions be taken to avoid explosions and fires from oxygen regulators containing aluminum:
>
> - If you are presently using high pressure oxygen regulators which contain any aluminum exposed to high-pressure oxygen, replace them with regulators made of brass. Consult the manufacturer if you don't know what material is used in your regulators.
> - If non-aluminum oxygen regulators are not available, it is recommended that you follow the precautions as described in the addendum to this advisory to minimize the risk of fires until brass replacement regulators become available.

ECRI (Emergency Core Research Institute) (http://www.mdsr.ecri.org/TOC/index.asp), in "Are Aluminum Oxygen Regulators Safe?" [2], states in its commentary on the Public Health Advisory:

FAQ ▶
What are the ignition mechanisms with valve fires?

> In these instances, the fires have been initiated through either of two mechanisms: (1) particle ignition, in which debris is blown from the cylinder into the high-pressure side of the regulator with sufficient energy to ignite the aluminum in the regulator, or (2) adiabatic compression ignition, in which the gas in the regulator is recompressed as the high-pressure oxygen enters the regulator; this creates a transient high temperature that ignites flammable materials in that space, resulting in the ignition of the regulator. Adiabatic compression ignition is less of a concern in the hospital setting because regulators are not likely to become contaminated with ignitable materials, such as oil and dirt, during use or maintenance in this environment.

This form of ignition is more of a concern in the prehospital setting (e.g., for emergency medical services).

ECRI further recommends:

- Particle ignition can typically be avoided by following basic compressed-gas safety practices. These include clearing the cylinder valve stem (by "cracking" the cylinder valve to release a short burst of gas) before attaching a regulator and ensuring that the regulator is in a no-flow state before attaching it to the cylinder. In the aluminum regulator fires that ECRI has investigated, such basic safety practices were violated. Also, while not a sure preventive measure, the use of a sintered inlet filter disk rather than an easily displaced mesh screen inlet filter can help reduce the fire risk. (One major regulator manufacturer has made this change to its regulators.)
- The risk of adiabatic compression ignition can be minimized both by keeping all regulators free of oils, dirt, and other combustible substances and by opening the cylinder valve slowly, rather than rapidly.

Extreme caution should be taken when opening cylinder valves. Valves should be opened slowly because of the phenomenon of adiabatic heating. There should also be a policy to ensure that valves and regulators are kept free from contaminants.

9.3.2 Cylinders and containers shall comply with 5.1.3.1.

Incidents have been reported of people forcing oxygen flowmeters into nitrous oxide or other gas outlets with sometimes fatal results. The Pin-Index Safety System can be defeated with enough force. Other incidents are known of pins being shorn off due to mechanical abuse, allowing unsuspecting staff members to defeat the intention of the Pin-Index Safety System and interchange gases. For this reason, it is important that staff are aware of the Pin-Index Safety System and report physical damage to the pins.

See A.9.5.1.2 for more information on the Pin-Index Safety System.

9.3.3 Cylinder valve outlet connections shall conform to CGA V-1, *Standard for Compressed Gas Cylinder Valve Outlet and Inlet Connections* (ANSI B57.1) (includes Pin-Index Safety System for medical gases). *(See 5.1.3.1.)*

9.3.4 When low-pressure threaded connections are employed, they shall be in accordance with the Compressed Gas Association standard for noninterchangeable, low-pressure connections for medical gases, air, and suction, CGA V-5, *Diameter-Index Safety System (Noninterchangeable Low Pressure Connections for Medical Gas Applications).*

9.3.5 Low-pressure quick-coupler connections shall be noninterchangeable between gas services.

9.3.6 Regulators and gauges intended for use in high-pressure service shall be listed for such service.

9.3.7 Pressure-reducing regulators shall be used on high-pressure cylinders to reduce the pressure to working pressures.

9.3.8 Approved regulators or other gas-flow control devices shall be used to reduce the cylinder pressure of every cylinder used for medical purposes. All such devices shall have connections so designed that they attach only to cylinders of gas for which they are designated.

Before being placed in service, all cylinders and containers should be checked for proper color coding, labeling, attached labeling, and Pin-Index Safety System or Diameter-Index Safety System fitting.

9.3.9* Equipment that will permit the intermixing of different gases, either through defects in the mechanism or through error in manipulation in any portion of the high-pressure side of any system in which these gases might flow, shall not be used for coupling cylinders containing compressed gases.

A.9.3.9 It is particularly important that the intermixing of oxidizing and flammable gases under pressure be scrupulously avoided. Such mixing may result in a violent explosion.

9.3.10 Cylinder valve outlet connections for oxygen shall be Connection No. 540 as described in CGA V-1, *Standard for Compressed Gas Cylinder Valve Outlet and Inlet Connections* (ANSI B57.1).

9.3.11 Cylinder valve outlet connections for nitrous oxide shall be Connection No. 326 as described in CGA V-1, *Standard for Compressed Gas Cylinder Valve Outlet and Inlet Connections* (ANSI B57.1).

9.4 Cylinder and Container Storage Requirements

FAQ ▶ What are some of the hazards associated with cylinders?

Cylinders and containers should never be left without some type of physical support such as a stand, a cart, or wall strapping. (See 9.7.2.3.) A high-pressure, gas-filled cylinder can create mechanical hazards from a sudden, uncontrollable release of its contents (e.g., from falling over and cracking open).

The storage criteria in Section 9.4 for nonflammable gas cylinders or containers are the same, whether for anesthetizing, respiratory therapy, or laboratory use. This section serves as a reminder that cylinders and containers must be stored properly. Note that the total volume of compressed gas being stored in the location determines whether 9.4.1, 9.4.2, or 9.4.3 applies.

Storage requirements in Chapter 5 take into consideration not only the cylinders and containers within the room, but also the piping distribution system connected to the manifold(s) in the room. The volumes referred to in this section are compressed volumes. Table C.13.5 gives cylinder nominal volumes in cubic inches and in liters.

9.4.1 Storage for nonflammable gases equal to or greater than 85 m^3 (3000 ft^3) compressed shall comply with 5.1.3.3.2 and 5.1.3.3.3.

9.4.2 Storage for nonflammable gases greater than 8.5 m^3 (300 ft^3) but less than 85 m^3 (3000 ft^3) compressed shall comply with the requirements in 9.4.2.1 through 9.4.2.3.

9.4.2.1 Storage locations shall be outdoors in an enclosure or within an enclosed interior space of noncombustible or limited-combustible construction, with doors (or gates outdoors) that can be secured against unauthorized entry.

9.4.2.2 Oxidizing gases, such as oxygen and nitrous oxide, shall not be stored with any flammable gas, liquid, or vapor.

9.4.2.3 Oxidizing gases such as oxygen and nitrous oxide shall be separated from combustibles or materials by one of the following:

(1) A minimum distance of 6.1 m (20 ft)

(2) A minimum distance of 1.5 m (5 ft) if the entire storage location is protected by an automatic sprinkler system designed in accordance with NFPA 13, *Standard for the Installation of Sprinkler Systems*
(3) An enclosed cabinet of noncombustible construction having a minimum fire protection rating of ½ hour

9.4.2.4 Liquefied gas container storage shall comply with 5.1.3.4.12.

9.4.2.5 Cylinder and container storage locations shall meet 5.1.3.3.1.7 with respect to temperature limitations.

Placing high-pressure cylinders near radiators, stoves, or other heat sources can cause the pressure to increase beyond the cylinder's pressure relief limit, resulting in uncontrolled venting. This situation is particularly dangerous if the heat source is also a source of ignition, such as a stove.

Small liquid containers, such as those used to provide metered oxygen therapy via mask or cannula in the home, or the larger reservoirs used to refill therapeutic devices present other significant hazards beyond those of frostbite from their liquid contents of approximately −184°C (−300°F). Liquid oxygen expands 860 times in the transition from liquid to the gaseous state. Therefore, what seems to be a small leak or spill can, in fact, release a significant quantity of 100 percent oxygen into the area around the container. In addition, liquid oxygen can cause certain greases or oils to ignite spontaneously if they come in contact with each other. All types of lotions, hair care products, lubricants, and oils should be kept away from any liquid oxygen reservoirs.

◀ **FAQ**
Is a liquid oxygen spill more severe than a gas leak?

9.4.2.6 Electrical fixtures in storage locations shall meet 5.1.3.3.2(5).

9.4.2.7 Cylinder protection from mechanical shock shall meet 5.3.13.1.3.

9.4.2.8 Cylinder or container restraint shall meet 5.3.13.1.3.

9.4.2.9 Smoking, open flames, electric heating elements, and other sources of ignition shall be prohibited within storage locations and within 6.1 m (20 ft) of outside storage locations.

9.4.2.10 Cylinder valve protection caps shall meet 5.3.13.1.3.

9.4.2.11 Gas cylinder and liquefied gas container storage shall comply with 5.1.3.4.12.

9.4.3 Storage for nonflammable gases with a total volume compressed equal to or less than 8.5 m^3 (300 ft^3) shall comply with the requirements in 9.4.3.1 and 9.4.3.2.

9.4.3.1 Individual cylinder storage associated with patient care areas, not to exceed 2100 m^2 (22,500 ft^2) of floor area, shall not be required to be stored in enclosures.

9.4.3.2 Precautions in handling these cylinders shall be in accordance with 9.7.2.

9.4.3.3 When small-size (A, B, D, or E) cylinders are in use, they shall be attached to a cylinder stand or to a therapy apparatus of sufficient size to render the entire assembly stable.

9.4.3.4 An individual cylinder placed in patient room for immediate use by a patient shall not be required to be stored in an enclosure.

9.4.3.5 Cylinders shall not be chained to portable or movable apparatus such as beds and oxygen tents.

9.4.4 Signs.

9.4.4.1 A precautionary sign, readable from a distance of 1.5 m (5 ft), shall be displayed on each door or gate of the storage room or enclosure.

9.4.4.2 The sign shall include the following wording as a minimum:

CAUTION
OXIDIZING GAS(ES) STORED WITHIN
NO SMOKING

Paragraph 9.4.4.2 requires a minimum amount of signage to warn facility staff and others of the presence of oxidizing gases. The contents of such rooms and enclosures can present a significant fire hazard.

9.5 Performance Criteria and Testing

9.5.1 Portable Patient Care Gas Equipment.

9.5.1.1* Anesthetic apparatus shall be subject to approval by the authority having jurisdiction.

A.9.5.1.1 If the sole source of supply of nonflammable medical gases, such as nitrous oxide and oxygen, is a system of cylinders attached directly to and supported by the device (such as a gas anesthesia apparatus) used to administer these gases, it is recommended that two cylinders of each gas be attached to the administering device.

9.5.1.2* Each yoke on anesthetic apparatus constructed to permit attachment of small cylinders equipped with flush-type valves shall have two pins installed as specified in CGA V-1, *Standard for Compressed Gas Cylinder Valve Outlet and Inlet Connections* (ANSI B57.1).

A.9.5.1.2 The Pin-Index Safety System consists of a combination of two pins projecting from the yoke assembly of the apparatus and so positioned as to fit into matching holes drilled into the cylinder valves. It is intended to provide against the possibility of error in attaching the flush-type valves, with which gas cylinders and other sources of gas supply are equipped, to gas apparatus having yoke connections.

9.5.1.3 Testing.

9.5.1.3.1 Interventions requiring testing shall include, but not be limited to, the following:

(1) Alteration of pipeline hose or fittings
(2) Alteration of internal piping
(3) Adjustment of selector switches or flush valves
(4) Replacement or repair of flowmeters or bobbins

9.5.1.3.2 After any adjustment or repair involving use of tools, or any modification of the gas piping supply connections or the pneumatic power supply connections for the anesthesia ventilator, or other pneumatically powered device if one is present, and before use on patients, the gas anesthesia apparatus shall be tested at the final common path to the patient to determine that oxygen and only oxygen is delivered from the oxygen flowmeters and the oxygen flush valve, if any.

9.5.1.3.3 Before the gas anesthesia apparatus is returned to service, each fitting and connection shall be checked to verify its proper indexing to the respective gas service involved.

9.5.1.3.4 Before the gas anesthesia apparatus is returned to service, an oxygen analyzer, or a similar device, shall be used to verify the oxygen concentration.

9.5.1.4* Yoke-type connections between anesthesia apparatus and flush-type cylinder valves (commonly used with anesthetic gas cylinders) shall be Connection No. 860 in accordance with CGA V-1, *Compressed Gas Cylinder Valve Outlet and Inlet Connections* (ANSI B57.1).

A.9.5.1.4 Fabrication specifications are contained in CGA V-1 (ANSI B57.1), *Standard for Compressed Gas Cylinder Valve Outlet and Inlet Connections*. Connection No. 860 shown in that document illustrates the system. Connection Nos. 870 (Oxygen, Medical), 880 (Oxygen-Carbon Dioxide Mixture), 890 (Oxygen-Helium Mixture), 900 (Ethylene), 910 (Nitrous Oxide), 920 (Cyclopropane), 930 (Helium), and 940 (Carbon Dioxide) are for specific medical gases and gas mixtures and utilize the basic dimensions of Connection 860.

9.5.2 Apparatus for Administering Respiratory Therapy.

9.5.2.1 Oxygen-delivery equipment intended to rest on the floor shall be equipped with a base designed to render the entire assembly stable during storage, transport, and use. If casters are used, they shall conform to Class C of U.S. Government Commercial Standard 223-59, *Casters, Wheels, and Glides for Hospital Equipment.*

9.5.2.2 Oxygen enclosures of rigid materials shall be fabricated of noncombustible materials.

9.5.2.3 Equipment supplied from cylinders or containers shall be designed and constructed for service at full cylinder or container pressure, or constructed for use with, or equipped with pressure-reducing regulators.

9.5.2.4 Humidification or reservoir jars containing liquid to be dispersed into a gas stream shall be made of clear, transparent material, impervious to contained solutions and medications, and shall permit observation of the liquid level and consistency.

Devices prefilled with sterile water are commonly used in hospitals today. These devices meet the requirements of 9.5.2.4 because they are clear and allow observation of the liquid level.

9.5.2.5 Humidifiers and nebulizers shall be equipped with provisions for overpressure relief or alarm if the flow becomes obstructed.

Alarms can be easily tested by briefly occluding the outlet port to see whether pressure relief occurs.

9.5.2.6 Humidifiers and nebulizers shall be incapable of tipping or shall be mounted so that any tipping or alteration from the vertical shall not interfere with function or accuracy.

9.5.3 Nonpatient Gas Equipment.

9.5.3.1 Carts and Hand Trucks.

9.5.3.1.1 Construction. Carts and hand trucks for cylinders and containers shall be constructed for the intended purpose, be self-supporting, and be provided with appropriate chains or stays to retain cylinders or containers.

9.5.3.1.2 Use. Carts and hand trucks that are intended to be used in anesthetizing locations or cylinder and container storage rooms communicating with anesthetizing locations shall comply with the appropriate provisions of 13.4.1.

9.5.3.2 Gas Equipment — Laboratory. Gas appliances shall be of an approved design and installed in accordance with NFPA 54, *National Fuel Gas Code*. Shutoff valves shall be legibly marked to identify the material they control.

9.6 Administration

9.6.1 Policies.

The FDA recommends the following from "Safe Practices for Handling and Operating Oxygen Equipment" [3] (http://www.fda.gov/cdrh/oxyreg.html), which can be used for training purposes as a summary of, and supplement to, much of the material in this chapter:

> Oxygen used in the medical profession can be very hazardous. Although oxygen does not burn, it does support combustion. A material which will not burn in air may burn in high pressure pure oxygen — such as the metal in oxygen regulators or cylinders. Comprehensive guidelines and training on safe practices for handling oxygen are available from several sources. . . . Some general guidelines for minimizing the chance of fire are provided below:

Storage, Maintenance and Handling:

- Do not allow smoking around oxygen.
- Store oxygen in clean, dry locations away from direct sunlight.
- Do not allow post valves, regulators, gauges, and fittings to come into contact with oils, greases, organic lubricants, rubber or any other combustible substance.
- Make sure that any cleaning, repair or transfilling of oxygen equipment is performed by qualified, properly trained staff.
- Do not work on oxygen equipment with ordinary tools. Designate special tools, clean them and store them for Use With Oxygen Equipment Only.
- Ensure that any components added to the regulator, e.g., gauge guards, are installed so that they do not block the regulator vent holes.
- Use plugs, caps and plastic bags to protect "off duty" equipment from dust and dirt.
- Particulate migration from the cylinder can be minimized by the installation of a standoff tube (bayonette) at the inlet of the post valve.

Use:

- Make sure that staff using oxygen equipment are adequately trained in its operation and in oxygen safety and have knowledge of manufacturers instructions for using the equipment.
- Visually inspect the post valve gasket and regulator inlet prior to installation. If they are not visually clean they should not be used.
- Momentarily open and close ("Crack") the post valve to blow out debris prior to installing a regulator.
- Ensure that the regulator is set with the flow knob in the off position before attaching it to the cylinder.
- Position the equipment so that valve is pointed away from the user and any other persons.
- Open the cylinder valve slowly and completely to minimize the heat produced and achieve the desired flow conditions within the equipment.
- Do not look at the regulator pressure gauge until the cylinder valve is fully opened.

9.6.1.1 Elimination of Sources of Ignition.

9.6.1.1.1 Smoking materials (e.g., matches, cigarettes, lighters, lighter fluid, tobacco in any form) shall be removed from patients receiving respiratory therapy.

FAQ ▶ What are the most common sources of ignition in areas of respiratory therapy?

Lighted cigarettes, cigars, and pipes are the most common sources of ignition where respiratory therapy is administered. Smoking regulations should be developed to eliminate the introduction of these ignition sources into the area of administration. (See 3.3.13, *Area of Administration,* and 9.6.1.1 for requirements on elimination of sources of ignition.) Alcohol, acetone, and other ignition sources used in conjunction with other respiratory care procedures — such as removal of tape residue from a patient's face post-extubation — however, are generally still present at the bedside.

It is very important that visitors, patients, and staff be informed of a facility's smoking policies to avoid jeopardizing the safety of patients, other visitors, and staff. A no-smoking policy should be developed for the entire facility to avoid confusion and to generally reduce the hazard from smoking.

9.6.1.1.2* No sources of open flame, including candles, shall be permitted in the area of administration.

A

A.9.6.1.1.2 Patients and hospital personnel in the area of administration should be advised of respiratory therapy hazards and regulations.

Visitors should be cautioned of these hazards through the prominent posting of signs *(see 9.4.4).*

9.6.1.1.3* Sparking toys shall not be permitted in any patient care area.

Young children and their families cannot be expected to understand the hazards associated with the administration of respiratory therapy. It is incumbent upon respiratory therapy personnel and other staff to explain these hazards and the measures necessary to prevent accidents/incidents.

A.9.6.1.1.3 Such toys have been associated with fire incidents in health care facilities.

A suggested text for precautionary signs for oxygen tent canopies and oxygen hoods used in pediatric nursing units is the following:

CAUTION: OXYGEN IN USE
ONLY TOYS APPROVED BY NURSES
MAY BE GIVEN TO CHILD

9.6.1.1.4 Nonmedical appliances that have hot surfaces or sparking mechanisms shall not be permitted within oxygen-delivery equipment or within the site of intentional expulsion.

The word *hot* is meant to be *hot to the touch.* To understand this requirement, it is important to carefully read the definition of *Oxygen-Delivery Equipment* (3.3.132 and A.3.3.132) and *Site of Intentional Expulsion* (3.3.170 and A.3.3.170). In practical terms, the only types of equipment where non-medical appliances might be inside oxygen-delivery equipment include closed incubators and oxygen tents, or possibly an oxygen hood. For further explanation, see 8.5.2.4 and the commentary following A.8.5.2.4.

9.6.1.2 Misuse of Flammable Substances.

Note that in 9.6.1.2.1, 9.6.1.2.2, and 9.6.1.2.3, restrictions on the use of flammable substances in oxygen-enriched atmospheres are not related to the amount of substance used (either momentarily or over a period of time) but simply to their use.

9.6.1.2.1 Flammable or combustible aerosols or vapors, such as alcohol, shall not be administered in oxygen-enriched atmospheres *(see B.6.1.11).*

9.6.1.2.2 Oil, grease, or other flammable substances shall not be used on/in oxygen equipment.

It is important that staff who service and clean oxygen equipment be supplied with nonflammable substances and be made aware of the hazards of using flammable substances.

9.6.1.2.3 Flammable and combustible liquids shall not be permitted within the site of intentional expulsion.

The *site of intentional expulsion* is defined in 3.3.170 as "all points within 0.3 m (1 ft) of a point at which an oxygen-enriched atmosphere is intentionally vented to the atmosphere." (See Exhibit 9.4.)

9.6.1.3 Servicing and Maintenance of Equipment.

9.6.1.3.1 Defective equipment shall be immediately removed from service.

9.6.1.3.2 Defective electrical apparatus shall not be used.

9.6.1.3.3 Areas designated for the servicing of oxygen equipment shall be clean, free of oil and grease, and not used for the repair of other equipment.

Exhibit 9.4 Site of intentional expulsion.

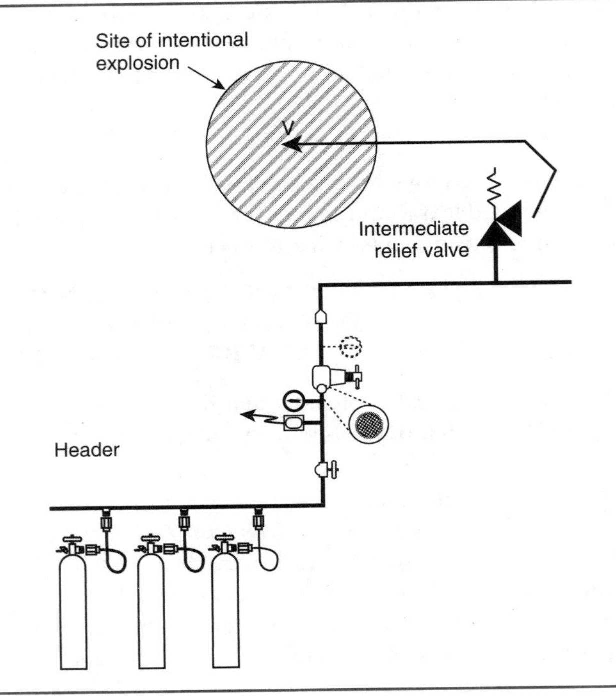

9.6.1.3.4 Service manuals, instructions, and procedures provided by the manufacturer shall be used in the maintenance of equipment.

9.6.1.3.5 A scheduled preventive maintenance program shall be followed.

9.6.2 Gases in Cylinders and Liquefied Gases in Containers.

The hazard posed by an oxygen-enriched atmosphere does not exist when oxygen is supplied to a room through piping but is not being used. It is when the oxygen is actually being administered that the precautions (policies) required by 9.6.2 must be taken. Staff should be taught to turn off piped oxygen when not in use in order to prevent its accumulation.

The attachment of a flowmeter (see Exhibit 3.4) to a station outlet would not automatically require the precautionary measures listed in this subsection, provided the flowmeter is in the off mode. However, once a device is connected to the flowmeter, the measures listed must be followed.

9.6.2.1 Qualification and Training of Personnel.

9.6.2.1.1* Personnel concerned with the application and maintenance of medical gases and others who handle medical gases and the cylinders that contain the medical gases shall be trained on the risks associated with their handling and use.

A.9.6.2.1.1 "Personnel" typically includes physicians, nurses, nursing assistants, respiratory therapists, engineers, technicians, and others.

9.6.2.1.2 The health care facilities shall provide programs of continuing education for their personnel.

9.6.2.1.3 Continuing education programs shall include periodic review of safety guidelines and usage requirements for medical gases and the cylinders. *(See Sections B.2 and B.6.)*

9.6.2.1.4 Equipment shall be serviced only by personnel trained in the maintenance and operation of the equipment.

9.6.2.2 Transfilling Cylinders.

9.6.2.2.1 Mixing of compressed gases in cylinders shall be prohibited.

Use of the term *mixing* in 9.6.2.2.1 is intended to mean the combining of two *different* gases. The combining of two different cylinders with the *same* gas is called *transfilling*. The mixing of some types of gases can cause an explosion.

◀ **FAQ**
What is the difference between *mixing* of gases and *transfilling* of gases?

Such mixing of different gases in cylinders should not be confused with the administration of various combinations of gases during surgery or respiratory therapy. The latter activity is the result of much research on combinations that do not create a hazard.

9.6.2.2.2 Transfer of gaseous oxygen from one cylinder to another shall be in accordance with CGA P-2.5, *Transfilling of High Pressure Gaseous Oxygen to be Used for Respiration.*

Although adherence to CGA Pamphlet P-2.5, *Transfilling of High Pressure Gaseous Oxygen to be Used for Respiration* [4], minimizes hazards, health care facilities need to ensure that the procedures in CGA P-2.5 are consistently followed. Patient, staff, and visitor safety can all be adversely affected if these procedures are not followed.

It should be noted that transfilling is allowed only for oxygen because procedures for other gases used in the medical environment have not yet been developed.

9.6.2.2.3 Transfer of any gases from one cylinder to another in patient care areas of health care facilities shall be prohibited.

CGA Pamphlet P-2.6, *Transfilling of Liquid Oxygen Used for Respiration* [5], outlines specific procedures to be followed when transferring liquid oxygen from one container to another. CGA Pamphlet P-2.7, *Guide for the Safe Storage, Handling, and Use of Portable Liquid Oxygen Systems in Healthcare Facilities* [6], was developed specifically for health care facilities, complementing CGA Pamphlet P-2.6 [5].

The term *prohibited* emphasizes concerns regarding transfilling gases between cylinders or mixing gases. The unpredictability of the results of these activities justifies this concern. (The term *transfilling,* as used throughout 9.6.2.2, applies only to the transfer of gaseous oxygen or oxygen-containing mixtures at high pressure.) See 9.6.2.3 regarding conditions under which transfilling is allowed. Mixing of compressed gases is never allowed. A cross-connection can be considered a mixing of gases and presents the same hazard as mixing of compressed gases (never allowed).

Also see 3.3.138, *Patient Care Area.*

9.6.2.3 Transferring Liquid Oxygen. Transferring of liquid oxygen from one container to another shall comply with 9.6.2.3.1 or 9.6.2.3.2, as applicable.

9.6.2.3.1 Transfer to reservoirs or portable units over 50 psi (344.74 kPa) shall include the following:

(1) A designated area is separated fom any portion of a facility wherein patients are housed, examined, or treated by a fire barrier of 1 hour fire-resistive construction.
(2) The area is mechanically ventilated, is sprinklered, and has ceramic or concrete flooring.
(3) the area is posted with signs indicating that transferring is occurring, and that smoking in the immediate area is not allowed.
(4) The individual filling the portable container has been properly trained in the filling procedures.

9.6.2.3.2 Transfer to portable containers at 50 psi (344.74 kPa) and under shall include the following:

(1) The area is well-ventilated and has noncombustible flooring.
(2) The area is posted with signs indicating that smoking in the area is not allowed.
(3) The individual filling the portable container has been properly trained in the filling procedure.

(4) The guidelines of CGA P-2.6, *Transfilling of Low-Pressure Liquid Oxygen to be Used for Respiration,* and CGA P-2.7, *Guide for the Safe Storage, Handling and Use of Portable Liquid Oxygen Systems in Health Care Facilities,* are met.

9.6.2.4 Ambulatory Patients. Ambulatory patients on oxygen therapy shall be permitted access to all flame and smoke free areas within the health care facility.

The use of portable oxygen systems has grown dramatically in the United States. Although the scope of NFPA 99 generally limits the requirements to the confines of health care facilities, the allowances and restrictions afforded to patients receiving oxygen therapy inside a health care facility should be accorded and followed by persons *outside* the facility. Paragraph 9.6.2.4 places some responsibilities on both the users and owners of establishments. Users need to be aware of the environment they are entering and whether or not a "no open flame" policy exists. And owners need to enforce whatever policy is established for designated areas. Appropriate signs warning that oxygen might be in use or directing oxygen users to places where they can safely sit should be posted. Ensuring the safety of all persons in an area or room can be further compounded if a language barrier exists.

Many people mistakenly believe that oxygen is a flammable or explosive gas. Paragraph 9.6.2.4 is intended to show that the use of oxygen is safe when reasonable precautions are taken. See Chapter 19 for further safety requirements for the home environment.

9.6.3 Use (Including Information and Warning Signs).

9.6.3.1 Labeling.

9.6.3.1.1 Equipment listed for use in oxygen-enriched atmospheres shall be so labeled.

See 3.2.6 for the definition of *Listed*. The wording of 9.6.3.1.1 should not be interpreted to mean that such equipment must be listed (see also 10.2.7.2 and 10.2.9.3).

9.6.3.1.2 Oxygen-metering equipment and pressure-reducing regulators shall be conspicuously labeled:

OXYGEN — USE NO OIL

9.6.3.1.3 Flowmeters, pressure-reducing regulators, and oxygen-dispensing apparatus shall be clearly and permanently labeled, designating the gas or mixture of gases for which they are intended.

9.6.3.1.4 Apparatus whose calibration or function is dependent on gas density shall be labeled as to the proper supply gas gauge pressure (kPa/psi) for which it is intended.

9.6.3.1.5 Oxygen-metering equipment, pressure-reducing regulators, humidifiers, and nebulizers shall be labeled with the name of the manufacturer or supplier.

9.6.3.1.6 Cylinders and containers shall be labeled in accordance with CGA C-7, *Guide to the Preparation of Precautionary Labeling and Marking of Compressed Gas Containers.* Color coding shall not be utilized as a primary method of determining cylinder or container content.

Patient safety depends on delivering the right gas to the patient. Failure to deliver the right gas can easily result in a fatality.

9.6.3.1.7 All labeling shall be durable and withstand cleansing or disinfection.

9.6.3.2* Signs.

A.9.6.3.2 Precautionary signs should be at least 21 cm × 28 cm (8 in. × 11 in.) in size.

Any material that can burn in air will burn more rapidly in the presence of oxygen.

Special signs and additional precautionary measures should be employed whenever foreign languages present a communication problem. *(See Figure A.9.6.3.2.)*

Any material that can burn in air will burn more rapidly in the presence of oxygen. No electrical equipment is allowed within an oxygen enclosure or within 1.5 m (5 ft) of it.

Figure A.9.6.3.2 A Suggested Minimum Text for Precautionary Signs.

NFPA 99 not only requires smoke-free health care facilities to post appropriate signs only at major entrances to meet the signage requirement, but it also requires a facility to strictly enforce no-smoking policies. With numerous signs prominently displaying a facility's smoke-free policy, and good enforcement of this policy, the level of protection discussed in A.9.6.3.2 is sufficient to prevent smoking-related fire hazards.

Exhibit 9.5 is an example of a label on an oxygen cylinder. If there is any doubt about the contents of a cylinder or container, a sample of the contents should be analyzed.

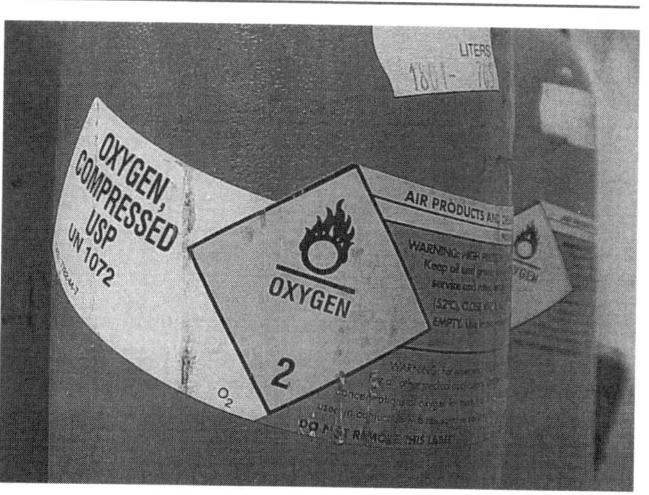

EXHIBIT 9.5 Sample labeling on an oxygen cylinder in a health care facility. (Courtesy of Rob Swift and Prince William Health System)

9.6.3.2.1 In health care facilities where smoking is not prohibited, precautionary signs readable from a distance of 1.5 m (5 ft) shall be conspicuously displayed wherever supplemental oxygen is in use and in aisles and walkways leading to that area; they shall be attached to adjacent doorways or to building walls or be supported by other appropriate means.

9.6.3.2.2 In health care facilities where smoking is prohibited and signs are prominently (strategically) placed at all major entrances, secondary signs with no-smoking language shall not be required.

9.6.3.2.3 The nonsmoking policies shall be strictly enforced.

9.6.3.3 Transportation, Storage, and Use of Equipment.

9.6.3.3.1 Flow-control valves on administering equipment shall be closed prior to connection and when not in use.

Releasing the pressure on the gauge by the flow control valve while the cylinder is not in use extends the life of the gauge itself.

9.6.3.3.2 Apparatus shall not be stored or transported with liquid agents in reservoirs.

9.6.3.3.3 Care shall be observed in attaching connections from gas services to equipment and from equipment to patients.

Accepted procedures should always be followed when making attachments.

9.6.3.3.4 Fixed or adjustable orifice mechanisms, metering valves, regulators, and gauges shall not be connected directly to high-pressure cylinders unless specifically listed for such use and provided with appropriate safety devices.

9.6.3.3.5 Equipment shall only be serviced by qualified personnel.

Serious harm to patients can result from improper maintenance on equipment. Many types of gas delivery equipment, such as ventilators and anesthesia machines, are used for life support.

9.7 Operation and Management of Cylinders

9.7.1 Administration. Administrative authorities of health care organizations shall provide policies and procedures for safe practices.

9.7.1.1 Purchase specifications shall include the following:

(1) Specifications for cylinders
(2) Marking of cylinders, regulators, and valves
(3) Proper connection of cylinders supplied to the facility
(4) Cylinders shall be permitted to be fitted with valves that include a means to slow the initial opening pressurization.

9.7.1.2 Training procedures shall include the following:

(1) Maintenance programs in accordance with the manufacturer's recommendations for the piped gas system
(2) Use and transport of equipment and the proper handling of cylinders, containers, hand trucks, supports, and valve protection caps
(3) Proper uses of the medical–surgical vacuum system in order to eliminate practices that reduce the system's effectiveness, such as leaving suction tips and catheters open when not actually aspirating, and using equipment arrangements that are improperly trapped or are untrapped
(4) Verify gas content and mechanical connection specificity of each cylinder or container prior to placing them into service.
(5) Annual training by the supplier on the operation of a bulk cryogenic system when provided.

9.7.1.3 Policies for enforcement shall include the following:

(1) Regulations for the storage and handling of cylinders and containers of oxygen and nitrous oxide
(2) Regulations for the safe handling of oxygen and nitrous oxide in anesthetizing locations
(3) Prompt evaluation of all signal warnings and all necessary measures taken to re-establish the proper functions of the medical gas and vacuum systems
(4) Organizational capability and resources to cope with a complete loss of any medical gas or vacuum system
(5) All tests required in 5.1.12.3 shall be successfully conducted prior to the use of any medical gas or vacuum piping system for patient care
(6) Locations intended for the delivery vehicle delivering cryogenic liquid to bulk cryogenic liquid systems shall remain open and shall not be used for any other purpose (e.g., vehicle parking, storage of trash containers)

9.7.2 Special Precautions for Handling Oxygen Cylinders and Manifolds. Handling of oxygen cylinders and manifolds shall be based on CGA G-4, *Oxygen*.

9.7.2.1 Oxygen cylinders, containers, and associated equipment shall be protected from contact with oil or grease. Specific precautions shall include the following:

(1) Oil, grease, or readily flammable materials shall never be permitted to come in contact with oxygen cylinders, valves, regulators, gauges, or fittings.
(2) Regulators, fittings, or gauges shall never be lubricated with oil or any other flammable substance.
(3) Oxygen cylinders or apparatus shall never be handled with oily or greasy hands, gloves, or rags.

9.7.2.2 Equipment associated with oxygen shall be protected from contamination. Specific precautions shall include the following:

(1) Particles of dust and dirt shall be cleared from cylinder valve openings by slightly opening and closing the valve before applying any fitting to the cylinder.
(2) The high-pressure valve on the oxygen cylinder shall be opened slowly before bringing the apparatus to the patient or the patient to the apparatus.
(3) An oxygen cylinder shall never be draped with any materials such as hospital gowns, masks, or caps.
(4) Cylinder-valve protection caps, where provided, shall be kept in place and be hand-tightened, except when cylinders are in use or connected for use.
(5) Valves shall be closed on all empty cylinders in storage.

9.7.2.3 Cylinders shall be protected from damage. Specific procedures shall include the following:

(1) Oxygen cylinders shall be protected from abnormal mechanical shock, which is liable to damage the cylinder, valve, or safety device.
(2) Oxygen cylinders shall not be stored near elevators, gangways, or in locations where heavy moving objects will strike them or fall on them.
(3) Cylinders shall be protected from the tampering of unauthorized individuals.
(4) Cylinders or cylinder valves shall not be repaired, painted, or altered.
(5) Safety relief devices in valves or cylinders shall never be tampered with.
(6) Valve outlets clogged with ice shall be thawed with warm — not boiling — water.
(7) A torch flame shall never be permitted under any circumstances to come in contact with cylinder valves or safety devices.
(8) Sparks and flame shall be kept away from cylinders.
(9) Even if they are considered to be empty, cylinders shall never be used as rollers, supports, or for any purpose other than that for which the supplier intended them.
(10) Large cylinders (exceeding size E) and containers larger than 45 kg (100 lb) weight shall be transported on a proper hand truck or cart complying with 9.5.3.1.
(11) Freestanding cylinders shall be properly chained or supported in a proper cylinder stand or cart.
(12) Cylinders shall not be supported by radiators, steam pipes, or heat ducts.

9.7.2.4 Cylinders and their contents shall be handled with care. Specific procedures shall include the following:

(1) Oxygen fittings, valves, regulators, or gauges shall never be used for any service other than that of oxygen.
(2) Gases of any type shall never be mixed in an oxygen cylinder or any other cylinder.
(3) Oxygen shall always be dispensed from a cylinder through a pressure regulator.
(4) The cylinder valve shall be opened slowly, with the face of the indicator on the regulator pointed away from all persons.

(5) Oxygen shall be referred to by its proper name, oxygen, not air, and liquid oxygen referred to by its proper name, not liquid air.
(6) Oxygen shall never be used as a substitute for compressed air.
(7) The markings stamped on cylinders shall not be tampered with because it is against federal statutes to change these markings without written authority from the Bureau of Explosives.
(8) Markings used for the identification of contents of cylinders shall not be defaced or removed, including decals, tags, stenciled marks, and the upper half of the shipping tag.
(9) The owner of the cylinder shall be notified if any condition has occurred that might permit any foreign substance to enter a cylinder or valve, giving details and cylinder number.
(10) Neither cylinders nor containers shall be placed in proximity of radiators, steam pipes, heat ducts, or other sources of heat.
(11) Very cold cylinders or containers shall be handled with care to avoid injury.

9.7.2.5 Oxygen equipment that is defective shall not be used until one of the following tasks has been performed:

(1) It has been repaired by competent in-house personnel.
(2) It has repaired by the manufacturer or his or her authorized agent.
(3) It has been replaced.

9.7.2.6 Regulators that are in need of repair or cylinders having valves that do not operate properly shall never be used.

9.7.3 Special Precautions for Making Cylinder and Container Connections.

9.7.3.1* Wrenches and tools used to connect respiratory therapy equipment shall not be required to be nonsparking.

A.9.7.3.1 Use of so-called nonsparking wrenches and tools is not necessary.

9.7.3.2 Cylinder valves shall be opened and connected in accordance with the following procedure:

(1) Make certain that apparatus and cylinder valve connections and cylinder wrenches are free of foreign materials.
(2) Turn the cylinder valve outlet away from personnel. Stand to the side — not in front and not in back. Before connecting the apparatus to cylinder valve, momentarily open cylinder valve to eliminate dust.
(3) Make connection of apparatus to cylinder valve. Tighten connection nut securely with a wrench.
(4) Release the low-pressure adjustment screw of the regulator completely.
(5) Slowly open cylinder valve to full open position.
(6) Slowly turn in the low-pressure adjustment screw on the regulator until the proper working pressure is obtained.
(7) Open the valve to the utilization apparatus.

9.7.3.3 Connections for containers shall be made in accordance with the container manufacturer's operating instructions.

9.7.4 Special Precautions for the Care of Safety Mechanisms.

9.7.4.1 Personnel using cylinders and containers and other equipment covered in this chapter shall be familiar with the Pin-Index Safety System and the Diameter-Index Safety System. Both are designed to prevent utilization of the wrong gas.

9.7.4.2 Safety relief mechanisms, noninterchangeable connectors, and other safety features shall not be removed, altered, or replaced.

9.7.5 Special Precautions — Storage of Cylinders and Containers.

9.7.5.1 Storage shall be planned so that cylinders can be used in the order in which they are received from the supplier.

9.7.5.2 If stored within the same enclosure, empty cylinders shall be segregated from full cylinders.

9.7.5.3 Empty cylinders shall be marked to avoid confusion and delay if a full cylinder is needed in a rapid manner.

9.7.5.4 Cylinders stored in the open shall be protected as follows:

(1) Against extremes of weather and from the ground beneath to prevent rusting
(2) During winter, against accumulations of ice or snow
(3) In summer, screened against continuous exposure to direct rays of the sun in those localities where extreme temperatures prevail

9.7.5.5 No cylinders containing oxygen or nitrous oxide, other than those connected to anesthetic apparatus, shall be kept or stored in anesthetizing locations.

9.8 Gas/Vacuum Systems Maintenance and Record Keeping

9.8.1 Permanent records of all tests required by 5.1.12.3.1 through 5.1.12.3.14 shall be maintained in the organization's files.

9.8.2 The supplier of the bulk cryogenic liquid system shall provide documentation of vaporizer(s) sizing criteria to the facility.

9.8.3 An annual review of bulk system capacity shall be conducted to ensure the source system has sufficient capacity.

9.8.4 Central supply systems for nonflammable medical gases shall conform to the following:

(1) Be inspected annually
(2) Be maintained by a qualified representative of the equipment owner
(3) Have a record of the annual inspection available for review by the authority having jurisdiction

9.8.5 A periodic testing procedure for nonflammable medical gas/vacuum and related alarm systems shall be implemented.

9.8.6 Whenever modifications are made or maintenance is performed that breaches the system, the verification tests specified in 5.1.12.3 shall be conducted on the downstream portions of the medical gas piping system.

9.8.7 A maintenance program shall be established for the following:

(1) The medical air compressor supply system in accordance with the manufacturer's recommendations.
(2) The facility shall establish a testing and calibration procedure that assures carbon monoxide monitors are calibrated at least annually or more often if recommended by the manufacturer.
(3)* Both the medical–surgical vacuum piping system and the secondary equipment attached to medical–surgical vacuum station inlets to ensure the continued good performance of the entire medical–surgical vacuum system.

Exhibit 9.6 illustrates a typical vacuum station inlet with a device connected to it. The receptacle and cover plate above the inlet are red, indicating that the inlet is wired to the essential electrical system.

A.9.8.7(3) Suction collection bottles that are used as part of patient treatment equipment should be equipped with an overflow shutoff device to prevent carryover of fluids into equipment of the piping system. It is recommended that a separate vacuum trap with shutoff be used between the suction collection bottle and the vacuum system station inlet.

(4) The WAGD system to assure performance.

9.8.8 Audible and visual alarm indicators shall meet the following requirements:

(1) Be periodically tested to determine that they are functioning properly
(2) Have the records of the test maintained until the next test is performed

9.8.9* Medical–surgical vacuum station inlet terminal performance, as required in 5.1.12.3.10.4, shall be tested as follows:

(1) On a regular preventive maintenance schedule as determined by the facility maintenance staff
(2) Based on flow of free air (Nl/min or SCFM) into a station inlet while simultaneously checking the vacuum level

A.9.8.9 The test can be conducted using a rotometer or other flow-measuring device, and a vacuum gauge, where both devices are fitted with the appropriate station inlet connector.

The test procedure will be to measure the flow with the station inlet wide open while simultaneously measuring the vacuum level at an adjacent wall station inlet or other station inlet on the same branch line.

It is recognized that this criterion might not be met by some existing systems. It is the responsibility of facility personnel, based on past experience and use, to determine the acceptable alternate performance criterion for their system(s).

9.9 Policies and Procedures

9.9.1 Administration.

Administrative authorities of health care organizations shall provide policies and procedures for safe practices.

9.9.1.1 Purchase specifications shall include the following:

(1) Specifications for cylinders
(2) Marking of cylinders, regulators, and valves
(3) Proper connection of cylinders supplied to the facility

9.9.1.2 Training procedures shall include the following:

(1) Maintenance programs in accordance with the manufacturer's recommendations for the piped gas system
(2) Use and transport of equipment and the proper handling of cylinders, containers, hand trucks, supports, and valve protection caps
(3) Proper uses of the medical–surgical vacuum system in order to eliminate practices that reduce the system's effectiveness, such as leaving suction tips and catheters open when not actually aspirating, and using equipment arrangements that are improperly trapped or are untrapped

EXHIBIT 9.6 Vacuum station inlet.

9.9.1.3 Policies for enforcement shall include the following:

(1) Regulations for the storage and handling of cylinders and containers of oxygen and nitrous oxide
(2) Regulations for the safe handling of oxygen and nitrous oxide in anesthetizing locations
(3) Prompt evaluation of all signal warnings and the performance of all necessary measures to reestablish the proper functions of the medical gas system
(4) The capability and resources of the organization to cope with a complete loss of any medical gas system
(5) All tests required in 5.3.12 successfully conducted prior to the use of any medical gas piping system for patient care

REFERENCES CITED IN COMMENTARY

1. FDA and NIOSH, Public Health Advisory "Explosions and Fires from Oxygen Regulators" (http://www.fda.gov/cdrh/oxyreg.html).
2. ECRI, Medical Device Safety Report "Are Aluminum Oxygen Regulators Safe?"
3. FDA, "Safe Practices for Handling and Operating Oxygen Equipment" (http://www.fda.gov/cdrh/oxyreg.html).
4. CGA Pamphlet P-2.5, *Transfilling of High Pressure Gaseous Oxygen to be Used for Respiration,* 2000 edition.
5. CGA Pamphlet P-2.6, *Low-pressure Transfilling of Liquid Oxygen to be Used for Respiration,* 1995 edition.
6. CGA Pamphlet P-2.7, *Guide for the Safe Storage, Handling, and Use of Portable Liquid Oxygen Systems in Healthcare Facilities,* 2000 edition.

CHAPTER 10

Manufacturer Requirements

The contemporary health care facility is filled with a myriad of sophisticated equipment manufactured for use in the delivery of patient care. In many cases, the safety of such equipment has major consequences for the well-being of patients and staff alike.

Chapter 10 addresses safety requirements for manufactured equipment used in health care facilities. At present, this chapter is devoted exclusively to electrical appliances that are related to patient care.

10.1* Applicability

This chapter applies to equipment manufactured for use in the delivery of patient care.

A.10.1 The application of requirements contained in this chapter for specific types of health care facilities can be found in Chapters 13 through 19.

10.2* Patient-Care–Related Electrical Appliances

A.10.2 It is the intent that Section 10.2 should not be used by authorities having jurisdiction over health care facilities to limit health care facilities' purchases to patient-care–related electrical appliances meeting these requirements. Rather, it is the intent to encourage equipment manufacturers to conduct the specified tests in order to ensure state-of-the-art electrical safety in their patient-care–related electrical appliances. Similarly, it is not the intent of the Technical Committee to require health care facilities to conduct tests using these manufacturer requirements to verify that their patient-care–related electrical appliances are in conformance with the requirements of this chapter. In this respect, it is the intent of the Committee that health care facilities perform only those tests specified in 8.4.1.

The requirements in Section 10.2 were developed to improve the safety of appliances manufactured for use in health care facilities. As in Chapters 4 through 9, this chapter does not specify where these requirements are applicable. Instead, their application is determined by references in Chapters 13 through 19, by specific references in other chapters (as in the case in Chapter 8), or by a facility or an authority choosing to enforce these requirements.

10.2.1 Mechanical Construction.

10.2.1.1 Separation of Patient Circuits. Patient-connected circuits within an appliance shall be separated or insulated from all other circuits within the appliance to prevent accidental contact with hazardous voltages or currents.

10.2.1.2 Mechanical Stability. The appliance shall be mechanically stable in the position of normal use. If the appliance is intended for use in an anesthetizing location, 13.4.1 shall apply.

10.2.2 Electrical Requirements — Appliances Equipped with Power Cords.

10.2.2.1* Attachment Plugs. Attachment plugs listed for the purpose shall be used on all cord-connected appliances.

A.10.2.2.1 Hospital grade listing is acceptable but not required.

FAQ ▶
Can a light duty plug be used in a health care facility?

In the past, health care facilities were frequently provided with molded or other light-duty plugs appropriate for household use but not for the severe conditions that can exist in hospitals. See Exhibit 10.1 for an example of a failed molded plug whose grounding connection has failed probably because of repeated flexing. Note that this would not be obvious on visual inspection.

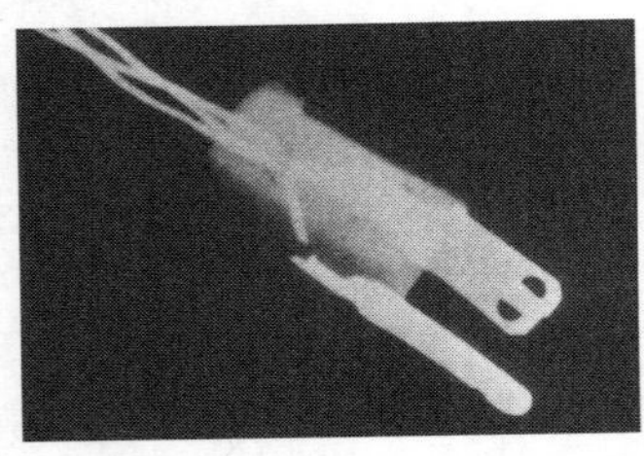

EXHIBIT 10.1 An X-ray of a conventional use molded plug.

Because of the design of these light-duty plugs it was possible that their inside ground connection, between the wire and the pin, could break and not be evident because the device itself would still be able to function. Although a hospital room might often seem like a domestic bedroom, the stresses and strains of patient care can subject equipment to the equivalent of heavy industrial use. Hazards such as these have led to the development of heavy-duty plugs that can withstand hospital abuse. These plugs are labeled *hospital grade* and are appropriately marked.

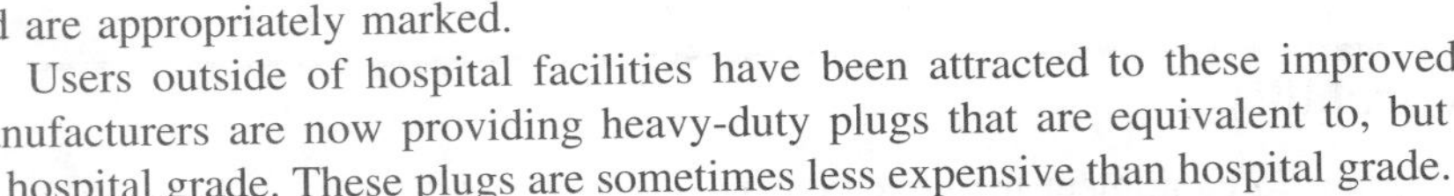

Users outside of hospital facilities have been attracted to these improved plugs, and manufacturers are now providing heavy-duty plugs that are equivalent to, but not labeled as, hospital grade. These plugs are sometimes less expensive than hospital grade. See Exhibit 10.2 for an example of a heavy-duty plug. The high-impact casing of this plug, along with a power cord that is also heavy-duty, prevents accidental damage or disconnection. The see-through cover of this particular model allows for quick plug inspection. It is the intent of this section to allow the use of such heavy-duty plugs. Household or other light-duty plugs, such as molded rubber plugs that secure the grounding pin only by rubber, are not acceptable for use in hospital facilities.

EXHIBIT 10.2 A typical heavy-duty plug for portable equipment.

10.2.2.1.1* Construction and Use. The attachment plug shall be a two-pole, three-wire grounding type.

A.10.2.2.1.1 See Sections 410.56, 410.57, and 410.58 of NFPA 70, *National Electrical Code*.

10.2.2.1.2 Appliances used in special locations or for special purposes shall be equipped with attachment plugs equipped with plugs approved for the location *(e.g., see 4.3.2.2.6)*.

10.2.2.1.3 Power cords of an appliance that do not require and do not contain a grounding conductor shall not be fitted with a grounding-type plug *(see 10.2.2.2.5)*.

10.2.2.1.4 Appliances supplied by other than 120 V single-phase systems shall use the grounding-type plug (cap) appropriate for the particular power system.

10.2.2.1.5 The grounding prong of the plug shall be the first to be connected to and the last to be disconnected from the receptacle.

By making the green wire longer than the phase conductors and the grounding prong on the plug longer than the phase prongs, the phase conductors will disengage first, as required by 10.2.2.1.5. (See Exhibit 10.3.) This order of disengagement is desired because it keeps the equipment grounded until the phase wire prongs are disengaged.

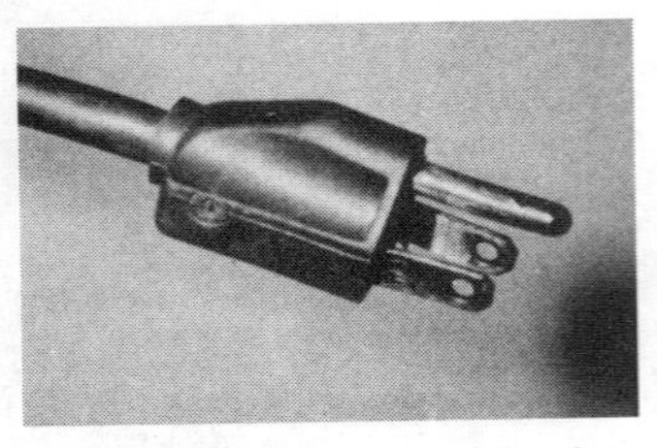

EXHIBIT 10.3 Receptacle and grounding prong of plug.

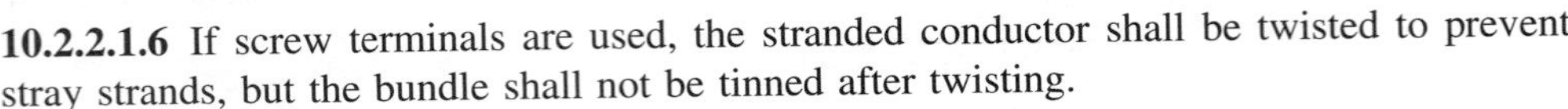

10.2.2.1.6 If screw terminals are used, the stranded conductor shall be twisted to prevent stray strands, but the bundle shall not be tinned after twisting.

It is the intent of 10.2.2.1.6 that twisted wires not be tinned. This position is based on experience and reports, such as in *Health Devices* [1], that indicate more occurrences of loosening connections with tinned, twisted wires than with untinned, twisted wires. No controlled studies of this issue have been conducted of late, however.

 **FAQ**
Why should twisted wires of attachment plugs be untinned?

Aluminum wire should be used only with plugs specifically designed for such wire.

10.2.2.1.7 If the conductor is not twisted, it shall be attached by an approved terminal lug.

10.2.2.1.8 The power-cord conductors shall be arranged so that the conductors are not under tension in the plug.

10.2.2.1.9 The grounding conductor shall be the last one to disconnect when a failure of the plug's strain relief allows the energized conductors to be disrupted.

10.2.2.1.10 Strain Relief. Strain relief shall be provided.

10.2.2.1.10.1 The strain relief shall not cause thinning of the conductor insulation.

10.2.2.1.10.2 The strain relief of replaceable plugs shall be capable of being disassembled.

10.2.2.1.10.3 Plugs shall be permitted to be integrally molded onto the cord jacket if the design is listed for the purpose.

10.2.2.1.11 Testing. The wiring of each cord assembly shall be tested for continuity and polarity at the time of manufacture, when assembled into an appliance, and when repaired.

10.2.2.2 Power Cords.

10.2.2.2.1 Material and Gauge.

10.2.2.2.1.1 The flexible cord, including the grounding conductor, shall be of a type suitable for the particular application, listed for use at a voltage equal to or greater than the rated power line voltage of the appliance, and have an ampacity, as given in Table 400.5(A) of NFPA 70, *National Electrical Code*, equal to or greater than the current rating of the device.

10.2.2.2.1.2* "Hard Service" (SO, ST, or STO) or "Junior Hard Service" (SJO, SJT, or SJTO) or equivalent listed flexible cord shall be used except where an appliance with a cord of another designation has been listed for the purpose.

A.10.2.2.2.1.2 "Hard Service" cord is preferable where the cord can be subject to mechanical abuse. A cord length of 3.1 m (10 ft) is recommended for general locations, and 5.5 m (18 ft) for operating rooms, but can be of a different length if designed for a specific location. See Table 400.4 of NFPA 70, *National Electrical Code*.

10.2.2.2.2 Grounding Conductor.

10.2.2.2.2.1 Each electric appliance shall be provided with a grounding conductor in its power cord.

10.2.2.2.2.2 The grounding conductor shall be no smaller than 18 AWG.

10.2.2.2.2.3 The grounding conductor of cords longer than 4.6 m (15 ft) shall be no smaller than 16 AWG.

10.2.2.2.2.4 Grounding conductors shall meet the resistance requirements of 10.2.13.2.

10.2.2.2.2.5 A grounding conductor in the power cord shall not be required for listed double-insulated appliances, but such a grounding conductor shall be permitted to be used to ground exposed conductive surfaces *(see 10.2.3.2)*.

10.2.2.2.3 Separable Cord Sets.

10.2.2.2.3.1 A separable power cord set shall be permitted to be used if it can be shown that an accidental disconnection does not pose a hazard.

10.2.2.2.3.2 Separable power cord sets shall be designed so that the grounding conductor is the first to be connected and the last to be disconnected.

10.2.2.2.3.3 Cord-set plugs and receptacles at the appliance shall be polarized in accordance with ANSI/NEMA WD 6, *Wiring Devices — Dimensional Requirements*. Appliances with separable cord sets shall meet the grounding-wire-resistance requirements of 10.2.13.2, Grounding Circuit Continuity — Measurement of Resistance, when the cord set is connected to the appliance.

10.2.2.2.3.4 Both the cord set and the means of connection to the appliance shall be listed for the purpose.

10.2.2.2.4 Connection to Circuit and Color Codes.

10.2.2.2.4.1* Power cords, regardless of whether intended for use on grounded or isolated power systems, shall be connected in accordance with the conventions of a grounded system.

A.10.2.2.2.4.1 See Sections 200.2 through 200.10 of NFPA 70, *National Electrical Code*.

10.2.2.2.4.2* The circuit conductors in the cord shall be connected to the plug and the wiring in the appliance so that any of the following devices, when used in the primary circuit, are connected to the ungrounded conductor:

(1) The center contact of an Edison base lampholder
(2) A solitary fuseholder
(3) A single-pole, overcurrent-protective device
(4) Any other single-pole, current-interrupting device

A.10.2.2.2.4.2 See Exception No. 2 to Section 210.5(b) of NFPA 70, *National Electrical Code*.

10.2.2.2.4.3 A second fuseholder or other overcurrent-protective device provided in the appliance shall be permitted to be placed in the grounded side of the line.

If a second overcurrent device is used in the grounded side of the power line in an appliance, it should preferably be ganged to the primary overcurrent device so that it is activated at the same time as the device in the ungrounded conductor.

10.2.2.2.5 Cords Without Grounding Conductors. The power cord of an appliance that does not require and does not contain a grounding conductor shall not be fitted with a grounding-type plug.

10.2.2.2.6 Testing. The wiring of each cord assembly shall be tested for continuity and polarity at the time of manufacture, when assembled into an appliance, and when repaired.

10.2.2.2.7 Cord Strain Relief.

10.2.2.2.7.1 Cord strain relief shall be provided at the attachment of the power cord to the appliance so that mechanical stress, either pull, twist, or bend, is not transmitted to internal connections.

10.2.2.2.7.2 A strain relief molded onto the cord shall be bonded to the jacket and shall be of compatible material.

10.2.2.2.8 Storage.

10.2.3 Wiring Within Appliances Equipped with Power Cords.

10.2.3.1 Protection of Wiring in Appliances. Within the appliance, the power conductors of the cord and the associated primary wiring (other than the grounding conductor) shall be mounted and dressed to minimize accidental electrical contact with the frame or exposed conductive parts of the appliance.

It has been previously noted that appliances in a health care facility might be subjected to severe physical abuse. In an emergency situation, the welfare of the appliances is secondary to the welfare of the patient, and equipment is often handled by relatively untrained personnel. Cord strain relief must therefore be well designed.

10.2.3.2* Grounding of Exposed Conductive Surfaces. All exposed conductive surfaces of an electric appliance that could become energized from internal sources shall be bonded together to provide electric continuity with the connection to the grounding conductor.

A.10.2.3.2 Size and location are the main criteria used in determining what is not likely to become energized and thus exempted from the bonding and grounding requirements. Items such as screws, nameplates, hinges, metal trim, handles, and other hardware are unlikely to become energized because of their size. If they are sufficiently isolated from internal sources they need not be grounded.

Also, it is unnecessary for exposed conductive surfaces to be grounded separately with individual or looped grounding wires if, by reliable contact or connection with other grounded metal portions (frame), these surfaces can maintain ground.

10.2.3.3 Replacement Connection. Ready replacement of the power cord shall be permitted except where the power cord is not intended to be replaced by the user.

10.2.3.4 Connection of the Grounding Conductor.

10.2.3.4.1 The grounding conductor shall be connected to the exposed metal or frame of the appliance by a terminal or bolt so that an electrical connection is always maintained.

10.2.3.4.2 The grounding connection shall remain intact during electrical or mechanical repair of the appliance, except during replacement of the power cord.

10.2.3.4.3 The grounding conductor shall be the last conductor to disconnect when a failure of the plug's strain relief at the appliance allows the energized conductors to be disrupted.

10.2.3.4.4 When a grounding conductor is not required and is not provided, the appliance shall be labeled to indicate that fact.

10.2.3.5 Connections with Grounding Conductor. Any component, such as a filter or test circuit, within an appliance that intentionally reduces the impedance between the energized conductors and the grounding conductor shall be in operation when the leakage current tests specified in 10.2.13.4 are performed.

10.2.3.6* Overcurrent Protection.

A.10.2.3.6 It is recommended that a listed overcurrent protective device be used in the power input circuit of all appliances.

◀ **FAQ**
Is an overcurrent device required in the power input circuit?

It is intended that overcurrent devices be permitted but not required. The annex text, however, recommends that such protection should be provided. If overcurrent protection is included, the requirements of 10.2.3.6 must be followed.

Overcurrent protection in an appliance is a way of protecting not only the appliance itself, but also the other appliances on the same branch circuit. The overcurrent protector opens when a fault within the appliance causes current to flow in excess of the overcurrent protector's rating. Because an appliance's overcurrent protection rating should be less than the rating of the branch circuit breaker, the branch circuit breaker will not open if a fault occurs in the appliance. When individual appliances are not protected in this way, a fault in one appliance could remove power from an entire branch circuit, a failure that could be dangerous to patients relying on the continuous operation of a number of medical electrical appliances.

10.2.3.6.1 An overcurrent protective device shall be permitted to be placed in any of the following locations:

(1) In the attachment plug
(2) In the power cord
(3) In the main body of the appliance

10.2.3.6.2 The overcurrent protective device shall precede any other components within the appliance, including the primary power-control switch.

10.2.3.6.3 Listed insulated terminal blocks or strips, listed connecting devices, and RFI filters for use on power systems shall be permitted to precede the overcurrent device *(see 10.2.3.5)*.

10.2.3.6.4 The use of overcurrent protective devices within the appliance shall be permitted.

Such internal overcurrent protective devices as permitted in 10.2.3.6.4 are not intended to serve as primary protective devices but rather to protect subcomponents of the appliance.

10.2.3.6.5 The power-control switch and overcurrent protective device shall be permitted to be combined into one component provided it is identified to indicate the combined function.

10.2.3.7 Primary Power-Control Switch.

10.2.3.7.1 A primary power-control switch when provided on an appliance shall interrupt all primary power conductors, including the neutral conductor.

10.2.3.7.2 The grounding conductor shall not be interrupted by the switch.

10.2.3.7.3 When the primary power wiring of an appliance is polarized, a primary power control switch shall not be required to interrupt the neutral conductor.

The polarization allowed in 10.2.3.7.3 must ensure that the proper connection of the appliance's neutral conductor is made to the neutral conductor of the building's electrical distribution system.

10.2.3.7.4 An in-line switch shall be permitted in a primary power cord only if the switch is listed with the appliance with which it is intended to be used.

It is recognized that there are hazards associated with in-line switches. For example, they are more easily damaged than a switch mounted on the chassis of an appliance. However, in some circumstances in-line switches could be the preferred way to control power. For example, a portable lamp whose location would make it inconvenient to use an on/off switch on the lamp base would be allowed to use an in-line switch. Therefore, the use of in-line switches is allowed, but only under the conditions specified.

10.2.3.8 Rack- or Cart-Mounted Equipment.

10.2.3.8.1 Each appliance mounted in an equipment rack or cart, when rated by the manufacturer as a stand-alone appliance, shall independently meet the requirements of 10.2.13.

Paragraph 10.2.3.8.1 refers to a condition where a single appliance is mounted on a cart and supplied by a single power cord, or several appliances are on a cart, with each supplied from a building receptacle by its own power cord. If several appliances are on a cart supplied from a receptacle that is part of the cart, so that one master power cord goes back to the building receptacle, then 10.2.3.8.2 applies.

10.2.3.8.2 When multiple appliances, as designated by the manufacturer, are mounted together in a cart or rack, and one power cord supplies power, the cart or rack shall meet the requirements of 10.2.13.

Requiring a rack or cart with one power cord takes into consideration the fact that all the leakage current passes through one main power cord. If the ground in this main power cord is broken, all the leakage current could pass through a person touching one of the appliances mounted on the rack or cart. Because of this cumulative effect, the entire system should be treated as one appliance and must adhere to the requirements of this chapter as one appliance.

10.2.4 Connectors and Connections to Devices.

10.2.4.1 Indexing of Receptacles for Patient Leads.

10.2.4.1.1 Receptacles on appliances shall be designed and constructed so that those contacts that deliver electric current in a way and of a magnitude greater than 500 μA, when measured in accordance with 10.2.13.5, are female and indexed.

It is not the intention of 10.2.4.1.1 to dictate design. However, it is recommended that careful study be given to connector selection. Inputs of multimodality monitoring equipment should be distinctive to avoid situations where, for example, an ECG signal could be confused with a pressure signal, resulting in improper signals and possible patient injury. In particular, great care should be exercised to clearly differentiate leads that deliver energy, such as powering pressure transducers, from those that only receive signals.

10.2.4.1.2 Receptacles and plugs shall be polarized if improper orientation can create a hazard.

10.2.4.2* Distinctive Receptacles for Patient Leads. Where reversal or misconnection of patient leads to an appliance constitutes a possible hazard (for example, reversal of active and dispersive electrodes of electrosurgical machines), distinctive, noninterchangeable connections shall be employed.

While this subsection specifically refers to the mating of patient leads and the receptacles on an appliance, it also implies that the lead connection design must be such that the lead cannot be inserted into a power receptacle. This could be a power receptacle on an appliance or a cart or a building receptacle.

A.10.2.4.2 The purpose of these requirements is to prevent interchanging connectors in any manner that permits the inadvertent delivery of a hazardous current to a patient. 

10.2.4.3 Patient Lead Connections.

10.2.4.3.1 Lead Termination. The connector, distal to the patient, on a patient lead shall be constructed so that the connector cannot be inserted to make contact with the live parts of a power receptacle or to engage any part of the appliance that can introduce a risk of electric shock, fire, or personal injury.

Paragraph 10.2.4.3.1 expands on the requirements in 10.2.4.1 and 10.2.4.2. Patient monitoring leads are being more widely used at the patient's bedside. The same patient leads can also be used in the home, where they are often applied by less-experienced persons more likely to make a mistake.

Some older models of patient leads used simple blade terminals as connectors to the appliance, which could also be inserted into power receptacles or extension cords. In one reported case, the color-coded ECG cables (white/black/green) were confused with the power line conductors (also white/black/green). Connection to the power line could be fatal. Although the incidence of such accidents is low, the problem can be a serious one due to the hazard level involved. Appliances are now designed with distinctive terminals. (See Exhibit 10.4.) Permanent adapters are available for the leads of existing appliances.

EXHIBIT 10.4 ECG leads, which have a special end configuration to prevent the lead from being accidentally inserted into a standard power outlet.

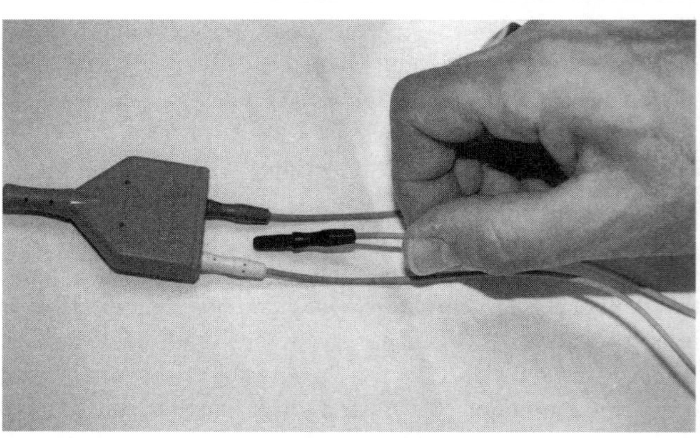

10.2.4.3.2 Isolated Patient Lead. The appliance connector of an isolated patient lead shall be constructed so that, when not inserted properly in the appliance, the end of the conductor of the lead cannot electrically contact any conductive surface.

10.2.5* Line Voltage Variations and Transients — General. All appliances shall be capable of operating within line voltage variations that conform with ANSI C84.1, *Voltage Ratings: Electric Power Systems and Equipment.*

Appliances, particularly those with digital terminal ports and controls, should be made electromagnetically resistant, such as with electromagnetic compatibility (EMC), to resist the effects of power line transients and other electromagnetic interference (EMI) and to limit their electrical signals as sources of EMI. For a further discussion of this subject, see the commentary following 8.2.5.

A.10.2.5 The design of an appliance intended for life support should minimize the effects on performance of transient, line voltage variations, or other electrical interference. The design of all appliances should minimize the production of line variations and transients.

10.2.6 General Design and Manufacturing Requirements.

10.2.6.1 Thermal Standards.

10.2.6.1.1 Electric appliances not designed to supply heat to the patient, and operated within reach of a nonambulatory patient, shall not have exposed surface temperatures in excess of 50°C (122°F).

10.2.6.1.2 Surfaces maintained in contact with the skin of patients and not intended to supply heat shall not be hotter than 40°C (104°F).

10.2.6.2 Toxic Materials.

10.2.6.2.1 Surfaces that contact patients shall be free of materials that commonly cause adverse reactions.

10.2.6.2.2 Coatings used on these surfaces shall conform to ANSI Z66.1, *Specifications for Paints and Coatings Accessible to Children to Minimize Dry Film Toxicity.*

10.2.6.3* Chemical Agents. Electric appliances containing hazardous chemicals shall be designed to facilitate the replenishment of these chemicals without spillage to protect the patient, the operating personnel, and the safety features of the appliance from such chemicals.

A.10.2.6.3 Preference should be given to the use of replaceable sealed canisters of chemicals.

10.2.6.4 Electromagnetic Compatibility. All appliances shall be designed so that they are capable of operating in a radio frequency electromagnetic environment where limits are established by IEC 60601-1-2, *Medical Electrical Equipment — General Requirements for Safety — Part 2: Collateral Standard: Electromagnetic Compatibility — Requirements and Tests.*

The problem of electromagnetic compatibility and interference is of rapidly increasing concern in health care facilities, resulting from the expanding use of electrical devices in general, and those using information processing components in particular. Such devices are inherently more subject to disturbance by electrical energy of low amplitude and over wide frequency ranges. Such disturbances can cause improper operation, give erroneous data, deliver improper therapy, or lead to electrical hazards.

Wireless communication is undergoing drastic changes in technology and regulatory control, with personal telephones, information transmission, entertainment, and so on. This technology has a potential for serious interference with health-care–related appliances. Facilities are attempting to control such interference by limiting access. However, manufacturers should be aware of the problems and design appliances to mitigate them.

10.2.6.5 Operation with Essential Electrical System.

10.2.6.5.1 General. Equipment (fixed or appliances) shall be designed to operate normally when energized by a standby power source that conforms to the requirements of Chapter 4.

10.2.6.5.2 Power Transfer.

10.2.6.5.2.1 Following transfer of power between the normal power system and the essential electrical system, a patient-care-related appliance shall resume function in the mode of operation that existed prior to the transfer.

10.2.6.5.2.2 If the appliance cannot maintain its mode of operation in the event of a power transfer, it shall default to a nonhazardous status and clearly indicate by audible or visible signals that its mode of operation has changed.

10.2.6.5.3 Programmable Appliances.

10.2.6.5.3.1 De-energization of the power supply of a programmable appliance shall not result in the loss or change of any part of the program or data required for normal operation.

10.2.6.5.3.2 Subparagraph 10.2.6.5.3.1 shall not apply to computers and programmable appliances that are not directly related to patient care.

10.2.6.5.3.3 Patient-care–related appliances that suffer a loss of program or vital data shall default to a start-up status and clearly indicate by audible or visual signals that their program or data has been altered or lost.

Pre-computer age appliances rarely were sensitive to brief interruptions of power, such as those that occur during the testing or use of the emergency electrical system. Computer hardware and software, however, can be extremely sensitive to even the briefest interruption of power.

Paragraph 10.2.6.5.3.3 does not govern design but is intended to alert manufacturers of patient-care–related appliances of the nature of this problem. It establishes performance requirements for new appliances, requiring that appliances be designed to default to a safe condition and provide warning if they can be affected by power interruption.

Facilities should ensure that existing appliances whose operating characteristics can be affected by loss of power do not become unsafe or give erroneous signals or data in the event of a power interruption. For further guidance on this subject, see the commentary following 8.2.4, 8.2.5, and 10.2.5.

10.2.7 Fire and Explosion Hazards.

10.2.7.1 Materials and Supplies.

10.2.7.1.1 Materials used in the construction of, and supplies for, electric appliances shall be noncombustible or flame retardant and impermeable to liquids (such as water and intravenous solutions) and gases to the extent practicable; or the materials used in the construction of, and supplies for, electric appliances shall not ignite from internal heating or arcing resulting from any and all possible fault conditions.

10.2.7.1.2 Materials used in the construction and operation of electric appliances shall be permitted to be combustible when it is essential to their intended function.

10.2.7.2* Oxygen-Enriched Atmospheres. Electric appliances employing oxygen, or that are intended to be used in oxygen-enriched atmospheres, shall comply with all of the following:

(1) Chapter 9
(2) Chapter 20
(3) All applicable provisions of this chapter

A.10.2.7.2 See also NFPA 53, *Recommended Practice on Materials, Equipment, and Systems Used in Oxygen-Enriched Atmospheres.*

10.2.7.3 Inhalation Anesthetizing Locations. Electric appliances used in inhalation anesthetizing locations shall comply with all of the following:

(1) Chapter 8
(2) Subsection 13.4.1
(3) All applicable provisions of this chapter

10.2.8 Instruction Manuals and Labels.

10.2.8.1 Manuals.

10.2.8.1.1 The manufacturer of the appliance shall furnish operator's, maintenance, and repair manuals with all units.

10.2.8.1.2 These manuals shall include operating instructions, maintenance details, and testing procedures and shall include the following where applicable:

(1) Illustrations that show location of controls
(2) Explanation of the function of each control
(3) Illustrations of proper connection to the patient and other equipment
(4) Step-by-step procedures for proper use of the appliance
(5) Safety considerations in application and in servicing
(6) Difficulties that might be encountered, and care to be taken if the appliance is used on a patient simultaneously with other electric appliances
(7) Schematics, wiring diagrams, mechanical layouts, parts lists, and other pertinent data for the appliance as shipped

(8) Functional description of the circuit
(9) Electrical supply requirements (i.e., volts, frequency, amperes, and watts), heat dissipation, weight, dimensions, output current, output voltage, and other pertinent data
(10) The limits of electrical supply variations — performance specifications of the appliance shall be given for the applicable limits of electrical supply variations
(11) Technical performance specifications including design levels of leakage current
(12) Instructions for unpacking, inspecting, installing, adjusting, and aligning
(13) Comprehensive preventive and corrective maintenance and repair procedures

10.2.8.1.3 The information itemized shall be permitted to be supplied in the form of a separate operating manual and a separate maintenance manual, except that the separate maintenance manual shall also include all the information included in the operating manual.

A manufacturer's provision of at least one complete set of manuals would satisfy the requirements of 10.2.8.1.3. For any additional sets, either complete or comprising just the operator or service portion, purchasers would have to discuss their needs with the manufacturer. Additional charges could be involved.

A complete manual set should be kept where the equipment is maintained. A copy of the operator's manual should be kept with the appliance.

◀ **FAQ**
What types of manuals are required to be supplied by the manufacturer?

10.2.8.2 Operating Instructions on Appliances. Condensed operating instructions shall be permanently attached to, or displayed on, any appliance that is intended to be used in emergency situations and that results in injury or death to the operator or patient if improperly used.

10.2.8.3 Labeling.

10.2.8.3.1 The manufacturer shall furnish, for all appliances, labels that are legible and that remain so after being in service for the expected life of the appliance under hospital service and cleaning conditions.

10.2.8.3.2 Controls and indicators shall be labeled to indicate their function.

10.2.8.3.3 Appliances shall be labeled with precautionary statements if applicable.

10.2.8.3.4 All appliance labeling shall include the following:

(1) Model numbers
(2) Date of manufacture
(3) Manufacturer's name
(4) Electrical ratings including voltage, frequency, current, and/or wattage of the device

10.2.8.3.5 Date of manufacture shall be permitted to be a code, if its interpretation is provided to the user.

10.2.8.3.6 Appliances shall be labeled to indicate if they are listed for use as medical equipment and have isolated patient leads.

10.2.8.3.7 Appliances intended for use in anesthetizing locations shall be labeled in an approved manner. *(See 13.4.1.)*

Anesthetizing Location is defined in 3.3.9 and also in A.3.3.9.

Adequate and appropriate labeling of appliances in anesthetizing locations, required by 10.2.8.3.7, is necessary to reduce the chance of misuse. Appliances are not required to be listed by Chapter 10, but if they are listed, they should be so labeled. Government agencies, such as the U.S. Food and Drug Administration, might have additional requirements for labeling.

10.2.9 Additional Requirements for Special Appliances.

10.2.9.1 Signal Transmission Between Appliances.

10.2.9.1.1* General. Signal transmission lines from an appliance in a patient location to remote appliances shall employ a signal transmission system designed to prevent hazardous current from flowing in the grounding interconnection of the appliances.

A.10.2.9.1.1 This can be accomplished by using a signal transmission system that is isolated from ground or presents a high impedance to ground; that employs a common signal grounding wire between appliances served from the same reference grounding point; that employs an additional grounding path between the common signal grounding wire and reference grounding point in the patient vicinity; or by other means intended to reduce potential differences in the patient care vicinity due to grounding currents to a safe level.

The annex material to 10.2.9.1.1 outlines several possible methods of preventing hazardous current levels. There might be others that are acceptable.

10.2.9.1.2 Outdoor Signal Transmission. Outdoor signal transmission lines from appliances attached to patients shall be equipped with surge protection appropriate to the type of transmission line used. Such appliances or signal transmission lines shall be designed to prevent a hazard to the patient from exposure of the lines to lightning, power contact, power induction, rise in ground potential, radio interference, and so forth.

10.2.9.2 Appliances Intended to Deliver Electrical Energy.

10.2.9.2.1* Conditions for Meeting Safety Requirements. Electrical-energy–delivering appliances shall conform to the leakage, grounding, and other requirements of this chapter when powered but not delivering energy.

A.10.2.9.2.1 When delivering energy, such appliances can deviate from these requirements only to the extent essential for their intended clinical function. Appliances that intentionally or that could inadvertently apply electrical energy to the patient or to components in contact with the patient require special safety considerations. Since there is a wide range of power levels, output frequencies, and purposes of appliances that apply electricity directly to patients or to patient-connected devices, it is not feasible to cite them in detail.

10.2.9.2.2 Specific Requirements by Type of Device.

10.2.9.2.2.1* Electrically Powered Transducers. Exposed metal parts of these devices shall be considered electrodes and meet the applicable requirements of 10.2.13.

A.10.2.9.2.2.1 Electrically powered transducers include pressure transducers, flowmeters, endoscopes, and so forth. The electrical energy is not intended to be applied to the patient but to a device that contacts the patient.

10.2.9.2.2.2 Connectors shall be designed to prevent inadvertent interchange of leads if interchange constitutes a hazard to the patient or operator.

The intent of 10.2.9.2.2.2 is to prohibit interchanges that could cause a shock hazard, not necessarily to prohibit all interchanges. Where the leads require a specific orientation of connection as, for example, in an electrocardiograph, the connections should be polarized or color-coded to ensure proper connections. This is particularly important if the appliance is a power source as in an electrosurgical unit. All leads must not be able to plug into a power receptacle or extension cord.

10.2.9.2.2.3* Patient Impedance Measuring Devices. For a particular application, the combination of frequency and current levels shall limit the applied current to the minimum necessary to achieve the medical purposes, and shall not exceed the limits given in 10.2.13.5. These limits shall be permitted to be exceeded if essential for the intended clinical function.

A.10.2.9.2.2.3 Assessment of physiologic functions by electric impedance measurements usually requires direct contact with the patient and injection of electric current.

Permission is given in 10.2.9.2.2.3 to exceed the lead leakage current limits to provide for those instances where the applied current necessary must exceed lead leakage limits to successfully measure impedance. Mitigating circumstances are that the duration is usually brief, the current is usually at a high frequency, and the patient is being closely observed.

10.2.9.2.2.4* Electrotherapeutic Devices. Appliances that require specific pulse forms or high power levels shall be designed to protect the operator and attendant personnel from accidental electric shock.

A.10.2.9.2.2.4 Electrotherapeutic devices include devices for electrosleep, electroanesthesia, and electroshock.

10.2.9.2.2.5* Electrosurgery. Electrosurgical devices shall meet the requirements of 10.2.9.2.1.

A.10.2.9.2.2.5 See Annex D for information on electrosurgical devices.

Electrosurgery uses high levels of continuous or pulsed radio frequency power. It presents some unique hazards. It generates sparks with the attendant ignition hazard. It generates radio frequency interference that could obstruct monitoring. It can cause burns at inadvertent ground return paths if its return circuit is inadequate. Demodulation products could contain components that cause fibrillation or stimulation. DC monitoring currents can cause chemical burns. Capacitive or inductive coupling can occur.

Electrosurgical unit output circuits are commonly designated as isolated or ground-referenced on the basis of their isolation at their operating (RF) frequency. No assumption about isolation at 60 Hz should be made unless the device is specifically labeled as having an "isolated patient circuit (60 Hz)," in which case the device is to conform to the requirements of 10.2.13.5.3.

10.2.9.2.2.6* Cardiac Defibrillation. Cardiac defibrillators shall be designed to protect the operator and attendant personnel from accidental electric shock.

A.10.2.9.2.2.6 Cardiac defibrillation applies high-voltage, short-duration pulses to the patient.

Exhibit 10.5 is an example of a defibrillator, an appliance intended to deliver high power to a patient.

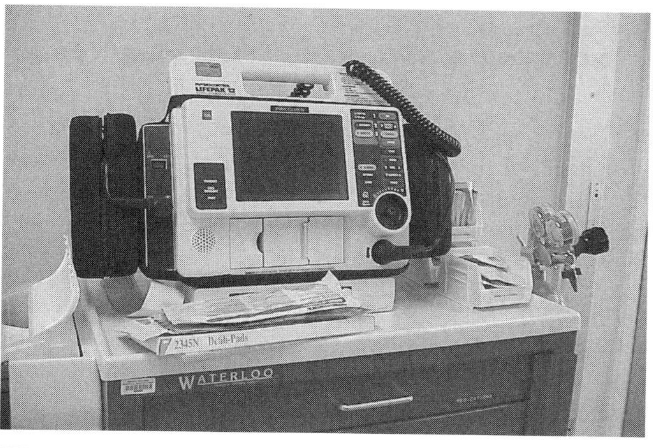

***EXHIBIT 10.5** A defibrillator unit, an example of an electronic device whose output is high-energy electricity that is applied directly to the patient's body. (Courtesy of Rob Swift and Prince William Health System)*

10.2.9.3 Electrical Equipment in Oxygen-Enriched Atmospheres. Appliances or part(s) of an appliance or system (e.g., pillow speaker, remote control, pulse oximeter probe) to be used in the site of intentional expulsion shall comply with one of the following:

(1) Be listed for use in oxygen-enriched atmospheres
(2) Be sealed so as to prevent an oxygen-enriched atmosphere from reaching electrical components. The sealing material shall be of the type that will still seal even after repeated exposure to water, oxygen, mechanical vibration, and heating from the external circuitry
(3) Be ventilated so as to limit the oxygen concentration surrounding electrical components to below 23.5 percent by volume
(4) Have both of the following characteristics:
   (a) No hot surfaces over 300°C (573°F), except for small (less than 2 W) hermetically sealed heating elements such as light bulbs.
   (b) No exposed switching or sparking points of electrical energy that fall to the right of the curve for the appropriate type of circuit illustrated in Figure 10.2.9.3(a) through Figure 10.2.9.3(f). The dc (or peak ac) open-circuit voltage and short-circuit current shall be used.

Paragraph 10.2.9.3 clarifies that an appliance, or parts of one, can be used within the site of intentional expulsion if it conforms to any one of four alternative methods of providing safety in an oxygen-enriched atmosphere.

In older editions of NFPA 99, only equipment listed for use in oxygen-enriched atmospheres [10.2.9.3(1)] was considered acceptable within the "site of administration," that is, 0.31 m (1 ft) around oxygen-delivery equipment. With greater experience it became evident that this distance was too restrictive. The concept of *site of administration* was replaced by the concept of *site of intentional expulsion* (see the commentary following 3.3.170 and following 8.5.2.4). This reduced the volume considered hazardous to 0.31 m (1 ft) from the vent(s) where oxygen-enriched air was "expelled" (or vented) from equipment. In addition three other safety measures were allowed for electrically powered devices within the site of intentional expulsion.

The curves in Figure 10.2.9.3(a) through Figure 10.2.9.3(f) illustrate minimum igniting currents for methane atmospheres and are from the former NFPA 493, *Standard for Intrinsically Safe Apparatus.* (NFPA 493 was withdrawn as an NFPA standard and cannot be referenced in other NFPA documents. However, the information contained in these graphics is still relevant.)

Extensive research [2] has concluded that under worst-case conditions the energy necessary to ignite dry cotton lint was somewhat greater than the minimum energy necessary to ignite methane atmospheres.

10.2.10 Low-Voltage Appliances and Appliances Not Connected to the Electric Power Distribution System.

10.2.10.1 General. Appliances and instruments operating from batteries or their equivalent, or from an external source of low voltage, or that are not connected to the electric power distribution system shall conform to all applicable requirements of Section 10.2. These appliances shall include communication systems except for telephones, signaling systems, entertainment systems, remote-control systems, and low-energy power systems.

10.2.10.2 Rechargeable Appliances. Battery-operated appliances that are rechargeable while in use shall meet all the requirements of 10.2.13.3.

10.2.10.3 Low-Voltage Connectors. Attachment plugs used on low-voltage circuits shall have configurations that do not permit interchangeable connection with circuits of other voltages.

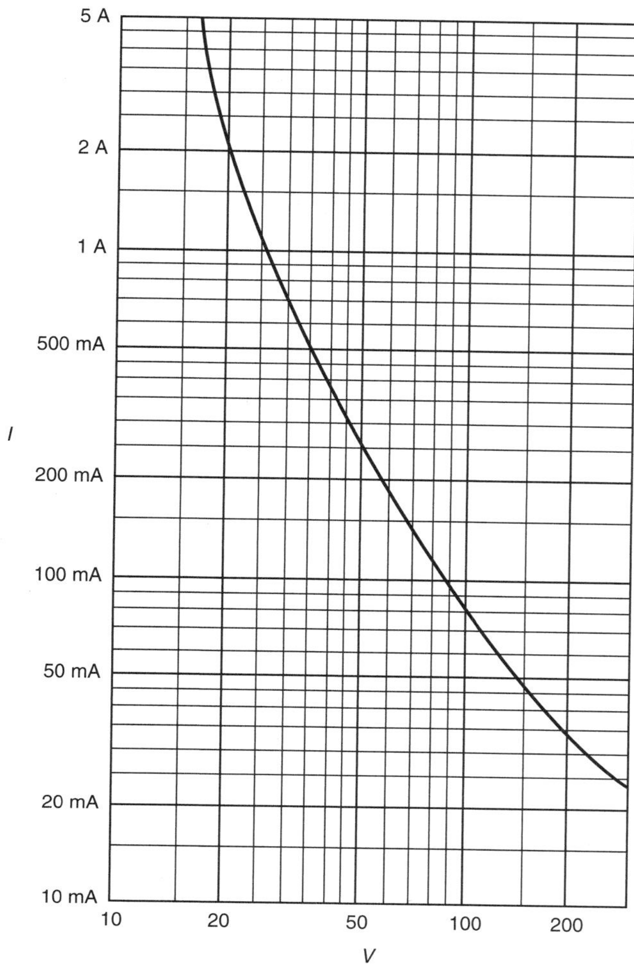

FIGURE 10.2.9.3(a) Resistance Circuits (L < 1 mH). Minimum igniting currents, applicable to all circuits containing cadmium, zinc, or magnesium.

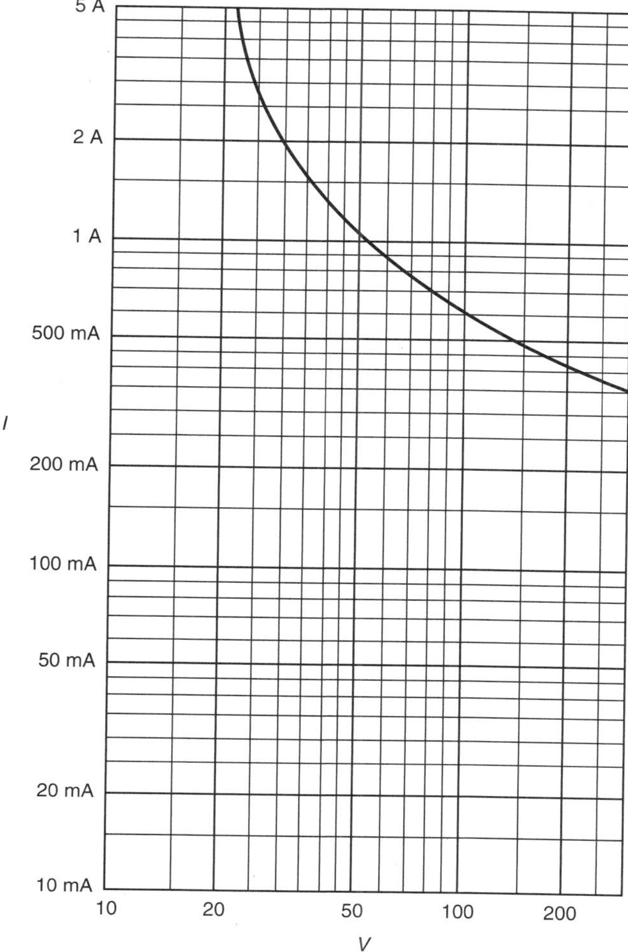

FIGURE 10.2.9.3(b) Resistance Circuits (L < 1 mH). Minimum igniting currents, applicable to circuits where cadmium, zinc, or magnesium can be excluded.

10.2.10.4 Isolation of Low-Voltage Circuits.

10.2.10.4.1 Circuits of 30 V (dc or ac rms) or less shall be electrically isolated from the power distribution system.

10.2.10.4.2 Grounded low-voltage circuits shall be permitted provided that load currents are not carried in the grounding conductor.

10.2.11* Cardiac Monitors and Electrocardiographs. Design of electrocardiographs, cardiac monitors, or blood-pressure monitors intended for use on patients in critical care shall include protection against equipment damage during defibrillation of the patient.

A.10.2.11 Monitoring of cardiac activity is crucial to effective defibrillation.

10.2.12* Direct Electrical Pathways to the Heart. The requirements of 10.2.12 shall apply only to manufacturers except where specifically noted.

A.10.2.12 This subsection is concerned with the patient who has either of two types of direct electrical connections to the heart. The obvious and most hazardous conductor comprises a

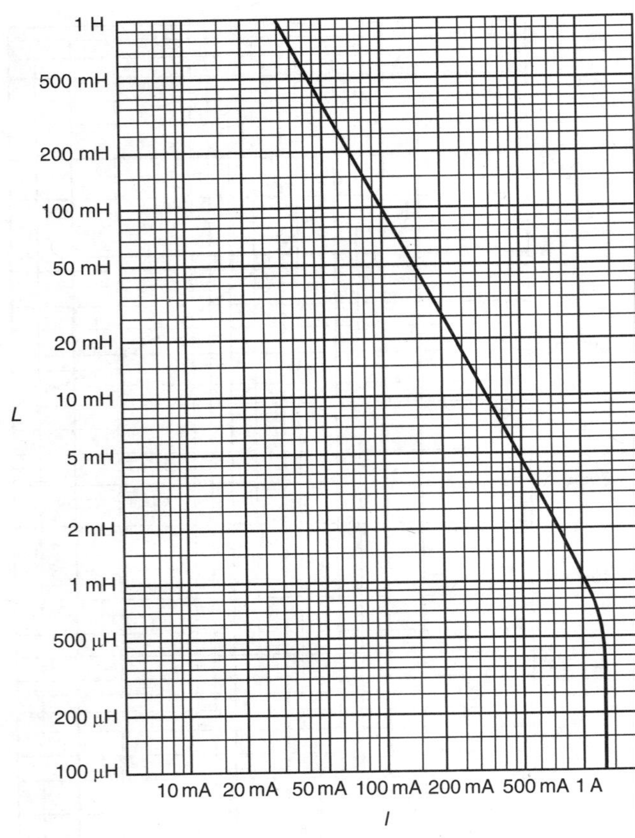

FIGURE 10.2.9.3(c) Inductance Circuits (L > 1 mH). Minimum igniting currents at 24 V, applicable to all circuits containing cadmium, zinc, or magnesium.

FIGURE 10.2.9.3(d) Inductance Circuits (L > 1 mH). Minimum igniting currents for various voltages, applicable to all circuits containing cadmium, zinc, or magnesium.

wire in contact with the heart muscle. This can be a pacemaker electrode, a guide wire, or a transthoracic or implanted electrode. The second type of conductor is a liquid column contained within a nonconductive catheter with the internal end in the heart.

In A.10.2.12, the term *transthoracic* refers to electrodes that enter the heart through the chest wall. A direct electrical pathway to the heart is not established by a simple invasive procedure to a peripheral vessel. To establish a direct electrical pathway, the end of the electrical probe or liquid-filled conductor inside the body must come in contact with the wall of the heart.

Although this section is intended primarily to guide manufacturers in the design of safe equipment, health care facility personnel also need to be aware of these design requirements so that they are not compromised. Some of the requirements listed apply specifically to facility operating personnel but were placed in this section because of their relationship to manufacturer's requirements. Grouping requirements for both allows facility personnel to appreciate the totality of the problem. A close relationship needs to be maintained between manufacturers and users in order to meet the requirements of this critical area of electrical safety.

10.2.12.1 Cardiac Electrodes.

10.2.12.1.1 General. Appliances that have isolated patient leads shall be labeled as having isolated patient leads in accordance with 10.2.13.5.

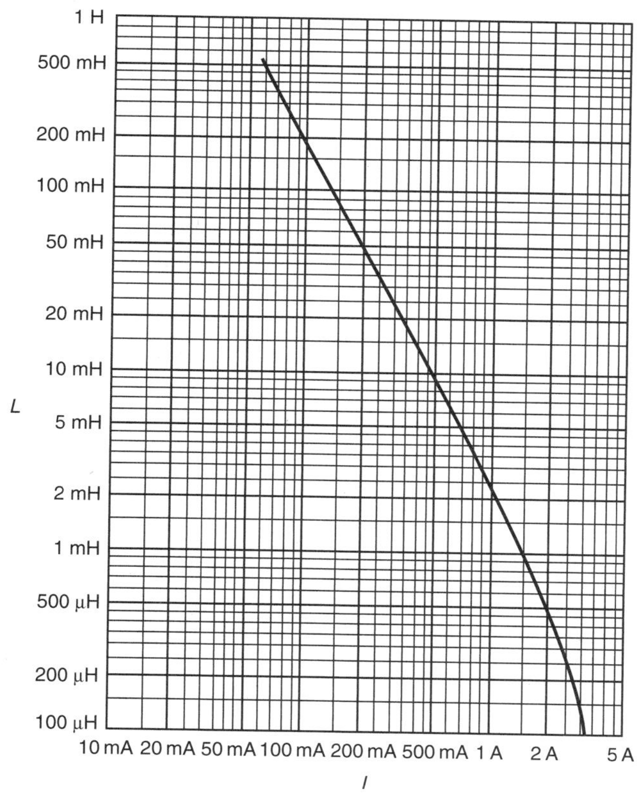

FIGURE 10.2.9.3(e) Inductance Circuits (L > 1 mH). Minimum igniting currents at 24 V, applicable only to circuits where cadmium, zinc, or magnesium can be excluded.

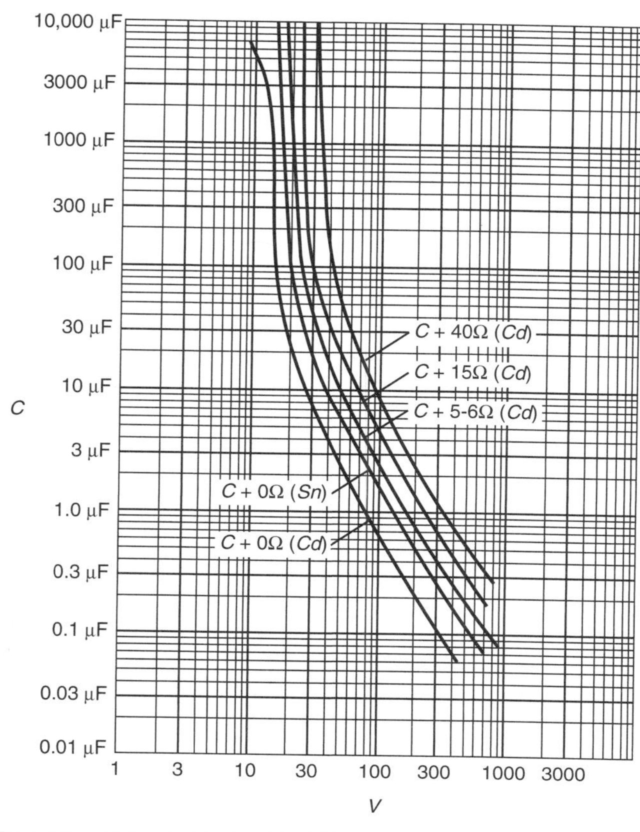

FIGURE 10.2.9.3(f) Capacitance Circuits Minimum Ignition Voltages. The curves correspond to values of current-limiting resistance as indicated. The curve marked Sn is applicable only where cadmium, zinc, or magnesium can be excluded.

10.2.12.1.2* Insulation of Cardiac Leads. Pacemaker leads and other wires intended for insertion into the heart, together with their adapters and connections to appliances, shall be insulated except for their sensing or stimulation areas.

A.10.2.12.1.2 The user is required to have a policy to protect pacing leads with external terminals from potentially hazardous contact with conductive surfaces *(see 8.5.2.1.5).*

10.2.12.1.2.1 Metal stylets or guide wires temporarily introduced into a vein or artery for purposes of positioning a catheter shall not be required to be insulated.

10.2.12.1.2.2 When guide wires are inside the heart, the operator shall exercise extreme care to ensure safe use.

10.2.12.1.2.3 When guide wires are used in conjunction with electrical devices (e.g., positioning catheters by use of ECG recordings), they shall be insulated as required by 10.2.12.1.2.

10.2.12.1.2.4 Insulated wires designed to be introduced through a surgical needle, or other special wires where it is not practicable to maintain insulation, shall not be required to maintain insulation during introduction or manipulation. At such times the operator shall take appropriate safeguards.

10.2.12.1.3 Safety Requirements for Cardiac Electrodes. The electrode catheter, fitting, and associated appliance, when assembled, shall meet the applicable requirements of 10.2.13.5.

10.2.12.1.4 Insulation of Pacemaker Connections. Uninsulated or open-type connectors shall not be used for external cardiac pacemaker terminals.

10.2.12.2 Liquid-Filled Catheters.

10.2.12.2.1* Cardiac Catheter System. Any conductive element of a liquid catheter system that comes in contact with the liquid column shall be insulated from ground and sources of electric energy.

A.10.2.12.2.1 A liquid catheter system can consist of the catheter itself, pressure transducers, electronic appliances, and associated accessories.

10.2.12.2.2 Nonconductive Cardiac Catheters. A nonconductive catheter containing a conductive liquid, when connected to its transducer, shall meet the applicable requirements of 10.2.13.5, for isolated patient leads, with the patient end of the liquid-filled catheter considered to be an electrode.

10.2.12.2.3 Conductive Cardiac Catheters.

10.2.12.2.3.1 If the liquid column is contained in a catheter made of conductive material having an electrical conductivity approximating that of blood, the system shall not require connection to an isolated patient lead.

10.2.12.2.3.2 Conductive catheters shall be identified.

10.2.12.3* Angiographic Catheters. Appliances used to inject contrast media into the heart or major vessels shall meet the same safety requirements as other liquid-filled catheter systems.

A.10.2.12.3 Although contrast injectors are not intended to apply electrical energy to the patient, they could deliver current from the power source and also could generate transient voltages large enough to be hazardous.

The contrast medium, not the injector, is the major hazard element. The injector, however, must be designed to reduce the hazard by not allowing the medium or the medium reservoir to be in contact with potential current sources.

10.2.13 Manufacturers' Tests for Safety of Patient-Care-Related Electrical Appliances.

10.2.13.1* General. The appliance manufacturer shall perform the testing to ensure that each finished appliance will meet the specified test limits of 10.2.13.

A.10.2.13.1 This section describes tests by manufacturers for the safe operation of an appliance. The tests in this subsection are in addition to the design requirements of the entire Section 10.2. Tests that are potentially destructive need only be performed by the manufacturer to ensure design compliance for new appliances.

The manufacturer needs to perform tests that are potentially destructive only to ensure design compliance for new appliances. Only those tests necessary to ensure that each appliance meets the requirements of this section must be performed on each individual appliance.

10.2.13.2 Grounding Circuit Continuity — Measurement of Resistance. For appliances that are used in the patient care vicinity, the resistance between the appliance chassis or any exposed conductive surface of the appliance and the ground pin of the attachment plug shall be less than 0.15 ohm under the following conditions:

(1) The cord shall be flexed at its connection to the attachment plug or connector.
(2) The cord shall be flexed at its connection to the strain relief on the chassis during the resistance measurement.

In the absence of a grounding conductor (as is the case in most listed double-insulated appliances), testing cannot be performed. However, if there is a grounding conductor, even if unnecessary, the test should be conducted, to avoid a possible misunderstanding on the part of the user of the significance of the grounding.

10.2.13.3* Leakage Current Tests.

A.10.2.13.3 For complex leakage current waveforms, a single reading from an appropriate metering system can represent the physiologically effective value of the composite waveform, provided that the contribution of each component to the total reading is weighted in accordance with 8.4.1.3.3 or 10.2.13.3.

This "weighting" can be achieved by a frequency–response-shaping network that precedes a flat-response meter, or by a meter whose own frequency response characteristic matches 8.4.1.3.3 or 10.2.13.3.

If the required performance is obtained by a meter with integral response shaping properties, then that meter should have a constant input resistance of 1000 ohms. (A high-input-impedance meter can be used by shunting a 1000-ohm resistor across the meter's input terminals.)

If, however, the required frequency response is obtained by a network that precedes an otherwise flat-response meter, then the input impedance of the network should be 1000 ohms ± 10 percent, over the frequency range from 0 to 1 MHz, and the frequency response of the network–meter combination should be substantially independent of the impedance of the signal source.

For maximum chassis leakage current allowed (i.e., 300 μA) below 1 kHz, this network will yield the limiting current of 10 mA above 30 kHz.

A suggested input network is shown in Figure A.10.2.13.3.

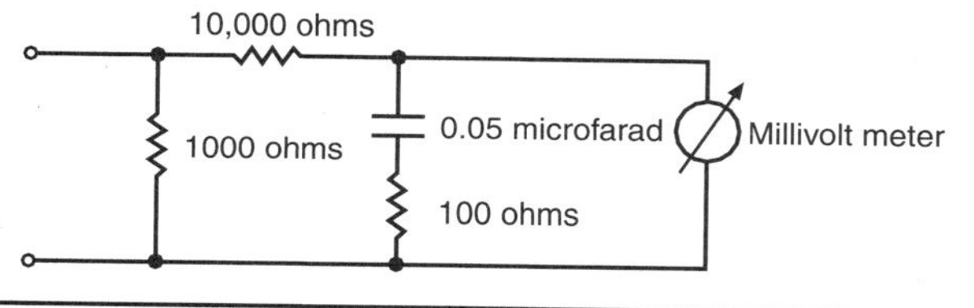

***FIGURE A.10.2.13.3** Leakage Current Measurements (1.0 millivolt meter reading corresponds to input current of 1.0 microampere).*

These currents usually derive from the line power by resistive paths, or capacitive or inductive coupling. However, they also include currents from other sources generated within the appliance and are measured by the tests described in Chapter 10.

These leakage current limits are based on acute events, for example, sensation, duration tetany, or ventricular fibrillation. Appliance design should aim to reduce such current as much as possible. In properly grounded appliances, maximum chassis leakage current is in the grounding conductor and not through the patient.

These tests are not known to be adequate where currents (such as dc or high frequency) are introduced into the patient for long periods and where low-level effects have to be considered. *(See also 8.4.1.3.3.)*

The suggested network in A.10.2.13.3 gives a proportional response up to 100 kHz. However, it is cautioned that the use of this network-meter combination was originally designed when the chassis leakage current limit was 100 μA to conform to a maximum leakage current limit of 10 mA per 8.4.1.3.3.3. For higher frequency values, this network-meter circuit is useable only to 30 kHz to meet the 10 mA limitation, which addresses thermal safety, not shock hazard.

When manufacturer requirements were placed in a separate chapter, some tests for manufacturers were not included. One test for hospitals was excluded as well. The tests in 10.2.13 are in the following sequence, the same as those for health care facilities in 8.4.1:

1. Chassis
   a. Permanently wired
   b. Cord-connected
2. Patient leads
   a. Lead-to-ground (non-isolated input)
   b. Lead–to-ground (isolated input)
   c. Isolated test (isolated input)
   d. Between leads (non-isolated input)
   e. Between leads (isolated input)

The values for leakage currents reflect exhaustive studies conducted on humans and dogs, actual measurements during cardiac surgery, and manufacturing capabilities. For further information, see A.10.2.13.4.3.

10.2.13.3.1 Techniques of Measurement. Each test shall be performed with the appropriate connection to a grounded ac power system.

10.2.13.3.2* Frequency of Leakage Current.

A.10.2.13.3.2 The limits for nonsinusoidal periodic, modulated, and transient waveforms remain to be determined.

For complex leakage current waveforms, a single reading from an appropriate metering system can represent the physiologically effective value of the composite waveform, provided that the contribution of each component to the total reading is weighted in accordance with 10.2.13.3.2.

10.2.13.3.2.1 The leakage current limits stated in 10.2.13.4 and 10.2.13.5 shall be rms values for sinusoidal waveforms up to 1 kHz. For frequencies above 1 kHz, the leakage current limits shall be the values given in 10.2.13.4 and 10.2.13.5 multiplied by the frequency, in kHz, up to a maximum of 10 mA.

For the reasoning behind a maximum value of 10 μA, see the commentary following A.8.4.1.3.3.

10.2.13.3.2.2 This "weighting" shall be achieved by a frequency-response–shaping network that precedes a flat response meter, or by a meter whose own frequency response characteristic matches 10.2.13.3.2.

10.2.13.3.3 Leakage Current in Relation to Polarity. Leakage current measurements shall be made as follows:

(1) With the polarity of the power line normal and reversed
(2) With the power switch of the appliance "on" and "off"
(3) With all operating controls in the positions to cause maximum leakage current readings

The leakage current limits in 10.2.13.4 and 10.2.13.5 shall not be exceeded under any of these conditions.

10.2.13.4 Leakage Current from Appliance to Ground.

10.2.13.4.1 Test Methods. The current shall be measured from the exposed conductive surfaces of the appliance to ground with all grounding conductors open at the end nearest the power receptacle. The appliance shall not be grounded by any other means. The current meter shall be inserted between the exposed conductive surfaces and ground. This test shall be made under the conditions of 10.2.13.3 and shall be made as illustrated in Figure 10.2.13.4.1.

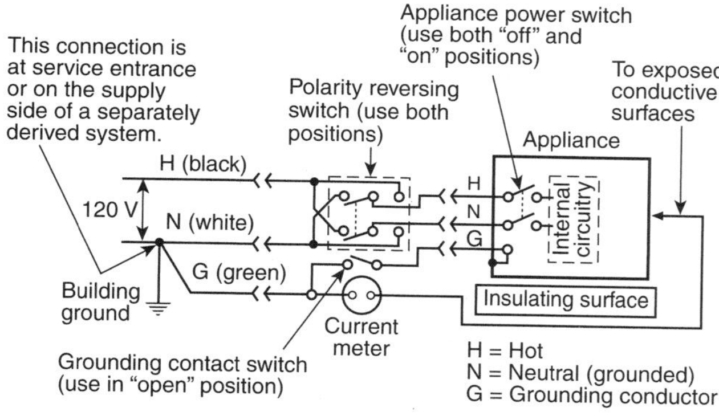

***FIGURE 10.2.13.4.1** Test Circuit for Measuring Leakage Current from Exposed Conductive Surfaces.*

Figure 10.2.13.4.1 reflects a better way to measure leakage current, that is, by connecting a probe to exposed conductive surfaces. The equipment addressed in 10.2.13.4.1 and in 8.4.2.2.1.1 also applies to non-patient care appliances intended for use in the patient care vicinity. These types of appliances are not intended to come in contact with the patient, but the possibility exists that they could do so.

10.2.13.4.2 Appliances with No Exposed Conductive Surfaces. When the appliance has no exposed conductive surface, one shall be simulated by placing a 10 cm × 20 cm (3.9 in. × 7.8 in.) bare metal foil in intimate contact with the exposed surface. This shall be considered the "exposed metal surface" of the appliance, and all appropriate tests shall be performed to the foil.

The dimensions of the metal foil required for use in 10.2.13.4.2 are considered to approximate the area of a hand touching an appliance. Hence, the leakage current measured here is a capacity-coupled area measurement rather than a point measurement. This test is a reasonable one for manufacturers of such appliances, particularly when appliances are covered with an insulating film but are not listed as double insulated.

10.2.13.4.3* Chassis Leakage Current Limits.

A.10.2.13.4.3 The chassis leakage current limits given in 10.2.13.4.3 and in other paragraphs, combined with the grounding wire requirements, are based on a concept of two layers of protection. Either the limited leakage current or an intact grounding system will provide protection. However, it is generally agreed that not only with medical equipment but also with conventional appliances, there should be two levels of protection. This means that both safeguards will have to fail before the subject is at hazard.

For general application (household appliances) the leakage current limit is generally set at 500 μA at 60 Hz. The limit of 500 μA is based on the work of Dalziel and others that indicates that different individuals in the general population will exhibit responses to electrical shock at differing levels. A small percentage, perhaps 5 percent, will react to a current level of 500 μA with an involuntary movement that could trigger a secondary accident. Some individuals are sensitive to an electric shock sensation as low as 100 μA. A reasonable compromise seems to be to set the limit at 500 for the general public. It should be noted that in 8.4.2.2.1, this is the limit for household-type appliances.

References for this material can be found in Annex G.

For equipment in the patient care vicinity it seems reasonable to reduce this limit to 300 μA, because of the special circumstances involved in hospitals. Some of these factors are as follow:

(1) Some patients could be wet or have some other low-impedance connection to the ground. For this reason, the assumption usually made for the general public that they are moderately insulated from ground is not valid.
(2) Patients are sick, tend to be unresponsive, tend to be obtunded, and might not be able to perform the evasive maneuvers that an alert adult would perform when experiencing an electrical shock.
(3) The nature of the patient's illness could exacerbate the response to electric shock.
(4) Hospital patients are increasingly in close proximity to more and more electrical equipment.
(5) Hospital equipment is subject to industrial-type abuse. It is handled roughly, is sometimes wet, and is sometimes not properly maintained. All of this increases the probability of deterioration and consequent increase in leakage.
(6) The economics of the problem has been considered. The medical appliance industry has responded to the requirement for 300 μA maximum leakage by designing equipment within that limit. It has been shown to be feasible and not unduly uneconomical. In the few cases where, for technical reasons, it is impractical to reach these limits, other solutions are available.
(7) It should be emphasized that the reduced leakage-current limit is not based on clear technical evidence but represents considered opinion. Therefore, if a particular appliance has a leakage current somewhat above 300 μA, it is not implied that it is dangerously unsafe. It does indicate that such an appliance should be examined to determine whether there is a reason for the higher leakage. If the leakage cannot be reduced it can be compensated for by more-intensive preventive maintenance to ensure that the grounding conductor is intact.
(8) It should be further noted that the shock hazards produced by these current levels apply to external contacts; that is, body surface ECG lead or a skin contact with the chassis of an appliance. These current values do not apply to intracardiac leads. For such leads, the hazard is not startle, involuntary muscular motion, or "let-go." It is frank fibrillation of the heart, and is caused at levels a factor of 1000 below those necessary to cause fibrillation by external contacts. It is impractical to provide protection to the patient who has an intracardiac lead by means of the control of chassis leakage current, isolated power systems, ground fault interrupter circuits, or other similar external devices. Protection for such patients can be achieved only by the protection of the intracardiac lead. This is discussed in 8.5.2.1.5. For such patients the limit of such leads has been placed at 10 μA with the ground intact (i.e., under normal conditions). Again there is a safety factor involved. The lower limit of hazardous currents seems to be about 100 μA at 60 Hz. A safety factor of 10 has been established because of most of the reasons just noted and because of the following:
    (a) Patients with intracardiac leads are usually ones whose hearts are already in jeopardy.
    (b) Such patients usually have even more electrical equipment near them than does the average patient.

(c) It has been shown to be economically quite feasible to maintain such leads at a limit of 10 μA with the ground intact (i.e., under normal conditions).

In early editions of NFPA 99, the chassis leakage limit was set at 100 μA. Based on further studies indicating that the safety factor originally used could be reduced without compromising patient safety, the limit was raised to 300 μA. Because all cord-connected patient care electrical appliances in a patient care vicinity are likely to come in contact with patients, this limit was set for all such appliances.

10.2.13.4.3.1 Cord-Connected Appliances. Cord-connected appliances that are intended for use in the patient care vicinity shall not exceed 300 μA of chassis leakage current as measured in 10.2.13.4.1.

10.2.13.4.3.2 Permanently Wired Equipment. Permanently wired equipment installed in the patient care vicinity shall not have leakage current from the frame to ground in excess of 5.0 mA. The leakage current shall be measured prior to installation by the installer and verified and accepted by the facility. This measurement shall be made in accordance with 10.2.13.4.1 while the equipment is temporarily insulated from ground.

The reference to *facility* in 10.2.13.4.3.2 reflects the fact that the paragraph requires both the manufacturer and the facility to participate in the test.

10.2.13.5 Lead Leakage Current Tests and Limits.

See the commentary following A.10.2.9.2.2.3.

10.2.13.5.1 Lead to Ground (Nonisolated Input).

10.2.13.5.1.1 The lead leakage current to ground shall be measured under the conditions of 10.2.13.3.

The test procedure and the limit for the lead to ground test for non-isolated inputs have been made more exacting for manufacturers than for users (i.e., health care facilities). For health care facilities, this test is to be conducted with the patient leads combined (connected together). For manufacturers, the test is to be conducted between each patient lead and ground and between combined patient leads and ground.

Making both individual and combined measurements is technically more accurate in the instance of active driven leads because the current would only be in the driven leads. Otherwise, their contribution of leakage current could be shunted off through another lead when measured in the combined configuration and the meter reading would be incorrect.

10.2.13.5.1.2 The test shall be made between each patient lead and ground and between the combined patient leads and ground.

10.2.13.5.1.3 The test shall be made with the patient leads active (e.g., in the case of a multilead instrument, the lead selector switch shall be advanced through all operating positions).

10.2.13.5.1.4 Each measurement shall be performed with the grounding conductors both opened and closed. For this purpose the grounding conductor shall be interrupted at the plug end of the appliance cord. Acceptable test configuration shall be as illustrated in Figure 10.2.13.5.1.4. The leakage current shall not exceed 100 μA.

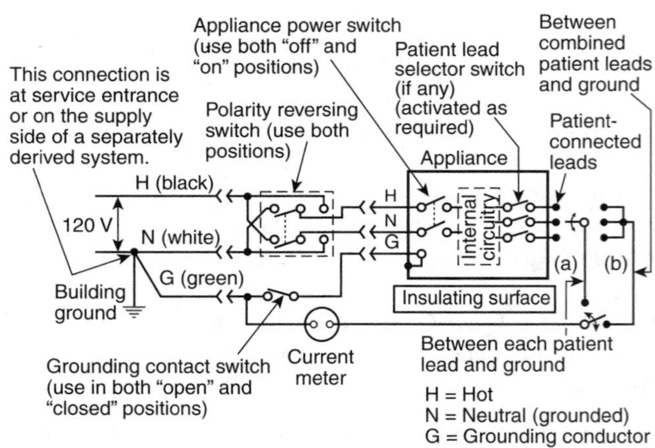

FIGURE 10.2.13.5.1.4 Test Circuit for Measuring Leakage Current Between Patient Leads and Ground (Nonisolated).

10.2.13.5.2 Lead to Ground (Isolated Input).

10.2.13.5.2.1 The leakage current to ground between each patient lead and ground shall be measured under the conditions of 10.2.13.3.

10.2.13.5.2.2 The test shall be made with the patient leads active (e.g., in the case of a multilead instrument, the lead selector switch shall be advanced through all operating positions).

10.2.13.5.2.3 Each measurement shall be performed with the grounding conductors both opened and closed. For this purpose the grounding conductor shall be interrupted at the plug end of the appliance cord. An acceptable test configuration shall be as illustrated in Figure 10.2.13.5.2.3. The leakage current shall not exceed 10 μA with the ground intact and 50 μA with the ground open.

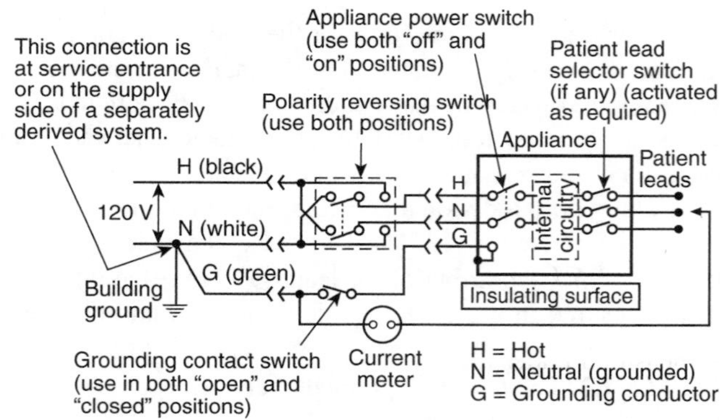

FIGURE 10.2.13.5.2.3 Test Circuit for Measuring Leakage Current Between Patient Leads and Ground (Isolated).

The leakage current limit was raised to 10 μA to conform to IEC 60601-1, *Medical Electrical Equipment — Part 1: General Requirements for Safety* [3].

10.2.13.5.3 Isolation Test (Isolated Input).

10.2.13.5.3.1 The isolation between each patient lead and ground for an appliance that has been labeled as having isolated patient leads shall be measured by observing the current produced by applying an external source of power-line frequency and voltage between the lead and ground while the leads are approximately 20 cm (8 in.) from a grounded conductive surface.

10.2.13.5.3.2 The isolation at the apparatus terminals to the patient cables shall be measured. An acceptable test configuration shall be as illustrated in Figure 10.2.13.5.3.2.

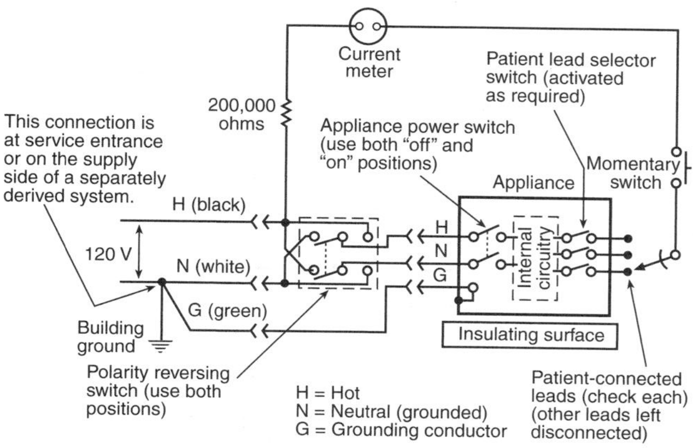

***FIGURE 10.2.13.5.3.2** Test Circuit for Measuring the Electrical Isolation of Isolated Patient Leads.*

10.2.13.5.3.3 At the patient end of the leads, the leakage current shall not exceed 50 μA and at the apparatus terminals, 25 μA.

10.2.13.5.3.4 Only appliances meeting the requirement of 10.2.13.5.3.3 shall be permitted to be identified as having isolated patient leads.

10.2.13.5.3.5 Safety precautions (such as including a resistance in series to limit the current, insulation of the meter, and a momentary switch) shall be taken to protect the operator. The following test procedures shall be followed for the indicated test conditions:

(1) In appliances without a power cord with ungrounded, exposed conductive surfaces, measurements shall be made with the exposed conductive surfaces temporarily grounded.
(2) If there is no exposed conductive surface, measurement shall be made with a simulated surface, as described in 10.2.13.4.2, that is also temporarily grounded.

10.2.13.5.4 Between Leads (Nonisolated Input).

10.2.13.5.4.1 The current between any pair of leads or any single lead and all others shall be measured under the conditions of 10.2.13.3. Each measurement shall be performed with the grounding conductors both opened and closed. For this purpose the grounding conductor shall be interrupted at the plug end of the appliance cord. An acceptable test configuration shall be as illustrated in Figure 10.2.13.5.4.1. The leakage current shall not exceed 50 μA.

10.2.13.5.4.2 Measuring leakage current between any single lead and all other leads shall be performed only to ensure the approval agency of design compliance.

10.2.13.5.5 Between Leads (Isolated Input).

10.2.13.5.5.1 The current between any pair of leads or any single lead and all others shall be measured under the conditions of 10.2.13.3. Each measurement shall be performed with the grounding conductors both opened and closed. For this purpose the grounding conductor shall be interrupted at the plug end of the appliance cord. An acceptable test configuration

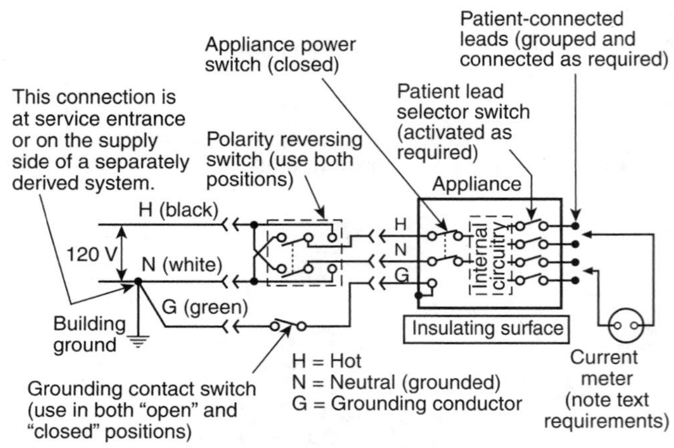

FIGURE 10.2.13.5.4.1 *Test Circuit for Measuring Leakage Current Between Patient Leads (Nonisolated and Isolated).*

shall be as illustrated in Figure 10.2.13.5.4.1. The leakage current shall not exceed 10 μA with the ground intact and 50 μA with the ground open.

10.2.13.5.5.2 Measuring leakage current between any single lead and all other leads shall be performed only to ensure the approval agency of design compliance.

REFERENCES CITED IN COMMENTARY

1. "Loosened Connections in Plug Tests," *Health Devices,* 4:75, 1975.
2. Lipschultz, A. and Barnard, T., "Perspectives on Electrical Equipment Used in Oxygen-Enriched Atmospheres," *Medical Instrumentation,* 18:4, July-August 1984.
3. IEC 60601-1, *Medical Electrical Equipment — Part 1: General Requirements for Safety,* 2004 edition.

CHAPTER 11

Laboratories

The goal of Chapter 11 is to assist the leadership of clinical laboratories located within health care facilities in establishing and maintaining a fire safe environment. This material is distinguished from the material in NFPA 45, *Standard on Fire Protection for Laboratories Using Chemicals* [1], by its focus on the potential presence of patients either within or in close proximity to the laboratory. The difference between these two primary standards increases in importance as laboratories providing in-patient care move out of hospitals and as freestanding laboratories expand their scope of services. 

Hazards particular to clinical laboratories, such as the presence of a variety of chemicals and automated testing equipment, are specifically addressed. More generally, an expectation is established for a safety program within and unique to the laboratory itself. The requirements of NFPA 99 are supported in more detail by a variety of standards, referenced within the commentary on this chapter, that are promulgated by other organizations.

11.1* Applicability

Most clinical laboratories use ignitible liquids, and many store flammable gases. Such application, along with the presence of considerable quantities of medical supplies and paper documents, contributes to the ignition fuel load. Any of the multiple items of electrical equipment in use can become an ignition source under the right conditions. Laboratory employees need to be aware of these hazards, know how best to prevent fire, and know how to prevent fire emergencies.

Patients incapable of self-preservation can occasionally be found in some clinical laboratories that are in or adjacent to patient care areas. The scope of this chapter was defined primarily for the protection of these patients.

Starting with the 2002 edition of NFPA 99, the requirements for piped medical gases in laboratories were moved into this chapter from Chapter 5, Gas and Vacuum Systems, where they were previously treated as Level IV systems. Because these systems are not used for direct patient care, the committees for both chapters supported the change to relocate the requirements under the direct purview of the laboratory.

A.11.1 The application of requirements contained in this chapter for specific types of health care facilities can be found in Chapters 6, 13, 14, 17, and 18.  

Some considerations in determining which document (NFPA 99 or NFPA 45) should be consulted first when designing or operating a laboratory in a health care facility (i.e., those laboratories under the jurisdiction of a health care facility as defined in Chapter 3 of NFPA 99) are shown in Table A.11.1 (Table A.1.3.2 in NFPA 45-1996, *Standard on Fire Protection for Laboratories Using Chemicals*, and Sections 1.1 and 11.1 in NFPA 99-2002). Sections 1.1 and 11.1 in NFPA 99–2002 should be reviewed in conjunction with the table.

TABLE A.11.1 *Using NFPA Documents for Laboratories in Health Care Facilities*

Location of Laboratory	*Primary Reference Document*
Laboratory in bldg. with inpatients	99
Laboratory in bldg. with outpatients incapable of self-preservation	99
Laboratory in a bldg. with outpatients capable of self-preservation	45

FAQ ▶ How should Table A.11.1 be used?

Table A.11.1 is an aid to users of NFPA 45 and NFPA 99 in determining which document applies to a particular laboratory. Patients "incapable of self-preservation" include bedridden hospitalized patients. The designation also includes nonhospitalized patients undergoing general anesthesia and patients under deep conscious sedation. For example, a clinical laboratory located within a hospital building and in a regular patient area would use NFPA 99 as its primary standard. An independent, freestanding clinical laboratory would refer directly to NFPA 45.

The more difficult decision regarding applicability concerns the degree of separation of a hospital laboratory from areas of direct patient care. Most hospital laboratories that are completely detached from their inpatient facility or that are separated from it by 2-hour construction should use NFPA 45. Paragraphs 18.1.2.2 and 19.1.2.2 of NFPA *101®, Life Safety Code®* [2], permit such facilities to be classified as business occupancies. Rare exceptions to this basic rule would be the presence of nonambulatory patients visiting the laboratory for phlebotomy and anesthetized patients brought to the laboratory for special studies. In such exceptional cases where four or more patients are litterborne, NFPA 99 would be the primary document even for freestanding clinical labs.

Over time, the adoption and enforcement of the provisions within this chapter have virtually eliminated hospital and other health care facility laboratories as a source of danger to patients and laboratory personnel. Property damage, however, remains a serious issue. Based on 1994 through 1998 averages, NFPA estimates that 100 fires reported to U.S. local fire departments occur in laboratories of health care facilities each year. These fires cause an estimated three nonfatal injuries and $420,000 in direct property damage per year. (These national estimates are based on fire department data from NFPA's annual survey of fire experience and the U.S. Fire Administration's National Fire Incident Reporting System [3].)

11.1.1* This chapter establishes criteria to minimize the hazards of fire and explosions in laboratories, as defined in Chapter 3. This section is not intended to cover hazards resulting from the misuse of chemicals, radioactive materials, or biological materials that will not result in fires or explosions.

The omission of coverage for protection from radiation, from infectious organisms, or from genetically active agents is not intended to minimize the seriousness of such hazards. Laboratory personnel must be aware of all those other types of hazards to be contained. These types of hazards are addressed in various OSHA standards, including *Occupational Exposure to Hazardous Chemicals in Laboratories* [4] and *Bloodborne Pathogens* [5]. By meeting with local fire authorities and providing appropriate signs, the laboratory's leadership can apprise fire responders of all the types of potential exposure that might be encountered in responding to an incident in the laboratory. Paragraphs 11.8.2.1 and 11.8.2.2 were added to underscore this goal.

Requirements and recommendations of other organizations and agencies, such as the Joint Commission on Accreditation of Healthcare Organizations (JCAHO), the College of American Pathologists (CAP), the Occupational Safety and Health Administration (OSHA), and any other applicable regulatory bodies should be reviewed and integrated with the requirements of this chapter to ensure that fire safety preparations and environmental, chemical, and biological safety precautions do not interfere with one another. As safety training programs in laboratory fire prevention and preparedness are developed, introduction to applicable fire codes can be integrated with other regulatory requirements.

A.11.1.1 Before a hazardous chemical is ordered, controls should be established to ensure that adequate facilities and procedures are available for receiving, storing, using, and disposing of the material. Information sources include the following:

NFPA 49, *Hazardous Chemicals Data*

NFPA 325, *Guide to Fire Hazard Properties of Flammable Liquids, Gases, and Volatile Solids*

NFPA 491, *Guide to Hazardous Chemical Reactions*

Note that NFPA 49 and NFPA 325 are available in the NFPA publication *Fire Protection Guide to Hazardous Materials*, 12th edition, 1997.

Class IA and IB flammable liquids in glass containers larger than the 1 qt (0.91 L) size should be transported in suitable containers of sufficient size to hold the contents of the glass containers.

Another source of information on hazardous chemicals is the material safety data sheets (MSDSs) provided by chemical manufacturers as a requirement of OSHA's *Hazard Communication Standard* [6].

Because of the nature of health care facility laboratory work, engineering and work-practice controls have been developed in NFPA 99 for use by all laboratories. Whereas construction and equipment requirements are applicable to new laboratories (per 1.3.2), safe work practices with respect to laboratory activities always apply.

11.1.2 Many of the requirements to protect against fire or explosion, such as those for hood exhaust systems, also serve to protect persons from exposure to nonfire health hazards of these materials.

11.1.3* NFPA 45, *Standard on Fire Protection for Laboratories Using Chemicals*, is the basic NFPA standard for laboratories that covers the construction, ventilation systems, and related fire protection of all laboratories in all facilities. However, this chapter (Chapter 11) has more stringent requirements for laboratories located in health care facilities. Where interface with existing NFPA or other consensus codes and standards occurs, reference is made to the appropriate source in the text.

A.11.1.3 Although NFPA 45 provides basic requirements and guidance for laboratory design, fire separation and sprinkler requirements are more stringent for laboratories in health care facilities. In addition, NFPA 99 has more stringent and realistic limitations of quantities of flammable liquids in laboratories, requires hood discharge above the roof, allows valves on emergency water supplies, encourages laboratory safety program activities, and recommends placement of flammable gas cylinders outside of the laboratory.

11.1.4 Where necessary, due to the special nature of laboratories, codes and standards are supplemented in this text so as to apply more specifically to buildings or portions of buildings devoted to laboratory usage.

11.2 Nature of Hazards

Section 11.2 has been continually revised over the years to include such items as fire loss prevention procedures and fire exit drill requirements. Laboratories using large quantities of explosive materials should be particularly observant of the safety procedures required in this section, in addition to any other practices required by enforcing authorities.

The development of a manual, as required by several regulatory organizations, can be helpful for identifying, listing, and implementing safety procedures for laboratory emergencies. A manual is also useful for documentation and review of procedures and as an orientation and educational tool for new employees.

11.2.1 Fire Loss Prevention.

11.2.1.1 Hazard Assessment.

11.2.1.1.1 An evaluation shall be made of hazards that may be encountered during laboratory operations before such operations are begun. The evaluation shall include hazards associated with following:

(1) Properties of the chemicals used
(2) Operation of the equipment
(3) Nature of the proposed reactions (e.g., evolution of acid vapors or flammable gases)

NFPA 704, *Standard System for the Identification of the Hazards of Materials for Emergency Response* [7], can greatly assist in evaluating the hazard potential of flammable and combustible liquids in a laboratory. Manufacturers' MSDSs, prepared according to the General Industry Standards [6] of the Occupational Safety and Health Administration of the Department of Labor, are also important sources of information on flammable and combustible liquids. MSDSs might be the only available source of information for purchased mixtures and proprietary formulations.

11.2.1.1.2 Periodic reviews of laboratory operations and procedures shall be conducted with special attention given to any change in materials, operations, or personnel.

Whenever new laboratory processes are introduced, the impact on fire protection and preparedness must be considered. Any safety considerations should be part of the written standard operating procedures of the laboratory. Many authorities recommend that these written procedures be reviewed and updated annually, although the Joint Commission on Accreditation of Healthcare Organizations requires only a triennial review of safety policies and procedures. The most stringent requirements should always be followed.

11.2.1.1.3* Unattended operations and automatic laboratory equipment shall be provided with periodic surveillance or with automatic monitoring devices to detect and report abnormal operation.

With appropriate training, periodic checks on unattended operations and automatic laboratory equipment can be performed by security personnel on their normal rounds, support service personnel (housekeeping, transport, etc.), or supervisors or other laboratory personnel in adjacent or nearby laboratories. The operation of such equipment can also be monitored electronically at a remote location. (See the requirements of 11.4.2.1.1 and 11.4.2.1.2.) The person(s) responsible for the operation of the equipment should inform personnel performing the periodic inspections of the following:

- What constitutes abnormal operation
- How often the equipment needs to be checked
- What actions should be taken if something abnormal is observed (e.g., an emergency shutdown switch/sequence, an emergency phone number)
- Safety issues and any requirements for personal protective equipment

Detailed instructions should be posted near the equipment, and the specifics of such checks should be included in the training of off-shift personnel who frequent the laboratory area. These instructions should display the date on which they were last revised, and a regular schedule for review and revision should be in place. These data are especially important for tissue processors, which are characteristically operated unattended at night and combine heat and combustible solvents. (See also 11.4.2.1.) The importance of safety checks cannot be overstated.

A.11.2.1.1.3 A safety check of the health care facility laboratory by designated laboratory personnel should be made prior to leaving the facility unattended.

11.2.1.1.4 When chemicals and reagents are ordered, steps shall be taken to determine the hazards and to transmit that information to those who will receive, store, use, or dispose of the chemicals.

The requirement of 11.2.1.1.4 also reflects the requirements in OSHA's *Hazard Communication Standard* [6], and in JCAHO's *Comprehensive Accreditation Manual for Pathology and Clinical Laboratory Services* [8], mandating that all individuals be aware of the hazardous materials in their workplace.

NFPA 704, *Standard System for the Identification of the Hazards of Materials for Emergency Response* [7], is intended for the benefit of fire fighters who are entering a hazardous zone and can also identify hazards for laboratory personnel who receive, store, use, or dispose of hazardous chemicals. Material safety data sheets are also good sources of this information.

11.2.1.2 Fire Prevention Procedures. Fire prevention procedures shall be established in accordance with Section 11.8.

The procedures for maintaining the laboratory's fire protection and prevention program are to be a structured program of inspection and maintenance within the laboratory's comprehensive safety program.

11.2.1.3 Emergency Procedures.

11.2.1.3.1 Procedures for laboratory emergencies shall be developed, including the following:

(1) Alarm activation
(2) Evacuation
(3) Equipment shutdown

The laboratory emergency procedures required by 11.2.1.3.1 should be custom-designed to address the specific hazards common to that location. Most laboratories must additionally consider alternative plans for evening, weekend, or holiday operation, when fewer staff are present, and for emergency conditions (severe weather, civil disorders, etc.), when staff resources might be altered. Those who will be responding to emergencies should review the laboratory's emergency procedures for clarity and for specific understanding of all plans. Emergency procedures should be reviewed with all employees at regular intervals. While not required, an annual employee update is suggested.

11.2.1.3.2 Procedures shall be developed for control of emergencies that could occur in the laboratory, including detailed plans for control operations by an emergency control group within the organization or a public fire department.

Careful consideration should be given to selecting the appropriate emergency control group. Laboratory policies should clearly specify those who are authorized to clean up specific types of spills. For example, only a limited number of people might be trained in appropriate cleanup of a mercury spill. In addition, definitions should be established for small and large spills. The definitions might be qualitative, such as, "A small spill is one that can be safely cleaned up by laboratory personnel using available materials and personal protective equipment." Other quantitative definitions might relate to the amount of material spilled or to a calculation of the exposure on the basis of various exposure limits.

Spills defined as "large" might imply a more complicated cleanup process and additional knowledge requirements. Many laboratories might choose to call the fire department hazardous materials team for a large spill, having discussed the response capabilities with them. If an internal response team is selected, it is important to ensure that training conform to the requirements of other regulatory standards, such as OSHA's *Hazardous Waste Operations and Emergency Response Standard* [9]. If the organization determines it is more appropriate that the public fire department respond, communication with that fire department about the mutual expectations and the nature of the hazards is essential. The local fire department might request an inventory of the hazardous materials stored and/or used in the laboratory.

11.2.1.3.3 Emergency procedures shall be established for controlling chemical spills.

FAQ ▶ Are there differences between spill kits?

As part of the emergency procedures required by 11.2.1.3.3, a chemical spill procedure and spill kit should be readily available to personnel who receive, store, use, and dispose of hazardous chemicals. The type of spill kit selected should be appropriate for the chemical hazards present in an area. For example, some chemicals, such as hydrofluoric acid and mercury, require a special spill kit. Kits containing neutralizers, absorbents, cleanup tools (scoops, brushes, boxes, or bags), and personal protective items (goggles, aprons, gloves) can be purchased or assembled by knowledgeable laboratory personnel. Potential users of any spill kit should be provided with written procedures and training in its use.

11.2.1.3.4* Emergency procedures shall be established for extinguishing clothing fires.

See the precautions in A.11.2.1.3.4 regarding the use of fire blankets.

A.11.2.1.3.4 Laboratory personnel should be thoroughly indoctrinated in procedures to follow in cases of clothing fires. The single most important instruction, one that should be stressed until it becomes second nature to all personnel, is to immediately drop to the floor and roll. All personnel should recognize that, in case of ignition of another person's clothing, they should immediately knock that person to the floor and roll that person around to smother the flames. Too often a person will panic if his or her clothing ignites and will run, resulting in more severe, often fatal burn injuries.

It should be emphasized that safety showers or fire blankets are of secondary importance. They should be used only when immediately at hand. It should also be recognized that rolling on the floor not only smothers the fire, but also helps to keep flames out of the victim's face and reduce inhalation of smoke.

Improper use of fire blankets can increase the severity of smoke and fire injuries if the blanket funnels smoke towards the face or if the blanket is not removed after the flames have been extinguished.

FAQ ▶ How is a fire blanket used?

Although NFPA 99 does not require that fire blankets be installed in the laboratory, as depicted in Exhibit 11.1, fire blankets can be a very effective means of extinguishing a clothing fire. If used improperly, however, they can also contribute to the degree of injury. For example, if used while the victim is in a standing position, a blanket can act as a chimney that delivers hot gases directly to the face and respiratory tract. Instructions for emergency action to extinguish clothing fires in a laboratory should emphasize the following procedures.

Stop, Drop, and Roll Procedure. If your clothes catch fire, stop immediately where you are, drop to the ground, roll over and over and back and forth, covering your face and mouth with your hands; this action will prevent flames from burning your face and smoke from entering your lungs. Roll over and over for a long time until the flames are extinguished. Cool the burn with cool water for 10–15 minutes. Call for help.

The stop, drop, and roll procedure should be an automatic reflex reaction.

Fire Blanket Procedure. To use a fire blanket on a person whose clothing is on fire, take the blanket to the victim. With the victim lying on the floor, slide the blanket across the victim *from the head toward the feet* (pushing flames and toxic gases away from the face) to smother flames. Remove all smoldering clothing immediately (do not allow the blanket to trap heat from remaining smoldering clothing). Note that fire blankets can be particularly harmful when synthetic fabrics are involved; they can increase the amount and severity of burns. Thus, *once the fire is extinguished, blankets should be immediately removed.*

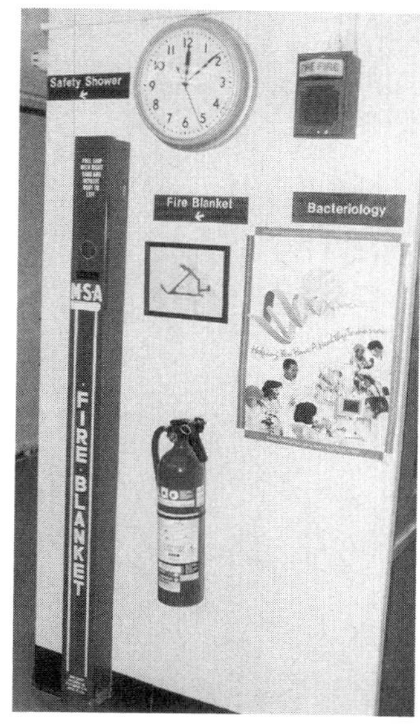

EXHIBIT 11.1 A well-organized safety area in the laboratory, including a fire blanket in a metal sleeve, as well as a portable fire extinguisher, a safety procedure reminder sign, and an egress map indicating the nearest exits.

11.2.1.4 Orientation and Training.

Orientation and training are particularly important for new personnel so that they can become familiar with specific procedures and features of a laboratory. Frequent in-service safety training programs can reinforce safety information to new staff and provide a valuable review to existing staff. Laboratory safety policies, procedures, and emergency plans should be coordinated with institution-wide emergency plans to avoid conflict and contradiction during an emergency.

More specific training requirements are found in OSHA's *Occupational Exposure to Hazardous Chemicals in Laboratories Standard* [4].

11.2.1.4.1 New laboratory personnel shall be taught general safety practices for the laboratory and specific safety practices for the equipment and procedures they will use.

11.2.1.4.2 Continuing safety education and supervision shall be provided, incidents shall be reviewed monthly, and procedures shall be reviewed annually.

11.2.1.4.3* Fire exit drills shall be conducted at least quarterly.

A.11.2.1.4.3 Interruption of essential services is not required.

11.2.1.4.4 Fire exit drills shall be so arranged that each person shall be included at least annually.

◀ **FAQ**
Should fire drills be announced?

Paragraph 11.2.1.4.4 implements exit drills for laboratories as specified in 18.7.1 and 19.7.1 of NFPA *101, Life Safety Code* [2]. Drills can be announced or unannounced, and an appropriate exit drill can involve only a subset of the entire laboratory staff at a time. Note that JCAHO does not allow more than 50 percent of the drills to be announced.

One should be mindful of the working hours of employees who may be on the premises only at night or on weekends. One drill per shift per quarter might be prudent, as well as required by some authorities. Each laboratory employee should be included in at least one drill over the course of a year.

11.3 Structure

Section 11.3 and Section 11.5 reflect current practices and correlate with requirements of NFPA *101, Life Safety Code* [2] (e.g., exit access travel distance, openings in corridor barriers, fire protection features).

11.3.1* Construction and Arrangement.

A.11.3.1 The types of construction are defined in NFPA 220, *Standard on Types of Building Construction*. Also, for a discussion of fire-resistive construction and fire resistance of

building materials and construction assemblies, see the NFPA *Fire Protection Handbook*. For information on the fire resistance, installation, and maintenance of fire doors, see NFPA 80, *Standard for Fire Doors and Fire Windows*.

The level of fire separation for laboratories is based on each laboratory's working supply of flammable or combustible liquids. The total amount of flammable or combustible liquids and the type of storage determine whether a laboratory is classified as an ordinary hazard or as a severe hazard. Quantities in excess of those identified in 11.7.2.3.1 and 11.7.2.3.2 are considered severe hazards.

11.3.1.1* Construction of laboratories shall comply with the requirements of NFPA 45, *Standard on Fire Protection for Laboratories Using Chemicals*, NFPA *101*, *Life Safety Code*, and with the additional requirements of 11.3.1.1.1 and 11.3.1.1.2.

A.11.3.1.1 NFPA 45 provides basic requirements and guidance for laboratory design, but fire separation and sprinkler requirements are more stringent for laboratories in health care facilities. In addition, NFPA 99 requires hood discharge above the roof, allows valves on emergency water supplies, and has other specific requirements based on the unique nature of facilities for care of patients who might be incapable of self-preservation.

11.3.1.1.1 Health care laboratories that are not protected by an automatic extinguishing system and that are not classified by the authority having jurisdiction as a severe hazard shall be separated from surrounding health care areas and from exit access corridors by a fire barrier wall with a minimum 1-hour fire resistant rating, and all openings protected by 1 hour-rated assemblies.

For ordinary hazard laboratories, NFPA 99 requires either a 1-hour fire separation with at least C-labeled, 45-minute-rated doors, or a smoketight room (equal to 30-minute walls and 20-minute doors for existing construction, 1-hour walls in new construction) protected by an automatic fire extinguishing system. For severe hazard laboratories, NFPA 99 requires either a 2-hour fire separation with at least B-labeled, 1-hour-rated doors or a 1-hour fire separation with at least C-labeled, 45-minute-rated doors and an automatic fire suppression system. (See Commentary Table 11.1.) It is the standard's intent that these requirements apply to laboratories separated by exit access corridors as well as exit corridors.

The term *by the authority having jurisdiction* was added to 11.3.1.1.1 to clarify who classifies the hazard level of laboratories.

COMMENTARY TABLE 11.1 *Separation Requirements*

Ordinary Hazard	*Severe Hazard*
<10 gal flammable liquids	>10 gal flammable liquids
or	or
<60 gal flammable liquids stored in a flammable liquids cabinet	>60 gal flammable liquids stored in a flammable liquids cabinet
requires	requires
1-hour separation with C-labeled 45-minute doors	2-hour separation with B-labeled 1½-hour doors
or	or
smoketight room with automatic fire extinguishing system	1-hour separation with C-labeled 45-minute doors and an automatic fire extinguishing system

11.3.1.1.2 Openings in a laboratory corridor barrier shall be permitted to be held open only by an automatic release device complying with the applicable requirements in NFPA *101*, *Life Safety Code*. 

Refer to Chapters 18 and 19 of NFPA *101, Life Safety Code* [2], for applicable health care facility requirements. Any automatic release device can hold open a door to a hazardous area if the device deactivates upon activation of a manual fire alarm system, a local smoke detector, or a complete fire detection or extinguishing system.

11.3.1.2 Interior finish in laboratories and means of egress shall comply with the applicable sections of NFPA *101*, *Life Safety Code*. 

11.3.2 Exit Details.

The requirements in 11.3.2 correlate with those of Chapter 18 and Chapter 19 in NFPA *101, Life Safety Code* [2], for health care facilities.

11.3.2.1* Any room arranged for laboratory work that has an area in excess of 92.9 m^2 (1000 ft^2) shall have at least two exit access doors remote from each other, one of which shall open directly onto a means of egress.

Exit access door requirements of 11.3.2.1 were revised in 1980 to make them less restrictive while still providing an equivalent degree of safety (e.g., one door could open to another room, assuming 1-hour fire-resistive-rated construction separated the two areas). Note that at least one door is required to open onto a means of egress.

A.11.3.2.1 A door to an adjoining laboratory work area is considered to be a second access to an exit. 

11.3.2.2 A second means of access to an exit shall be provided for any laboratory work areas in which hazards exist as required by 3.4.1 of NFPA 45, *Standard on Fire Protection for Laboratories Using Chemicals*. 

Laboratory areas smaller than 92.9 m^2 (1000 ft^2) also need a second means of egress if the hazard potential warrants it, as defined in 3.4.1 of NFPA 45, *Standard on Fire Protection for Laboratories Using Chemicals* [1].

11.3.2.3 Travel distance between any point in a laboratory unit and an exit access door shall not exceed 22.9 m (75 ft).

Paragraph 11.3.2.3 emphasizes the importance of not creating tenuous situations in laboratories. The requirements of 11.3.2 are somewhat more restrictive than specified in 18.2.6 and 19.2.6 of NFPA *101, Life Safety Code* [2]. Exhibit 11.2 illustrates travel distance. 

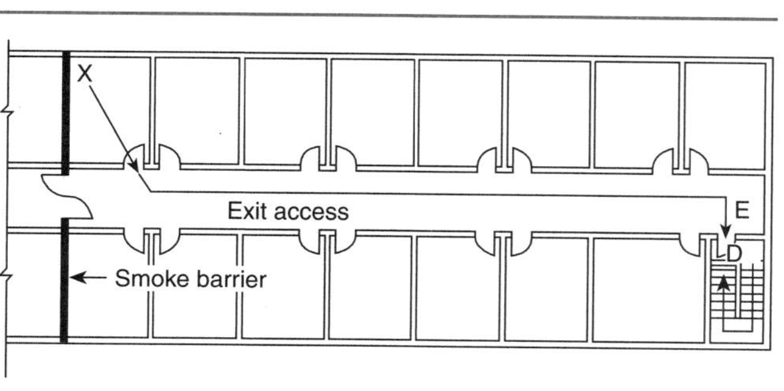

***EXHIBIT 11.2** Travel distance measurement. (Source: Life Safety Code Handbook, 2003, Exhibit 18/19.19.)*

11.3.2.4 Exit access doors from laboratories shall meet the requirements of NFPA *101*, *Life Safety Code*.

11.3.2.5 Laboratory corridors constituting access to an exit shall meet the requirements of NFPA *101*, *Life Safety Code*.

It should be noted that the width of corridors that constitute access to an exit vary, depending on the occupancy classification of a laboratory, per NFPA *101* [2]. For example, if properly separated from the rest of a health care facility, the laboratory is classified as business/industrial; if the laboratory is not separated, it is classified as health care. If the laboratory is used by patients on litters or beds, the requirement of 11.3.2.7 takes precedence.

11.3.2.6 Corridors shall be maintained clear and unobstructed at all times.

FAQ ▶ What are some examples of objects that can obstruct the corridor width?

Although a corridor can be built in accordance with NFPA *101, Life Safety Code* [2], criteria, the effective width of corridors can be narrowed by the placement of objects in the corridors (e.g., water coolers, boxes, chairs, temporary equipment). (Sections 18.2.3 and 19.2.3 of NFPA *101* detail the means of egress capacity requirements for health care occupancies.)

11.3.2.7 Laboratory corridors, used for the transporting of patients in beds or litters, and constituting access to an exit, shall be not less than 243.8 cm (96 in.) in clear and unobstructed width.

Paragraph 11.3.2.7 takes into consideration those laboratory corridors (or portions therein) that constitute an access to an exit and through which patients in beds or litters might be wheeled. This paragraph applies only to laboratories performing in vivo procedures requiring patients to be transported into the laboratory for the test or procedure. This requirement, it should be noted, is applicable only to new construction. The 243.8 cm (96 in.) value allows for the need to turn a bed around in the corridor and for beds to pass each other. This is the same value as required in Chapter 18 of NFPA *101, Life Safety Code* [2], for patient areas in new health care occupancies. (See Exhibit 11.3.)

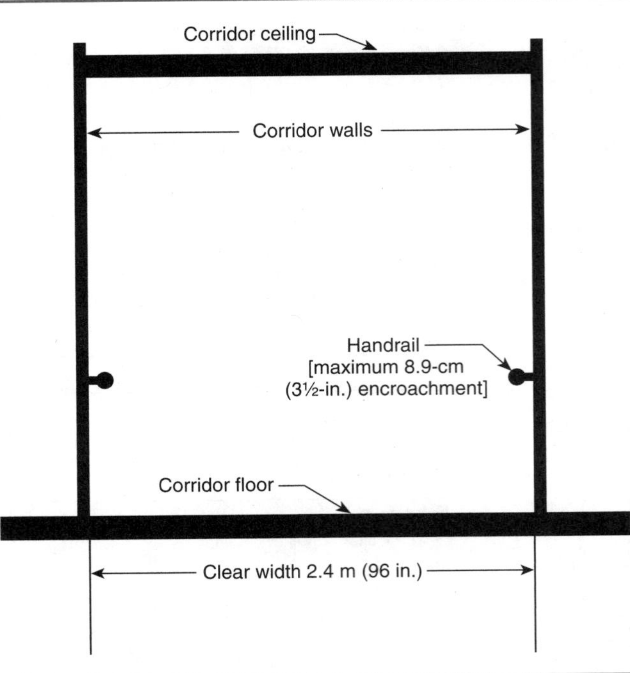

***EXHIBIT 11.3** Clear width in corridor. (Source: Life Safety Code Handbook, 2003, Exhibit 18/19.6.)*

11.3.3 Exhaust Air.

Exhaust air shall conform to Section 6.3.

11.3.4* Ventilation.

Ventilation shall comply with 6.4.2 and with the requirements of NFPA 45, *Standard on Fire Protection for Laboratories Using Chemicals.*

A.11.3.4 Subsection 6.4.3 gives ventilation requirements that are specific for laboratories in health care facilities and are in addition to the basic laboratory ventilation requirements contained in Chapter 6 of NFPA 45.

11.3.5 Fume Hoods.

Fume hoods shall conform to 6.4.3 and 6.6.2.

11.4 Equipment

For general safety requirements for electrical appliances used in laboratories, see Chapter 8.

11.4.1 General.

Laboratory apparatus shall comply with the requirements of NFPA 45, *Standard on Fire Protection for Laboratories Using Chemicals.*

11.4.2 Equipment Employing Liquids.

11.4.2.1* Tissue processors and similar automatic equipment that release ignitable (flammable or combustible) vapors into the ambient workspace shall be operated at least 1.52 m (5 ft) from the storage of combustible materials, unless separated by 1-hour fire-resistive construction.

Paragraph C.11.1 includes descriptions of four tissue processor fires that were fueled by combustible reagents in containers stored below the processor. The intent of 11.4.2.1 is to isolate equipment capable of igniting such reagents during unattended periods of operation. Although a flammable safety cabinet less than 1.52 m (5 ft) away would satisfy the 1-hour construction requirement of 11.4.2.1, great care should be exercised in the location of combustible reagent storage near equipment intended to be operated in an unattended mode.

This section applies only to equipment that operates on an open system principle. (Newer equipment operates on a closed-system basis.) Distillation apparatus for the recycling and reuse of xylenes and alcohols, increasingly prevalent among clinical laboratories, is characteristically designed to be a closed system, but such systems qualify as "similar automatic equipment" if they release combustible vapors. Paragraph C.11.1.6 relates a fire incident in Tennessee in 1984 that began in a xylene distillation apparatus.

A.11.4.2.1 Tissue processors that operate as a closed system contain ignitible vapor hazards within the processor and thus do not pose a hazard requiring a 1.52 m (5 ft) separation.

11.4.2.1.1 All new tissue processors and similar automatic equipment that release ignitable vapors shall be provided with the following safeguards and interlocks as part of a monitored audible and visual alarm:

(1) Low liquid level
(2) High vapor

11.4.2.1.2 The safeguards above shall be connected to an audible alarm in a constantly attended location.

FAQ ▶ Why is an audible alarm required for a tissue processor?

Unattended tissue processors are common ignition sources of laboratory fires. The low liquid level and high vapor safeguards and interlocks are readily available on new tissue processor models. The requirement to have an audible alarm in a constantly attended location takes into account the minimal staffing that might be present in some laboratories on some shifts.

Exhibit 11.4 shows a closed-system tissue processor.

11.4.2.2* Unattended laboratory operations employing flammable or combustible reagents shall be conducted in an area equipped with an automatic fire extinguishing system.

Paragraph 11.2.1.1.3 contains the general requirements for unattended operation and automatic laboratory equipment. Paragraph 11.4.2.2 contains requirements specifically for those unattended operations or equipment that employs flammable or combustible reagents. It is based on knowledge of actual fires involving unattended experiments where no automatic fire protection was present.

Exhibit 11.4 Closed-system tissue processor.

Routine operations performed by tissue processors, solvent recycling apparatus (see Exhibit 11.5), and other automated equipment increase the possibility of fire due to the repetitive nature of the process and the casual attitude that can accompany routine operations. Special attention needs to be directed toward the design and installation of the automatic fire detection and extinguishing equipment specifically intended for such unattended operation.

Laboratory occupancies in health care facilities often contain very expensive equipment that could be destroyed or become extremely hazardous if exposed to an accidental discharge from a sprinkler system. One design consideration to eliminate any possibility of an accidental discharge from a sprinkler system is through the installation of a preaction system. This type of system is defined in NFPA 13, *Standard for the Installation of Sprinkler Systems* [10], as "a sprinkler system employing automatic sprinklers that are attached to a piping system that contains air that might or might not be under pressure, with a supplemental detection system installed in the same areas as the sprinklers." Actuation of the fire detection system opens a valve that permits water to flow into the sprinkler piping system and to be discharged from any sprinklers that are open (usually as a result of fire). Thus, no water needs to be within the sprinkler stationed over special equipment. It is only when the fire detection system senses fire or heat that water is released into the sprinkler piping system.

A.11.4.2.2 One method of safeguarding unattended processes is to place the equipment in a pan large enough to contain any spilled materials, preferably within a fume hood protected by some form of automatic fire extinguishment or detection.

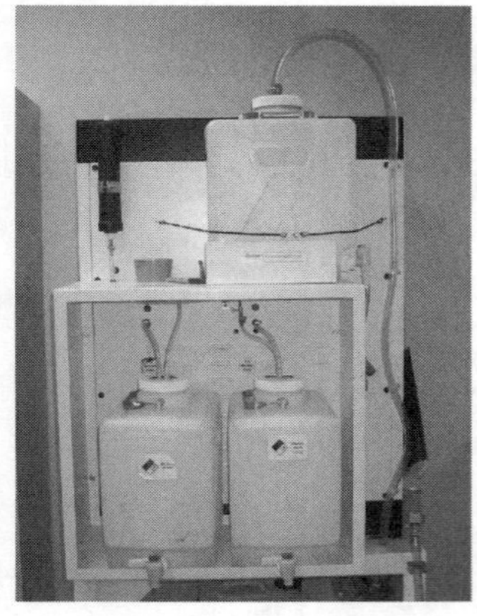

EXHIBIT 11.5 A closed-system solvent recycling apparatus.

11.5* Fire Protection

A.11.5 Examination of laboratory fire records demonstrates the extra vulnerability of premises with substantial amounts of combustible contents. The use of noncombustible shelving, benches, and furniture will reduce production of smoke and damage to facilities, with substantial savings where expensive laboratory equipment is present, even in sprinklered areas.

Self-contained breathing apparatus should be considered for equipping personnel for rescue operations in areas with special fire hazards. Training is required for effective use of such equipment. It is desirable to coordinate equipment and training with local fire department personnel.

11.5.1* Automatic fire-extinguishing protection shall be provided in all laboratories, including associated storage rooms, under either of the following conditions:

(1) Laboratories are not separated from surrounding areas by at least 1-hour fire-resistive construction with door openings protected by Class C self-closing fire doors, and employ quantities of flammable, combustible, or hazardous materials less than that which would be considered severe.
(2) Laboratories are not separated from surrounding areas by at least 2-hour fire-resistive construction with door openings protected by Class B self-closing doors, and employ quantities of flammable, combustible, or hazardous materials considered severe.

Paragraph 11.3.1.1.1 contains requirements for automatic fire extinguishing systems with respect to separation requirements that comply with NFPA 45, *Standard on Fire Protection for Laboratories Using Chemicals* [1]. (See the commentary following 11.3.1.1.1 for further information.) Paragraph 11.5.1 adds to that criteria specific to laboratories within health care facilities based not only on the degree of hazard present, but also on the separation of the laboratory from other areas of the facility.

Table A.11.5.1 provides one method to determine the level of hazard present in the laboratory. Laboratories employing hazardous material rated as less than severe, and not separated by a 1-hour-rated wall, should have an automatic fire extinguishing system.

The annex text calls attention to the fact that some types of extinguishing systems other than water should be reviewed for use in such areas as computer rooms and/or laboratory areas (which may or may not be sprinklered) with a significant amount of automated laboratory equipment.

A.11.5.1 Where there is a need to reduce equipment damage and facilitate return to service, consideration should be given to an approved gaseous agent total flooding system in laboratories.

The hazard level of a laboratory is considered severe if quantities of flammable, combustible, or hazardous materials are present that are capable of sustaining a fire condition of sufficient magnitude to breach a 1-hour fire separation.

To determine the combustible content or heat potential of flammable or combustible materials capable of breaching or penetrating a 1-hour–rated fire separation, one method is included in the 19th edition of the NFPA *Fire Protection Handbook*, where formulas and tables for calculating the equivalence of time versus fire severity are given. Specific reference is made to Section 12.5, Confinement of Fire in Buildings, and Tables A.1, A.2, and A.3 for heat of combustion (Btu/lb) for materials common to laboratories.

Note that the weights of combustible contents in Tables 12.5.1, 12.5.2, and 12.5.3 are those of ordinary combustible materials taken at 8000 Btu/lb. For converting other than ordinary combustibles to pounds per square foot (psf), divide the total Btu value by 8000/Btu/lb.

The method described, it should be noted, is only one of several methods for calculating the hazard level of a laboratory with regard to combustibles breaching a 1-hour fire separation.

Table A.11.5.1 can be used as a guide in making the determination of the combustible content or heat potential of flammable or combustible materials capable of breaching or penetrating a 1-hour–rated fire separation.

TABLE A.11.5.1 *Guide for Determining Fire Separation Rating*

	Hazard	
Wall Rating	***Not Severe***	***Severe***
Less than 1 hour	Automatic fire extinguishing system required	Not allowed
1 hour	No automatic fire extinguishing system required	Automatic fire extinguishing system required
2 hour	No automatic fire extinguishing system required	No automatic fire extinguishing system required

11.5.2 Automatic fire extinguishment and fire detection systems, where required, shall be connected to the facility fire alarm system and shall be arranged to immediately sound an alarm.

Subsection 11.5.2 is applicable only if an automatic fire detection and extinguishing system is installed. If a laboratory were excluded by one of the criteria in 11.5.1, no connection to a facility sprinkler system would be required; however, a review of appropriate fire/smoke detectors connected to the facility fire alarm system should be made.

11.5.3 Portable fire extinguishers suitable for the particular hazards shall be located so that they will be readily available to personnel in accordance with NFPA 10, *Standard for Portable Fire Extinguishers*.

In addition to the selection, distribution, inspection, maintenance, and recharging of portable fire extinguishers as specified in NFPA 10, *Standard for Portable Fire Extinguishers* [11], 18.7.2 and 19.7.2 of NFPA *101, Life Safety Code* [2], set forth operational plans and staff responsibilities in a fire emergency. NFPA 10 includes provisions within the fire plan for fire extinguishment. Familiarity with selection, extinguishing characteristics, and the location, operation, and use of fire extinguishers should be incorporated into new employee orientation, periodic retraining, and instruction on fire exit drills. Considerations such as minimizing damage to equipment, specimens, or records contained in the laboratory could warrant the installation of such alternatives to water extinguishing systems as a gaseous agent total flooding system.

FAQ ▶ **Can a non-water extinguishing agent be used to protect the laboratory?**

See Exhibit 11.6 for an example of a fire extinguisher cabinet whose curved Plexiglas® increases extinguisher visibility while protecting the unit from damage. The three-dimensional sign shown above the cabinet in the illustration calls further attention to the extinguisher location but is not required.

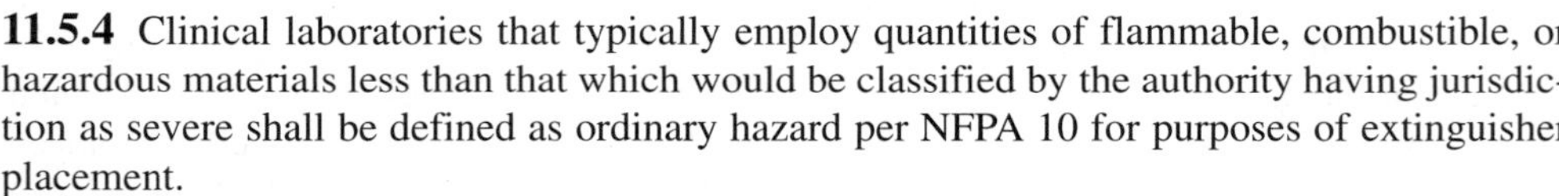

11.5.4 Clinical laboratories that typically employ quantities of flammable, combustible, or hazardous materials less than that which would be classified by the authority having jurisdiction as severe shall be defined as ordinary hazard per NFPA 10 for purposes of extinguisher placement.

Subsection 11.5.4 is intended to clarify the placement of portable fire extinguishers in relation to the amount of hazardous material.

EXHIBIT 11.6 *A typical fire extinguisher cabinet with door.*

11.6* Emergency Shower

Where the eyes or body of any person can be exposed to injurious corrosive materials, suitable fixed facilities for quick drenching or flushing of the eyes and body shall be provided within the work area for immediate emergency use.

A.11.6 Showers should be controlled by a nonautomatic shutoff device. Although a self-closing shower valve (favored by most designers) would minimize flooding of the building if, for example, the shower were maliciously activated, it does not afford maximum help to the injured user. Since a person would have to use one hand to keep the valve open, efforts to remove clothing or wipe away offending materials would be greatly hampered.

Although emergency showers are rarely used, their use when necessary can mean the difference between superficial burns and serious disfigurement, or loss of life. In some cases where such showers have not been activated for long periods, they have been found inoperative. It is essential that emergency showers be provided and tested from time to time to determine that their valves are in good operating condition. Advance planning needs to be made to handle the water that will flow in a test.

Floor drains in areas of hospitals and other health care facilities are likely to dry out if the floors are not wet-mopped regularly, and dry traps can permit passage of gases, vapors, odors, and vermin. Since a floor drain will be of great value if a safety shower is used, resulting in the release of several hundred gallons of water, it is recommended that floor drains be filled with water regularly, or in new construction that some plumbing be provided to fill the traps manually, automatically, or incidentally by plumbing design.

Another consideration is to be sure that all holes in floor slabs that have not been sealed around pipes to prevent the passage of smoke be so sealed, and in a manner that will prevent water from flowing to lower floors from the discharge of an emergency shower or sprinkler head.

Wall-mounted portable eye wash stations do not contain an adequate supply of water for the 15-minute flushing recommended by chemical manufacturers.

Previous editions of the standard have stated that floor drains were "not recommended" because they tended to dry out and permit entry of noxious gases into the laboratory. Paragraph A.11.6 recommends that floor drains be installed (and maintained) because of the overriding value of such drains in cleaning up after a drenching shower.

Maintenance requirements for emergency showers and eyewash stations are based on ANSI Z358.1, Standard *for Emergency Eyewash and Shower Equipment* [12], which requires that showers be activated weekly and inspected annually.

See Exhibits 11.7, 11.8, and 11.9 for photographs of one safety shower and two types of eyewash units. Showerheads on flexible water lines at sink locations can be useful for eye flush and skin or clothing spills. (See 11.8.1.3 for inspection procedures.) Shutoff valves for showers allow repair, replacement, and testing without necessitating the shutdown of an entire sprinkler system.

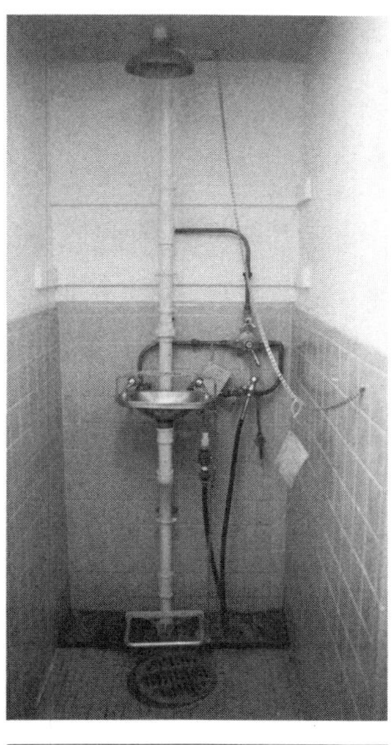

EXHIBIT 11.7 *A combination one-point operation eye wash and shower. Eye and body contamination with chemical or body fluid substances can be flushed.*

11.6.1 Fixed eye baths shall be designed and installed to avoid injurious water pressure.

Although portable eye wash stations might meet the need to provide a measure of safety immediately adjacent to a hazard, they do not meet the requirement of OSHA *Standard for Medical Services and First Aid* [13], which requires that 1.5 L (0.4 gal) be delivered per minute for a total of 15 minutes.

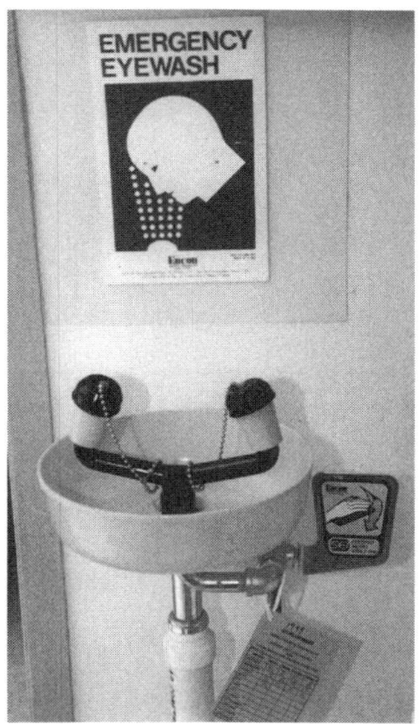

EXHIBIT 11.8 *A conventional one-point operation plumbed eyewash, with signage to ensure location visibility from any area within the acceptable travel distance, and an inspection tag.*

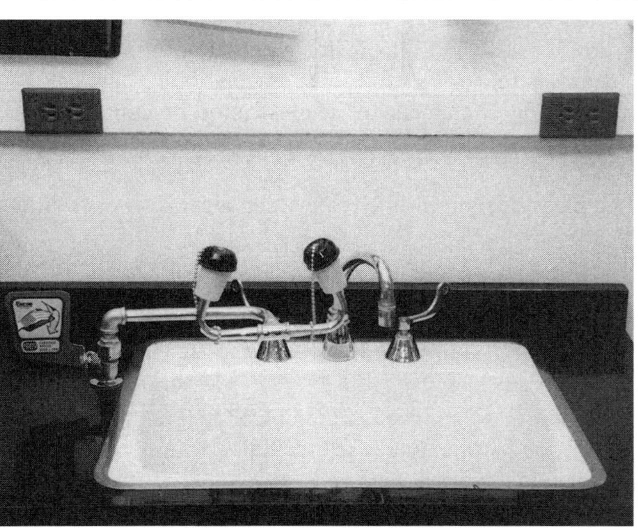

EXHIBIT 11.9 *A one-point operation swing-out eye wash that combines accessibility, space, and utility considerations.*

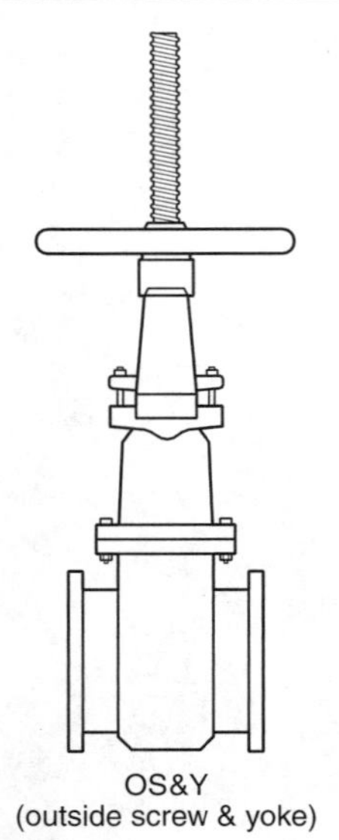

EXHIBIT 11.10 An outside screw and yoke sprinkler system water control valve.

ANSI Z358.1, *Standard for Emergency Eyewash and Shower Equipment* [12], also addresses eyewash maintenance requirements, which include weekly activation.

11.6.2 If shutoff valves or stops are installed in the branch line leading to safety drenching equipment, the valves shall be as follows:

(1) OS & Y (outside stem and yoke)
(2) Labeled for identification
(3) Sealed in the open position

OS & Y–type valves were selected because of their reliability and ease in determining whether they are open or closed. Other types could be used if they can be demonstrated to be equivalent in character and performance. (See 1.4.2 regarding the subject of equivalency.) An example of an OS & Y valve is shown in Exhibit 11.10.

11.6.3 The installation of wall-mounted portable eye-wash stations shall not preclude the adherence to the provisions of Section 11.6.

11.7 Flammable and Combustible Liquids

The material in Section 11.7 correlates with NFPA 30, *Flammable and Combustible Liquids Code* [14], which contains general requirements for such liquids. Unless otherwise noted, the term *liquids* in this section refers to flammable or combustible liquids.

11.7.1 General.

Flammable and combustible liquids shall be handled and used with care and with knowledge of their hazardous properties, both individually and in combination with other materials with which they can come in contact.

11.7.2* Storage and Use.

A.11.7.2 Plastic containers are sometimes used to avoid breakage problems posed by glass containers or contamination problems with metal containers. Plastic containers need to be chosen with particular attention to their compatibility with the liquid to be contained. For example, polyethylene containers are generally unsuitable for aldehydes, ketones, esters, higher molecular-weight alcohols, benzene, toluene, various oils, silicone fluids, and halogenated hydrocarbons. In addition to labeling containers for identification of contents, it is important to label plastic containers for identification of their constituent materials to avoid misuse.

In some cases, listed or labeled stainless steel or tin-lined safety containers offer a solution to contamination problems.

11.7.2.1* Flammable and combustible liquids shall be used from and stored in approved containers in accordance with NFPA 30, *Flammable and Combustible Liquids Code*, and NFPA 45, *Standard on Fire Protection for Laboratories Using Chemicals.*

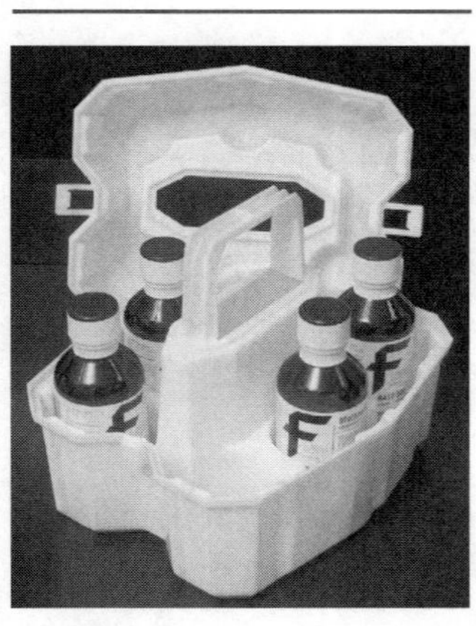

EXHIBIT 11.11 Chemical carrier.

To determine the maximum size container for a flammable or combustible liquid, the liquid's hazard classification must be known [15]. The maximum size container can be determined from Commentary Table 11.2 [14], for maximum allowed size.

Glass containers are often put in safety carrying devices, such as the one shown in Exhibit 11.11, for transport within the laboratory.

A.11.7.2.1 Table A.11.7.2.1 is a portion of Table 4.2.3 in NFPA 30, *Flammable and Combustible Liquids Code*. NFPA 45 provides more specific guidance for use of flammable and combustible liquids in laboratories, in addition to basic requirements set forth in NFPA 30.

TABLE A.11.7.2.1 *Maximum Allowable Size of Containers and Portable Tanks*

	Flammable Liquids			*Combustible Liquids*	
Container Type	***Class IA***	***Class IB***	***Class IC***	***Class II***	***Class III***
Glass	1 pt	1 qt	1 gal	1 gal	5 gal
Metal (other than DOT drums) or approved plastic	1 gal	5 gal	5 gal	5 gal	5 gal
Safety cans	2 gal	5 gal	5 gal	5 gal	5 gal

For SI units: 1 pt = 0.49 L; 1 qt = 0.95 L; 1 gal = 3.8 L.

11.7.2.2 Storage cabinets for flammable and combustible liquids shall be constructed in accordance with Section 4.3 of NFPA 30, *Flammable and Combustible Liquids Code.*

Storage cabinets for flammable and combustible liquids are to be constructed in accordance with Section 6.3 of NFPA 30, *Flammable and Combustible Liquids Code* [14]. Such a storage cabinet, fabricated from sheet metal, is shown in Exhibit 11.12.

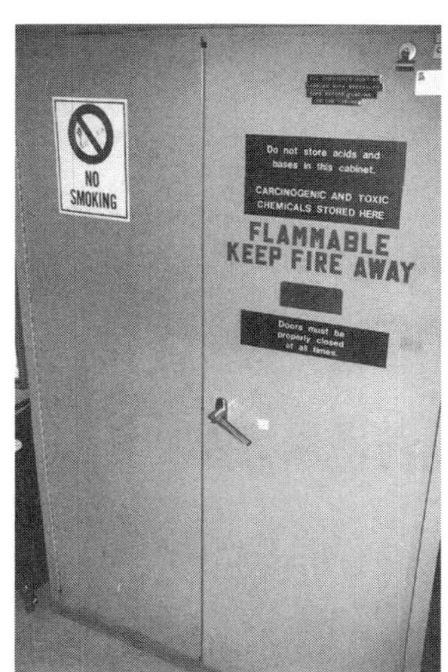

EXHIBIT 11.12 *Laboratory flammable liquids cabinet with necessary and appropriate warning signs.*

11.7.2.3* In laboratories not classified by the authority having jurisdiction as very small work areas, established laboratory practice shall limit working supplies of flammable or combustible liquids.

A few very small laboratories might have a need to store quantities larger than those listed in Table A.11.7.2.1. In any case, the listed amounts specify maximum quantities. Laboratories should have on hand only the minimum amounts necessary for safe laboratory operation, as noted in A.11.7.2.3.

Depending on quantity and type, chemicals within a laboratory, particularly flammable liquids, can constitute a serious fire hazard. Careful consideration should be given to the quantities and reactive qualities of chemicals stored in a laboratory. A systematic review of chemical inventory by qualified laboratory personnel can aid in providing the most appropriate (safe) level of flammable storage within the laboratory.

A.11.7.2.3 The goal is to keep the fuel load to a limit that is as low as is practicable. In no case should excessive amounts be stored. Constant effort needs to be exerted to prevent the overstocking of hazardous chemicals. The laboratory manager can help keep stocks at a safe level by encouraging small and more frequent requisitions, by developing a reliable stock inventory system, by assuring convenient and prompt deliveries from the central stock room, by selecting brands that are the most popular and not necessarily the cheapest, and by discouraging (except perhaps for large-scale research-type projects) the practice of purchasing the largest containers, including bulk supplies in 55 gal (208.2 L) drums.

11.7.2.3.1 The total volume of Class I, II, and IIIA liquids outside of approved storage cabinets and safety cans shall not exceed 3.78 L (1 gal) per 9.29 m^2 (100 ft^2).

The allowable quantities in 11.7.2.3.1 parallel the hazard assessment procedure used by NFPA 45, *Standard on Fire Protection for Laboratories Using Chemicals* [1]. The allowable quantities are proportional to the size of the laboratory.

COMMENTARY TABLE 11.2 *Maximum Allowable Size — Containers, Intermediate Bulk Containers, and Portable Tanks*

Type	*Flammable Liquids*			*Combustible Liquids*	
	Class IA	*Class IB*	*Class IC*	*Class II*	*Class III*
Glass	0.5 L (1.05 pt)	1 L (1.05 qt)	5 L (1.3 gal)	5 L (1.3 gal)	20 L (5.3 gal)
Metal (other than drums) or approved plastic	5 L (1.3 gal)	20 L (5.3 gal)	20 L (5.3 gal)	20 L (5.3 gal)	20 L (5.3 gal)
Safety cans	10 L (2.6 gal)	20 L (5.3 gal)	20 L (5.3 gal)	20 L (5.3 gal)	20 L (5.3 gal)
Metal drum (e.g., UN 1A1 or 1A2)	450 L (119 gal)	450 L (119 gal)	450 L (119 gal)	450 L (119 gal)	450 L (119 gal)
Approved metal portable tanks and IBCs	3000 L (793 gal)	3000 L (793 gal)	3000 L (793 gal)	3000 L (793 gal)	3000 L (793 gal)
Rigid plastic IBCs (UN 31H1 or 31H2) and composite IBCs with rigid inner receptacle (UN31HZ1)	NP	NP	NP	3000 L (793 gal)	3000 L (793 gal)
Composite IBCs with flexible inner receptacle (UN31HZ2) and flexible IBCs (UN13H, UN13L, and UN13M)	NP	NP	NP	NP	NP
Bag-in-Box Nonbulk	NP	NP	NP	NP	NP
Polyethylene UN 1H1, or as authorized by DOT exemption	5 L (1.3 gal)	20 L (5.3 gal)*	20 L (5.3 gal)*	450 L (119 gal)	450 L (119 gal)
Fiber drum NMFC or UFC Type 2A; Types 3A, 3B-H, or 3B-L; or Type 4A	NP	NP	NP	450 L (119 gal)	450 L (119 gal)

Note: NP — Not permitted.
*For Class IB and IC water-miscible liquids, the maximum allowable size of plastic container is 230 L (60 gal), if stored and protected in accordance with Table 6.8.2(g) of NFPA 30, *Flammable and Combustible Liquids Code,* 2003 edition.
Source: NFPA 30, *Flammable and Combustible Liquids Code,* 2003 edition, Table 6.2.3.

11.7.2.3.2 The total volume of Class I, II, and IIIA liquids, including those contained in approved storage cabinets and safety cans, shall not exceed 7.57 L (2 gal) per 9.29 m^2 (100 ft^2).

Approved storage cabinets are described in Section 6.3, Design Construction and Capacity of Storage Cabinets, of NFPA 30, *Flammable and Combustible Liquids Code* [14]. Approved cabinets can be of either metal (Exhibit 11.13) or wood (Exhibit 11.14), as long as the materials and construction techniques appropriate for each are followed. One advantage of wooden cabinets is that they often can be constructed locally or in-house and custom designed to fit into the space available, as opposed to locating a manufactured cabinet to fit the desired space.

11.7.2.3.3 No flammable or combustible liquid shall be stored or transferred from one vessel to another in any exit access corridor or passageway leading to an exit.

Paragraph 11.7.2.3.3 applies to laboratories separated by exit access corridors as well as exit corridors.

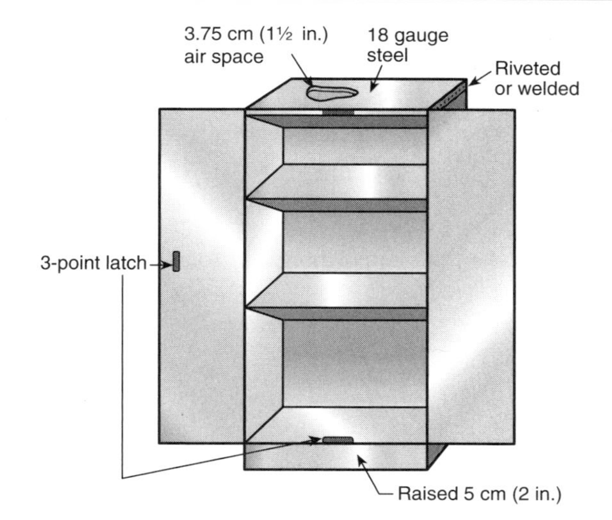

EXHIBIT 11.13 *Metal cabinets whose construction is acceptable.*

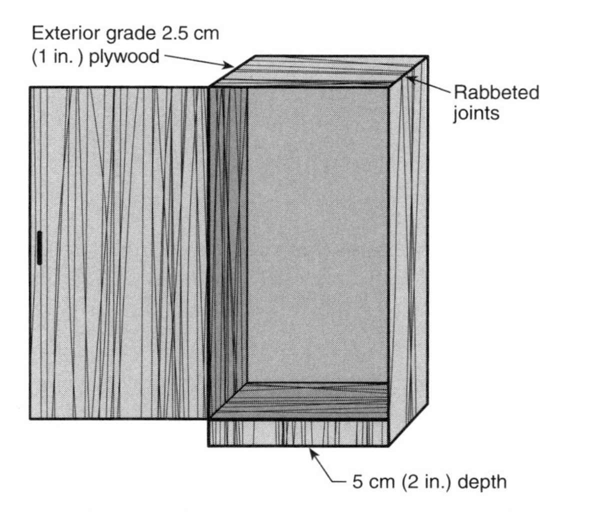

EXHIBIT 11.14 *Wooden cabinets whose construction is acceptable. A three-point latch is not required on the doors because wood does not tend to warp or distort when exposed to fire, as metal does.*

11.7.2.3.4 Approved flammable or combustible inside liquid storage area(s) designed, constructed, and operated in accordance with NFPA 30, *Flammable and Combustible Liquids Code*, shall be available within any health care facility regularly maintaining a reserve storage capacity in excess of 1135.5 L (300 gal).

Reference to NFPA 30, *Flammable and Combustible Liquids Code* [14], refers authorities having jurisdiction, designers, and users to the appropriate requirements for storage areas for flammable liquids.

11.7.2.3.5 Quantities of flammable and combustible liquids for disposal shall be included in the total inventory.

11.7.2.4 Venting of storage cabinets shall be permitted.

11.7.2.4.1 Storage cabinets with approved flame arresters shall be permitted to be exhausted through a fume hood exhaust system.

11.7.2.4.2 Construction of the venting duct within the laboratory shall be equal to the rating of the cabinet.

FAQ ▶
Is venting necessary?

The purpose of the venting criteria of 11.7.2.4.2 is to provide safety guidelines to those laboratories that choose to vent. It should be noted, however, that venting is optional. Reasons for electing to vent include preventing a buildup of positive pressure within cabinets and reducing the accumulation of fumes that pose a fire hazard.

11.7.2.5 Flammable or combustible liquids shall not be positioned as follows:

(1) Near Bunsen burners
(2) Near ovens
(3) Near hot pipes and valves
(4) Near other sources of heat
(5) In corridors

Exhaust canopies do not represent a potential ignition source for flammable or combustible materials and therefore are not a hazard and not included in the list.

11.7.2.6* Class I flammable liquids shall not be stored in ordinary refrigerators, freezers, or coolers.

Hazards are associated with the storage of ignitible liquids in any type of refrigerator (i.e., vapors can build up with no way to vent them). Alternative means for storage of such liquids exist, as noted in 11.7.2.1, 11.7.2.2, and 11.7.2.4.1. Paragraph 11.7.2.6 applies only to Class I flammable liquids.

A.11.7.2.6 *Walk-in Thermal-Controlled Boxes.* Procedures likely to result in toxic or flammable atmospheres should be discouraged within "walk-in" refrigerators or other types of temperature-controlled boxes. A warning sign such as the following should be posted on every box:

DANGER
NOT EXPLOSIONPROOF
NOT VENTILATED
GROUND ALL ELECTRICAL EQUIPMENT
DO NOT STORE DRY ICE

New boxes should include at least the following features:

(1) A latch that can be released by a person inside the box when the door is locked from the outside

(2) Latch and door frames designed to allow actuation under all conditions of freezing

(3) A floor with a nonconductive surface

(4) Neoprene matting to insulate up to 10,000 V

(5) A view-window in the door

(6) An independently circuited high-temperature thermostat and alarm (for warm boxes)

(7) Vaporproof duplex electrical receptacles

(8) An alarm that can be heard throughout the occupied work area and an alarm button at the inside door frame that will keep operating after actuation

(9) Conduits sealed (in cold boxes) in a manner to prevent accumulation of water vapor such as in the globe protectors of the light fixtures

(10) Adjustable exhaust vent and air intake of at least 15 CFM for general ventilation, with provisions for installing a flexible hose and miniature canopy in a manner to provide local ventilation at a specific work site. As explosionproof laboratory apparatus becomes available, it should be substituted for less safe equipment used in enclosed thermal-control boxes.

Non-Walk-in Refrigerators. The use of domestic refrigerators for the storage of typical laboratory solvents presents a significant hazard to the laboratory work area. Refrigerator temperatures are almost universally higher than the flash points of the flammable liquids most often stored in them. In addition to vapor accumulation, a domestic refrigerator contains readily available ignition sources, such as thermostats, light switches, and heater strips, all within or exposing the refrigerated storage compartment. Furthermore, the compressor and its circuits are typically located at the bottom of the unit, where vapors from flammable liquid spills or leaks can easily accumulate.

Explosionproof refrigeration equipment is designed to protect against ignition of flammable vapors both inside and outside the refrigerated storage compartment. This type is intended and recommended for environments such as pilot plants or laboratory work areas where all electrical equipment is required to be explosionproof.

The design concepts of the flammable material storage refrigerators are based on the typical laboratory environment. The primary intent is to eliminate ignition of vapors inside the storage compartment from sources also within the compartment. In addition, flammable material storage refrigerators incorporate such design features as thresholds, self-closing latch doors, friction latches or magnetic door gaskets, and special methods for the inner shell. All of these features are intended to control or limit the loss potential should an exothermic reaction occur within the storage compartment. Finally, the compressor and its circuits and controls are often located at the top of the unit to further reduce the potential for ignition of floor-level vapors. In general, the design features of a commercially available flammable material storage refrigerator are such that they provide several safeguards not available through modification of domestic models.

Every laboratory refrigerator should be clearly labeled to indicate whether or not it is acceptable for storage of flammable materials. Internal laboratory procedures should ensure that laboratory refrigerators are being properly used. The following are examples of labels that can be used on laboratory refrigerators:

DO NOT STORE FLAMMABLE SOLVENTS
in this refrigerator

NOTICE
This is not an "explosionproof" refrigerator, but it has been designed to permit storage of materials producing flammable vapors. Containers should be well stoppered or tightly closed.

Smoking in health care facilities is not permitted by other regulatory organizations. Therefore, there is no need to post signs stating this fact.

Safety standards and safe work practices are often not introduced until accidents begin to happen. Better, safer equipment is developed once the hazards present themselves, as was the case with the storage of diethyl ether in the early 1970s. Laboratories often stored diethyl ether in the cold to retard vaporization and the formation of dangerous peroxides. The volatility of diethyl ether, a Class IA liquid (as defined in NFPA 30, *Flammable and Combustible Liquids Code* [14]), was such that, even when refrigerated at a temperature range of 4°C to 6°C (39°F to 43°F), easily ignitible vapors could accumulate. Explosions would occur when electrical switches or lamps within conventional refrigerator cabinets ignited these vapors. These violent accidents led to the development of explosionproof refrigerators, which greatly reduced the risk that these flammable vapors would ignite. Examples of design changes included the use of thermostats with sealed or externally mounted contact points and the absence of lights inside refrigerators.

11.7.2.6.1 If Class I flammable liquids are stored under refrigeration (e.g., for analytical purposes), the storage devices shall be listed flammable materials storage refrigerators or refrigerators listed for Class I, Division 1, Group C locations in accordance with NFPA 70, *National Electrical Code*.

Modification of clinical lab refrigerators by health care personnel was tacitly condoned in the past; this is no longer the case. Refrigerators storing flammable material must be tested and listed by an organization acceptable to the authority having jurisdiction.

11.7.2.6.2 The outside doors of refrigerators shall be labeled to denote whether or not they are acceptable for storage of flammable liquids.

Laboratory refrigerators should be clearly labeled to indicate their appropriate use. (See Exhibit 11.15.)

EXHIBIT 11.15 Laboratory refrigerator label.

11.7.2.6.3 If the refrigerator is not listed for the purpose, the warning shall be worded to prohibit all storage of flammable liquids.

11.7.3 Transfer of Flammable or Combustible Liquids.

Transfer from bulk stock containers to smaller containers shall be made in storage rooms as described in NFPA 30, *Flammable and Combustible Liquids Code*, or within a fume hood having a face velocity of at least 30.5 m (100 ft) per minute.

11.7.4 Handling of Flammable and Combustible Liquids.

Procedures and policies for handling flammable and combustible liquids must be incorporated into laboratory practices and must also be monitored to ensure that they are in effect. General requirements for policies, procedures, and training are contained in 11.2.1.4.

11.7.4.1 Flammable liquids and combustible liquids with flash points lower than 93.3°C (200°F) (Class I, II, and IIIA liquids) shall be heated in hoods or with special local exhaust ventilation if the quantities exceed 10 mL, or if the liquid is heated to within 16.6°C (30°F) of the flash point of the liquid.

Paragraph 11.7.4.1 is a refinement of previous guidelines on heating flammable and combustible liquids, using the flash point as the hazard criterion. Thus, laboratory personnel must know the flash point of the type of liquid they are using.

11.7.4.2 Heating Flammable or Combustible Liquids.
11.7.4.2.1 Flammable or combustible liquids shall be heated with hot water, steam, or an electric mantle, depending upon their boiling points.

11.7.4.2.2 Open flames shall not be employed.

Paragraphs 11.7.4.2.1 and 11.7.4.2.2 reaffirm the prohibition of open flames when heating any flammable or combustible liquid.

11.7.5* Disposal of Hazardous Materials.

Disposal of hazardous materials shall be accomplished off the premises by a disposal specialist or at a safe location away from the health care facility by competent personnel using procedures established in concurrence with the authority having jurisdiction.

Disposal of hazardous materials in accordance with 11.7.5 is possible by any disposal specialist or by whatever procedures comply with applicable regulation and are acceptable to the authority having jurisdiction.

A.11.7.5 Because disposal techniques for various hazardous materials produced in hospital research involve complicated problems, they cannot be adequately discussed herein. Such materials include the toxic product of mixing sodium cyanide and acids in the drain system; nuisance or alarming odors such as produced by mercaptans or lutidine; violently water-reactive solids or liquids like phosphoric anhydride and thionyl chloride; potential explosives like picric acid; strong oxidizers like perchloric acid; and radioactive, pathogenic, corrosive, or potentially harmful wastes, such as television picture tubes, syringes, and aerosol cans.

Many chemicals can be disposed of at the bench through the ingenuity of the chemist, such as the reacting of small quantities of potassium with tertiary butyl alcohol.

Flammable and combustible liquids that are miscible with water in all proportions can be flushed down a drain within a laboratory room in quantities not exceeding 1 pt (0.45 L), thoroughly mixed with at least 3 gal (11.4 L) of cold water. This precaution for minimizing flammable vapor concentrations in building drains could be unacceptable to pollution-control authorities.

Vaporization should not be used for routine disposal of liquids.

Drain lines and traps from laboratory benches, safety showers, hood floors, mechanical equipment rooms, storage rooms, and so forth, should have water added at regular intervals to assure that traps will not be the source of flammable or toxic vapor release. Where self-priming traps are provided, an annual inspection for proper operation should be made. Addition of mineral oil or similar liquids is sometimes used to reduce evaporation of water from traps.

Federal regulations (i.e., those of the U.S. Environmental Protection Agency) and state regulations should be reviewed with regard to the way hazardous material, including gases, liquids, and solids, is disposed. Some materials might be appropriate for disposal via the drain or sewer system, but the local water reclamation district should be consulted prior to establishing a policy.

11.8* Maintenance and Inspection

A.11.8 Comprehensive discussions of the goals and procedures to provide safe working conditions in clinical laboratories are available from the National Committee for Clinical Laboratory Standards.

11.8.1* Procedures.

The laboratory safety program addressed in Section 11.8 should be part of, and coordinated with, the facility-wide safety program and be in accordance with the Chemical Hygiene Plan required by OSHA [6]. The integration of fire protection with biohazard protection and radiation safety is important for the success of the laboratory safety program and should help define the specific fire prevention and preparedness process as directed in 11.2.1.2. Preventive maintenance programs and electrical safety tests and inspections must encompass appropriate laboratory equipment.

A.11.8.1 For adequate laboratory safety, careful maintenance and watchfulness are imperative.

All hazards associated with clinical laboratories and their functioning should be under the purview of the laboratory safety officer. The provisions of A.11.8.1 help ensure that the most qualified individual is appointed.

Large laboratories might require the expertise and resources of a safety committee. The responsibilities of the safety officer can be delegated among the members of such a committee. Committees comprised of workers of different job classifications and levels of training often are the best way to determine the employees' need to know about fire protection and prevention practices. Discussions in such committees should include review of incidents, accidents, drills, and procedures, with the goal of reducing the level of hazards.

11.8.1.1* A safety officer shall be appointed to supervise safe practices in the laboratory.

A.11.8.1.1 This individual can be the safety officer for the health care facility or can be a specifically designated laboratory safety officer.

11.8.1.1.1 Responsibilities shall include ensuring that the equipment and preparation for fire fighting are appropriate for the special fire hazards present.

11.8.1.1.2 These responsibilities shall be in addition to surveillance of hazards attendant to the following:

(1) Caustics
(2) Corrosives
(3) Compressed gases
(4) Electrical installations
(5) Other hazards indigenous to laboratories in health care facilities

11.8.1.1.3 The safety officer shall also supervise the periodic education of laboratory personnel including the following:

(1) New employee orientation
(2) The nature of combustible and flammable liquids and gases
(3) First aid

(4) Fire fighting
(5) The use of protective equipment
(6) Unsafe conditions observed or reported

11.8.1.1.4 The laboratory safety officer shall prepare and supervise the proper completion of a safety checklist that can be preserved for the record.

11.8.1.2* The laboratory safety officer shall supervise operations and equipment related to safe operations and practices, including such items as the following:

(1) Ventilating provisions
(2) Fire protection apparatus
(3) Periodic flushing of sinks, emergency showers, and eye wash units
(4) Shelf stocks and storage of flammable and combustible materials and caustic and corrosive liquids shall be reviewed at appropriate, regular intervals

A.11.8.1.2 Regulations should be adopted for routine housekeeping and laboratory cleanup practices.

The laboratory safety officer should make periodic inspections of the laboratory premises to determine that electric cords in use are of adequate conductor size with safe insulation and that circuits are not overloaded through the use of multiple taps.

Several good laboratory safety checklists are available, such as the one developed by the College of American Pathologists Inspection and Accreditation Program *(see Annex G)*. The laboratory safety officer could augment or modify one of these for his or her own facility if he or she so wished.

11.8.1.2.1 A system of prompt reporting of defective equipment and its prompt repair shall be instituted, and periodic inspections shall be made of all electrical and gas equipment.

11.8.1.2.2 Periodic inspection shall be made of all electrical and gas equipment.

11.8.1.3 Periodic safety inspection shall include the testing of all emergency showers, eye baths, and other emergency equipment.

Periodic safety inspections can be conducted by the laboratory safety officer or incorporated into other safety programs. The frequency of the inspection should meet appropriate regulatory requirements, such as those of the American National Standards Institute for safety showers and eye baths.

11.8.1.4* There shall be a written procedure for the disposal of hazardous waste in accordance with local, state, and federal hazardous material and waste regulations.

Paragraph 11.8.1.4 requires a written procedure (rather than a system) for the disposal of hazardous waste. The requirement makes the language enforceable and aligns it with the requirements of various regulatory organizations. The reference to environmental standards reflects concern for safety and environmental protection when disposing of hazardous chemicals.

A.11.8.1.4 Information sources for safe handling, storage, and emergency response to spills or fires in hazardous materials include NFPA 49, *Hazardous Chemicals Data*.

Another good source for a safety checklist is the National Committee for Clinical Laboratory Standards, 940 West Valley Road, Suite 1400, Wayne, PA 19087-1898; (610) 688-0100.

Hazards particular to each laboratory should be evaluated to determine frequency of inspection. However, the Joint Commission on Accreditation of Healthcare Organizations requires that hazard surveillance of nonpatient care areas be conducted at least annually.

11.8.2 Identification of Hazards.

11.8.2.1* All doors leading to laboratories in health-related facilities shall be marked with signage indicating the fire hazards of materials when significant quantities, as defined below, are intended to be used within the area.

A.11.8.2.1 The identification system of NFPA 704, *Standard System for the Identification of the Hazards of Materials for Emergency Response*, can be used on doors leading to laboratories as well as on doors of approved flammable liquid storage cabinetry and on doors of refrigerators. *(See C.11.2.3.)*

Unlike a research or academic chemistry laboratory where a simple signage system is difficult to apply, the quantity and variety of ignitible liquids in clinical laboratories is characteristically modest. The Committee on Laboratories continues to recommend the use of NFPA 704, *Standard System for the Identification of the Hazards of Materials for Emergency Response* [7], on doors leading to laboratories and on cabinets because of its widespread recognition by the fire service. In those facilities that choose to use NFPA 704 signage, laboratory personnel should be familiar with the symbols as well. A summary of this signage system is reproduced in C.11.2.3.

***EXHIBIT 11.16** The NFPA 704 Diamond System for labeling (e.g., chemicals).*

Exhibit 11.16 is a replica of the "NFPA 704 diamond." Numbers used range from 0 to 4, with 4 being the most hazardous (e.g., a "4" in the flammability box means extremely flammable; a "0" in the flammability box means "will not burn"). Several color arrangements are allowed:

1. The background of each square is the color listed, and numbers are some contrasting color (e.g., black, white).
2. The background is white, and the color of numbers corresponds to the color assigned for hazard.

Any special hazards are indicated by the use of a symbol, for example,

~~W~~ means avoid the use of water because of an unusual reactivity to water.

OX means materials possess oxidizing properties.

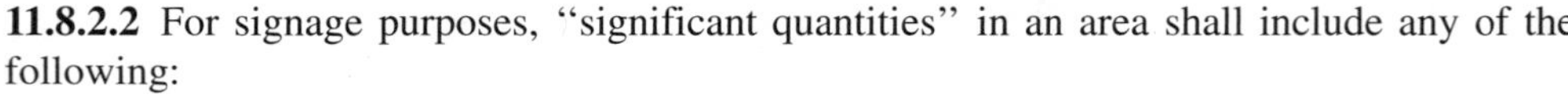

means materials possess radioactivity hazards.

11.8.2.2 For signage purposes, "significant quantities" in an area shall include any of the following:

(1) Hazardous materials in glass containers that are 3.8 L (1 gal) in size or larger
(2) Compressed gases or cryogenic liquids in containers that are greater than 12.7 cm (5 in.) in diameter and 38 cm (15 in.) in length
(3) Dry hazardous chemicals in containers in excess of 2.27 kg (5 lb)
(4) Aggregate quantities of hazardous materials exceeding 91 kg (200 lb), or flammable liquids exceeding 38 L (10 gal)

The signage on entry ways or safety cabinetry should reflect the presence of "significant quantities" of materials, as defined by NFPA 99, to avoid the overuse and overreaction to labeling.

11.8.2.3* All doors leading to laboratories, laboratory work areas, and laboratory storage areas shall be identified with signs to warn emergency response personnel of unusual or severe hazards that are not directly related to the fire hazards of contents.

Paragraph 11.8.2.3 emphasizes the laboratory's responsibility to alert emergency personnel concerning significant environmental hazards other than those directly relevant to fire control.

The wording or symbols used are immediately recognizable to those approaching the laboratory in response to a fire emergency.

A.11.8.2.3 Examples of severe or unusual hazards that might require signage include, but are not limited to, biohazards, radioactive chemicals, carcinogens, mutagens, teratogens, and high energy lasers.

11.8.2.4 It shall be the responsibility of the laboratory safety officer to ensure periodically that the signage properly indicates the nature of the materials being used within the identified space.

Other laboratory personnel, in addition to the safety officer, are urged to become familiar with this ID system as well.

11.8.2.5 It shall be the duty of the senior person responsible for activities in respective laboratory areas to inform the laboratory safety officer of changes in protocol and procedures that involve variations in the fire and associated hazards of materials used in individual spaces.

Laboratory personnel and facility-wide disaster planners must coordinate closely to ensure that hazards related to laboratories are identified and properly addressed in the facility's disaster plans. (See also Chapter 12.)

11.9 Transfer of Gases

11.9.1 Transfer of gaseous oxygen shall be in accordance with 9.6.2.2.

For background on this allowance, see the commentary following 9.6.2.2.3.

11.9.2 Transfer of all other gases from one cylinder to another within the laboratory shall be prohibited.

11.9.3 Transfer of liquid oxygen shall be in accordance with 9.6.2.3.

11.10 Laboratory Gas Cylinder Storage for Nonpiped Use

Section 11.10 refers only to *nonpiped* gases, that is, to freestanding cylinders and containers. Specifications for laboratory piped systems have been moved from Chapter 5 to Section 11.11, but other piped medical gas and vacuum system requirements remain in Chapter 5.

11.10.1 Cylinder and Container Management.

Requirements shall be in accordance with 5.1.3.1.1.

11.10.2 Storage Requirements (Location, Construction, Arrangement; Any Quantity; Flammable and Nonflammable Gases).

11.10.2.1 Storage shall be in cylinders complying with 5.1.3.1.1.

11.10.2.2 Flammable gas cylinder storage for a laboratory, if inside any health care facility, shall be in a separate room or enclosure with the following characteristics:

(1) Reserved exclusively for that purpose

(2) Having a fire-resistance classification of at least 2 hours
(3) Ventilated *(See E.6.8 of Annex E.)*

Paragraph 11.10.2.2 applies to the storage of individual flammable gas cylinders. Requirements for a storage area used to connect cylinders for a manifold system are listed in 11.11.1.1. The 2-hour fire resistance requirement in 11.10.2.2(2) is consistent with federal regulations and NFPA *101, Life Safety Code* [2].

The following recommendations for ventilation within a room or an enclosure where flammable gas cylinders are stored should be considered:

1. There should be eight air changes per hour.
2. Air should be ceiling-supplied and floor exhausted (with physical separation between each as great as possible).
3. Exhaust should be discharged to the exterior.

Although either a gravity or a mechanical ventilation system is allowed, a mechanical one would require additional electrical safety and emergency power requirements. (See Chapter 4 for emergency power requirements.)

Flammable and oxidizing gases must not be stored or utilized in a common room in any type of health care facility.

11.10.2.2.1 When a laboratory is intended to be routinely and frequently operated with flammable gases supplied from a manifold compressed system, storage shall comply with 11.11.1.1.

11.10.2.2.2 Cylinders in storage shall be kept in racks or secured in position.

11.10.2.3 Rooms or enclosures for storage of cylinders shall be well ventilated.

Whereas 11.10.2.3 applies to all storage locations, specific requirements for flammable gas cylinder storage rooms in laboratories are identified in 11.10.2.2.

11.10.2.4 Electrical equipment in flammable-gas storage areas shall comply with NFPA 70, *National Electrical Code*, for Class I, Division 2 locations.

11.10.2.5 Enclosures for storage of nonflammable gases shall have at least 1-hour fire-resistive construction, in accordance with 5.1.3.3.2.

FAQ ▶
Can nonflammable and flammable gas cylinders be stored in the same room?

Note that 11.10.2.5 addresses the storage of only nonflammable gas cylinders. A fire resistance–rated separation is required between flammable and nonflammable gases. In addition, the storage of flammable and nonflammable gases in the same enclosure is prohibited.

11.10.2.6* Use of Gases. Gases shall be handled and used with care and with knowledge of their hazardous properties, both individually and in combination with other materials with which they can come in contact. *(See NFPA 49, Hazardous Chemicals Data, and NFPA 491, Guide to Hazardous Chemical Reactions.)*

A.11.10.2.6 The precautions outlined in CGA P-1, *Safe Handling of Compressed Gases in Containers*, and CGA P-2, *Characteristics and Safe Handling of Medical Gases*, should be observed. *(See Annex B.)* These publications cover such items as moving and storage of cylinders, labeling, withdrawing of cylinder contents, and handling of leaking cylinders. Cryogenic fluids are to be used only in containers designed for the purpose, such as a double-walled thermos bottle.

Caps are to be replaced promptly after each use to prevent the solidification of atmospheric water vapor in the pouring neck, which otherwise could convert a safe cylinder into a potential bomb.

Protective clothing and eye shields should be used to prevent burns from issuing gases or spilled liquids. Effects of flammable and oxidizing properties are intense and demand special fire protection measures and handling. Inadvertent saturation of clothing by oxygen or spills on asphalt flooring, for example, require prompt and accurate corrective measures. Ample ventilation is needed to prevent hazardous concentrations, for example, of nitrogen, which could cause asphyxiation. For routine cooling operations, liquid air or oxygen should never be used as substitutes for liquid nitrogen.

11.10.2.7 Cylinders. In a laboratory, gas cylinders being held for prompt use shall not exceed 2 days' working needs, except as permitted in 11.11.1.1. Cylinders shall be in racks or secured in position.

11.10.2.8 Working Supplies. The aggregate accumulation of cylinders at any one working station shall not exceed one extra cylinder for each cylinder actually connected for use. All cylinders shall be secured in a rack or secured in an upright position.

11.10.3 The total quantity and size of cylinders containing oxygen, flammable gas, liquefied flammable gas, and gas with Health Hazard Ratings of 3 or 4 shall comply with Chapter 8 of NFPA 45, *Standard on Fire Protection for Laboratories Using Chemicals.*

11.10.4 The number of reserve cylinders within general laboratory work areas shall not exceed one week's working supply.

11.11 Piped Gas Systems

Those systems previously designated as Level 4 are now designated as laboratory piped gas systems and thus are addressed in this chapter.

11.11.1 Source.

11.11.1.1 When a laboratory is intended to be routinely and frequently operated with flammable gases supplied from a manifold compressed system, the containers shall meet either of the following requirements:

(1) Be in a separate room having a fire-resistance classification of at least 1 hour and be ventilated in accordance with 5.1.3.3.2, and 5.1.3.3.3
(2) Be located outside of the building and connected to the laboratory equipment by a permanently installed piping system

There may be local ordinances on the issue of flammable gas cylinders inside occupied buildings. As always, compliance should be with the most stringent requirement.

11.11.1.1.1 Wherever the volume and nature of the gas, in the judgment of the laboratory safety officer or other authority having jurisdiction, do not offer a hazard, the requirement for the remote locations of the cylinder in 11.11.1.1 shall be permitted to be waived.

11.11.1.2 A laboratory intended to be routinely and frequently operated with nonflammable gases supplied from a manifold compressed system shall meet the following requirements:

(1) The manifold within the laboratory shall consist of not more than six cylinders.
(2) Manifolds larger than six cylinders shall conform to 11.11.1.1.
(3) Cylinders shall be secured in position.

Six cylinders are considered a reasonable breakpoint. Although the gases involved are nonflammable, the quantity stored inside a laboratory working area should not be open-ended.

11.11.1.3 A pressure-reducing valve shall be connected to each gas cylinder and adjusted to a setting to limit pressure in the piping system at the minimum required gas pressure.

11.11.1.4 Pressure regulators shall be compatible with the gas for which they are used.

11.11.1.5 Piping systems shall not be used for gases other than those for which they are designed and identified.

11.11.1.5.1 If a system is to be converted for use with a gas other than that for which it was originally installed, the following procedure shall be performed:

(1) It shall be inspected for suitability for the proposed gas.
(2) It shall be purged with an inert gas (such as nitrogen).
(3) It shall be cleaned when oil, grease, or other readily oxidizable materials are present.
(4) It shall be pressure tested in accordance with the appropriate piping standard.

11.11.1.5.2 Each outlet of such a system shall be identified by chemical name and specifically converted for use with the successor gas.

11.11.2 Distribution.

11.11.2.1* Piping systems for fuel gases, such as manufactured gas, natural gas, and LP-Gas, shall comply with NFPA 54, *National Fuel Gas Code*, and NFPA 58, *Liquefied Petroleum Gas Code*.

A.11.11.2.1 Piping systems supplying medical gases to patients should be reserved exclusively for that purpose so as to protect the patients from administration of gas other than that intended for their use. Therefore laboratory gas piping systems should not be used to pipe gas for use by hospital patients. This warning is also intended to apply to piping systems intended to supply gas to patients within a laboratory facility. Such a system should not be used to supply laboratory equipment other than that directly involved with the patient procedure.

11.11.2.2 Piping systems for gaseous hydrogen shall comply with NFPA 50A, *Standard for Gaseous Hydrogen Systems at Consumer Sites*.

11.11.2.3 Piping systems for nonflammable gases shall comply with Level 1 gas systems as specified in Chapter 5.

11.11.2.4 Piping systems for acetylene shall comply with NFPA 51, *Standard for the Design and Installation of Oxygen–Fuel Gas Systems for Welding, Cutting, and Allied Processes*.

11.11.2.5 Supply and discharge terminals of piping systems shall be legibly and permanently marked at both ends with the name of the gas piping, after testing, to establish their content and continuity.

11.11.3 Piped Vacuum Systems. See 5.1.3.6.

11.11.3.1 Source. (Reserved)

11.11.3.2* Distribution. Where only one set of vacuum pumps is available for a combined medical–surgical vacuum system and an analysis, research, or teaching laboratory vacuum system, such laboratories shall be connected separate from the medical–surgical system directly to the receiver tank through its own isolation valve and fluid trap located at the receiver. Between the isolation valve and fluid trap, a scrubber shall be permitted to be installed.

A.11.11.3.2 Any laboratory (such as for analysis, research, or teaching) in a hospital that is used for purposes other than direct support of patient therapy should preferably have its own self-supporting vacuum system, independent of the medical–surgical vacuum system. A small laboratory in patient care areas used in direct support of patient therapy should not be required to be connected directly to the receiver or have fluid traps, scrubbers, and so forth, separate from the rest of the medical–surgical vacuum system.

A separate vacuum system for nonpatient purposes is recommended by A.11.11.3.2 for several reasons. Laboratories often require levels, operating ranges, and displacements of vacuum that differ from those for patient care areas. These differences, including usage rates, make planning difficult, particularly if coordination of the laboratory system with the patient system is included. Laboratory systems are also much more likely to aspirate vapors, fumes, and/or liquids of unusual nature, including exotic chemicals that could contaminate the patient vacuum system and damage pumps and other system components.

If a separate laboratory vacuum source (receiver tank) is not possible, laboratory piping needs to be connected directly into the receiver tank(s), as already noted. (This allowance for one source is not permitted for piped medical air systems.) Requirements were revised by requiring a separate isolation valve and fluid trap for the laboratory piping system to prevent material suctioned from laboratories from getting into the patient vacuum system. Scrubbers are needed only when waste products are extremely hazardous.

11.11.4 Piped WAGD Systems. (Reserved)

11.11.5 Performance Criteria and Testing (Gas, Vacuum, WAGD).

Paragraph 5.1.10.10.11.2 requires installers of medical gas and vacuum systems to meet the certification requirements of ANSI/ASSE 6010, *Professional Qualification Standard for Medical Gas and Vacuum System Installers* [16]. This requirement also applies to laboratory systems, as does a similar requirement for the certification of medical gas verifiers according to ANSI/ASSE 6030, *Professional Qualifications Standard for Medical Gas Systems Verifiers* [17], which is referenced in 5.1.12.3.1.3.

11.11.5.1 Piped Gas Systems. Piped gas systems shall be tested in accordance with 5.1.12.

11.11.5.2 Piped Vacuum Systems. (Reserved)

11.11.5.3 WAGD Systems. (Reserved)

11.11.6 Administration. (Reserved)

REFERENCES CITED IN COMMENTARY

1. NFPA 45, *Standard on Fire Protection for Laboratories Using Chemicals,* 2004 edition.
2. NFPA *101*®, *Life Safety Code*®, 2006 edition.
3. NFPA Annual Survey and National Fire Incident Reporting System (U.S. Fire Administration).
4. Title 29, Code of Federal Regulations, Part 1910.1450, "Occupational Exposure to Hazardous Chemicals in Laboratories Standard," U.S. Government Printing Office, Washington, DC.
5. Title 29, Code of Federal Regulations, Part 1910.1200, "Bloodborne Pathogens Standard," U.S. Government Printing Office, Washington, DC.
6. Title 29, Code of Federal Regulations, Part 1910.1200, OSHA, "Hazard Communication Standard," U.S. Government Printing Office, Washington, DC.
7. NFPA 704, *Standard System for the Identification of the Hazards of the Materials for Emergency Response,* 2001 edition.

8. JCAHO *Comprehensive Accreditation Manual for Pathology and Clinical Laboratory Services,* 2001 update.

9. Title 29, Code of Federal Regulations, Part 1910.120, OSHA, "Hazardous Waste Operations and Emergency Response Standard," U.S. Government Printing Office, Washington, DC.

10. NFPA 13, *Standard for the Installation of Sprinkler Systems,* 2002 edition.

11. NFPA 10, *Standard for Portable Fire Extinguishers,* 2002 edition.

12. ANSI Z358.1, *American National Standard for Emergency Eyewash and Shower Equipment,* 2004.

13. Title 29, Code of Federal Regulations, Part 1910.151, "Medical Services and First Aid Standard," U.S. Government Printing Office, Washington, DC.

14. NFPA 30, *Flammable and Combustible Liquids Code,* 2003 edition.

15. NFPA's *Fire Protection Guide to Hazardous Materials,* 2002.

16. ANSI/ASSE 6010, *Professional Qualification Standard for Medical Gas and Vacuum System Installers,* 2001.

17. ANSI/ASSE 6030, *Professional Qualifications Standard for Medical Gas Systems Verifiers,* 2001.

CHAPTER 12

Health Care Emergency Management

The terrorist attacks of September 11, 2001, have taken the United States to a higher level of emergency management. Within the past few years, natural disasters have hit the health care industry hard. Tropical Storm Allison (June 2001) forced the evacuation of several hospitals in Houston, and ice storms in the Northeast left many health care facilities without power for extended periods of time. In 2003, 31 patients died in two separate nursing home fires. The 2004 Florida hurricanes severely damaged many health care facilities, displacing thousands of patients.

All of these disasters demonstrate that a health care facility must operate, if at all possible, during the disaster and recovery period. The community cannot fully recover without health care. In any particular geographical area, a hazard vulnerability analysis (HVA), which is part of an emergency operations plan (EOP), can be used to determine the type of disasters for which a facility needs to be prepared. The goal of Chapter 12 is to provide a framework within which health care facilities can develop an effective EOP.

Chapter 12 covers essential items that the EOP must cover, management of the plan, as well as education and drills. Annexes A and C provide additional information for the user.

12.1* Applicability

A.12.1 Such facilities include, but are not limited to, hospitals, clinics, convalescent or nursing homes, and first-aid stations (disaster receiving stations). Such facilities could be formally designated by a government authority as disaster treatment centers. Such facilities would not normally include doctors' or dentists' offices, medical laboratories, or school nurseries, unless such facilities are used for treatment of disaster victims. National bioterrorism preparedness efforts call for the use of schools and other large public facilities to provide facilities for mass immunization.

Table A.12.1 illustrates how the various components of this chapter relate to either the day-to-day emergency management program or the emergency operations plan or EOP.

Any facility that provides medical care for people and will need to continue their care through and after a disaster — such as hospitals, long-term care assisted living facilities, and clinics — is within the scope of this standard, as noted in A.12.1. All health care facilities must work with the emergency agencies of their communities to see where they "fit" into the emergency plan.

Some disasters result in the need to open different types and numbers of acute care beds. For example, a biological contamination affecting large numbers of people could require the need for more isolation beds than normally exist. Long-term care facilities in any given

TABLE A.12.1 *How NFPA 99 Chapter 12 Elements Relate to the Emergency Management Program (EMP) or the Emergency Operations Plan (EOP)*

NFPA 99	*Chapter 12*	*EMP*	*EOP*
12.1	Applicability	X	
12.2	Responsibilities		
	12.2.1 Authority Having Jurisdiction	X	
	12.2.2 Senior Management	X	
	12.2.3 Emergency Management Committee	X	
12.3	General Requirements		
	12.3.1 Declaration of Emergency		X
	12.3.2 Activation of Plan		X
	12.3.3 Components		
	12.3.3.1 Personnel Identification		X
	12.3.3.2 Continuity of Essential Systems		X
	12.3.3.3 Staff Management		X
	12.3.3.4 Patient Management		X
	12.3.3.5 Logistics		X
	12.3.3.6 Security		X
	12.3.3.7 Public Affairs		X
	12.3.3.8 Operational Recovery		X
	12.3.3.9 Staff Education	X	
	12.3.3.10 Drills	X	

region might receive patients from a long-term care wing or building of a local hospital. By moving these patients to a remote long-term care facility, the beds within this wing/building could then be used for isolation or acute care.

FAQ ▶
How might a disaster affect the operations of the facility?

Disasters could alter a facility's structure, utilities, staffing, supplies, communications, and medical care services. These functions must be addressed in every emergency operations plan to ensure, as far as possible, the safety of patients, staff, and visitors during a disaster and throughout recovery. An emergency department's trauma room(s), ambulatory surgery, and labor and delivery room(s) could be considered as supplementary operating rooms, whereas an auditorium or large training room could provide for less critical or walk-in patients. Access, site control, staff, and medical supplies must be considered in the planning assessments and be included in the plan.

See Exhibit 12.1 for an example of a trauma room within the emergency center of a hospital. It could serve as an additional or backup operating room during a disaster.

12.1.1 This chapter is applicable to any health care facility that is intended to provide medical care during an emergency or maintain services for patients during a disaster and for the protection of visitors and staff.

12.1.2* This chapter provides those with the responsibility for the emergency management program in health care facilities with a framework to assess, mitigate, prepare for, respond to, and recover from disasters of any origin. This chapter is intended to aid in developing, maintaining, and evaluating effective emergency management programs. For additional information on emergency management programs, see NFPA 1600, *Standard on Disaster/Emergency Management and Business Continuity Programs.*

The framework for an emergency management program is outlined in Commentary Table 12.1.

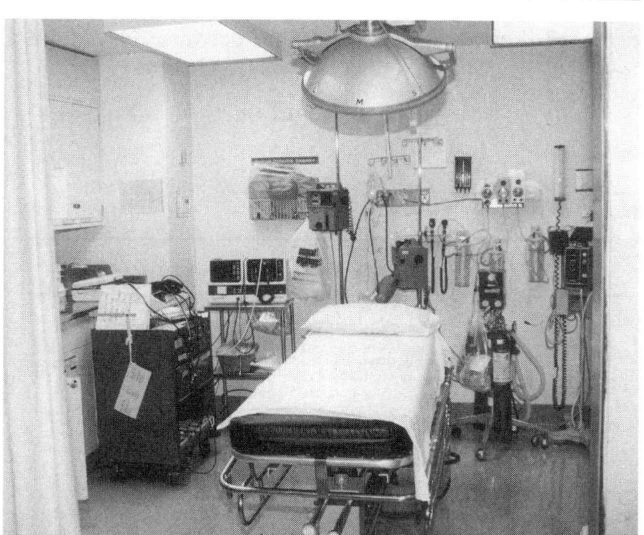

EXHIBIT 12.1 *Trauma room.*

COMMENTARY TABLE 12.1 *Emergency Management Program Framework*

Action	*Description*
Assessment	A hazard vulnerability analysis (see A.12.2.3.1) is an assessment of a disaster that could affect a health care facility. The facility's ability to "handle" these disasters is necessary.
Mitigate	These assessments often reveal ways to lessen (mitigate) the effects of a particular disaster. For example, some facilities in flood-prone areas locate critical utilities above the high water mark.
Prepare	All threats cannot be mitigated. Health care facilities in a community can prepare for the possibility of a disaster-forced evacuation by entering into mutual aid agreements to receive each other's patients.
Respond	The response part of the emergency operations procedure contains action guidelines for staff during a particular disaster.
Recover	The community needs the health care facility to remain operational, if at all possible. The recovery procedure must start with actions staff will take immediately after patients are out of immediate danger through the return to pre-disaster conditions.

A.12.1.2 An emergency management program (formerly known as a disaster plan or internal/external plan) encompasses activities across four phases: mitigation, preparedness, response, and recovery. Mitigation activities are those designed to reduce or eliminate the impact of hazards. Preparedness activities include those that build organizational and individual capabilities to deal with disasters. Response activities include all necessary actions to stop ongoing negative effects of a disaster, and recovery activities are those that restore the organization, its employees, and the community back to normal.

The Joint Commission for the Accreditation of Healthcare Organizations (JCAHO) has incorporated Comprehensive Emergency Management as a central theme of its emergency management standards. See Annex G for JCAHO publications.

NFPA 1600, *Standard on Disaster/Emergency Management and Business Continuity Programs*, is an internationally accepted framework for an emergency program. NFPA 99,

Chapter 12 recognizes this overall structure and provides additional information useful to health care organizations. Table A.12.1.2 illustrates the relationship between the elements of NFPA 99, Chapter 12 and NFPA 1600.

TABLE A.12.1.2 *How NFPA 99 Chapter 12 Relates to NFPA 1600*

NFPA 1600	***NFPA 99 Chapter 12***
Introduction	
Scope	12.1.1 Applicability
Purpose	12.1.2 Framework
Program Management	
Policy	12.2.1 Authority Having Jurisdiction
Program Coordinator	12.2.2 Senior Management
Program Committee	12.2.3 EM Committee
Program Assessment	12.2.3 EM Committee
Program Elements	
General	—
Laws and Authorities	—
Hazard Identification and Risk Assessment	A.12.3.1 Hazard Identification
Hazard Management (Mitigation)	—
Resource Management	A.12.3.3.5 Resource Assessment
Planning	12.3.3 Emergency Management Plan
Direction, Control, and Coordination	A.12.2.3 Incident Command System
Communications and Warning	A.12.3.3.2(7) Communications
Operations and Procedures	12.3.3.1 Identification of Personnel
	12.3.3.2 Continuity of Essential Systems
	12.3.3.3 Staff Management
	12.3.3.4 Patient Management
	12.3.3.6 Security
	12.3.3.10 Operational Recovery
Logistics and Facilities	12.3.3.5 Logistics
Training	12.3.3.8 Staff Education
Exercises, Evaluations, and Corrective Actions	12.3.3.9 Drills
Public Education and Information	12.3.3.7 Public Affairs
Finance and Administration	—

12.2 Responsibilities

12.2.1* Authority Having Jurisdiction (AHJ).

The authority having jurisdiction shall be cognizant of the requirements of a health care facility with respect to its uniqueness for continued operation of the facility in an emergency.

The community, as well as patients, needs health care facilities to remain operational, if at all possible, during a disaster and through full recovery. To accomplish this, the assistance of community public agencies is needed. That assistance takes several forms, including the following:

◀ FAQ
What type of services might a public agency provide?

1. Assistance in obtaining industrial and potable water
2. Locating backup emergency generators
3. Local police helping supply trucks to reach the health care facility
4. Transporting staff who cannot use normal means of transportation
5. Code enforcers working with health care facilities to keep people in the building safe while allowing the facility to remain operational as work progresses toward full recovery

A.12.2.1 In time of disaster all persons are subject to certain constraints or authorities not present during normal circumstances. The emergency operations plans written by a health care facility should be reviewed and coordinated with such authorities so as to prevent confusion. Such authorities include, but are not limited to, civil authorities (such as a fire department, police department, public health department, or emergency medical service councils), Centers for Disease Control, Federal Bureau of Investigation, and emergency management or military authorities. See Annex G for publications explaining how the out-of-hospital response is organized to multiple, and mass, casualty incidents.

Further, an authority having jurisdiction can impose upon the senior management of the facility the responsibility for participating in a community emergency management program.

12.2.2 Senior Management.

Each health care organization shall have plans necessary to respond to a disaster or an emergency. Each health care organization shall have an individual or group, often known as an emergency management committee, as appropriate, with the authority for developing, implementing, exercising, and evaluating the emergency management program.

12.2.3* Emergency Management Committee.

As required by 12.2.2, senior management of a health care facility is responsible for ensuring that their facility can function during any emergency situation. The emergency management committee addressed in 12.2.3 is responsible for developing the emergency operations plan. This plan should address all applicable hazards, as developed in the hazard vulnerability analysis. (See A.12.2.3.1.) The committee's responsibility includes developing the emergency plan, implementing the plan, educating and training the staff, and evaluating the plan to ensure that it can and will work effectively.

A.12.2.3 The membership of the EMC should include a chairperson, the emergency program coordinator, and representatives from key areas within the organization, such as the administration office, physicians, nursing, infection control, facilities engineering, safety/industrial hygiene, purchasing/fiscal, security, and other critical operating unit managers.

12.2.3.1* The emergency management committee shall have the responsibility for the emergency management program within the facility, under the supervision of designated leadership. The program shall be based on realistic conceptual events and operating capacity thresholds.

A.12.2.3.1 The emergency management committee should base the entity's program on a hazards vulnerability analysis (HVA). The HVA determines whether the following types of hazards are applicable and the impacts each might have on mission critical systems:

(1) Natural disasters
(2) Technological/industrial disasters
(3) Civil/political disasters

For further information on how to conduct the HVA, see NFPA 1600, *Standard on Disaster/Emergency Management and Business Continuity Programs*, and other publications listed in Annex G. See C.12.3.5 for descriptions of sample protocols for common hazards.

12.2.3.2* The emergency management committee shall model the emergency operations plan on an incident command system (ICS) in coordination with local emergency response agencies.

A.12.2.3.2 The incident command system (ICS) (also referred to as the incident management system, or IMS) is a system having an identified chain of command that adapts to any emergency event. The ICS consists of eight key elements: common terminology, integrated communications, modular organization, unified command structure, manageable span of control, consolidated action plans, comprehensive resource management, and pre-designated incident facilities. These allow emergency responders from hospitals and all involved organizations to respond to an incident and be familiar with the management concepts and terminology of other responders. It also facilitates the request and processing of mutual aid requests.

A widely accepted structure of an ICS is illustrated in Figure A.12.2.3.2.

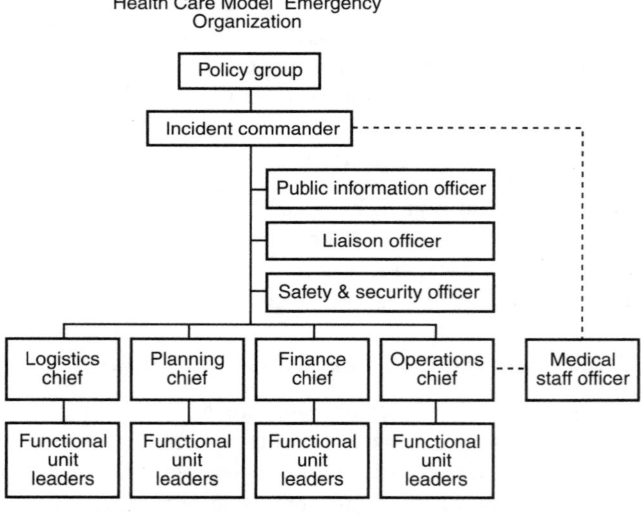

FIGURE A.12.2.3.2 *Health Care Model Emergency Organization.*

A policy group consists of senior managers constituted to provide decisions related to items or incident decisions not in the emergency management program.

The command staff consists of the incident commander and support staff. This support staff consists of the public information officer, liaison officer, and safety officer.

In addition to the command staff, there are four sections, each with a section chief responding directly to the incident commander: plans section, logistics section, operations section, and finance section.

Due to the nature of a health care facility, one deviation from the traditional ICS is made to show a line of medical control. Note the advisory position of the "medical staff officer."

The use of an incident command system (ICS), covered in A.12.2.3.2, is a nationally recognized system to manage a disaster. Under this plan, key individuals within the health care facility are given disaster job titles, follow an organizational chart, and complete an action checklist.

An ICS strives to ensure that staff operate within the scope of their knowledge and do not overlook important actions during a disaster. This management system must be compatible with local emergency agencies and health care facilities.

12.3 General Requirements

12.3.1* When a facility declares itself in a disaster mode, or when the authority having jurisdiction declares that a state of disaster exists, the emergency operations plan shall be activated.

A.12.3.1 In emergency situations that occur without warning and impact the facility, staff at the scene of the problem are expected to follow established protocols to protect life, notify others, and conserve property. Senior management can establish an Incident Command Post (ICP) near the scene, or support one that is established by responding public safety agencies. In emergency situations with warning or whose impacts require extended periods to resolve, senior management report to the facility's Emergency Operations Center (EOC). Not all incidents require an EOC.

Both the ICP and the EOC provide centralized locations for information collection, display, coordination, documentation, and dissemination. When both are established, the ICP focuses on tactical activities currently underway, and the EOC focuses on strategies for the next operational period(s), resource issues, etc.

See Annex G for publications on the Incident Command (Management) System.

12.3.2* The decision to activate the emergency operations plan shall be made by the authority designated within the plan, in accordance with the facility's activation criteria. The decision to terminate shall be made by the designated authority in coordination with the authority having jurisdiction and other civil or military authorities involved.

◀ **FAQ**
What steps are involved in activating the EOP?

Leadership staff must know how to activate the facility's emergency operations plan (EOP). All staff must be aware of the facility's procedure for alerting appropriate people, once they discover a disaster situation or the strong possibility of one.

For example, if the facility's communications position receives a telephone bomb threat, they could alert their supervisor or someone nearby. This position could alert the administrator-on-call, who could activate the facility's bomb threat procedure from the EOP. Or, upon discovery of a fire, a staff person could call out the facility's fire code word, alerting staff in the area of the fire situation. The building fire alarm system would then be activated, which would prompt activation of the fire procedure from the EOP.

A.12.3.2 By basing the planning of health care emergency management on realistic conceptual events, the program reflects those issues or events that are predictable for the environment the organization operates in. Thus, such conceptual planning should focus on issues, such as severe weather typical in that locale; situations that can occur due to close proximity of industrial or transportation complexes; or earthquake possibilities due to local seismic activity. Planning for these events should also focus on the capacity of the health care organization to provide services in such an emergency. Capacity thresholds are different for all facilities, but have to do with issues such as the availability of emergency departments, operating suites and operating beds, as well as logistical response and facility utilities. Planning should also incorporate knowledge available in the disaster research about how individuals, small groups, organizations, communities and societies behave during emergencies and disasters. See Annex G for information sources on disaster research. There is no way to plan for all possible emergencies, but by focusing on logical conceptual events and operating capacity thresholds, the health care organization can develop realistic plans as well as guidelines for staff to activate those plans.

12.3.3 The emergency operations plan, as a minimum, shall include the components detailed in 12.3.3.1 through 12.3.3.8 and training and drills (12.3.3.9 and 12.3.3.10) as necessary for effectiveness.

The requirements of 12.3.3 are essential for a successful emergency operations plan. Actual disasters have shown these items to be important, and they must be addressed in every EOP. More information can be found in Annexes A and C. Individual departmental emergency management plans must be implemented, and each must be a subset of the facility's overall plan. A department should not have a plan that is totally independent of the rest of the facility.

12.3.3.1* Identification of Emergency Response Personnel. All personnel designated or involved in the emergency operations plan of the health care facility shall be supplied with a means of identification, which shall be worn at all times in a visible location. Specific means of identification for incident command system (ICS) personnel shall be provided, such as vests, baseball caps, or hard hats.

A.12.3.3.1 Where feasible, photo identifications or other means to assure positive identification should be used.

Visitor and crowd control create the problem of distinguishing staff from visitors. Such identification should be issued to all facility personnel, including volunteer personnel who might be utilized in disaster functions.

Note that care should be taken to assure that identification cards are recalled whenever personnel terminate association with the health care facility.

Members of the news media should be asked to wear some means of identification, such as the press card, on their outside garments so that they are readily identifiable by security guards controlling access to the facility or certain areas therein. Clergy also will frequently accompany casualties or arrive later for visitations and require some means of identification.

Consideration should be given to a method of identifying staff called to a facility during an emergency. Without proper identification, it could be impossible to get by police roadblocks. Having a phone contact for key organizations to confirm identity and carrying facility identification at all times can eliminate potential problems.

A form of identification different from that normally worn daily by the staff must be established for staff in the command center. Many incident command systems also have designated colors for key personnel to be worn at the time of a disaster.

During actual disasters, hospitals found that it was necessary to quickly address credentialing of doctors and nurses who had come from other facilities to help. The development of an emergency credentialing policy among community health care facilities is recommended. The Joint Commission Accreditation of Healthcare Facilities has a guideline on disaster credentialing.

12.3.3.2* Continuity of Essential Building Systems. When designated by the emergency operations plan to provide continuous service in a disaster or emergency, health care facilities shall establish contingency plans for the continuity of essential building systems, as applicable:

Many disasters result in the loss of essential building systems (utilities), without which a health care facility cannot adequately care for patients. Commentary Table 12.2 lists examples of services that might be lost following failure of a building utility. Annexes A and C give examples of effective procedures for loss of essential building systems and subsequent services.

***COMMENTARY TABLE 12.2** Lost Services and Building Utilities*

Essential Building System	*Possible Service Lost*
Electricity (emergency power systems)	• Life support systems • Lab testing • Pharmacy • Diagnostic imaging • Information systems • Lighting • Fire protection systems • Heating, ventilation, air conditioning • Elevators
Water	• Sewage service • Dishwashing service • Laundry service • Fire sprinkler service • Liquid consumption • Spill clean-up • Patient bathing
Ventilation	• Heating and cooling • Isolation service • Lab and research fume removal
Fire protection systems	• Fire detection • Automatic alarm reporting
Fuel source (natural gas)	• Heating and cooling • Sterilization services • Cooking • Laundry
Medical gas & vacuum systems	• Piped-in oxygen, nitrous oxide • Suction service
Communication systems	• Internal and external telephone service • Fax • E-mail • Nurse call system

A.12.3.3.2 For essential building systems, consideration should be given to the installation of exterior building connectors to allow for the attachment of portable emergency utility modules.

Water storage systems should be inventoried and protected to the greatest extent possible.

During an emergency within a facility or outside a facility, several essential building services must be continued; otherwise, patients will have to be evacuated. These services require that the facility have contingency plans that are part of the overall emergency preparedness plan. Many vendors in the surrounding areas can provide these services. However, as recent disasters have shown, the whole community can be affected. Therefore, a facility should have backup agreements with vendors up to 90 miles away or with national suppliers. It is up to the facility to make the necessary arrangements and provide hookups for these systems to be used.

It should be noted that several types of water are used in health care facilities. These include potable water, fire protection water, and water used by sanitation and building environmental control systems. See Exhibit 12.2 for an example of a fire pump used to supply water for sprinkler and standpipe systems. A plan should be in place to separate the potable water from the system water. System water can be pumped in from a number of sources. Potable water can be distributed in bottles or cans. Dietary department supplies of milk, juices, soda, and so on, can often be adequate for liquid consumption. This supply can be supplemented by stored bottled water. A plan should be based on three days to two weeks of no outside services.

***EXHIBIT 12.2** Fire pumps used in a hospital. Key staff members need to know how these function.*

(1)* Electricity

A.12.3.3.2(1) See Sections 4.4, 4.5, and 4.6 for types of essential electrical systems for health care facilities.

(2) Water
(3) Ventilation
(4) Fire protection systems
(5) Fuel sources
(6) Medical gas and vacuum systems (if applicable)
(7)* Communication systems

A.12.3.3.2(7) Emergency internal and external communication systems should be established to facilitate communication with security forces and other authorities having jurisdiction as well as internal patient care and service units in the event normal communication methods are rendered inoperative.

The basic form of communication in a disaster is the telephone system. As part of the contingency plan to maintain communication, a plan for restoring telephone systems or using alternate systems is necessary. Typically, the first line of internal defense for a system outage is strategically placed power-failure telephones that are designed to continue to function in the event of system failure. Plans for external outages and load control should include the use of pay phones that have first priority status in external system restoration.

Contingency plans should also contain strategies for the use of radio-frequency communications to supplement land-line usage. The plan should include a means to distribute and use two-way radio communication throughout the facility. A plan for the incorporation and use of amateur radio operators should also be considered.

It should be recognized that single-channel radio communication is less desirable than telephone system restoration due to the limited number of messages that can be managed. Cellular telephones, although useful in some disaster situations, should not be considered a contingency having high reliability due to their vulnerability to load control schemes of telephone companies. Portable e-mail devices, satellite telephones and audio- and video-conferencing services are useful tools to link key staff and organizations.

An increase in telephone traffic can almost always be expected in a disaster. A means of expanding telephone service quickly and efficiently must be included in any emergency operations plan. Pre-arranged unlisted telephone numbers can be of crucial importance.

◀ **FAQ**
What are the different methods of communication during a disaster?

Installation of pay telephones should be considered in more than just the traditional places, such as a lobby. At least one telephone should be located near, or even in, the disaster control center(s). Cellular phones should be considered. However, because of load control, they should not be the only source of backup systems.

One of the best methods for communication within a facility during a disaster is through a messenger system. This need became apparent during response to the bombing of the Murrah Federal Office Building in Oklahoma City in 1995. Rescuers from different agencies did not have a common radio channel during this incident. The use of normal and cellular telephone service was lost because these systems became quickly overloaded (because of use by rescuers and also by the general public, who were calling in associated emergencies from the bomb blast). Messengers or "runners" were the most effective form of communication among agencies.

Many amateur radio clubs are willing to provide communications services during emergencies. These clubs can set up operations and can provide contact with resources outside the facility and disaster area. These organizations can be reached through a local emergency management office.

12.3.3.3* Staff Management. Planning shall include the alerting and managing of all staff and employees in a disaster, as well as consideration of all of the following:

(1) Housing
(2) Transportation of staff and staff family
(3) Critical incident stress management

A.12.3.3.3 Management of staff and employees allows for the best and most effective use of the entity's human resources during disaster operations. Consideration should be given to both personnel on-hand and those that can be alerted. Specifically, staff management includes the following:

(1) Assignment of roles and responsibilities
(2) Method for identifying human resource needs to include status of families
(3) Method for recalling personnel and augmenting staff
(4) Management of space (housing, day care, etc.)
(5) Management of staff transportation
(6) Critical incident stress debriefing (Many case histories show that not only victims but also rescuers and treatment/handler staff bear serious emotional or even mental scars from their traumatic experiences. Emergency room and ambulance staff can also benefit from such help when stress has been acute.)

Staff management is an essential element for a successful emergency operations plan. Staff assignments and procedures should be clear and concise. It is important that any staff placed in a position of authority understand the position, its responsibilities, the hazards of particular disasters, the chain of command they are to follow, and who reports to their position.

The well-being of the staff is also essential. To maintain the proper staff well-being, management must provide time for rest, sleeping accommodations, and nourishment. Of most concern to the staff are their families and their homes. News from the outside should be distributed as part of the public information officer's and human service director's responsibilities.

During the Florida hurricanes of August and September 2004, health care facilities reported that the homes of up to one-third of their staff were damaged or destroyed. To help employees and enable them to work, the following steps were taken:

1. Free health care services for the immediate families were offered.
2. Funds were established to help with personal losses.
3. Furniture was stored and homes were tarped to prevent more damage.
4. Salary advances were approved.

Other types of disasters — such as the Sars Epidemic in Toronto (2003), and Tropical Storm Allison in Houston (2001) — illustrate the importance of adequate staffing during a disaster and through recovery. The more a facility is understaffed, the higher the likelihood of staff burnout.

The extra staffing required during a disaster is often obtained by calling back to work off-duty personnel. This practice can work for the short term; however, as times goes on, the facility can "run out" of staff.

Popular health care incident command systems include a progressive planning section for staff management following the disaster. Health care mutual aid plans in central and western New York lend volunteer off-duty staff from nonaffected facilities to disaster-struck facilities.

Depending on the type of emergency, there must be contingency plans for staff transportation to and from the facility. Inclement weather could require four-wheel drive vehicles to transport the staff. The public information officer should have a script in place to request this type of service through the news media; or the liaison officer could request such help through the local office of emergency management. Any plan should include pick-up and drop-off points, weather updates, and fuel provisions as appropriate. Pick-up and drop-off points should be off-site because the disaster could prohibit staff from driving directly to the facility.

There is awareness that traumatic incidents can affect staff and their ability to maintain patient care. This problem is often not recognized until a staff member collapses or a serious misjudgment occurs. Senior management should be mindful of this potential problem because it can occur at any level. Some of this stress can be acute and might affect staff members throughout their lives unless dealt with immediately. Making staff aware of this potential problem is now understood to be another important factor that needs to be addressed in emergency preparedness planning. Many organizations have employee assistance programs that offer stress debriefing.

12.3.3.4* Patient Management. Planning shall include provisions for management of patients, particularly with respect to clinical and administrative issues.

A.12.3.3.4 The plans should focus also on modification or discontinuation of nonessential patient services, control of patient information, and admission/discharge and transfer of patients. Emergency transfer plans need to consider the proper handling of patient personal property and medical records that will accompany the patient as well as assurance of continuity of quality care. Evaluation of space, patient transport resources, and a process to ensure patient location information should be included.

An assessment of the damage sustained as a result of a disaster to the facility's structure, utilities, and operations will provide the health care facility's incident command information regarding the type of care they must provide for patients presently in the building.

Besides the normal patient medical management, medical control through the medical care director (operations section) could require that patients be discharged or transferred to other facilities. Preplanning with other facilities as to what type and number of patients they could take in a disaster situation has shown to be helpful in situations such as the 2001 Houston floods and the Florida hurricanes of August and September 2004. It is important that the emergency operations plan take into account patient medical records, medications, and personal items. It is imperative that patients be closely tracked as they are transferred to another facility. Staff and supplies for receiving facilities must also be preplanned.

Special transportation for neonatal care patients, cardiac, surgical or critical care patients, and other similar cases should be part of the patient management plan. A receiving area or areas should be set up for incoming patients. These areas could have separate locations, depending on the severity of the patients' medical condition. Recent disasters such as at the World Trade Center attacks or Tropical Storm Allison in Houston in 2001 show that entire communities can be involved in the situation. Agreements with health care facilities outside of local areas are important.

12.3.3.5* Logistics. Planning for disasters shall include as a minimum stockpiling or ensuring immediate or at least uninterrupted access to critical materials such as the following:

(1) Pharmaceuticals
(2) Medical supplies
(3) Food supplies
(4) Linen supplies
(5) Industrial and potable (drinking) waters

The primary mission of a health care facility is to provide clinical care for patients. Key logistical items are needed to support the clinical care staff, among them pharmaceuticals, medical supplies, linen, food, and water.

Staff interviews of health care facilities that have experienced actual disasters showed the following priority of logistical items needed to manage facility patients, and to enable them to admit new patients. Note: Some items carry equal importance.

- Structural components
- Utilities
  - Electrical power — primary and emergency backup
  - Life support equipment and power to such critical areas as the following:
    - Emergency department
    - Surgery
    - Intensive care units
    - Laboratory
    - Diagnostic imaging
    - Pharmacy
    - Dialysis
    - Emergency operations center
  - Lighting
  - Heating, ventilation, air conditioning
  - Elevators

  - Water supplies
    - Domestic
    - Industrial
  - Water removal systems
- Medical gas
  - Oxygen
  - Nitrous oxide
  - Vacuum
- Sterilization equipment
- Communications
  - Telephone
  - Nurse call system
  - Information systems
- Food and liquids
- Fire protection and life safety systems
- Staff housing
- Physician offices

A.12.3.3.5 It will be essential to assess these kinds of resources currently available within the health care facility itself, and within the local community as a whole. Community sources identification can be effectively performed by the local disaster council, through the cooperation of local hospitals individually or collectively through local hospital associations, nursing homes, clinics, and other outpatient facilities, retail pharmacies, wholesale drug suppliers, ambulance services, and local medical–surgical suppliers and their warehouses.

Knowing the location and amount of in-house and locally available medical and other supply sources, a given health care facility could then desire to stockpile such additional critical material and supplies as could be needed to effectively cope with the disaster situation. Stockpiling of emergency supplies in carts should be considered as they facilitate stock rotation of outdated supplies, provide a locally secured environment, and are easily relocated to alternate site locations both within and outside the facility.

See Annex G for information about mutual aid and the Emergency Management Assistance Compact.

12.3.3.6* Security. Security plans shall be developed to meet the needs of the facility.

A.12.3.3.6 Prior to a disaster, facilities should formally coordinate their security needs with local law enforcement agencies.

The health care institution will find it necessary to share its emergency operations plans with local law enforcement agencies, or better still involve them in the process of planning for security support during disasters. The information should at least include availability of parking for staff, patients, and visitors, and normal vehicular, emergency vehicular, and pedestrian traffic flow patterns in and around the facility. The extent of the security and traffic control problems for any given health care facility will depend upon its geographical location, physical arrangement, availability of visitor parking areas, number of entrances, and so forth.

Crowd Control. Visitors can be expected to increase in number with the severity of the disaster. They should not be allowed to disrupt the disaster functioning of the facility. Ideally, a visitor's reception center should be established away from the main facility itself, particularly in major disasters. Volunteer personnel such as Red Cross, Explorer Scouts, or other helpers can be utilized as liaisons between the visitors and the health care facility itself.

Vehicular Traffic Control. Arrangement for vehicular traffic control into and on the facility premises should be made in the disaster planning period. It will be necessary to direct ambulances and other emergency vehicles carrying casualties to triage areas or the emergency room entrance, and to direct incoming and outgoing vehicles carrying people, supplies, and equipment. Charts showing traffic flow and indicating entrances to be used, evacuation routes to be followed, and so forth, should be prepared and included in the emergency operations plan. Parking arrangements should not be overlooked.

Internal Security and Traffic Control. Internal security and traffic control are best conducted by facility trained personnel, that is, regular health care facility security forces, with reinforcements as necessary. Potential additional assistance from the local law enforcement agencies should be coordinated in the disaster planning phase. Upon activation of the emergency operations plan, security guards should be stationed at all unlocked entrances and exits to the extent possible. Entrance to the facility should be restricted to personnel bearing staff identification cards and to casualties. In the case of major access corridors between key areas of the facility, pedestrian traffic should be restricted to one side of the corridor, keeping one side of the corridor free for movement of casualties. Traffic flow charts for internal traffic should also be prepared in the planning phase, as is the case with external traffic control.

Other Considerations. The following should also be considered:

(1) Notification protocols
(2) Response criteria
(3) Maintaining sensitive areas security
(4) Safeguarding property/equipment
(5) Backup communication
(6) Maintaining critical security systems
(7) Alternate site security
(8) Security to/from evacuated/alternate sites
(9) Security at evacuated facilities

Allowing the general public access to an operational area during a disaster makes it very difficult for health care providers to administer patient care. It also creates an unsafe condition for everyone. Access control plays an important part of any emergency situation. Crimes and terrorist activity have shown the importance of protecting patient support areas of labs and pharmacies.

During the planning stages, the person responsible for security should establish which resources are available both within the facility and with outside agencies.

Disaster situations are also a prime time for the violation of recognized safety practices. Security on rounds is often the "safety eyes" for the facility. Staff will be tempted to lift objects and people without sufficient help, which can result in musculo-skeletal injuries. Hygiene practices are apt to be foregone, resulting in a potential for a variety of exposures. Equipment might clutter walkways, posing trip hazards. Exit/egress paths and other emergency equipment might become blocked and inaccessible. These, along with a multitude of other safety violations, must be evaluated by a dedicated individual who will ensure that staff, patients, and visitors are afforded appropriate protection.

The facility should have a specific plan for managing the large number of visitors who might seek access to the facility during an emergency. The facility could very well be operating under uncertain and possibly dangerous conditions, and staff will need to be flexible but firm in handling each situation. September 11 demonstrated the need for health care facilities to at least separate visitors into the following categories:

1. Responsible parties of in-patients
2. Public, searching for missing persons

Beeper systems, e-mail addresses, and other tools in use before a disaster can serve as a framework for establishing staff access lists.

Language barriers can make even the best disaster plans ineffectual. Valuable time can be lost trying to convey emergency directions or procedures to those who speak languages other than the one predominantly spoken in the facility. Signs in the languages that are often heard in the halls of a facility can help. (See also NFPA 170, *Standard for Fire Safety and Emergency Symbols* [1], for symbols that are widely used in the United States.)

As noted in A.12.3.3.6, traffic control is essential during any emergency situation, whether patients are being transported to another facility or are being brought to the facility. An example of one traffic control plan assigns facility security officers to handle the internal security operations and the local police department or other government agency to control the traffic patterns outside the facility. As with evacuation routes, traffic control patterns, both internal and external, should be preplanned and made part of the master emergency preparedness plan. Plans should also address the issues of staff who have been requested to return to the facility, such as how they should enter the campus, where they must park, and provision of offsite parking and transportation to the facility.

If health care facility personnel are utilized for traffic control, basic instructions are essential. Orange traffic vests or some other suitable form of identification also should be provided to signify their authority and to provide a measure of personal safety (i.e., so that they are more easily seen).

Some facilities have no security force. Such facilities must consider how security procedures can be put into action quickly in an emergency.

To minimize security requirements during disaster conditions, points of access and egress to buildings should be "secured" (being careful not to create a dangerous situation in terms of emergency egress from the facility). All staff and employees can be required to enter and leave the facility through easily controlled points marked with signs hung on doors directing people to active entrances and exits. Some facilities use staff from departments around the building to "guard" all doors during an emergency lockdown of the building.

It should be noted that the request for military support and the invoking of martial law are mutually exclusive. Military support could be necessary in some situations because of the capability or manpower it can provide to an area. Preplanning with these groups and local law enforcement is important.

Health care facilities are prepared to handle victims. They also need to handle the concerned families and friends of the victims. A professional and efficient program for visitor control during the disaster will be important. During the terrorist attacks in New York City on September 11, 2001, several visitors arrived at the same time for each person in the hospital and emergency room. Other people entered hospitals, trying to locate family and friends. How the public later perceives the "handling" of visitors is quite important. Identifying visitors with special badges; listing the names of visitors and the patients they are seeing or seeking; and being prompt, courteous, and considerate in the handling of information and requests are all important factors in the visitor center.

Prerecorded telephone messages relating to the health care facility's operational status and patient information points can help relieve congested telephone lines.

It is good practice to have a first-aid cart at the visitor control center for treating visitors' medical problems that result from the anxiety and shock of the emergency situation.

Visitors might also have to accompany injured family members for a variety of reasons, including language barriers. Staff should not try to enforce normal rules that might ordinarily exclude visitors from certain areas or procedures if this situation exists.

See Exhibit 12.3 for an example of the emergency protocol procedures for fire and emergency response, as well as accidental exposure to biohazards; these procedures are printed on the front and back of a red plastic card and affixed to all ID card badge holders. All employees and volunteers wear an ID badge.

12.3.3.7* Public Affairs.

A.12.3.3.7 Because of the intense public interest in disaster casualties, news media representatives should be given as much consideration as the situation will permit. Ideally, news media personnel should be provided with a reception area, with access to telephone communication

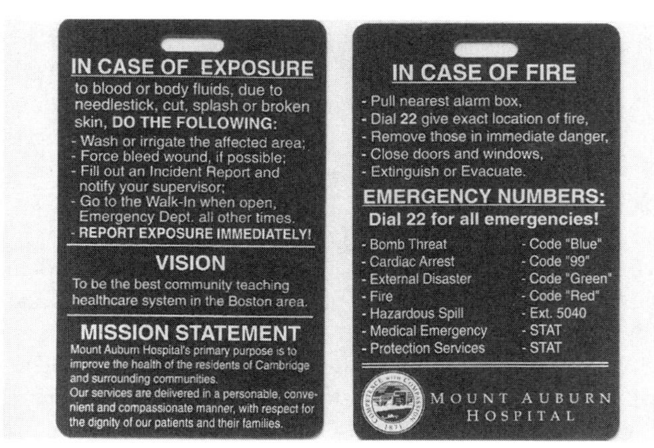

EXHIBIT 12.3 *Emergency protocol procedures on an ID badge.*

and, if possible, an expediter who, though not permitted to act as spokesman for news releases, could provide other assistance to these individuals. News media personnel should not be allowed into the health care facility without proper identification. To alert off-duty health care staff and for reassuring the public, use of broadcast media should be planned. Media representatives should be requested to wear some means of identification for security purposes.

◀ **FAQ**
How should the media requests be addressed?

All health care facility personnel should be advised on handling media requests, especially during emergency preparedness implementation. It is suggested that all media requests be forwarded to one person in one location. Preplanning with media personnel can ease the strain of dealing with requests under trying circumstances.

Under the scope of the incident command officer (ICO), one person serves as the public information officer (PIO). This person should be in direct contact with the incident commander to communicate with the news media. In the emergency preparedness planning phase, this person should determine where the news media will be staged (and the media's level of access to the facility), issue press credentials, and handle all news releases from the ICO.

The PIO should also notify the media of staff recall and where the staff should report. A person from the PIO staff should monitor radio and television transmissions to determine whether the information is correct and should keep the PIO briefed on any breaking news so the staff can be informed.

It is important to issue press releases at a scheduled time. If the press does not receive the information on a timely basis, they may report inaccurate information or attempt to enter the disaster scene.

Emergency agencies that have responded to the disaster will also have public information officers to address the news media. It is important that all persons assigned to the PIO position confer to ensure consistent information is being given to the news media.

12.3.3.7.1 Health care facilities shall have a designated media spokesperson to facilitate news releases.

12.3.3.7.2 An area shall be designated where media representatives can be assembled, where they will not interfere with the operations of the health care facility.

12.3.3.8* Operational Recovery. Plans shall reflect measures needed to restore operational capability to pre-disaster levels. Fiscal aspects shall be considered because of restoration costs and possible cash flow losses associated with the disruption.

Aside from the responsibilities associated with federal and state health agencies or accrediting organizations to provide a standard of care or insurance considerations to preserve the facility's resources, it is important to consider the community commitment associated with the facility's mission. During a catastrophic event or emergency, citizens within a community know that a health care facility will render treatment and care. Facilities of all types need to assess their role and responsibility in the community and the community's expectations. Individual facilities should consider these considerations not only in their assessment and planning activities but also in collaboration among all facilities in an area.

The magnitude of an event during the 1980s was not recognized until a review of data determined that a number of hospitals had received patients with similar symptoms and diagnoses, leading to the conclusion that numerous restaurant salad bars had intentionally been contaminated with salmonella. Reporting mechanisms that enable health departments to discover clusters or indications of widespread events are no longer as uncommon. There have been incidences of hospitals communicating among themselves regarding bed availability and their capabilities for patient care, thereby reducing the potential for one or two facilities to become overburdened during a disaster. Collaboration also enhances command operations at the disaster site and provides for a greater continuity of care during the emergency medical services transport phase and transfer to an emergency department.

Brainstorming during assessment can bring to light the potential for smoke from a wildland fire in an urban area, vapor cloud from a hazardous materials incident on an adjacent transportation route, or lack of public utilities for two weeks due to an ice storm. Following significant blizzards in the late 1970s, many facilities in various regions developed transportation plans in order to assist staff in getting to the workplace during crises. However, changes in staff and the cyclic nature of these types of events sometimes can result in laxity regarding these considerations in emergency management plans.

An emergency management plan is intended to establish a process that is realistic and can be implemented before, during, and after any emergency situation. This standard is the framework that is essential for designing an emergency management plan.

A.12.3.3.8 Recovery measures could involve a simple repositioning of staff, equipment, supplies, and information services; or recovery could demand extensive cleanup and repair. It can, under certain circumstances, identify opportunities for structural and nonstructural mitigation efforts. Filing of loss claims might require special approaches.

Health care facilities should have access to cash or negotiable instruments to procure immediately needed supplies.

Studies show that an emergency operations plan must include not only actions to deal with a disaster *while* it is occurring, but also steps to take *after* the crisis stage has passed and a facility has begun to return to a normal state of operation.

Recovery of a health care facility appears to have three stages:

1. *Immediate recovery.* Internal actions taken until outside services (supplies and staff) can reach the facility.
2. *Long-term temporary recovery.* Actions and equipment that would allow the facility to operate at some level until operations return to pre-disaster conditions.
3. *Full recovery.* The return of the facility to pre-disaster conditions.

A priority of logistical items and departments that need to be recovered is noted in the commentary following 12.3.3.5.

Recovery can be as simple as cleaning up one area of the facility or as complicated as finding suitable buildings, supplies, and equipment to continue some services until the facility is back to normal operation. Recovery can also involve long-range planning for both financial and architectural efforts. A key element is computer software backup and data backup. Because most health care facilities are computerized, arrangements for data storage should be made off premises. In addition, arrangements should be made to find equivalent systems to run the software and access the data in case the emergency impairs the computer network.

Disasters have shown two priorities in recovering information systems: patient data, including clinical equipment and medication dispensing, and patient billing.

Patient care is always the first priority. But if the financial systems go down, like any business, the impact to the organization can be catastrophic. The reality is, if money is not coming in the door and there is no payroll system, the facility will be out of business fast.

It is also imperative to have appropriate insurance coverage, including coverage for business interruption and insurance riders for floods and earthquakes. In the 2004 Florida hurricanes, the cash flow loss was higher than the cost of the disaster itself.

A suggested business plan of action based on previous disasters includes the following points:

- Ensure good insurance coverage.
- Know the source of funds (insurance, FEMA) and request loans against what you will be paid.
- Activate lines of credit with vendors and banks.
- Do not liquidate stocks — use stocks and other investments as collateral for loans and credit lines.
- Have the finance section chief (health care incident command system) work with other section chiefs to keep up-to-date records of disaster-related expenses.
- Ensure that doctors have offices and that the hospital can provide services to get patients in the door.
- Activate billing as soon as possible.
- Activate payroll as soon as possible.

Correspondence with the facility insurance agent or insurance company should be started as soon as the emergency has been mitigated. It is important to note that good record keeping is a must for claims reporting. (See Exhibit 12.4.)

12.3.3.9 Staff Education.

12.3.3.9.1 Each health care facility shall implement an educational program. This program shall include an overview of the components of the emergency management program and concepts of the incident command system. Education concerning the staff's specific duties and responsibilities shall be conducted.

12.3.3.9.2 General overview education of the emergency management program and the incident command system shall be conducted at the time of hire. Department/staff specific education shall be conducted upon reporting to their assignments or position and annually thereafter.

For additional guidance (education) for staff, see the commentary following A.12.3.3.7 on media response.

After the emergency operations plan has been formulated, each staff member should attend an educational session explaining the overall scope of the plan. It is important that this education take place for all full-time and part-time employees and volunteers. Contract employees or agency personnel (e.g., temporary nursing agency personnel) should also know what is expected in an emergency. Training of temporary staff has always been a challenge. It is important that leadership staff have a thorough knowledge of the procedures to guide their staff in a crisis.

Many different types of disasters can affect a health care facility. It would be impossible for staff to commit to memory the complete procedure for each disaster that could befall the

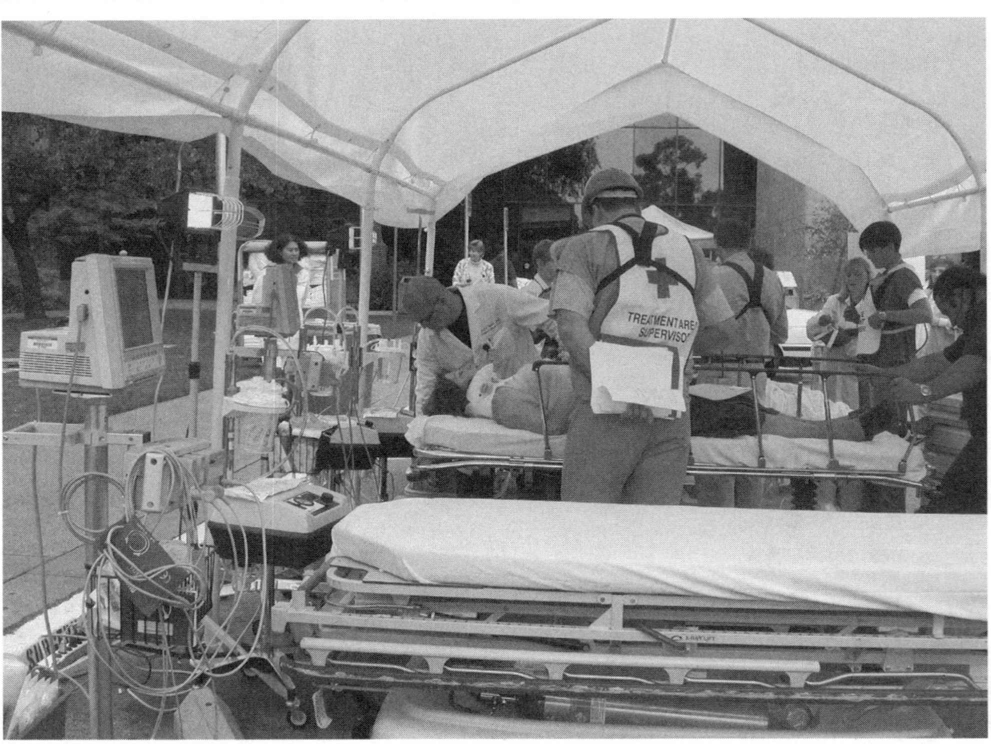

Exhibit 12.4 Recovery teams/equipment from Florida hurricane.

facility. For a few disasters, such as fire, the discovering staff person would not have time to reference a manual to determine the first steps to be taken. In the case of a fire, that person must immediately react and call out the pre-established fire code word, remove the patient from immediate danger, ensure someone has pulled the fire alarm upon hearing the fire code word shouted out, close the door to contain the fire, and extinguish the fire if it is safe to do so.

For most other disasters, such as loss of water, staff must know that there is a procedure for their department and position to follow. There is time for the staff to look up the guidelines and take appropriate actions.

Therefore, the most effective training is an overview of the emergency operations plan and a review of the highlights or algorithm of individual procedures. (See Exhibit 12.5.) As the standard points out, training can occur at the time of new hire orientation and annually within departments.

12.3.3.10* Drills. Each organizational entity shall implement two or more specific responses of the emergency operations plan during each year, at least one of which shall rehearse mass casualty response for health care facilities with emergency services, disaster receiving stations, or both.

A.12.3.3.10 Experiences show the importance of drills to rehearse the implementation of all elements of a specific response including the entity's role in the community, space management, staff management, and patient management activities.

To consider an exercise a drill, the following aspects are typically incorporated and documented: a general overview of the scenario, activation of the disaster plan, evaluation of all involved participants/departments, a critique session following the drill, and any identified follow-up training to correct or improve any deficiencies. See Annex G for publications on exercise design, management and evaluation.

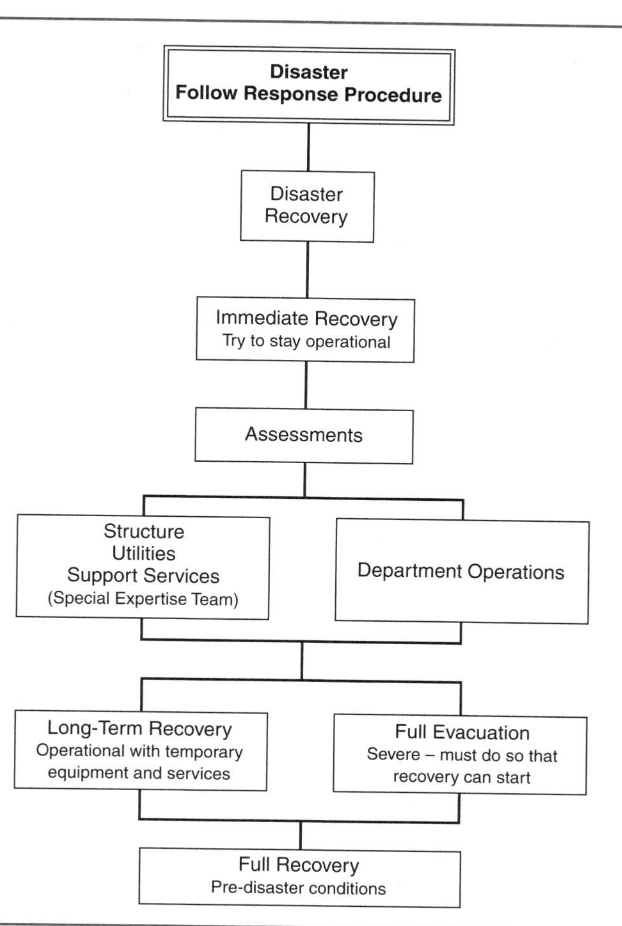

Exhibit 12.5 *Algorithm for recovery procedure*

Health care facilities should conduct disaster drills at least semi-annually.

Those rehearsals of an emergency management plan should be as realistic as possible. Preparation for rehearsals should involve the following: procedural knowledge, walk-through familiarizations, and discussions after the walk-through to resolve questions or problems.

It would be very helpful to involve as many outside agencies as possible that might respond to a real emergency. Simulation of patient management and movement is also helpful in evaluating the emergency management plan; it should not, however, involve actual patients.

During a simulation, volunteers who have been made to look like victims and counseled on typical behavior for specific injury types can provide a level of realism for all staff, particularly those who might not have dealt with the trauma of viewing, transporting, or attending to an injured victim. During the rehearsal, staff members can ascertain whether they will be able to handle the duties expected of them.

All parts of the emergency operations plan should be tested, including media and visitors' functions, security and traffic control, as well as loss of essential building systems that are necessary to continue serving patients. To decide which type of disaster to practice during the drill, the hazard vulnerability analysis (HVA) should be consulted to determine which disasters place the facility at the highest risk. Based on the HVA, the type of disasters practiced during drill situations should rotate so the same drill scenarios are not carried out each time a drill is conducted. The only exception would be the required annual mass casualty drill. Even during this drill, the scenario should change.

It cannot be stressed enough that emergency operations plans should not only be developed in coordination with local fire and emergency management agencies, but should also be rehearsed in coordination with these same groups. Plans cannot be developed in isolation.

REFERENCES CITED IN COMMENTARY

1. NFPA 170, *Standard for Fire Safety and Emergency Symbols,* 2006 edition.

CHAPTER 13

Hospital Requirements

Electrical hazards to life and property, a great concern in the 1970s, have decreased significantly in recent years. The reduction in hazards has come about partly through the improved design and quality of electrical appliances and improved materials and techniques used in gas and vacuum systems. The development of sophisticated, but ever-smaller, circuitry has also ensured that it is no longer necessary for a patient to be deliberately grounded in order to obtain noise-free signals. Successive levels of isolation have also separated the patient from accidental exposure to line voltage. The universal installation of grounding receptacles has profoundly reduced the danger of electric shock from domestic appliances and cord-connected devices in the hospital.

Exhibit 13.1 is one example of a hospital fire involving medical equipment. The fire, which involved smoking materials and an air flotation mattress, was fed by oxygen released from the piped oxygen distribution system.

With recognition that the hospital environment was hostile and abusive to equipment, industrial-grade fittings and cables became the rule for connectors and power cords, respectively. Exhibit 13.2 is one example of such improved equipment. However, these items are the weakest link in the safety chain, and they require regular inspection, testing, and repair when needed. The measures created to establish electrical "safety" were straightforward, inexpensive, and effective.

Although electrical hazards in health care facilities have certainly decreased, they have not been eliminated. Scattered fatalities due to electrical shock have occurred in recent

EXHIBIT 13.1 *A Petersburg, VA, hospital, where five patients died in a 1994 fire.*

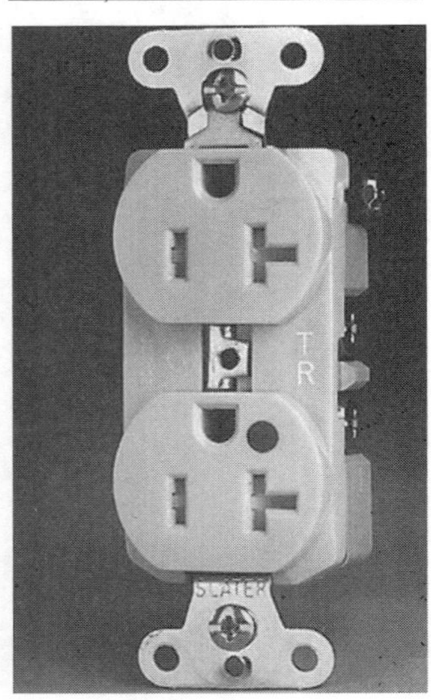

EXHIBIT 13.2 *A hospital-grade receptacle, identified by a green dot on its face. (Courtesy of Pass and Seymour/Legrand)*

decades. All of these incidents, however, have involved children and were caused by an inattentive or untrained attendant. Training and verification of qualifications remain a vital part of any electrical safety program.

As noted in Chapter 1, Chapters 13 through 19 and Chapter 21 are "facility" chapters. These facility chapters usually recommend the type or level of protection that is needed for the facility. In most cases the chapter will refer back to the requirements of Chapters 4 through 12 that are applicable to specific facilities. Chapter 13 lists requirements that are specific for hospital facilities. The definition of *hospital* appears in 3.3.70.

13.1 Applicability

This chapter applies to hospitals as defined in Chapter 3. As used in this chapter, the term *hospital* (except where it obviously refers to the physical structure) shall mean the entity and that portion of its internal governing structure that has the responsibility for the elements of hospital operation covered by this chapter, including building design, purchasing specifications, inspection procedures, maintenance schedules, and training programs affecting such use.

13.2* Responsibilities

The governing body of hospitals shall have the responsibility of protecting the facilities (for patient care and clinical investigation) and the personnel employed therein.

A.13.2 It is understood that the individuals who are responsible will vary from one hospital to another, although in most cases the hospital's administration exercises the concomitant authority. It is further recognized that fulfillment of this responsibility frequently occurs by means of delegating appropriate authority to staff, consultants, architects, engineers, and others.

13.2.1 Governing Body.

To achieve the performance criteria of Chapters 1 through 12, the governing body of the hospital shall be permitted to assign responsibility to appropriate hospital personnel, consultants, architects, engineers, or others.

13.2.2 Policies.

The hospital shall ensure that policies are established and maintained that permit the attending physician to satisfy the emergency needs of any patient that could supersede the requirements of this chapter. Each such special use shall be clearly documented and reviewed to attempt to have future similar needs met within the requirements of this chapter.

13.2.3 Electricity.

It shall be the responsibility of the hospital to provide an environment that is reasonably safe from the shock and burn hazards that are attendant with the use of electricity in patient care areas.

13.2.3.1 The hospital shall establish policies and procedures related to the safe use of electric appliances.

13.2.3.2 Each hospital shall be permitted to select a specific electrical safety program that is appropriate to its particular needs.

13.2.3.3 The physical protection afforded by the installation of an electrical distribution system that meets the requirements of this chapter and the purchase of properly constructed and tested appliances shall be augmented by having designated departments of the facility assume responsibility for the continued functioning of the electrical distribution system *(see Chapter 4)* and the inspection, testing, and maintenance of electrical appliances *(see Chapter 8)*.

13.2.3.3.1 The hospital shall adopt regulations and practices concerning the use of electric appliances and shall establish programs for the training of physicians, nurses, and other personnel who might be involved in the procurement, application, use, inspection, testing, and maintenance of electrical appliances for the care of patients.

13.2.4 Patient Care Areas.

Areas of a hospital in which patient care is administered are classified as general care areas or critical care areas, either of which shall be permitted to be classified as a wet location. The governing body of the facility shall designate the following areas in accordance with the type of patient care anticipated and with the following definitions of the area classification *(see definition of Patient Care Area in Chapter 3)*:

(1) General Care Area *(see Chapter 3)*
(2) Critical Care Area *(see Chapter 3)*
(3) Wet Location *(see Chapter 3)*

Patient care areas are categorized as *general care* and *critical care*. (See 3.3.138.1 and 3.3.138.2 for the definitions of these terms.) Patients in different areas may be at different levels of risk of electrical exposure. Distinct requirements for each category of patient care area are necessary.

It is important to note that the governing body of the facility is responsible for the designation of areas as general care or critical care. This designation can and should be done in consultation with medical staff and engineering staff, taking into consideration the conditions and practices of the facility. Although this requirement places responsibility on the facility, it also provides the facility with an opportunity to safeguard its own operations, rather than leaving the designations to an outside agency.

Variations in patient care area categorization within facilities can be expected. For example, general surgical recovery rooms might have conditions quite different from eye surgery recovery rooms. There is also confusion regarding the term *invasive procedures* as used in the definition of *critical care areas*. A new definition of *invasive procedures* was added to this edition of the standard to provide further guidance when analyzing critical care areas. See 3.3.83 for this definition.

Many differences of opinion exist on just what constitutes a wet location. The two terms *patient care areas* and *wet locations* are not mutually exclusive. Patient care areas may be wet locations, but a wet location is not necessarily a patient care area.

See the commentary on *wet location* following A.3.3.185 for an explanation of the term and 4.3.2.2.8.1 for electrical requirements for wet locations.

13.2.5 Anesthesia.

It shall be the responsibility of the governing body of the hospital to designate anesthetizing locations.

Many NFPA 99 users often wonder whether a location that uses only intravenous medication to perform anesthesia is considered an anesthetizing location. The answer is no. NFPA 99 recognizes only nonflammable inhalation anesthetic agents to induce analgesia or general anesthesia.

13.3 General Requirements

The subsections of the facility chapters are formatted to correlate with core Chapters 4 through 12. See Commentary Table 13.1 for more information.

***COMMENTARY TABLE 13.1** Chapter–Subsection Correlation*

Core Chapter	Facility Section
Chapter 4, Electrical Systems	X.3.4 Electrical Distribution System
Chapter 5, Gas and Vacuum Systems	X.3.5 Gas and Vacuum System Requirements
Chapter 6, Environmental Systems	X.3.6 Environmental System Requirements
Chapter 7, Materials	X.3.7 Material Requirements
Chapter 8, Electrical Equipment	X.3.8 Electrical Equipment Requirements
Chapter 9, Gas Equipment	X.3.9 Gas Equipment Requirements
Chapter 10, Manufacturer Requirements	X.3.10 Reserved
Chapter 11, Laboratories	X.3.11 Laboratories
Chapter 12, Health Care Emergency Management	X.3.12 Emergency Management

13.3.1 Reserved.

13.3.2 Reserved.

13.3.3 Reserved.

13.3.4 Electrical System Requirements.

13.3.4.1 Electrical Distribution System. The electrical distribution system for patient care areas shall conform to the requirements in Chapter 4, Electrical Systems. These requirements shall apply to new construction. Existing installations shall not need to be modified, provided that they meet the operational safety requirements in 4.3.3.2 and 4.3.3.3.

13.3.4.2 Essential Electrical Distribution System. The essential electrical distribution system shall conform to a Type 1 system, as described in Chapter 4.

13.3.4.3 Hospitals shall be permitted to serve the essential electrical system needs of contiguous or same-site facilities with the generating equipment of the hospital.

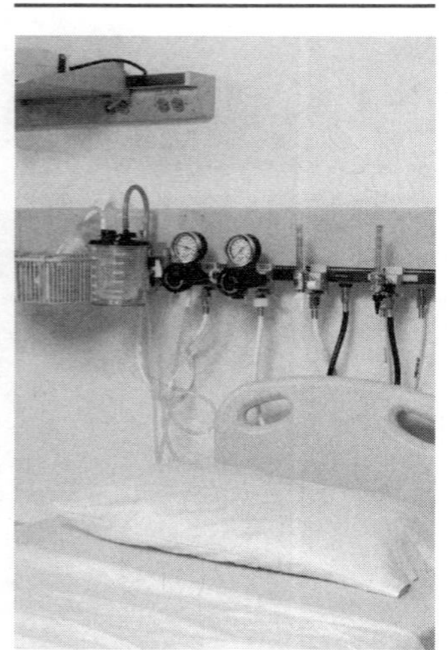

***EXHIBIT 13.3** Typical general care bed setup.*

Exhibit 13.3 shows a general care hospital bed setup. The essential electrical receptacles are shown in Exhibit 13.4.

13.3.5 Gas and Vacuum System Requirements.

FAQ ▶
How is the level of the gas and vacuum system determined for a particular hospital?

Readers are reminded that the term *Level* is used only as a designator. The term is, in actuality, defined by the criteria provided for each of the various Levels listed in Chapter 5 (e.g., for Level 1 gas and vacuum system requirements, see Section 5.1).

The facility chapters do not mandate the level of gas and vacuum systems. The user must determine the appropriate level on the basis of an analysis of their facility and usage.

EXHIBIT 13.4 Receptacles for essential electrical system.

A facility that uses gas or vacuum systems to sustain life will require a higher-level system than a facility that does not.

13.3.5.1 General. Where medical gas, instrument air, vacuum, and WAGD systems are installed they shall conform to the requirements for the appropriate level. Systems conforming to different levels within the same building shall be permitted. The appropriate level shall be determined as follows:

(1) All systems shall comply to Level 1 if any part of the systems are Level 1, except where both of the following apply:
  (a) The system(s) is entirely separate from the Level 1 system(s) (i.e., is stand-alone) and is not connected to Level 1 sources or distribution pipelines.
  (b) The occupancy to be served and the function of that occupancy is distinct from other occupancies in the building.

Hospitals are required to use a Level 1 gas and vacuum system unless there is a separate facility with a separate gas or vacuum system within that building, and then the possibility of compromising the hospital's gas and vacuum system has been eliminated. In that case, the separate facility in the hospital is not required to be a Level 1 system.

(2) Medical gas and vacuum systems shall be permitted to be Level 2 systems only where the following apply:
  (a) Paragraphs 13.3.5.1(1)(a) and 13.3.5.1(1)(b) apply.
  (b) Patients served by the system(s) are not dependent on mechanical ventilation or assisted mechanical ventilation at any time, including during administration of anesthesia.

◀ **FAQ**
Can a hospital have a Level 2 gas and vacuum system?

A hospital is allowed to have a Level 2 gas and vacuum system if it meets all the requirements of a separate facility and separate systems and the patients are not dependant on mechanical ventilation or assisted mechanical ventilation. A Level 2 system is not as reliable as a Level 1 system because of the lack of redundancies. As a result, a Level 2 system has restrictions on the type of equipment and needs of the patient utilizing a Level 2 system.

(3) Medical gas and vacuum systems shall be permitted to be Level 3 systems only where the following apply:
  (a) Paragraphs 13.3.5.1(1)(a) and 13.3.5.1(1)(b) and 13.3.5.1(2)(b) apply.
  (b) The patient population, during or subsequent to treatment, are not dependent for life on the gases or vacuum system(s), and the treatment(s) that the facility will

perform can be completed without detrimental effect on patient outcomes in the event of sudden loss of the gas or vacuum system(s).

(c)* The total of all gases in cylinders or containers, except nitrogen, connected and in storage at one time does not exceed 85 m^3 (3000 ft^3) at standard temperature and pressure (STP), except that 142 m^3 (5000 ft^3) (STP) shall be permitted if oxygen is stored in a DOT Specification 4L (cryogenic liquid) cylinder.

Level 3 systems have many restrictions on their use because of the lack of redundancies. In addition to meeting all the criteria for a Level 2 and Level 1 system, as specified in 13.3.5.1(1) and (2), there are restrictions based on the patient's need for the gas or vacuum to stay alive. Additionally, a Level 3 system spreads the risk by limiting the amount of gas that can be stored and the number of treatment facilities served by the system.

A.13.3.5.1(3)(c) It is the intent to provide a simple, safe piping system for small facilities. Although the number of use points could be a consideration, it was felt that actual gas use is a more accurate indicator of complexity. Applications involving a storage in excess of 85 m^3 (3000 ft^3) would have a complexity warranting installation in accordance with the provisions of Level 1 patient gas distribution systems.

Although the principal intent is to provide simple installations for single treatment facilities, numerous applications exist where a remote use point creates essentially a second treatment facility or where the supply system might be shared by another health care professional such as other dentist, podiatrist, oral surgeon, or general medicine practitioner. The addition of another treatment facility requires incremental safety precautions.

A maximum of two single treatment facilities also approximates the limit with which a 85 m^3 (3000 ft^3) supply system can provide [143 m^3 (5000 ft^3) when liquid oxygen is used].

It is acknowledged that older user analgesia equipment has offered a nitrous oxide lockout device that requires a minimum of 3 L/min oxygen flow. However, a reasonable percentage of older equipment without this safety feature is in daily use. The storage and piping system is based upon the potential use, either initially or subsequently, of one of the older style analgesia equipment in one of the single treatment facilities. The quantity of 85 m^3 (3000 ft^3), or 143 m^3 (5000 ft^3) if liquid oxygen storage, is to be taken as the total combined storage of gases if there is more than one supply system in the single treatment facility.

(d) The system(s) supplies not more than two adjoining single treatment facilities.

13.3.5.2 Where nitrous oxide or halogenated agents are intended to be administered, a patient WAGD shall be installed and conform to Level 1 WAGD systems in Chapter 5.

Paragraph 13.3.5.2 correlates with 5.1.3.7 in Chapter 5, Gas and Vacuum Systems. It is important to remove the excess anesthetic agents from the room so as to not affect the medical staff. Therefore, a Level 1 WAGD system is required to ensure the gases are exhausted.

Exhibit 13.5 shows the extensive amount of electronic equipment and medical gas/vacuum outlets in a patient care area.

13.3.6* Environmental System Requirements. (Reserved)

A.13.3.6 See 13.4.1 for requirements for anesthetizing locations, and 13.3.8.2 and 13.3.11 for requirements for laboratories.

13.3.7 Material Requirements. (Reserved)

13.3.8 Electrical Equipment Requirements.

13.3.8.1* Patient Care Areas. Electrical appliances shall conform to Chapter 8.

A.13.3.8.1 The requirements of Chapter 8 apply to all electrical appliances. Chapter 8 requirements and procedures are intended to be implemented by the hospital to evaluate

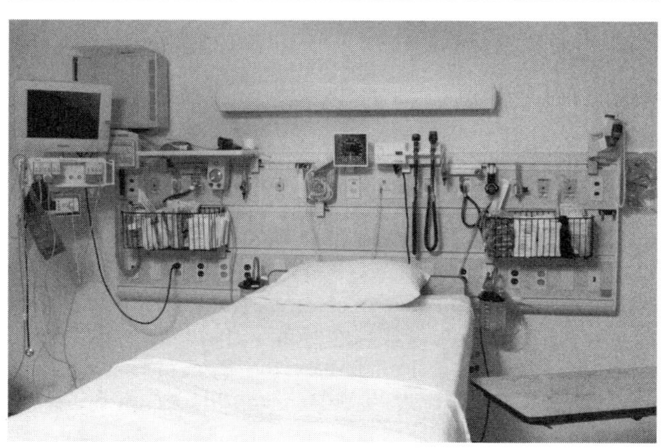

EXHIBIT 13.5 *The range of electronic equipment and medical gas and vacuum system outlets used in a typical intensive care patient unit.*

existing equipment or to evaluate new equipment as part of routine incoming inspection procedures for all appliances in patient care areas. *(See 8.4.1 and 8.4.2.2.1.)*

13.3.8.2* Laboratories. Equipment shall conform to the nonpatient electrical equipment requirements in Chapter 8.

A.13.3.8.2 See 8.4.2.2.2 for performance criteria; see 8.5.2.5 for policies. 

13.3.9 Gas Equipment Requirements.

13.3.9.1 Patient. Equipment shall conform to the patient equipment requirements in Chapter 9.

13.3.9.2 Nonpatient. Equipment shall conform to the nonpatient equipment requirements in Chapter 9.

13.3.10 Reserved.

13.3.11* Laboratories.

Laboratories in hospitals shall comply with the requirements of Chapter 11 as applicable and the requirements of NFPA 45, *Standard on Fire Protection for Laboratories Using Chemicals*, as applicable. 

A.13.3.11 NFPA 45, *Standard on Fire Protection for Laboratories Using Chemicals*, establishes basic requirements for all laboratories using chemicals, but important additional requirements are contained in Chapter 11 and in Chapters 5, 6, and 8. 

13.3.12 Emergency Management.

Hospitals shall comply with the provisions of Chapter 12 for emergency management planning, as appropriate.

13.4* Specific Area Requirements

A.13.4 This is in addition to any applicable requirements in Section 13.3. 

Paragraph A.13.4 is an important reminder that stresses the structure of NFPA 99 and of how requirements are to be applied for each type of facility in Chapters 13 through 19 and Chapter 21. For example, Section 13.3, *General Requirements*, applies to all hospitals. Section

EXHIBIT 13.6 Example of a hospital isolated power system with built-in isolation transformer, line isolation monitor, and grounded busbar. (Courtesy of Square D Co.)

13.4, *Specific Area Requirements,* applies to specific areas within hospitals (e.g., 13.4.1 covers anesthetizing locations). It should be clearly understood that the requirements of Section 13.4 cannot be considered alone, but must be applied in conjunction with the requirements of Section 13.3. Section 13.4 requirements can be considered as supplementary to any of the general requirements listed in Section 13.3.

13.4.1 Anesthetizing Locations.

Because of the special hazards associated with anesthetizing locations, Chapter 13 has highlighted some important safety concepts.

During the initial development of fire and explosion precautions for hospital operating suites, it became apparent that one of the principal sources of ignition of flammable anesthetic gases was static electricity. As a result of studies conducted by the Bureau of Mines, a number of precautions were developed to deal with static electricity. These precautions included all of the following:

1. Installation of conductive flooring
2. Maintenance of a relative humidity of 50 percent to 55 percent
3. Elimination of garments and drapes made from synthetic fibers
4. Use of conductive and antistatic materials
5. Compliance with Class 1, Group C requirements for suction, pressure, or insufflation (for tonsillectomy) equipment and for other portable equipment
6. Compliance with Class 1, Group C requirements for receptacles and switches in hazardous locations
7. Use of conductive shoes or conductive shoe covers and the testing of their efficacy before personnel entered flammable anesthetizing locations
8. Use of isolation transformers to supply ungrounded electric power, along with ground contact indicators (today line isolation monitors are used), to detect whether the ungrounded power was being compromised

See Exhibits 13.6 and 13.7 for examples of hospital isolated power system equipment.

FAQ ▶ Are there still fire hazards in the operating rooms even though nonflammable anesthetic agents are used?

These precautionary measures reduced the number of fire incidents in operating rooms. (See Exhibit 13.8.) Nonflammable anesthetic gases eventually replaced flammable anesthetic gases, further reducing fires in operating rooms. Fires were not eliminated, however, as flammable agents such as alcohol, flammable prepping agents, and bone cement can still be found in anesthetizing locations. These flammable agents, combined with a large combustible load in the operating room and the use of oxidizing agents (oxygen and nitrous oxide), have not as yet been fully addressed by health care facilities experts. In addition, the extensive use of electrosurgical units, which create a combination of sparks and small flames, also is a matter of concern. (See further commentary on this subject following 13.4.1.2.10.)

Although there are no restrictions on the *types of fabric* worn by personnel or used for draping patients in nonflammable anesthetizing locations, institutions should be sure that such materials are not highly combustible. The increased use of flammable liquids, the presence of oxygen, and sparks and small flames caused by cautery and electrosurgical devices pose a problem should a fire involving these materials occur. (Oxygen, although not a flammable gas, greatly enhances combustion once it has begun.)

Some conductive floors are still in existence in anesthetizing rooms. The low conductivity of these floors is no longer an issue for static control because flammable anesthetics are no longer used. The low conductive flooring can pose an electrical hazard and therefore is still a concern for some people.

13.4.1.1 General.

13.4.1.1.1 Scope.

13.4.1.1.1.1 The purpose of 13.4.1 is to establish performance and maintenance criteria for anesthetizing locations and for equipment and facilities ancillary thereto in order to safeguard patients and health care personnel from fire, explosion, electrical, and related hazards associated with the administration of inhalation anesthetics.

13.4.1.1.1.2 Subsection 13.4.1 applies to all anesthetizing locations and related storage areas within hospitals in which inhalation anesthetics are administered.

Although the requirements of 13.4.1 apply to all anesthetizing locations, they are not retroactive to existing locations. Paragraph 1.3.2 states that the application of NFPA 99 is for new construction and new equipment except as modified by the individual chapters. Chapter 13 does not specifically state the requirements of 13.4.1 are retroactive.

13.4.1.1.1.3 Subsection 13.4.1 is intended to provide requirements to protect against explosions or fires, electric shock, mechanical injury from compressed gases or compressed gas cylinders, or anoxia from erroneous gas connections and similar hazards, without unduly limiting the activities of the surgeon or anesthesiologist. This principle, without minimizing any of the aforementioned dangers, recognizes that the physicians shall be guided by all the hazards to life that are inherent in surgical procedures carried out in anesthetizing locations.

13.4.1.1.1.4 Subsection 13.4.1 does not cover animal operative facilities unless the animal operative facility is integral to a hospital.

13.4.1.1.1.5 The provisions of 13.4.1 do not apply to the manufacture, storage, transportation, or handling of inhalation anesthetics prior to delivery to the consuming health care facility. They do not apply to any use other than in an anesthetizing location and related storage areas.

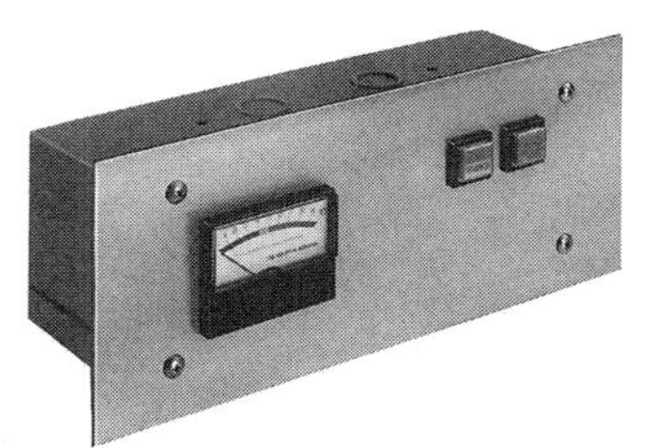

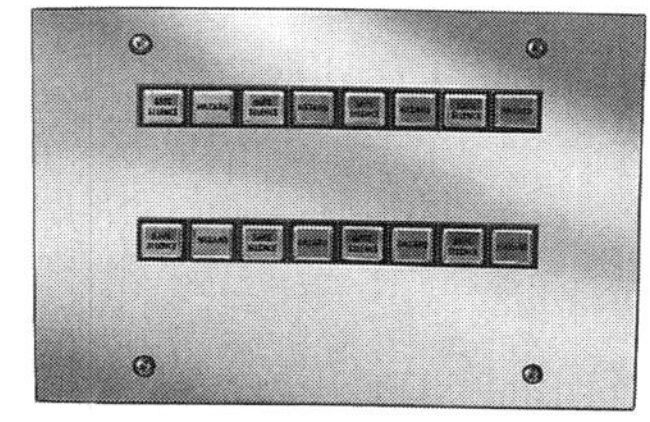

EXHIBIT 13.7 Line isolation monitor (top) for use with isolated power systems, remote indicator alarm (middle), and multiple annunciator panel (bottom), which can monitor several operating rooms from a central location, such as a nurses' station. (Courtesy of Square D Co.)

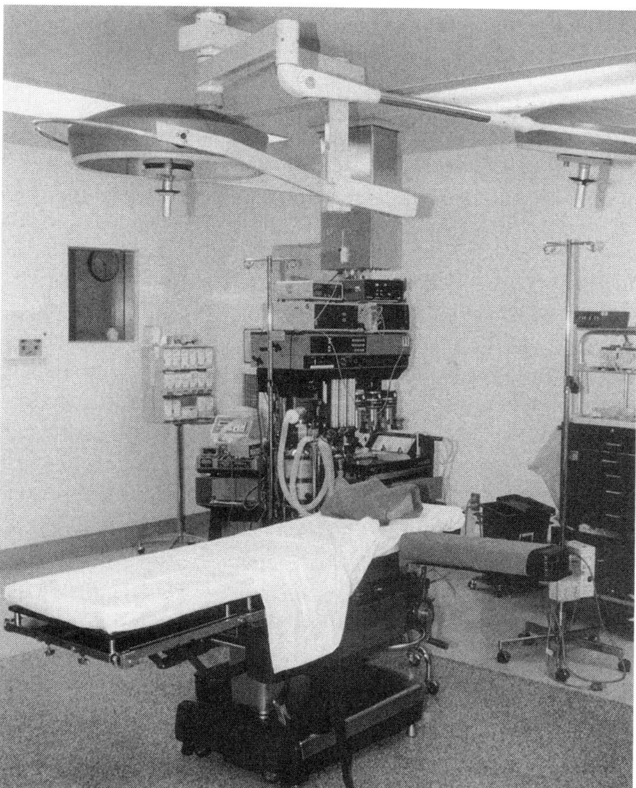

EXHIBIT 13.8 A typical operating room setup.

13.4.1.1.2 Purpose. Subsection 13.4.1 contains the requirements for administration and maintenance that shall be followed as an adjunct to physical precautions specified in 13.4.1.2.

13.4.1.1.3* Recognition of Hazards and Responsibility.

A.13.4.1.1.3 In determining whether existing construction or equipment does or does not constitute a hazard to life, due consideration should be given to the record of incidents or accidents of the facility in question and whether equipment used in the facility is subject to documented preventive maintenance. Absence of incidents and accidents, and the existence of a well-documented preventive maintenance program covering all electrical equipment used in anesthetizing locations in the facility, indicates that minimal hazard to life exists.

For example, isolated power systems would not be required in existing anesthetizing locations in health care facilities meeting the above criteria.

The hazards involved in the use of inhalation anesthetic agents can be successfully mitigated only when all of the areas of hazard are fully recognized by all personnel, and when the physical protection provided is complete and is augmented by attention to detail by all personnel of administration and maintenance having any responsibility for the functioning of anesthetizing locations. Since 13.4.1.1 and 13.4.1.2 are expected to be used as a text by those responsible for the mitigation of associated hazards, the requirements set forth herein are frequently accompanied by explanatory text.

Responsibility for the maintenance of safe conditions and practices in anesthetizing locations falls mutually upon the governing body of the hospital, all physicians using the anesthetizing locations, the administration of the hospital, and those responsible for hospital licensing, accrediting, or other approval programs.

13.4.1.1.3.1 Inasmuch as the ultimate responsibility for the care and safety of patients in a hospital belongs to the governing board of the hospital, that body, in its responsibility for enforcement of requirements contained in this chapter, shall determine that adequate regulations with respect to anesthesia practices and conduct in anesthetizing locations have been adopted by the medical staff of the hospital and that adequate regulations for inspection and maintenance are in use by the administrative, nursing, and ancillary personnel of the hospital.

13.4.1.1.3.2 By virtue of its responsibility for the professional conduct of members of the medical staff of the hospital, the organized medical staff shall adopt regulations with respect to the use of inhalation anesthetic agents and to the prevention of electric shock and burns *(see C.13.3)* and through its formal organization shall ascertain that these regulations are regularly adhered to.

13.4.1.1.3.3 In meeting its responsibilities for safe practices in anesthetizing locations, the hospital administration shall adopt or correlate regulations and standard operating procedures to ensure that both the physical qualities and the operating maintenance methods pertaining to anesthetizing locations meet the standards set in this chapter. The controls adopted shall cover the conduct of professional personnel in anesthetizing locations, periodic inspection to ensure the proper grounding of dead metal *(see 4.3.3.2),* and inspection of all electrical equipment, including testing of line isolation monitors.

It is the intent that changes to future editions of 13.4.1.1.3.3 be applied judiciously to existing facilities (similar to NFPA *101®*, *Life Safety Code®* [1], which specifically differentiates between new and existing occupancies). Paragraph A.13.4.1.3 is a further clarification with respect to the specific issue of existing anesthetizing locations that do not have isolated power systems.

Note again that a patient care area that is designated as a wet location would require an added level of electrical protection. [See the commentary following 13.4.1.2.6.1(F).]

13.4.1.1.4 Rules and Regulations.

13.4.1.1.4.1 Hospital authorities and professional staff shall jointly consider and agree upon necessary rules and regulations for the control of personnel concerned with anesthetizing locations. Upon adoption, rules and regulations shall be prominently posted in the operating room suite. Positive measures shall be necessary to acquaint all personnel with the rules and regulations established and to ensure enforcement.

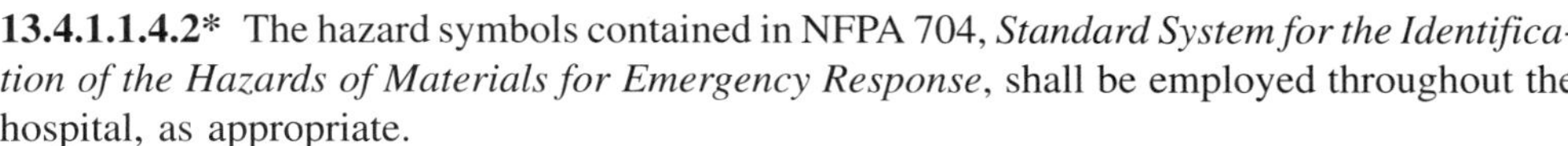

13.4.1.1.4.2* The hazard symbols contained in NFPA 704, *Standard System for the Identification of the Hazards of Materials for Emergency Response*, shall be employed throughout the hospital, as appropriate.

A.13.4.1.1.4.2 Use of such hazard symbols is particularly important in the operating suite and in gas and volatile liquid storage facilities.

NFPA 704 provides a simple method for identifying an area's level of hazard. Fire departments are familiar with NFPA 704, *Standard System for the Identification of the Hazards of Materials for Emergency Response* [2], and can quickly interpret the document's coding and take appropriate measures when extinguishing a fire in that area. Once an area's level of hazard has been identified, the area should be checked periodically to determine whether the assigned coding is still applicable.

For further details on the "704 diamond," see the commentary following A.11.8.2.1.

13.4.1.2 Requirements for ALL Anesthetizing Locations.

The requirements of 13.4.1.2 apply to all anesthetizing locations, but these requirements are not retroactive. The requirements of NFPA 99 apply for new construction.

The term *ALL* applies to all the anesthetizing locations in a hospital, not just a select number of them.

13.4.1.2.1 Ventilation. Ventilation of anesthetizing locations shall conform to 6.4.1 and 6.6.1.

13.4.1.2.2 Germicides.

13.4.1.2.2.1 Medicaments, including those dispersed as aerosols, shall be permitted to be used in anesthetizing locations for germicidal purposes, for affixing plastic surgical drape materials, for preparation of wound dressing, or for other purposes.

13.4.1.2.2.2 Liquid germicides used in anesthetizing locations, whenever the use of cautery or electrosurgery is contemplated, shall be nonflammable.

13.4.1.2.2.3* Whenever flammable aerosols are employed, sufficient time shall be allowed to elapse between deposition and application of drapes to permit complete evaporation and dissipation of any flammable vehicle remaining.

A.13.4.1.2.2.3 Some tinctures and solutions of disinfecting agents can be flammable, and can be used improperly during surgical procedures. Tipping containers, accidental spillage, and the pouring of excessive amounts of such flammable agents on patients expose them to injury in the event of accidental ignition of the flammable solvent.

◀ **FAQ**
What are the hazards of flammable germicides and what are the ignition sources?

There are differences between 13.4.1.2.2.2 and 13.4.1.2.2.3 — specifically the form of germicide, liquid or aerosol. The use of flammable liquid germicides when cautery or electrosurgery is contemplated is of concern. In particular, the bulk flammable liquid germicides can be hazardous because of the amount of liquid present and the potential for an overabundance of material used or potentially spilled. The hazard is reduced with unit-dose, controlled application of the flammable germicide. In this case, there is a limited amount of flammable liquid in an applicator, thus reducing the potential for overuse or spills.

There have been some documented combustion incidents, including "Fire Following Use of Electrocautery During Emergency Percutaneous Transtracheal Ventilation [3]." (It is a widely held belief that most incidents are never reported in the literature. They occur but are not reported or written up for publication.)

At the time of this writing, a Tentative Interim Amendment (TIA) is being processed to allow the use of flammable germicides where electrosurgery is contemplated as long as the flammable liquid is in unit-doses and is allowed to completely evaporate. In addition, any solution that has been absorbed into some material must be removed because it may not dry during surgery. Combustion is likely if the electrosurgical device emits a spark near the wet area.

With the ban on the use of fluorocarbons as propellants (liquid Freon® had been a popular skin degreasing agent), manufacturers of aerosol products have had to seek alternative agents, some of which can be highly flammable (e.g., isobutane, propane). Nitrous oxide, an oxidizing agent that is equal to oxygen in supporting combustion, is also employed as a propellant. With the commercial disappearance of the old, quite inexpensive Freons, care must be taken to ensure that all vapors have dissipated if flammable propellant degreasers are used.

13.4.1.2.3 Smoking and Open Flames. Smoking and open flames shall be prohibited in all anesthetizing locations.

13.4.1.2.4* Electrical Safeguards.

See the introductory commentary following the Chapter 13 heading on the subject of electrical hazards.

A.13.4.1.2.4 Physical safeguards built into the anesthetizing locations or storage areas will not provide protection unless safe practices are followed and good maintenance is provided.

13.4.1.2.4.1 Scheduled inspections and written reports shall be maintained.

13.4.1.2.4.2 Rules to require prompt replacement of defective electrical equipment shall be adopted and rigidly enforced.

13.4.1.2.4.3 Personnel working in anesthetizing locations shall be instructed in these electrical safeguards.

13.4.1.2.4.4 Members of the professional staff shall be required to submit for inspection and approval any special equipment they wish to introduce into anesthetizing locations. Such equipment shall meet the requirements for the protection against electric shock as given in Chapter 8 *(see 8.4.1.1).*

13.4.1.2.4.5 Line-powered equipment that introduces current to the patient's body shall have the output circuit isolated from ground to ensure against an unintentional return circuit through the patient. Equipment whose output circuit is grounded or ground-referenced shall be permitted, provided that the design provides equivalent safety to an isolated output.

From a safety perspective, it is very important that electrical and mechanical appliances be tested before they are used on patients.

13.4.1.2.5 Electric Connections and Testing.

13.4.1.2.5.1 Administrative authorities shall ascertain that electric maintenance personnel are completely familiar with the function and proper operation of ungrounded electric circuits required by E.6.6.2. The significance of the signal lamps and audible alarms installed to indicate accidental grounds shall be explained to all personnel affected. A permanent sign shall be installed close to the position of the signal lamps to indicate their significance.

Circuits in the panel boxes shall be clearly labeled, distinguishing between grounded and ungrounded, emergency and normal circuits, so that immediate recognition is possible.

13.4.1.2.5.2 Extension cords shall not be connected to lighting fixtures in anesthetizing locations under any circumstances.

13.4.1.2.6 Electrical Systems.

See the introductory commentary following the Chapter 13 heading on the subject of electrical hazards.

13.4.1.2.6.1 Wiring in Anesthetizing Locations.

(A) Wiring. Installed wiring shall be in metal raceway or shall be as required in NFPA 70, *National Electrical Code*, Sections 517.60 through 517.63.

(B) Raceway. Such distribution systems shall be run in metal raceways along with a green grounding wire sized no smaller than the energized conductors.

(C) Grounding to Raceways. Each device connected to the distribution system shall be effectively grounded to the metal raceway at the device.

(D) Installation. Methods of installation shall conform to Articles 250 and 517 of NFPA 70, *National Electrical Code*.

(E) Battery-Powered Emergency Lighting Units. One or more battery-powered emergency lighting units shall be provided as required in Section 700.12(E) of NFPA 70, *National Electrical Code*. Such lights shall be wired to circuits serving general area lighting. Testing shall be in accordance with 4.3.4.2.

Emergency lighting is a very important feature of occupant and patient safety, particularly in anesthetizing locations. Emergency lighting provides illumination to complete tasks and for egress during evacuation. These battery-powered emergency lights are designed to supply emergency lighting for 1½ hours of continuous use.

For medical practitioners performing invasive procedures on a patient under anesthesia, the short delay (generally less than 10 seconds) between loss of normal power and transfer of the automatic transfer switch to the on-site generator can seem like an eternity. Battery-powered lights are intended to bridge this gap.

◄ **FAQ**
Why are battery-operated emergency lights required in the operating room?

To ensure that emergency lighting will work when called upon, the battery-operated units need to be tested on a regular basis. Functional testing needs to be conducted every month for 30 seconds to determine whether the batteries are charged and that light bulbs are not burned out. This is just a functional test to determine whether the unit is working and that there are no gross failures. What is not known is whether the batteries have degraded or the charging system has failed and will not supply lighting for 1½ hours. Consequently, an annual test is required to ensure the unit can provide emergency lighting for 1½ hours.

(F) If an anesthetizing location is a wet location the provisions of 4.3.2.2.8 shall apply.

Wet locations pose unique hazards to both patients and hospital staff. For example, standing fluids on the floor pose the possibility of electrical shock. Paragraph 4.3.2.2.8 allows two methods to protect against this hazard. One method limits the ground-fault current through the power supply design of an isolated power system (IPS). The second method uses a ground-fault circuit interrupter (GFCI). An IPS does not interrupt the power during a fault whereas a GFCI does. Hospital staff should determine where an interruption of power can be tolerated and where it cannot and then choose the appropriate method of protection.

13.4.1.2.6.2 High-voltage wiring for X-ray equipment shall be effectively insulated from ground and adequately guarded against accidental contact.

13.4.1.2.6.3 Anesthetizing Location Receptacles. Receptacles for use in anesthetizing locations shall be listed for the use. In anesthetizing locations of new and existing construction having receptacles on isolated and grounded power, all receptacles shall be identified as to whether they are on isolated or grounded power.

13.4.1.2.6.4 Approved permanently installed equipment shall be permitted to be supplied through a grounded single-phase or three-phase distribution system if installed in accordance with E.6.6.3.

Fixed equipment would be bolted to structural metal and thus be permanently grounded. The equipment would also be grounded through flexible metallic conduit. In the event of an electrical fault within the equipment, the case of the equipment could not be raised to a potentially hazardous level for personnel who might be grounded.

Equipment covered in E.6.6.3 operates at 24 V or less and is supplied by an isolating transformer or from isolated power at line voltage.

Article 517 of NFPA 70, *National Electrical Code®* [4], permits nonmetallic conduit for circuits other than branch circuits serving patient care areas [see 517.30(C)(3)(1) in NFPA 70]. With this change, 13.4.1.2.6.3 might merit reconsideration, inasmuch as it is observed that some equipment (e.g., the electrically powered operating table) can be fixed only to studs set in concrete.

13.4.1.2.6.5* Unless the requirements of 13.4.1.2.6.6 are met, an isolation transformer shall not serve more than one operating room except as provided in 13.4.1.2.6.7. If an induction room serves more than one operating room, the isolated circuits of the induction room shall be permitted to be supplied from the isolation transformer of any one of the operating rooms served by that induction room.

Although one transformer cannot serve more than one operating room in new facilities, there is no restriction on using more than one transformer in one operating room. The purpose of 13.4.1.2.6.5 is to reduce cumulative leakage current from tripping line isolation monitor alarms.

A.13.4.1.2.6.5 For purposes of 13.4.1, anesthetic induction rooms are considered part of the operating room or rooms served by the induction rooms.

13.4.1.2.6.6 The requirements of 13.4.1.2.6.5 shall not apply in existing hospitals where one isolation transformer is serving more than one inhalation anesthetizing location, provided the system has been installed in accordance with requirements previously found in 13.4.1 of NFPA 99 (as taken from former NFPA 56A) where such systems were permitted.

The purpose of paragraph 13.4.1.2.6.6 is to avoid the necessity of having a 208 V or 240 V transformer in each room (in addition to any other isolation transformers for regularly used 120 V equipment) to supply high-voltage devices used only occasionally. In some installations, a push-button system is used to lock out all the circuits except those in the room where the high-voltage device will be used. This requirement ensures that only one high-voltage device is used at a time.

13.4.1.2.6.7 Isolation transformers shall be permitted to serve single receptacles in several patient areas when the receptacles are reserved for supplying power to equipment requiring 150 V or higher (e.g., items such as portable X-ray units) and when the receptacles and mating plugs are not interchangeable with the receptacles on the local isolated power system.

13.4.1.2.6.8 Switches in Anesthetizing Locations. Switches controlling ungrounded circuits within or partially within an inhalation anesthetizing location shall have a disconnecting pole for each conductor.

13.4.1.2.7 Gases.

13.4.1.2.7.1 Storage Locations or Manifold Enclosures for Oxygen and Nitrous Oxide. The location and ventilation of storage rooms or manifold enclosures for oxygen and nitrous oxide shall comply with Chapters 5 and 6.

13.4.1.2.7.2 Nonflammable Medical Gas Piping Systems. Oxygen and nitrous oxide manifolds and piping systems that supply anesthetizing locations shall comply with Chapter 5.

13.4.1.2.8 Anesthetic Apparatus. Anesthetic apparatus shall conform to the requirements in 9.5.1.

13.4.1.2.9 Electrical Equipment. See 13.3.8.1.

13.4.1.2.10 Fire Loss Prevention.

Paragraph 13.4.1.2.10 is one part of a multipart response to several fatal operating room fires that occurred in 1990. This section addresses electrical appliances that are most likely to be ignition sources in anesthetizing locations. It is intended for operating room staff as well as those responsible for appliances used in operating rooms (e.g., biomedical engineers and technicians and risk managers).

Why are precautions and training necessary when flammable anesthetics are no longer used? A little history might help explain this apparent dichotomy.

Knowledge of the particulars might have been vague, but operating room personnel came to appreciate that the cyclopropane and ether used for anesthesia were highly flammable substances that might even explode if ignited when mixed with oxygen. Despite this awareness of the dangers involved with performing surgery, the electrosurgical unit (ESU) was, in fact, often employed while a flammable anesthetic was being administered to the patient. The ESU was, however, employed with circumspection and utilized only if there was no effective alternative, as in surgery on the brain.

By the 1970s, flammable anesthetics were being phased out. Operating room fires that did not involve flammable anesthetics, however, were still being reported. Surgeons were regularly employing the ESU; in fact, knot tying to control "bleeders" had become an overnight antiquity. Although the hazard of flammable anesthetics had been eliminated, the hazard of electricity had taken its place.

Then came a second event that would further aggravate the problem. The pulse oximeter (the oxygen-saturation monitor) became a resounding commercial success. By 1985, it had become a designated component of "the standard of care" and keeping the patient's oxygen saturation at 100 percent became commonplace. This new tool would come to be joined by still another influence that would have a multiplying effect.

At the same time, performing outpatient surgery under local anesthesia, accompanied by sometimes heavy sedation, became a strong trend. Oxygen was administered by a loose-fitting mask, by nasal cannula, or through a hose under the tented drapes (for facial or head surgery) even in the operating field. Because eyelashes or facial hair, along with dry gauze sponges, can readily be ignited even by a battery-operated cautery, it should have come as no surprise that flash fires occurred with increasing frequency. The number of these flash fires, however, was tiny relative to the number of operations performed. The right set of circumstances had to exist for an adverse event to occur, so the majority of hospital personnel and patients were spared any first-hand experience of the fire risk.

The medical literature abounds with candid reports of fires associated with the ESU and, more recently, lasers. However, according to some anesthesiologists, no reliable data exist concerning the actual incidence of operating room fires.

13.4.1.2.10.1 Hazard Assessment.

(A) An evaluation shall be made of hazards that could be encountered during surgical procedures. The evaluation shall include hazards associated with the properties of electricity, hazards associated with the operation of surgical equipment, and hazards associated with the nature of the environment.

(B) Periodic reviews of surgical operations and procedures shall be conducted with special attention given to any change in materials, operations, or personnel.

13.4.1.2.10.2 Fire Prevention Procedures. Fire prevention procedures shall be established.

13.4.1.2.10.3 Emergency Procedures.

(A) Procedures for operating room/surgical suite emergencies shall be developed. Such procedures shall include alarm actuation, evacuation, and equipment shutdown procedures, and provisions for control of emergencies that could occur in the operating room including specific detailed plans for control operations by an emergency control group within the organization or a public fire department.

(B) Emergency procedures shall be established for controlling chemical spills.

(C) Emergency procedures shall be established for extinguishing drapery, clothing, or equipment fires.

13.4.1.2.10.4 Orientation and Training.

(A) New operating room/surgical suite personnel, including physicians and surgeons, shall be taught general safety practices for the area and specific safety practices for the equipment and procedures they will use.

(B) Continuing safety education and supervision shall be provided, incidents shall be reviewed monthly, and procedures shall be reviewed annually.

(C) Fire exit drills shall be conducted periodically.

REFERENCES CITED IN COMMENTARY

1. NFPA *101®*, *Life Safety Code®*, 2006 edition.
2. NFPA 704, *Standard System for the Identification of the Hazards of Materials for Emergency Response,* 2001 edition.
3. Bowdle, T. A., Glenn, M., Colston, H., and Eisele, D., "Fire Following Use of Electrocautery During Emergency Percutaneous Transtracheal Ventilation," *Anesthesiology* 1987;66: 697–698.
4. NFPA 70, *National Electrical Code®*, 2005 edition.

CHAPTER 14

Other Health Care Facilities

Chapter 14 covers the facilities that are not covered by Chapter 13 and Chapters 15 through 21, including facilities such as ambulatory health care centers, clinics, medical/dental offices, and psychiatric and obstetrical services. Many of these facilities were grouped because the "label" or designation given to a building did not always reflect the health care provided to the patients inside the structure. (See Exhibit 14.1.) Grouping often led to problems of interpretation by the authority having jurisdiction as to the proper designation for the facility. Some facilities — such as hospitals, nursing homes, and limited care facilities — are classified correctly and do not cause confusion. Their designations did not change in the chapter headings.

14.1 Applicability

This chapter applies to other health care facilities not covered in Chapters 13 and 15 through 21.

14.2 Responsibilities

The governing body of these facilities shall have the responsibility of protecting the facilities (for patient care and clinical investigation) and the personnel employed therein.

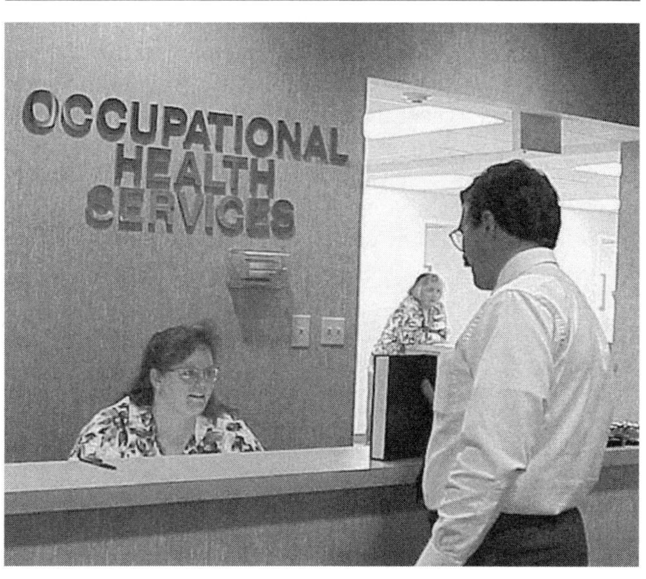

Exhibit 14.1 *Increasingly complex procedures are performed in medical and dental offices. (Courtesy of Rob Swift and Prince William Health System)*

14.3 General Requirements

The subsections of the facility chapters are formatted to correlate with core Chapters 4 through 12. See Commentary Table 14.1 for more information.

COMMENTARY TABLE 14.1 *Chapter/Subsection Correlation*

Core Chapter	*Facility Section*
Chapter 4, Electrical Systems	X.3.4 Electrical Distribution System
Chapter 5, Gas and Vacuum Systems	X.3.5 Gas and Vacuum System Requirements
Chapter 6, Environmental Systems	X.3.6 Environmental System Requirements
Chapter 7, Materials	X.3.7 Material Requirements
Chapter 8, Electrical Equipment	X.3.8 Electrical Equipment Requirements
Chapter 9, Gas Equipment	X.3.9 Gas Equipment Requirements
Chapter 10, Manufacturer Requirements	X.3.10 Reserved
Chapter 11, Laboratories	X.3.11 Laboratories
Chapter 12, Health Care Emergency Management	X.3.12 Emergency Management

14.3.1 Reserved.

14.3.2 Reserved.

14.3.3 Reserved.

14.3.4 Electrical System Requirements.

14.3.4.1 Electrical Distribution System. For ambulatory health care centers, the electrical distribution system for patient care areas shall conform to the requirements in Chapter 4, Electrical Systems. These requirements shall apply to new construction. Existing installations shall not need to be modified, provided that they meet the operational safety requirements in 4.3.3.2 and 4.3.3.3 *(see 1.3.2).*

Paragraph 14.3.4.1 was modified to emphasize that its requirements are for new construction only. The AHJ may determine there is a safety concern with an existing installation and, if so, the AHJ is authorized to make the requirement retroactive.

14.3.4.2 Essential Electrical Distribution System. The essential electrical distribution system shall conform to a Type 3 system as described in Chapter 4.

Readers are reminded that the term *Type* is used only as a designator. The term is, in actuality, defined by the criteria provided for each of the various system types listed in Chapter 4 (e.g., for Type 1 essential electrical system requirements, see Section 4.4).

See the commentary following 17.3.4.2.2(1) regarding the term *electrical life support equipment.*

14.3.4.2.1 If electrical life support equipment is required, the essential electrical distribution system shall conform to a Type 1 system as described in Chapter 4.

14.3.4.2.2 If critical care areas are present, the essential electrical distribution system shall conform to a Type 1 system as described in Chapter 4.

14.3.5 Gas and Vacuum System Requirements.

The facility chapters do not mandate the level of gas and vacuum systems. The user must determine the appropriate level on the basis of an analysis of their facility and its usage. A facility that utilizes gas or vacuum systems to sustain life will require a higher-level system than a facility that does not.

Readers are reminded that the term *Level* is used only as a designator. The term is, in actuality, defined by the criteria provided for each of the various levels listed in Chapter 5 (e.g., for Level 1 gas and vacuum system requirements, see Section 5.1).

◀ **FAQ**
How is the level of the gas and vacuum system determined for a particular facility?

14.3.5.1 General. Where medical gas, instrument air, vacuum, and WAGD systems are installed they shall conform to the requirements for the appropriate level. Systems conforming to different levels within the same building are permitted. The appropriate level shall be determined as follows:

(1) All systems shall comply with Level 1 requirements if any part of the systems are Level 1, except under both of the following conditions:
   (a) The system(s) is entirely separate from the Level 1 system(s) (i.e., is stand-alone) and is not connected to Level 1 sources or distribution pipelines.
   (b) The occupancy to be served and the function of that occupancy is distinct from other occupancies in the building.

Other health care facilities are required to have a Level 1 gas and vacuum system unless there is a separate facility with a separate gas or vacuum system within that building. Thus the possibility of compromising the health care facility's gas and vacuum system has been eliminated. In that case, the separate facility in the health care facility is not required to be a Level 1 system.

(2) Medical gas and vacuum systems shall be permitted to be Level 2 systems only where both of the following conditions exist:
   (a) Paragraphs 14.3.5.1(1)(a) and 14.3.5.1(1)(b) apply.
   (b) Patients served by the system(s) are not dependent on mechanical ventilation or assisted mechanical ventilation at any time, including during administration of anesthesia.

The other health care facility is allowed to have a Level 2 gas and vacuum system if it can meet all the requirements of a separate facility, and of separate systems, and the patients are not dependent on mechanical ventilation or assisted mechanical ventilation. A Level 2 system is not as reliable as a Level 1 system because of the lack of redundancies. As a result, a Level 2 system has restrictions on the type of equipment and needs of the patient utilizing a Level 2 system.

(3) Medical gas and vacuum systems shall be permitted to be Level 3 systems only where both of the following conditions exist:
   (a) Paragraphs 14.3.5.1(1)(a) and 14.3.5.1(1)(b) and 14.3.5.1(2)(b) apply.
   (b) The patient population, during or subsequent to treatment, are not dependent for life on the gases or vacuum system(s), and the treatment(s) that the facility will

perform can be completed without detrimental effect on patient outcomes in the event of sudden loss of the gas or vacuum system(s).

(c)* The total of all gases in cylinders or containers, except nitrogen, connected and in storage at one time does not exceed 85 m^3 (3000 ft^3) STP, except that 142 m^3 (5000 ft^3) at STP shall be permitted if oxygen is stored in a DOT Specification 4L (cryogenic liquid) cylinder.

Level 3 systems have many restrictions because of the lack of redundancies. In addition to meeting all the criteria for a Level 2 and Level 1 system as specified in 13.3.5.1(1) and (2), there are restrictions on the needs of the patient and on the gas or vacuum to keep the patient alive. Additionally, a Level 3 system spreads the risk by limiting the amount of gas that can be stored and the number of treatment facilities served by the system.

A.14.3.5.1(3)(c) It is the intent to provide a simple, safe piping system for small facilities. Although the number of use points could be a consideration, it was felt that actual gas use is a more accurate indicator of complexity. Applications involving a storage in excess of 85 m^3 (3000 ft^3) would have a complexity warranting installation in accordance with the provisions of Level 1 patient gas distribution systems.

Although the principal intent is to provide simple installations for single treatment facilities, numerous applications exist where a remote use point creates essentially a second treatment facility or where the supply system might be shared by another health care professional such as other dentist, podiatrist, oral surgeon, or general medicine practitioner. The addition of another treatment facility requires incremental safety precautions.

A maximum of two single treatment facilities also approximates the limit with which a 85 m^3 (3000 ft^3) supply system can provide [143 m^3 (5000 ft^3) when liquid oxygen is used].

It is acknowledged that older user analgesia equipment has offered a nitrous oxide lockout device that requires a minimum of 3 L/min oxygen flow. However, a reasonable percentage of older equipment without this safety feature is in daily use. The storage and piping system is based upon the potential use, either initially or subsequently, of one of the older style analgesia equipment in one of the single treatment facilities. The quantity of 85 m^3 (3000 ft^3), or 143 m^3 (5000 ft^3) if liquid oxygen storage, is to be taken as the total combined storage of gases if there is more than one supply system in the single treatment facility.

(d) The system(s) supplies not more than two adjoining single treatment facilities.

14.3.5.2 Where nitrous oxide or halogenated agents are intended to be administered, a patient WAGD shall be installed and conform to Level 1 WAGD systems in Chapter 5.

14.3.6 Environmental Systems. (Reserved)

14.3.7 Material Requirements. (Reserved)

14.3.8 Electrical Equipment Requirements.

14.3.8.1 Patient Care Areas. If critical care areas are present, electrical appliances shall conform to Chapter 8.

14.3.8.2 Laboratories. Equipment shall conform to 8.4.2.2 and Section 8.5.

14.3.9 Gas Equipment Requirements — Patient.

Gas equipment shall conform to the patient equipment requirements in Chapter 8.

14.3.10 Reserved.

14.3.11 Laboratories.

Laboratories covered in this chapter shall comply with requirements in Chapter 11 as applicable and the requirements of NFPA 45, *Standard on Fire Protection for Laboratories Using Chemicals*, as applicable.

14.3.12 Emergency.

Facilities covered by this chapter shall comply with the provisions of Chapter 12 for emergency preparedness planning, as appropriate.

14.4 Specific Area Requirements

14.4.1 Anesthetizing Locations.

If anesthetizing locations are present, they shall comply with the requirements of 13.4.1.

Subsection 14.4.1 requires that all anesthetizing locations comply with the same criteria as hospitals. Even though the designation of the facility might be different, the hazards associated with anesthetizing locations are the same. Therefore, the requirements for anesthetizing locations in other health care facilities are the same as for hospitals.

14.4.1.1 Wiring.

14.4.1.1.1 Wiring. Installed wiring shall be in metal raceway or shall be as required in Sections 517.60 through 517.63 of NFPA 70, *National Electrical Code.*

14.4.1.1.2 Raceway. Such distribution systems shall be run in metal raceways along with a green grounding wire sized no smaller than the energized conductors.

14.4.1.1.3 Grounding to Raceways. Each device connected to the distribution system shall be effectively grounded to the metal raceway at the device.

14.4.1.1.4 Installation. Methods of installation shall conform to Articles 250 and 517 of NFPA 70, *National Electrical Code.*

14.4.1.1.5 Battery-Powered Emergency Lighting Units. One or more battery-powered emergency lighting units shall be provided as required in Section 700.12(e) of NFPA 70, *National Electrical Code*. Testing shall be in accordance with 4.3.4.2.

For medical practitioners performing invasive procedures on a patient under anesthesia, the short delay (generally less than 10 seconds) between loss of normal power and transfer of the automatic transfer switch to the on-site generator can seem like an eternity. Battery-powered lights are intended to bridge this gap.

CHAPTER 15

Reserved

In the 2005 edition of NFPA 99, Chapter 15 has been reserved for future use.

CHAPTER 16

Reserved

In the 2005 edition of NFPA 99, Chapter 16 has been reserved for future use.

CHAPTER 17

Nursing Home Requirements

Chapter 17 specifies the requirements from core Chapters 4 through 12 that apply to nursing homes. As noted in Chapter 1, Chapters 13 through 19 and Chapter 21 are "facility" chapters. The term *nursing home* is defined in 3.3.129.

According to the American Health Care Association, as of June 2004, there were 16,149 Medicare or Medicaid certified nursing homes in the United States. These facilities housed 1.78 million beds and served 1.44 million patients [1]. Fire safety in nursing homes has improved dramatically over the past 36 years. Fire incident data from NFPA indicate that fire fatalities from multiple-death fires (*multiple-death fires* is defined as a fire that claims three or more lives) in nursing homes from 1966 to 1975 averaged 15.8 deaths per year. With the proper application of modern codes and standards, the nursing home fire safety record is a true success story. Fire fatalities from multiple-death fires in nursing homes from 1981 to 2000 dropped to an average of 1.25 deaths per year [2]. This is an impressive fire safety record for any sleeping-type occupancy. Looking at all fire deaths, not just multiple-fire deaths, from 1997 to 2001, there was an average of six fire deaths in facilities that care for the aged with nursing staff, and in unclassified or unknown-type facilities that care for the aged. If residential board and care facilities are included in the data, there was an average of 9 deaths per year [3].

17.1 Applicability

This chapter applies to nursing homes, as defined in Chapter 3.

17.2 Responsibilities

The governing body of nursing homes shall have the responsibility of protecting the facilities (for patient care and clinical investigation) and the personnel employed therein.

17.3 General Requirements

The subsections of the facility chapters are formatted to correlate with core Chapters 4 through 12. See Commentary Table 17.1 for more information.

17.3.1 Reserved.

17.3.2 Reserved.

COMMENTARY TABLE 17.1 Chapter/Subsection Correlation

Core Chapter	Facility Section
Chapter 4, Electrical Systems	X.3.4 Electrical Distribution System
Chapter 5, Gas and Vacuum Systems	X.3.5 Gas and Vacuum System Requirements
Chapter 6, Environmental Systems	X.3.6 Environmental System Requirements
Chapter 7, Materials	X.3.7 Material Requirements
Chapter 8, Electrical Equipment	X.3.8 Electrical Equipment Requirements
Chapter 9, Gas Equipment	X.3.9 Gas Equipment Requirements
Chapter 10, Manufacturer Requirements	X.3.10 Reserved
Chapter 11, Laboratories	X.3.11 Laboratories
Chapter 12, Health Care Emergency Management	X.3.12 Emergency Management

17.3.3 Reserved.

17.3.4 Electrical System Requirements.

17.3.4.1 Electrical Distribution System. (Reserved)

17.3.4.2 Essential Electrical Distribution System.

17.3.4.2.1 Unless the requirements of 17.3.4.2.2 are met, essential electrical distribution systems shall conform to the Type 2 systems as described in Chapter 4.

17.3.4.2.2 The requirements of 17.3.4.2.1 shall not apply to any freestanding nursing home that performs all of the following:

(1) Maintains admitting and discharge policies that preclude the provision of care for any patient or resident who needs to be sustained by electrical life support equipment

The term *electrical life support equipment* in 17.3.4.2.2(1) more accurately reflects the type of equipment that would require a generator set supplying ac power. Only if a device supports life and requires ac electricity to function is an essential electrical system required. (See the definition of *electrical life support equipment* in 3.3.37.)

(2) Offers no surgical treatment requiring general anesthesia

(3) Provides an automatic battery-powered system or equipment that will be effective for at least 1½ hours and is otherwise in accordance with NFPA *101*, *Life Safety Code*, and NFPA 70, *National Electrical Code*, and that will be capable of supplying lighting of at least 1 ft-candle to exit lights, exit corridors, stairways, nursing stations, medication preparation areas, boiler rooms, and communication areas. This system shall also supply power to operate all alarm systems.

The functioning time and light level required for an automatic battery-powered system are in agreement with Chapter 7 of NFPA *101*®, *Life Safety Code*® [4]. Although reference is made to battery-powered systems for supplying emergency power in 17.3.4.2.2(3), any suitable method of supplying electric power would be acceptable, provided the criterion of 1½ hours of electric power is met. It was not the intent that a battery-powered system had to be provided or was the only means by which emergency power could be provided. The requirement is for "an automatic battery-powered system or equipment." This is an alternative. Item (3) simply allows a battery-powered system to be used under certain conditions. A regular emergency generator system is acceptable. It should be noted that, if a generator set is used, it must meet the applicable requirements for generator sets as listed in Chapter 4.

17.3.4.2.3 Nursing homes that meet the requirement in 17.3.4.2.2 shall be permitted to use a battery system or self-contained battery integral with equipment in lieu of the alternate power source required in 4.4.1.1.4.

17.3.4.2.4 If patients are admitted who need to be sustained by electrical life support equipment, the essential electrical system from the source to that portion of the facility where such patients are treated shall conform to a Type 1 system as described in Chapter 4.

The electrical requirements are less stringent when patients are not on electrical life support equipment. When this is the case, the alternate source of power is allowed to be a battery backup integral with the equipment. However, when the patient is dependent on electrical life support equipment, the level of power must be at a higher level in order to supply power in the event of the primary power failing. In this case, the requirement is a Type 1 system.

◀ **FAQ**
When is it appropriate to use a battery backup integral with the equipment?

17.3.5 Gas and Vacuum System Requirements.

This section reflects the effort to have the level of risk to the patient (based on life support) determine the level (or complexity) of the systems (electrical, gas, vacuum, etc.) required in the facility.

The facility chapters do not mandate the level of gas and vacuum systems. The user must determine the appropriate level based on an analysis of the facility and its usage. A facility that utilizes gas or vacuum systems to sustain life will require a higher-level system than a facility that does not.

◀ **FAQ**
How is the level of the gas and vacuum system determined for a particular nursing home?

Readers are reminded that the term *Level* is used only as a designator. The term is, in actuality, defined by the criteria provided for each of the various levels listed in Chapter 5 (e.g., for Level 1 gas and vacuum system requirements, see Section 5.1).

17.3.5.1 General. Where medical gas, instrument air, vacuum, and WAGD systems are installed, they shall conform to the requirements for the appropriate level. Systems conforming to different levels within the same building are permitted. The appropriate level shall be determined as follows:

(1) All systems shall comply with Level 1 requirements if any part of the systems are Level 1, except under both of the following conditions:
    (a) The system(s) is entirely separate from the Level 1 system(s) (i.e., is stand-alone) and is not connected to Level 1 sources or distribution pipelines.
    (b) The occupancy to be served and the function of that occupancy is distinct from other occupancies in the building.

Nursing homes are required to have a Level 1 gas and vacuum system unless there is a separate occupancy within the building and it has a separate gas or vacuum system. The possibility of compromising the nursing home gas and vacuum system has been eliminated. In that case, the separate facility in the nursing home is not required to be a Level 1 system.

(2) Medical gas and vacuum systems shall be permitted to be Level 2 systems only where both of the following conditions exist:
   (a) Paragraphs 17.3.5.1(1)(a) and 17.3.5.1(1)(b) apply.
   (b) Patients served by the system(s) are not dependent on mechanical ventilation or assisted mechanical ventilation at any time, including during administration of anesthesia.

The nursing home is allowed to have a Level 2 gas and vacuum system if it can meet all the requirements of a separate facility, and of separate systems, and the patients are not dependent on mechanical ventilation or assisted mechanical ventilation. A Level 2 system is not as reliable as a Level 1 system because of the lack of redundancies. As a result, a Level 2 system has restrictions on the type of equipment and needs of the patient utilizing a Level 2 system.

(3) Medical gas and vacuum systems shall be permitted to be Level 3 systems only where both of the following conditions exist:
   (a) Paragraphs 17.3.5.1(1)(a) and 17.3.5.1(1)(b) and 17.3.5.1(2)(a) apply.
   (b) The patient population, during or subsequent to treatment, are not dependent for life on the gases or vacuum system(s), and the treatment(s) that the facility will perform can be completed without detrimental effect on patient outcomes in the event of sudden loss of the gas or vacuum system(s).
   (c)* The total of all gases in cylinders or containers, except nitrogen, connected and in storage at one time does not exceed 85 m^3 (3000 ft^3) at STP, except that 142 m^3 (5000 ft^3) at STP shall be permitted if oxygen is stored in a DOT Specification 4L (cryogenic liquid) cylinder.

Level 3 systems have many restrictions because of the lack of redundancies. In addition to meeting all the criteria for a Level 2 and Level 1 system as specified in 13.3.5.1(1) and (2), there are restrictions on the needs of the patient on the gas or vacuum to keep the patient alive. Additionally, a Level 3 system spreads the risk by limiting the amount of gas that can be stored and the number of treatment facilities served by the system.

A.17.3.5.1(3)(c) It is the intent to provide a simple, safe piping system for small facilities. Although the number of use points could be a consideration, it was felt that actual gas use is a more accurate indicator of complexity. Applications involving a storage in excess of 85 m^3 (3000 ft^3) would have a complexity warranting installation in accordance with the provisions of Level 1 patient gas distribution systems.

Although the principal intent is to provide simple installations for single treatment facilities, numerous applications exist where a remote use point creates essentially a second treatment facility or where the supply system might be shared by another health care professional such as other dentist, podiatrist, oral surgeon, or general medicine practitioner. The addition of another treatment facility requires incremental safety precautions.

A maximum of two single treatment facilities also approximates the limit with which a 85 m^3 (3000 ft^3) supply system can provide [143 m^3 (5000 ft^3) when liquid oxygen is used].

It is acknowledged that older user analgesia equipment has offered a nitrous oxide lockout device that requires a minimum of 3 L/min oxygen flow. However, a reasonable percentage of older equipment without this safety feature is in daily use. The storage and piping system is based upon the potential use, either initially or subsequently, of one of the older style analgesia equipment in one of the single treatment facilities. The quantity of 85 m^3 (3000 ft^3), or 143 m^3 (5000 ft^3) if liquid oxygen storage, is to be taken as the total combined storage of gases if there is more than one supply system in the single treatment facility.

(d) The system(s) supplies not more than two adjoining single treatment facilities.

17.3.5.2 Reserved.

17.3.5.3 Reserved.

17.3.6 Environmental Systems. (Reserved)

17.3.7 Material Requirements. (Reserved)

17.3.8 Electrical Equipment Requirements.

17.3.8.1 Patient Care Areas. (Reserved)

17.3.8.2 Laboratories. Equipment shall conform to 8.4.2.2 and Section 8.5.

17.3.9 Gas Equipment Requirements.

17.3.9.1 Patient. Equipment shall conform to requirements for patient equipment in Chapter 9.

17.3.10 Reserved.

17.3.11* Laboratories.

Laboratories in nursing homes shall comply with the requirements of Chapter 11, as applicable.

A.17.3.11 This is in addition to other nursing home requirements listed in Section 17.3.

17.3.12 Emergency Management.

Nursing homes shall comply with the provisions of Chapter 12 for emergency management planning, as appropriate.

REFERENCES CITED IN COMMENTARY

1. "Executive Summary," *Facts & Trends: The Nursing Facility Sourcebook,* American Health Care Association, Chantilly, VA, 2001.
2. Gage-Babcock & Associates, Inc., Analysis of NFPA Fire Incident Data, prepared for the American Health Care Association, Chantilly, VA, April, 2001.
3. NFPA data from Fire Data Analysis Department.
4. NFPA *101*®, *Life Safety Code*®, 2006 edition.

CHAPTER 18

Limited Care Facility Requirements

Chapter 18 specifies the requirements from core Chapters 4 through 12 that apply to limited care facilities. As noted in Chapter 1, Chapters 13 through 19 and Chapter 21 are "facility" chapters.

The term *limited care facility* is defined in 3.3.97. The Technical Committee on Safety to Life first defined *limited care facility* in the 1988 edition of NFPA *101*®, *Life Safety Code*® [1]. The term *limited care facility* replaced the terms *custodial care facility* and *supervisory care facility* for life safety purposes. For operational safety purposes, the Technical Correlating Committee on Health Care Facilities reviewed NFPA 99, voted to follow suit, and revised the definition to correlate with that of the Safety to Life Committee.

18.1 Applicability

This chapter applies to limited care facilities, as defined in Chapter 3.

18.2 Responsibilities

The governing body of limited care facilities shall have the responsibility of protecting the facilities (for patient care and clinical investigation) and the personnel employed therein.

18.3 General Requirements

The subsections of the facility chapters are formatted to correlate with core Chapters 4 through 12. See Commentary Table 18.1 for more information.

18.3.1 Reserved.

18.3.2 Reserved.

18.3.3 Reserved.

18.3.4 Electrical System Requirements.

18.3.4.1 Electrical Distribution System. (Reserved)

18.3.4.2 Essential Electrical Distribution System.

18.3.4.2.1 Unless the requirements of 18.3.4.2.2 are met, essential electrical distribution systems shall conform to the Type 2 systems as described in Chapter 4.

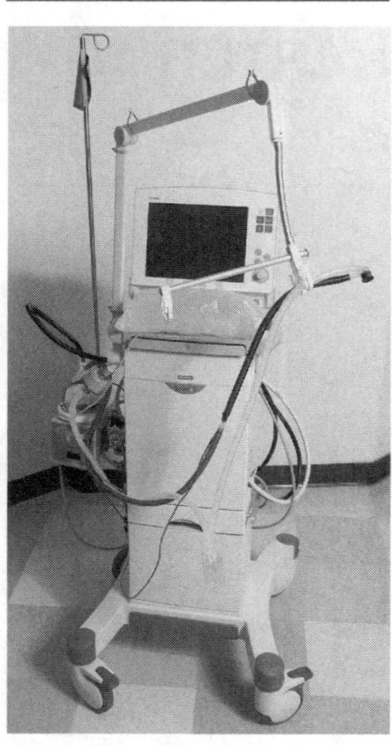

EXHIBIT 18.1 Ventilator.

***COMMENTARY TABLE 18.1** Chapter/Subsection Correlation*

Core Chapter	*Facility Section*
Chapter 4, Electrical Systems	X.3.4 Electrical Distribution System
Chapter 5, Gas and Vacuum Systems	X.3.5 Gas and Vacuum System Requirements
Chapter 6, Environmental Systems	X.3.6 Environmental System Requirements
Chapter 7, Materials	X.3.7 Material Requirements
Chapter 8, Electrical Equipment	X.3.8 Electrical Equipment Requirements
Chapter 9, Gas Equipment	X.3.9 Gas Equipment Requirements
Chapter 10, Manufacturer Requirements	X.3.10 Reserved
Chapter 11, Laboratories	X.3.11 Laboratories
Chapter 12, Health Care Emergency Management	X.3.12 Emergency Management

18.3.4.2.2 The requirements of 18.3.4.2.1 shall not apply to any freestanding limited care facility that performs all of the following:

(1) Maintains admitting and discharge policies that preclude the provision of care for any patient or resident who needs to be sustained by electrical life support equipment.

The term *electrical life support equipment* as used in 18.3.4.2.2(1) more accurately reflects the type of equipment that would require a generator set supplying ac power. Only if a device supports life and requires ac electricity to function is an essential electrical system required. (See 3.3.37, *Electrical Life Support Equipment.*)

Exhibit 18.1 illustrates electrical life support equipment used in a hospital.

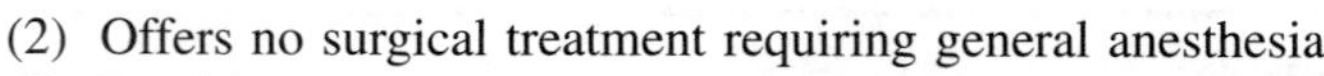

(2) Offers no surgical treatment requiring general anesthesia.

(3) Provides an automatic battery-powered system or equipment that will be effective for at least 1½ hours and is otherwise in accordance with NFPA *101*, *Life Safety Code*, and NFPA 70, *National Electrical Code*, and that will be capable of supplying lighting of at least 1 ft-candle to exit lights, exit corridors, stairways, nursing stations, medication preparation areas, boiler rooms, and communication areas. This system shall also supply power to operate all alarm systems.

The duration of power and light level required in 18.3.4.2.2 are in agreement with Chapter 7 of NFPA *101*®, *Life Safety Code*® [2]. Although reference is made to battery-powered systems for supplying emergency power in 18.3.4.2.2(3), any suitable method of supplying electric power would be acceptable, provided the criterion of 1½ hours of electric power is met. It was not the intent that a battery-powered system had to be provided or was the only means by which emergency power could be provided. The requirement for "an automatic battery-powered system or equipment" is an alternative. Subparagraph (3) simply allows a battery-powered system to be used under certain conditions. A regular emergency generator system is acceptable. It should be noted that, if a generator set is used, it must meet the applicable requirements for generator sets as listed in Chapter 4.

18.3.4.2.3 Limited care facilities that meet the requirements in 18.3.4.2.2 shall be permitted to use a battery system or self-contained battery integral with equipment in lieu of the alternate power source required in 4.4.1.1.4.

◀ **FAQ**
When is it appropriate to use a self-contained battery integral with the equipment?

Sources of power for essential electrical systems (EES) are covered under 4.4.1. Two types of sources are allowed for an EES: an on-site generator set (4.4.1.1) and a battery system (4.4.1.2) meeting the requirements of Article 700 of NFPA 70, *National Electrical Code®* [3]. Paragraph 18.3.4.2.3 allows a third alternative — a self-contained battery integral with the equipment. An integral battery is allowed because the use of electrical life support equipment is restricted and the duration of the alternate source of power is only 1½ hours.

18.3.5 Gas and Vacuum System Requirements.

The facility chapters do not mandate a level of gas and vacuum systems. The user must determine the appropriate level on the basis of an analysis of the facility and its usage. A facility that utilizes gas or vacuum systems to sustain life will require a higher-level system than a facility that does not.

Readers are reminded that the term *Level* is used only as a designator. The term is, in actuality, defined by the criteria provided for each of the various levels listed in Chapter 5 (e.g., for Level 1 gas and vacuum system requirements, see Section 5.1).

18.3.5.1 General. Where medical gas, instrument air, vacuum, and WAGD systems are installed, they shall conform to the requirements for the appropriate level. Systems conforming to different levels within the same building are permitted. The appropriate level shall be determined as follows:

(1) All systems shall comply with Level 1 requirements if any part of the systems are Level 1, except under both of the following conditions:
  (a) The system(s) is entirely separate from the Level 1 system(s) (i.e., is stand-alone) and are not connected to Level 1 sources or distribution pipelines.
  (b) The occupancy to be served and the function of that occupancy is distinct from other occupancies in the building.

Nursing homes are required to have a Level 1 gas and vacuum system unless there is a separate facility with a separate gas or vacuum system within that building, in which case the possibility of compromising the nursing home gas and vacuum system has been eliminated and the separate facility in the nursing home is not required to be a Level 1 system.

(2) Medical gas and vacuum systems shall be permitted to be Level 2 systems only where both of the following conditions exist:
  (a) Paragraphs 18.3.5.1(1)(a) and 18.3.5.1(1)(b) apply.
  (b) Patients served by the system(s) are not dependent on mechanical ventilation or assisted mechanical ventilation at any time, including during administration of anesthesia.

A nursing home is allowed to have a Level 2 gas and vacuum system if it can meet all of the requirements of a separate facility, of separate systems, and the patients are not dependent on mechanical ventilation or assisted mechanical ventilation. A Level 2 system is not as reliable as a Level 1 system because of the lack of redundancies. As a result, a Level 2 system has restrictions on the type of equipment and needs of the patient utilizing a Level 2 system.

(3) Medical gas and vacuum systems shall be permitted to be Level 3 systems only where all of the following conditions exist:
   (a) Paragraphs 18.3.5.1(1)(a) and 18.3.5.1(1)(b) and 18.3.5.1(2)(b) apply.
   (b) The patient population, during or subsequent to treatment, are not dependent for life on the gases or vacuum system(s), and the treatment(s) that the facility will perform can be completed without detrimental effect on patient outcomes in the event of sudden loss of the gas or vacuum system(s).
   (c)* The total of all gases in cylinders or containers, except nitrogen, connected and in storage at one time does not exceed 85 m^3 (3000 ft^3) at STP, except that 142 m^3 (5000 ft^3) at STP shall be permitted if oxygen is stored in a DOT Specification 4L (cryogenic liquid) cylinder.

Level 3 systems have many restrictions on the use of this system because of the lack of redundancies. In addition to meeting all the criteria for a Level 2 and Level 1 system as specified in 13.3.5.1(1) and (2), there are restrictions on the needs of the patient and on the gas or vacuum to keep the patient alive. Additionally, a Level 3 system spreads the risk by limiting the amount of gas that can be stored and the number of treatment facilities served by the system.

A.18.3.5.1(3)(c) It is the intent to provide a simple, safe piping system for small facilities. Although the number of use points could be a consideration, it was felt that actual gas use is a more accurate indicator of complexity. Applications involving a storage in excess of 85 m^3 (3000 ft^3) would have a complexity warranting installation in accordance with the provisions of Level 1 patient gas distribution systems.

Although the principal intent is to provide simple installations for single treatment facilities, numerous applications exist where a remote use point creates essentially a second treatment facility or where the supply system might be shared by another health care professional such as other dentist, podiatrist, oral surgeon, or general medicine practitioner. The addition of another treatment facility requires incremental safety precautions.

A maximum of two single treatment facilities also approximates the limit with which a 85 m^3 (3000 ft^3) supply system can provide ([143 m^3 (5000 ft^3) when liquid oxygen is used].

It is acknowledged that older user analgesia equipment has offered a nitrous oxide lockout device that requires a minimum of 3 L/min oxygen flow. However, a reasonable percentage of older equipment without this safety feature is in daily use. The storage and piping system is based upon the potential use, either initially or subsequently, of one of the older style analgesia equipment in one of the single treatment facilities. The quantity of 85 m^3 (3000 ft^3), or 143 m^3 (5000 ft^3) if liquid oxygen storage, is to be taken as the total combined storage of gases if there is more than one supply system in the single treatment facility.

   (d) The system(s) supplies not more than two adjoining single treatment facilities.

18.3.6 Environmental Systems. (Reserved)

18.3.7 Material Requirements. (Reserved)

18.3.8 Electrical Equipment Requirements.

18.3.8.1 Patient Care Areas. (Reserved)

18.3.8.2 Laboratories. Equipment shall conform to 8.4.2.2 and Section 8.5.

18.3.9 Gas Equipment Requirements. (Reserved)

18.3.10 Reserved.

18.3.11* Laboratories.

Laboratories in limited care facilities shall comply with the requirements of Chapter 11, as applicable.

A.18.3.11 This is in addition to other limited care facility requirements listed in Section 18.3.

18.3.12 Emergency Management.

Limited care facilities shall comply with the provisions of Chapter 12 for emergency management planning, as appropriate.

REFERENCES CITED IN COMMENTARY

1. NFPA *101*®, *Life Safety Code*®, 1988 edition.
2. NFPA *101*®, *Life Safety Code*®, 2006 edition.
3. NFPA 70, *National Electrical Code*®, 2005 edition.

CHAPTER 19

Electrical and Gas Equipment for Home Care

Chapter 19 provides another facet of safety in the use of medical appliances. It is not intended to imply that a home is a health care facility; rather that the use of medical appliances in the home can pose the same hazards as in health care facilities and that appropriate safety requirements should therefore apply.

Two major forces are driving the growing use of medical appliances in the home. First, advances in technology have made many complex appliances easier to operate by nonmedical personnel. Second, the escalating cost of health care delivery has forced patients to leave hospitals while they still might need treatment requiring medical appliances. Every indication is that the trend toward home health care will continue to grow. Safety standards need to address this trend.

Chapter 19 opens what will probably be a long debate on how best to establish requirements for the use of medical appliances in home health care and to achieve safety levels equivalent to those in health care facilities.

19.1* Applicability

This chapter applies to home care, as defined in Chapter 3.

A.19.1 As part of the current decentralization of health care modalities, traditionally the province of hospitals, patients are being treated at home using electrical and gas appliances that, if used in a health care facility, would come under the purview of this standard. 

19.2 Responsibilities

It shall be the responsibility of the equipment supplier, which could be a hospital, an equipment rental company, or an equipment sales company, to perform the following:

(1) Appropriately instruct the equipment user to operate the equipment safely. This shall include written instructions, demonstrations, and periodic review of the use.
(2) Provide instruction on user maintenance of the equipment, provide supervision of the maintenance, and provide such higher level maintenance as is appropriate.

Because nonprofessional, relatively unskilled persons will most likely use home care equipment, safety is a shared responsibility. The term *supplier* can be a single entity (e.g., a hospital) or it can be a chain of entities (e.g., a doctor, a hospital, an equipment rental company, a service company). There should be a clear understanding of how these various parties share the legal and moral burdens of responsibility.

19.3 Equipment

19.3.1 Reserved.

19.3.2 Reserved.

19.3.3 Reserved.

19.3.4 Reserved.

19.3.5 Reserved.

19.3.6 Reserved.

19.3.7 Reserved.

19.3.8 Electrical Equipment Requirements.

Electrical equipment used in the home for health care shall conform to such requirements of Chapter 8 as applicable.

A home is a significantly different environment from that of a hospital or other health care facility, and the demands on electrical equipment vary. The electrical power system in a home can vary more than that in a health care facility, placing more demand on equipment, or the amount of time the equipment is actually in use can be less than in a health care facility, creating less of a demand on equipment. Equipment should be designed and used to achieve an appropriate safety level.

19.3.9 Gas Equipment Requirements.

Gas equipment used in the home for health care shall conform to such requirements of Chapter 9 as applicable.

FAQ ▶ **In what form is oxygen used in the home environment and what are the potential hazards?**

Oxygen is the primary medical gas used in the home environment. Historically, high-pressure gas cylinders have been the equipment of choice to deliver oxygen to the patient. Recently, however, the use of liquid oxygen has surged because its expansion ratio to vapor is about 860:1. Consequently, it can deliver a greater volume of oxygen for a given volume. Liquid oxygen also poses new hazards that must be considered, including ventilation, burns from freezing, and reactions with hydrocarbon fuels resulting from spills when transferring liquid oxygen into the containers. Paragraph 9.6.2.3 specifies the safety precautions and requirements for transferring liquid oxygen.

CHAPTER 20

Hyperbaric Facilities

The Chapter 20 organization differs from that of the other occupancy chapters. Chapter 20 is more or less an independent chapter with very few references to the core chapters of NFPA 99. Many of the requirements for hyperbaric chambers are unique and are not found in the core chapters.

Several changes are worth noting for the 2005 edition:

1. The ventilation rates for Class B chambers have been specified.
2. Fire alarm requirements have been added to the requirements for Class B and Class C chambers.
3. Mechanical ventilation is now required for spaces or consoles that have an oxygen-enriched atmosphere.
4. The grounding references have been updated per NFPA 70, *National Electrical Code®* *(NEC®)* [1].
5. The requirements for the types of clothing and the types of materials that are allowed in the chambers are more stringent.

For additional information on specific regulatory issues related to the safe operation of clinical hyperbaric medicine facilities, see Supplement 2, Regulatory Issues Affecting the Safety of Clinical Hyperbaric Medicine Facilities.

20.1 Applicability

20.1.1 This chapter shall apply to new facilities.

20.1.2 This chapter shall also apply to the altered, renovated, or modernized portion of an existing system or individual component.

20.1.3 Existing construction or equipment shall be permitted to be continued in use when such use does not constitute a distinct hazard to life.

This document contains requirements that affect hyperbaric chamber manufacturers, hyperbaric facility designers, and personnel operating hyperbaric facilities. Even if existing facilities are not required to modify equipment, it would be prudent for personnel to implement the portions of this standard that are operational/procedural in nature.

20.1.4* Scope.

The scope of this chapter shall be as specified in 1.1.20.

A.20.1.4 Chapter 20 does not apply to respiratory therapy employing oxygen-enriched atmospheres at ambient pressures. See Chapter 9.

20.1.5 Classification of Chambers.

20.1.5.1 General. Chambers shall be classified according to occupancy in order to establish appropriate minimum essentials in construction and operation.

20.1.5.2* Occupancy. Hyperbaric chambers shall be classified according to the following criteria:

(1) Class A — Human, multiple occupancy
(2) Class B — Human, single occupancy
(3) Class C — Animal, no human occupancy

A.20.1.5.2 Chambers designed for animal experimentation but equipped for access of personnel to care for the animals are classified as Class A for the purpose of Chapter 20.

FAQ ▶ What are the differences between Class A, B, and C chambers?

Hyperbaric chambers are classified according to occupancy. Although they are defined by number of occupants, it is generally understood that there is little diversity within each classification. Class A chambers are large, made of steel with small viewports, compressed with air, and deliver oxygen to patients through special masks or hoods (Exhibits 20.1 and 20.2).

Class B chambers are small, made mostly of acrylic, are compressed with oxygen, and deliver oxygen to patients in the chamber environment (Exhibit 20.3). Class C chambers are used for research and to treat animals (Exhibit 20.4).

In the past, most hyperbaric chambers were military, hospital based, or attached to a university. This is no longer the case. Recent years have seen a rapid growth in the number of hyperbaric facilities and hyperbaric chamber manufacturers. A wide variety of chamber sizes and configurations are currently available. There are small Class A chambers (Exhibit 20.5), Class B chambers designed to be compressed with air (Exhibit 20.6), and Class C chambers designed to medically treat animals (at least one version is specifically designed for treating horses). Although the most common shape is still cylindrical, there are also chambers of other shapes, including L-shaped and rectangular (Exhibit 20.7).

EXHIBIT 20.1 Outside view of Class A chamber. (Photo courtesy of International ATMO, San Antonio, Texas)

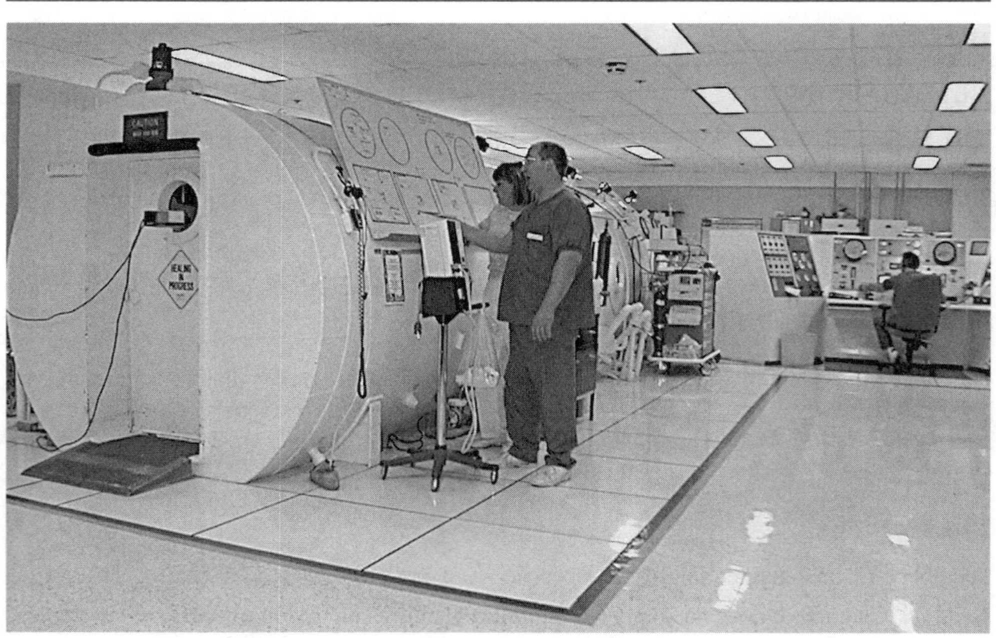

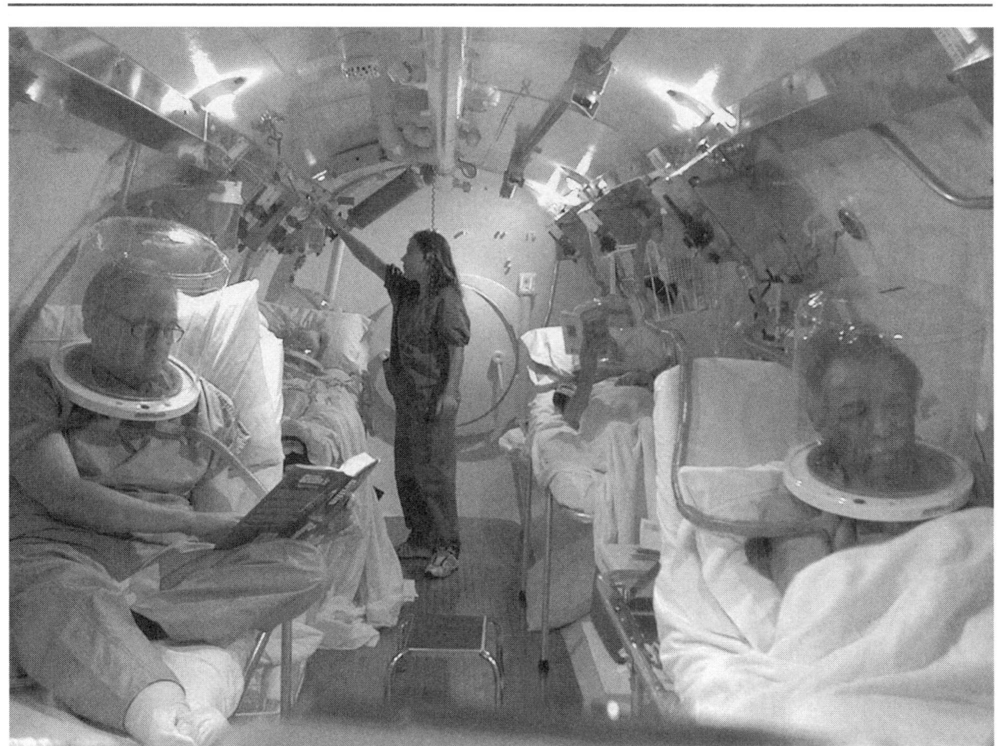

EXHIBIT 20.2 *Inside view of Class A chamber. (Photo courtesy of International ATMO, San Antonio, Texas)*

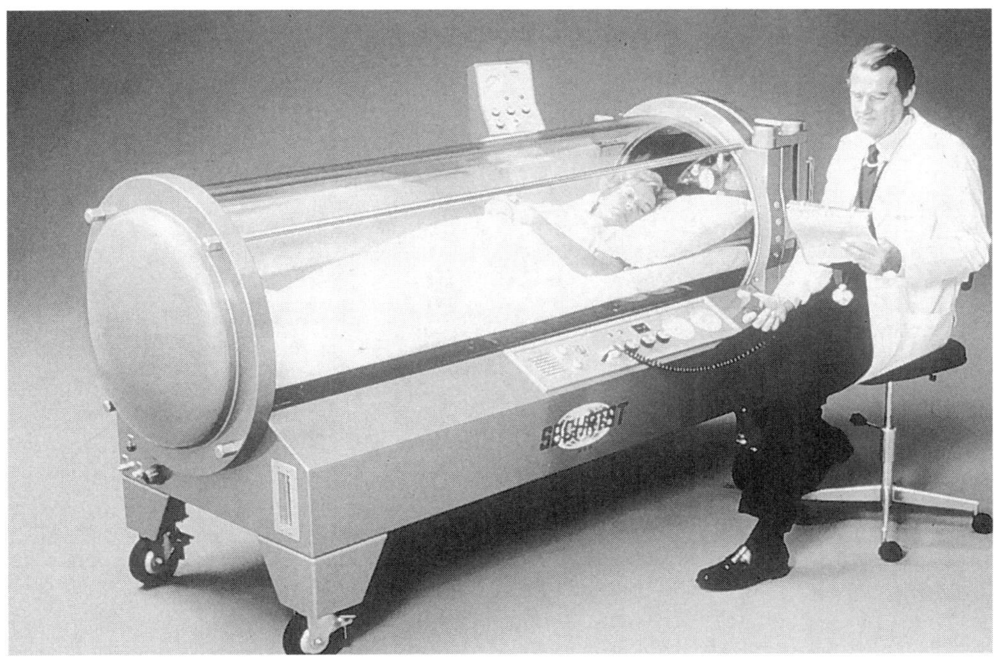

EXHIBIT 20.3 *Class B chamber. (Photo courtesy of Sechrist Industries, Anaheim, California)*

EXHIBIT 20.4 *Class C chamber used for animal research. (Photo courtesy of David Davolt)*

EXHIBIT 20.5 *Class A chamber designed for two patients. (Photo courtesy of Perry Baromedical, Riviera Beach, Florida)*

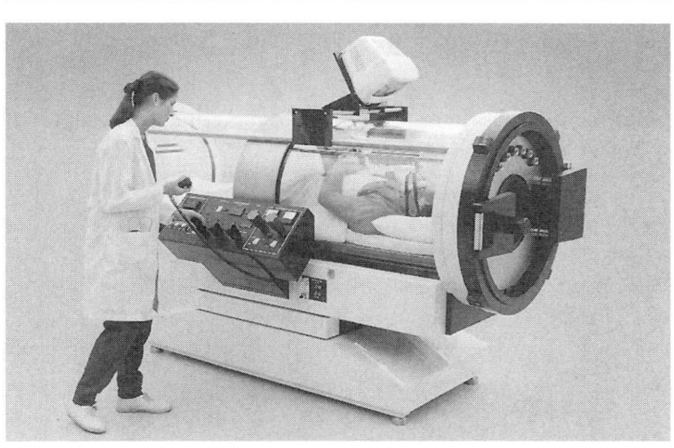

EXHIBIT 20.6 *Class B chamber designed for air pressurization. (Photo courtesy of Nth Systems, San Antonio, Texas)*

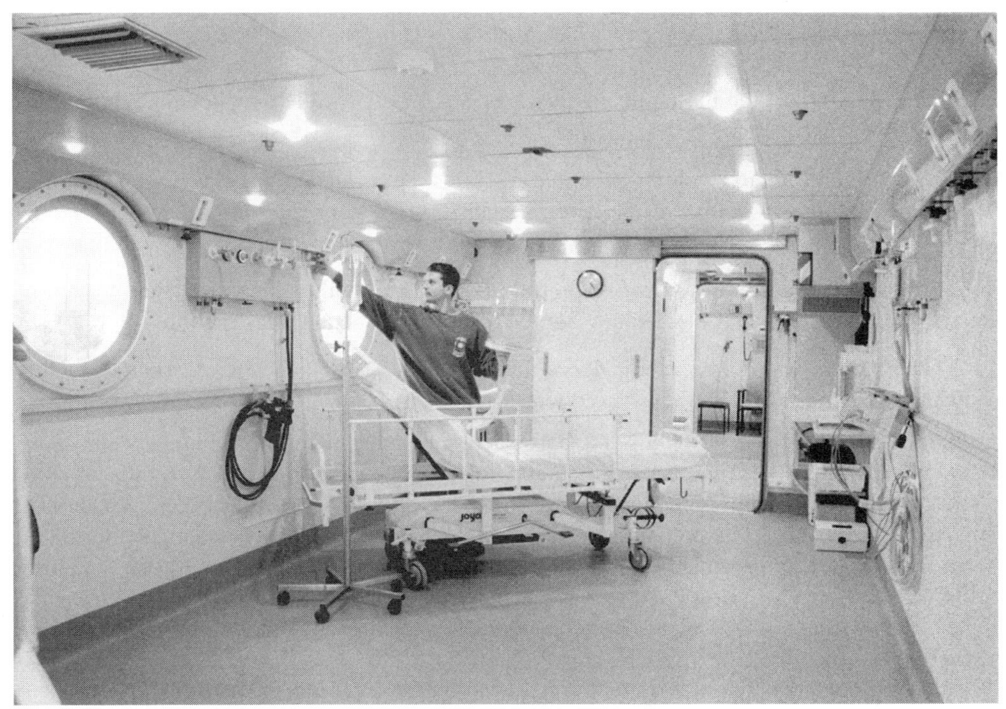

EXHIBIT 20.7 *Interior of rectangular Class A chamber. (Photo courtesy of Fink Engineering, Cheltenham, Victoria, Australia)*

20.1.6 Nature of Hazards. See Section B.7.

For additional information on the nature of hyperbaric hazards, see Annex C, Section C.20.

20.2 Construction and Equipment

20.2.1 Housing for Hyperbaric Facilities.

20.2.1.1 For Class A chambers located inside a building, the chamber(s) and all ancillary service equipment shall be protected by 2-hour fire-resistant–rated construction.

20.2.1.1.1* Free-standing, dedicated buildings containing only a Class A chamber(s) and ancillary service equipment shall not be required to be protected by 2-hour fire-resistant–rated construction.

A.20.2.1.1.1 For guidance on minimum construction requirements, depending on occupancy classification, see NFPA *101*, *Life Safety Code*.

The reason for 2-hour fire-resistant–rated construction is the consideration that it could take some time to decompress and evacuate a Class A chamber in the event of fire in an adjacent area. If the Class A chamber and support equipment are the only things in a freestanding building, there is no adjacent area. The same logic applies to trailer- or vehicle-mounted facilities that are not contiguous to a health care facility and therefore have no adjacent area.

Previous editions of this standard allowed an exception to 2-hour fire-resistant–rated construction for "chambers . . . not permanently affixed to a foundation." This exception was removed from the standard to eliminate the impression that egress of hyperbaric chamber occupants should be accomplished by disconnecting the chamber from its facility connections and removing the chamber from the area. Once installed, almost all chamber designs currently in service (even those that are not permanently affixed to a foundation) are permanent from an emergency egress point of view.

20.2.1.1.2 Trailer or vehicle-mounted facilities shall be permitted without a 2-hour fire-resistant–rated perimeter.

20.2.1.1.3 When trailer or vehicle-mounted facilities are located contiguous to a health care facility, or another structure, a 2-hour fire-resistant–rated barrier shall be placed between the facility and the contiguous structure.

20.2.1.1.4 Where building exterior walls form part of the facility boundary, that portion of the facility boundary shall not require 2-hour fire-resistant–rated construction.

20.2.1.1.5* If there are connecting doors through such common walls of contiguity, they shall be at least B-label, 1½-hour fire doors.

A.20.2.1.1.5 Characteristics of building construction housing hyperbaric chambers and ancillary facilities are no less important to safety from fire hazards than are the characteristics of the hyperbaric chambers themselves. It is conceivable that a fire emergency occurring immediately outside a chamber, given sufficient fuel, could seriously endanger the life or lives of those inside the chamber. Since the service facilities such as compressors, cooling equipment, reserve air supply, oxygen, and so forth, will in all probability be within the same building, these will also need protection while in themselves supplying life-maintaining service to those inside.

20.2.1.1.6 When used for hyperbaric procedures, the room or rooms housing the Class A or Class B chambers shall be for the exclusive use of the hyperbaric operation.

20.2.1.1.7 Service equipment (e.g., compressors) shall be permitted to be located in multi-use spaces meeting the requirements of 20.2.1.1.

20.2.1.1.8 The supporting foundation for any chamber shall be designed to support the chamber.

Hyperbaric chambers come in a wide variety of sizes and weights. It is important for facility designers to know the total weight load and the point load of the chamber(s) that will go into a facility.

20.2.1.1.8.1 If on-site hydrostatic testing will be performed, the chamber supporting foundation shall be designed to support an additional water weight.

20.2.1.2 A hydraulically calculated automatic wet pipe sprinkler system meeting the requirements of NFPA 13, *Standard for the Installation of Sprinkler Systems*, shall be installed in the room housing a Class A chamber and in any ancillary equipment rooms.

20.2.1.2.1 Class A chambers not contiguous to a health care facility, and located in a mobile vehicle-mounted facility shall not be required to be protected as specified in 20.2.1.2.

Sprinkler protection is a prudent loss-limiting measure for all hyperbaric facilities. However, this allowance acknowledges the difficulty of providing sprinkler protection to a mobile vehicle.

20.2.1.2.2* Chamber room sprinkler heads shall be an approved type equipped with fusible elements.

A.20.2.1.2.2 In addition to the functions of building protection, the chamber room sprinkler system should be designed to ensure a degree of protection to chamber operators and occupants who likely will not be able to immediately evacuate the premises in the event of a fire.

20.2.1.2.3 The element temperature ratings shall be as low as possible, consistent with the requirements against false operation in NFPA 13.

20.2.1.3 The room or rooms housing Class B and Class C chambers shall be afforded sprinkler protection in accordance with 20.2.1.2.

20.2.1.3.1 Chambers not contiguous to a health care facility, and located in a mobile vehicle-mounted facility shall not be required to have sprinkler protection as specified in 20.2.1.2.

Paragraph 20.2.1.3.1 applies specifically to Class B and C chambers. The intent of this allowance is the same as the intent of 20.2.1.2.1.

20.2.1.4 Nonflammable gases shall be permitted to be piped into the hyperbaric facility.

Paragraph 20.2.1.4 contains a facility construction requirement dealing with storage and handling of gases within a hyperbaric facility. This issue should be addressed during the facility design process.

20.2.1.4.1 Shutoff valves accessible to facility personnel shall be provided for such piping at the point of entry to the room housing the chamber.

20.2.1.4.2 Storage and handling of nonflammable gases shall meet the applicable requirements of Chapter 5, Gas and Vacuum Systems, of this document and NFPA 50, *Standard for Bulk Oxygen Systems at Consumer Sites.*

20.2.2 Fabrication of the Hyperbaric Chamber.

20.2.2.1* Chambers for human occupancy, and their supporting systems, shall be designed and fabricated to meet ANSI/ASME PVHO-1, *Safety Standard for Pressure Vessels for Human Occupancy*, by personnel qualified to fabricate vessels under such codes.

A.20.2.2.1 Other chapters in NFPA 99 contain many requirements that could appear to relate to hyperbaric facilities but could be inappropriate. The requirements of other chapters in NFPA 99 should be applied to hyperbaric facilities only where specifically invoked by this chapter.

20.2.2.2 The chamber shall be stamped in accordance with ANSI/ASME PVHO-1, *Safety Standard for Pressure Vessels for Human Occupancy.*

20.2.2.3 As a minimum, animal chambers shall be designed, fabricated, and stamped to meet ANSI/ASME Section VIII, Division 1 code requirements.

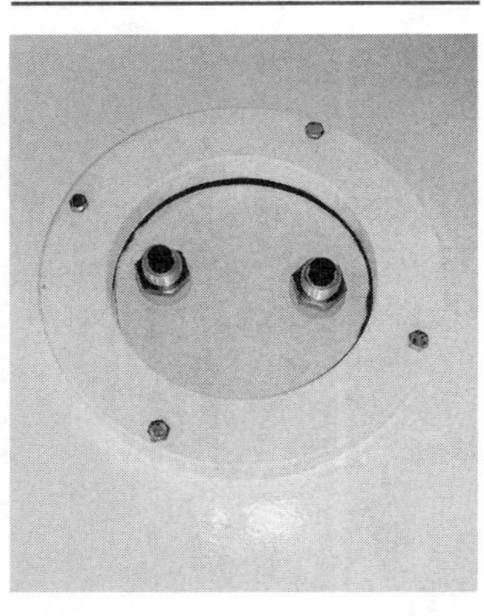

***EXHIBIT 20.8** Acrylic viewport on Class A chamber replaced with plate for two electrical penetrators. (Photo courtesy of International ATMO, San Antonio, Texas)*

20.2.2.4 The floor of a Class A chamber shall be designed to support equipment and personnel necessary for the operation of the chamber according to its expected purpose.

20.2.2.4.1 The floor of Class A chambers shall be noncombustible.

20.2.2.4.2 If the procedures to be carried out in the Class A hyperbaric chamber require antistatic flooring, the flooring shall be installed in accordance with the provisions of 13.4.1.

20.2.2.4.3 If a bilge is installed, access to the bilge shall be provided for cleaning purposes.

20.2.2.4.4 If the interior floor of a Class A chamber consists of removable floor (deck) plates, the plates shall be mechanically secured and electrically bonded to the chamber to ensure a positive electrical ground and to prevent movement of the plate, which could cause injury to personnel.

20.2.2.5 The interior of Class A chambers shall be unfinished or treated with a finish that is one of the following:

(1) Inorganic-zinc–based
(2) High-quality epoxy
(3) Flame resistant

20.2.2.5.1 If the interior of a Class A chamber is treated (painted) with a finish listed in 20.2.2.5, the cure procedure and minimum duration for each coat of finish to off-gas shall be in accordance with the manufacturer's application instructions and material safety data sheets.

FAQ ▶
What are the concerns with fresh paint on the chamber?

There are two concerns relating to fresh paint on the chamber. The first is that flammable vapors not be introduced into the chamber. The second is that chamber occupants not be exposed to toxic fumes.

20.2.2.5.2* If sound-deadening materials are employed within a hyperbaric chamber, they shall be flame resistant as defined in Chapter 3.

A.20.2.2.5.2 Many commercial sound-deadening materials that might be flame resistant are porous and will absorb water from activation of the fire-suppression system and retain odor. Metallic panels that contain a large quantity of small holes or are made of wire mesh and are installed about 1 in. (2.5 cm) away from the chamber wall can be used to form an acoustic baffle. These panels should be made from corrosive-resistant materials such as stainless steel or aluminum and can be painted in accordance with 20.2.2.5.1.

20.2.2.6* Viewing ports, access ports for piping and wiring or monitoring, and related leads shall be installed during initial fabrication of the chamber.

A.20.2.2.6 Prudent design considerations suggest that at least 50 percent excess pass-through capacity be provided, for future use, given the difficulty of adding pass-throughs to the chamber after it is constructed and tested.

20.2.2.6.1 Access ports in Class A chambers, for monitoring, and other electrical circuits shall be housed in enclosures that are weatherproof both inside and outside the chamber for protection in the event of sprinkler activation.

20.2.2.6.2 Viewports and penetrator plates shall be designed and fabricated according to ANSI/ASME PVHO-1, *Safety Standard for Pressure Vessels for Human Occupancy.*

Paragraph 20.2.2.1 covers the design and fabrication of viewports and penetrator plates for a new chamber. However, users of existing chambers can modify these components. Modification most commonly involves replacing damaged viewports or adding or altering penetrator plates to add extra pass-through capacity. (See Exhibit 20.8.) This paragraph emphasizes the importance of replacement parts and modifications meeting the requirements of ANSI/ASME PVHO-1, *Safety Standard for Pressure Vessels for Human Occupancy* [2]. This issue is also addressed in 20.3.4.1.6.

20.2.3 Illumination.

20.2.3.1 Unless designed for chamber use, sources of illumination shall be mounted outside the pressure chamber and arranged to shine through chamber ports or through chamber penetrators designed for fiberoptic or similar lighting.

20.2.3.1.1 Lighting fixtures used in conjunction with viewports shall be designed so that temperature ratings for the viewport material given in ANSI/ASME PVHO-1 are not exceeded.

◀ **FAQ**
What are the concerns when acrylic plastics are used?

The heat from adjacent light sources can melt acrylic plastic if it reaches a temperature of approximately 93°C (200°F). Although this standard addresses only the potential damage of acrylics from a hot light source, there are other concerns. A number of things weaken acrylic, including the following:

1. Physical damage (scratch or gouge)
2. Exposure to physical stress (compression/decompression of the chamber)
3. Exposure to ultraviolet radiation (sunlight or other strong UV source)
4. Exposure to a variety of chemicals, including chlorinated hydrocarbons (i.e., methylene chloride, carbon tetrachloride), aromatic solvents (i.e., turpentine, benzene, toluene), ethyl/methyl alcohol, and organic acids (i.e., acetic acid, phenols, Lysol®)

Because acrylics are an integral part of the chamber pressure boundary (pressure hulls, viewports, and light pipes), the pressure integrity of the chamber depends on appropriate care of its acrylic components.

Acrylics should be routinely inspected for physical damage and crazing. Crazing is a visual sign that acrylic has weakened. It develops slowly over time and can be difficult to detect in its early stages. It usually appears as a series of very fine cracks on the outer surface of the acrylic. (See Exhibit 20.9.) Information about inspection, repair, replacement, and documentation of chamber acrylics can be found in ANSI/ASME PVHO-2, *Safety Standards for Pressure Vessels for Human Occupancy: In-service Guidelines for PVHO Acrylic Windows* [3].

EXHIBIT 20.9 Section of acrylic plastic from a Class B chamber hull showing extensive crazing on outer surface. (Photo courtesy of International ATMO, San Antonio, Texas)

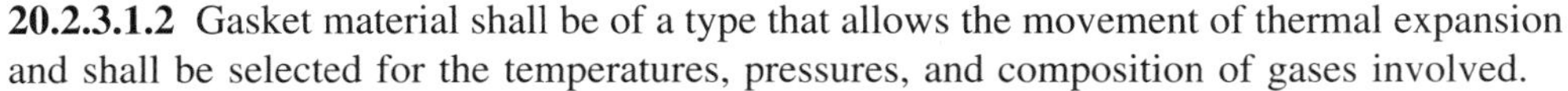

20.2.3.1.2 Gasket material shall be of a type that allows the movement of thermal expansion and shall be selected for the temperatures, pressures, and composition of gases involved.

20.2.3.1.2.1 Gaskets or O-rings shall be confined to grooves or enclosures, which will prevent their being blown out or squeezed from the enclosures or compression flanges.

20.2.3.2 Lighting permanently installed inside the chamber and portable lighting for temporary use inside the chamber shall meet the requirements of 20.2.7.3.15.

20.2.3.3 Emergency lighting for the interior of the chamber shall be provided.

Although not the only lighting options, chamber interiors are normally lit one of two ways. Either sufficient ambient room light enters the chamber through its acrylic components, or additional light sources are added to project light into the chamber. In either case, at least part of this lighting needs to be connected to an emergency power source. It is not the intent of 20.2.3.3 to require all chambers to have special "emergency" lighting installed inside the chamber.

20.2.4 Chamber Ventilation.

20.2.4.1 Ventilation of Class A Chambers.

20.2.4.1.1 The minimum ventilation rate for a Class A chamber shall be 0.085 actual m^3 (3 actual ft^3) per minute of air per chamber occupant who is not using a breathing-mask overboard dump system that exhausts exhaled gases.

20.2.4.1.1.1 The minimum threshold rate shall be 0.085 actual m^3 (3 actual ft^3) per minute.

The intent of 20.2.4.1.1.1 is that a Class A chamber be ventilated at a minimum rate, even if all occupants are using a breathing circuit with overboard dump of exhaled gases.

20.2.4.1.1.2 Provision shall be made for ventilation during nonpressurization of Class A chambers as well as during pressurization.

The intent of 20.2.4.1.1.2 is that the chamber design allow for ventilation during compression of the chamber and while the chamber is at operating pressure. See the commentary following 20.2.8.4.2 for information about oxygen pooling.

20.2.4.1.2* Ventilation shall not be required when saturation operations are conducted in the chamber, provided that carbon dioxide removal and odor control are accomplished and that the monitoring requirements of 20.2.8.4.1 and 20.2.8.5 are met.

A.20.2.4.1.2 Experience and practice can dictate the need for a threshold ventilation rate in excess of the minimum specified for sanitary reasons. It is recommended that consideration be given, if necessary, to the use of odor filters in the chamber circulation system as a means of keeping sanitary ventilation rate requirements to a minimum.

20.2.4.1.3 Individual breathing apparatus shall be available inside a Class A chamber for each occupant for use in the event that the chamber atmosphere is fouled by combustion or otherwise.

Analysis of hyperbaric chamber fires has shown that several fatalities were caused by asphyxia from the unbreathable atmosphere. Hyperbaric burning rate tests also have shown that smoke will quickly fill the chamber in the event of fire. Because the goal is to minimize the exposure to a potentially harmful contaminant in the chamber atmosphere, it is prudent to have the breathing apparatus immediately available and to train all chamber occupants on proper use of the apparatus.

20.2.4.1.3.1 The breathing mixture supplied to breathing apparatus shall be independent of chamber atmosphere.

20.2.4.1.3.2 The breathing gas supply shall be designed for simultaneous use of all breathing apparatus.

20.2.4.1.3.3 Breathing apparatus shall function at all pressures that can be encountered in the chamber.

20.2.4.1.3.4 In the event of a fire within a chamber, provision shall be made to switch all breathing apparatus to an air supply that is independent of the chamber atmosphere.

20.2.4.2 Sources of Air for Chamber Atmospheres.

There are two fundamental concerns about chamber air sources. First, the chamber environment must be breathable air. Measures must be taken to ensure the quality of this breathing air source. Second, some contaminants that could be introduced into the chamber environment are fuel sources and thereby increase the fire risk.

20.2.4.2.1* Sources of air for chamber atmospheres shall be such that toxic or flammable gases are not introduced.

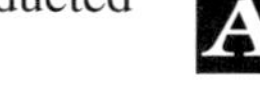

A.20.2.4.2.1 If intakes are located where it could be possible for maintenance to be conducted in the immediate vicinity, a warning sign should be posted.

20.2.4.2.2 Compressor intakes shall be located away from air contaminated by exhaust from activities of vehicles, internal combustion engines, stationary engines, or building exhaust outlets.

Even if the original intake location is appropriate, potential sources of contamination could enter the area later. It is important to be alert to possible contaminants near the intake.

20.2.4.2.3 Air supply for chamber atmosphere shall be monitored as required in 20.2.8.6.

20.2.4.2.4 The use of conventional oil-lubricated compressors shall be permitted provided they are fitted with air treatment packages designed to produce medical air, and they meet the monitoring requirements of 20.2.8.6.

The specifications for "medical air" quality would be appropriate for hyperbaric air compressors except for the dewpoint limit in the medical air standard. The annex note for paragraph 20.2.4.3.2 recommends that the chamber interior maintain 50 to 70 percent relative humidity. The dryness of medical air conflicts with this recommendation.

20.2.4.2.4.1 The air treatment packages shall include automatic safeguards.

20.2.4.2.5 Air compressor installations shall consist of two or more individual compressors with capacities such that required system flow rates can be maintained on a continuous basis with any single compressor out of operation unless 20.2.7.2.4 is satisfied.

20.2.4.2.5.1 Each compressor shall be supplied from separate electrical branch circuits.

20.2.4.2.6 Air compressor installations that supply medical air to piped gas systems as well as to hyperbaric facilities shall meet the requirements of 5.1.3.5.3 in Chapter 5 and the requirements of this chapter.

20.2.4.2.7 Air compressor installations that are used exclusively for hyperbaric facilities shall meet the requirements of this chapter only.

Chapter 5 contains requirements for medical air compressor installations. These include a level of redundancy, monitoring, and alarm capabilities not necessary for an air compressor installation dedicated to a hyperbaric facility.

◀ **FAQ**
If the compressors are used for hyperbaric facilities only, is it necessary to comply with Chapter 5 of NFPA 99?

20.2.4.3 Temperature and Humidity Control.

20.2.4.3.1 Warming or cooling of the atmosphere within a Class A chamber shall be permitted by circulating the ambient air within the chamber over or past coils through which a constant flow of warm or cool water or water/glycol mixture is circulated.

20.2.4.3.2* Class A chambers that are not used in the capacity of an operating room shall maintain a temperature that is comfortable for the occupants [usually 22° ± 2°C (75° ± 5°F)].

A.20.2.4.3.2 Subsection 13.4.1 specifies a desirable temperature of 20°C (68°F). It is impractical to maintain such a temperature during pressurization, but efforts should be made in the design and operation of thermal control systems to maintain the temperature as close to 22°C (75°F) as possible. The air-handling system of all Class A chambers should be capable of maintaining relative humidity in the range of 50 to 70 percent during stable depth operations.

The thermal control system should be designed to maintain the temperature below 29°C

(85°F) during pressurization, if possible, and above 19°C (65°F) during depressurization, if possible.

20.2.4.3.3 Whenever the Class A chamber is used as an operating room, it shall be ventilated and the air supply thereto shall be conditioned according to the minimum requirements for temperature for hospital operating rooms as specified in 13.4.1.

20.2.4.3.3.1 If inhalation anesthetic agents are being utilized (e.g., nitrous oxide, methoxyflurane, halothane), a closed anesthetic system with exhaled-gas scavenging and overboard dumping shall be employed.

20.2.4.3.3.2 Flammable inhalation anesthetics (i.e., cyclopropane, ethyl ether, ethylene, and ethyl chloride) shall not be employed.

20.2.4.3.4 Dehumidification shall be permitted through the use of cold coils.

20.2.4.3.5 Humidification by the use of an air-powered water nebulizer shall be permitted.

20.2.4.3.6 Noncombustible packing and nonflammable lubricant shall be employed on the fan shaft.

20.2.4.4 Ventilation of Class B Chambers.

20.2.4.4.1* The minimum ventilation rate for a Class B chamber shall be 0.0283 m^3/min (1 actual ft^3/min).

A.20.2.4.4.1 Ventilation can be provided by closed or open circuit systems.

20.2.4.4.2 Class B chambers not designed for 100 percent oxygen environment shall comply with the monitoring requirements of 20.2.8.4.

20.2.4.5 Emergency Depressurization and Facility Evacuation Capability.

The intent of 20.2.4.5 is that the design of the chamber not create a long delay in evacuating chamber occupants. This requirement is different for Class A and Class B chambers because of the relative difference in volume of gas that must be exhausted.

20.2.4.5.1 Class A chambers shall be capable of depressurizing from 3 ATA (304.0 kPa) to ambient pressure in no more than 6 minutes.

20.2.4.5.2 Class B chambers shall be capable of depressurizing from 3 ATA (304.0 kPa) to ambient pressure in no more than 2 minutes.

20.2.4.5.3* A source of breathable gas allowing unrestricted mobility shall be available outside a Class A or B chamber for use by personnel in the event that the air in the vicinity of the chamber is fouled by smoke or other combustion products of fire.

Adding Class B chambers to this requirement is new to this edition of the standard. Considering how rapidly a fire in a chamber room would fill the room with smoke, it is prudent to have protection for the chamber operator(s). Although a self-contained breathing apparatus (SCBA) meets this requirement, this standard allows for other types of protection. Be aware that if an SCBA is employed, the user must follow the OSHA regulations specific to SCBAs.

A.20.2.4.5.3 The intent of this requirement is to allow facility staff to evacuate the facility and avoid breathing contaminated air. This requirement can be met using either a self-contained breathing apparatus, smoke hood with integral filter/air supply, or similar technology.

The number of units available should be adequate to meet facility staffing.

The breathing duration of the personal protection devices should be predicated upon the time necessary for evacuation of the facility.

Facility evacuation time should be determined during fire drills conducted by the hyperbaric facility.

20.2.5 Fire Protection in Class A Chambers.

20.2.5.1 General Requirements.

20.2.5.1.1 A fire suppression system consisting of independently supplied and operating handline and deluge type water spray systems shall be installed in all Class A chambers.

The deluge and handlines should be two separate systems. The most important issue is to prevent a common point of failure that would disable all fire suppression capability.

20.2.5.1.2 Design of the fire suppression system shall be such that failure of components in either the handline or deluge system will not render the other system inoperative.

20.2.5.1.3 System design shall be such that activation of either the handline or the deluge system shall automatically cause the following:

(1) Visual and aural indication of activation shall occur at the chamber operator's console.
(2) All ungrounded electrical leads for power and lighting circuits contained inside the chamber shall be disconnected.
(3) Emergency lighting *(see 20.2.3.3)* and communication, where used, shall be activated.

20.2.5.1.3.1 Intrinsically safe circuits, including sound-powered communications, shall be permitted to remain connected when either the handline or the deluge system is activated.

20.2.5.1.4* A fire alarm signaling device shall be provided at the chamber operator's control console for signaling the emergency fire/rescue network of the institution containing the hyperbaric facility.

A.20.2.5.1.4 This requirement does not preclude the use of an alarm system affording direct fire department contact.

20.2.5.1.4.1 Trailer or vehicle-mounted facilities not contiguous to a health care facility shall conform to the requirements of one of the following:

(1) Comply with 20.2.5.1.4 or
(2) Have a means for immediately contacting the local fire department.

20.2.5.1.5* Fire blankets and portable carbon dioxide extinguishers shall not be installed in or carried into the chamber.

A.20.2.5.1.5 Experience has shown that fire blankets, portable carbon dioxide extinguishers, and other methodology intended to "snuff out" fires by excluding air are not effective in controlling fires in oxygen-enriched atmospheres. Valuable time can be lost in attempting to use such devices.

20.2.5.1.6 Booster pumps, control circuitry, and other electrical equipment involved in fire suppression system operation shall be powered from a critical branch of the emergency electrical system as specified in 20.2.7.2.2.1.

20.2.5.1.7 Signs prohibiting the introduction of flammable liquids, gases, and other articles not permitted by this chapter into the chamber shall be posted at the chamber entrance(s).

Analysis of hyperbaric chamber fires has shown that the introduction of ignition sources into the chamber has been a major factor in chamber fires worldwide. Chamber design alone cannot prevent fires. Diligence in tightly controlling items that go into the chamber (both

◀ **FAQ**
What are the major ignition factors in chamber fires?

ignition sources and fuel sources) is extremely important. There should be a constant reminder to hyperbaric facility staff and patients of prohibited items.

20.2.5.1.8 The fire suppression system shall be permitted to be supplied from the local potable water service.

Designers should not be discouraged from using potable water sources in the fire suppression system. Potable water is commonly used in hyperbaric facilities to fill fire suppression water storage tanks. Also, it is feasible to run handlines directly off of the potable water source, as long as the performance criteria of 20.2.5.3.7 and 20.2.5.3.7.1 are met.

The building sprinkler system water supply is not necessarily the appropriate water source for fire suppression in hyperbaric chambers. The water in building sprinkler systems is dirtied by the black iron piping and could affect the operation of components of the chamber fire suppression system (i.e., activation valves).

Even when potable water is used, there are still concerns. Rusting of water storage tanks and piping components is common. Hard water deposits can form in pipes, valves, and nozzles. Water with high quantities of dissolved solids (i.e., well water) can grow organisms that eat through stainless steel. With all of these concerns, attention should be given to the source and quality of fire suppression water.

20.2.5.2 Deluge System Requirements. A fixed water deluge extinguishing system shall be installed in all chamber compartments that are designed for manned operations.

20.2.5.2.1 In chambers that consist of more than one chamber compartment (lock), the design of the deluge system shall meet the requirements of 20.2.5.2 when the chamber compartments are at different depths (pressures).

20.2.5.2.2 The deluge system in different compartments (locks) shall operate independently or simultaneously.

20.2.5.2.3 Fixed deluge systems shall not be required in chamber compartments that are used strictly as personnel transfer compartments (locks), and for no other purposes.

These transfer compartments are still required to have fire suppression capability. Paragraph 20.2.5.3.2 requires at least one handline in transfer compartments.

20.2.5.2.4* Manual activation and deactivation deluge controls shall be located at the operator's console and in each chamber compartment (lock) containing a deluge system.

A.20.2.5.2.4 More than one control station could be required in a compartment (lock) depending on its size.

20.2.5.2.4.1 Controls shall be designed to prevent unintended activation.

20.2.5.2.5 Water shall be delivered from the fixed discharge nozzles as specified in 20.2.5.2.7 within 3 seconds of activation of any affiliated deluge control.

20.2.5.2.6* Average spray density at floor level shall be not less than 81.5 L/min/m^2 (2 gpm/ft^2) with no floor area larger than 1 m^2 (10.76 ft^2) receiving less than 40.75 L/min/m^2 (1 gpm/ft^2).

A.20.2.5.2.6 Experience has shown that when water is discharged through conventional sprinkler heads into a hyperbaric atmosphere, the spray angle is reduced because of increased resistance to water droplet movement in the denser atmosphere. This is so even though the water pressure differential is maintained above chamber pressure. Therefore, it is necessary to compensate by increasing the number of sprinkler heads. It is recommended that spray coverage tests be conducted at maximum chamber pressure.

Some chamber configurations, such as small-diameter horizontal cylinders, could have a very tiny "floor," or even no floor at all. For horizontal cylinder chambers and spherical chambers, "floor level" should be taken to mean the level at ¼ diameter below the chamber centerline or actual "floor level," whichever gives the larger floor area.

20.2.5.2.7 There shall be water available in the deluge system to maintain the flow specified in 20.2.5.2.6 simultaneously in each chamber compartment (lock) containing the deluge system for 1 minute.

20.2.5.2.7.1 The limit on maximum extinguishment duration shall be governed by the chamber capacity (bilge capacity also, if so equipped) and/or its drainage system.

20.2.5.2.8 The deluge system shall have stored pressure to operate for at least 15 seconds without electrical branch power.

20.2.5.3 Handline System Requirements. A handline extinguishing system shall be installed in all chamber compartments (locks).

20.2.5.3.1 At least two handlines shall be strategically located in treatment compartments (locks).

20.2.5.3.2 At least one handline shall be located in each personnel transfer compartment (lock).

20.2.5.3.3 If any chamber compartment (lock) is equipped with a bilge access panel, at least one handline shall reach the bilge area.

20.2.5.3.4 Handlines shall have a 1.27 cm (0.5 in.) minimum internal diameter and shall have a rated working pressure greater than the highest supply pressure of the supply system.

20.2.5.3.5 Each handline shall be activated by a manual, quick-opening, quarter-turn valve located within the compartment (lock).

20.2.5.3.5.1 Hand-operated, spring-return to close valves at the discharge end of handlines shall be permitted.

20.2.5.3.6 Handlines shall be equipped with override valves that are accessible to personnel outside the chamber.

20.2.5.3.7 The water supply for the handline system shall be designed to ensure a 345 kPa (50 psi) minimum water pressure above the maximum chamber pressure.

20.2.5.3.7.1 The system shall be capable of supplying a minimum of 18.9 L/min (5 gpm) simultaneously to each of any two of the handlines at the maximum chamber pressure for a period of not less than 4 minutes.

A duration of at least 4 minutes is specified in 20.2.5.3.7.1 to give designers guidance for the appropriate size of storage tanks.

20.2.5.4 Automatic Detection System Requirements. Automatic fire detection systems shall not be required.

Automatic detection systems and automatic activation of the fire suppression deluge are different issues. Automatic detection systems are common in Class A chambers. Less common are automatic activation systems. To work, automatic activation must include automatic detection. Neither of these systems is required by this standard.

20.2.5.4.1 Surveillance fire detectors responsive to the radiation from flame shall be employed.

20.2.5.4.1.1 Type and arrangement of detectors shall be such as to respond within 1 second of flame origination.

20.2.5.4.2* The number of detectors employed and their location shall be selected to cover the chamber interior.

A.20.2.5.4.2 Additional detectors are recommended to avoid "blind" areas if the chamber contains compartmentation.

20.2.5.4.3 The system shall be powered from the critical branch of the emergency electrical system or shall have automatic battery back-up.

20.2.5.4.4 If used to automatically activate the deluge system, the requirements for manual activation/deactivation in 20.2.5.2.4 and deluge system response time in 20.2.5.2.5 shall still apply.

20.2.5.4.5 The system shall include self-monitoring functions for fault detection and fault alarms and indications.

20.2.5.4.6 Automatic fire detection equipment, when used, shall meet the applicable requirements in 20.2.7.3.

20.2.5.5* Testing Requirements. The deluge and handline systems shall be functionally tested at least semiannually per 20.2.5.2.7 for deluge systems and 20.2.5.3.7 for handline systems. Following the test, all valves shall be placed in their baseline position.

A.20.2.5.5 The primary focus for the semiannual test of a water-based extinguishing system is to ensure water flow through the system (i.e., inspector's test). Other vitally important benefits are the activation of water flow devices, alarm appliances, and notification and annunciator systems.

A hyperbaric fire suppression system is a critical safety device that might sit idle for long periods of time and then be expected to work flawlessly the moment it is activated. There are many different configurations of hyperbaric fire suppression systems. It is prudent to perform maintenance and testing of a particular fire suppression system as often as appropriate for its particular components. Many users have increased the frequency of testing their own fire suppression system because of maintenance issues they identified.

More information about testing can be found in NFPA 25, *Inspection Testing and Maintenance of Water-Based Fire Protection Systems* [4].

20.2.5.5.1 If a bypass system is used, it shall not remain in the test mode after completion of the test.

FAQ ▶
What are the concerns regarding bypass systems?

A bypass system should allow functional testing without spraying fire suppression water into the chamber interior. This should encourage more frequent testing of the fire suppression system. The concern with allowing a bypass is that the system could be left in bypass mode after the test, then not be operational in the event of fire.

20.2.5.5.2 During initial construction, or whenever changes are made to the installed deluge system that will affect the spray pattern, testing of spray coverage to demonstrate conformance to the requirements of 20.2.5.2.6 shall be performed at surface pressure, and at maximum operating pressure. The requirements of 20.2.5.2.6 shall be satisfied under both conditions.

20.2.5.5.3 A detailed record of the test results shall be maintained and a copy sent to the hyperbaric facility safety director.

20.2.6 Fire Protection in Class B and Class C Chambers.

Class B and Class C chambers shall not be required to comply with 20.2.5.

20.2.6.1 Signs prohibiting the introduction of flammable liquids, gases, and other articles not permitted by this chapter into the chamber shall be posted at the chamber entrance(s).

Analysis of hyperbaric chamber fires has shown that the introduction of ignition sources into the chamber has been a major factor in chamber fires worldwide. Chamber design alone cannot prevent fires. Diligence in tightly controlling items that go into the chamber (both ignition sources and fuel sources) is extremely important. There should be a constant reminder to hyperbaric facility staff and patients of prohibited items.

20.2.6.2 A fire alarm signaling device shall be provided within the room housing the chamber(s) for signaling the emergency fire/rescue network of the institution containing the hyperbaric facility.

20.2.6.2.1 Trailer or vehicle-mounted facilities not contiguous to a health care facility shall conform to the requirements of one of the following:

(1) Comply with 20.2.6.2
(2) Have a means for immediately contacting the local fire department

20.2.7 Electrical Systems.

20.2.7.1 General.

20.2.7.1.1 The requirements of NFPA 70, *National Electrical Code*, or local electrical codes shall apply to electrical wiring and equipment in hyperbaric facilities within the scope of this chapter, except as such rules are modified in 20.2.7.

20.2.7.1.2 All hyperbaric chamber service equipment, switchboards, panels, or control consoles shall be located outside of, and in the vicinity of, the chamber.

20.2.7.1.3 Console or module spaces containing both oxygen piping and electrical equipment shall be either one of the following:

(1) Mechanically or naturally ventilated
(2) Continuously monitored for excessive oxygen concentrations whenever the electrical equipment is energized

20.2.7.1.4 For the fixed electrical installation, none of the following shall be permitted inside the chamber:

(1) Circuit breakers
(2) Line fuses
(3) Motor controllers
(4) Relays
(5) Transformers
(6) Ballasts
(7) Lighting panels
(8) Power panels

20.2.7.1.4.1* If motors are to be located in the chamber, they shall meet the requirements of 20.2.7.3.14.

A.20.2.7.1.4.1 It is recommended that system design be such that electric motors not be located inside the chamber.

20.2.7.1.5 All electrical equipment connected to or used in conjunction with hyperbaric patients shall comply with the requirements of Chapter 8, Electrical Equipment, and with the applicable paragraphs of 20.2.7.3.

20.2.7.1.6 In the event of activation of the room sprinkler system, electrical equipment shall be protected from sprinkler water but need not remain functional if manual means to control and decompress the chamber are provided.

20.2.7.2 Electrical Service.

20.2.7.2.1 All hyperbaric facilities shall contain an electrical service that is supplied from two independent sources of electric power.

20.2.7.2.1.1 All hyperbaric facilities for human occupancies shall contain an electrical service that is supplied from two independent sources of electric power.

20.2.7.2.1.2 For hyperbaric facilities using a prime-mover-driven generator set, it shall be designated as the "emergency system" and shall meet the requirements of Chapter 4 of this standard for hyperbaric systems based in health care facilities.

20.2.7.2.1.3 Article 700, Emergency Systems, of NFPA 70, *National Electrical Code*, shall apply to hyperbaric systems located in facilities other than health care facilities.

Health care facilities should already have appropriate emergency power systems in place to support the entire facility (including the hyperbaric facility). If the hyperbaric facility is not part of a health care facility, there could be no emergency power system available. The purpose of 20.2.7.2.1.3 is to ensure that all hyperbaric facilities have appropriate emergency power sources.

20.2.7.2.2 Electrical equipment associated with life support functions of hyperbaric facilities shall be connected to the critical branch of the emergency system; that is, such equipment shall have electrical power restored within 10 seconds of interruption of normal power. Such equipment shall include, but is not limited to the following:

(1) Electrical power outlets located within the chamber
(2) Chamber emergency lighting, whether internally or externally mounted
(3) Chamber intercommunications
(4) Alarm systems, including fire detectors
(5) Chamber fire suppression system equipment and controls
(6) Other electrical controls used for chamber pressurization and ventilation control
(7) A number of chamber room lights (either overhead or local) to ensure continued safe operation of the facility during a normal power outage

20.2.7.2.2.1 Booster pumps in the chamber fire suppression system shall be on separate branch circuits serving no other loads.

20.2.7.2.3 Electric-motor-driven compressors and auxiliary electrical equipment normally located outside the chamber and used for chamber atmospheric control shall be connected to the equipment system *(see Chapter 4)* or the emergency system *(see* NFPA 70, *National Electrical Code, Article 700)*, as applicable.

20.2.7.2.4 Electric-motor–driven compressors and auxiliary electrical equipment shall be arranged for delayed-automatic or manual connection to the alternate power source so as to prevent excessive current draw on the system during restarting.

20.2.7.2.5 When reserve air tanks or non-electric compressor(s) to maintain pressure and ventilation airflow within the chamber and supply air for the chamber pressurization are provided, the compressor(s) and auxiliary equipment shall not be required to have an alternate source of power.

20.2.7.2.6 Electrical control and alarm systems design shall be such that hazardous conditions (e.g., loss of chamber pressure control, deluge activation, spurious alarms) do not occur during power interruption or during power restoration.

20.2.7.3* Wiring and Equipment Inside Class A Chambers. The following general rules shall be satisfied in the use of electrical devices and equipment. The requirements under 20.2.7.3 are intended to protect against the elevated fire risks known to exist in a pressurized air environment and shall not be construed as classifying the chamber interior as a Class I (as defined in NFPA 70, *National Electrical Code*, Article 500) hazardous location.

A.20.2.7.3 This subsection contains requirements for the safe use of electrical equipment in the hyperbaric, oxygen-enriched environment of the Class A chamber.

20.2.7.3.1 Equipment or equipment component installed in or used in the chamber shall not present an explosion or implosion hazard under the conditions of hyperbaric use.

20.2.7.3.2 All equipment shall be rated, or tested and documented, for intended hyperbaric conditions prior to use.

20.2.7.3.3 Only the electrical equipment necessary for the safe operation of the chamber and for required patient care shall be permitted in the chamber.

20.2.7.3.4 Only portable equipment necessary for the logistical and operational support shall be permitted in the chamber during manned pressurization.

20.2.7.3.5 Where conformance with Class I, Division 1 requirements is specified in 20.2.7.3.7, conformance with Class I, Division 2 requirements is permitted to be substituted.

20.2.7.3.6 Conductor Insulation. All conductors inside the chamber shall be insulated with a material classified as flame resistant as defined in Chapter 3.

20.2.7.3.6.1 Insulation classified as flame retardant shall not be required on conductors that form an integral part of electrical equipment approved for use inside the chamber, including patient leads.

20.2.7.3.6.2 Insulation shall not be required on ground conductors inside of a conduit.

20.2.7.3.7 Wiring Methods.

20.2.7.3.7.1 Fixed wiring shall be installed in threaded RMC or IMC conduit utilizing the following waterproof components:

(1) Threaded metal joints
(2) Fittings
(3) Boxes
(4) Enclosures

20.2.7.3.7.2 A continuous ground shall be maintained between all conductive surfaces enclosing electrical circuits and the chamber hull using approved grounding means.

20.2.7.3.7.3 All threaded conduit shall be threaded with an NPT standard conduit cutting die that provides a 1.9 cm taper per 0.3 m (0.75 in. taper per ft).

20.2.7.3.7.4 All threaded conduit shall be made wrenchtight to prevent sparking when fault current flows through the conduit system.

20.2.7.3.7.5 Wiring classified as intrinsically safe for any group location and installed in accordance with Article 504, Intrinsically Safe Systems, of NFPA 70, *National Electrical Code*, shall be permitted.

20.2.7.3.7.6 Threaded, liquidtight flexible metal conduit installed in accordance with Article 351 of NFPA 70, *National Electrical Code*, shall be permitted when protected from damage by physical barriers such as equipment panels.

20.2.7.3.8 Drainage. Means of draining fixed conduit and fixed equipment enclosures shall be provided.

20.2.7.3.9 Flexible Electrical Cords. Flexible cords used to connect portable utilization equipment to the fixed electrical supply circuit shall meet all of the following requirements:

(1) Be of a type approved for extra-hard utilization in accordance with Table 400.4 of NFPA 70, *National Electrical Code*
(2) Include a ground conductor
(3) Meet the requirements of Article 501.11 of NFPA 70, *National Electrical Code*

20.2.7.3.9.1 The normal cord supplied with the device shall be permitted when the portable device is rated at less than 2 A and the cord is positioned out of traffic and protected from physical abuse.

Prior to the 1999 edition of this standard, the electrical requirements of Chapter 20 prohibited the use of most patient care equipment without modification of the equipment. These modifications usually voided the manufacturer warranty. The intent of 20.2.7.3.9.1 is to allow unmodified medical equipment to be used, provided the equipment meets all other requirements of this standard.

20.2.7.3.10* Receptacles Installed Inside the Chamber.

A.20.2.7.3.10 It should be recognized that interruption of any powered circuit, even of very low voltage, could produce a spark sufficient to ignite a flammable agent.

20.2.7.3.10.1 Receptacles shall be waterproof.

20.2.7.3.10.2 Receptacles shall be of the type providing for connection to the grounding conductor of the flexible cord.

20.2.7.3.10.3 Receptacles shall be supplied from isolated power circuits meeting the requirements of 20.2.7.4.2.

20.2.7.3.10.4 The design of the receptacle shall be such that sparks cannot be discharged into the chamber environment when the plug is inserted or withdrawn under electrical load.

20.2.7.3.10.5 One of the following shall be satisfied to protect against inadvertent withdrawal of the plug under electrical load:

(1) The receptacle-plug combination shall be of a locking type.
(2) The receptacle shall carry a label warning against unplugging under load, and the power cord shall not present a trip hazard for personnel moving in the chamber.

20.2.7.3.11 Switches. Switches in the fixed wiring installation shall be waterproof.

20.2.7.3.11.1* Switch make and break contacts shall be housed in the electrical enclosure so that no sparks from arcing contacts can reach the chamber environment.

A.20.2.7.3.11.1 It is recommended that all control switching functions inside the chamber be accomplished using intrinsically safe circuits that control power and control circuits located outside of the chamber.

20.2.7.3.12* Temperature. No electrical equipment installed or used in the chamber shall have an operating surface temperature in excess of 85°C (185°F).

A.20.2.7.3.12 It is the intention of this paragraph that equipment used in the chamber be incapable of igniting, by heating, any material or fabric that could come into contact with the surface of the equipment.

To give a frame of reference, Commentary Table 20.1 shows the relative ignition temperatures of four materials in both air and oxygen at different absolute pressures.

COMMENTARY TABLE 20.1 *Minimum Hot Plate Ignition Temperatures of Six Combustible Materials in Oxygen–Nitrogen Mixtures at Various Total Pressures*

		Ignition Temperature (°C)			
		Total Pressure (atm)			
Material	*Oxidant*	*1*	*2*	*3*	*4*
Cotton sheeting	Air	465	440 (425)[a]	385	365
	42% O_2, 58% N_2	390	370	355	340
	100% O_2	360	345	340	325
Cotton sheeting, treated[b]	Air	575	520 (510)[a]	485 (350)[a]	370 (325)[a]
	42% O_2, 58% N_2	390 (350)[a]	335	315	295
	100% O_2	310	—	300	285
Conductive rubber sheeting	Air	480	395	370	375
	42% O_2, 58% N_2	430	365	350	350
	100% O_2	360	—	345	345
Paper drapes	Air	470	455	425	405
	42% O_2, 58% N_2	430	—	400	370
	100% O_2	410	—	365	340
Nomex fabric	Air	>600	>600	>600	560
	42% O_2, 58% N_2	550	540	510	495
	100% O_2	520	505	490	470
Polyvinyl chloride sheet	Air	>600	—	495	490
	42% O_2, 58% N_2	575	—	370	350
	100% O_2	390	—	350	325

[a]Values in parentheses indicate the temperature at which material glowed.
[b]Cotton sheeting treated with DuPont® X-12 fire retardant; amount of retardant equal to 12 percent of cotton specimen weight.
Source: NFPA 53, *Recommended Practice on Materials, Equipment, and Systems Used in Oxygen-Enriched Atmospheres,* 2004 edition, Table F.3.2.8 [5].

20.2.7.3.13 Exposed Live Electrical Parts. There shall be no exposed live electrical parts.

20.2.7.3.13.1 Exposed live electrical parts that are intrinsically safe shall be permitted.

20.2.7.3.13.2 Exposed live electrical parts that constitute patient monitoring leads, which are part of electromedical equipment, shall be permitted provided that they meet the requirements of 20.2.7.3.17.

20.2.7.3.14 Motors. Motors shall meet one of the following requirements:

(1) Article 501.8(A)(1) of NFPA 70, *National Electrical Code*, for the chamber pressure and oxygen concentration 
(2) Be of the totally enclosed types meeting Article 501.8(A)(2) or 501.8(A)(3) of NFPA 70, *National Electrical Code.*

20.2.7.3.15* Lighting. Lighting installed or used inside the chamber shall be rated for a pressure of 1½ times the chamber working pressure. Permanently installed fixtures shall meet the following requirements:

A.20.2.7.3.15 It is strongly recommended that high-intensity local task lighting be accomplished using through-hull fiber optic lights. Many high-intensity lights will not meet the temperature requirements specified in this subparagraph. 

(1) Be rated and approved for Class I (Division 1 or 2) classified areas
(2) Have lens guards installed
(3) Be located away from areas where they would experience physical damage from the normal movement of people and equipment

20.2.7.3.15.1 Ballasts and other energy storage components that are part of the lighting circuit shall be installed outside the chamber in accordance with 20.2.7.1.4.

20.2.7.3.15.2 Portable fixtures intended for spot illumination shall be shatterproof or protected from physical damage.

20.2.7.3.16 Low-Voltage, Low-Power Equipment. The requirements of 20.2.7.3.16 shall apply to sensors, signaling, alarm, communication, and remote control equipment installed or used in the chamber for operation of the chamber.

20.2.7.3.16.1* Equipment shall be isolated from main power by one of the following means:

(1) Design of the power supply circuit
(2) Opto-isolation
(3) By other electronic isolation means

A.20.2.7.3.16.1 The requirement for isolation from mains supply in (1) is not the same as the requirement in 20.2.7.4.2 that circuits supplying power to portable utilization equipment inside the chamber be isolated, monitored, and alarmed.

It is recommended that intrinsically safe sensors and controls be used whenever possible.

20.2.7.3.16.2 Circuits such as headset cables, sensor leads, and so forth, not enclosed as required in 20.2.7.3.7, shall meet one of the following requirements:

(1) Be part of approved intrinsically safe equipment
(2) Be limited by circuit design to no more than 28 V and 0.5 A under normal or circuit fault conditions

20.2.7.3.16.3 Chamber speakers shall be of a design in which the electrical circuitry and wiring is completely enclosed.

20.2.7.3.16.4 Electrical rating of chamber speakers shall not exceed 28 V rms and 25 W.

20.2.7.3.16.5 Battery-operated, portable intercom headset units shall meet the requirements of 20.2.7.3.17.5 for battery-operated devices.

20.2.7.3.17* Portable Patient Care–Related Electrical Appliances.

A.20.2.7.3.17 These requirements are only the minimum requirements for electrical safety. There are many other safety concerns that should be addressed on a case-by-case basis. Meeting the requirements of this subparagraph does not indicate that proper device performance will occur in the hyperbaric environment, and that the device will be safe for use with patients.

20.2.7.3.17.1 The appliance shall be designed and constructed in accordance with Chapter 10.

20.2.7.3.17.2 The electrical and mechanical integrity of the appliance shall be verified and documented through an ongoing maintenance program as required in Chapter 8.

20.2.7.3.17.3 The appliance shall conform to the requirements of 20.2.7.3.1 and 20.2.7.3.12.

20.2.7.3.17.4 Appliances that utilize oxygen shall not allow oxygen accumulation in the electrical portions of the equipment under normal and abnormal conditions.

20.2.7.3.17.5 Battery-Operated Devices. Battery-operated devices shall meet the following requirements:

(1) Batteries shall be fully enclosed and secured within the equipment enclosure.
(2) Batteries shall not be damaged by the maximum chamber pressure they are exposed to.
(3) Batteries shall be of a sealed type that does not off-gas during normal use.
(4) Batteries or battery-operated equipment shall not undergo charging while located in the chamber.
(5) Batteries shall not be changed on in-chamber equipment while the chamber is in use.
(6) The equipment electrical rating shall not exceed 12 V and 48 W.

20.2.7.3.17.6 Cord-Connected Devices. Cord-connected devices shall meet the following requirements:

(1) All portable, cord-connected equipment shall have an on–off power switch.
(2) The equipment electrical rating shall not exceed 120 V and 2 A unless the electrical portions of the equipment are inert-gas purged.
(3) The plug of cord-connected devices shall not be used to interrupt power to the device.

20.2.7.4 Grounding and Ground Fault Protection.

20.2.7.4.1 All chamber hulls shall be grounded to an electrical ground or grounding system that meets the requirements of Article 250, Grounding, Section III, Grounding Electrode System, of NFPA 70, *National Electrical Code*.

20.2.7.4.1.1 Grounding conductors shall be secured as required by Article 250, Section III, Grounding Conductor Connections, of NFPA 70, *National Electrical Code*.

20.2.7.4.1.2 The material, size, and installation of the grounding conductor shall meet the requirements of Article 250, Section VI, Grounding Conductors, of NFPA 70, *National Electrical Code*, for equipment grounding conductors.

20.2.7.4.1.3 The resistance between the grounded chamber hull and the electrical ground shall not exceed 1 ohm.

20.2.7.4.2 In health care facilities, electrical power circuits located within the chamber shall be supplied from an ungrounded electrical system equipped with a line isolation monitor with signal lamps and audible alarms.

20.2.7.4.2.1 Such circuits shall meet the requirements of Article 517.160, Isolated Power Systems, and 517.160(B), Line Isolation Monitor, of NFPA 70, *National Electrical Code*. Branch circuits shall not exceed 125 V or 15 A.

20.2.7.4.3 Wiring located both inside and outside the chamber, which serves line level circuits and equipment located inside the chamber, shall meet the grounding and bonding requirements of Article 501.16 of NFPA 70, *National Electrical Code*.

20.2.7.5 Wiring Outside the Chamber.

20.2.7.5.1 Those electrical components that must remain functional for the safe termination of a dive following activation of the room sprinkler system shall be enclosed in waterproof housing.

20.2.7.5.1.1 All associated conduits shall meet the following requirements:

(1) Be waterproof
(2) Meet the requirements of NFPA 70, *National Electrical Code*
(3) Be equipped with approved drains

20.2.7.5.2* All other electrical devices outside the chamber shall meet the requirements of NFPA 70.

A.20.2.7.5.2 It is necessary that these circuits be protected from exposure to water from the room sprinkler system protecting the chamber housing in the event of a fire in the vicinity of the chamber while it is in operation.

20.2.7.6 Additional Wiring and Equipment Requirements inside Class B Chambers. The requirements in 20.2.7.6 shall apply to Class B chambers whether they are pressurized with oxygen or with air.

20.2.7.6.1 Electrical equipment inside Class B chambers shall be restricted to communication functions and patient physiological monitoring leads.

20.2.7.6.1.1 Circuits shall be designed to limit the electrical energy to wire leads into the chamber under normal or fault conditions to no more than 28 V and 0.5 W.

20.2.7.6.1.2 Communication wires shall be protected from physical damage and from coming into contact with flammable materials in the chamber by barriers or conduit.

20.2.7.6.1.3 Patient monitoring leads shall be part of approved electromedical apparatus meeting the requirements in 20.2.7.3.17.

20.2.7.6.2 Lighting inside the chamber shall be supplied from external sources.

20.2.7.6.3 No electrical circuit in a Class B chamber shall operate at a temperature exceeding 60°C (140°F).

Notice in Commentary Table 20.1 that the ignition temperatures of materials are lower in oxygen than in air. This is the reason for the maximum temperature difference between Class A and Class B chambers described in 20.2.7.3.12 and 20.2.7.6.3.

20.2.8 Communications and Monitoring.

20.2.8.1 General.

20.2.8.1.1 Detectors, sensors, transducers, and communications equipment located inside the chamber shall meet the requirements of 20.2.7.3.16.

20.2.8.1.2 Wiring methods in the chamber shall meet the applicable requirements in 20.2.7.3.

20.2.8.1.3 The following equipment shall be installed outside the chamber or shall meet the requirements of 20.2.7.3.16:

(1) Control equipment
(2) Power amplifiers
(3) Output transformers
(4) Monitors associated with communications and monitoring equipment

20.2.8.2* Intercommunications.

A.20.2.8.2 Intercommunications equipment is mandatory for safe operation of a hyperbaric facility.

20.2.8.2.1* An intercommunication system shall connect all personnel compartments (locks) and the chamber operator's control console.

A.20.2.8.2.1 It is recommended that multiple compartment (lock) Class A chambers be equipped with multiple channel systems, and that, in addition, a sound-powered telephone or surveillance microphone be furnished.

20.2.8.2.2 Oxygen mask microphones shall be intrinsically safe at the maximum proposed pressure and 95 ± 5 percent oxygen.

20.2.8.3 Combustible Gas Detection.

20.2.8.3.1 The chamber atmosphere shall be continuously monitored for combustible gas concentrations whenever any volatile agents are used in the chamber *(see 20.2.4.3.3.1)*.

The reference to 20.2.4.3.3.1 might be misleading because flammable anesthetic agents are prohibited from the chamber elsewhere in this standard. This monitoring requirement exists in case a flammable gas other than an anesthetic agent is used.

20.2.8.3.1.1 The monitor shall be set to provide audible and visual alarms at 10 percent lower explosive limit (LEL) for the particular gas used.

Information about LELs can be found in A.20.3.1.5.2.2(2).

20.2.8.4 Oxygen Monitoring.

20.2.8.4.1 Oxygen levels shall be continuously monitored in any chamber in which nitrogen or other diluent gas is added to the chamber to reduce the volumetric concentration of oxygen in the atmosphere.

20.2.8.4.1.1 Oxygen monitors shall be equipped with audible and visual alarms.

20.2.8.4.2 Oxygen levels shall be continuously monitored in Class A chambers when breathing mixtures containing in excess of 21 percent oxygen by volume are being breathed by patients or attendants and/or any flammable agents are present in the chamber.

It has been demonstrated that when there is an oxygen leak in a Class A chamber, oxygen will pool in the area close to the leak. An oxygen anaylzer with a sample port only a few feet away from the leak might not indicate elevated oxygen percentage. This failure can occur even when there is active ventilation through the chamber. It is prudent to have some means of stirring the atmosphere in the chamber so that pooling of oxygen or other gases can be minimized.

20.2.8.4.2.1 Audible and visual alarms shall indicate volumetric oxygen concentrations in excess of 23.5 percent.

The requirements of Chapter 20 dealing with electrical wiring and electrical equipment are based on the atmosphere in the hyperbaric chamber being approximately 21 percent oxygen. An elevated oxygen percentage is associated with lower ignition temperatures and increased flame spread rate.

Exhibit 20.10 shows the effect of oxygen percentage on the flame spread rate.

20.2.8.5 Carbon Dioxide Monitoring. The chamber atmosphere shall be monitored for carbon dioxide levels during saturation operations whenever ventilation is not used.

20.2.8.6* Chamber Gas Supply Monitoring. The air supply of Class A and Class B chambers shall be sampled for concentrations of carbon monoxide.

The appropriate frequency of sampling varies. If chamber air is supplied by a compressor, and the compressor air intake is located where carbon monoxide contamination is possible, it might be prudent to continuously sample for carbon monoxide at the intake.

◀ **FAQ**
How often should the air be sampled for carbon monoxide?

A.20.2.8.6 The purity of the various gas supplies should be assured. It is recommended that air be sampled at the air intake location at times when the intake air is likely to have maximum impurities (e.g., when vehicles or stationary engines upwind of the intake are running).

A purity statement for any cryogenic or high pressure cylinder gas should be supplied by the vendor.

A

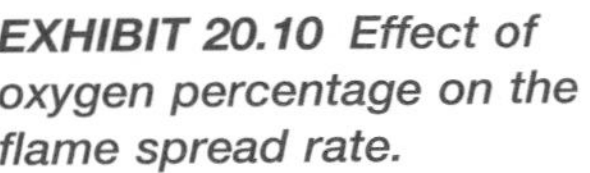

EXHIBIT 20.10 Effect of oxygen percentage on the flame spread rate.

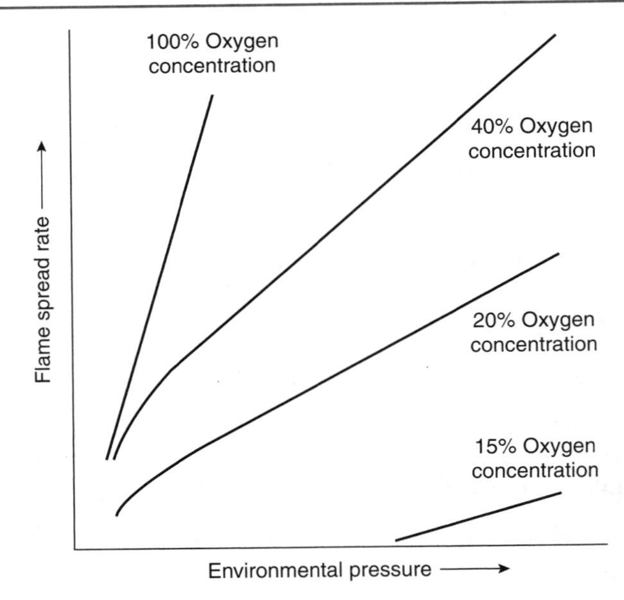

Gas cylinder purity statements should be cross referenced, where possible, with the delivered gas.

For additional verification, some facilities have installed sampling ports for monitoring oxygen and other gases.

20.2.8.6.1 Air supplied from oil-lubricated compressors capable of contaminating the compressor output due to wear or failure shall be continuously monitored for volatilized hydrocarbons as well as carbon monoxide at a location downstream from the oil filter when the compressors are running.

20.2.8.6.2* As a minimum, the air supplied to Class A chambers shall meet the requirements for CGA Grade D.

A.20.2.8.6.2 CGA Grade D permits quantities of hydrocarbons and water in air. In piping systems where air and oxygen might be used interchangeably, hydrocarbon buildup can occur and increase the risk of fire when oxygen is used. There is also a concern about pneumatic components being fouled and functionally impaired by hydrocarbons or water from compressed air. Ideally, there should be no condensed hydrocarbons in an oxygen system and no liquid water in pneumatic control systems.

20.2.8.6.3 As a minimum, the air supplied to Class B chambers shall meet the requirements for CGA grade D with the additional limit of no condensable hydrocarbons.

20.2.8.7* Electrical monitoring equipment used inside the chamber shall comply with the applicable requirements of 20.2.7.

A.20.2.8.7 The frequency of such monitoring should depend on the location of the air intake relative to potential sources of contamination.

20.2.8.8* Closed-circuit TV monitoring of the chamber interior shall be employed for chamber operators who do not have direct visual contact of the chamber interior from their normal operating location.

A.20.2.8.8 It is recommended that information about the status of an anesthetized or otherwise monitored patient be transmitted to the inside chamber attendants via the intercommunications system. As an alternative, the monitor indicators can be placed adjacent to a chamber viewport (or viewports) for direct observation by inside personnel.

20.2.9 Other Equipment and Fixtures.

20.2.9.1 All furniture permanently installed in the hyperbaric chamber shall be grounded.

20.2.9.2 Exhaust from all classes of chambers shall be piped outside of the building.

20.2.9.2.1 The point of exhaust shall not create a hazard.

20.2.9.2.2 The point of exhaust shall not allow reentry of gases into the building.

20.2.9.2.3 The point of exhaust shall be protected by the provision of a minimum of 0.3 cm mesh screen and situated to prevent the intrusion of rain, snow or airborne debris.

20.2.9.2.4 The point of exhaust shall be identified as an oxygen exhaust by a sign prohibiting smoking or open flame.

20.2.9.3 The supply piping for all air, oxygen, or other breathing mixtures from certified commercially supplied flasks shall be provided with a particulate filter of at least 10 microns or finer.

20.2.9.3.1 The filter shall meet the construction requirements of ANSI/ASME PVHO-1, *Safety Standard for Pressure Vessels for Human Occupancy*, and be located as close as practical to the source.

20.3 Administration and Maintenance

20.3.1 General.

20.3.1.1 Purpose. Section 20.3 contains requirements for administration and maintenance that shall be followed as an adjunct to physical precautions specified in Section 20.2.

20.3.1.2* Recognition of Hazards. The nature and recognition of hyperbaric hazards are outlined in Annex B of this document and shall be reviewed by the safety director.

To broaden his or her knowledge base with regard to hazards, a safety director should seek additional training and reference material outside this document.

A.20.3.1.2 The hazards involved in the use of hyperbaric facilities can be mitigated successfully only when all of the areas of hazard are fully recognized by all personnel and when the physical protection provided is complete and is augmented by attention to detail by all personnel of administration and maintenance having any responsibility for the functioning of the hyperbaric facility. Since Section 20.3 is expected to be used as a text by those responsible for the mitigation of hazards of hyperbaric facilities, the requirements set forth are frequently accompanied by explanatory text.

20.3.1.3 Responsibility.

20.3.1.3.1 Personnel having responsibility for the hyperbaric facility, and those responsible for licensing, accrediting, or approving institutions or other facilities in which hyperbaric installations are employed, shall establish and enforce programs to fulfill the provisions of this chapter.

20.3.1.3.2* Each hyperbaric facility shall designate an onsite hyperbaric safety director to be in charge of all hyperbaric equipment and the operational safety requirements of this chapter.

Some organizations manage multiple hyperbaric facilities in different regions and have designated a single safety director for all of their facilities. There must also be an individual at each facility designated as safety director, per 20.3.1.3.2.

◀ **FAQ**
Can a single safety director be responsible for multiple facilities in different locations?

A.20.3.1.3.2 The complexity of hyperbaric chambers is such that one person should be designated chamber operator, such as one in a position of responsible authority. Before starting a hyperbaric run, this person should acknowledge, in writing, in an appropriate log, the purpose of the run or test, duties of all personnel involved, and a statement that he or she is satisfied with the condition of all equipment. Exceptions should be itemized in the statement.

Safety, operational, and maintenance criteria of other organizations are published, for example, in the Undersea & Hyperbaric Medical Society Safety Committee documents and the Compressed Gas Association pamphlets, and should be reviewed by the safety director. The safety director should serve on the health care facility safety committee.

Due to a conflict of responsibility, the same individual should not serve as both Medical Director and Safety Director.

20.3.1.3.2.1 The safety director shall participate with facility management personnel and the hyperbaric physician(s) in developing procedures for operation and maintenance of the hyperbaric facility.

20.3.1.3.2.2 The safety director shall make recommendations for departmental safety policies and procedures.

20.3.1.3.2.3 The safety director shall have the authority to restrict or remove any potentially hazardous supply or equipment items from the chamber.

20.3.1.3.3* The governing board shall be responsible for the care and safety of patients and personnel.

A.20.3.1.3.3 It is incumbent upon the governing body to insist that rules and regulations with respect to practices and conduct in hyperbaric facilities, including qualifications and training of hyperbaric personnel, be adopted by the medical or administrative staff of the institution, and that regulations for inspection and maintenance are in use by the administrative, maintenance, and ancillary (and in the case of a hospital, nursing and other professional) personnel.

In meeting its responsibilities for safe practices in hyperbaric facilities, the administration of the facility should adopt or correlate regulations and standard operating procedures to ensure that both the physical qualities and the operating maintenance methods pertaining to hyperbaric facilities meet the standards set in Chapter 20. The controls adopted should cover the conduct of personnel in and around hyperbaric facilities and the apparel and footwear allowed. They should cover periodic inspection of static-dissipating materials and of all electrical equipment, including testing of ground contact indicators.

20.3.1.3.4* By virtue of its responsibility for the professional conduct of members of the medical staff of the health care facility, the organized medical staff shall adopt and enforce regulations with respect to the use of hyperbaric facilities located in health care facilities.

A.20.3.1.3.4 It is recommended that training of hyperbaric chamber personnel be closely monitored, following the guidelines and publications of the Undersea & Hyperbaric Medical Society, Baromedical Nurses Association, and the National Board of Diving and Hyperbaric Medical Technology.

20.3.1.3.4.1 The safety director shall participate in the development of these regulations.

20.3.1.3.5* The safety director shall ensure that electrical, monitoring, life support, protection, and ventilating arrangements in the hyperbaric chamber are inspected and tested as part of the routine maintenance program of the facility.

A.20.3.1.3.5 In the case of a hyperbaric facility located in a hospital, hospital licensing and other approval bodies, in meeting their responsibilities to the public, should include in their inspections not only compliance with requirements for physical installations in hyperbaric facilities, but also compliance with the requirements set forth in Section 20.3.

20.3.1.4 Rules and Regulations.

20.3.1.4.1* General. The administrative, technical, and professional staffs shall jointly develop policies for management of the hyperbaric facility.

A.20.3.1.4.1 It is recommended that all personnel, including trainees and those involved in the operation and maintenance of hyperbaric facilities, and including professional personnel and (in the case of hospitals) others involved in the direct care of patients undergoing hyperbaric therapy, be familiar with Chapter 20. Personnel concerned should maintain proficiency in the matters of life and fire safety by periodic review of this chapter, as well as any other pertinent material.

Positive measures are necessary to acquaint all personnel with the rules and regulations established and to assure enforcement. Training and discipline are necessary.

20.3.1.4.1.1 Upon adoption, policies shall be available in the facility.

20.3.1.4.2 The medical director of hyperbaric medicine and the safety director shall jointly develop the minimum staff qualifications, experience, and complement based on the following:

(1) The number and type of hyperbaric chambers in use
(2) Maximum treatment capacity
(3) The type of hyperbaric therapy normally provided

The *UHMS Guidelines for Hyperbaric Facility Operation,* published by the Undersea and Hyperbaric Medical Society, offers guidance on hyperbaric facility staffing [6].

20.3.1.4.3 All personnel, including those involved in maintenance and repair of the hyperbaric facility, shall be trained on the purpose, application, operation, and limitations of emergency equipment.

20.3.1.4.4 Emergency procedures specific to the hyperbaric facility shall be established.

20.3.1.4.4.1* All personnel shall be trained on emergency procedures.

A.20.3.1.4.4.1 All full and part-time personnel should receive training in emergency management appropriate to their job description.

20.3.1.4.4.2 Personnel shall be trained to control the chamber and decompress occupants when all powered equipment has been rendered inoperative.

20.3.1.4.5* Emergency procedures and fire training drills shall be conducted at least annually and documented by the safety director.

The requirement in 20.3.1.4.5 to conduct emergency procedures drills highlights the importance of practicing the emergency plans specific to the hyperbaric facility (i.e., medical emergency in the chamber, fire in the chamber, contaminated breathing gas). It is also important to document emergency preparedness.

A.20.3.1.4.5 A calm reaction (without panic) to an emergency situation can be expected only if the recommendations are familiar to and rehearsed by all concerned.

20.3.1.4.6* When an inspection, test, or maintenance procedure of the fire suppression system results in the system being placed OUT OF SERVICE, a protocol shall be followed that notifies appropriate personnel and agencies of the planned or emergency impairment.

A sign indicating the fire suppression system is OUT OF SERVICE shall be conspicuously placed on the operating console until the fire suppression system is restored to service.

Fire suppression capability must not be disabled without conspicuous and appropriate notification.

A.20.3.1.4.6 A suggested outline for emergency action in the case of fire is contained in C.20.2.

20.3.1.4.7 During chamber operations with occupant(s) in a chamber, the operator shall be physically present, and shall maintain visual or audible contact with the control panel or the chamber occupant(s).

20.3.1.5 General Requirements.

20.3.1.5.1* Potential Ignition Sources.

A.20.3.1.5.1 The immediate vicinity of the chamber is defined as the area around the chamber from which activation of the flame detector can occur. Flame detectors can be prematurely activated by certain radiation sources.

20.3.1.5.1.1 The following shall be prohibited from inside the chamber and the immediate vicinity outside the chamber:

(1) Smoking
(2) Open flames
(3) Hot objects

FAQ ▶ Can warming devices that operate at elevated temperatures at normal atmosphere be considered a hazard if used in an oxygen-enriched atmosphere at elevated pressures?

Air-activated warming devices have become increasingly popular as over-the-counter pain relief. Normal operating temperature for these devices is approximately 49°C (120°F) at 1 atmosphere absolute in air. The temperature of these devices has been shown to reach at least 110°C (230°F) at 3 atmospheres absolute in 100 percent oxygen. This temperature is far above the maximum allowed in 20.2.7.3.12 and 20.2.7.6.3 and certainly hot enough to burn the skin of a patient.

20.3.1.5.1.2 The following shall be prohibited from inside the chamber:

(1) Personal warming devices (i.e., therapeutic chemical heating pads, handwarmers, pocket warmers)
(2) Cell phones and pagers
(3) Sparking toys
(4) Personal entertainment devices

20.3.1.5.2 Flammable Gases and Liquids.

20.3.1.5.2.1 Flammable agents (including devices such as laboratory burners employing bottled or natural gas and cigarette lighters) shall be prohibited inside the chamber and from the proximity of the compressor intake.

20.3.1.5.2.2 For Class A chambers, flammable agents used for patient care, such as alcohol swabs, parenteral alcohol-based pharmaceuticals, and topical creams, shall be permitted in the chamber if the following conditions are met:

(1) Such use is approved by the safety director, or other authority having jurisdiction.

(2)* The quantities of such agents are limited so that they are incapable of releasing sufficient flammable vapor into the chamber atmosphere to exceed the LEL for the material.

A.20.3.1.5.2.2(2) Allowable quantities for (2) can be determined from the chamber volume, flammable agent vapor density, and lower explosive limit (LEL). Experience has shown that increased pressure has little effect on LEL for a given flammable gas and oxygen concentration. A safety factor of 10 is recommended. Flammable liquids should be confined to nonbreakable, nonspill containers.

Sample Determination. Example of Limiting Quantity of Flammable Agent Substance: Isopropyl alcohol (2-propanol)

LEL = 2%/vol. (irrespective of chamber pressure)

Vapor density = 2.1 relative to air

Liquid density = 786 g/L

Air density = 0.075 lb/ft^3 at STP

The limiting case occurs at the lowest ambient pressure, that is, 1 atmosphere:

$$\begin{aligned}\text{Alcohol vapor density at LEL} &= 0.02 \times 2.1 \times 0.075 \\ &= 0.00315 \text{ lb/ft}^3 \\ &= 1.43 \text{ g/ft}^3\end{aligned}$$

For a relatively small 500 ft^3 chamber, this implies:

$1.43 \times 500 = 715$ g alcohol vapor at LEL

Using a safety factor of 10 to account for uneven vapor concentrations gives 71.5 g = 91 ml alcohol.

One could conclude that even 90 ml of alcohol is more than would be needed for almost any medical procedure. The above calculation also does not account for the mitigating effect of ventilation.

Many "inert" halogenated compounds have been found to act explosively in the presence of metals, even under normal atmospheric conditions, despite the fact that the halogen compound itself does not ignite in oxygen, or, in the case of solids such as polytetrafluoroethylene, is self-extinguishing. Apparently these materials are strong oxidizers whether as gases, liquids (solvents, greases), or solids (electrical insulation, fabric, or coatings). Some halogenated hydrocarbons that will not burn in the presence of low-pressure oxygen will ignite and continue to burn in high-pressure oxygen. Customarily, Class A chambers maintain internal oxygen concentration that does not exceed 23.5 percent.

Parts of this chapter deal with the elements required to be incorporated into the structure of the chamber to reduce the possibility of electrostatic spark discharges, which are a possible cause of ignition in hyperbaric atmospheres. The elimination of static charges is dependent on the vigilance of administrative activities in materials, purchase, maintenance supervision, and periodic inspection and testing. It cannot be emphasized too strongly that an incomplete chain of precautions generally will increase the electrostatic hazard. For example, conductive flooring can contribute to the hazard unless all personnel wear conductive shoes, all objects in the room are electrically continuous with the floor, and humidity is maintained.

The limitations on the use in the chamber of alcohol and other agents that emit flammable vapors in 20.3.1.5.2.2 should be strictly observed and such restrictions should be prominently posted.

(3) A safety factor shall be included to account for the localized concentrations, stratification, and the absence of ventilation.
(4) The oxygen monitoring requirement of 20.2.8.4.2 is observed.

20.3.1.5.2.3 Flammable liquids, gases, or vapors shall not be permitted inside any Class B chamber.

20.3.1.5.3* Personnel.

A.20.3.1.5.3 The number of occupants of the chamber should be kept to the minimum number necessary to carry out the procedure.

20.3.1.5.3.1 Antistatic procedures as directed by the safety director shall be employed whenever atmospheres containing more than 23.5 percent oxygen by volume are used.

FAQ ▶
What are some of the antistatic procedures?

Paragraph 20.3.1.5.3.1 addresses two issues. First, antistatic procedures are necessary when the oxygen percentage of the environment is high. This is always the case inside an oxygen compressed Class B chamber. Second, the safety director is responsible for antistatic procedures. These procedures might include, but are not limited to, grounding, ground testing, humidity control, laundering techniques, and textile selection.

20.3.1.5.3.2 In Class A and Class B chambers with atmospheres containing more than 23.5 percent oxygen by volume, electrical grounding of the patient shall be ensured by the provision of a high-impedance conductive pathway in contact with the patient's skin.

This high-impedance conductive pathway is usually accomplished with a "grounding strap." (See Exhibit 20.11.) The chamber itself is required to have a low-impedance ground to the building. When the patient is electrically connected to the chamber, it is important that the connection be a high-impedance conductive pathway. This connection allows dissipation of static charge but also prevents electric shock of the patient. Should the chamber be exposed to a surge of energy, the high-impedance pathway will limit the energy that can travel to the patient.

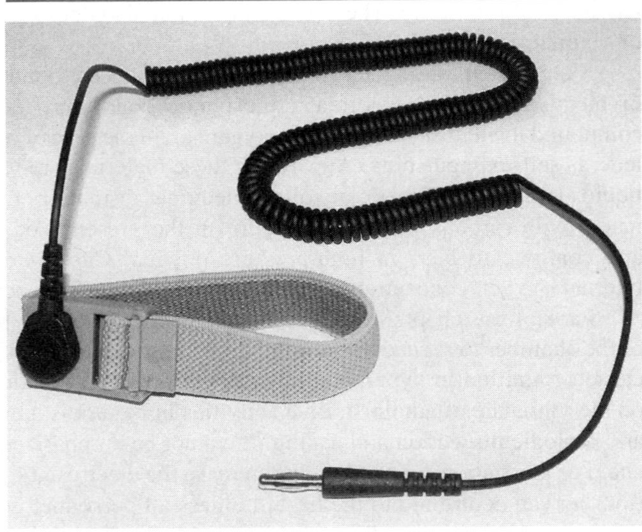

***EXHIBIT 20.11** Typical grounding strap used in an oxygen-filled hyperbaric chamber. (Photo courtesy of International ATMO, San Antonio, Texas)*

20.3.1.5.3.3 Shoes having ferrous nails that make contact with the floor shall not be permitted to be worn in Class A chambers.

20.3.1.5.4* Textiles.

A.20.3.1.5.4 It is recommended that all chamber personnel should wear garments of the overall or jumpsuit type, completely covering all skin areas possible, and as tightfitting as possible. It can be impractical to clothe some patients (depending upon their disease or the site of any operation) in such garments. Hospital gowns of flame-resistant textile should be employed in such a case.

The requirement for tightfitting overall or jumpsuit garments for chamber personnel was moved to advisory text (i.e., A.20.3.1.5.4) in the last edition. The recommendation was also altered to include garments that this standard allows for patients and garments approved for surgical personnel. With this relaxation in the standard for chamber personnel garments, care must still be taken not to introduce otherwise prohibited textiles or significant static producers.

20.3.1.5.4.1 Silk, wool, or synthetic textile materials shall not be permitted in Class A or Class B chambers unless the fabric meets the flame resistant requirements of 20.3.1.5.4.5.

It is important to remember that all textiles are fuel sources in the chamber. Synthetic fabrics (i.e., polyester, rayon, nylon) are not permitted because they tend to be good fuel sources and better producers of static charge. Even flame-resistant textiles can burn in the hyperbaric chamber, but they are allowed by 20.3.1.5.4.1 because they have higher ignition temperatures.

20.3.1.5.4.2 Garments fabricated of 100 percent cotton or a blend of cotton and polyester fabric shall be permitted in Class A chambers equipped with fire protection as specified in 20.2.5, and in Class B chambers.

It is impractical to require only flame-resistant textiles in chambers, so other fabrics have been allowed. The allowance of a blend of cotton and polyester fabric is new in this edition of the standard.

Previous editions allowed an "antistatic blend of cotton and polyester" because of one specific fabric — a blend of cotton and polyester with steel fibers to make it conductive. This blended fabric was intended for surgical scrubs, but its conductive properties made it a good choice for hyperbaric garments. From a static electricity standpoint, the conductive properties of the fabric actually afford some protection that cotton fabric does not. Unfortunately, this particular fabric is no longer made.

Selection of textiles for the hyperbaric chamber should be based on ignition temperature and static-producing properties.

20.3.1.5.4.3 The physician or surgeon in charge, with the concurrence of the safety director, shall be permitted to use prohibited items in the chamber that are one of the following:

(1) Suture material
(2) Alloplastic devices
(3) Bacterial barriers
(4) Surgical dressings
(5) Biological interfaces

Paragraph 20.3.1.5.4.3 recognizes that patients with wounds might require the use of certain products specifically prohibited by this standard. If one of these products is allowed, it should be based on specific knowledge of the oxygen compatibility and ignition temperature of the product. It should also be a one-time exception. Although a "blanket exception" is not prohibited by this standard, it undermines the intent of prohibiting the items in the first place.

20.3.1.5.4.4 Physician and safety director approval to use prohibited items shall be stated in writing for all prohibited materials employed *(see A.20.3.1.3.2).*

20.3.1.5.4.5 Where flame resistance is specified, the fabric shall meet the requirements set forth for the small-scale test in NFPA 701, *Standard Methods of Fire Tests for Flame Propagation of Textiles and Films*, in an atmosphere equivalent to the maximum oxygen concentration and pressure proposed for the chamber.

20.3.1.5.5 The use of flammable hair sprays, hair oils, and skin oils shall be forbidden for all chamber occupants/patients as well as personnel.

20.3.1.5.5.1 Whenever possible, patients shall be stripped of all clothing, particularly if it is contaminated by dirt, grease, or solvents, and then reclothed. *(See A.20.3.1.5.4.)*

20.3.1.5.5.2 All cosmetics, lotions, and oils shall be removed from the patient's body and hair.

20.3.1.5.6 All other fabrics used in the chamber such as sheets, drapes, and blankets shall conform to 20.3.1.5.4.1 and 20.3.1.5.4.2.

20.3.1.5.7 Clothing worn by patients in Class A or B chambers and personnel in Class A chambers shall conform to the following:

(1) Be issued by the hyperbaric facility or specifically approved by the safety director for hyperbaric use
(2) Be uncontaminated
(3) Be devoid of prohibited articles prior to chamber pressurization

FAQ ▶ **Why is it important to have the facility supply the patient clothing used in the chamber?**

Analysis of hyperbaric chamber fires has shown that the ignition mechanism can be concealed in patient clothing. For this reason, many hyperbaric facilities either remove the pockets or sew the pockets shut on facility-issued patient clothing.

In normal use, clothing can be exposed to petroleum products, flammable liquids, and vapors. For this reason, many hyperbaric facilities do not allow the facility-issued patient clothing to leave the facility.

20.3.2 Equipment.

20.3.2.1 All equipment used in the hyperbaric chamber shall comply with Section 20.2, including the following:

(1) All electrical and mechanical equipment necessary for the operation and maintenance of the hyperbaric facility
(2) Any medical devices and instruments used in the facility

20.3.2.1.1 Use of unapproved equipment shall be prohibited. *(See 20.3.1.5.4.3.)*

A formal process should be in place and documented to evaluate and approve chamber equipment. It should incorporate assessment of compliance with all applicable requirements of this standard, including the following:

1. Potential release of energy into the chamber environment
2. Potential release of toxic gases into the chamber environment
3. Damage from exposure to maximum chamber pressure
4. Functional performance at different chamber pressures (up to maximum chamber pressure)

20.3.2.1.2 The following devices shall not be operated in the hyperbaric chamber unless approved by the safety director for such use:

(1) Portable X-ray devices
(2) Electrocautery equipment
(3) High-energy devices

20.3.2.1.3 Photographic equipment employing the following shall not remain in the chamber when the chamber is pressurized:

(1) Photoflash
(2) Flood lamps

20.3.2.1.4 Lasers shall not be used under any condition.

20.3.2.1.5 Equipment known to be, or suspected of being, defective shall not be introduced into any hyperbaric chamber or used in conjunction with the operation of such chamber until repaired, tested, and accepted by qualified personnel and approved by the safety director *(see 20.3.1.3.2).*

20.3.2.1.6* Paper brought into the chamber shall be stored in a closed metal container. Containers used for paper storage shall be emptied after each chamber operation.

Analysis of hyperbaric chamber fires has shown that an abundance of burnable materials has been a contributing factor in several fire mishaps worldwide.

A.20.3.2.1.6 The use of paper should be kept to an absolute minimum in hyperbaric chambers.

20.3.2.1.7 Equipment that does not meet the temperature requirements of Article 500.8(A), 500.8(B), and 500.8(C) of NFPA 70, *National Electrical Code*, shall not be allowed in the chamber.

20.3.2.2* The following shall be all metal to the extent possible:

(1) Oxygen containers
(2) Valves
(3) Fittings
(4) Interconnecting equipment

A.20.3.2.2 Users should be aware that many items if ignited in pressurized oxygen-enriched atmospheres are not self-extinguishing. Iron alloys, aluminum, and stainless steel are, to various degrees, in that category as well as human skin, muscle, and fat, and plastic tubing such as polyvinyl chloride (Tygon®). Testing for oxygen compatibility is very complicated. Very little data exist and many standards still have to be determined. Suppliers do not normally have facilities for testing their products in controlled atmospheres, especially high-pressure oxygen. Both static conditions and impact conditions are applicable. Self-ignition temperatures normally are unknown in special atmospheres.

20.3.2.3 The following shall be compatible with oxygen under service conditions:

(1) Valve seats
(2) Gaskets
(3) Hose
(4) Lubricants

20.3.2.4 Equipment used inside the chamber requiring lubrication shall be lubricated with oxygen-compatible flame-resistant material.

20.3.2.4.1 Factory-sealed antifriction bearings shall be permitted to be used with standard hydrocarbon lubricants in Class A chambers that do not employ atmospheres of increased oxygen concentration.

20.3.2.5* Equipment made of the following shall be prohibited from the chamber interior:

(1) Cerium
(2) Magnesium
(3) Magnesium alloys

Recently, concern has been raised about the potential fire risk of titanium products in the hyperbaric chamber. If a piece of titanium is broken in hyperbaric oxygen, enough energy can be produced by the stress fracture to ignite the titanium in the high-oxygen environment. This is not a concern in hyperbaric air.

◀ **FAQ**
Is titanium a hazard in a hyperbaric chamber?

A.20.3.2.5 See A.20.3.2.2.

20.3.2.6* In the event that radiation equipment is introduced into a hyperbaric chamber, hydrocarbon detectors shall be installed.

A.20.3.2.6 Radiation equipment, whether infrared or roentgen ray, can make hyperbaric chambers even more hazardous.

20.3.2.6.1 In the event that flammable gases are detected in excess of 1000 ppm, radiation equipment shall not be operated until the chamber atmosphere is cleared.

20.3.3 Handling of Gases.

20.3.3.1 The institution's administrative personnel shall develop policies for safe handling of gases in the hyperbaric facility *(see 20.3.1.5.2 and C.20.1.1.3.2).*

20.3.3.2 Oxygen and other gases shall not be introduced into the chamber in the liquid state.

20.3.3.3 Flammable gases shall not be used or stored in the chamber or in the hyperbaric facility.

20.3.3.4* Pressurized containers of gas shall be permitted to be introduced into the hyperbaric chamber, provided that the container and its contents are approved for such use by the safety director.

A.20.3.3.4 Quantities of oxygen stored in the chamber should be kept to a minimum.

20.3.4 Maintenance.

20.3.4.1 General.

20.3.4.1.1 The hyperbaric safety director shall ensure that all valves, regulators, meters, and similar equipment used in the hyperbaric chamber are compensated for use under hyperbaric conditions and tested as part of the routine maintenance program of the facility.

The appropriate frequency for this type of maintenance varies with different equipment. The intent of 20.3.4.1.1 is to ensure that testing of these equipment items is not overlooked.

20.3.4.1.1.1 Pressure relief valves shall be tested and calibrated as part of the routine maintenance program of the facility.

20.3.4.1.2 The hyperbaric safety director shall ensure that all gas outlets in the chambers are labeled or stenciled in accordance with CGA C-4, *Standard Method of Marking Portable Compressed Gas Containers to Identify the Material Contained.*

20.3.4.1.3 Before piping systems are initially put into use, it shall be ascertained that the gas delivered at the outlet is shown on the outlet label and that connecting fittings are checked against their labels, in accordance with Sections 5.1 through 5.3.

20.3.4.1.4 The requirements set forth in Section 5.1 concerning the storage, location, and special precautions required for compressed gases shall be followed. Reserve supplies and master alarm signals shall meet the requirements of Section 5.2.

20.3.4.1.5 Storage areas for hazardous materials shall not be located in the room housing the hyperbaric chamber *(see 20.2.1).*

20.3.4.1.5.1 Flammable gases, except as provided in 20.3.1.5.2.2(1), shall not be used or stored in the hyperbaric room.

20.3.4.1.6 All replacement parts and components shall conform to original design specification.

20.3.4.2 Maintenance Logs.

20.3.4.2.1 Installation, repairs, and modifications of equipment related to a chamber shall be evaluated by engineering personnel, tested under pressure, and approved by the safety director.

20.3.4.2.1.1 Logs of all tests shall be maintained.

20.3.4.2.2 Operating equipment logs shall be maintained by engineering personnel.

20.3.4.2.2.1 Operating equipment logs shall be signed before chamber operation by the person in charge *(see A.20.3.1.3.2).*

20.3.4.2.3 Operating equipment logs shall not be taken inside the chamber.

20.3.5 Electrical Safeguards.

20.3.5.1 Electrical equipment shall be installed and operated in accordance with 20.2.7.

20.3.5.1.1 All electrical circuits shall be tested in accordance with the routine maintenance program of the facility.

20.3.5.1.1.1 Electrical circuit test shall include the following:

(1) A ground fault check to verify that no conductors are grounded to the chamber
(2) A test of normal functioning *(see 20.2.7.2.2)*

20.3.5.1.2 In the event of fire, all nonessential electrical equipment within the chamber shall be deenergized before extinguishing the fire.

20.3.5.1.2.1 Smoldering, burning electrical equipment shall be deenergized before extinguishing a localized fire involving only the equipment *(see 20.2.5).*

20.3.6* Electrostatic Safeguards.

A.20.3.6 The elimination of static charges is dependent on the vigilance of administrative supervision of materials purchased, maintenance, and periodic inspection and testing.

20.3.6.1 Administration. (Reserved)

20.3.6.2 Maintenance.

20.3.6.2.1* Conductive Floors. See E.6.6.8, Reduction in Electrostatic Hazard, for recommendations on chambers containing conductive floors.

A.20.3.6.2.1 The requirements of E.6.6.8 apply.

20.3.6.2.2 Furniture Used in the Chamber.

20.3.6.2.2.1 Conductive devices on furniture and equipment shall be inspected to ensure that they are free of wax, lint, or other extraneous material that could insulate them and defeat the conductive properties.

20.3.6.2.2.2* Casters or furniture leg tips shall not be capable of impact sparking.

A.20.3.6.2.2.2 Ferrous metals can cause such sparking, as can magnesium or magnesium alloys if contact is made with rusted steel.

20.3.6.2.2.3 Casters shall not be lubricated with oils or other flammable materials.

20.3.6.2.2.4 Lubricants shall be oxygen compatible and flame resistant.

20.3.6.2.2.5 Wheelchairs and gurneys with bearings lubricated and sealed by the manufacturer shall be permitted in Class A chambers where conditions prescribed in 20.2.8.4 are met.

20.3.6.2.3* Conductive Accessories. Conductive accessories shall meet conductivity and antistatic requirements.

The conductive property of a material in the chamber is an important part of the ground path. Conductive properties can change over time. In oxygen-enriched environments, some materials deteriorate faster; and typical cleaning products can diminish the conductive properties of some materials. It is important to ensure that grounding is not defeated by the loss of conductive properties.

A.20.3.6.2.3 Conductive accessories can include belting, rubber accessories, plastics, covers, and sheeting. For more information see E.6.6.8, Reduction in Electrostatic Hazard, in Annex E.

20.3.6.2.4* Materials containing rubber shall be inspected as part of the routine maintenance program of the facility, especially at points of kinking.

A.20.3.6.2.4 Materials containing rubber deteriorate rapidly in oxygen-enriched atmospheres.

20.3.6.3 Fire Protection Equipment. Electrical switches, valves, and electrical monitoring equipment associated with fire detection and extinguishment shall be visually inspected before each chamber pressurization. Fire detection equipment shall be tested each week and full testing, including discharge of extinguishing media, shall be conducted annually. Testing shall include activation of trouble circuits and signals.

The intent of a visual inspection before each chamber pressurization is to ensure that fire detection and suppression capabilites are in a ready state. Procedures vary with different equipment configurations but would include inspections to ensure the following:

1. Electrical components are powered on.
2. Activation switches are enabled.
3. Pneumatic components have sufficient pressure.
4. Water supply is available.
5. Water flow valves are open.
6. Handlines are accessible.
7. The system is not in bypass mode.

The testing requirements of 20.2.5.5 call for at least semiannual testing of deluge and handlines. That requirement is not in conflict with 20.3.6.3. The requirements of 20.2.5.5 deal with only functional testing, whereas this paragraph deals with annual testing of the entire fire suppression system (all components), including the functional test required by 20.2.5.5.

20.3.6.4* Housekeeping. A housekeeping program shall be implemented whether or not the facility is in regular use.

A.20.3.6.4 It is absolutely essential that all areas of, and components associated with, the hyperbaric chamber be kept meticulously free of grease, lint, dirt, and dust.

20.3.6.4.1 The persons assigned to this task shall be trained in the following:

(1) Potential damage to the equipment from cleaning procedures
(2) Potential personal injury
(3) Specific cleaning procedures
(4) Equipment not to be cleaned

REFERENCES CITED IN COMMENTARY

1. NFPA 70, *National Electrical Code®,* 2005 edition.
2. ANSI/ASME PVHO-1, *Safety Standard for Pressure Vessels for Human Occupancy.* American Society of Mechanical Engineers, New York, NY, 1997.
3. ANSI/ASME PVHO-2, *Safety Standard for Pressure Vessels for Human Occupancy: In-service Guidelines for PVHO Acrylic Windows*. American Society of Mechanical Engineers, New York, NY, 2004.
4. NFPA 25, *Inspection, Testing, and Maintenance of Water-Based Fire Suppression Systems,* 2002 edition.
5. NFPA 53, *Recommended Practice on Materials, Equipment, and Systems Used in Oxygen-Enriched Atmospheres,* 2004 edition.
6. Workman, W. T., UHMS Guidelines for Hyperbaric Facility Operation. Undersea and Hyperbaric Medical Society, Kensington, MD, 2004.

Additional References of Interest

Beeson, H. D., Stewart, W. F. and Woods, S. S., *Safe Use of Oxygen and Oxygen Systems: Guidelines for Oxygen System Design, Materials Selection, Operations, Storage, and Transportation*, American Society for Testing and Materials, West Conshohocken, PA, 2000.

Burman, F., *Risk Assessment Guide for the Installation and Operation of Clinical Hyperbaric Facilities* (3rd edition), International ATMO, Inc., San Antonio, TX, 2002.

Hink, J., and Jansen, E., "Titanium in a Hyperbaric Oxygen Environment May Pose a Fire Risk," *Aviation, Space and Environmental Med*, 2003, 74(12): 1301–1302.

Johnson, R. P., *Technical Report 1622: Acrylic Light Pipes for Interior Illumination of Hyperbaric Chambers*, Naval Command, Control and Ocean Surveillance Center, San Diego, CA, 1996.

NFPA 77, *Recommended Practice on Static Electricity,* 2000 edition.

Raleigh, G., Rivard, R., and Fabus, S., "Air-Activated Warming Devices in the Hyperbaric Environment: Effects of Oxygen and Pressure," *Undersea Hyper Med*, 2005, 32(3).

Sheffield, P. J., and Desautels, D. A., "Hyperbaric and Hypobaric Chamber Fires: A 73-year Analysis," *Undersea Hyper Med,* 1997, 24(3): 153–164.

Sheffield, P. J., Hewitt, M., and Sheffield, R. B., "Fire Risk in Hyperbaric Facilities: Could Oxygen Pooling Be A Factor?" *Proceeding of the Fourteenth International Congress on Hyperbaric Medicine*, Best Publishing, Flagstaff, AZ, 2002, pp. 305–311.

Stachiw, J. D., *Handbook of Acrylics for Submersibles, Hyperbaric Chambers, and Aquaria*, Best Publishing, Flagstaff, AZ, 2003.

Workman, W. T., *Hyperbaric Facility Safety: A Practical Guide*, Best Publishing, Flagstaff, AZ, 1999.

CHAPTER 21

Freestanding Birthing Centers

Many freestanding birthing centers use the same equipment and systems as hospitals, nursing homes, and other health care facilities. This equipment includes patient-care-related appliances and gas-powered medical equipment to perform procedures where the loss of electrical power would cause electrical incidents or patient injury or to install piped medical gas or vacuum systems. Because these facilities use the same equipment, they should comply with the requirements for such equipment or systems.

21.1 Applicability

This chapter applies to freestanding birth centers, as defined in Chapter 3.

21.2 Responsibilities (Reserved)

21.3 General Requirements

21.3.1 Reserved.

21.3.2 Reserved.

21.3.3 Reserved.

21.3.4 Electrical System Requirements.

Electrical systems used in freestanding birthing centers shall conform to such requirements of Chapter 4 as applicable.

Chapter 21 does not specify the appropriate type of electrical service to be used but simply imposes a general requirement to follow the requirements of Chapter 4, as applicable. Therefore, the user and the AHJ should determine which type of electrical service to provide. The user should review the requirements of Type 1, Type 2, and Type 3 systems to determine the level of acceptable risk they wish to take for a freestanding birthing center. In addition, the user can review the electrical requirements of Chapter 13, Hospitals; Chapter 14, Other Health Care Facilities; Chapter 17, Nursing Homes; and Chapter 18, Limited Care Facilities to determine whether the functional operations of the birthing center are similar to any of those facilities.

21.3.5 Gas and Vacuum System Requirements.

Gas and vacuum systems used in freestanding birthing centers shall conform to such requirements of Chapter 5 as applicable.

FAQ ▶
What level gas and vacuum system is required for a freestanding birthing center?

Chapter 21 does not specify the appropriate level of gas and vacuum service to be used but instead applies a general requirement to follow the requirements of Chapter 5, as applicable. Therefore, the user and the AHJ should determine which type of gas or vacuum service to provide. Because there is no guidance, the user can use the criteria specified in 13.3.5, 14.3.5, 17.3.5, or 18.3.5 to assist in determining the appropriate level for a gas or vacuum system. The requirements of these sections allow the user to select a Level 1, Level 2, or Level 3 system after an analysis of the system use and patient needs has been conducted.

21.3.6 Reserved.

21.3.7 Reserved.

21.3.8 Electrical Equipment Requirements.

Electrical equipment used in freestanding birthing centers shall conform to such requirements of Chapter 8 as applicable.

21.3.9 Gas Equipment Requirements.

Gas equipment used in freestanding birthing centers shall conform to such requirements of Chapter 9 as applicable.

ANNEX A

Explanatory Material

Annex A is not a part of the requirements of this NFPA document but is included for informational purposes only. This annex contains explanatory material, numbered to correspond with the applicable text paragraphs.

The material contained in Annex A of NFPA 99 is not part of the requirements of this standard but is included with the standard for informational purposes only. For the convenience of readers of this handbook, Annex A text is interspersed among the text of Chapter 1 through Chapter 21 and, therefore, is not repeated here.

ANNEX B

Nature of Hazards

This annex is not a part of the requirements of this NFPA document but is included for informational purposes only.

Annex B covers the hazards associated with electrical systems and equipment, gas and vacuum systems and equipment, environmental systems, flammability of materials, and hyperbaric chambers.

B.1 Electrical Systems Hazards

The hazards attendant to the use of electricity include electrical shock, thermal injury, and interruption of power.

B.1.1 Fire and Explosions.

Electrical systems can be subject to the occurrence of electrical fires. Grounding systems, over-current protective devices, and other subjects discussed in this standard could be intended for fire prevention as well as other purposes. This aspect of electrical systems is the primary focus of other NFPA standards and will not be emphasized herein.

B.1.2 Shock.

B.1.2.1 General. The major concern in this chapter is electric shock resulting from degradation or some type of failure within normally safe electrical appliances or the facility's electrical distribution system. The defect could be in the wiring, in a component, or the result of deteriorating insulation. The failure could be caused by mechanical abuse or by improper use of the equipment.

Hospital service presents unusually severe environmental stress to equipment, similar to hard industrial use. Appliances are frequently subjected to large mechanical stresses in the course of being transported around the facility. Patients and staff, particularly those in operating rooms, critical care areas, clinical laboratories and some physical therapy areas, are frequently surrounded by exposed, electrically grounded conductive surfaces that increase the risk of serious injury in the event of certain types of electrical failure.

Electricity passing through the body can stimulate excitable tissue, causing pain, involuntary muscle contractions, convulsions, or ventricular fibrillation. Also, electricity can cause tissue necrosis due to heat, chemical imbalance, or arcing. The effect of electricity depends upon the applied voltage, the magnitude of the current, the duration of application, whether the current is direct or alternating, the frequency of the current, and the size and location of the electrodes at which the current enters and leaves the body. The conductivity and dielectric strength of the skin is often a factor in determining the outcome of contact with electrified conductors.

Electrocution resulting from contact with equipment connected to ordinary branch circuit (i.e., less than 250 V at about 60 Hz) is usually a consequence of sustained ventricular fibrillation. When applied directly to the heart, voltages of less than 100 mV rms, 60 Hz can cause sustained ventricular fibrillation and death.

B.1.2.2 Control. Control of electric shock hazard requires the limitation of electric current that might flow in an electric circuit involving the patient's body and is accomplished through a variety of alternative approaches.

B.1.2.2.1 Shock Prevention. See Figure B.1.2.2.1(a). Since electric shock results from the effect of an electric current flowing through a part of the human body, the following three conditions should be satisfied simultaneously before a patient or staff member can be shocked:

(1) One part of the body in contact with a conductive surface (Point 1)
(2) A different part of the same body in contact with a second conductive surface (Point 2)
(3) A voltage source that will drive current through the body between those two points of contact (Point 3)

In the general case, six or seven independent and separable factors should combine simultaneously to satisfy these three conditions. *[See Figure B.1.2.2.1(b).]*

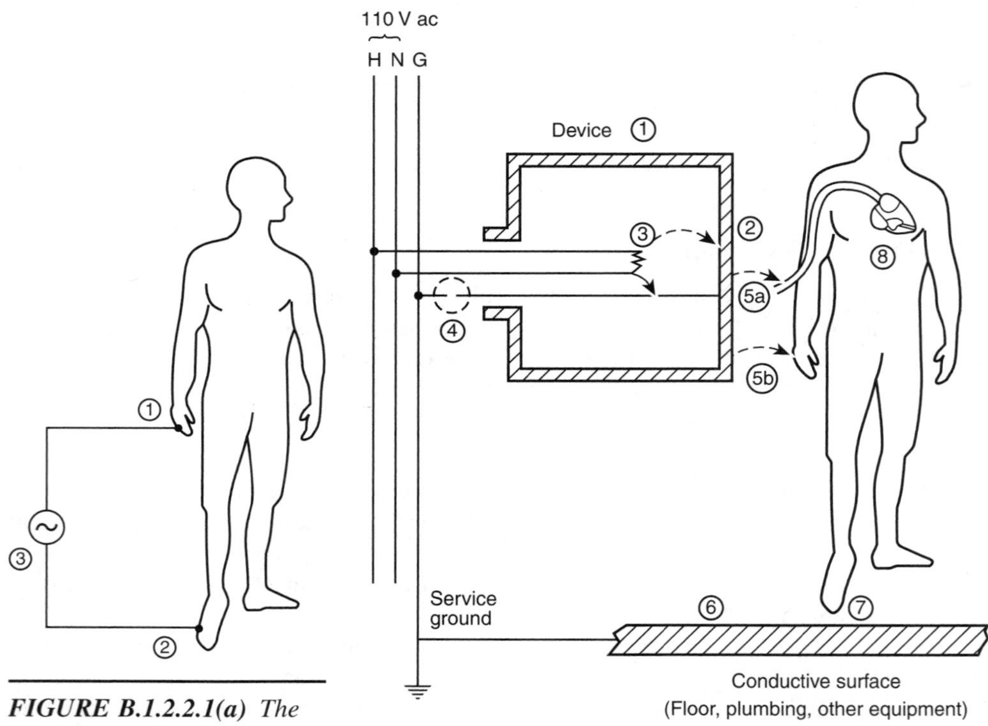

FIGURE B.1.2.2.1(a) *The Three Basic Conditions Required to Produce an Electric Shock.*

FIGURE B.1.2.2.1(b) *General Factors That Should Be Considered When Analyzing Electrical Safety.*

Several separate factors should be analyzed when evaluating a potential electric shock hazard. The following numbers refer to points in Figure B.1.2.2.1(b):

(1) The likelihood that a piece of line-powered equipment will be within reach of the patient
(2) The possibility of direct exposure of a "live" 110-V conductor through a damaged line cord or attachment plug. The likelihood that the equipment will have exposed metal parts that through some reasonably credible accident could become "live"

(3) The likelihood that equipment is accidentally damaged or malfunctions in some way and the metal becomes "live," that is, electrified
(4) The likelihood of the exposed metal parts not being grounded or accidentally becoming ungrounded
(5) The likelihood that the patient (or member of staff, or visitor) will make good contact with this exposed, potentially live surface
(6) The likelihood that a second exposed conductive surface that is, or that could through a reasonably credible event become, grounded is also within reach
(7) The likelihood that the patient (or member of staff, or visitor) will make good contact with this grounded, or potentially grounded, surface
(8) The probability that the resultant current flow will be sufficient to cause an injury

The chance of a patient actually sustaining an electric shock is a product of the likelihood that each of the events in (1) through (8) will occur. If the likelihood of occurrence of any one event is very close to zero, then the risk of electric shock will be very close to zero. Put another way, six or seven links in a chain need to be intact in order for a shock to be sustained. If any one link can be made extremely weak, by design or operating procedure, the chance of receiving a shock will be minimal.

Working to minimize the occurrence of one factor (i.e., one safety factor) can achieve one layer of protection. A second layer of protection is achieved by working to make the chance of occurrence of a second factor in the overall chain also very close to zero. However, extending this process to minimize the occurrence of all factors can lead to overdesign, overspecification, and less than cost-effective utilization of resources to control any problem.

Consider briefly each of the component factors. First, more could be done operationally to ensure that the minimum amount of line-powered equipment is within reach of the patient. Second, equipment that does not have a significant amount of exposed metal is to be preferred. Third, the staff should be instructed to report all obviously damaged equipment, even if it is still functional. Fourth, all grounding circuits should be tested frequently. Fifth, minimize the amount of grounded metal that is within reach of the patient. Avoid when possible attaching any grounded leads directly to the patient. Do not deliberately ground any metal part, such as a curtain rail or a metal cabinet, that cannot become accidentally "live." Insulate the patient from ground as much as possible.

In consideration of these objectives, four basic principles can be examined to avoid electric shock:

(1) Shock prevention by insulating and enclosing
(2) Shock prevention by grounding
(3) Shock prevention by device design
(4) Shock prevention through user procedures

B.1.2.2.2 Shock Prevention by Insulation and Enclosure. Physical provisions should be made to prevent personal hazardous contact between energized conductors or between an energized conductor and ground.

B.1.2.2.2.1 Noninsulated current-carrying conductors, which could produce hazardous currents, should be protected from contact through suitable enclosure.

B.1.2.2.2.2 Energized conductors, which could produce hazardous currents when not in protective enclosures, should be insulated by materials suitable to the voltage and environment.

In order to minimize the probability of completing a hazardous circuit, exposed conductive surfaces not likely to be energized from internal sources should not be intentionally grounded. Insulated covering of such surfaces is desirable.

Note that past measures recommended by earlier editions of NFPA standards and other standards associated with equipotential grounding and bonding of "dead metal" served to increase the likelihood that a patient or staff member would complete an undesirable pathway for electric shock.

Also note that this principle does not intend to mandate construction of an insulated environment, but rather to avoid intentional grounding of otherwise dead metal surfaces.

B.1.2.2.3 Shock Prevention by Grounding. A grounding system for fault currents should be supplied for two reasons: to minimize the fraction of the fault current that might flow through an individual during the fault condition and to operate overcurrent devices in order to minimize the possibility of damage and fire. This grounding system should also be utilized to provide a safe path for leakage currents.

B.1.2.2.3.1 Unless doubly insulated, each line-powered electrical appliance within the patient care vicinity should have a grounding wire, which normally carries the leakage current directly to ground, in the same power cable as the energized conductors.

B.1.2.2.3.2 Each receptacle for line-powered electrical appliances should provide a low-impedance grounding connection and path.

B.1.2.2.4 Shock Prevention by Device Design. Leakage current should be minimized. New device designs should not intentionally provide a low-impedance path at 60 Hz from patient to ground.

B.1.2.2.5 Shock Prevention Through User Procedures. A total electrical safety program incorporates the best features of design, manufacture, inspection, maintenance, and operation. The design should be such that limited departures from ideal conditions of maintenance and use will not cause unreasonable risks.

Where existing equipment that does not meet new-equipment requirements is to be used, such use is permissible if procedures of use and maintenance can establish an equivalent level of safety.

User procedures should include the establishment of the following:

(1) A policy to prohibit the connection of nonisolated input equipment to externalized intracardiac electrodes
(2) User educational and training programs
(3) A testing and routine maintenance program

B.1.3 Thermal. (Reserved)

B.1.4 Interruption of Power.

The normal source of power will fail at some point. In this case, a secondary source of power is required for life safety features such as lighting, communications, alarms, and more. In addition, there is a need to maintain power to complete medical procedures and activities as well as the need to power building equipment such as fans, motors, and pumps.

B.1.4.1 General. Medical and nursing sciences are becoming progressively more dependent on electrical apparatus for the preservation of life of hospitalized patients. For example, year by year more cardiac operations are performed, in some of which the patient's life depends on artificial circulation of the blood. In other operations, life is sustained by means of electrical impulses that stimulate and regulate heart action. In still others, suction developed by electrical means is routinely relied on to remove body fluids and mucus that might otherwise cause suffocation. In another sense, lighting is needed in strategic areas in order that precise procedures can be carried out, and power is needed to safeguard such vital services as refrigerated stores held in tissue, bone, and blood banks.

Interruption of normal electrical service in health care facilities can be caused by catastrophes such as storms, floods, fires, earthquakes, or explosions; by failures of the systems supplying electrical power; or by incidents within the facility. For all such situations, electrical systems should be planned to limit internal disruption and to provide for continuity of vital services at all times. Outages might be corrected in seconds or might require hours for correction. This indicates that the system or protection needs to be designed to cope with the longest probable outage.

Selecting vital areas and functions considered to be essential, designing safeguards to ensure continuity in these circuits, and maintaining the electrical and mechanical components of such essential services so that they will work when called on are complex problems that warrant standardized guidance for regulating agencies, governing boards, and administrators of health care facilities and architects and engineers concerned with their construction. Such guidance is offered in Chapter 4.

Chapter 4 is predicated on the basic principle of achieving dependability. It is intended to recognize the different degrees of reliability that can result from varying approaches to electrical design. Therefore, its requirements have been developed to allow the designer the flexibility needed to achieve a reliable electrical system.

B.1.4.2 Need to Maintain Power. Interruption of the supply of electric power in a facility can be a hazard. Implementation of the requirements of Chapter 4 serves to maintain the required level of continuity and quality of electrical power for patient care electrical appliances.

Extensive commentary is included in A.3.3.85, following the definition of *isolated power system,* on the history of these systems as used in anesthetizing locations and as related to electrical and personnel safety. Additional commentary follows 4.4.2.1.4.4, discussing the 10-second limit within which the restoration of electric power is to occur in the event of the loss of normal power to a health care facility.

The phrase *continuity of power* is a bit of a misnomer. It can have several meanings, depending on the context in which it is used. For some, it refers to the supply of electric power to a facility and to the presence of some mechanism to switch to a second source of power if the first source is interrupted (either the source itself stops supplying power or the wires carrying the power to a facility are accidentally or intentionally cut). For others, this phrase refers to equipment that allows electric power to continue to flow to a particular device even though one of several types of electrical faults has occurred that would normally stop the flow of electricity within the device. It is necessary to know or ascertain whether the term is intended to refer to the incoming electric power to a facility or the electric power being supplied to a specific device.

For the purposes of NFPA and this document, the phrase *continuity of power* falls within the context of the overall fire or electrical safety of people and property. Although other concerns, such as the interruption of medical procedures or the efficacy of an appliance, are related, NFPA does not have the authority to make judgments or set standards in these other areas.

In the early 1960s, when the then Committee on Hospitals began to address the issue of emergency power, the question of how long facilities could tolerate loss of power until emergency power came on-line was discussed. A brief period of time (up to 10 seconds) was considered acceptable in view of the technology of the day and the medicine/surgery being practiced. Today, some in medicine do not want or cannot accept any loss of power. They contend that a loss of power for even a fraction of a second, or even just a power surge, can be damaging because of medicine's reliance on computers and the type of procedures performed. Loss of power would mean a shutdown of the computer and reprogramming or resetting after restoration of power. Because computers are now used (either alone or as part of a device) to store data, to control pumps, and for other uses, recycling in the middle of a critical surgical procedure could be detrimental to the patient. With some medical procedures involving very intricate movements, such as neuro-microsurgery or cardiac bypass surgery, a sudden loss of light could be harmful to the patient.

Others in medicine do not believe that a 10-second downtime is serious enough to warrant the installation of equipment to prevent intervals of lost power. They believe that physicians are quite capable of continuing to care for patients during a short, temporary loss of power. The important points here are "short" and "temporary." Note that an electrical feeder fault within a facility will not allow power from any source to flow beyond the fault. It will also mean no power to all devices downstream from the fault, irrespective of a system that allows power to continue to flow to appliances for certain appliance faults.

The debate over isolated power systems (IPSs) in anesthetizing locations includes the issue of continuous power because of the way IPSs function. In a grounded electrical system, an electrical fault either trips the equipment's internal fuse or trips a branch circuit breaker. IPSs react to certain electrical faults by activating an alarm while allowing power to continue to flow to equipment. An IPS, however, is not a source of power, like a generator set that actually provides power. The original intended use of IPS was to provide electrical and personnel safety in the presence of flammable anesthetics, not to allow appliances to continue operating during certain electrical faults within the appliance. However, the use of flammable anesthetics has practically stopped, and more and more electrical appliances are being used and relied on in anesthetizing locations, a fact that needs to be evaluated in terms of electrical and personnel safety.

Health care facilities must be certain of their electrical needs and dependency and of the length of time, if any, power outage in various areas can be tolerated.

B.1.5 RF Interference.

See Annex D.

B.2 Gas and Vacuum System Hazards

B.2.1 Gas Systems.

Oxygen and nitrous oxide, the gases normally used for relative analgesia and as components of general anesthesia, are strong oxidizing gases, and individually or as a mixture, support combustion quite readily.

FAQ ▶ Is nitrous oxide an oxidizing gas?

Nitrous oxide will, in fact, support combustion in the absence of oxygen.

Inhalation gases or vapors introduce fire, chemical, mechanical, and electrical hazards that are all interrelated. Any mixture of inhalation gases will support combustion. In an oxygen-enriched atmosphere, materials that are flammable and combustible in air ignite more easily and burn more vigorously. Combustible materials that could be found near patients who are to receive respiratory therapy include hair oils, oil-based lubricants, skin lotions, facial tissues, clothing, bed linen, tent canopies, rubber and plastic articles, gas supply and suction tubing, ether, alcohols, and acetone.

Even a patient's body hair can be considered a combustible if the right circumstances and a high enough concentration of oxygen exist. The very fine, barely visible hairs over apparently "hairless" areas of the body can trap oxygen and are particularly susceptible to burning. For example, in an oxygen-enriched environment in which atmosphere escapes from a hand resuscitator and envelops the patient's torso, a cardiac defibrillator can cause a spark if adequate contact gel is not used. If such a spark occurs while oxygen is in use as just described, the patient's body hair could ignite.

It is rare to find anesthetics such as cyclopropane and ether at the bedsides of patients on respiratory therapy or under any medical care. Because cyclopropane is no longer available commercially in the United States, reference to it was dropped in the 1999 edition. Ether has been included in the requirements to draw attention to the possibility that flammable gases might be moved near patients (although it is very unlikely).

A particular hazard exists when oxygen or nitrous oxide equipment becomes contaminated with oil, grease, or other combustible materials. Such contaminants will ignite readily and burn more rapidly in the presence of high oxygen concentrations and make it easier to ignite less combustible materials with which they come in contact.

The hazard posed by contaminants is particularly true when the gas pressures are operating at a high level.

Any mixture of breathing gases used in respiratory therapy will support combustion. In an oxygen-enriched atmosphere, materials that are combustible and flammable in air ignite more easily and burn more vigorously. Materials not normally considered to be combustible can be so in an oxygen-enriched atmosphere.

An oxygen-enriched atmosphere normally exists in an oxygen tent, croup tent, incubator, and similar devices when supplemental oxygen is being employed in them. These devices are designed to maintain a concentration of oxygen higher than that found in the atmosphere.

A hazard exists if either oxygen or nitrous oxide leaks into a closed space, creating an oxygen-enriched atmosphere.

Oxygen-enriched atmospheres can exist in the immediate vicinity of all oxygen administration equipment. *(See Chapter 3 for the definition of Site of Intentional Expulsion.)*

The transfer of liquid oxygen from one container to another container can create an oxygen-enriched atmosphere within the vicinity of the containers. If oxygen is supplied by a container that stores the oxygen as a liquid, there will be a small amount of oxygen vented into the vicinity of the container after a period of nonuse of the equipment. Larger amounts of oxygen will be vented if the container is accidentally tipped over or placed on its side. This venting can create an oxygen-enriched atmosphere if the container is stored in a confined space.

Most of the hazards addressed in B.2.1 involve oxygen equipment at any pressure. Previously, reference had been to high-pressure oxygen equipment, which can accentuate the problems. High pressures are not needed for an oxygen-enriched atmosphere to develop.

A hazard exists if improper components are employed to connect equipment containing pressurized oxygen or nitrous oxide during respiratory therapy administration.

The occurrence of a fire requires the presence of combustible or flammable materials, an atmosphere of oxygen or other oxidizing agents, and a source of ignition. Combustible materials can be unavoidably present when oxygen is being administered, but flammable liquids and gases and ignition sources are avoidable.

Sources of ignition include not only the usual ones in ordinary atmospheres, but others that become significant hazards in oxygen-enriched atmospheres such as the following:

(1) Open flames, burning tobacco, and electric radiant heaters are sources of ignition.
(2) The discharge of a cardiac defibrillator can serve as a source of ignition.

Such occurrences as cited in B.2.1(2) have been documented. In many of these instances, the rush of activities surrounding the patient resulted in the removal of the patient's mask or cannula without the oxygen supply to it being shut off. Flash fires developed when defibrillators were discharged.

(3) Arcing and excessive temperatures in electrical equipment are sources of ignition. Electrically powered oxygen apparatus and electrical equipment intended for use in an oxygen-enriched atmosphere are sources of ignition if electrical defects are present.

Electrically powered coagulation and cutting devices with energy levels of 10 W to 400 W are common open-spark sources in or near oxygen-enriched atmospheres. (For further details, see Annex D, The Safe Use of High-Frequency Electricity in Health Care Facilities.) An electrical safety inspection program should be instituted to detect such problems before equipment deteriorates to the point that it can cause ignition.

(4) Electrical equipment not conforming to the requirements of 8.5.2.4.1, which can include, but is not limited to, electric razors, electric bed controls, hair dryers, remote television controls, and telephone handsets, can create a source of ignition if introduced into an oxygen-enriched atmosphere.

(5) A static discharge having an energy content that can be generated under normal conditions in respiratory therapy will not constitute an ignition source as long as easily ignited substances (such as alcohols, acetone, oils, greases, or lotions) are not present.

A study by R.J. Plano [1] confirmed that blankets and sheets do not present a fire hazard from static sparks inside an oxygen tent. Therefore, there is an even lower hazard when oxygen is administered by cannula. Static discharge is not the same condition as that of spark-generating toys, moreover, which are a definite hazard inside oxygen tents.

Reference to substances such as ether and cyclopropane were deleted because they are no longer used in the United States as inhalation anesthetics.

(6) Rapid opening of cylinder valves can cause sudden increase in downstream gas pressure and temperature caused by the adiabatic heat of recompression with consequent ignition of combustible materials in contact with the hot gas downstream, including the valve seat. Sudden compression or recompression of a gas to high pressure can generate large increase in temperature [up to 1093°C (2000°F)] that can ignite any organic material present, including grease. *(See also* NFPA 53, *Recommended Practice on Materials, Equipment, and Systems Used in Oxygen-Enriched Atmospheres.)*

B.2.2 Medical–Surgical Vacuum Systems.

There are potential fire and explosion hazards associated with medical gas central piping systems and medical–surgical vacuum systems. The various components are usually not independent isolated components, but are parts of a larger system dedicated to total patient care and safety.

Many of these components are covered by existing standards to minimize the fire, explosive, and patient safety hazard. The potential for mistaken interconnection with oxidizing gases and for under-capacity requiring extended overheated operation all present potential hazards or compound other hazardous conditions that should be properly addressed. Although the potential for these problems exists, the Piping Committee on Medical Gas and Vacuum Systems is unaware of the actual occurrence of any significant fire-related hazards with medical–surgical vacuum systems.

There are also potential hazards to patients in the unplanned shutdown or failure of the systems secondary to a fire and/or the inability of the system to provide adequate levels of performance under normal or emergency situations. There is also the potential for mistaken interconnection with pressurized nonflammable medical gas systems.

B.2.3 Waste Anesthetic Gas Disposal.

There are potential fire and explosion hazards associated with the gases that are removed from the anesthesia machine by the WAGD system. These gases typically include oxygen, nitrous oxide, and halogenated anesthetics. There are also potential hazards to patients and staff resulting from exposure to these gases or from improper interface between the very low pressures in the breathing circuit and the high vacuum present in some WAGD systems.

There is also the hazard of interconnection between the WAGD system and the other medical gas systems, and especially the medical–surgical vacuum system.

Any mixture of breathing gases used in respiratory therapy will support combustion. In an oxygen-enriched atmosphere, materials that are combustible and flammable in air ignite more easily and burn more vigorously. Materials not normally considered to be combustible can be so in an oxygen-enriched atmosphere.

It is also important to consider the hazards associated with WAGD discharge. The discharge vents should be marked with signage to alert anyone in the area of the potential of hazardous gases discharged from the vent.

◀ **FAQ**
Should signage be provided at WAGD discharge vents?

B.2.3.1 Toxicity During Respiratory Therapy Administration. Chemical hazards can be associated with the presence of residual sterilant in high-pressure equipment.

Some breathing mixtures can decompose in contact with hot surfaces and produce toxic or flammable substances.

Smoldering combustion of flammable substances can occur with the production of significant amounts of toxic gases and fumes.

B.2.3.2 Safety (Mechanical Injury, Cross-Connection, and So Forth). A large amount of energy is stored in a cylinder of compressed gas. If the valve of a cylinder is struck (or strikes something else) hard enough to break off the valve, the contents of the cylinder could be discharged with sufficient force to impart dangerous reactive movement to the cylinder.

B.2.3.3 Mechanical Hazards During Respiratory Therapy Administration. Cylinders and containers can be heavy and bulky and can cause personal injury or property damage (including to the cylinder or container) if improperly handled. In cold climates, cylinders or containers stored outdoors or in unheated ventilated rooms can become extremely cold. A hazardous situation could develop if these cylinders or containers are heated.

Improper maintenance, handling, or assembly of equipment can result in personal injury, property damage, or fire.

A hazardous condition exists if cylinders or containers are improperly located so that they can become overheated or tipped over. If a container is tipped over or placed on its side, liquid oxygen could be spilled. The liquid can cause frostbite on contact with skin.

See the commentary following 9.4.2.5.

A hazardous condition exists if there is improper labeling of cylinders or containers or inattention to the manufacturer's label or instructions.

The index safety systems that are intended to make it impossible to connect cylinders of the wrong gas to a system must not be modified or otherwise defeated. Between 1996 and 2000, at least nine deaths occurred in facilities when an employee field-modified the pigtail and/or cylinder outlet to introduce a lethal gas (e.g., nitrogen, argon, carbon dioxide) into an oxygen system. See also the commentary following 9.3.2 and 9.3.8. Also see A.9.5.1.2.

A hazardous condition exists if care is not exercised in making slip-on and other interchangeable connections when setting up equipment.

Safety features, including relief devices, valves, and connections, are provided in equipment and gas supply systems. Altering or circumventing these safety features by means of adapters creates a hazardous condition.

Extreme danger to life and property can result when compressed gases are mixed or transferred from one cylinder to another. A hazardous condition exists if devices, such as fixed or adjustable orifices and metering valves, are directly connected to cylinders or systems without a pressure-reducing regulator.

See the commentary following 9.6.2.2.1.

Hazardous conditions are created when pressure-reducing regulators or gauges are defective.

B.2.3.4 Manufactured Assemblies. Specific hazards associated with manufactured assemblies are the same as those listed above as well as additional hazards resulting from improper assembly, separation and leakage resulting from hidden semipermanent connections, improper connection resulting in cross-connection, and blockage and flow problems resulting from damage to hose, and so forth.

Without defined requirements, it is impossible to maintain the high quality of safety that is prescribed for piped gas systems if the total system requirements are not extended to include the many different manufactured assemblies being installed today. Thus, manufactured assemblies are deemed to require the same system integrity as the remainder of the piped system.

B.3 Environmental System Hazards

See Electrical Systems Hazards (Section B.1) and Gas Equipment Hazards (Section B.6).

B.4 Flammability of Materials Hazards

B.4.1 Flammable Materials. (Reserved)

B.4.2 Toxicity of Products of Combustion.

Many substances, when subjected to a fire, undergo a chemical change resulting in a new toxic product. This is especially true of many plastic substances. Many highly toxic combustion products can cause sudden unconsciousness, cardiovascular collapse, and severe injury or death, even though the person injured is relatively remote from the fire. These combustion products have been found to cause injury after passing through halls, ventilating systems, and even electrical conduit.

B.4.3 Chemical Burns. (Reserved)

B.4.4 Safety. (Reserved)

B.4.5 Radioactivity. (Reserved)

B.5 Electrical Equipment Hazards

See Section B.1 for related electrical hazards.

B.5.1 Fire and Explosion.

Transmission of electricity generates heat. The normal operating temperature of a device is a function of material and design. Equipment or wiring faults can cause abnormal temperature increases. These abnormal temperatures can cause fire and explosions. Use of oxygen or other oxidizing agents lowers ignition temperatures. Normal operating temperatures of equipment not designed for use in oxygen-enriched atmospheres can cause fires if used in oxygen-enriched atmospheres. See B.6.1.14 for other ignition hazards.

B.5.2 Electrical Shock.

B.5.2.1 Elimination of Shock Hazards.

B.5.2.1.1 Personnel are cautioned to be aware of the hazards presented by defective or improperly employed electrical equipment *(see B.5.2.2)* and to avoid the use of defective electrical equipment *(see 8.5.2.2.4).*

Training covering electrical hazards and safe practices should be conducted to make personnel sensitive to the problem of shock hazards. Such training should occur during orientation and should be periodically reviewed.

B.5.2.1.2 Adequate grounding for electrical equipment is an important safeguard against fire and electric shock *(see 4.3.3.1 and 8.4.1.2.1.1).*

B.5.2.2 Effects of Moisture. Moisture, in the form of liquids, vapors, or mists, can degrade insulation to the point where fire, equipment malfunction, and electric shock hazard become a threat. Moisture can enter equipment as a result of defective seals, leaks, or inadvertent spillage. Vessels containing liquids should not be placed on electrical equipment. See 4.3.2.2.8.

B.5.3 Burns.

B.5.3.1 Heated Surfaces. Sustained skin contact with surfaces of equipment that have temperatures in excess of 42°C (107°F) can cause burns. Caution is required when exposing patients to warmed surfaces, particularly when the patients are helpless.

B.5.3.2 High-frequency electromagnetic fields, particularly those from electrosurgical generators and from lasers, are used to intentionally destroy tissue. Inadvertent burns, or ignition of combustible materials, is a hazard. See Annex D.

B.5.4 Interruption of Power. (Reserved)

Even brief interruptions of power can cause some equipment to malfunction, particularly appliances with computer components, such as physiological monitoring systems. Readers are referred to essential electrical system requirements described in Chapter 4, which allow a switchover time of up to 10 seconds. If an appliance cannot tolerate even this brief interruption, special power provisions might need to be arranged.

Requirements for the manufacture of patient-care-related electrical appliances were added in 1993 to ensure that new appliances would not malfunction because of brief interruptions of power (as might occur when normal power is interrupted and then restored by the essential electrical system). Older equipment might not be designed to meet this new criterion, and health care personnel should be aware of potential hazards posed by these older appliances, particularly those with computer components. (See the commentary following 10.2.6.5.3.3.)

B.5.5 RF Interference. See Annex D.

Radio frequency interference (RFI) and *electromagnetic interference* (EMI) refer to electromagnetic radiation from outside sources. Such radiation can affect the proper operation of medical devices. Sources of RFI and EMI can be a radio station transmitting tower, portable telephones, electric power lines, or even other medical devices. A related term, *electromagnetic compatibility* (EMC), denotes the ability of a device to function properly in the presence of disturbing electromagnetic fields.

Some cellular telephones, because of their operating characteristics, have been shown to activate the alarm signals of older smoke and heat detectors and to interfere with the operation of medical equipment. Facilities that experience these problems should contact the manufacturers of the suspect phones to learn how to mitigate the problem. The facility should develop a policy to address the restriction of cellular phones or other equipment that produces RFI or EMI.

The increasing proliferation of electrical devices in health care facilities, along with their increased sophistication (making them more prone to gross and subtle failures), demands heightened awareness of these potential hazards. Specific recommendations and requirements for ameliorating the problems of RFI and EMI are being studied by many agencies.

B.5.6 Mechanical Injury. (Reserved)

B.6 Gas Equipment Hazards

See Electrical Systems Hazards (Section B.1) for electrical hazards associated with gas equipment.

B.6.1 Fire and Explosions.

B.6.1.1 Oxygen and nitrous oxide, the gases normally used for relative analgesia and as components of general anesthesia, are strong oxidizing gases and individually or as a mixture support combustion quite readily.

Nitrous oxide will, in fact, support combustion in the absence of oxygen.

B.6.1.2 Inhalation gases or vapors introduce fire, chemical, mechanical, and electrical hazards that are all interrelated. Any mixture of inhalation gases will support combustion. In an oxygen-enriched atmosphere, materials that are flammable and combustible in air ignite more easily and burn more vigorously. The materials that could be found on or near patients include hair oils, oil-based lubricants, skin lotions, clothing, linens, paper, rubber, alcohols, acetone, and some plastics.

See the commentary following the second paragraph of B.2.1.

B.6.1.3 A hazard exists if any of the components of an oxygen or nitrous oxide supply system become contaminated with oil or grease.

This is particularly true with high-pressure systems where the adiabatic heating of recompressed gases can ignite combustible materials.

B.6.1.4 Sources of ignition can include open flames, burning tobacco, electric heating coils, defective electrical equipment, and adiabatic heating of gases.

Sudden compression or recompression of a gas to high pressure can generate large increase in temperature [up to 1093°C (2000°F)] that can ignite any organic material present, including grease. *(See also* NFPA 53, *Recommended Practice on Materials, Equipment, and Systems Used in Oxygen-Enriched Atmospheres.)*

Temperatures hot enough to melt some plastics used in respiratory care equipment do not normally seem dangerous. These same temperatures become extremely dangerous in an oxygen-enriched atmosphere because, instead of melting the plastics, such temperatures are sufficient to cause ignition of these materials.

B.6.1.5 A hazard exists if either oxygen or nitrous oxide leaks into a closed space, creating an oxygen-enriched atmosphere.

B.6.1.6 A hazard exists if improper components are employed to connect equipment containing pressurized oxygen or nitrous oxide.

B.6.1.7 The occurrence of a fire is dependent on the presence of combustible or flammable materials, an atmosphere of oxygen or other oxidizing agents, and a source of ignition. When combustible materials are present and oxygen is being administered, flammable liquids and gases and ignition sources are to be avoided.

B.6.1.8 Any mixture of breathing gases used in respiratory therapy will support combustion. In an oxygen-enriched atmosphere, materials that are combustible and flammable in air ignite more easily and burn more vigorously. Materials not normally considered to be combustible change their characteristics in an oxygen-enriched atmosphere.

B.6.1.9 Combustible materials that could be found near patients who are to receive respiratory therapy include hair oils, oil-based lubricants, skin lotions, facial tissues, clothing, bed linen, tent canopies, rubber and plastic articles, gas-supply and suction tubing, ether, alcohols, and acetone.

See the commentary following the second paragraph of B.2.1.

B.6.1.10 A particular hazard exists when oxygen equipment becomes contaminated with oil, grease, or other combustible materials. Such contaminants will ignite readily and burn more rapidly in the presence of high oxygen concentrations and make it easier to ignite less combustible materials with which they come in contact.

B.6.1.11 An oxygen-enriched atmosphere normally exists in an oxygen tent, croup tent, incubator, and similar devices when supplemental oxygen is being employed in them. These devices are designed to maintain a concentration of oxygen higher than that found in the atmosphere.

Oxygen-enriched atmosphere exists in the immediate vicinity of all oxygen administration equipment. *(See also 3.3.170, Site of Intentional Expulsion, and A.3.3.170.)*

B.6.1.12 The transfer of liquid oxygen from one container to another container can create an oxygen-enriched atmosphere within the vicinity of the containers.

Liquid oxygen expands 860 times when transitioning from a liquid to a gas. A small spill of liquid oxygen can create an oxygen-enriched atmosphere in the vicinity of the spill.

B.6.1.13 If oxygen is supplied by a container that stores the oxygen as a liquid, there will be a small amount of oxygen vented into the vicinity of the container after a period of nonuse of the equipment. Larger amounts of oxygen will be vented if the container is accidentally tipped over or placed on its side. This venting may create an oxygen-enriched atmosphere if the container is stored in a confined space.

See the commentary following the eighth paragraph of B.2.1.

B.6.1.14 Sources of ignition include not only the usual ones in ordinary atmospheres, but others that become significant hazards in oxygen-enriched atmospheres *(see B.6.1.7 and B.6.1.8)* such as the following:

See the commentary following B.2.1(3).

(1) Open flames
(2) Burning tobacco

See the commentary following 9.6.1.1.1.

(3) Electric radiant heaters

(4) The discharge of a cardiac defibrillator

See the commentary following B.2.1(2).

(5) Arcing and excessive temperatures in electrical equipment
(6) Electrically powered oxygen apparatus and electrical equipment intended for use in an oxygen-enriched atmosphere if electrical defects are present

See the commentary following B.2.1(3).

(7) Electrical equipment not conforming to the requirements of 8.5.2.4.1, which includes, but is not limited to, the following:
   (a) Electric razors
   (b) Electric bed controls
   (c) Hair dryers
   (d) Remote television controls and telephone handsets if introduced into an oxygen-enriched atmosphere *(see 8.5.2.4.1)*
(8) Rapid opening of cylinder valves, which can cause sudden increase in downstream gas pressure and temperature caused by the adiabatic heat of recompression, with consequent ignition of combustible materials in contact with the hot gas downstream, including the valve seat

See the commentary following Section 9.4.

A static discharge having an energy content that can be generated under normal conditions in respiratory therapy will not constitute an ignition source as long as easily ignited substances (such as alcohols, acetone, oils, greases, or lotions) are not present.

B.6.2 Toxicity.

B.6.2.1 Chemical hazards can be associated with the presence of residual sterilant in high-pressure equipment.

B.6.2.2 Some breathing mixtures decompose when in contact with heat and produce toxic or flammable substances *(see 9.6.1)*.

B.6.2.3 Smoldering combustion of substances may produce toxic gases and fumes.

B.6.3 Mechanical.

B.6.3.1 A large amount of energy is stored in a cylinder of compressed gas. If the valve of a cylinder is struck (or strikes something else) hard enough to break off the valve, the contents of the cylinder could be discharged with sufficient force to impart dangerous reactive movement to the cylinder.

B.6.3.2 Cylinders and containers can be heavy and bulky and can cause personal injury or property damage (including to the cylinder or container) if improperly handled. In cold climates, cylinders or containers stored outdoors or in unheated ventilated rooms can become extremely cold *[see 9.7.2.4(11) and 9.7.2.1(3)]*. A hazardous situation could develop if these cylinders or containers are heated *[see 9.7.2.4(10)]*.

See the commentary following Section 9.4.

B.6.3.3 Improper maintenance, handling, or assembly of equipment can result in personal injury, property damage, or fire.

B.6.3.4 A hazardous condition exists if cylinders or containers are improperly located so that they become overheated or tipped over. If a container is tipped over or placed on its side, liquid oxygen could be spilled. The liquid can cause frostbite on contact with skin.

See the commentary following 9.4.2.5.

B.6.3.5 A hazardous condition exists if there is improper labeling of cylinders or containers or inattention to the manufacturer's label or instructions.

See the commentary following 9.3.8.

B.6.3.6 A hazardous condition exists if care is not exercised in making slip-on and other interchangeable connections when setting up equipment.

B.6.3.7 Safety features, including relief devices, valves, and connections, are provided in equipment and gas supply systems. Altering or circumventing these safety features by means of adapters creates a hazardous condition.

B.6.3.8 Extreme danger to life and property can result when compressed gases are mixed or transferred from one cylinder to another.

See the commentary following 9.6.2.2.1.

B.6.3.9 A hazardous condition exists if devices, such as fixed or adjustable orifices and metering valves, are directly connected to cylinders or systems without a pressure-reducing regulator.

B.6.3.10 Hazardous conditions are created when pressure-reducing regulators or gauges are defective.

B.6.4 Electric Shock.

See B.5.2 for additional information.

B.7 Hyperbaric Hazards

Chapter 20 for the use of hyperbaric facilities is intended to provide protection against fire, explosion, and other hazards without unduly limiting the activities of professional personnel involved in patient (in the case of hospitals) or other care. This principle, without minimizing the hazards, recognizes that professional personnel shall be guided by all of the hazards to life that are inherent in and around hyperbaric treatment procedures.

B.7.1 Potential hazards involved in the design, construction, operation, and maintenance of hyperbaric facilities are formidable.

B.7.2 The navies of the world have established an enviable safety record in their use of hyperbaric facilities for deep-sea-diving research, training, and operations. A knowledge of this safety record should not lull hyperbaric personnel into a false sense of security, however. The potential hazards remain. Where civilian personnel — patients, experimental subjects, and chamber attendants — are involved, an appreciation of these hazards and their mitigation becomes even more important. For a discussion of hazards, see information in C.20.

Other military organizations have also maintained equally impressive hyperbaric chamber safety records. The United States Air Force, which requires very aggressive initial and recurring training, is an excellent example. Air force operators are routinely exposed to hyperbaric chamber operations and practice a variety of emergency response procedures.

Civilian medical facilities are urged to follow the military's lead by developing their own comprehensive training program and devoting the time necessary to conduct training. Training is particularly important because medical facilities can house nonambulatory patients who may be completely unfamiliar with the chambers and their operational features. Training should include not only hazard recognition and prevention, but emergency responses to accidents as well. Additionally, all medical treatment facilities are encouraged to develop a safety awareness program for all prospective patients. They too must understand the hyperbaric environment and its potential hazards.

REFERENCE CITED IN COMMENTARY

1. Plano, R. J., *Modern Hospital,* vol. 95, no. 3, September 1960.

ANNEX C

Additional Explanatory Notes to Chapters 1–20

This annex is not a part of the requirements of this NFPA document but is included for informational purposes only.

Annex C provides additional explanatory information on the main requirements of the standard. Often times this material includes additional details to Annex A or provides examples, history, or sample procedures or processes.

C.1 Reserved

C.2 Reserved

C.3 Reserved

C.4 Additional Information on Chapter 4

C.4.1 Typical Hospital Wiring Arrangement.

See Figure C.4.1. Separate transfer switches for each branch, as shown, are required only if dictated by load considerations. Smaller facilities can be served by a single transfer switch.

C.4.2 Maintenance Guide for an Essential Electrical System.

This generalized maintenance guide is provided to assist administrative, supervisory, and operating personnel in establishing and evaluating maintenance programs for emergency electric generating systems. See Figure C.4.2.

C.4.3 Suggested Format for Listing Functions to Be Served by the Essential Electrical System in a Hospital.

It may be advantageous, in listing the specific functions for a given construction project or building review, to list them, at the outset, by geographical location within the project, in

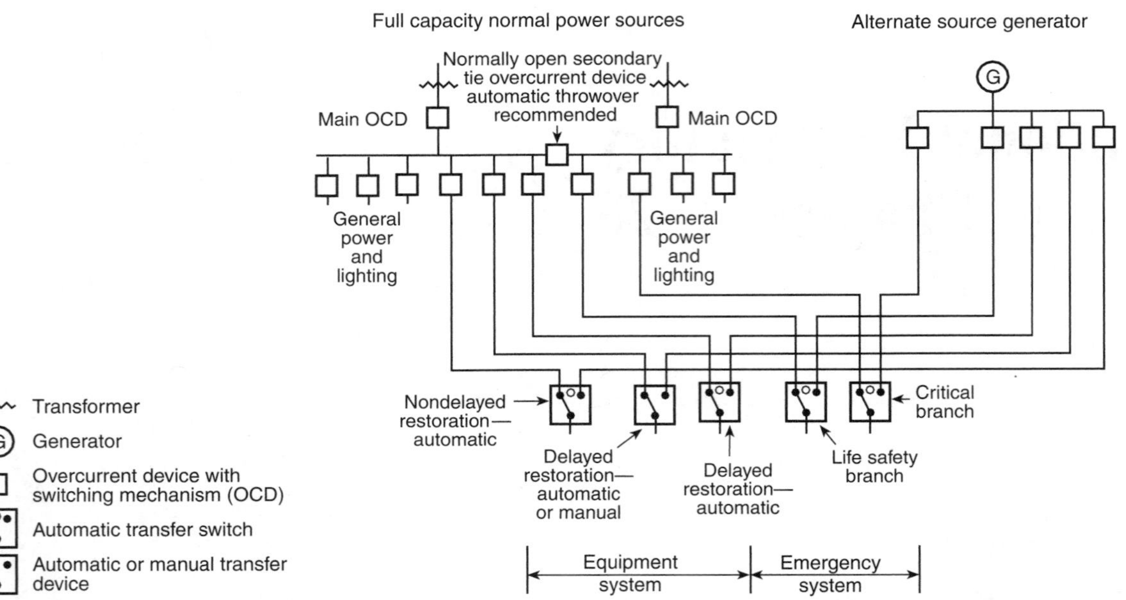

FIGURE C.4.1 Typical Hospital Wiring Arrangement.

order to ensure comprehensive coverage. Every room or space should be reviewed for possible inclusion of the following:

(1) Lighting (partial or all)
(2) Receptacles (some or all)
(3) Permanently wired electrical apparatus

The format suggested herein is offered as a convenient tool, not only for identifying all functions to be served and their respective time intervals for being reenergized by the alternate electric source, but also for documenting other functions that were considered, discussed, and excluded as nonessential. This last column is considered worthy of attention. *(See Figure C.4.3.)* It may be that the hospital engineer or the reviewing authority will wish to keep on file a final copy of the list, which would be the basis for the electrical engineer's detailed engineering design.

Although this suggested format is intended for use by a hospital it may, with suitable changes, be useful for other health care facilities.

C.5 Additional Information on Chapter 5

Numbers in brackets refer to paragraphs in Chapter 5 of text.

C.5.1 Initial Testing of Nonflammable Medical Piped Gas Systems (Level 1 Systems).

The commentary in Annex C contains only general recommendations. Testing requirements are listed in 5.1.12, 5.2.12, and 5.3.12. The recommendations in this annex apply to a Level 1 piped gas system, although portions might be applicable to a Level 2 or Level 3 piped gas system.

MAINTENANCE GUIDE

Monthly

a. Testing of generator sets and transfer switches under load and operating temperature conditions at least every 30 days. A 30-minute exercise period is an absolute minimum, or the engine manufacturer's recommendations should be followed.

b. Permanently record all available instrument readings during the monthly test.

c. During the monthly test, check the following system or systems applicable to your installation:

Natural Gas or Liquid Petroleum Gas System:
- ❑ Operation of solenoids and regulators
- ❑ Condition of all hoses and pipes
- ❑ Fuel quantity

Gasoline Fuel System:
- ❑ Main tank fuel level
- ❑ Operation of system

Diesel Fuel System:
- ❑ Main tank fuel level
- ❑ Day tank fuel level
- ❑ Operation of fuel supply pump and controls

Turbine Prime Movers:
- ❑ Follow manufacturer's recommended maintenance procedure

Engine Cooling System:
- ❑ Coolant level
- ❑ Rust inhibitor in coolant
- ❑ Antifreeze in coolant (if applicable)
- ❑ Adequate cooling water to heat exchangers
- ❑ Adequate fresh air to engine and radiators
- ❑ Condition of fan and alternator belts
- ❑ Squeeze and check condition of hose and connections
- ❑ Functioning of coolant heater (if installed)

Engine Lubricating System:
- ❑ Lubricating oil level
- ❑ Crankcase breather not restricted
- ❑ Appearance of lubricating oil
- ❑ Correct lubricating oil available to replenish or change
- ❑ Operation of lubricating oil heater (if installed)
- ❑ Oil pressure correct

Engine Electrical Starting System:
- ❑ Battery terminals clean and tight
- ❑ Add distilled water to maintain proper electrolyte level
- ❑ Battery charging rate
- ❑ Battery trickle charging circuit operating properly
- ❑ Spare batteries charged if provided

Engine Compressed Air Starting System:
- ❑ Air compressor operating properly
- ❑ Air compressor lubricating oil level
- ❑ Spare compressed air tanks full
- ❑ Main compressed air tanks full
- ❑ Drain water from compressed air tanks

Engine Exhaust System:
- ❑ Condensate trap drained
- ❑ No exhaust leaks
- ❑ Exhaust not restricted
- ❑ All connections tight

Transfer Switch:
- ❑ Inside clean and free of foreign matter
- ❑ No unusual sounds
- ❑ Terminals and connectors normal color
- ❑ Condition of all wiring insulation
- ❑ All covers tight
- ❑ Doors securely closed

General:
- ❑ Any unusual condition of vibration, deterioration, leakage, or high surface temperatures or noise
- ❑ Maintenance manuals, service log, basic service tools, jumpers, and supplies readily available
- ❑ Check and record the time intervals of the various increments of the automatic start-up and shutdown sequences
- ❑ Overall cleanliness of room
- ❑ No unnecessary items in room

d. After the monthly test: Take prompt action to correct all improper conditions indicated during test. Check that the standby system is set for automatic start and load transfer.

Quarterly

a. On generator sets:

Engine Electrical Starting System:
- ❑ Check battery electrolyte specific gravity
- ❑ Check battery cap vents

Engine Lubricating System:
- ❑ Check lubricating oil (or have analyzed if part of an engineered lube oil program)

b. Fuel System:
- ❑ Drain water from fuel filters (if applicable)
- ❑ Drain water from day tank (if applicable)
- ❑ Check fuel gages and drain water from main fuel tanks
- ❑ Inspect all main fuel tank vents

(NFPA 99, 1 of 2)

FIGURE C.4.2 Maintenance Guide for an Essential Electrical System.

MAINTENANCE GUIDE (Continued)

Semiannually

a. On generator sets:

Engine Lubricating System:
- ❑ Change oil filter (if sufficient hours)
- ❑ Clean crankcase breather

Fuel System:
- ❑ General inspection of all components
- ❑ Change fuel filter
- ❑ Change or clean air filter

Governor:
- ❑ Check all linkages and ball joints
- ❑ Check oil level (if applicable)
- ❑ Observe for unusual oil leakage

Generator:
- ❑ Check brush length and pressure
- ❑ Check appearance of slip rings and clean if necessary
- ❑ Blow out with clean, dry compressed air

Engine Safety Controls:
- ❑ Check operation of all engine-operating alarms and safety shutdown devices (generator not under load during this check)

Exhaust System:
- ❑ Check condition of mufflers, exhaust lines, supports, and connections

Ignition System:
- ❑ Spark ignition engines
- ❑ Replace points and plugs
- ❑ Check ignition timing
- ❑ Check condition of all ignition leads

Generator:
- ❑ Clean generator windings
- ❑ Check generator bearings
- ❑ Measure and record resistance readings of generator windings using insulation tester (megger)

Engine Control:
- ❑ General cleaning
- ❑ Check appearance of all components
- ❑ Check meters

b. Transfer Switch:
- ❑ Inspect transfer switch and make repairs or replacements if indicated

c. On main switchgear and generator switchgear:
- ❑ Operate every circuit breaker manually
- ❑ Visually check bus bars, bracing, and feeder connections for cleanliness and signs of overheating

Annually

a. On generator sets:

Fuel System:

Diesel:
- ❑ Analyze fuel for condition (replace if required)

Gasoline:
- ❑ Replace fuel

Natural Gas or Liquefied Petroleum Gas:
- ❑ Examine all supply tanks, fittings, and lines

Lubricating Systems:
- ❑ Change oil
- ❑ Change oil filter
- ❑ Replace carburetor air filter

Cooling System:
- ❑ Check condition and rod-out heat exchangers if necessary
- ❑ Change coolant on closed systems
- ❑ Clean exterior of all radiators
- ❑ Check all engine water pumps and circulating pumps
- ❑ Examine all duct work for looseness
- ❑ Clean and check motor-operated louvers

Every Three Years

a. System Controls:
- ❑ Reevaluate the settings of the voltage sensing and time delay relays

b. Main Switchgear and Generator Switchgear:
- ❑ Determine whether changes to the electrical supply system have been made that require a revision of the main circuit breaker, fuse, or current-limiting bus duct coordination.
- ❑ Calibrate and load test main circuit breakers. Spot-check bus bar bolts and supports for tightness. Obtain and record insulation tester readings on bus bars and circuit breakers. Obtain and record insulation tester readings on internal distribution feeders.

Periodically

a. Prime Mover Overhaul:
- ❑ Each prime mover should have a periodic overhaul in compliance with the manufacturer's recommendation or as conditions warrant.

b. Connected Load:
- ❑ Update the record of demand and connected load and check for potential overload.

(NFPA 99, 2 of 2)

FIGURE C.4.2 *Continued*

Essential Electrical Systems

Hospital ____________________ Date __________

Room no.	Room name	Function served*	Emergency system		Equipment system		Non-essential
			Life safety branch	Critical branch	Delayed auto.**	Delayed manual	

* Indicate precise lighting, receptacles, and/or equipment. Use a separate line for each function.

** Indicate time interval.

FIGURE C.4.3 Essential Electrical Systems.

C.5.1.1 [5.1.3.4.6.1] The pressure relief valve, set at 50 percent above normal line pressure, should be tested to assure proper function prior to use of the system for patient care.

C.5.1.2 [5.1.3.5.2] The proper functioning of the safety valve, automatic drain, pressure gauge, and high-water-level sensor should be verified before the system is put into service.

C.5.1.3 [5.1.9.2.4; 5.1.3.4.10, 5.1.3.4.12, and 5.1.3.4.13] Changeover Warning Signal.

(1) Start a flow of gas from an outlet of the piping system.
(2) Close the shutoff valve or cylinder valves on the primary supply of the manifold *[see Figure A.5.1.3.4.9(a) and Figure A.5.1.3.4.9(b)]*, or the primary unit of the alternating bulk supply to simulate its depletion *(see Figure A.5.1.3.4.13)*. Changeover should be made to the secondary supply or the alternate bulk unit.
(3) Check main-line pressure gauge to ensure maintenance of the desired pressure.
(4) Check signal panels for activation of the proper changeover signal.
(5) Silence the audible signal; visual signal should remain.
(6) Open the valves closed in Step (2). Close the valve on the secondary supply or alternate bulk unit. When changeover back to original primary supply has occurred, reopen the valve. This will reinstate system to its original status.
(7) Check signal panels for deactivation of warning signals.
(8) Stop flow of gas from the piping system.

C.5.1.4 [5.1.9.2.4; 5.1.3.4.10, 5.1.3.4.12, and 5.1.3.4.13] Reserve-In-Use Warning Signal.

(1) Start a flow of gas from the piping system.
(2) Close the proper shutoff valves to simulate depletion of the operating supply. Reserve should begin to supply the piping system.

(3) Check the main-line pressure gauge. Pressure should remain at the desired level.
(4) Check the master signal panels to determine that the reserve-in-use signals have been activated.
(5) Silence the audible signal. Visual signal should remain.
(6) Open the shutoff valves closed in Step (2).
(7) Check master signal panels for deactivation of the warning signals.
(8) Stop the flow of gas from the piping system.

C.5.1.5 [5.1.9.2.4; 5.1.3.4.12, 5.1.3.4.13, 5.1.3.4.15, and 5.1.3.8.2.3] Reserve Supply Low.

(1) Start a flow of gas from the piping system.
(2) Close all operating supply shutoff valves (to use pressure from the reserve).
(3) Close the reserve supply shutoff valve or, if necessary, the reserve cylinder valves, depending on the exact location of the actuating switch (to reduce pressure on the actuating switch, simulating loss of reserve).
(4) Open the operating supply valves closed in Step (2) (so that only the "reserve low" signal should be activated).
(5) Check the master signal panels for activation of the proper signal.
(6) Silence the audible signal. Visual signal should remain.
(7) Open reserve supply valve or cylinder valves closed in Step (3).
(8) Check master signal panels for deactivation of the warning signals.
(9) Stop flow of gas from the piping system.

Note on Liquid Bulk Reserves. This type of reserve requires an actuating switch on the contents gauge and another actuating switch for the gas pressure being maintained in the reserve unit. Reduced contents or gas pressure in the reserve unit would indicate less than a day's supply in reserve.

Simulation of these conditions requires the assistance of the owner or the organization responsible for the operation and maintenance of the supply system as it will vary for different styles of storage units.

C.5.1.6 [5.1.9.2.4] High or Low Pressure in Piping System. Initial test of the area alarms covered in 5.1.9.3 can be done at the same time.

(1) Increase the pressure in the piping system to the high-pressure signal point (20 percent above normal pressure).
(2) Check all master signal panels (and area signals) to ensure that the properly labeled warning signal is activated; also check main-line pressure gauge and area gauges to ensure their function.
(3) Silence the audible signal. Visual signal should remain.
(4) Reduce piping system pressure to the normal. A flow from the system is required to lower the pressure and permit readjustment of the line regulator.
(5) Check all signal panels for deactivation of the signals.
(6) Close main-line shutoff valve.
(7) Continue the flow from the system until pressure is reduced to the low-pressure signal point (20 percent below normal).
(8) Check all signal panels for activation of the properly labeled warning signal; also check main-line gauge and area pressure gauges to ensure their function.
(9) Silence the audible signal. Visual signal should remain.
(10) Open main-line shutoff valve.
(11) Check main-line gauge for proper line pressure.
(12) Check all signal panels for deactivation of warning signals.

C.5.1.7 [5.1.9.3] This signal should be initially tested at the time the tests of C.5.1.6 are performed.

C.5.2 Retesting and Maintenance of Nonflammable Medical Piped Gas Systems (Level 1 Systems).

C.5.2.1 [5.1.3.4.10] These systems should be checked daily to assure that proper pressure is maintained and that the changeover signal has not malfunctioned. Periodic retesting of the routine changeover signal is not necessary as it will normally be activated on a regular basis.

C.5.2.2 [5.1.3.4.12] These systems should be checked daily to assure that proper pressure is maintained and that the changeover signal has not malfunctioned. Periodic retesting of the routine changeover signal is not required. Annual retesting of the operation of the reserve and activation of the reserve-in-use signal should be performed.

C.5.2.3 [5.1.3.4.12] If the system has an actuating switch and signal to monitor the contents of the reserve, it should be retested annually.

C.5.2.4 [5.1.3.4.13] Maintenance and periodic testing of the bulk system is the responsibility of the owner or the organization responsible for the operation and maintenance of that system.

The staff of the facility should check the supply system daily to ensure that medical gas is ordered when the contents gauge drops to the reorder level designated by the supplier. Piping system pressure gauges and other gauges designated by the supplier should be checked regularly, and gradual variation, either increases or decreases, from the normal range should be reported to the supplier. These variations might indicate the need for corrective action.

Periodic testing of the master signal panel system, other than the routine changeover signal, should be performed. Request assistance from the supplier or detailed instruction if readjustment of bulk supply controls is necessary to complete these tests.

C.5.2.5 [5.1.8.2.3] The main-line pressure gauge should be checked daily to ensure the continued presence of the desired pressure. Variation, either increases or decreases, should be investigated and corrected.

C.5.2.6 [5.1.3.5.15] Quarterly rechecking of the location of the air intake should be made to ensure that it continues to be a satisfactory source for medical compressed air.

The quarterly check recommended in C.5.2.6 might include the following:

◀ **FAQ**
What comprises the quarterly check?

1. A physical inspection for accumulations of debris around the intake
2. An examination of the immediate area around the intake for new exhausts that could pollute air being drawn in or for any changes that might affect the air circulation in the area of the intake
3. An examination of Environmental Protection Agency reports on air quality in the locality

If any of these examinations raise concerns about the air purity or quality, a more detailed purity examination should be conducted.

C.5.2.7 [5.1.3.5.14] Proper functioning of the pressure gauge and high-water-level sensor should be checked at least annually. Check the receiver drain daily to determine if an excessive quantity of condensed water has accumulated in the receiver.

C.5.2.8 [5.1.3.5] An important item required for operation of any medical compressed air supply system is a comprehensive preventive maintenance program. Worn parts on reciprocating compressors can cause high discharge temperatures resulting in an increase of contaminants in the discharge gas. Adsorber beds, if not changed at specified time intervals, can become saturated and lose their effectiveness. It is important that all components of the system be maintained in accordance with the manufacturers' recommendations. It is important that any instrumentation, including analytical equipment, be calibrated routinely and maintained in operating order. Proper functioning of the dew point sensor should be checked at least annually.

C.5.2.9 [5.1.9] When test buttons are provided with signal panels, activation of the audible and visual signals should be performed on a regular basis (monthly).

C.5.2.10 [5.1.9.2.4] Changeover Warning Signals. As these are routine signals that are activated and deactivated at frequent intervals, there is no need for retesting UNLESS they fail. If the reserve-in-use signal is activated because both units of the operating supply are depleted without the prior activation of the changeover signal, it should be repaired and retested.

C.5.2.11 [5.1.9.2.4] Reserve-In-Use Warning Signal. All components of this warning signal system should be retested annually in accordance with Steps (2) through (7) of the procedure given in C.5.1.4. Audible and visual signals should be tested periodically during the year (monthly).

C.5.2.12 [5.1.9.2.4] Reserve Supply Low (Down to an Average One-Day Supply) High-Pressure Cylinder or Liquid Reserve. All components of these signal warning systems should be retested annually in accordance with Steps (2) through (8) of the procedure given in C.5.1.5. If test buttons are provided, audible and visual signals should be periodically tested throughout the year (monthly).

C.5.2.13 [5.1.9.2.4] The medical compressed air system alarms in 5.1.3.5.14 should be checked at least annually.

C.5.2.14 [5.1.8.2.2(1)] This pressure gauge should be checked on a daily basis to ensure proper piping system pressure. A change, increase or decrease, if noted, can give evidence that maintenance is required on the line pressure regulator and could thus avoid a problem.

C.5.2.15 [5.1.9] Annual retesting of all components of warning systems, if it can be done without changing piping system line pressure, should be performed.

C.5.2.16 [5.1.9] If test buttons are provided, the retesting of audible and visual alarm indicators should be performed monthly.

C.5.2.17 [5.1.4] Shutoff valves should be periodically checked for external leakage by means of a test solution or other equally effective means of leak detection safe for use with oxygen.

C.5.2.18 [5.1.5] Station outlets should be periodically checked for leakage and flow. Instructions of the manufacturer should be followed in making this examination.

Flow rates for a given pressure vary among systems due to the differences among manufacturers and among the various models of a manufacturer. A recommended value for existing systems is not included. What is important, however, is the consistency of readings over a period of time after a facility has determined what the minimum acceptable flow rates are for the devices intended for connection to the system.

C.5.3 Oxygen Service–Related Documents. The following publications can be used for technical reference:

(1) ASTM G 63, *Standard Guide for Evaluating Nonmetallic Materials for Oxygen Service*
(2) ASTM G 88, *Standard Guide for Designing Systems for Oxygen Service*

(3) ASTM G 93, *Practice for Cleaning Methods and Cleanliness Levels for Material and Equipment Used in Oxygen-Enriched Environments*
(4) ASTM G 94, *Standard Guide for Evaluating Metals for Oxygen Service*

C.6 Reserved

C.7 Reserved

C.8 Reserved

C.9 Additional Information on Chapter 9

C.9.1 Medical Safeguards, Respiratory Therapy.

C.9.1.1 General.

C.9.1.1.1 Personnel setting up, operating, and maintaining respiratory therapy equipment, including suction apparatus, should familiarize themselves with the problems of the use of each individual unit.

C.9.1.1.2 Personnel must be aware of the exact location of equipment in storage to facilitate emergency use.

C.9.1.1.3 Suction tubing employed in a hazardous location is to be electrically conductive.

C.9.2 Glossary of Respiratory Therapy Terminology.

C.9.2.1 Arrhythmia. Irregularity of heartbeats.

C.9.2.2 Asphyxia. Suffocation from lack of oxygen and an accumulation of carbon dioxide.

C.9.2.3 Aspiration. Removal of accumulated mucus by suction.

C.9.2.4 Bronchi. The two primary divisions of the trachea.

C.9.2.5 CPAP. Continuous positive airway pressure.

C.9.2.6 CPR. Cardiopulmonary resuscitation.

C.9.2.7 Croup Tent. Equipment utilized to provide environmental control inside a canopy in relation to oxygen concentration, temperature, humidity, and filtered gas.

C.9.2.8 Cyanosis. A bluish discoloration of skin and mucus membranes due to excessive concentration of reduced hemoglobin in the blood.

C.9.2.9 Defibrillate. Use of electrical shock to synchronize heart activity.

C.9.2.10 Diffusion. Transfer of gases across the alveolar capillary membrane.

C.9.2.11 EKG, ECG. Electrocardiogram.

C.9.2.12 Hemoglobin. The chemical compound in red blood cells that carries oxygen.

C.9.2.13 Hypoxia. An abnormally decreased supply or concentration of oxygen.

C.9.2.14 IMV. Intermittent mandatory ventilation.

C.9.2.15 IPPB. Intermittent positive pressure breathing.

C.9.2.16 PEEP. Positive end expiratory pressure.

C.9.2.17 Respiration. The exchange by diffusion of gases between the alveoli, the blood, and the tissue.

C.9.2.18 RLF. A disease entity of the premature infant causing blindness.

The definition of *RLF* (retrolental fibroplasia) makes no reference to oxygen because there are questions in the medical community concerning the role oxygen plays in the production of RLF.

C.9.2.19 Thorax. The chest; the upper part of the trunk between the neck and the abdomen.

C.9.2.20 Trachea. The windpipe leading from the larynx to the bronchi.

C.9.2.21 Ultrasonic Nebulizer. A device that produces sound waves that are utilized to break up water into aerosol particles.

C.9.2.22 Ventilation. Movement of air into and out of the lungs.

C.9.2.23 Ventilator. Machine used to support or assist nonbreathing or inadequately breathing patient.

C.9.3 Suggested Fire Response, Respiratory Therapy.

Suggested procedure in the event of fire involving respiratory therapy apparatus.

C.9.3.1 General. Fires in oxygen-enriched atmospheres spread rapidly, generate intense heat, and produce large volumes of heated and potentially toxic gases. Because of the immediate threat to patients and personnel, as well as the damage to equipment and possible spread to the structure of the building, it is important that all personnel be aware of the steps necessary to save life, to preserve limb, and, within reason, to extinguish or contain the fire.

C.9.3.2 Steps to Take in Event of Fire.

C.9.3.2.1 The following steps are recommended in the event of a fire, in the approximate order of importance:

(1) Remove the patient or patients immediately exposed from the site of the fire if their hair and clothing are not burning; if they are burning, extinguish the flames. *(See C.9.3.4 and C.9.3.5.)*
(2) Sound the fire alarm by whatever mode the hospital fire plan provides.
(3) Close off the supply of oxygen to the therapy apparatus involved if this step can be accomplished without injury to personnel. *(See C.9.3.3.)*
(4) Carry out any other steps specified in the fire plan of the hospital. For example:
   (a) Remove patients threatened by the fire
   (b) Close doors leading to the site of the fire
   (c) Attempt to extinguish or contain the fire *(See C.9.3.4.)*
   (d) Direct fire fighters to the site of the fire
   (e) Take whatever steps necessary to protect or evacuate patients in adjacent areas

C.9.3.3 Closing Off of Oxygen Supply.

C.9.3.3.1 In the event of a fire involving respiratory therapy equipment connected to an oxygen station outlet, the zone valve supplying that station is to be closed.

C.9.3.3.1.1 All personnel are cautioned to be aware of the hazard of such a step to other patients receiving oxygen supplied through the same zone valve. Steps should be taken to minimize such hazards, realizing that closing the valve is of foremost importance.

C.9.3.3.2 In the case of oxygen therapy apparatus supplied by a cylinder or container of oxygen, it is desirable to close the valve of the cylinder or container, provided that such closure can be accomplished without injury to personnel.

Note that metallic components of regulators and valves can become exceedingly hot if exposed to flame. Personnel are cautioned not to use their bare hands to effect closure.

C.9.3.4 Extinguishment or Containment of Fire.

C.9.3.4.1 Fire originating in or involving respiratory therapy apparatus generally involves combustibles such as rubber, plastic, linen, blankets, and the like. Water or water-based extinguishing agents are most effective in such fires.

C.9.3.4.1.1 Precautions should be observed if electrical equipment is adjacent to or involved in the fire, because of the danger of electrocution of personnel if streams of water contact live 115-V circuits.

C.9.3.4.1.2 Before attempting to fight such a fire with water or a water-based extinguishing agent, such electrical apparatus should be disconnected from the supply outlet, or the supply circuit deenergized at the circuit panel.

C.9.3.4.1.3 If such deenergization cannot be accomplished, water should not be employed. *(See C.9.3.4.2.)*

C.9.3.4.2 Fires involving or adjacent to electrical equipment with live circuits can be fought with extinguishers suitable for Class C fires, in accordance with NFPA 10, *Standard for Portable Fire Extinguishers.*

Note that chemical extinguishers are not effective against fires in oxygen-enriched atmospheres unless the source of oxygen is shut off. See C.9.3.3 for closing off oxygen supply.

C.9.3.5 Protection of Patients and Personnel.

C.9.3.5.1 Because of the intense heat generated, serious and even fatal burns of the skin or of the lungs from inhaling heated gases are possible sequelae to the oxygen-enriched-atmosphere fire. Thus, it is essential that patients be removed from the site of the fire whenever practical.

Note that where a nonambulatory patient is connected to a burning piece of therapy equipment, it might be more practical as the initial step to remove the equipment and/or extinguish the fire than to remove the patient.

C.9.3.5.2 The large quantities of noxious gases produced constitute a threat to life from asphyxia, beyond the thermal burn problem.

C.9.3.5.2.1 Personnel are cautioned not to remain in the fire area after patients are evacuated if quantities of gaseous combustion products are present.

C.9.3.6 Indoctrination of Personnel.

C.9.3.6.1 It is highly desirable that personnel involved in the care of patients, including nurses, aides, ward secretaries, and physicians, irrespective of whether or not they are involved in respiratory therapy practices, be thoroughly indoctrinated in all aspects of fire safety, including the following:

(1) The location of zone valves of nonflammable medical gas systems where employed, and the station outlets controlled by each valve.

(2) The location of electrical service boxes, and the areas served thereby.
(3) The location of fire extinguishers, indications for their use, and techniques for their application.
(4) The recommended methods of evacuating patients, and routes by which such evacuation is accomplished most expeditiously. Reference should be made to the facility's fire plan.
(5) The steps involved in carrying out the fire plan of the hospital.
(6) The location of fire alarm boxes, or knowledge of other methods, for summoning the local fire department.

C.9.4 Typical Gas Cylinders. See Table C.13.5.

C.10 Reserved

C.11 Additional Information on Chapter 11

C.11.1 Fire Incidents in Laboratories.

The following descriptions of laboratory fires are selected from previous editions of NFPA 99 and from the National Fire Incident Reporting System data base.

C.11.1.1 Iowa, October 1980. A hospital fire, originating in a second-floor pathology laboratory, occurred when electrical wires arced and ignited cloth towels placed under beakers. The beakers contained tissue samples, alcohol, and formaldehyde. The contents of the beakers caused the fire to spread to other larger containers of chemicals in the lab.

There was a 20- to 30-minute delay in detection of this fire because there was no automatic smoke detection equipment in the laboratory. Smoke detectors in the air ducts located in the hallways did operate when the smoke filtered out of the lab. There was no automatic sprinkler system.

No other specifics were reported as to the cause of the electrical arcing.

Direct property damage was estimated at $20,000.

C.11.1.2 Pennsylvania, December 1980. A small fire, of electrical nature, broke out in a hospital laboratory. The fire involved a condensate drip tray that was used to dissipate water from a refrigerator unit. The probable fire scenario was that a short circuit resulted from the aging rubber insulation of the cord. The unit is always left "on."

No direct property damage was reported for this fire. There were no automatic sprinklers in the lab area of the hospital. There were heat detectors in the area, but no smoke detectors. The fire generated large amounts of smoke.

C.11.1.3 Rhode Island, October 1981. A fire occurred in a blood bank/donor lab in a hospital. A patient was lying on one of three contour couches in the donor room giving blood. The technician pushed a button to raise the couch, then heard a pop, and saw flames and smoke coming from the couch. The technician tried unsuccessfully to extinguish the fire with a portable fire extinguisher.

A supervisor pulled the manual pull station and the fire department arrived within 3 minutes.

One civilian and one fire fighter were injured in the fire.

There was extensive smoke and soot damage in the area. Direct property damage was estimated at $12,000. The fire occurred in an unsprinklered building.

The cause of the fire was determined to be a short circuit in the wiring in the motor of the couch.

C.11.1.4 New Jersey, April 1982. A small hospital fire occurred in a processing laboratory where tissue samples are cut and mounted in metal or polypropylene cassettes and then run through a processor. In the processor, the mounted samples are dipped in a series of baths. The cassettes were stored in polystyrene cabinets.

The cause of the fire was undetermined. Damage was confined to a 6-ft^2 area in the corner of the tissue lab. The fronts of the cassette cabinets suffered partial melting and some cassettes had the paraffin melted. It was estimated that 80 percent of the specimen cassettes were intact and salvageable.

Total direct property damage was estimated at $70,000 and business interruption at $4,000.

A single sprinkler head operated and extinguished the fire. The waterflow alarm was received by the hospital switchboard and the municipal dispatching service.

C.11.1.5 Massachusetts, April 1982. A tissue laboratory in a hospital was the scene of a fire that resulted in $50,000 in direct property damage. An additional $50,000 was lost due to business interruption.

The tissue lab was located in the pathology area of the lab building and housed 11 tissue processing machines. Eight of the machines were used to dehydrate tissue samples in a xylene concentrated solution or an alcohol solution.

When a technician left the room at 5:15 p.m., all the machines were functioning properly. Twenty minutes later, a waterflow and smoke detection alarm was received at the command center with direct transmission to the fire department. Two sprinkler heads helped control the fire. The fire was extinguished by the fire department using a 1½-in. hand line from an interior standpipe. The fire was attributed to the jamming of one of the baskets of a processing machine as it was being moved from one carriage to another. The motor failed to shut down as it should have, overheated, and eventually ignited the flammable xylene and alcohol solutions.

C.11.1.6 Tennessee, May 1984. The overheating of xylene inside a distiller located in the hospital lab resulted in a fire. Apparently, the escaping flammable vapors were ignited by ordinary electrical equipment in the room. Prompt and effective automatic sprinkler activation helped minimize fire damage.

The fire occurred in a fourth floor histology lab. Among the contents of the lab were small xylene stills for reclaiming used solvent, and also tissue processing equipment. A technician had filled the distiller with xylene. Some time later, another person working in the area of the distiller noticed that an odor was coming from the unit and that the solution had a brown color to it. This employee left to find someone to inspect the distiller. This employee returned with another worker to find a grayish haze around the console. Just after leaving the room, the employees saw smoke coming from under the door. A "Code Red" was sounded and the lab was evacuated. The technician who originally was running the machine returned at the sound of the alarm and tried to turn off the instrument by crawling on the floor, but was unable to do so because of the smoke and smell of xylene.

Property loss was estimated at $150,000, and business interruption resulted in an additional $15,000.

C.11.1.7 Florida, December 1985. A fire broke out in a hospital pathology lab and resulted in $100,000 in property damage, and an additional $2,000 in business interruption. The pathology lab analyzes tissue samples from patients. These samples are preserved in an embedding center using paraffin as the preserving agent.

The cause of the fire was determined to be the failure of a thermostat that controls the temperature of the heating element that melts the paraffin in the tissue embedding center.

The fire damaged two tissue-embedding centers, an ultrasonic cleaner, two light fixtures, a wood wall cabinet, as well as damaging the wall and ceiling. Microscopes, computer terminals, measuring equipment, and tissue slides and samples were among the items damaged by smoke and soot. The fire damage was confined to the lab.

An employee smelled smoke coming from the lab and noticed that the lab door was hot. A security guard was called immediately and pulled the alarm at a manual station in the hallway. The fire department extinguished the fire with dry chemicals and an inside hose stream located in the hallway. There were no heat or smoke detectors inside the pathology lab. The building was unsprinklered.

C.11.1.8 New York, April 1988. A hospital laboratory was the scene of a $250,000 fire. The fire started when a professor was sterilizing a pair of scissors using the "flaming" procedure. The "flaming" method involves dipping an item into alcohol and then burning off that alcohol with a Bunsen burner. The professor carried out the procedure once, then tried to do it a second time because he thought he had contaminated the scissors. During the second attempt, the alcohol he dipped the scissors into ignited because the scissors were still hot. The container of alcohol was dropped and the fire spread to nearby combustibles, including other flammable liquids.

A security guard noticed the fire and immediately pulled the alarm signaling the fire department and hospital fire brigade. The fire department responded promptly and extinguished the fire.

There were no automatic sprinklers in the fire area. Three civilians were injured in the fire.

C.11.1.9 California, April 1989. The thermostat of a low-temperature lab oven (incubator) malfunctioned, causing the oven to overheat. The unit heated to approximately 200 degrees overnight, causing a smoldering fire. An employee discovered the fire in the sixth-floor laboratory in the medical center when he arrived early to work. His first action was to shut off the incubator, after which he called the fire department.

Fire destroyed the contents of the incubator, and the incubator itself needed repairs due to exposure to dry powder agent. Smoke damage also occurred in the lab and hallway. Property damage was estimated at $1,000.

An alarm sounded after the fire department had used an extinguisher on the fire. The type of alarm was not reported.

C.11.1.10 California, November 1989. Four fire fighters were injured at a fire in a pathology lab at a multi-story hospital medical center when they were exposed to toxic chemical debris and human tissue. The fire originated in a stainless steel cabinet that had two glass-windowed doors. There were two pieces of equipment in the cabinet that were used to process tissue by dipping trays of tissues into a series of containers. The machines were about 20 years old.

The official cause of the fire was listed as a malfunctioning piece of electrically powered lab equipment igniting volatile flammable liquid. The exact point of failure could not be determined.

Automatic detection equipment was present and operated. There was no automatic sprinkler system present in the lab. Direct property loss was estimated at $325,000. No estimates were given for business interruption.

C.11.1.11 Michigan, March 1981. A building that housed various analytical research and development laboratories was the scene of a $60,000 fire. The laboratory involved in the fire was used essentially for liquid and gas chromatography.

The fire occurred when solvent leakage inside, or adjacent to, a liquid chromatograph ignited from an electrical source. Apparently, a small amount of solvent was spilled for up to 25 minutes and subsequently ignited. The fire burned through a plastic tube feeding a waste solvent container on a shelf. The spilled waste solvent intensified the fire. Liquid chromatography uses solvents of methanol and iso-octane.

An employee first heard a crackling and then saw flames at the base of the liquid chromatography instrument. Employees immediately attacked the fire with a dry chemical fire extinguisher. Also, two sprinkler heads operated, limiting the spread of fire within the laboratory. The fire department received a waterflow alarm, a manual fire alarm box, and several phone calls. Fire fighters found the fire nearly out on arrival because of sprinkler activation and consumption of the spilled liquid.

C.11.1.12 Virginia, June 1981. A small fire occurred in a laboratory that manufactures interferon. During this process, red and white blood cells are separated, and the white cells are placed in beakers with nutrients. A virus is introduced to the white cell cultures, which then produce the interferon. A centrifuge is used to separate the interferon from the white cells. The process is carried out in a small refrigerated room isolated from other areas by insulated metal panel walls and ceiling.

In the early afternoon, an employee stabilized a magnetic stirring rod that had been banging the side of one of the glass beakers.

Minutes later, personnel noticed smoke and fire within the refrigerated room and immediately extinguished the fires with extinguishers. The fire department also was notified.

Alcohol spilling onto the electrical parts of the magnetic stirrer caused the fire. The spilling was caused by inadequate supervision of the magnetic stirrer.

The fire resulted in $235,000 in direct property damage and an additional $40,000 in business interruption. Metal walls and ceiling panels, some laboratory equipment, and an unknown quantity of interferon were destroyed or damaged in the fire.

There were no automatic detection or suppression systems in the building. There were manual pull stations and portable extinguishers.

C.11.1.13 Tissue Processor Fire. Operated 24 hours per day, but unattended from 11 p.m. to 7 a.m., a tissue processor was suspected of causing $200,000 damage because the incident occurred after 11 p.m. and there were no detectors or automatic extinguishing equipment in the laboratory. Flammable liquids in glass containers stored in an open shelf below the equipment contributed to the intensity of the fire.

Aside from damage to the laboratory, electrical cables in the corridor near the incident shorted and caused power to be interrupted in the hospital. Fire doors closed, but the fire alarm was not sounded.

C.11.1.14 Hot Plate Fires. Acetone, being poured at the sink in a patient treatment lab, was ignited by a nearby hot plate that had just been turned off. The technician dropped the container, which was metal and which, fortunately, fell in an upright position. The patient was safely evacuated, but the fire was intense enough to melt the sweated water pipe fittings of the window ventilator.

Petroleum ether caught fire while a chemist was pouring it in a fume hood from its large glass container — presumably ignited by a nearby hot plate that had recently been turned off. He dropped the glass container on the floor and ran from the room. The bottle broke; ignition caused enough pressure to blow open the lab escape hatch and slam the entrance door shut.

C.11.1.15 Refrigerator Explosion. Eighty ml of diazomethane dissolved in ether detonated in a domestic-type refrigerator. The door blew open, the frame bowed out, and the plastic lining ignited, causing a heavy blanket of soot to be deposited far down the adjoining corridor. *(See 11.7.2.5.)*

C.11.1.16 Pressure Filter Fire. At an eastern hospital pharmacy, a fire-conscious technician prepared for pressure filtering of 50 gal (220 L) of isopropyl alcohol by placing a towel on a table adjacent to the pump; in the event of fire he planned to smother flames of alcohol inadvertently spilled on his person. As he attempted to turn on the pump, the defective switch ignited alcohol on his hands. Instinctively, he reached for the towel as he had previously rehearsed in his mind but, in doing so, he tripped over the hose that was conducting alcohol by gravity from a large open kettle to the suction side of the pump. The hose slipped from its fittings, thereby dumping 50 gal (220 L) of the flaming solvent onto the floor. He escaped with minor injuries, but the pharmacy was destroyed. (Many fires are intensified by an unfortunate sequence of minor unsafe practices that in themselves seem almost too insignificant to worry about.)

C.11.1.17 Water Bath Fire. When the thermostat on a water bath malfunctioned, the bath overheated, causing the acrylic lid to sag and contact the heater elements. A fire resulted. Heater equipment should always be protected by overtemperature shutoffs. (Based on *DuPont Safety News*, June 14, 1965.)

C.11.1.18 Peroxide Explosion. A distillation apparatus exploded within a lab fume hood. It was caused by the detonation of the residual peroxide. The drawn sash prevented injury, although the electric mantle was torn to shreds. The investigator was using "some isopropyl ether," which had been kept in a clear glass bottle. He allowed the distillation to continue to dryness.

Investigators should become more aware of the nature of ether peroxide formations. Dioxane and ethyl and isopropyl ethers are the most common offenders. Age, sunlight, air space above liquid, and clear glass containers help to create these explosive peroxides. Test frequently for peroxide; filter out peroxides through a column of 80 mesh Alorco activated alumina, as suggested by Dasler and Bauer, *Ind. Eng. Chem. Anal.*, Ed. 18, 52 (1964). Never leave distillations unattended.

C.11.2 Related Definitions, Laboratories.

The following definitions are taken from other NFPA documents and are critical to the understanding of Chapter 11.

C.11.2.1 The following definitions are taken from NFPA 30, *Flammable and Combustible Liquids Code*:

Flammable Liquid. Any liquid that has a closed-cup flash point below 100°F (37.8°C), as determined by the test procedures and apparatus set forth in 1.7.4.1 through 1.7.4.4. Flammable liquids are classified as Class I as follows: *Class I Liquid* — any liquid that has a closed-cup flash point below 100°F (37.8°C) and a Reid vapor pressure not exceeding 40 psia (2068.6 mm Hg) at 100°F (37.8°C), as determined by ASTM D 323, *Standard Method of Test for Vapor Pressure of Petroleum Products (Reid Method)*. Class I liquids are further classified as follows: (1) Class IA liquids — those liquids that have flash points below 73°F (22.8°C) and boiling points below 100°F (37.8°C); (2) Class IB liquids — those liquids that have flash points below 73°F (22.8°C) and boiling points at or above 100°F (37.8°C); (3) Class IC liquids — those liquids that have flash points at or above 73°F (22.8°C), but below 100°F (37.8°C). [**30:**3.3.25.2]

Combustible Liquid. Any liquid that has a closed-cup flash point at or above 100°F (37.8°C), as determined by the test procedures and apparatus set forth in 1.7.4.1 through 1.7.4.4. Combustible liquids are classified as Class II or Class III as follows: (1) *Class II Liquid* — any liquid that has a flash point at or above 100°F (37.8°C) and below 140°F (60°C); (2) *Class IIIA* — any liquid that has a flash point at or above 140°F (60°C), but below 200°F (93°C); (3) *Class IIIB* — any liquid that has a flash point at or above 200°F (93°C). [**30:**3.3.25.1]

C.11.2.2 The following definition is also taken from NFPA 30, *Flammable and Combustible Liquids Code*:

Flash Point. The minimum temperature of a liquid at which sufficient vapor is given off to form an ignitible mixture with the air, near the surface of the liquid or within the vessel used, as determined by the appropriate test procedure and apparatus specified in 1.7.4. [**30:**3.3.16]

C.11.2.3 The following definitions are based on NFPA 704, *Standard System for the Identification of the Hazards of Materials for Emergency Response*.

C.11.2.3.1 Health Hazard. A health hazard is any property of a material that, either directly or indirectly, can cause injury or incapacitation, either temporary or permanent, from exposure by contact, inhalation, or ingestion. Table C.11.2.3.1 is extracted from NFPA 704 and defines degrees of health hazard.

C.11.2.3.2 Flammability Hazard. Flammability describes the degree of susceptibility of materials to burning. The form or condition of the material, as well as its inherent properties, affects its flammability. Table C.11.2.3.2 is extracted from NFPA 704 and defines degrees of flammability hazard.

TABLE C.11.2.3.1 *Degrees of Health Hazards*

*Degree of Hazard**	*Criteria*
4 — Materials that, under emergency conditions, can be lethal.	Gases whose LC_{50} for acute inhalation toxicity is less than or equal to 1000 parts per million (ppm). Any liquid whose saturated vapor concentration at 20°C (68°F) is equal to or greater than ten times its LC_{50} for acute inhalation toxicity, if its LC_{50} is less than or equal to 1000 ppm. Dusts and mists whose LC_{50} for acute inhalation toxicity is less than or equal to 0.5 milligrams per liter (mg/L). Materials whose LD_{50} for acute dermal toxicity is less than or equal to 40 milligrams per kilogram (mg/kg). Materials whose LD_{50} for acute oral toxicity is less than or equal to 5 mg/kg.
3 — Materials that, under emergency conditions, can cause serious or permanent injury.	Gases whose LC_{50} for acute inhalation toxicity is greater than 1000 ppm but less than or equal to 3000 ppm. Any liquid whose saturated vapor concentration at 20°C (68°F) is equal to or greater than its LC_{50} for acute inhalation toxicity, if its LC_{50} is less than or equal to 3000 ppm and that does not meet the criteria for degree of hazard 4. Dusts and mists whose LC_{50} for acute inhalation toxicity is greater than 0.5 mg/L but less than or equal to 2 mg/L. Materials whose LD_{50} for acute dermal toxicity is greater than 40 mg/kg but less than or equal to 200 mg/kg. Materials that are corrosive to the respiratory tract. Materials that are corrosive to the eye or cause irreversible corneal opacity. Materials that are corrosive to skin. Cryogenic gases that cause frostbite and irreversible tissue damage. Compressed liquefied gases with boiling points at or below −55°C (−66.5°F) that cause frostbite and irreversible tissue damage. Materials whose LD_{50} for acute oral toxicity is greater than 5 mg/kg but less than or equal to 50 mg/kg.

TABLE C.11.2.3.1 Continued

*Degree of Hazard**	*Criteria*
2 — Materials that, under emergency conditions, can cause temporary incapacitation or residual injury.	Gases whose LC_{50} for acute inhalation toxicity is greater than 3000 ppm but less than or equal to 5000 ppm. Any liquid whose saturated vapor concentration at 20°C (68°F) is equal to or greater than one-fifth its LC_{50} for acute inhalation toxicity, if its LC_{50} is less than or equal to 5000 ppm and that does not meet the criteria for either degree of hazard 3 or degree of hazard 4. Dusts and mists whose LC_{50} for acute inhalation toxicity is greater than 2 mg/L but less than or equal to 10 mg/L. Materials whose LD_{50} for acute dermal toxicity is greater than 200 mg/kg but less than or equal to 1000 mg/kg. Compressed liquefied gases with boiling points between −30°C (−22°F) and −55°C (−66.5°F) that can cause severe tissue damage, depending on duration of exposure. Materials that are respiratory irritants. Materials that cause severe but reversible irritation to the eyes or lacrimators. Materials that are primary skin irritants or sensitizers. Materials whose LD_{50} for acute oral toxicity is greater than 50 mg/kg but less than or equal to 500 mg/kg.
1 — Materials that, under emergency conditions, can cause significant irritation.	Gases and vapors whose LC_{50} for acute inhalation toxicity is greater than 5000 ppm but less than or equal to 10,000 ppm. Dusts and mists whose LC_{50} for acute inhalation toxicity is greater than 10 mg/L but less than or equal to 200 mg/L. Materials whose LD_{50} for acute dermal toxicity is greater than 1000 mg/kg but less than or equal to 2000 mg/kg. Materials that cause slight to moderate irritation to the respiratory tract, eyes, and skin. Materials whose LD_{50} for acute oral toxicity is greater than 500 mg/kg but less than or equal to 2000 mg/kg.
0 — Materials that, under emergency conditions, would offer no hazard beyond that of ordinary combustible materials.	Gases and vapors whose LC_{50} for acute inhalation toxicity is greater than 10,000 ppm. Dusts and mists whose LC_{50} for acute inhalation toxicity is greater than 200 mg/L. Materials whose LD_{50} for acute dermal toxicity is greater than 2000 mg/kg. Materials whose LD_{50} for acute oral toxicity is greater than 2000 mg/kg. Materials that are essentially nonirritating to the respiratory tract, eyes, and skin.

*For each degree of hazard, the criteria are listed in a priority order based upon the likelihood of exposure.

TABLE C.11.2.3.2 Degrees of Flammability Hazards

Degree of Hazard	*Criteria*
4 — Materials that will rapidly or completely vaporize at atmospheric pressure and normal ambient temperature or that are readily dispersed in air and will burn readily.	Flammable gases. Flammable cryogenic materials. Any liquid or gaseous material that is liquid while under pressure and has a flash point below 22.8°C (73°F) and a boiling point below 37.8°C (100°F) (i.e., Class IA liquids). Materials that ignite spontaneously when exposed to air. Solids containing greater than 0.5 percent by weight of a flammable or combustible solvent are rated by the closed cup flash point of the solvent.
3 — Liquids and solids that can be ignited under almost all ambient temperature conditions. Materials in this degree produce hazardous atmospheres with air under almost all ambient temperatures or, though unaffected by ambient temperatures, are readily ignited under almost all conditions.	Liquids having a flash point below 22.8°C (73°F) and having a boiling point at or above 37.8°C (100°F) and those liquids having a flash point at or above 22.8°C (73°F) and below 37.8°C (100°F) (i.e., Class IB and Class IC liquids). Materials that on account of their physical form or environmental conditions can form explosive mixtures with air and that are readily dispersed in air. Flammable or combustible dusts with representative diameter less than 420 microns (40 mesh). Materials that burn with extreme rapidity, usually by reason of self-contained oxygen (e.g., dry nitrocellulose and many organic peroxides). Solids containing greater than 0.5 percent by weight of a flammable or combustible solvent are rated by the closed cup flash point of the solvent.
2 — Materials that must be moderately heated or exposed to relatively high ambient temperatures before ignition can occur. Materials in this degree would not under normal conditions form hazardous atmospheres with air, but under high ambient temperatures or under moderate heating could release vapor in sufficient quantities to produce hazardous atmospheres with air.	Liquids having a flash point at or above 37.8°C (100°F) and below 93.4°C (200°F) (i.e., Class II and Class IIIA liquids). Solid materials in the form of powders or coarse dusts of representative diameter between 420 microns (40 mesh) and 2 mm (10 mesh) that burn rapidly but that generally do not form explosive mixtures with air. Solid materials in a fibrous or shredded form that burn rapidly and create flash fire hazards, such as cotton, sisal, and hemp. Solids and semisolids that readily give off flammable vapors. Solids containing greater than 0.5 percent by weight of a flammable or combustible solvent are rated by the closed cup flash point of the solvent.
1 — Materials that must be preheated before ignition can occur. Materials in this degree require considerable preheating, under all ambient temperature conditions, before ignition and combustion can occur.	Materials that will burn in air when exposed to a temperature of 815.5°C (1500°F) for a period of 5 minutes in accordance with Annex D [of NFPA 704]. Liquids, solids, and semisolids having a flash point at or above 93.4°C (200°F) (i.e., Class IIIB liquids).

TABLE C.11.2.3.2 Continued

Degree of Hazard	*Criteria*
1 — Materials that must be preheated before ignition can occur. Materials in this degree require considerable preheating, under all ambient temperature conditions, before ignition and combustion can occur.	Liquids with a flash point greater than 35°C (95°F) that do not sustain combustion when tested using the *Method of Testing for Sustained Combustibility*, per 49 CFR 173, Appendix H or the UN *Recommendations on the Transport of Dangerous Goods, Model Regulations*, 11th revised edition, and the related *Manual of Tests and Criteria*, 3rd revised edition. Liquids with a flash point greater than 35°C (95°F) in a water-miscible solution or dispersion with a water noncombustible liquid/solid content of more than 85 percent by weight. Liquids that have no fire point when tested by ASTM D 92, *Standard Test Method for Flash and Fire Points by Cleveland Open Cup*, up to the boiling point of the liquid or up to a temperature at which the sample being tested shows an obvious physical change. Combustible pellets with a representative diameter greater than 2 mm (10 mesh). Most ordinary combustible materials. Solids containing greater than 0.5 percent by weight of a flammable or combustible solvent are rated by the closed cup flash point of the solvent.
0 — Materials that will not burn under typical fire conditions, including intrinsically noncombustible materials such as concrete, stone, and sand.	Materials that will not burn in air when exposed to a temperature of 816°C (1500°F) for a period of 5 minutes in accordance with Annex D [of NFPA 704].

C.11.2.3.3 Reactivity (Instability) Hazards. Reactivity describes the ability of a material to chemically react with other stable or unstable materials. For purposes of this hazard identification system, the other material is water, if reaction with water releases energy. Reactions with common materials other than water can release energy violently, but are beyond the scope of this identification system.

Unstable materials are those that, in the pure state or as commercially produced, will vigorously polymerize, decompose, or condense, become self-reactive, or undergo other violent chemical changes.

Stable materials are those that normally have the capacity to resist changes in their chemical composition, despite exposure to air, water, and heat encountered in fire emergencies. Table C.11.2.3.3 is extracted from NFPA 704 and defines degrees of reactivity (instability) hazards.

C.12 Additional Information on Chapter 12

C.12.1 Emergency Management Program Development.

For those new to the emergency management field, and/or for those seeking to re-structure an existing program, a sample program development process is illustrated in Figure C.12.1.

C.12.1.1 Program Development Steps and Activities.

TABLE C.11.2.3.3 *Degrees of Instability Hazards*

Degree of Hazard	***Criteria***
4 — Materials that in themselves are readily capable of detonation or explosive decomposition or explosive reaction at normal temperatures and pressures.	Materials that are sensitive to localized thermal or mechanical shock at normal temperatures and pressures. Materials that have an instantaneous power density (product of heat of reaction and reaction rate) at 250°C (482°F) of 1000 W/mL or greater.
3 — Materials that in themselves are capable of detonation or explosive decomposition or explosive reaction, but that require a strong initiating source or that must be heated under confinement before initiation.	Materials that have an instantaneous power density (product of heat of reaction and reaction rate) at 250°C (482°F) at or above 100 W/mL and below 1000 W/mL. Materials that are sensitive to thermal or mechanical shock at elevated temperatures and pressures.
2 — Materials that readily undergo violent chemical change at elevated temperatures and pressures.	Materials that have an instantaneous power density (product of heat of reaction and reaction rate) at 250°C (482°F) at or above 10 W/mL and below 100 W/mL.
1 — Materials that in themselves are normally stable, but that can become unstable at elevated temperatures and pressures.	Materials that have an instantaneous power density (product of heat of reaction and reaction rate) at 250°C (482°F) at or above 0.01 W/mL and below 10 W/mL.
0 — Materials that in themselves are normally stable, even under fire conditions.	Materials that have an instantaneous power density (product of heat of reaction and reaction rate) at 250°C (482°F) below 0.01 W/mL. Materials that do not exhibit an exotherm at temperatures less than or equal to 500°C (932°F) when tested by differential scanning calorimetry.

Subsection C.12.1.1 is an effort to help a health care facility design or update its emergency operations plan (EOP). When designing the response portion of the EOP, many facilities find it helpful to place those procedures applicable to any disaster in an infrastructure section. All specific disasters would be listed separately. For example, the infrastructure approach would include the following:

- Activation of plan
- Key persons and general staff disaster alert
- Incident command system
- Disaster internal and external communications
- Disaster staffing
- Emergency building lockdown
- Full building evacuation plans

Specific disaster procedures would include the following:

- Natural disasters
- Technological disasters
- Human events

C.12.1.1.1 Designate the Emergency Management Committee (EMC), Identify Operating Unit Roles, and Assign Responsibilities. The EMC is a multi-disciplinary commit-

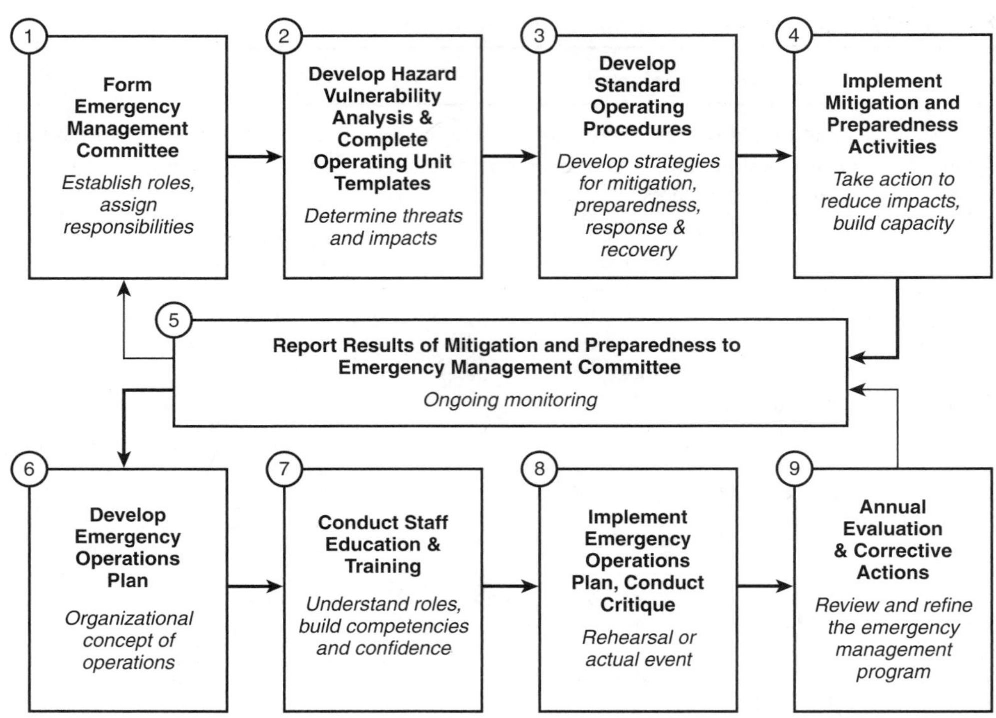

FIGURE C.12.1 *Emergency Management Program Development Process.*

tee established to coordinate and oversee the emergency management program, and have a close relationship with the Safety Committee.

The functions of the EMC include defining the role of the organization in the community wide emergency management program; conducting/reviewing a Hazard Vulnerability Analysis (HVA) which addresses all hazards that threaten the facility; developing/reviewing Standard Operating Procedures (SOPs) that address hazards identified in the HVA; developing/reviewing the emergency operations plan and coordinate it with other health care organizations in the community wide emergency management program; assigning roles and responsibilities of operating unit managers and key operators/managers; overseeing the development and maintenance of the EMP; ensuring that all employees have received appropriate training; conducting an annual evaluation of the effectiveness of the program, and ensuring a telephone roster of key personnel responsible for critical operations is kept current.

C.12.1.1.2 Conduct a Hazard Vulnerability Analysis (HVA) and Complete Operating Unit Templates. The HVA is a systematic approach to assessing the probability and consequence of hazards, threats and events that might affect the continued operation of the health care facility and surrounding community. Figure C.12.1.1.2(a) illustrates a sample HVA format.

The emergency management committee oversees the HVA process to ensure that all major threats to the facility are accounted for and assessed. Input to the HVA by operating unit managers is very important. Once a list of priority hazards, threats and events has been compiled, managers should complete an operating unit template for their particular service or department. Some threats to individual operating units are so severe that they might interrupt the continuity of critical operations in the facility. The operating unit template is a unit-level contingency plan, useful in staff education, drills, and actual events. Figure C.12.1.1.2(b) shows a sample operating unit template.

Type of Event	Severity Classification — Low, Moderate, High				Rank
	Probability	Human Impact	Property Impact	Operational Impact	
	Likelihood this will occur within 1 year	*Possibility of death or injury*	*Physical losses and damage*	*Interruption of services*	*Score of 2 or higher in any category requires a SOP*
Score	*0 = N/A 1 = Low 2 = Moderate 3 = High*	*0 = N/A 1 = Low 2 = Moderate 3 = High*	*0 = N/A 1 = Low 2 = Moderate 3 = High*	*0 = N/A 1 = Low 2 = Moderate 3 = High*	*SOP required — yes or no?*
(hazard type)					

 NFPA 99 (p. 1 of 1)

FIGURE C.12.1.1.2(a) *Sample Hazards Vulnerability Analysis (HVA) Format.*

Operating Unit: ______________________ Operating Unit Manager: ______________________

Mission Critical System	Potential Problems	Contact for Assistance in Preparing	Mitigation Actions	If this mission critical system is interrupted, then: Assess situation for:	Action required:
(Lighting)					
(Electrical Power)					
(Steam Distribution)					
(HVAC)					
(Room or Hood Exhaust)					
(Water Delivery)					
(Waste Stream)					
(Communications)					

 NFPA 99 (p. 1 of 1)

FIGURE C.12.1.1.2(b) *Sample Operating Unit Template.*

C.12.1.1.3 Review the Hazard Vulnerability Analysis (HVA) and Determine Priorities for Developing Standard Operating Procedures (SOPs). Using the input submitted by operating unit managers, the committee must prioritize threats/events and develop a list of SOPs that must be developed to address those hazards. Figure C.12.1.1.3 displays a sample Standard Operating Procedure format.

C.12.1.1.4 Implement Mitigation and Preparedness Strategies. Using the SOPs developed for prioritized threats/events, develop and implement actions that will eliminate or reduce the impact of adverse events to the facility and build capabilities to manage them. The committee should review the SOPs to identify resources needed for mitigation and preparedness, develop cost estimates or resources required, and submit the resource request to the Director for funding. The committee is responsible for tracking mitigation and preparedness planning activities until completed.

C.12.1.1.5 Report Results of Mitigation and Preparedness Activities to the Emergency Management Committee. Operating unit managers and the emergency program coordinator should regularly report results of mitigation and preparedness activities to the committee. Reports should include mitigation activities taken that effectively reduced or eliminated adverse impacts to the facility; mitigation activities that did not reduce or eliminate adverse impacts to the facility operation; and recommendations for mitigation and preparedness activities, budget, and timelines.

C.12.1.1.6 Develop, Publish and Distribute the Emergency Operations Plan (EOP). NFPA 1600, *Standard on Disaster/Emergency Management and Business Continuity Programs*, Section 3.6, describes four types of planning: strategic administrative (preparedness) planning, mitigation planning, recovery planning, and emergency operations planning.

The Federal Emergency Management Agency, now part of the Department of Homeland Security, issues guidance on the development of emergency operations plans, or EOPs. The EOP is designed to address all hazards and it accomplishes this through its organization by functions, not departments, hazards, or individuals. Flexibility is a key feature of this type of format, as only the functions needed to address the problems are activated, not the entire plan. This type of EOP format (a Basic Plan and Functional Annexes) is that used by communities, states, and the Federal Response Plan. *(See Annex G, Informational References.)*

C.12.1.1.7 Train Staff on the Emergency Operations Plan (EOP). See 12.3.3.8.

C.12.1.1.8 Test and Evaluate the Emergency Operations Plan in Response to a Drill or Actual Event. See 12.3.3.9.

C.12.1.1.9 Conduct an Annual Review of the Effectiveness of the Emergency Management Program. See NFPA 1600 for additional information on program evaluation and corrective actions.

C.12.2 Personnel Notification and Recall.

Medical staff, key personnel, and other personnel needed will be notified and recalled as required. In order to relieve switchboard congestion, it is desirable to utilize a pyramidal system to recall individuals who are off duty or otherwise out of the facility. Under the pyramidal system, an individual who has been notified will notify two other individuals, who in turn will each notify two other individuals, and so on. A current copy of the notification and recall roster, with current home and on-call telephone numbers, will be maintained at the hospital switchboard at all times. In case the pyramidal system is to be utilized, each individual involved in the system has to maintain a current copy of the roster at all times, in order that each knows whom they are to notify and the telephone numbers concerned. It is essential that key personnel rosters be kept current.

____
(Name of facility)

Standard Operating Procedure #: ____________________ ________________
(Date)

SUBJECT: ____
(Insert Hazard, Threat, or Event Name)

1. Description of hazard, threat, or event: ____________________

2. Impact on mission critical systems: ____________________

3. Operating units and key personnel with responsibility: ____________________

4. Mitigation and Preparedness Activities
   a. Hazard reduction strategies and resource issues: ____________________
   b. Preparedness strategies and resource issues: ____________________

5. Response and Recovery Activities
   a. Hazard control strategies and resource issues: ____________________
   b. Hazard monitoring strategies: ____________________
   c. Recovery strategies and resource issues: ____________________

6. Notification Procedures
   a. Internal: ____________________
   b. External: ____________________

7. Specialized staff training: ____________________

8. References and further assistance: ____________________

9. Review date: ____________________

____________________ ____________________
(Name) (Position/Title)

 (NFPA 99, p. 1 of 1)

FIGURE C.12.1.1.3 *Sample Standard Operating Procedure Format.*

When setting up staff recall procedures, facilities might find it helpful to list staff by proximity to the facility. The greater the distance one must travel to reach the facility, the more difficult it will be to return to the facility quickly.

It can also be helpful to list staff who have pre-agreed to come to the facility immediately when requested at the time of a disaster. This list often includes staff who do not have family commitments, such as small children, to attend to first.

C.12.3 Special Considerations and Protocols.

Fire is a deadly disaster for a health care facility. The actions taken at the first discovery of fire could determine whether patients live or die. It is one of the few disasters for which the procedures must be committed to memory. Additionally, if staff are expected to react appropriately, they must have realistic training.

The key procedures in a health care facility's fire plan are as follows:

R **R**emove anyone in immediate danger while calling out a fire code word for assistance.
A **A**ctivate the fire alarm.
C **C**lose the door to contain the fire.
E **E**xtinguish the fire upon discovery if you know you can do so safely and quickly, and **E**vacuate as directed by the person in charge.

NOTE: The priority of these procedures depends on the scenario at the time of the fire.

Additional important fire considerations include the following:

- Who meets the fire department?
- Who automatically responds to the fire area to help?
- What are the department-specific procedures?
  - Support departments. If the fire is in your area, to which area do you evacuate?
  - High-acuity areas. If the fire is in the surgical suite, what actions should the OR team take to sustain the life of the patient while handling the fire and evacuating the fire area, as necessary?

C.12.3.1 Fire and Explosion. In the event that the health care facility need not be completely evacuated immediately, the actions staff should take when they are alerted to a fire are detailed in Sections 18.7, 19.7, 20.7, and 21.7 of NFPA *101*, *Life Safety Code*.

C.12.3.2 Severe Storm. The warning system operated by the National Oceanic and Atmospheric Administration will, in most cases, provide adequate time to permit the health care facility to take certain precautions, and if disaster appears inevitable, to activate the Health Care Emergency Management Plan in advance of the disaster event. Assuming evacuation is not feasible, some precautions include the following:

(1) Draw all shades and close all drapes as protection against shattering glass.
(2) Lower all patient beds to the low position, wherever possible.
(3) Place blankets on patients/residents.
(4) Close all doors and windows.
(5) Bring indoors those lawn objects that could become missiles.
(6) Remove all articles from window ledges.
(7) Relocate patients/residents to windowless hallways or rooms.

The U.S. Weather Bureau, as a result of studies, no longer recommends that windows on a particular side of a building be kept open during severe windstorms.

C.12.3.3 Evacuation. Evacuation can be partial or total. It might involve moving from one story to another, one lateral section or wing to another, or moving out of the structure. Even partial evacuations can involve all categories of patients; where these are people who would not routinely be moved, extraordinary measures might be required to support life. It is also necessary to ensure movement of supplies in conjunction with any evacuation. Decisions to evacuate might be made as a result of internal problems or under menace of engulfing external threats. In all cases, the following considerations govern:

(1) Move to pre-designated areas, whether in the facility, nearby, or in remote zones. Evacuation directives will normally indicate destinations. Note that it is recommended to predesign a mutual aid evacuation plan with other health care facilities in the community. *(See Annex G, U.S. Government Publication 3152, Hospitals and Community Emergency Response–What you Need to Know, on the subject of health care community mutual aid and evacuation planning.)*

It should again be noted that, although movement (particularly evacuation to the outside) is the least desired action for a health care facility to take, it might be necessary in some emergencies. A facility must be prepared for situations when total evacuation is necessary, as has occurred in the past in health care facilities.

(2) Ensure movement of equipment, supplies, and medical records to accompany or meet patients and staff in the new location.

Patients on electrical life-support equipment require added consideration when evacuating to a new location. Plans are necessary for both the physical needs of such patients during the move and in the new location.

(3) Execute predetermined staffing plans. Some staff will accompany patients; others will rendezvous in the new location. Maintenance of shifts is more complex than normal, especially when some hard-to-move patients stay behind in the threatened location, and when staff might be separated from their own relocated families.
(4) Protection of patients and staff (during and after movement) against the threatening environment has to be provided.
(5) Planning has to consider transportation arrangements and patient tracking.

An increase in certain activities, such as the production and transportation of toxic chemicals and the number of arson incidents, has increased the probability of evacuation of health care facilities in times of emergency involving these activities. Natural events such as hurricanes, tornadoes, and volcanic eruptions can also necessitate such action. For example, the nuclear accident at the Three Mile Island Nuclear Plant in Pennsylvania (March 28, 1979) and the eruption of Mount St. Helens (May 18, 1980) required the temporary evacuation of hospitals in those areas.

For most incidents, facilities require only an internal patient relocation plan because of the defend-in-place concept. This concept considers facilities to be composed of many zones that can provide safe areas of refuge. However, facilities also should be prepared for outside relocation of patients if certain internal conditions, such as the interruption of both normal and emergency electrical power, or external events require it.

A well-organized relocation plan incorporates most components of an evacuation plan on a unit-by-unit or zone-by-zone basis, as necessary. If an evacuation is ordered, additional consideration should be given to the adequate care of patients once they have left the confines (and protection) of the facility. This would include providing shelter adjacent to the facility or transportation to another facility, the transferring of the patient's medical records and any vital supplies, and staff support for each patient.

C.12.3.4 High Profile. Admission of a high-profile person to a health care facility in an emergency creates two sets of problems that might require partial activation of the Health Care Emergency Management Plan. These problems are security and reception of news media.

C.12.3.4.1 Security. Provision of security forces in this situation might be provided by a governmental agency or private security forces. However, activation of facility security forces might be required to prevent hordes of curious onlookers from entering facility work areas and interfering with routine facility functioning. Routine visiting privileges and routine visiting hours might need to be suspended in parts of the facility.

C.12.3.4.2 Reception of News Media. The news media reception plans will need to be activated. In this instance, additional communications to the news reception center will be required. Additional telephones and telephone lines can be installed on an emergency basis on request to the local telephone company.

C.12.3.5 Other Protocols as Deemed Desirable. These should follow a number of additional protocols for internal disasters, to be determined by the hazards vulnerability analysis.

C.12.3.6 Activation of Emergency Utility Resources. In the planning phase, backup utility resources will have been stockpiled and arrangements made for mutual aid when required. Such utilities include electrical power, water, and fuel. Through prior coordination with the local office of emergency preparedness or fire department, mobile generators and auxiliary pumps can be obtained in the internal disaster situation. Through these same sources arrangements could be made to supply water tank trucks. Obviously, such planning is in addition to routine planning, in which all health care facilities maintain emergency electrical power and, in those areas requiring central heating in winter, backup supplies of oil, coal, or gas. Priorities for use of available power (e.g., air circulation but not air conditioning) have to be determined. Sanitation requirements can become overriding in prolonged disasters, and even an ordinary strike by garbage collectors can cause difficulties.

Actual disasters have shown the importance of agreements between health care facilities and contractors, local and remote, for such things as backup emergency generators. Local emergency management offices are responsible for serving the entire community and might not be able to respond immediately to a health care facility in need.

It is also imperative that a facility know which size generator is needed and how that generator will be connected to the building.

C.12.3.7 Civil Disturbance. Large-scale civil disturbances in recent years have shown that health care facilities and their personnel are not immune to the direct effects of human violence in such disturbances. Hospitals in large urban areas have to make special provisions in their disaster plans to ensure the physical safety of their employees in transit from the hospital exit to and from a secure means of transportation to their homes. In extreme cases it might be necessary to house employees within the health care facility itself during such civil disturbances. Examples of direct attacks or sniping are extremely rare.

Another aspect of civil disturbances not to be overlooked in facility security planning is the possibility that a given health care facility might have to admit and treat large numbers of prisoners during such emergencies; however, security guards for such patients will normally be provided by the local police department.

Provisions for securing windowed areas on lower floors that could be subject to items being thrown from hostile crowds should be included in the civil disturbance plan. Items such as heavy window screens, guards, substantial drapes, or window shades might be considered as reasonable precautions.

C.12.3.8 Bomb Threats. The disaster potential inherent in the telephoned bomb threat warrants inclusion of this disaster contingency in the Health Care Emergency Management Plan. Experience has shown that facility personnel have to accompany police or military bomb demolition personnel in searching for the suspected bomb, because speed is of the essence and only individuals familiar with a given area can rapidly spot unfamiliar or suspicious objects or condition in the area. This is particularly true in health care facilities. The facility switchboard operator has to be provided with a checklist to be kept available at all times, in order to obtain as much information as possible from the caller concerning the location of the supposed bomb, time of detonation, and other essential data, which have to be considered in deciding whether or not to evacuate all or part of the facility.

The response of police and fire authorities to bomb threats varies considerably from locality to locality. Knowing exactly what assistance local authorities provide dictates the level of involvement of the health care facility in responding to a bomb threat. A facility's plans should reflect the requirements or suggestions of local authorities.

C.12.3.9 Radioactive Contamination. Emergency management planning has to consider the possibility of radioactive materials being released from nuclear reactors or transportation accidents, acts of terrorism, as well as from internal spills. These incidents could require that health care staff and patients be sheltered. Shelter areas can be selected in existing structures and should be planned for during the design of new facilities or additions. Similarly, plans also have to consider radiation dose control and decontamination of victims or staff personnel and public safety in connection with nuclear accidents or incidents such as reactor excursions.

Radioactive contamination plans should consider both internal and external emergencies. Transportation accidents involving radioactive materials can contaminate rescue workers as well as victims, a possibility that should be considered in the development of any contamination plan. NFPA 801, *Standard for Fire Protection for Facilities Handling Radioactive Materials* [1], covers this subject, including a section (see Section 7.2) specifically addressing hospital activities.

C.12.3.10 Hazardous Materials. There are at least three major sources of concern with regard to nonradioactive hazardous materials not related to the intentional use of chemical agents to harm people (*see Weapons of Mass Destruction, C.12.3.12*). The first is the possibility of a large spill or venting of hazardous materials near the facility; this is especially likely near major rail or truck shipping routes, near pipelines, or near heavy manufacturing plants. Second, every facility contains within its boundaries varying amounts of such materials, especially in the laboratory and custodial areas. A spill of a highly volatile chemical can quickly contaminate an entire structure by way of the air ducts. Finally, contaminated patients can pose a risk to staff, though on a more localized basis. Usually removal of their clothing will reduce the risk materially. In any case, staff has to be prepared to seek advice on unknown hazards. This type of advice is not usually available from poison centers, but rather from a central referral, such as CHEMTREC, and its toll-free emergency information service number (800-424-9300).

See Annex G for publications concerning hazardous materials regulations and reports on various types of chemical protective equipment.

The response of health care facilities to an incident involving nonradioactive hazardous materials ranges from localization and sealing off of contaminated areas or persons to the complete evacuation of the facility. Emergency management plans need to consider both extremes.

Regulatory laws and instructions that govern the response to threats from the use of hazardous materials have been adopted of late. Facilities need to be aware of any regulations governing the use or shipment of hazardous materials.

C.12.3.11 Volcanic Eruptions. Although most of the direct effects of a volcanic eruption are covered in other protocols for disasters (fire, explosion, etc.), it is necessary to make special provisions for functioning in areas of heavy to moderate ash fall. This hazard can exist hundreds of miles downwind from the eruption.

Volcanic ash is actually finely pulverized rock blown out of the volcano. Outside the area of direct damage, the ash varies from a fine powder to a coarse sand. General housekeeping measures can exclude much ash. It should be noted, however, that people move about freely during and after ash fall.

Ash fall presents the following four problems for health care facilities:

(1) People require cleanup (brushing, vacuuming) before entering the building.
(2) Electromechanical and automotive equipment and air-filtering systems require special care because of the highly abrasive and fine penetration nature of the ash.

Ash penetration can even result in the short-circuiting of devices' electrical systems.

(3) Increased flow of patients with respiratory complaints can be expected.
(4) Eye protection is required for people who have to be out in the dust. (No contact lenses should be worn; goggles are suggested.) Dust masks are available that are approved by the National Institute for Occupational Safety and Health (NIOSH) and are marked TC-21 plus other digits.

Although the threat of volcanic eruptions is not as widespread as other potential disasters, incidents such as the 1980 eruption of Mount St. Helens in Washington demonstrate the need to address this subject. Volcanoes of the Mount St. Helens type are present from Alaska to California, although the effects of major volcanic eruptions might not be confined to these areas. The entire northwest of the United States, as well as portions of Canada, for example, have experienced the effects of the Mount St. Helens eruption.

C.12.3.12 Weapons of Mass Destruction. Weapons of Mass Destruction or WMD are defined as any weapon or device that is intended, or has the capability, to cause death or serious bodily injury to a significant number of people through the release, dissemination, or impact of: toxic or poisonous chemicals or their precursors; a disease organism; or radiation or radioactivity. A complete index of chemical, biological, and radiological agents and treatment recommendations can be found at the following web site: http://www.bt.cdc.gov/agent/index.asp.

Many federal departments and agencies are involved in supporting WMD preparedness and response activities at the State and local level. The Department of Health and Human Services manages two cooperative grant programs administered by the Centers for Disease Control and Prevention (CDC) and the Health Resources Services Administration (HRSA). These programs are aimed at enhancing the readiness of the public health and hospital system *(see the following web link for a description of these initiatives: http://www.bt.cdc.gov/planning/continuationguidance/pdf/activities_attachments.pdf.)*

The Department of Justice maintains a help line (1-800-368-6498) offering technical assistance in nonemergency cases providing information on the following subjects: detection equipment; personal protective equipment; decontamination systems and methods; physical properties of WMD materials; signs and symptoms of WMD exposure; treatment of exposure to WMD materials; toxicology information; federal response assets; and applicable laws and regulations. For reporting actual or potential acts of terrorism, health care facilities should contact their local or state health departments. The National Response Center (1-800-424-8802) can link callers to technical experts.

See Annex G for publications relating to WMD preparedness for health systems.

As of the printing of this edition of Chapter 12 of NFPA 99, the health care industry is approximately 3.5 years removed from the September 11, 2001, terrorist attacks on the United States. Much research and education have been conducted, and a great deal of equipment has been purchased to enable the health care industry to diagnose, report on, and treat various biological agents; to decontaminate individuals following exposure to biological agents; and to prevent the spread of infectious disease.

It is important for health care facilities to work with the community to stock appropriate amounts of prophylactics, to practice decontamination, and to train medical staff to diagnose agents in weapons of mass destruction.

It is also important for health care facilities to have procedures in place to protect the facility when the Office of Homeland Security (OHS) declares a high (orange) state of alert. In this situation, typical procedures might include protecting building utilities, screening packages and mail entering the building, and screening people entering the building.

If the Office of Homeland Security takes the country to red alert, the health care facility should activate a building's lock-down procedure. Each of the color codes carries specific actions that should be followed. Health care personnel must know these color codes and develop appropriate procedures. It is important to stay prepared.

C.13 Additional Information on Chapter 13

C.13.1 Nature of Hazards — Anesthetizing Locations.

C.13.1.1 General. The environment of the modern operating room poses numerous hazards, even in those rooms in which flammable agents are prohibited.

C.13.1.2 Hazards Present in All Anesthetizing Locations.

C.13.1.2.1 Electric Shock and Spark Hazards — High-Frequency Burn.

C.13.1.2.1.1 When a human body becomes the connecting link between two points of an electric system that are at different electric potentials, the person is likely to suffer an electric shock or high-frequency burns. When there is a highly conductive pathway from outside the body to the heart or great vessels, small electric currents could cause ventricular fibrillation. If a conductive material bridges two points of an electric system that are different electric potentials, the contact is likely to create a spark or an arc and intense heating of one or more of the conductors involved.

C.13.1.2.1.2 Electric equipment that is defective or has a faulty ground produces a definite shock hazard if connected to conventional grounded electric circuits and employed in the presence of purposely conductive flooring, as installed in corridors adjacent to operating rooms, or wet flooring as might be encountered in sterilizing or scrub rooms during use.

C.13.1.2.1.3 Improper use of the high-frequency electrosurgical unit, alone or in combination with certain items of medical monitoring equipment, can cause serious high-frequency burns to the patient or to personnel. *(See Annex D, The Safe Use of High-Frequency Electricity in Health Care Facilities.)*

C.13.1.2.2 Toxicologic Hazards.

C.13.1.2.2.1 The use of some modern nonflammable inhalation anesthetic agents with high-flow techniques and in the absence of venting of the exhaled gases to the atmosphere can create low-grade toxicity in personnel who work regularly in the operating room *(see E.3.5)*.

C.13.1.2.3 Mechanical Hazards.

C.13.1.2.3.1 A large amount of energy is stored in a cylinder of compressed gas. If the valve of a cylinder is struck (or strikes something else) hard enough to break off the valve, the contents of the cylinder can be discharged with sufficient force to impart dangerous reactive movement to the cylinder.

C.13.1.2.3.2 A hazard exists when hospital personnel attempt to transfer the contents of one compressed gas cylinder into another.

C.13.1.3 Hazards Related to the Use of Flammable Substances.

C.13.1.3.1 Flammable Anesthetic Agents.

C.13.1.3.1.1 The use of flammable anesthetic agents is attended by considerable fire and explosion risk because these agents form flammable mixtures with air, oxygen, or nitrous oxide. In many cases, these mixtures are violently explosive. Fatal accidents have resulted from explosions of such mixtures during anesthesia.

C.13.1.3.1.2 The following inhalation agents are considered flammable during conditions of clinical use in anesthesia: cyclopropane, diethyl ether, ethyl chloride, and ethylene.

The flammability of a compound can be reduced by substitution of a halogen (fluorine, chlorine, or bromine) for hydrogen at one or more positions in the molecular structure. Several inhalational anesthetics are thus halogenated. Halogenated agents are not necessarily nonflammable under all conditions.

Conflicting reports in the literature as to flammability limits probably represent differences in experimental techniques. Both the nature of the source of ignition and the configuration of the test chamber are critical. Some agents can be ignited only under optimal conditions never duplicated in clinical anesthesia. In one study, ignition of chloroform in oxygen could be obtained only in a closed steel bomb with a fuse producing an ignition temperature of 1093°C to 1649°C (2000°F to 3000°F) and with a chloroform concentration of 20 percent to 25 percent.

Trichloroethylene, used in concentrations higher than recommended, is flammable in oxygen and nitrous oxide. Methoxyflurane is nonflammable in concentrations obtainable at room temperature; however, a heated vaporizer can produce flammable mixtures.

Halothane, enflurane, and isoflurane are nonflammable under almost all conditions encountered in clinical anesthesia. High concentrations of nitrous oxide increase the range of flammability. Given laboratory conditions employing a closed tube, zero humidity, and sufficient ignition energy (far greater than that obtainable from incidental static electricity) it is possible to ignite a mixture of 4.75 percent halothane in 30 percent oxygen provided the balance of the atmosphere is nitrous oxide. If the oxygen concentration in a mixture with nitrous oxide is allowed to fall to 20 percent, 3.25 percent halothane is flammable. In these same nitrous oxide-oxygen atmospheres, the corresponding minimal flammable concentrations of enflurane are 5.75 percent and 4.25 percent, respectively, and of isofluorane, 7.0 percent and 5.25 percent. *(See Cruice, 1974.)*

The fact that halothane has for years been widely employed without significant problems relating to flammability suggests that the data in the preceding paragraph are of more theoretical than practical concern.

C.13.1.3.1.3 The use of closed rebreathing systems for the administration of flammable anesthetic agents normally tends to restrict the region likely to be hazardous. To secure a reasonable measure of protection, however, it has been found necessary to apply certain basic safeguards in any room in which these agents are used.

C.13.1.3.2 Flammable Medicaments, Including Aerosol Products.

C.13.1.3.2.1 Medicaments, including those dispersed as aerosols, frequently are used in anesthetizing locations for germicidal purposes, for affixing plastic surgical drape materials, for preparation of wound dressings, or for other purposes.

C.13.1.3.2.2 A particular hazard is created if cautery or high-frequency electrosurgical equipment is employed following use of a flammable medicament for preparation of the skin *(see C.13.1.3.2.1)*, since the liquid remaining on the skin or vapors pocketed within the surgical drapes can be ignited.

Fire incidents have been reported involving flammable germicides used for operating room procedures involving cautery, electrosurgery, or lasers. Although these products are fast-drying, in some situations the flammable liquid can pool or absorb into material or fabric. Alcohol is one of the most effective agents in killing microorganisms and is an effective skin degreaser.

When a flammable liquid germicide is used, several precautions should be followed in order to reduce the risk of fire in conjunction with a potential ignition source:

1. The quantity of germicide should be controlled with a unit dose applicator.
2. The germicide should be completely evaporated before electrosurgery, cautery, or a laser is used.
3. Any solution-soaked material must be removed.
4. Pooling of the flammable germicide must be avoided.

C.13.1.3.3 Sources of Ignition.

C.13.1.3.3.1 Potential sources of ignition of flammable anesthetics in anesthetizing locations include all of the following:

(1) Fixed electric equipment
(2) Portable electric equipment
(3) Accumulation of static electricity
(4) Electrosurgical equipment
(5) Open flames and heated objects above the ignition temperature of the flammable gases in use.

Other potential sources of ignition are percussion sparks, ignition of oxidizing and flammable gases from accidental mixing under pressure (9.3.9), and ignition from improper handling of oxygen cylinders (9.4.3.3, 9.4.3.5, and 9.7.2).

The Technical Committee on Anesthesia Services is cognizant of suggestions that the detonation of ether peroxides formed by the oxidation of ether over a period of time can be a cause of explosions in anesthesia machines. Frequent emptying of the ether bottle and cleaning of the ether evaporator inside anesthetizing locations is a simple and desirable precaution.

Many types of hospital construction afford reasonable protection against lightning hazards. However, because of the storage and use of combustible anesthetic agents, the increased protection offered by the installation of lightning rods might be desirable for some types of buildings, particularly those of wood (frame) construction in outlying areas. Lightning protection, if installed, should conform to the requirements of NFPA 780, *Standard for the Installation of Lightning Protection Systems.*

C.13.1.3.3.2 Experience indicates that the ignition of flammable mixtures by electrostatic spark is a great hazard. Electrostatic charges can accumulate on personnel and metallic equipment. Electrostatic charges can set up dangerous potential differences only when separated by materials that are electrically nonconducting. Such insulators act as barriers to the free movement of such charges, preventing the equalization of potential differences. A spark discharge can take place only when there is no other available path of greater conductivity by which this equalization can be effected. Such a spark can ignite a flammable mixture of gases.

C.13.1.3.3.3 In many cases, the hazards of electric shock and electrostatic discharge coexist. Measures to mitigate one hazard might enhance the other, however. It is necessary, therefore, to weigh both hazards in recommending precautionary measures for either.

An example of the inverse relationship cited in C.13.1.3.3.3 is a damp or highly humid environment where the hazard of electric shock is increased but electrostatic discharge is decreased.

C.13.1.3.3.4 An obvious and, hence, less frequent cause of the ignition of flammable anesthetic agents is by open flame or hot materials at or above the ignition temperature of the agents. The lowest ignition temperature in air of any of the anesthetic agents mentioned in C.13.1.3.1.2 is that of diethyl ether: 180°C (365°F). The most effective safeguard against this source of ignition is a constant vigilance on the part of the operating room personnel to prevent the introduction of sources of flames and hot objects into the anesthetizing locations *(see 13.4.1.2.3)*.

C.13.1.4 Hazards that Can Be Present in Nonflammable Anesthetizing Locations.

C.13.1.4.1 Electrostatic Hazard.

C.13.1.4.1.1 Conductive flooring is not a requirement for nonflammable anesthetizing locations. The uncontrolled use of static-producing materials in such locations, however, can lead to any of the following:

(1) Electrostatic discharge through sensitive components of electronic equipment, causing equipment failure
(2) Inadvertent use of these materials in flammable anesthetizing locations where mixed facilities exist *(see definition of Mixed Facility in E.1.6)*
(3) Impaired efficiency because of electrostatic clinging
(4) The involuntary movement of personnel subject to electrostatic discharges

C.13.1.4.2 Hazard of Flammable Substances.

C.13.1.4.2.1 Nonflammable anesthetizing locations are neither designed nor equipped for the use of any flammable substances, be they inhalation anesthetic agents or medicaments containing benzene, acetone, or the like. A hazardous situation is created any time any such flammable substance is inadvertently or intentionally introduced into a nonflammable anesthetizing location *(see also C.13.1.3.2)*.

C.13.1.5 Hazards that Can Be Present in Mixed Facilities.

C.13.1.5.1 Mixed facilities contain both flammable and nonflammable anesthetizing locations. Movable furniture, portable equipment, and conductive accessories intended for sole use in nonflammable anesthetizing locations might be introduced inadvertently into a flammable anesthetizing location, with the attendant dangers of ignition of flammable gas mixtures from electrical or electrostatic sparks.

C.13.1.5.2 Personnel working in mixed facilities might not take the proper precautions in reference to wearing apparel and the use of conductive grounding devices when entering flammable anesthetizing locations.

C.13.1.5.3 A particular hazard exists if regulations *(see E.8)* are not adopted, posted, and complied with or if the anesthetizing locations are not identified as noted in E.6.7.5.

C.13.2 Related Hazards and Safeguards, Anesthetizing Locations.

C.13.2.1 General.

C.13.2.1.1 The gas anesthesia apparatus and anesthetic ventilators constitute essential items (in most cases) for the administration of inhalation anesthesia. The safe use of these devices is predicated upon their cleanliness and proper function, as well as an understanding of their proper operation, maintenance, and repair.

C.13.2.2 Selection of a Gas Anesthesia Apparatus.

C.13.2.2.1 The individual selecting a gas anesthesia apparatus, either for initial purchase or for application in a given case, should be certain that the apparatus is the proper one for the given application or applications and that it is in good repair. See C.13.2.3, Suggested Method for Ensuring Proper Delivery of Oxygen and Nitrous Oxide; C.13.2.4, Disposable Masks, Bags, Tubing, and Bellows; and C.13.2.5, Decontamination and Routine Cleaning of Reusable Items.

C.13.2.3 Suggested Method for Ensuring Proper Delivery of Oxygen and Nitrous Oxide.

C.13.2.3.1 This method is recommended to prevent delivery of a gas different from that indicated by the flowmeters and to detect mixing of gases inside the machine that can result in delivery of dangerous gas mixtures to the patient. Both of the following materials are needed:

(1) 91.5 cm (3 ft) of anesthesia delivery hose
(2) An accurate oxygen meter, analyzer, or detector *(see 9.5.1)*. This device can be of the paramagnetic, platinum electrode, gas chromatographic, or mass spectrometer type.

C.13.2.3.2 Detailed steps of a method of testing anesthesia machines to assure the absence of hazard due to crossed connections between oxygen and nitrous oxide follow.

C.13.2.3.2.1 Premises. It is reasonable to conclude that no hazardous cross-connections or cross-leakages are present if gas from the only source available is delivered by only those valves intended for that gas, and that no gas is delivered by those valves when their intended source is unavailable, but other sources are available.

It is not necessary to know the composition of a gas in order to determine the extent of the circuit it supplies.

The operation of the oxygen circuit is independent, but the operation of some or all of the other circuits might be at least partially dependent on the operability of the oxygen circuit, for example, fail-safe valves.

C.13.2.3.2.2 Method. All anesthesia machines have at least one source of oxygen. This can be a large cylinder, one or two small cylinders, or a pipeline supply. Some machines have two such sources, and a very few have all three. Each should be tested separately. Proceed as follows:

(1) Disconnect all gas sources and open all needle valves and flush valves until all gas has stopped flowing from the machine outlet. Then close all needle valves and flush valves. Be certain that all cylinder pressure gauges read zero. Connect an oxygen cylinder to an oxygen hanger yoke and open the cylinder valve. Pressure must rise in the corresponding oxygen pressure gauge only. Close the cylinder valve.
(2) Repeat Step (1) exactly for each oxygen hanger yoke, including any fed by high-pressure lines from large cylinders. Leave the cylinder in the last hanger yoke tested, with the cylinder valve open.
(3) Open in succession and leave open all the needle valves for gases other than oxygen. Briefly open any flush valve for a gas other than oxygen. No flow should occur at the

machine outlet. An easy way to test for gas flow is to simply place the machine outlet tube in a glass of water and observe bubbling. Stand clear when flush valves are operated.

(4) Open and close in succession each of the oxygen needle valves, including any that provide an independent source of oxygen for vaporizers, and the oxygen flush valve. Flow should occur at the associated flowmeter or the machine outlet each time a valve is opened.

(5) If the machine is equipped for a pipeline oxygen supply, close the oxygen cylinder valve and open the oxygen flush valve. When gas stops flowing at the machine outlet, close the flush valve and all needle valves and connect the oxygen pipeline inlet to an oxygen pipeline outlet with the oxygen supply hose. Then repeat Steps (3) and (4).

(6) Since it is now established that oxygen is delivered to the oxygen needle and flush valves, and is not delivered to any other needle or flush valve, it remains to be determined that oxygen and oxygen alone is also available to perform any other function for which it is essential. A valve that shuts off the supply of any other gas to the appropriate needle valve in the event of oxygen supply pressure failure, commonly called a "fail-safe" valve, performs such a function. It should be tested as follows:

   (a) Disconnect the pipeline supply and open the oxygen flush valve until flow stops at the machine outlet, then close the flush valve. Install a cylinder of nitrous oxide in one hanger yoke, open the cylinder valve, and note the pressure on all cylinder pressure gauges. Only the nitrous oxide gauge should show any pressure.

   (b) Open in succession and leave open all the needle valves for gas other than nitrous oxide. Briefly open any flush valve for a gas other than nitrous oxide. No flow should occur at the machine outlet, nor at any flowmeter. Note that an easy way to test for gas flow is to simply place the machine outlet tube in a glass of water and observe bubbling. Stand clear when flush valves are operated.

   (c) Open and close in succession each of the nitrous oxide needle valves and nitrous oxide flush valves. If any delivers flow, all should do so.

   (d) If neither the nitrous oxide needle valves nor the nitrous oxide flush valve delivers flow, open the oxygen cylinder valve and repeat Steps (b) and (c). Each nitrous oxide needle valve and flush valve should deliver flow to the machine outlet.

   (e) Close the nitrous oxide cylinder valve and open a nitrous oxide needle valve until all gas stops flowing, then remove the nitrous oxide cylinder and close the needle valve. Repeat Steps (a) through (d) using any other nitrous oxide yoke.

   (f) If the machine is equipped for a pipeline nitrous oxide supply, close the nitrous oxide cylinder valve and open a nitrous oxide needle valve until all gas stops flowing, then close all needle valves and flush valves. Connect the nitrous oxide pipeline inlet to a nitrous oxide pipeline outlet with the nitrous oxide supply hose. Then repeat Steps (b) through (d).

C.13.2.4 Disposable Masks, Bags, Tubing, and Bellows.

C.13.2.4.1 It is well-recognized that newer technologies often lead to the introduction of new equipment and techniques, which in turn might lead to new hazards, or the potentiation of old ones. For example, the use of disposable and nondistensible conductive accessories potentiate the hazards of excessive airway pressures. These components should be employed only when it is assured that system pressure cannot become excessive.

C.13.2.4.1.1 Many plastic items are combustible. Most of these materials will emit toxic compounds when subjected to thermal decomposition. Special care has to be exercised during storage, use, and disposal of these items in order to preclude accidental ignition. Due consideration has to be given to on-site storage of trash prior to removal from the operating suite. The presence of these items on the hospital premises contributes significantly to the solid waste disposal problem facing the modern hospital.

C.13.2.4.1.2 The Technical Committee on Gas Delivery Equipment recommends that purchasing policies of an institution, as well as the practices of individual physicians and nurses, take into consideration the multiple problems posed by plastic items, and limit purchases and use of them to those items deemed essential for the proper function of the institution.

C.13.2.5 Decontamination and Routine Cleaning of Reusable Items.

C.13.2.5.1 Under certain circumstances, infectious organisms can be cultured from the breathing passages of ventilators, anesthesia valves, absorbers, tubing, bags, masks, and connectors. Some of these organisms can remain viable for many days. Although evidence that cross-infection from such sources can and does occur is very scanty, it is suggested that the user of such equipment consider implementation of one of the following methods. Mechanical cleansing with soap and water should precede sterilization. Alternative approaches to routine cleansing include the following:

(1) Mechanical cleansing with soap and water, followed by air drying in a stream of compressed air
(2) Mechanical cleansing with soap and water, followed by exposure to a preparation such as dialdehyde solution
(3) Mechanical cleansing with soap and water, followed by ethylene oxide, steam, or dry heat sterilization

C.13.2.5.2 Following gross contamination, the step outlined in C.13.2.5.1(2) or C.13.2.5.1(3) should be employed.

Note that whenever ethylene oxide or dialdehyde is used, care has to be taken to ensure complete removal of residuals.

Also note that recommendations for cleansing and sterilization supplied by the manufacturer of the item of equipment should be followed.

C.13.2.5.2.1 External contamination of the gas anesthesia apparatus, ventilator, and other equipment employed on and around the patient at least at weekly intervals, as well as immediately after use in an infectious case, is likewise recommended.

C.13.3 Text of Suggested Signs and Posters for Inhalation Anesthetizing Locations.

See Figure C.13.3.

C.13.4 Suggested Procedures in the Event of a Fire or Explosion, Anesthetizing Locations.

C.13.4.1 General. Fires in hospitals pose unique problems for hospital personnel, patients, and fire service personnel. Hospitals store and use relatively large quantities of flammable and combustible substances. Oxygen-enriched atmospheres are often employed in medical therapy and are utilized routinely during administration of anesthesia. The presence of flammable and combustible substances and oxygen-enriched atmospheres under the same roof with nonambulatory patients presents an extra-hazardous situation. All hospital personnel should understand the steps to take to save life, preserve limb, and contain smoke and/or limit fire until the fire department arrives. It is recommended that the procedures delineated herein, or similar ones, become a part of the fire safety regulations of every hospital.

C.13.4.2 Steps to Take in the Event of a Fire or Explosion.

C.13.4.2.1 The following steps, listed in the approximate order of their importance, should be taken by all personnel, should fire occur. If an explosion occurs, and it is not followed

SET (1)
REGULATIONS FOR SAFE PRACTICE IN NONFLAMMABLE ANESTHETIZING LOCATIONS

The following rules and regulations have been adopted by the medical staff and administration.
NFPA 99-2005, subsection 13.4.1, Anesthetizing Locations, shall apply in all inhalation anesthetizing locations.

________________ ____

(Insert Date) (Insert Name of Hospital Authority)

The use or storage of any of the following flammable agents or germicides shall be prohibited from all operating rooms, delivery rooms, and other anesthetizing locations in this hospital.

By reason of their chemical composition, these agents present a hazard of fire or explosion:

cyclopropane **ethyl chloride**
diethyl ether **ethylene**

(1) Nonflammable Anesthetizing Location.

a. *Definition*. The term *nonflammable anesthetizing location* shall mean any anesthetizing location designated for the exclusive use of nonflammable anesthetizing agents.

(2) Equipment.

a. No electrical equipment except that judged by the Engineering Department of ____________________ Hospital as being in compliance with NFPA 99-2005, subsection 13.4.1, Anesthetizing Locations, shall be used in any anesthetizing location.

b. When a physician wishes to use his or her personal electrical equipment, it shall first be inspected by the Engineering Department and, if judged to comply with NFPA 99-2005, subsection 13.4.1, Anesthetizing Locations, it shall be so labeled.

c. Photographic lighting equipment shall be of the totally enclosed type or so constructed as to prevent the escape of sparks or hot metal particles.

(3) Personnel.

Smoking shall be limited to dressing rooms and lounges, with doors leading to the corridor closed.

(4) Practice.

a. The use or storage of flammable anesthetic agents shall be expressly prohibited in a nonflammable anesthetizing location.

b. If cautery, electrosurgery, or a hot or arcing device is to be used during an operation, flammable germicides or flammable fat solvents shall not be applied for preoperative preparation of the skin.

c. A visual (lighted red lamp) or audible warning signal from the line isolation monitor serving an anesthetizing location indicates that the total hazard current has exceeded allowable limits. This suggests that one or more electrical devices is contributing an excessively low impedance to ground, which might constitute a fault that would expose the patient or hospital personnel to an unsafe condition should an additional fault occur. Briefly and sequentially unplugging the power cord of each electrical device in the location will usually cause the green lamp to light, showing that the system has been adequately isolated from ground, when the potentially defective device has been unplugged. The continuing use of such a device, so identified, should be questioned, but not necessarily abandoned. At the earliest opportunity the device should be inspected by the hospital engineer or other qualified personnel and, if necessary, repaired or replaced.

d. Transportation of patients while an inhalation anesthetic is being administered by means of a mobile anesthesia machine shall be prohibited, unless deemed essential for the benefit of the patient in the combined judgment of the surgeon and anesthesiologist.

e. If, in the combined judgment of the anesthesiologist responsible for the administering of the anesthetic and the surgeon performing the operation, the life of the patient would be jeopardized by not administering a flammable anesthetic agent, the following steps shall be taken:

1. Both surgeon and anesthesiologist involved in the case shall attest to the reason for administering a flammable anesthetic in a nonflammable anesthetizing location on the patient's record and in the operating room register.
2. The hazard of static sparks shall be reduced by electrically interconnecting the patient, operating room table, anesthesia gas machine, and anesthesiologist by wet sheets or other conductive materials. Conductive accessories shall be used for the electrically conductive pathways from the anesthesia gas machine to the patient.
3. If cautery, electrosurgery, or electrical equipment employing an open spark is to be used during an operation, flammable anesthetics shall not be used. Flammable germicides or flammable fat solvents shall not be applied for the preoperative preparation of the field.

(5) Enforcement.

It shall be the responsibility of

____

(Name)

(an anesthesiologist or other qualified person appointed by the hospital authority to act in that capacity) to enforce the above regulations.

NFPA 99 (p. 1 of 1)

FIGURE C.13.3 *Text of Suggested Signs and Posters for Inhalation Anesthetizing Locations.*

by fire, follow the procedure outlined under C.13.4.2.2. If a fire follows an explosion, proceed as follows:

(1) Remove the immediately exposed patient or patients from the site of the fire, if their hair or clothing is not burning. If they are burning, extinguish the flames *(see C.13.4.4 and C.13.4.5)*.
(2) Sound the fire alarm by whatever mode the hospital fire plan provides. Note that it is assumed that each hospital has a fire plan, prepared in consultation with representatives of the local fire department. In such a plan, immediate notification of the local fire department is essential.
(3) Close off the supply of oxygen, nitrous oxide, and air to any equipment involved, if this step can be accomplished without injury to personnel *(see C.13.4.3)*.
(4) Close doors to contain smoke and isolate fire.
(5) Remove patients threatened by the fire.
(6) Attempt to extinguish or contain the fire *(see C.13.4.4)*.
(7) Direct the fire fighters to the site of the fire.
(8) Take whatever steps are necessary to protect or evacuate patients in adjacent areas.

Note that in the event of a fire in an operating room while an operative procedure on an anesthetized patient is in progress, it might be necessary to extinguish the fire prior to removing the patient from the room.

Note also that during an operation, it can be more hazardous to move patients than to attempt to extinguish or contain the fire. The attending physician has to determine which step would present the lesser hazard — hurriedly terminating an operative procedure or continuing the procedure and exposing the members of the operating team and the patient to the hazards stemming from the fire.

C.13.4.2.2 The following steps are recommended in the event of an explosion involving inhalation anesthesia apparatus:

(1) Disconnect the patient from the apparatus.
(2) Procure a new gas anesthesia apparatus and make every effort to save the life of the patient and prevent injury to the patient.

C.13.4.2.3 It is essential that all equipment involved in a fire or explosion be preserved for examination by an authority attempting to determine the cause. Additionally, pertinent administrative data, including photographs, should be recorded. The report should state the following:

(1) Whether wearing apparel of all persons in the room at the time of the fire or explosion had to meet the requirements listed in Annex E
(2) Whether portable equipment, low-voltage instruments, accessories, and furniture had to meet the requirements listed in Annex E
(3) Whether the ventilating system was being operated in accordance with 6.4.2

C.13.4.2.3.1 The area involved, with all involved items in place, should be closed off and secured for later examination by a responsible authority.

C.13.4.3 Closing Off Oxygen, Nitrous Oxide, and Air Supply.

C.13.4.3.1 In the event of a fire involving equipment connected to an oxygen, nitrous oxide, and air station outlet, the zone valve supplying that station is to be closed *[see C.13.4.6.1(1)]*.

C.13.4.3.1.1 Immediately, all patients receiving oxygen through the same zone valve have to be supplied with individual oxygen cylinders.

Note that each gas line to an operating room should have an individual zone valve *(see Section 5.1)*. Thus, closing of all valves to one room would not endanger patients in other rooms.

C.13.4.3.2 If fire involves apparatus supplied by a cylinder of oxygen, it is desirable to close the cylinder valve, if this can be done without injuring personnel.

Note that metal components of regulators and valves can become excessively hot if exposed to flame. Personnel are cautioned not to use their bare hands to effect closure.

C.13.4.4 Extinguishment or Containment of Fire.

The issue of fire extinguisher use inside operating rooms is very complicated because of the unusual environment during surgery, when one person, the patient, is either unconscious or immobile, his or her internal body cavity is exposed, and sterile conditions must be maintained. In addition, although staff are always present during surgery, they might not be able to respond to a fire immediately. Finally, the effects of extinguishers, including water-based extinguishers, can be adverse to the patient.

Portable halon extinguishers had been promoted, with some controversy, for use in operating rooms. Halon, however, has all but been completely phased out due to environmental concerns, and alternative "clean-agents" are continuing to be developed (e.g., FE-36, carbon dioxide, Halotron 1, Cleanguard, FM-200).

Also contributing to the uncertainty of fire extinguisher use in operating rooms is the extensive use of oxygen and the resultant creation of an oxygen-enriched atmosphere.

NFPA *101*®, *Life Safety Code*® [2], and NFPA 10, *Standard for Portable Fire Extinguishers* [3], offer some general criteria for fire extinguisher placement. One of the best solutions for fighting operating room fires is, of course, taking steps to *prevent* fire from occurring in the first place. Prevention involves reviewing the proper methods for procedures that can create hazards (e.g., the use of flammable liquids), as well as educating staff on the need to prevent incidents.

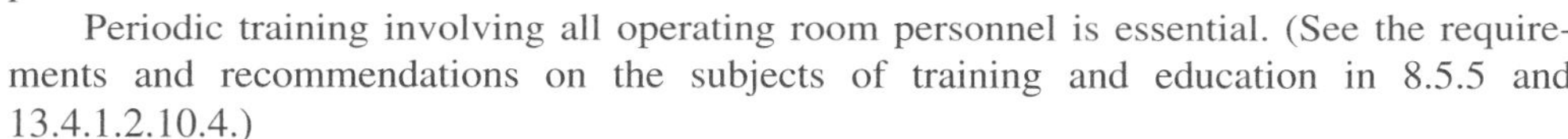

Periodic training involving all operating room personnel is essential. (See the requirements and recommendations on the subjects of training and education in 8.5.5 and 13.4.1.2.10.4.)

C.13.4.4.1 Fire originating in or involving inhalation anesthesia apparatus generally involves combustibles such as rubber. Water or water-based extinguishing agents are most effective in such fires.

Precautions should be taken if line-powered electrical equipment is adjacent to or involved in fire, because of the danger of electrocution of personnel if streams of water contact live circuits.

Before attempting to fight fire with water or a water-based extinguishing agent, electrical apparatus should be disconnected from the supply outlet, or the supply circuit deenergized at the circuit panel.

If such deenergization cannot be accomplished, water should not be employed *(see C.13.4.4.3).*

C.13.4.4.2 Fires involving, or adjacent to, electrical equipment with live circuits have to be fought with extinguishers suitable for Class C fires in accordance with NFPA 10, *Standard for Portable Fire Extinguishers.*

C.13.4.4.3 Fire extinguishers are classified according to the type of fire for which each is suited.

C.13.4.4.3.1 Fires involving ordinary combustibles such as rubber, plastic, linen, wool, paper, and the like are called Class A fires. These can be fought with water or water-based extinguishing agents. Hose lines are suitable for this purpose. Portable extinguishers suitable for Class A fires are identified with the letter A contained in a (if colored) green triangle.

C.13.4.4.3.2 Class B fires involve flammable liquids and should be fought only with an extinguisher identified by the letter B contained in a (if colored) red square.

C.13.4.4.3.3 Class C fires involve electrical equipment and should be fought only with an extinguisher identified by the letter C contained in a (if colored) blue circle.

C.13.4.4.3.4 Carbon dioxide and some dry chemical extinguishers are labeled for Class B and Class C fires. Some dry chemical units can be used for all three types *(see* NFPA 10, *Standard for Portable Fire Extinguishers, Annex F).*

C.13.4.5 Protection of Patients and Personnel.

C.13.4.5.1 Serious and even fatal burns of the skin or lungs, from inhaling heated gases, are possible. Thus, it is essential that patients be removed from the scene of the fire whenever practical. Where an anesthetized patient is connected to a burning piece of equipment, it might be more practical as the initial step to remove the equipment and/or extinguish the fire than to remove the patient.

C.13.4.5.2 Noxious gases produced by fire constitute a threat to life from asphyxia, beyond the thermal burn problem.

Personnel are cautioned not to remain in the fire area after patients are evacuated, unless they are wearing proper emergency apparatus.

C.13.4.6 Indoctrination of Personnel.

C.13.4.6.1 It is highly desirable that personnel involved in the care of patients, including nurses, aides, ward secretaries, and physicians, irrespective of whether they are involved in anesthesia practices, be thoroughly indoctrinated in all aspects of fire safety, including the following:

(1) Location of zone valves of nonflammable medical gas systems and the station outlets controlled by each valve
(2) Location of electrical service boxes and the areas served thereby
(3) Location and proper use of fire extinguishers *(see C.13.4.4)*
(4) Recommended methods and routes for evacuating patients *(see Chapter 12)*
(5) Steps involved in carrying out the fire plan of the hospital
(6) Location of fire alarm boxes, or knowledge of other methods for summoning the fire department

C.13.4.6.2 To ensure that personnel are familiar with the procedures outlined above, regular instructive sessions and fire drills should be held.

C.13.5 Cylinder Table.

See Table C.13.5.

C.14 Additional Information on Chapter 14

C.14.1 Typical Gas Cylinder Table, Anesthetizing Locations.

(See Table C.13.5.)

C.14.2 Text of Suggested Regulations for Nonflammable Inhalation Anesthetizing Locations and Gas Storage Areas in Nonhospital-Based Ambulatory Care Facilities. The following rules and regulations have been adopted. The requirements of 13.4.1 of NFPA 99-2005 shall apply to all anesthetizing locations and gas storage areas in this facility.

TABLE C.13.5 *Typical Medical Gas Cylinders' Volume and Weight of Available Contents. [All Volumes at 70°F (21.1°C)].*

Cylinder Style and Dimensions	Nominal Volume (in.³/L)	Contents	Name of Gas: Air	Carbon Dioxide	Cyclo-propane	Helium	Nitrogen	Nitrous Oxide	Oxygen	Mixtures of Oxygen: Helium	Mixtures of Oxygen: CO_2
B	87/1.43	psig		838	75				1900		
3½ in. O.D.	L	370	375				200				
× 13 in.											
8.89 × 33	cmlb-oz	1–8		1–7¼				—			
cm											
		kg		0.68	0.66				—		
D	176/2.88	psig	1900	838	75	1600	1900	745	1900	*	*
4½ in. O.D.		L	375	940	870	300	370	940	400	300	400
× 17 in.											
10.8 × 43		lb-oz	—	3–13	3–5½	—	—	3–13	—	*	*
cm											
		kg	—	1.73	1.51	—	—	1.73	—	*	*
E	293/4.80	psig	1900	838		1600	1900	745	1900	*	*
4¼ in. O.D.		L	625	1590		500	610	1590	660	500	660
× 26 in.											
10.8 × 66		lb-oz	—	6–7		—	—	6–7	—	*	*
cm											
		kg	—	2.92	—	—	2.92		—	*	*
M	1337/21.9	psig	1900	838		1600	2200	7.45	2200	*	*
7 in. O.D.		L	2850	7570	2260	3200	7570		3450	2260	3000
× 43 in.											
17.8 × 109		lb-oz	—	30–10		—	—	30–10	122 ft³	*	*
cm											
		kg	—	13.9	—	—	13.9		—	*	*
G	2370/38.8	psig	1900	838		1600		745		*	*
8½ in. O.D.		L	5050	12,300		4000	13,800	4000	5330		
× 51 in.											
21.6 × 130	lb-oz	—	50–0		—	56–0	*	*			
cm											
		kg	—	22.7		—		25.4	*	*	
H or K	2660/43.6	psig	2200			2200	2200	745	2200†		
9¼ in. O.D.		L	6550			6000	6400	15,800	6900		
× 51 in.											
23.5 ×											
130 cm											
		lb-oz	—			—	—	64	244 ft³		
		kg	—			—	—	29.1			

Notes: These are computed contents based on nominal cylinder volumes and rounded to no greater variance than ±1%.

* The pressure and weight of mixed gases will vary according to the composition of the mixture.

†275 ft³/7800 L cylinders at 2490 psig are available upon request.

Source: *With permission from the Compressed Gas Association, Inc.*

The use of any of the following flammable agents shall be prohibited from the premises. By reason of their chemical composition, these agents present a hazard of fire or explosion.

(1) Cyclopropane
(2) Divinyl ether
(3) Ethyl ether
(4) Fluroxene
(5) Ethyl chloride
(6) Ethylene

Smoking shall be limited to those areas of the premises not directly connected with the anesthetizing location or the location for storage of compressed gas cylinders.

Compressed gas cylinders shall be connected to the manifold, and otherwise handled and stored, as provided in Chapter 14 of NFPA 99-2002.

Defective electrical equipment shall not be used on the premises.

Gas pipeline alarm systems shall be monitored, and responsible personnel notified of any fall in pressure or alarm condition.

C.15 Reserved

C.16 Reserved

C.17 Reserved

C.18 Reserved

C.19 Reserved

C.20 Additional Information on Chapter 20

C.20.1 Nature of Hazards.

C.20.1.1 Fire and Explosion.

C.20.1.1.1 The occurrence of a fire requires the presence of combustible or flammable materials, an atmosphere containing oxygen or other oxidizing agent(s), and heat or energy source of ignition.

Note that certain substances such as acetylenic hydrocarbons can propagate flame in the absence of oxygen.

C.20.1.1.2 Under hyperbaric conditions utilizing compressed air, the partial pressure of oxygen is increased. Leakage of oxygen into the atmosphere of the chamber (for example, from improper application of respiratory therapy apparatus) can further increase markedly the oxygen partial pressure.

C.20.1.1.2.1 The flammability or combustibility of materials generally increases as the partial pressure of oxygen increases, even when the percentage of oxygen in the gas mixture remains constant. Materials that are nonflammable or noncombustible under normal atmospheric conditions can become flammable or combustible under such circumstances.

C.20.1.1.3 Sources of Fuel.

C.20.1.1.3.1 Materials that might not ignite in air at atmospheric pressure or require relatively high temperatures for their ignition but that burn vigorously in 100 percent oxygen include, but are not necessarily limited to, the following: tricresyl phosphate (lubricant); certain types of flame-resistant fabrics; silicone rubber; polyvinyl chloride; asbestos-containing paint; glass fiber-sheathed silicone rubber-insulated wire; polyvinyl chloride-insulated asbestos-covered wire and sheet; polyamides; epoxy compounds; and certain asbestos blankets.

Note that flammable lubricants are used widely in equipment designed for conventional use, including shafts, gear boxes, pulleys and casters, and threaded joints, which are coupled and uncoupled.

Even if a lubricant is not "flammable," it could be undesirable for use in the hyperbaric environment because it is most likely hydrocarbon based.

C.20.1.1.3.2 The flammability of certain volatile liquids and gases containing carbon and hydrogen is well known. Hazards and safeguards for their use in oxygen-enriched atmospheres at ambient pressure are well-documented in 13.4.1 of NFPA 99. See also NFPA 325, *Guide to Fire Hazard Properties of Flammable Liquids, Gases, and Volatile Solids*, now part of the NFPA *Fire Protection Guide to Hazardous Materials.*

Note that repeated reference to subsection 13.4.1 is made throughout Chapter 20. These references do not imply, and should not be construed to mean, that flammable anesthetics can or should be employed in or around hyperbaric facilities.

C.20.1.1.3.3 Human tissues will burn in an atmosphere of 100 percent oxygen. Body oils and fats, as well as hair, will burn readily under such circumstances.

C.20.1.1.3.4 When a conventional loose cotton outergarment, such as scrub suits, dresses, and gowns employed in hospital operating suites, is ignited in an atmosphere of pure oxygen, the garment will become engulfed in flame rapidly and will be totally destroyed within 20 seconds or less.

If such a garment is ignited in a compressed air atmosphere, the flame spread is increased. When oxygen concentration exceeds 23.5 percent at elevated total pressure, flame spread is much more rapid, and at 6 ATA, is comparable to 95 ± 5 percent at 1 ATA. Flame spread in air (21 percent oxygen) is somewhat increased at 6 ATA, but not to the level of 95 ± 5 percent at 1 ATA.

Combustible fabrics have tiny air spaces that become filled with oxygen when exposed to oxygen-enriched environments. Once removed to atmospheric air (e.g., room air outside the chamber), the fabric will burn, if ignited, almost as rapidly as if it were still in the oxygen environment. This hazard will remain until the oxygen trapped in the air spaces in the fabric has had time to diffuse out and be replaced by air.

Chamber personnel should remain continuously alert to the phenomenon of tiny air spaces that fill with oxygen, as discussed in the last paragraph of C.20.1.1.3.4. If any clothing or similar fabric catches fire, corrective action must be instantaneous. Burning clothes should be removed from the body as quickly as possible.

This phenomenon is also an issue when defibrillating a patient just removed from an oxygen-filled chamber. The bedding and clothing should be stripped away before attempting to defibrillate.

C.20.1.1.3.5 Oil-based or volatile cosmetics (facial creams, body oils, hair sprays, and the like) constitute a source of fuel that is highly flammable in an oxygen-enriched atmosphere.

Even if cosmetics are not oil-based or volatile, they are still fuel sources that are not necessary in the hyperbaric chamber. One of the strategies to control fire risk is to minimize the total fuel load.

C.20.1.1.4 Sources of Ignition.

C.20.1.1.4.1 Sources of ignition that might be encountered in a hyperbaric chamber include, but are not necessarily limited to, the following: defective electrical equipment, including failure of high-voltage components of radiological or monitoring equipment; heated surfaces in broken vacuum tubes or broken lamps used for general illumination, spot illumination, or illumination of diagnostic instruments; the hot-wire cautery or high-frequency electrocautery; open or arcing switches, including motor switches; bare defibrillator paddles; overheated motors; and electrical thermostats.

C.20.1.1.4.2 Sources of ignition that should not be encountered in a hyperbaric facility, but that might be introduced by inept practice, include the following: lighted matches or tobacco, static sparks from improper use of personal attire, electrical wiring not complying with 20.2.7, cigarette lighters, and any oil-contaminated materials that present a spontaneous heating hazard.

Before anyone enters a chamber for hyperbaric therapy, a thorough check should be made to ensure that potential ignition sources are not taken into the chamber. Cigarette lighters, warmers, and toys have been responsible for igniting several chamber fires. In the reported hyperbaric chamber fires, there have been very few survivors.

C.20.1.1.4.3 In oxygen-enriched atmospheres, the minimum energy necessary to ignite flammable or combustible materials is reduced in most instances below the energy required in atmospheres of ambient air.

C.20.1.2 Mechanical Hazards.

C.20.1.2.1 General.

C.20.1.2.1.1 A large amount of potential energy is stored in even a small volume of compressed gas. In hyperbaric chambers of moderate or large size, the potential energy of the chamber's compressed atmosphere, if released suddenly, can produce devastating destruction to adjacent structures and personnel, as well as to structures and personnel remote from the site of the chamber. Such sudden release could result from failure of the vessel structure, its parts, or its piping.

C.20.1.2.1.2 A particular hazard can be created if individuals attempt to drill, cut, or weld the vessel in a manner contrary to ASME *Boiler and Pressure Vessel Code.*

C.20.1.2.2 The restriction on escape and the impedance to rescue and fire-fighting efforts posed by the chamber create a significant hazard to life in case of fire or other emergency.

C.20.1.2.2.1 A particular hazard exists to chamber personnel in the event of a fire within the structure housing the chamber. Inability to escape from the chamber and loss of services of the chamber operator would pose serious threats to the lives of all occupants of the chamber.

C.20.1.2.2.2 All personnel involved in hyperbaric chamber operation and therapy, including patients and family, have to be made aware of the risks and hazards involved. Fire prevention is essential. Extinguishment of a fire within a Class B chamber is impossible. Extinguishment of a fire within a Class A chamber is only possible utilizing equipment already installed in such a chamber, and then often only by the efforts of the occupants of such a chamber or the chamber operator.

In Class B chambers, fire prevention measures are more restrictive than in Class A chambers due to the elevated oxygen level in Class B chambers.

C.20.1.2.3 The necessity for restricting viewing ports to small size limits the vision of chamber operators and other observers, reducing their effectiveness as safety monitors.

C.20.1.2.4 Containers and enclosures can be subjected to collapse or rupture as a consequence of the changing pressures of the hyperbaric chamber. Items containing entrained gas include, but are not necessarily limited to, the following: ampuls, partially filled syringes, stoppered or capped bottles, cuffed endotracheal tubes, and pneumatic cushions employed for breathing masks or aids in positioning patients. The rupture of such containers having combustible or flammable liquids would also constitute a severe fire or explosion hazard.

C.20.1.2.4.1 The sudden collapse of containers from high external pressures will result in adiabatic heating of the contents. Therefore the collapse of a container of flammable liquid would constitute a severe fire or explosion hazard both from heating and from a spill of the liquid. *(See 20.3.1.5.2 and C.20.1.1.3.2.)*

C.20.1.2.5 Other mechanical hazards relate to the malfunction, disruption, or inoperativeness of many standard items when placed in service under pressurized atmospheres. Hazards that might be encountered in this regard are implosion of illuminating lamps and vacuum tubes; overloading of fans driving gas at higher density; and inaccurate operation of standard flowmeters, pressure gauges, and pressure-reducing regulators.

Note that illuminating lamps or vacuum tubes, which implode, or overloaded fans, are sources of ignition.

C.20.1.3 Pathophysiological, Medical, and Other Related Hazards.

C.20.1.3.1 Exposure of pregnant chamber occupants to hyperbaric atmospheres might result in fetal risk.

C.20.1.3.2 Medical hazards that can be encountered routinely include compression problems, nitrogen narcosis, oxygen toxicity, and the direct effects of sudden pressure changes.

C.20.1.3.2.1 Inability to equalize pressure differentials between nasopharynx (nose) and nasal sinuses or the middle ear can result in excruciating pain and might cause rupture of the eardrum or hemorrhage into the ear cavity or nasal sinus.

C.20.1.3.2.2 The breathing of air (78 percent nitrogen) under significant pressures (as by chamber personnel breathing chamber atmosphere) can result in nitrogen narcosis, which resembles alcoholic inebriation. The degree of narcosis is directly related to the amount of pressurization. Nitrogen narcosis results in impairment of mental functions, loss of manual dexterity, and interference with alertness and ability to think clearly and act quickly and intelligently in an emergency.

C.20.1.3.2.3 Oxygen toxicity can develop from breathing oxygen at partial pressures above 0.50 atmospheres absolute for a significant length of time. Oxygen toxicity can affect the lungs (pain in the chest, rapid shallow breathing, coughing), nervous system (impaired consciousness and convulsions), or other tissues and organs, or combinations thereof.

The minimum threshold for pulmonary oxygen toxicity is a dose of oxygen (partial pressure, or pO_2) of approximately 450 mmHg over approximately 24 hours. Hyperbaric oxygen doses are in the range of 1520 to 2280 mmHg pO_2. At these higher doses, the timeline shortens considerably.

The minimum threshold for central nervous system (CNS) oxygen toxicity is a pO_2 of approximately 1200 mmHg. The duration of exposure before onset of CNS oxygen toxicity varies greatly in different individuals but shortens as the pO_2 increases. At a pO_2 of 1200 mmHg it might be measured in hours, and at a pO_2 of 3000 mmHg it is measured in minutes.

In a hyperbaric chamber, the maximum oxygen dose delivered is 2280 mmHg because of CNS oxygen toxicity.

C.20.1.3.2.4 Direct effects of reduction in pressure can include inability to equalize pressures between the nasopharynx and sinuses or middle ear, expansion of gas pockets in the gastrointestinal tract, and expansion of trapped gas in the lungs.

C.20.1.3.2.5 The presence of personnel within the cramped confines of the hyperbaric chamber in close proximity to grounded metallic structures on all sides creates a definite shock hazard if accidental contact is made with a live electrical conductor or a defective piece of electrical equipment. Such accidental contact also could be a source of ignition of flammable or combustible materials. *(See C.20.1.1.4.)*

C.20.1.3.3 Medical hazards that are not ordinarily encountered during hyperbaric oxygen therapy, but that might arise during malfunction, fire, or other emergency conditions, include electric shock and fouling of the atmosphere of the chamber with oxygen, nitrous oxide, carbon dioxide, carbon monoxide, pyrolysis products from overheated materials, or the toxic products of combustion from any fire.

C.20.1.3.3.1 Increased concentrations of carbon dioxide within the chamber, as might result from malfunction of the systems responsible for monitoring or removal thereof, can be toxic under increased pressures.

C.20.1.3.3.2 The development of combustion products or gases evolved from heated nonmetallics within the closed space of the hyperbaric chamber can be extremely toxic to life because of the confining nature of the chamber and the increased hazards of breathing such products under elevated pressure.

Note that extreme pressure rises have accompanied catastrophic fires in confined atmospheres. These pressures have driven hot, toxic gases into the lungs of victims as well as exceeding the structural limits of the vessel in at least one case.

C.20.1.3.4 Physiological hazards include exposure to high noise levels and decompression sickness. Rapid release of pressurized gases can produce shock waves and loss of visibility.

C.20.1.3.4.1 During hyperbaric therapy, and especially during compression, the noise level within the chamber becomes quite high. Such a level can be hazardous because it is distractive, interferes with communication, and can produce permanent sensory-neural deafness.

C.20.1.3.4.2 Decompression sickness (bends, caisson worker's disease) results from the elution into the bloodstream or extravascular tissues of bubbles of inert gas (mainly nitrogen) that becomes dissolved in the blood and tissue fluids while breathing air at elevated pressures for a significant period of time.

Note that rapid decompression of the chamber can occur if the pressure relief valve is damaged from exposure to a fire external to the chamber or from the venting of hot products of combustion from within the chamber.

C.20.1.3.4.3 The use of decompression procedures will prevent immediate escape from the Class A chamber by occupants during emergency situations.

Note that these procedures are not followed if chamber occupants are exposed to a "no-decompression exposure" [compression to less than 2 atmospheres absolute (ATA) air], or when compressed to 2 ATA or higher pressures and breathing 100 percent oxygen.

In Class A chambers, one or more of the occupants might be breathing air (rather than 100 percent oxygen) during the hyperbaric exposure. This is usually the case when a medical attendant is inside the chamber with patients. Breathing air at hyperbaric pressures could require a slow decompression to prevent decompression sickness. In severe cases, decompression sickness can be crippling or fatal. This risk does not exist if 100 percent oxygen is breathed (rather than air). In Class B chambers, the single occupant is almost always breathing 100 percent oxygen.

C.20.1.3.4.4 The sudden release of gas, whether by rupture of a container or operation of a device such as used in fire fighting, will produce noise, possible shock waves, reduced or obscured visibility, and temperature changes. The initial effect might be to cool the air, but resulting pressure rises will cause adiabatic heating.

C.20.1.3.5 In summary, the hazards of fire and related problems in hyperbaric systems are real. By the very nature of the hyperbaric atmosphere, increased partial pressures of oxygen are present routinely. Flammability and combustibility of materials are increased. Ignition energy is lowered. Both immediate escape and ready entry for rescue are impeded. Finally, attendants within the chamber, through effects of the elevated noise level and nitrogen pressure, might be unable to respond to emergencies quickly and accurately.

C.20.2 Suggested Procedures to Follow in Event of Fire in Class A Chambers.

The procedures contained in C.20.2 are adopted from those employed by the U.S. Air Force. These procedures are published herein only as a guide for those who are preparing procedures for their own hyperbaric facilities. Their publication herein is not to be construed as implying that they become a literal part of the standard procedure in any hyperbaric facility.

The procedures listed in C.20.2.1 and C.20.2.2 reflect the emergency practices of the U.S. Air Force.

C.20.2.1 Fire Inside Chamber. For fire inside the chamber the following procedures should be performed:

(1) *Inside Observer:*
  (a) Advise outside.
  (b) Don breathing air mask.
  (c) Activate fire suppression system and/or hand-held hoses.
(2) *Console Operator:*
  (a) Maintain chamber depth.
  (b) Activate the fire suppression system, if needed.
  (c) Ensure breathing gas is compressed air.
  (d) Notify the fire department by activating fire alarm station or telephone.
  (e) Note time of fire and record progress of events.
(3) *Hyperbaric Chamber (System) Technician (Outside):*
  (a) Stand by with a fire extinguisher.
  (b) Assist in unloading chamber occupants.
(4) *Physician/Safety Monitor (Outside):*
  (a) Direct operations and assist crew members wherever necessary.
  (b) Terminate procedure as soon as possible.
(5) *Other Personnel:* Stand by to evacuate chamber personnel.

C.20.2.2 Fire Outside Chamber. For fire outside the chamber the following procedures should be performed:

(1) *Console Operator:*
   (a) Notify the inside observer to stand by for emergency return to normal atmospheric pressure.
   (b) Notify fire department by activating fire alarm station or telephone.
   (c) Change chamber breathing gas to compressed air.
   (d) Don fire mask.
   (e) Note time of fire and record progress of events.
(2) *Hyperbaric Chamber (System) Technician (Outside):*
   (a) Ensure that compressor intake is drawing outside air.
   (b) Man fire extinguisher.
   (c) Help chamber operator to don fire mask.
(3) *Physician/Safety Monitor (Outside):*
   (a) Direct operations.
   (b) Determine whether procedure should be terminated.
(4) *Other Personnel:* Stand by to evacuate chamber personnel.

C.20.3 Suggested Procedures to Follow in Event of Fire in Class B Chambers.

For a fire in a hyperbaric room or hyperbaric chamber, the procedure to follow is essentially the same as anywhere else: **R**escue, **A**larm, **C**onfine, **E**xtinguish (RACE). In order to rescue chamber occupants, the chamber must be decompressed. Decompression lengthens the egress time and could require additional personnel to accomplish. Aside from the egress time, this procedure is no different from any other area.

It is important to note that most Class B chambers are pneumatic devices and require gas supply pressure to operate a rapid decompression function. This is the same gas supply as the chamber compression gas (usually oxygen). If the oxygen source is turned off (as in the procedure in C.20.3.1), rapid decompression capability could be disabled.

C.20.3.1 For fires within facility not involving the chamber, the following procedure should be performed:

(1) Turn off oxygen source.
(2) Decompress chamber.
(3) Remove patient and evacuate to safe area.

C.20.3.2 For fire within chamber, the following procedure should be performed:

(1) Turn off oxygen source.
(2) Decompress chamber.
(3) Remove patient.

The chamber door will probably be very hot. There may still be fire in the chamber, or it may rekindle when the door is opened. Exercise caution and have someone stand by with a hand-held fire extinguisher.

(4) Sound fire alarm of facility.
(5) Evacuate area.
(6) Attempt to suppress fire, or close door and await arrival of fire service personnel.

C.20.4 See Table C.20.4.

TABLE C.20.4 Pressure Table

Atmosphere Absolute (ATA)	mm Hg	psia	psig	Equivalent Depth in Seawater		mm Hg Oxygen Pressure of Compressed Air	mm Hg Oxygen Pressure of Oxygen-Enriched Air (23.5%)
				ft	m		
1	760	14.7	0	0	0	160	179
1.5	1140	22	7.35	16.5	5.07	240	268
2.0	1520	29.4	14.7	33.1	10.13	320	357
2.5	1900	36.7	22.0	49.7	15.20	400	447
3.0	2280	44.1	29.4	66.2	20.26	480	536
3.5	2660	51.4	36.7	82.7	25.33	560	625
4.0	3040	58.8	44.1	99.2	30.40	640	714
5.0	3800	73.5	58.8	132.3	40.53	800	893

Notes:

1. The oxygen percentage in the chamber environment, not the oxygen partial pressure, is of principal concern, as concentrations above 23.5 percent oxygen increase the rate of flame spread. Thirty percent oxygen in nitrogen at 1 ATA (228 mm Hg pO_2) increases burning rate. However, 6 percent oxygen in nitrogen will not support combustion, regardless of oxygen partial pressure (at 5 ATA, 6 percent oxygen gives 228 mm Hg pO_2).

2. The Subcommittee on Hyperbaric and Hypobaric Facilities recommends that one unit of pressure measurement be employed. Since a variety of different units are now in use, and since chamber operators have not settled upon one single unit, the above table includes the five units most commonly employed in chamber practice.

REFERENCES CITED IN COMMENTARY

1. NFPA 801, *Standard for Fire Protection for Facilities Handling Radioactive Materials*, 2003 edition.
2. NFPA *101*®, *Life Safety Code*®, 2006 edition.
3. NFPA 10, *Standard for Portable Fire Extinguishers*, 2002 edition.

General References

Sheffield, P. J., and Desautels, D. A., "Hyperbaric and Hypobaric Chamber Fires: A 73-year Analysis." *Undersea Hyper Med,* 1997, 24(3): 153–164.

U.S. Navy Diving Manual (Revision 4). Naval Sea Systems Command, Arlington, VA, 1999.

ANNEX D

The Safe Use of High-Frequency Electricity in Health Care Facilities

This annex is not a part of the requirements of this NFPA document but is included for informational purposes only.

D.1 Introduction

The late Dr. Carl W. Walter, chairman of what was the Committee on Hospitals in the 1960s, appointed a subcommittee to draft a document on the safe use of high-frequency medical devices. A document had been considered necessary for some time because high-frequency electrosurgery could and did cause injuries to patients and staff. The result was NFPA 76CM, *Safe Use of High-Frequency Electrical Equipment in Hospitals,* a manual that was adopted in 1970 and upgraded to a recommended practice in 1975.

This recommended practice, which became Appendix E in the 1984 edition of NFPA 99 and is now this Annex D, is a valuable guide to the safe use of this energy and equipment and is highly recommended reading for anesthesiologists, anesthetists, operating room nurses, surgeons, and those who maintain and service high-frequency electrical equipment. Because high-frequency electrosurgery is often used in anesthetizing locations, readers should study this material in conjunction with 13.4.1.

Although Annex D contains recommendations and information, not requirements, users and manufacturers should note that these recommendations have generally been accepted as good practice for many years. Although not intended to be incorporated into law, these recommendations have been referenced in litigation and have afforded valuable advice.

Annex D contains relatively little commentary compared to other chapters in NFPA 99 because the text itself incorporates a great deal of explanatory material.

D.1.1 Purpose.

The purpose of this annex is to provide information and recommendations for the reduction of electrical and thermal hazards associated with the use of high-frequency electricity in health care facilities.

D.1.2 Scope.

This annex covers principles of design and use of electrical and electronic appliances generating high-frequency currents for medical treatment in hospitals, clinics, ambulatory care facilities, and dental offices, whether fixed or mobile.

Annex D covers many of the principles of design and use, but not all. Those features that relate to fire and burn hazards have been emphasized.

D.1.2.1 This annex does not cover communication equipment, resuscitation equipment (e.g., defibrillators), or physiological stimulators used for anesthesia, acupuncture, and so on.

D.1.2.2 This annex does not cover experimental or research apparatus built to order, or under development, provided such apparatus is used under qualified supervision and provided the builder demonstrates to the authority having jurisdiction that the apparatus has a degree of safety equivalent to that described herein.

D.1.3 Frequency Range.

For the purposes of this annex, high frequency is intended to mean any electrical energy generated in the radio-frequency range from approximately 100 kHz (100,000 cyc/sec) to microwave frequencies.

D.1.4 Intended Use.

This annex is intended for use by operating personnel practicing the electrical or the medical arts, as well as apparatus designers. It thus contains material of an informative nature as well as recommendations.

D.1.5 Responsibility of the Governing Body.

It is the responsibility of the governing body of the health care facility to provide its staff, patients, and visitors with an environment that is reasonably safe from the shock and burn hazards associated with the use of high-frequency electricity. In order to discharge this obligation, the governing body is permitted to delegate appropriate authority to its medical staff, consultants, architects, engineers, and others. *(See Section D.5 for further information.)*

D.1.6 Interpretations.

The National Fire Protection Association does not approve, inspect, or certify any installation, procedure, equipment, or material. With respect to this annex, its role is limited solely to an advisory capacity. The acceptability of a particular piece of equipment, installation, or procedure is a matter between the health care facility and the authority having jurisdiction. However, in order to assist in the determination of such acceptability, the National Fire Protection Association has established interpretation procedures. These procedures are outlined in the NFPA *Regulations Governing Committee Projects*.

D.1.7 General Introduction.

The flow of electric energy at conventional power frequencies is generally understood and predictable. As the frequency is increased to the radio-frequency range, that is, above 100 kHz (100,000 cyc/sec), the electric current might not be restricted to obvious conductive paths and consequently can have effects not generally appreciated.

High-frequency power-generating equipment can present a hazard to the patient or to the operator by the nature of its use, or by its electrical interference with other apparatus in contact with or implanted within the patient. Since the equipment usually requires direct connections to the patient, it can also present a current path through the body tissues for electrical faults occurring within it or in other equipment.

It should be kept in mind that this annex is intended for use by operating personnel practicing the electrical or the medical arts, as well as apparatus designers. Some of the comments might appear overly simple, since it was considered desirable to err on the side of clarity rather than conciseness.

Some statements in this annex concerning waveforms, frequency, and so on, refer to specific designs of apparatus that are in common use. These are cited for illustrative purposes only. Other techniques for accomplishing the same medical purposes have been developed. This annex is not intended to assess the relative merits of any of these techniques, but rather to provide guidelines for the safe use of any type of high-frequency, power-generating, medical equipment.

This annex indicates circumstances and procedures that can produce hazards during the use of high-frequency electrosurgical or diathermy equipment, and it suggests protective measures against such hazards. This annex is concerned specifically with electrical effects and safety. The high-frequency power generated by these devices can interfere with the operation of other apparatus such as physiological monitors or pacemakers. The mechanisms of heat generation in body tissues by high-frequency energy needs to be understood and controlled to be effective therapeutically, while avoiding unwanted burning. The arc that is likely to occur when an energized high-frequency electrode contacts tissues can be an ignition source for flammable vapors and gases. Although referenced in this annex, full recommendations for safety from explosion hazards in the presence of flammable anesthetic agents are given in Annex E of this standard and should be consulted for detailed specifications. Surgical effects of electrosurgery are described in Section D.6 of this annex. A recommendation for the clinical use of electrosurgical equipment is outlined in Section D.7 of this annex. These sections are included because there is little available in the medical literature on the effective and safe use of these powerful electrical therapeutic instruments.

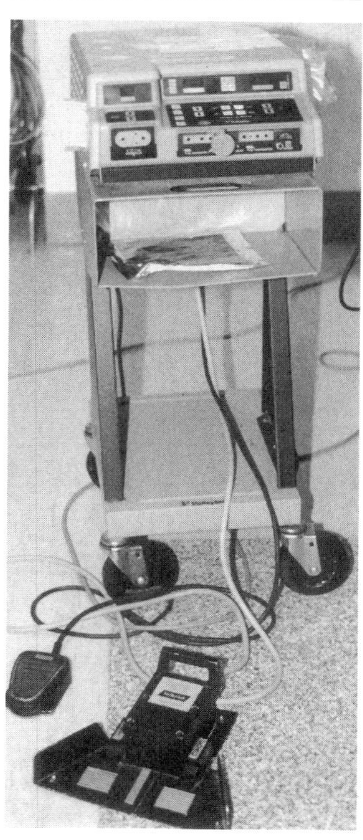

EXHIBIT D.1 *Typical electrosurgical unit used in surgery.*

The commonly used waveforms, frequencies, and energies were arrived at largely through experience and can be varied a great deal. Research has been conducted on the mechanisms for therapeutic action, but no optimum design has been developed (assuming that there is such an optimum). Therefore, technical descriptions have been kept general, with the understanding that a variety of designs could achieve equivalent therapeutic results.

D.2 High-Frequency Equipment

D.2.1 Types of Apparatus.

D.2.1.1 Electrosurgery.

The frequency used for electrosurgery is not critical. The frequency range indicated, 0.1 MHz to 5 MHz, is well above the possibility of stimulating nerve or muscle but not so high that there is excessive radiation of power from leads or electrodes. (See Exhibit D.1.)

Although electrical currents in the 0.1 to 5 MHz frequency range would not directly stimulate nerve or muscle, the waveform might be heavily modulated and could therefore produce stimulating effects. A good discussion of electrical stimulation can be found in Bruner and Leonard, *Electricity, Safety, and the Patient* [1].

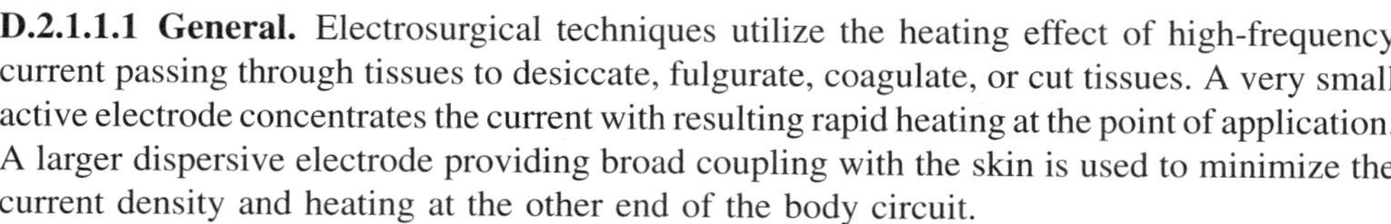

D.2.1.1.1 General. Electrosurgical techniques utilize the heating effect of high-frequency current passing through tissues to desiccate, fulgurate, coagulate, or cut tissues. A very small active electrode concentrates the current with resulting rapid heating at the point of application. A larger dispersive electrode providing broad coupling with the skin is used to minimize the current density and heating at the other end of the body circuit.

D.2.1.1.2 Electrocoagulation and Fulguration. Coagulation and fulguration procedures generally employ a damped sine waveform or a train of low duty–cycle pulses. The frequency is in the 0.1- to 5-MHz (million cycles per second) region, but a wide spectrum of high frequencies also could be generated.

D.2.1.1.3 Electrocutting. High-frequency cutting of tissue is more effective with an undamped sinusoidal current or continuous pulse train. Most electrosurgical equipment provides a selection of coagulating current, cutting current, or a blended output.

D.2.1.1.4 Electrosurgical Oscillators. Electrosurgical oscillators operate in the general range of 0.5 MHz to 5.0 MHz with average output power capabilities as high as 500 watts. The actual amount of power required depends on the type of electrode used, the modality (cutting or coagulating), the operative procedure, and the conditions surrounding the operating field. In open-air cutting or coagulating, the power will generally range from 50 to 100 watts. In a transurethral resection, higher power might be required because of the bypassing effect of the irrigating fluid around the electrode. An electrosurgical unit must have a relatively low output impedance (typically 100 to 1000 ohms) in order to match the tissue electrical load and to limit open-circuit peak voltage with its attendant danger of insulation failure of electrodes, surgical handles, and so on.

Note that most older instruments used a spark gap oscillator to generate highly damped radio-frequency sine waveforms, often modulated at 120 Hz, characterized by high peak voltages and low duty cycle, for coagulating purposes. Newer instruments use solid-state circuits to generate complex pulse trains with similar characteristics. Limited studies indicate that the frequency range is not very critical, but that the low duty–cycle train is the key to the coagulating process. A continuous, unmodulated sine waveform or pulse train, delivering a high average power generated by a vacuum tube or solid state oscillator, is used for free cutting with little or no hemostasis. Higher duty–cycle, moderately damped waveforms are used when a greater degree of hemostasis is desired while cutting. *(See Section D.6 of this annex.)*

D.2.1.2 Electrocautery. Electrocautery is a surgical technique that utilizes a heated electrode or glowing wire to conduct heat to the tissue. It usually uses power frequency (60 Hz) current at low voltage to heat the electrode and hence is not a high-frequency device. It is described here because of possible confusion in terminology. In electrocautery there is no intentional passage of current through the tissues. While the voltage and frequency are low, these are patient-connected devices using electrical power, and appropriate precautions should be used. *(See Chapter 8 in the requirements portion of this document.)*

Hazards of patient-care-related electrical appliances, particularly with respect to power-line operation, are addressed in Chapter 8. Readers are urged to read that chapter because the appliances discussed in Annex D could pose power-line frequency hazards, even in the standby state.

D.2.1.3 Neurosurgical Lesion Generator. Specialized instruments with lower power, 1 to 30 watts, are used in neurosurgery to make carefully delineated lesions in neural tissue. They employ continuous waveform radio-frequency power. Some designs use stereotactic instruments or neural signals for position control, and temperature measurement for size control. The temperature rise is limited to achieve tissue protein denaturation but not gross tissue destruction.

Other types of high-frequency devices are used for dental work, cardiac lesions, and other special surgical purposes. Although the specific designs differ, the same general safety principles apply for all types of uses.

D.2.1.4 Radio-Frequency Diathermy.

D.2.1.4.1 General. Diathermy utilizes the heating effect of the passage of a high-frequency current or an electromagnetic field in body tissues. In contrast to electrosurgery, it applies a relatively even heat distribution within the tissue well below a temperature that would cause tissue destruction. Diathermy equipment operates at 27.12 MHz, with some older units at 13.56 MHz. These frequencies are assigned for this purpose by the Federal Communications Commission with rigid regulations regarding frequency control, harmonics, or spurious radiation. *(See Section D.9.)*

Both magnetic and electric radio-frequency fields can have undesirable effects — such as heating of tissues, cataracts in the eye, and neurological disturbances — on general nonpatient populations. These fileds are regulated by safety rules generally based on ANSI/IEEE C95.1, *Standard for Safety Levels with Respect to Human Exposure to Radio Frequency Electromagnetic Fields, 3 kHz to 300 GHz* [2]. These regulations apply to medical staff and visitors at risk of exposure to radio-frequency fields. Patients who are exposed to radio-frequency fields for therapeutic reasons are generally exempt from these regulations. Exposure time for these patients is relatively short, and the medical benefits far outweigh the risks. In addition to ANSI/IEEE C95.1, a valuable source of information on radio-frequency fields is NCRP Report No. 67, *Radio-Frequency Electromagnetic Fields — Properties, Quantities and Units, Biophysical Interaction, and Measurements* [3].

D.2.1.4.2 Dielectric or Spaced-Plate Diathermy. With spaced-plate applicators, heating is the result of alternating current in the tissues caused by the high potential difference between the electrodes. This alternating electric field permeates the interposed tissues, which act as lossy dielectrics between capacitor plates.

D.2.1.4.3 Inductive Diathermy. The high-frequency current of inductive diathermy is passed through a coil or coils to produce rapidly reversing magnetic fields through the tissue. Heating is caused by eddy currents set up by the alternating magnetic field.

D.2.1.5 Microwave Diathermy. Microwave energy is radiated from a reflector, usually parabolic, air-spaced from the tissue. The energy is "beamed" like light to the intended area. The depth of penetration and intensity of heating are determined by the spacing and energy output of the microwave source. The assigned medical frequency is 2450 MHz. Electromagnetic energy at this frequency has an appropriate combination of penetration and absorption in tissue.

D.2.1.6 Ultrasonic Diathermy. Ultrasonic energy in the high-frequency range (approximately 0.05 MHz to 5 MHz) is also used for therapeutic heating and for making lesions. It should be noted that the energy modality is mechanical (acoustic) and not electrical, and hence some of the hazards described herein do not apply. However, these are patient-connected devices employing substantial electrical power, and appropriate precautions must be used.

D.2.1.7 Hyperthermia. Heating, controlled in spatial distribution and temperature, can be applied to tumors as a therapeutic adjunct to other therapeutic techniques. Techniques similar to diathermy can be used, often with implanted antennas or coupling devices.

Hyperthermia operates in high-level fields that are usually at microwave frequencies because they can raise the temperature of tissue under good spatial control, enhancing the tumoricidal effects of simultaneous ionizing radiation. The electrical safety concerns of hyperthermia should be considered carefully because this technique often uses experimental systems and can be applied while the patient is isolated in an ionizing radiation chamber.

D.2.1.8 Medical Lasers. The spatial and frequency coherence properties of laser-generated radiation allow the localized deposition of large amounts of energy in tissue. This can be used for cutting, coagulation, or photochemoactivation. This apparatus per se is an electrical device, subject to the requirements of Chapter 8 (in the requirements portion of this document), but the peculiar hazard is the result of the unusual optical properties of this radiation.

Light amplification by stimulated emission of radiation (laser) technology is well established, despite its use in surgery for only the last twenty years or so. Although not a high-frequency device in the same sense as other types listed in D.2.1, laser technology does have properties that pose unique hazards, as well as hazards similar to those of high-frequency devices.

Medical laser use of electromagnetic radiation in the infrared and visible spectrums is not usually considered high-frequency electricity in the radio-frequency sense of the term. However, in medical use, these devices apply thermal energy to cause cutting and coagulation of tissue analogous to electrosurgery.

Although both modalities are thermal in effect, electrosurgery involves direct contact with a flow of current, whereas lasers use a radiated beam of energy without the need for direct contact with the intended target (i.e., location on body). The laser beam can be focused, reflected or piped, and pointed at intended or unintended targets.

Many of the risks from thermal hazards in electrosurgery apply to lasers — for example, burns in unintended places — and to ignition of drapes and flammable liquids. Lasers present added hazards as well. Laser beams that operate in the invisible radiation spectrum can be reflected from surgical tools and other metallic devices that in visible light appear dull and nonreflective. Such reflection can cause unintended injury to the patient or attendant staff if hit by a misdirected laser beam. Thus, surgeons must receive specific training in the use of lasers.

Lasers are also used as spatial localizing beams. Although they are usually very low power, prolonged exposure to such beams by the patient or staff should be avoided. The eye is a particularly sensitive target because the lens can focus a beam on the retina.

See D.3.8.2 and accompanying commentary for further information and guidance. See also NFPA 115, *Standard for Laser Fire Protection* [4], for more general laser safety guidance.

D.2.2 Properties of High-Frequency Circuits.

D.2.2.1 General. In low-frequency apparatus, the circuit elements are usually discrete components, physically obvious, interconnected by wires or other conductors. At higher frequencies, distributive elements and less obvious forms of coupling (capacitive, inductive, and radiative) become increasingly important. Since these properties might not be fully appreciated by personnel using high-frequency medical equipment, this section reviews some aspects of them.

D.2.2.2 Nonconductive Coupling.

D.2.2.2.1 Capacitive. Any two conductors separated by a dielectric constitute a capacitor through which alternating current will pass. This capacitor has a reactance that varies inversely with frequency. Thus, when a conductive material is placed near a conductor carrying high-frequency current, some of the high-frequency energy can be transferred to this material. This coupling might exist, for example, between an electrosurgical power cable and an adjacent input lead of an electrocardiograph. Similarly, a low-impedance ground path might be presented by the capacitance between an electrode lead and its grounded metal shield. Capacitive coupling exists at all frequencies but is relatively more significant at higher frequencies.

D.2.2.2.2 Inductive. Energy might also be transferred without an obvious interconnection by the magnetic field that surrounds all current paths. This effect is used in the familiar transformer but could also produce coupling between two adventitiously placed adjacent wires. If a large conductor is placed in a magnetic field, the coupling could induce circulating current in the conductor. These "eddy currents" generate heat as would any other current in the conductor. Inductive coupling could be affected relatively little by shielding intended to inhibit capacitive coupling.

D.2.2.3 Skin Effect. Because of self-induced eddy currents, high-frequency current could be confined to the surface of metal conductors. This "skin effect" can cause a simple conductor to have a much higher effective impedance at high frequencies than it would have at low frequencies.

Skin effect should not be confused with the change of impedance of a patient's skin. Living tissue is a complex electrical system of ionic conductors and capacitors. The skin contact impedance shows a marked decrease at higher frequencies largely because of capacitive coupling through the poorly conductive outer skin layers.

D.2.2.4 Modulation and Detection. The high-frequency currents present in medical apparatus often have complex waveforms. The frequency and amplitude of the oscillations can vary. The peaks of successive oscillations form an "envelope" of the signal, or modulation. Thus a 1-MHz radio-frequency waveform might be modulated by a 120-Hz signal. When such a waveform passes through a nonlinear circuit element, other frequency waveforms are produced, including some at the modulating frequency (in this example, 120 Hz). Since the contact between an electrode and tissue, and the tissue itself, contain nonlinear elements, low-frequency currents could be present when high-frequency currents pass through the body.

D.2.2.5 Electromagnetic Radiation.

D.2.2.5.1 General. In the radio-frequency region, energy is also propagated by direct radiation through air or other media. This is the basis of radio communication and microwave diathermy and can produce undesired effects in other high-frequency apparatus.

Long Wires and Antennas. At sufficiently high frequencies, a conductor such as a simple wire can become "electrically long" and constitute a complex circuit element. In free space this length is governed by the following relation:

$$\lambda f = 300$$

where λ is the wavelength, in meters, f is the frequency, in megahertz, and 300 is the velocity of light, in meters per microsecond. The velocity is less in other media. If the conductor is an appreciable fraction of a wavelength, it is no longer a simple resistive conductor. It could have a large impedance and become an effective antenna. If the length approaches $\frac{1}{4}\lambda$ (or more), it could be part of the resonant output system of the apparatus.

D.2.2.5.2 Sources of High-Frequency Radiation. *Electrosurgical Equipment Radiation.* Such radiation derives from the following:

(1) The active cable
(2) The dispersive return cable
(3) Electrical power lines (minimized by filtering)
(4) Direct radiation from components, especially the spark gap and associated wiring (minimized by proper cabinet design)
(5) Radio-frequency current paths through the patient and from the patient to ground via alternative paths, such as capacitive coupling to the table

Since the operating frequency is relatively low and the leads in the output circuit are electrically short, radiation from them is at a low level. Generally, interference with other equipment is caused by the conduction of high-frequency energy through common power lines or by capacitive and inductive coupling. Interference can be minimized by proper shielding and filtering.

Diathermy Equipment Radiation. Such radiation derives from the following:

(1) Electromagnetic radiation from the applicators and their connecting cables. The amount of radiation is dependent on the treatment level and on the orientation of the drum or spaced plates and can be influenced by the placement of the leads.
(2) At 27.12 MHz, a quarter wavelength ($\frac{1}{4}\lambda$) is 2.76 m (about 10.9 ft). The "ground" wire in the supply cable might be low impedance only at a low frequency, so that the

cabinet of the diathermy acts as the "ground" plane for the unit and under unusual conditions might be at appreciable high-frequency voltage above power supply ground.

(3) A patient under treatment with spaced plates is in a strong electric field and is a conductor at some voltage above ground, as evidenced by the fact that he or she can receive a burn by touching a bare metal part of the cabinet. Since diathermy equipment is used to produce heat in tissues without direct contact with the body, the energy transferred must be by means of induction from resonant electrodes or applicators. This energy can be picked up by adjacent equipment, such as remote monitoring systems or by power lines, and can be difficult to control. Physical separation is the best solution since the signals attenuate rapidly with distance and interposed walls and building structures. The construction of shielded rooms might be necessary if the radiation problem is serious. The radiation from components and supply cable must be kept low to meet Federal Communications Commission requirements.

Microwave Therapy Radiation. Such radiation is at extremely high frequency and short wavelength. A quarter wavelength in tissue is about 3 cm (1.18 in.). The electrical properties of tissue at these high frequencies are complex and need to be investigated further.

Only limited commentary on microwave therapy radiation is possible at this time, given the complexity of the subject and the need for further investigation. The use of microwave radiation as a source of energy for hyperthermia in cancer therapy is expanding. Care must be taken to avoid injuries when microwave radiation is used for this purpose. See also the commentary following D.2.1.7.

D.3 The Hazard

D.3.1 Hazards Covered.

This annex is concerned with the hazards that can exist during the use of high-frequency power equipment in the health care facility. The danger can be to the patient, the operating personnel, or to other equipment. Some of these problems are common to all electrical apparatus and are the subject of other manuals and codes. These are appropriately referenced. The following kinds of hazards are considered:

(1) Radio-frequency interference *(see D.3.2)*
(2) High-frequency burns *(see D.3.3)*
(3) Low-frequency electrical shock *(see D.3.4)*
(4) Explosions and fire *(see D.3.5)*
(5) Complications of the use of the apparatus *(see D.3.6)*
(6) Direct current burns *(see D.3.7)*
(7) Nonionizing radiation burns and ignition *(see D.3.8)*

D.3.2 Radio-Frequency Interference.

D.3.2.1 General. The high-frequency output of therapeutic equipment can propagate by radiation or other coupling through air, tissue, or current conductors to affect the operation of other equipment, that is, by distorting or obscuring displayed data, blocking normal operation, or causing damage through thermal or electrical breakdown. The extent of the effect will depend upon operating frequency, power level, intercoupling of circuits, distance, and the sensitivity and selectivity of the affected apparatus. This could be of particular concern if the affected apparatus is computer-based since some digital circuits are very sensitive to interference.

The hazards of radio-frequency interference (RFI) have become a subject of increasing concern in recent years because of the proliferation of diagnostic and monitoring devices based on digital circuitry. Some of these devices are extremely sensitive to RFI but can exhibit this sensitivity in ways that are not immediately obvious, such as in random malfunctions or the production of erroneous data. If such devices are to be used in conjunction with high-frequency apparatus, or will be in close proximity to such apparatus, the entire system should be checked for compatibility. These concerns apply not only to electrosurgical apparatus, but also to diathermy, hyperthermia, or other techniques that might radiate or conduct significant high-frequency energy.

See Exhibit D.2 for an example of a sign prohibiting cellular phone use in an area where high-frequency medical equipment is used. Cellular phones have been reported to interfere with medical monitoring equipment and fire alarm systems. As a result, some facilities have restricted their use in certain locations.

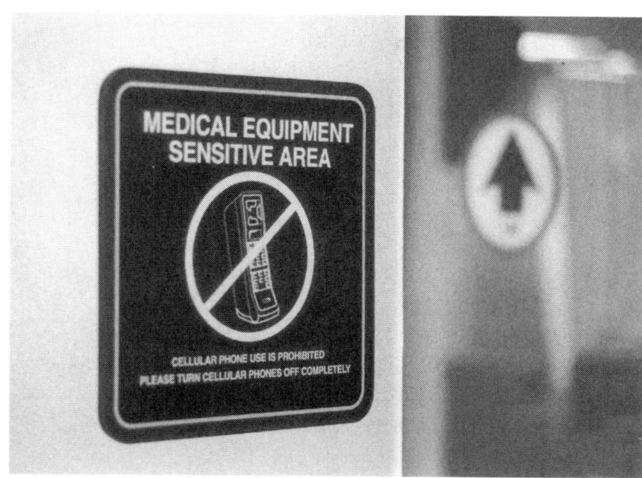

EXHIBIT D.2 *A sign denoting an area housing high-frequency medical equipment.*

D.3.2.2 Equipment in Contact with Patient. High-frequency currents flowing through body tissues can be conducted directly to equipment having input electrodes on or in the patient, or can be capacitively or inductively coupled to implanted sensors, to affect their operation. The performance of implanted pacemakers can be disrupted, particularly those having sensing circuits. The pacemaker manufacturer's literature should be consulted before using high-frequency equipment on a patient with a pacemaker.

D.3.2.3 Equipment in Patient Area — No Direct Contact. Telemetering and similar equipment in the immediate vicinity of the patient can be affected by energy radiated from high-frequency sources. The degree of interference depends on the strength of the interfering radiation and on the sensitivity of the affected equipment to the interfering signal. Before new configurations of equipment are utilized, they should be checked to ensure that no unacceptable interference could occur.

D.3.2.4 Equipment in Remote Areas. Equipment in remote areas can be affected by radiated energy or by energy conducted through power lines. Intensive care areas adjacent to treatment or operating areas are examples. In extreme cases shielding might be necessary, but spatial separation is usually adequate. If such interference occurs, the equipment should be modified or locations changed to reduce the interference to an acceptable level.

D.3.3 High-Frequency Burns.

D.3.3.1 Electrosurgical Equipment. When electricity flows in a conductor, heat is generated at a rate proportional to the product of the resistance and the square of the current. This thermal effect is the basis of function for electrosurgical and dielectric diathermy equipment. In the case of electrosurgical equipment, the cutting electrode is made very small to produce a high current density and consequently a very rapid temperature rise at the point of contact with tissue. The high-frequency current is intended to flow through the patient to the dispersive electrode. The dispersive electrode provides a large contact with skin to minimize the current density at that end of the patient circuit. However, when the resistance between the body and the dispersive electrode is excessive, significant current can flow via alternative paths. The relative areas are indicated in Figure D.3.3.1. If the dispersive electrode presents too small a contact area, deep tissue burns can result not only at the dispersive electrode but also at other sites. *(See also Section D.6 of this annex.)*

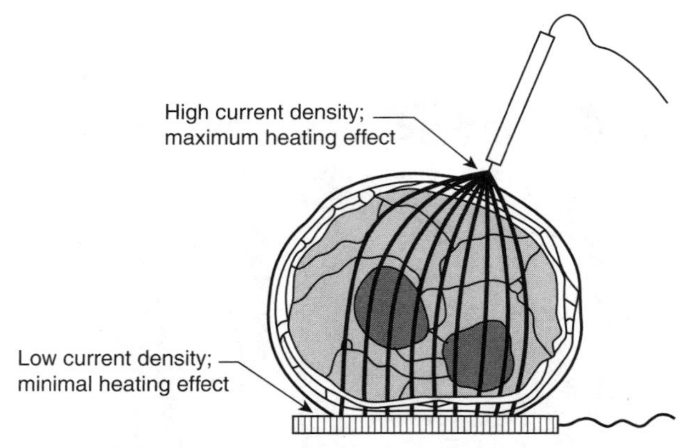

FIGURE D.3.3.1 *Relative Current Densities at Contact with Patient.*

Note that the optimum characteristics and area of tissue contact for a dispersive electrode are matters of controversy. Factors pertinent to tissue injury include adequacy of gel, anatomic placement and orientation of the electrode, edge phenomena, and principles of fabrication (such as proprietary pregelled pads as opposed to metal foil or plate). Additional considerations are the manner of use of the ESU and the adequacy of skin perfusion (related to body temperature, circulatory integrity, and pressure points).

Thermal probes, monitoring electrodes, intravascular wires, or incidental contacts with metal furniture such as operating tables, IV poles, or instrument trays could provide better opportunities for return paths for current, particularly if the preferred path is inadequate.

Historical experience suggests that 1 cm^2 for each 1.5 watts of applied power appears to offer a generous margin of safety for most applications using gelled metal plates. Continuing research might establish confidence in the utilization of less generous contact areas in view of modern practices and equipment.

The issue of contact size of the dispersive electrode becomes more complex as the number of devices connected to the patient increases (i.e., as the number of possible alternative paths for current to flow increases). Techniques such as thermography have been used to quantitatively study increases in skin temperature at the dispersive electrode and other sites. These studies indicate that maximum heating takes place along the edges of the electrode, particularly the edge of the dispersive electrode closest to the active electrode.

Note that the optimum characteristics and area of tissue contact for a dispersive electrode are matters of controversy. Factors pertinent to tissue injury include adequacy of gel, anatomic placement and orientation of the electrode, edge phenomena, and principles of fabrication (such as proprietary pregelled pads as opposed to metal foil or plate). Additional considerations are the manner of use of the ESU and the adequacy of skin perfusion (related to body temperature, circulatory integrity, and pressure points).

Thermal probes, monitoring electrodes, intravascular wires, or incidental contacts with metal furniture such as operating tables, IV poles, or instrument trays could provide better opportunities for return paths for current, particularly if the preferred path is inadequate.

Historical experience suggests that 1 cm^2 for each 1.5 watts of applied power appears to offer a generous margin of safety for most applications using gelled metal plates. Continuing research might establish confidence in the utilization of less generous contact areas in view of modern practices and equipment.

D.3.3.1.1 Burns from Inadequate Dispersive Electrode Contact. Inadequate contact with a dispersive electrode can result from the following:

(1) Electrode area too small for application
(2) Electrode not in adequate contact with tissue
(3) Electrode insulated from the skin by interposition of bedding, clothing, or other unintended material

With the advent of a multitude of configurations and designs (e.g., pregelled, electrically conductive adhesive, capacitively coupled, and combinations), and since each type presents application requirements peculiar to its design, the manufacturers' instructions should be carefully read and followed.

When electrosurgical equipment is brought into use after the start of an operating procedure and after the patient has been draped, extreme care is necessary in the placement and attachment of the dispersive electrode to be sure that proper contact is made directly with the skin and that there is no intervening insulating material. Electrode paste is useful to reduce the impedance of the contact between the electrode and the patient's skin. In a prolonged procedure, this should be checked periodically to ensure that the paste has not dried up.

It should be recognized that while a dispersive electrode might be making proper and sufficient contact with a patient at the beginning of an operation, conditions requiring repositioning of the patient can arise. This repositioning might reduce or completely eliminate contact with the electrode, and burns might result. Electrode placement must be checked whenever the patient is moved.

Electrode paste reduces impedance of the contact but by itself does not ensure good contact. Care should be used when electrodes are first applied, and they should be checked periodically during long procedures.

A variety of pregelled electrodes are now widely used. However, if opened and exposed to the air for too long before being used, or if insufficient gel is supplied by the manufacturer, or if the gel is removed by careless handling, their advantage of ease is lost. Pregelled electrodes often have minimally adequate surface area. Care needs to be taken, therefore, to ensure that all available surface area is used.

Capacitively coupled electrodes do not use conductive gel. However, instructions must be followed carefully to ensure good electrical contact.

D.3.3.1.2 Burns from Uneven Electrode Contact. Pressure points caused by bony protuberances or irregularities in electrode surface can concentrate current flow with resulting excessive temperature rise. Loose skin overhanging the edges of the electrode, or areas pinched by sliding a plate beneath the patient without lifting the patient sufficiently contribute to the burn hazard. See Figure D.3.3.1.2.

Some heat is generated at the dispersive electrode contact, but it normally is carried away by the circulation of blood under the skin, so that the temperature rise is small. However, at pressure points or after prolonged pressure, the blood flow could be impeded, so that adequate cooling is not obtained. Skin and subcutaneous tissue blood flow could be altered by body temperature, anesthetic agents, and other drugs used during surgery. The effect could vary with the patient's age and clinical condition. The significance of these factors is not always fully appreciated.

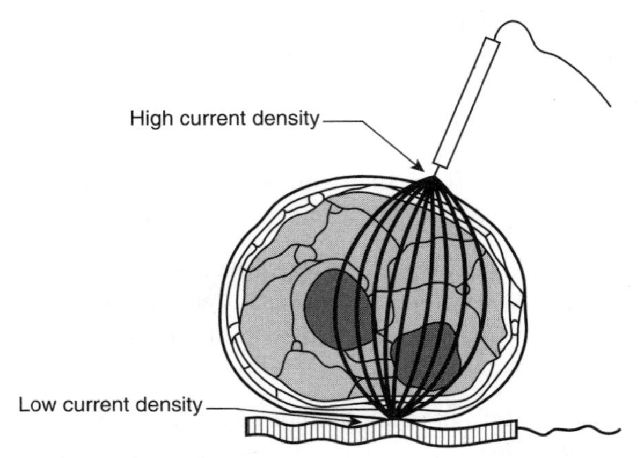

FIGURE D.3.3.1.2 High Current Density at Irregularity of Electrode.

D.3.3.1.3 Burns at Unintended Current Paths with Various Types of Electrosurgical Units. Normally, the current from the active electrode flows through the patient to the dispersive electrode and then back to the generator via the dispersive cable as shown in Figure D.3.3.1.3(a) through Figure D.3.3.1.3(c). If other paths are available, the current will divide among the several paths.

The effect of alternate paths will vary depending on the type of electrosurgical unit employed.

Electrosurgical Unit with a Grounded Dispersive Electrode and No Dispersive Cable Continuity Monitor. Normally the high-frequency current will flow as shown in Figure D.3.3.1.3(a). If the dispersive cable is broken and the unit is activated, then the current could flow through unintended ground paths as shown in Figure D.3.3.1.3(b) and Figure D.3.3.1.3(c).

Electrosurgical Unit with a Grounded Dispersive Electrode and a Dispersive Cable Continuity Monitor. If an electrosurgical unit has a dispersive cable monitor, the break in the dispersive cable shown in Figure D.3.3.1.3(b) can be detected, and the machine inactivated.

Care should be taken not to activate these kinds of ESUs until the active electrode is about to contact the patient. Similarly, activation should be terminated as soon as possible after removing the active electrode. When the active electrode is away from patient contact, other radio frequency leakage paths might have lower impedance and carry the current. The problem is of particular concern when finger-operated pencil electrodes are used, because it is very easy to activate the electrode before it is in contact with the patient.

Paragraph 8.5.2.3 governs the use of ESUs, with the intent of avoiding fires. Electrodes that are resting in the surgical field, or that are allowed to dangle in the drapes when contaminated, can be particularly dangerous if inadvertently activated. The growing use of multiple ESUs in complicated procedures exacerbates the problem.

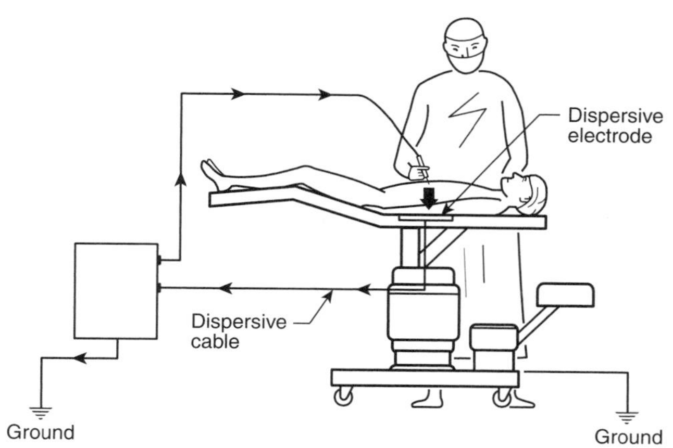

FIGURE D.3.3.1.3(a) *Correct Flow of High-Frequency Current from Electrosurgery Through Tissue to Dispersive Electrode and Patient Cord Back to Generator.*

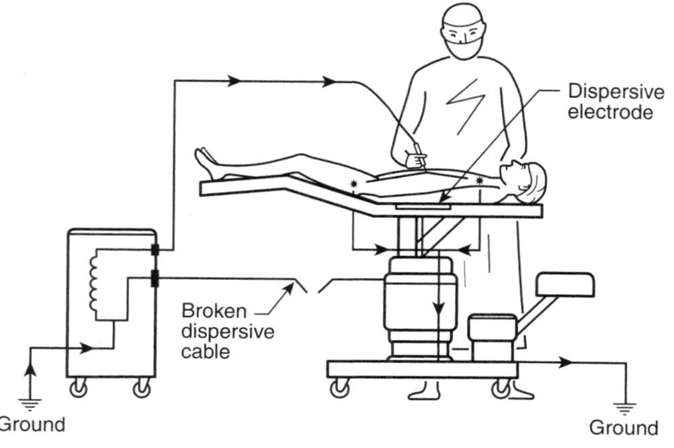

FIGURE D.3.3.1.3(b) *Alternate Return Paths to Ground When Normal Return Path Through Patient Cord Is Broken.*

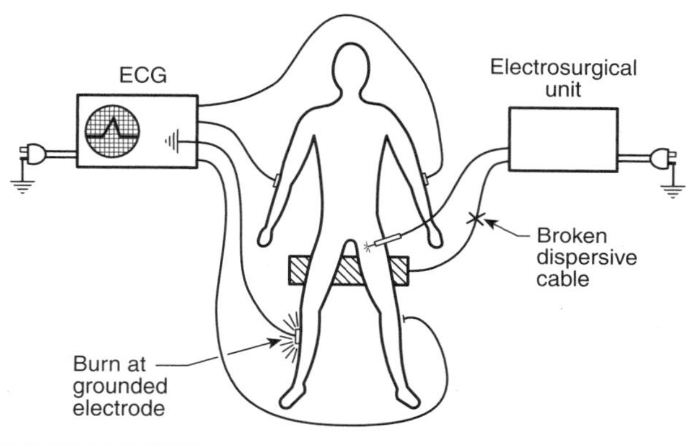

FIGURE D.3.3.1.3(c) *Alternate Return Path to Ground Through Grounded Electrode of ECG.*

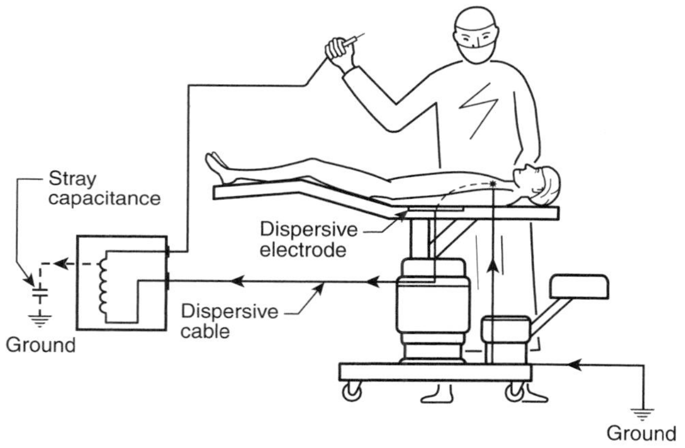

FIGURE D.3.3.1.3(d) *Stray Current Flow from an RF Isolated Electrosurgical Unit.*

Electrosurgical Unit with an RF Isolated Output Circuit (Floating Output). Because RF isolation is inherently imperfect, stray RF currents (leakage currents) can flow from the electrodes to any grounded conductor contacting the patient as shown in Figure D.3.3.1.3(d). This stray RF current is greatest when the unit is activated with the active electrode not in contact with the patient.

D.3.3.1.4 Dispersive Cable Monitoring Circuits. The incorporation of a monitoring circuit will warn of a broken dispersive electrode cable. However, the monitoring circuit does not ensure that the dispersive electrode contact with the body is adequate and might lead to a false sense of security on the part of the surgeon or attendant.

To ensure alarm with broken cable but with alternate ground paths as shown in Figure D.3.3.1.3(b), the dispersive cable monitor should alarm if the series resistance [R in Figure D.3.3.1.4(a)] exceeds 150 ohms.

Note that the monitoring current might produce interference on an ECG display.

If an electrosurgical unit has its dispersive cable connected as shown in Figure D.3.3.1.4(b), with a capacitor between it and ground, the dispersive cable monitor circuit might not respond to an alternate ground path.

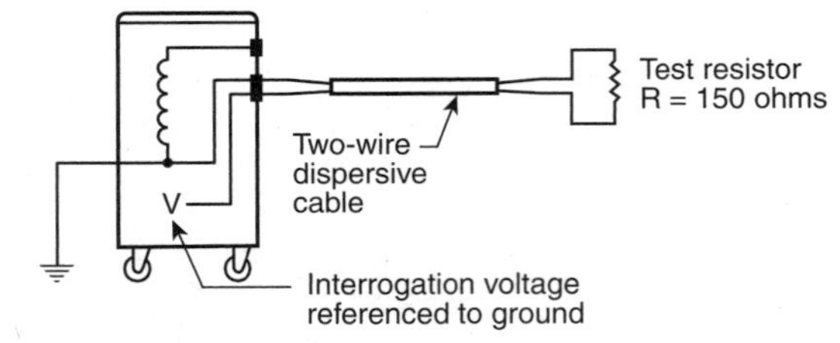

FIGURE D.3.3.1.4(a) *Trip-Out Resistance R.*

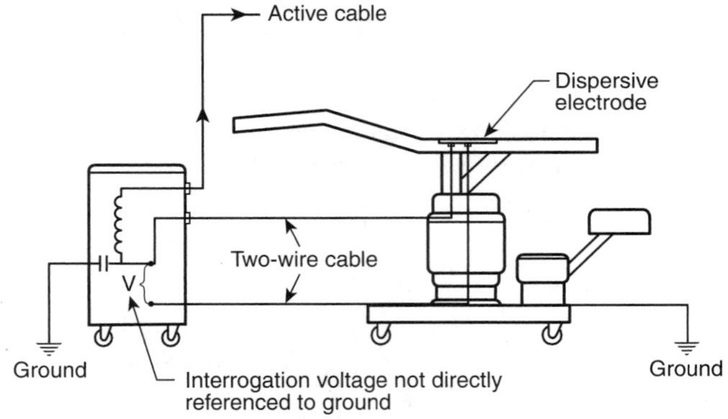

FIGURE D.3.3.1.4(b) *Electrosurgical Unit with a dc Isolated Patient Plate.*

Whether or not a monitoring circuit is provided, the method of attachment of the dispersive electrode should be such that the cable connector cannot be readily disconnected accidentally. A clip-on type of connection can be used only if it meets this criterion.

D.3.3.1.5 Other Causes of Burns at Unintended Current Paths. These can be caused by the following:

(1) Other electrodes providing direct or capacitance-coupled ground returns. Needle electrodes are often used for ECG or other physiological monitoring procedures. The subcutaneous application of these needles provides good connection to the patient, but their small surfaces could produce high-current densities, especially if they are near the operating site. They should be used with great care when electrosurgery is employed. *(See Section D.7 of this annex.)*
(2) Proximity of high-frequency leads to other wires, causing capacitive or inductive coupling, with resultant current in electrodes attached to the patient.

D.3.3.2 Diathermy. Radio-frequency diathermy can induce currents that cause excessive heating in metal devices in the dielectric field (e.g., bone pins, dental fillings, metal sutures, implanted electrodes and leads), producing burns in the adjacent tissue and jeopardizing the tolerance of the metal in the tissues. The magnetic field of inductive diathermy can cause eddy currents that produce a similar effect in implanted metals.

D.3.4 Low-Frequency Shocks (60 Hz).

D.3.4.1 General. Depending on the type of electrosurgical unit employed, the dispersive electrode can present a direct or low-impedance ground path for a fault current emanating from other equipment connected to the patient. The dispersive electrode can be connected in either of two ways:

(1) An electrosurgical unit with a grounded dispersive electrode that provides a direct path for low-frequency current. *[See Figure D.3.3.1.4(a).]*
(2) An RF grounded (low-frequency isolated) electrosurgical unit with capacitance between the electrodes and ground will provide isolation from low-frequency currents inversely proportional to the value of the capacitor (i.e., the smaller the capacitor, the better the low-frequency isolation). *[See Figure D.3.3.1.4(b).]*

D.3.4.2 Equipment Faults. Insulation failure or loose wiring in power-operated devices used for surgery, such as bone saws and dye injectors, or monitoring equipment such as an ECG, can result in high voltage being applied to the patient through contact with the device.

D.3.4.3 Equipment Not Isolated from Power Lines. Low-voltage power sources of older design, which use an autotransformer, do not provide isolation from the main power lines. Contact of the patient with the frame or other exposed conductive surfaces of the device could apply full-line voltage to a grounded patient. This is often true of power sources for resectoscope lights, electrocautery units, stimulators, and other low-voltage devices commonly used in conjunction with electrosurgery, particularly in urology. Such low-voltage equipment should not be used unless provided with an isolated power supply.

D.3.4.4 Rectified Modulation. A peculiar hazard exists in electrosurgical equipment where the high-frequency energy is modulated at low frequencies, as in the coagulating mode. The contact between the active electrode and the tissue can demodulate the high-frequency current, generating power frequency components. If a low-impedance path is present through the apparatus and ground back to the patient, hazardous current levels might be generated. Thus, the application of what is believed to be solely high-frequency current might also be the application of dangerous low-frequency currents.

D.3.5 Explosion and Fire.

D.3.5.1 General. Since electrosurgery operates on the basis of tissue destruction by high-frequency arcs, it must be used with great caution when flammable anesthetic, disinfecting, or cleaning agents are employed. If the medical procedure requires the simultaneous use of electrosurgery and flammable agents, the responsible surgeon must be fully aware of the risks he or she is taking. *(See Section E.6 in Annex E.)*

The caution counseled in D.3.5.1 also applies to the use of surgical lasers or other appliances that generate localized high energy.

D.3.5.2 Explosions in Hollow Organs. The intestines, especially the colon, can contain flammable mixtures of hydrogen, hydrogen sulfide, methane, and oxygen. These gases are readily ignited and can burn explosively and disrupt organs. Hence, special precautions are necessary in surgery on the colon and paracolonic tissue. During laparoscopy, the abdominal cavity should be filled with a nonflammable gas, such as CO_2. When fulguration is done through a sigmoidoscope, an indwelling suction device is used to remove flammable gases. Explosive mixtures of hydrogen and oxygen form by electrolysis of electrolyte solutions used to distend the bladder during fulguration or resection. Isomolar solutions of crystalloids are used to avoid this complication.

In a large portion of the U.S. population, methane is a normal constituent of flatulent gas. It is prudent therefore to assume that methane is present in all cases and to take appropriate measures before the use of electrosurgery. Such measures include evacuating the colon, filling the colon with nonflammable gas, or clamping.

D.3.5.3 Explosions During Operations on Head, Neck, Oropharynx, and in Body Cavities. Flammable mixtures of anesthetic agents can persist in the exhaled air of patients for long periods, and such mixtures can persist in hollow viscera and body cavities. Electrosurgical equipment should not be used for operations on the head, neck, oropharynx, or body cavities during or following the administration of a flammable anesthetizing agent.

D.3.5.4 Ignition of Combustibles in Mouth or Oropharynx during Oxygen Administration. A hot needle or blade can ignite combustibles such as dry sponges, lubricants on endotracheal tubes, or the endotracheal tube itself. In the presence of an oxygen-enriched atmosphere, a major conflagration can occur, resulting in severe burns to the mouth, oropharynx, or the respiratory tract. Wet sponges are employed when electrosurgery is contemplated in the mouth or oropharynx. It is necessary to exercise care to ensure that the blade, needle, or hot metal particles do not contact the endotracheal tube. It is not advisable to use lubricants in these circumstances. *(See* NFPA 53, *Recommended Practice on Materials, Equipment, and Systems Used in Oxygen-Enriched Atmospheres, for details.)*

Note that nitrous oxide will dissociate with heat to produce an oxygen-enriched atmosphere that readily supports combustion.

D.3.5.5 Fire from Flammable Germicides and Defatting Agents. The vapors from flammable solutions of disinfecting agents, or fat solvents left on the skin or saturating the drapes, can persist for long periods and be ignited by the arc that occurs when a high-frequency electrode contacts tissue. Nonflammable germicides or detergents should be used when the use of electrosurgery is contemplated.

Ether is an excellent defatting agent but is extremely flammable. However, it is still occasionally found, labeled "defatting agent," in operating rooms.

D.3.5.6 Fires from Microwave Heating. Microwave ovens are frequently used in health care facilities to dry towels or linens, or to heat compresses or applicators. Although they are intended to heat at relatively low temperatures, they can cause fires by a kind of spontaneous combustion. A thick, tight cloth pack, particularly if there is metal or greasy material in the interior, can have a significant internal temperature rise and smolder. On opening and exposing this heated material to air, the cloth may spontaneously begin to burn.

Care should be taken to ensure that metal or other foreign materials are not left in such packs.

D.3.6 Complications of Electrosurgery.

D.3.6.1 General. Electrosurgery provides a method of cutting and hemostasis. It is an adjunct rather than a substitute for the scalpel, scissors, and hemostatic ligature. It always results in some tissue destruction and affects cells beyond the point of contact. Unless precautions are taken, electrosurgery could be followed by the complications of impaired tissue healing, enhanced risk of infection, surface burns, and explosion. It is effective in cutting muscle and in obtaining hemostasis of small or moderately sized blood vessels. It is also effective in excising and dissecting malignant lesions when primary healing is not important.

D.3.6.2 Tissue Damage. Electrosurgery always destroys tissue. The damage extends radially from the needle or blade electrode. Too much power, especially damped sinusoidal coagulating currents, results in excessive destruction of tissue. When organs or tissues are isolated, as when on a stretched pedicle, current and heat concentrate in the pedicle and could destroy the circulation. Skin flaps and fascia could be overheated. Contact of the high-frequency electrode with instruments or retractors in the wound could result in accidental burns. Defective or extra-thin gloves can result in burns to the surgeon's fingers.

D.3.6.3 Special Electrosurgical Instruments. Some surgical techniques require special instrumentation such as a resectoscope for transurethral resections or a laparoscope for tubal ligations. Since it is desired to keep the size of these instruments to a minimum, electrical distances are also minimal. To allow minimal separation, electrical insulation is used to provide isolation between various portions of these instruments. Complications during surgery can occur for the following reasons:

(1) The instrument has an insufficient amount of insulating material.
(2) The insulation has cracks.
(3) The instrument has a poor grade of insulating material.
(4) The insulation gets wet.
(5) More than normal power settings are required of the electrosurgical unit.

With all electrosurgical instruments the manufacturer's recommendations should be followed. *(See Section D.7 in this annex.)*

The special types of electrosurgical devices covered in D.3.6.3, as well as those discussed in D.3.6.4, should be specially examined before each use for signs of insulation failure.

D.3.6.4 Use of Surgical Instruments to Deliver Electrosurgical Current. When electrosurgical current is intentionally delivered through a surgical instrument, insulation might be needed so that only the desired portion of the instrument is exposed. This will preclude undesired contact with the patient or operator.

D.3.6.5 Use of Hand Controls. The use of pencil-type electrodes that include hand controls, particularly multiple electrodes on the same electrosurgical unit, or contact-activated electrodes presents special problems because of ease of misuse and inadvertent activation. Appropriate holsters should be provided to house electrodes in the sterile field when not in use.

Fires, as well as patient burns and injuries, associated with these types of hand controls have been reported. These controls operate differently than do older, simpler ones and are more vulnerable to incorrect use because of their sensitive activation mechanism (a slight touch of a finger). Manufacturers have designed these devices for ease of use, but it is the user (the surgeon) who must study the operating characteristics of these controls and learn how to use them as intended. See also 8.5.2.3.1 and the accompanying commentary.

D.3.7 Direct Current Burns.

Some electrosurgical devices utilize low direct currents to interrogate the continuity of leads in the dispersive electrode cable. The interruption of current can then be used to inhibit the operation of the machine. An alarm system is sometimes activated as well. *(See D.3.3.1.4.)*

Where the dc voltage is referenced to ground, an inadvertent ground could provide a pathway for small direct currents to flow from the interrogation circuitry through the patient to ground.

The burns that can be produced due to the application of dc voltage are generally not thermal burns, as high-frequency ones are. Rather, they are electrochemical ones, caused by the production of caustic agents at the cathode site and chlorine gas at the anode.

The threshold level of voltage required to support electrolytic burning is close to 3 volts dc. The active electrolytic threshold depends in a complex way on many factors, some of which are electrode material, viscosity of electrolytic medium, and the chemical composition of electrolytic medium.

The amount of caustic and acidic products formed depends on the cumulative amount of current that flows through the electrolytic medium. The longer the current flows, the greater the quantity produced. Tissue fluids are converted chiefly to sodium and potassium hydroxides, and chlorine gas. Saline-soaked pads, jellies, and so on, could thus be rendered caustic.

D.3.8 Nonionizing Radiation Burns and Ignition.

D.3.8.1 Radio-Frequency Devices. In electrosurgery or diathermy it is intended to apply significant energy to the tissue of a patient for a desired therapeutic effect. However, the attendant staff are also subjected to some level of radiant energy. While this hazard is usually insignificant, peculiar circumstances might warrant closer attention. The nature of radio-frequency hazard and recommended levels are addressed in ANSI C95.1, *Safety Levels of Electromagnetic Radiation with Respect to Personnel.*

D.3.8.2 Medical Laser Devices. Laser radiation does not present the same type of hazard as lower-frequency electromagnetic energy, nor does it have the ionizing effects of X-rays and radioisotopes. However, the concentration of energy in a narrow beam is high enough to destroy tissue or to ignite combustible materials in its path. These issues are addressed in ANSI Z136.1, *Safe Use of Lasers*, and in ANSI/Z136.3, *Safe Use of Lasers in Health Care Facilities*. The former (Z136.1) addresses general safety aspects of lasers; the latter (Z136.3) provides guidance for lasers specifically for use in health care facilities.

Laser systems have rapidly become a valuable tool in the therapeutic and diagnostic medical appliances field. These systems are now being utilized in various medical applications, ranging from surgical instruments to pattern refractometers and teletherapy alignment scanning devices used for patient positioning.

Laser systems differ from one another in regard to their names, active laser mediums, wavelengths generated, power outputs, operating modes, and clinical applications. The beam generated by a laser system is very powerful because it possesses the unique characteristics of monochromaticity and coherency. Hazards from the use of laser systems include optical radiation (hazards to the eye and skin), fire ignition (especially in an oxygen-enriched environment), chemical emissions, and RF emissions that could affect other systems in close proximity to the laser system. Laser systems are classified in four control groups according to their output power and risk.

Electrical accidents (without injury), accidental shock of personnel, and electrocutions and fires in operating rooms have been reported as a result of the use of lasers. Thus, only trained professionals should be permitted to use and maintain laser systems. The extremely high energies and voltages present in the power supplies of many lasers require that institutions establish hazard-control policies and procedures. All precautionary labels should be visible, and warning devices should be operational.

Suggested safety measures for using laser systems in the operating theater include the following:

1. An institutional laser safety committee should be established to help develop, monitor, and evaluate policies and procedures relating to the safe use of medical lasers.
2. Laser systems should be properly registered and calibrated before their first use. It is important to plan for their incorporation into a maintenance program.
3. Surgeons and other operating room (OR) personnel should be trained in, and familiar with, the guidelines of laser radiation safety as outlined by respective state agencies.
4. Lighted or clearly marked signs indicating when lasers are in use in the room should be posted on OR door(s). No one should enter or exit an OR when a laser is actually being used.
5. OR personnel should be aware that the laser beam, although invisible for most systems, can ignite flammable or combustible materials, inflict third-degree burns, and be reflected off shiny or even dull, light metal or invisible glass surfaces, causing severe eye injuries.
6. OR personnel should be aware that the visible He-Ne laser system aiming beam can also cause eye injuries.
7. Appropriate safety glasses, either plastic or glass and fitted with sideguards, should be worn by everyone in the OR.

8. The patient's eyes should be covered with moist eye pads or protected with proper goggles.
9. A laser surgeon and assistant should have attended a laser training course prior to attempting laser surgery. In addition, the surgeon should have satisfied all the requirements for laser surgery privileges as set out by the laser safety committee of the particular institution.
10. Lasers should not be used with or around alcohol preps, ether, and other flammable anesthetic gases.
11. Laser systems should be locked when not in use. Access keys should be kept by one person, preferably an OR nurse specifically in charge of the OR where the laser system is used.
12. An in-house qualified person should be trained to troubleshoot minor problems with laser systems, for example, problems involving gasflow gauges, water temperature, mirror adjustments, or the microscope and the microsled. The laser system needs to be maintained in accordance with the manufacturer's guidelines and checked prior to each operation. Cooling fan(s) and radiator(s) should be cleaned periodically.
13. Ideally, only one foot pedal should be used for a laser system.
14. Nonreflective or blackened retractors and other instruments must be used during laser surgery because the laser beam can reflect off shiny instruments.
15. The laser system should be put on standby whenever the surgeon is performing a nonlaser maneuver (such as suturing). After all laser procedures are accomplished for an individual case, the laser system should be turned off immediately. (The surgeon should make this determination.)
16. Flame-retardant drapes and surgical gowns should be used. In addition, portions of the patient's skin not involved with surgery must be protected, such as by saline-soaked gauze or towels.
17. The patient's breathing circuit and oxygen hoses should be well protected. One method of protection is to cover the hoses with aluminum foil and towels.

Site preparation for laser system installation is critical because most laser systems require special utilities. For example, electrical specifications might require a 3-phase, 208 VAC, 50 ampere service. For systems that use water, requirements might include a minimum flow rate of 17.6 L/min at 345 kPa (4 gal/min at 50 psi), with an input temperature of not higher than 15°C (60°F) and water conductivity of less than 100 micro-ohms. Because of spillage problems, water systems might require that an area be designated as a wet location, therefore necessitating a GFCI or isolated power system.

Because a loss of circulating water can cause system overheating problems, it is a good practice to connect the water pump to a circuit on the essential electrical system. This connection enables the pump to continue operating if normal power is interrupted. If the emergency power fails, or the pump itself fails, the laser system should also have sensors to detect loss of pumping action and shut the system down before overheating occurs. If the laser is self-contained, the coolant level and filtering system, including hoses, should be inspected routinely.

A sample site installation is illustrated in Exhibit D.3.

In summary, practitioners who use laser systems should be aware of laser technology and its limitations, have a good working knowledge of the equipment, and be specially trained in its proper use. They should also be aware of two unique safety-related laser issues:

1. Laser energy can travel over distances and can interact with flammable material (i.e., ignite it).
2. The effect of laser radiation on tissue ranges from absorption, coagulation, and vaporization in the short term, to photochemical effects in the long term. It is thus important for staff to control not only the area immediately around the laser instrument itself, but also

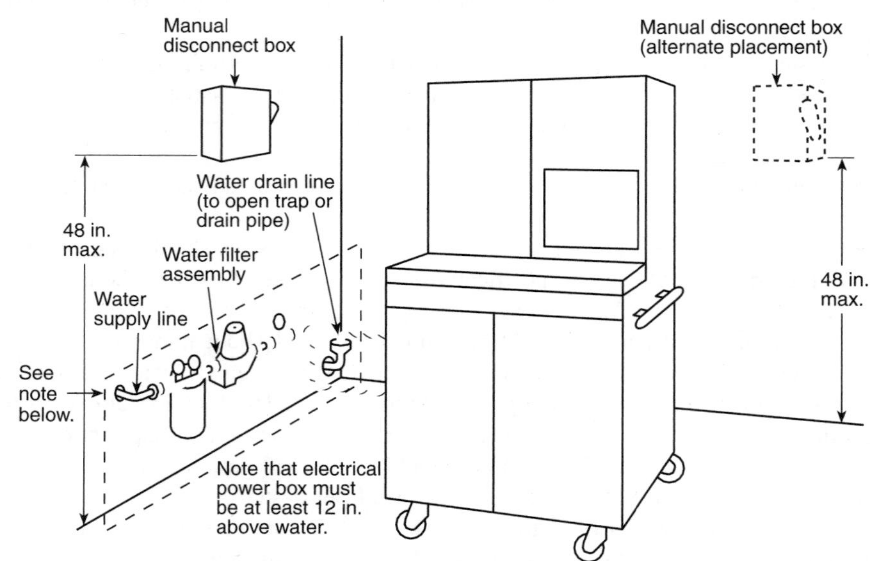

EXHIBIT D.3 *One type of installation for a laser system.*

the total environment in which the system is being used. If both fire hazard and optical radiation are closely controlled, the medical community can take full advantage of the benefits of laser systems without unnecessary risks. A sample procedure for approval of new lasers is shown in Exhibit D.4.

For more information and material on lasers, see the Laser Institute of America's *Laser Safety Guide* [5]. Other publications on laser safety include *Guide for Control of Laser Hazards* [6]; ANSI Z136, *Standards for the Safe Use of Lasers* [7]; and ANSI Z136.3, *Safe Use of Lasers in Health Care Facilities* [8]. See the sample inspection checklist in Exhibit D.5 and the sample user application for new lasers in Exhibit D.6.

D.4 Equipment Safety Measures

D.4.1 General.

D.4.1.1 Equipment Requirements. Special requirements for anesthetizing locations are discussed in 13.4.1 in the requirements portion of this standard. Additional considerations outlined in this section are primarily performance recommendations, which should be implemented in the manner indicated or by other equivalent methods.

The general electrical safety requirements of Chapter 8 apply to high-frequency appliances. In particular, when in standby mode, high-frequency equipment must meet the patient lead leakage requirements. In large, high-power equipment, it can be difficult to meet the chassis leakage current limits. Isolation transformers, redundant grounds, or other special techniques might be necessary.

D.4.1.2 Applicability. These recommendations apply to the high-frequency equipment itself to reduce its potential as a source of radio-frequency interference, burns, shock, and explosion. Recommendations are also made relating to other associated electrical appliances to make them less susceptible to malfunction in the presence of the high-frequency apparatus.

EXHIBIT D.4 *Sample procedure for approval of new lasers.*

APPLICATION FORM FOR NEW LASERS

PROCEDURE FOR APPROVAL OF NEW LASERS AT ______________ HOSPITAL

1. The Chief of the Service or his or her designee shall submit an application requesting approval of new lasers to the Laser Committee.
2. The Laser Committee shall meet to discuss and decide on the application. The committee may invite the Chief of the Service or his or her designee to make a presentation.

PROCEDURE FOR GRANTING LASER PRIVILEGES AT ______________ HOSPITAL

1. Candidate applies to the Chief of Service and submits documentation of having received hands-on instruction in the use of a particular laser.
2. The Chief of Service approves and authorizes members of his or her staff for laser privileges. (Note: The Chief of Service should have the Laser Committee's approval of the guidelines that are used to grant laser privileges to physicians.)
3. The Chief of Service is responsible for sending copies of the approval of such physicians to the Medical Staff Office with the request to distribute to the following staff:
   - Chairperson of Laser Committee
   - Laser Safety Officer
   - Operating Room Supervisor(s)
4. Annually, the Chief of Service is responsible for sending the list of residents who have been approved to use lasers only under direct supervision of approved physicians to the following staff:
   - Chairperson of Laser Committee
   - Chief Operating Room Nurse
   - Office of Medical Staff Affairs

D.4.2 High-Frequency Apparatus.

D.4.2.1 Input Power Circuits. Input power circuits should be provided with low-pass filters, electrostatically shielded isolation transformers, or other means for preventing the injection of high-frequency energy into the power lines. The use of a simple capacitive low-pass filter might introduce excessive line-to-ground leakage, which should be taken into account.

D.4.2.2 Output Circuits. High-frequency output circuits should be provided with isolation, high-pass filters, or other means to isolate these circuits from low-frequency voltages and rectified currents that could be produced in the patient circuit.

Specialized low-power equipment such as a neurosurgical lesion generator, where precise control is important, might have the return (dispersive) electrode directly connected to ground.

Whereas precise radio frequency control can be achieved in several ways, direct connection to ground has many operational advantages. Because the devices identified in the second paragraph's exception are used only briefly during an operation, and when the electrosurgical unit is not in use, the committee considered this exception to be acceptable.

Isolated outputs are desirable practice for protection against 60-Hz electric shock. In some circumstances, however, the effective operation of devices individually or in combination might dictate connection, by the user, of a dispersive electrode to an equipment grounding conductor or to another grounding point. Such grounding will defeat any radio-frequency isolation existing in the electrosurgical unit.

Note that in electrosurgery, low-frequency or faradic currents can result from a rectifica-

EXHIBIT D.5 *Sample laser inspection checklist.*

SEMIANNUAL LASER INSPECTION CHECKLIST

Laser: ______________________

Serial Number: ______________________

Date							
Location							
Laser Classification (labeled on unit)							
Area: Laser operation must take place in controlled area posted with suitable warning signs							
Warning Signs: Warning logo on laser must state maximum output, pulse duration, and laser median or emitted wavelength							
Housing: No modifications in manufacturer's design							
Date of Last Calibration							
Safety Glasses: Available and appropriate for laser type							
Date of Last Inspection							
Completed by:	______	______	______	______	______	______	______

tion phenomenon occurring between the active electrode and body tissue during arcing. These low-frequency currents could constitute an electric shock hazard to the patient, as discussed in D.3.4.

D.4.2.3 Dispersive Cable Continuity Monitor.

D.4.2.3.1 In electrosurgical apparatus, a monitor circuit can be incorporated to indicate that the connection to the dispersive electrode is intact. This monitor should not utilize currents that could be a shock or burn hazard to the patient or that could interfere with other instruments.

D.4.2.3.2 It is preferable that the dispersive cable continuity monitor also indicate that the plate is in contact with the patient, but this should not result in increased hazard to the patient or surgeon.

EXHIBIT D.6 *Sample user application for new laser.*

SAMPLE USER APPLICATION FOR NEW LASER

Application for User of New Laser at ____ANYTOWN____ *Hospital*

I. APPLICANT

Name ____________________ Title ____________________

Department ____________________ Tel. No. ____________________

II. PROJECT

Description of laser use ____

____

____

Guidelines for laser use [safety measures (attach literature and manuals)].

Is this use investigational? ❑ Yes ❑ No

If yes, attach a copy of the Institutional Review Board application and Board approval (if available).

Anticipated duration of the project ____________________

III. LASER

Manufacturer ____

Model No. ____________________ Serial No. ____________________

Description (Ar, Kr, CO_2, etc.) ____________ Class ____________________

Emission levels ____________________ Continuous power ____________________

Pulsed

Pulse width ____________ Pulse rate ____________ Pulse power ____________

Emission wavelength ____________________ Fixed or mobile ____________________

Special accessories or preparation for installation needed ____________________

____

Aiming laser (if used) ____

Emission level ____________________ Emission wavelength ____________________

IV. OPERATIONAL SAFEGUARDS

Has this system been registered by the Laser Safety Office with the State's Department of Health, Bureau of Radiation Control? ❑ Yes ❑ No

Will an in-service education program on this laser be provided to appropriate hospital staff? ❑ Yes ❑ No

When? ____________________ By whom? ____________________

How often, by whom, and by what method will the output of the laser be calibrated? ____________

____

Are adequate safety glasses supplied or available for personnel when this laser is used? ❑ Yes ❑ No

I am familiar with the "Regulations for the Control of Laser Radiation Hazards" and the administrative procedures established by this hospital's Laser Safety Committee and will abide by them.

____________________________ ____________________

Laser applicant Date

D.4.2.3.3 There should be a suitable caution notice against defeat of the dispersive cable continuity-monitoring circuit. This could take the form of a label on the apparatus itself and explanatory material in the operating manual.

D.4.2.4 Foot Switches.

D.4.2.4.1 Electrically powered foot switches for use in flammable anesthetizing locations are to be explosionproof or approved as intrinsically safe, as described by Section E.6 in Annex E.

D.4.2.4.2 All foot switches should be provided with features to prevent accidental operation to a degree consistent with the need for facility of operation.

D.4.2.5 Power-Supply Cord.

D.4.2.5.1 The power-supply cord for high-frequency equipment should incorporate a separate grounding conductor connected to the grounding contact in the attachment cap (plug).

D.4.2.5.2 Where a detachable power supply cord set is used, the design of the connectors at the instrument end should prevent accidental disconnection.

D.4.2.6 FCC Regulations.

D.4.2.6.1 Shortwave diathermy should meet all requirements of Part 18, *Industrial, Scientific and Medical Service*, of the Rules and Regulations of the Federal Communications Commission. *(See Section D.9, Informational and Referenced Publications and Articles, in this annex.)*

D.4.2.6.2 The power line filter must prevent the 13.56-MHz or 27.12-MHz energy from feeding back into the power line.

D.4.3 Protection of Associated Apparatus.

D.4.3.1 Input Power Circuits. The introduction of high-frequency energy into patient monitors or other apparatus by inductive coupling or radiation to the power supply cord, or by conduction on the power supply lines, should be minimized. Low-pass filters or shielding in the power input circuits of equipment could introduce excessive leakage paths from line to ground, in which case they should not be used.

D.4.3.2 Signal Input Circuits.

D.4.3.2.1 Low-pass filters can be incorporated in the signal input circuits of patient monitoring equipment to limit the flow of high-frequency currents from body electrodes to the equipment. Since the attenuation of the higher frequencies can be achieved by providing a low-impedance path to ground, such filters can increase the possibility of burns where small electrodes are used.

D.4.3.2.2 Isolation of input circuits from high-frequency signals can be accomplished by automatically disconnecting the input terminals when the high-frequency device is energized.

D.4.3.2.3 Short-circuiting of input terminals might be effective in protecting signal input circuits but care should be taken that a low-resistance path is not provided for the high-frequency currents.

D.4.3.3 Patient Monitoring Electrodes.

D.4.3.3.1 High-frequency current densities at a monitoring, electrode-to-skin interface can be reduced by the use of a large surfaced electrode. Needle electrodes normally should not be employed during an electrosurgical procedure, but if this mode of monitoring is judged necessary it should be done with extreme care.

D.4.3.3.2 In the application of inductive diathermy, remote placement of patient monitoring electrodes might eliminate high-frequency burns.

D.4.3.3.3 Where possible, all physiological monitoring circuits with conductive contacts of small surface area on or in the body should present a high impedance to the passage of high-frequency current between the contacts and ground.

D.4.3.4 Cardiac Pacemakers. Cardiac pacemakers, particularly external pacemakers of the demand type, can be susceptible to interference. Their input circuits require careful design to minimize these effects.

D.4.3.5 Low-Voltage Electrical Devices.

D.4.3.5.1 Low-voltage power sources for endoscopy illuminators and other devices should incorporate transformers with isolated secondary circuits so that there is no possibility of patient contact with the primary power source.

D.4.3.5.2 Exposed metal parts of line-operated low-voltage sources should be kept to a minimum. The chassis and exposed metal parts likely to become energized, if any, should be connected to ground through a third wire in the power supply cord or protected by double insulation when no grounding conductor is used. Low-voltage sources for devices that should have this protection include resectoscopes, stimulators, pumps, and photographic equipment. Small exposed surfaces not likely to come energized, particularly those that contact the patient, should not be grounded.

D.4.3.5.3 A particular problem exists with resectoscopes used in conjunction with electrosurgical apparatus for urological procedures. These devices often have small clearances and insulation resulting in capacitively coupled RF currents. Repeated use could damage the insulation and expose the operator and patient to high-frequency burns. These devices should be designed to withstand high RF voltages in addition to low voltages used for illumination.

The patient is not the only one who can receive a burn from defective equipment or changes that occur in the active or dispersive electrode during an operation. The surgeon can be burned as well. Care of the apparatus should be of particular concern because increasing numbers of operative procedures are being performed in walk-in clinics without full support from an operating room ancillary staff.

D.5 Administration and Maintenance

D.5.1 Responsibility.

D.5.1.1 Administration. Responsibility for the maintenance of safe conditions surrounding the use of high-frequency equipment falls mutually upon the governing body of the health care facility, the administration, the physicians using the equipment, and all personnel concerned with the application of the equipment to the patient.

Given the litigious climate in the United States today and the hazards surrounding the use of high-frequency equipment, everyone associated with high-frequency appliances shares the responsibility for their safe use. Burns and other problems allegedly associated with the use of high-frequency apparatus are common reasons for liability litigation.

D.5.1.2 Medical Staff. It is important that the organized medical staff of the health care facility adopt regulations and practices with respect to the use of anesthetics and electrical devices in the presence of high-frequency energy, and jointly with the facility authorities set up requirements for training physicians, nurses, and other personnel who might be involved in the procurement, application, use, or maintenance of equipment used in conjunction with high-frequency equipment.

D.5.1.3 Qualifications for Use of Electrosurgery. No physician should attempt electrosurgery unless he or she is first adept with the scalpel and hemostat. Except for endoscopic surgery or when excising malignancy, sharp dissection provides safer surgery with more predictable wound healing.

The physician who chooses electrosurgery should know how to adjust the electrosurgical unit at his or her disposal. The physician is responsible for the proper placement of the dispersive electrode and the selection of the mode of attaching other electronic equipment to the patient.

D.5.2 Personnel, Training, and Clearance.

D.5.2.1 Qualifications for Use of High-Frequency Equipment. All personnel concerned with the application of high-frequency equipment, including surgeons, nurses, operating room technicians, and orderlies, should be fully cognizant of the potential hazards associated with its use, as outlined in Section D.3 of this annex.

Surgical lasers, for example, can be very hazardous if misused. Personnel must be specifically qualified in the use of these devices. Surgical lasers are also sensitive to mechanical disturbances, such as misalignment of the aiming and power beams, and ancillary staff must be instructed in their safe handling. The recommendations contained in this section for electrosurgical devices apply to laser systems where relevant.

D.5.2.2 Instruction Manuals. A complete instruction manual for each model of apparatus should be conveniently available for reference at the location of use. *(See D.5.3.2 in this annex.)*

D.5.2.3 Operating Instructions on Apparatus. Information necessary for the safe use of the apparatus, in the form of condensed operating instructions, should be visibly and permanently displayed on, or attached to, the appliance itself.

D.5.2.4 Qualifications for Use of Monitoring Equipment in Presence of High-Frequency Currents. All personnel concerned with the application of monitoring or auxiliary apparatus that might be used in the same area as the high-frequency apparatus, or that might be in contact with the patient to whom high-frequency power is applied, should be fully cognizant of the hazards presented by that equipment in the presence of high-frequency energy.

D.5.2.5 In-Service Training. The health care facility administration should institute an obligatory in-service training program for the surgical staff and others involved in the use of high-frequency energy sources. With the current rapid changes in medical device technology, many techniques that were appropriate a short time in the past are no longer so. There is a great potential for patient injury and fire ignition if these high-powered energy devices are improperly used. Education and retraining are essential to avoid these hazards.

The section on in-service training was added in 1993 to remind those responsible for the safety of patients and staff of the need for training and appropriate periodic retraining on the use of high-frequency, high-energy medical devices. New equipment should never be used until it has been inspected for safety and proper operation and appropriate training has been conducted.

D.5.3 Maintenance.

D.5.3.1 Periodic Maintenance. For the continued safe operation of high-frequency apparatus, a schedule of periodic preventive maintenance should be established. It is the responsibility of the health care facility to see that this program is effective. Because of the complex nature of this apparatus and associated electrical equipment, repairs should be made by qualified service personnel. Service could be provided by a competent internal engineering group, the manufacturer, or other reliable agency.

D.5.3.2 Instruction Manuals. Proper maintenance, as well as safe use, requires that the manufacturer provide operator's or user's manuals with all units. These manuals should include operating instructions, maintenance details, and calibration and testing procedures. The manuals should include the following:

(1) Illustrations showing location of controls
(2) Explanation of the function of each control
(3) Illustrations of proper connection to the patient and to other equipment
(4) Step-by-step procedures for proper use of the apparatus
(5) Safety considerations in application and in servicing
(6) Effects of probable malfunction on safety
(7) Difficulties that might be encountered, and cautions to be observed, if the apparatus is used on a patient simultaneously with other electrical appliances
(8) Principles of operation
(9) Functional description of the circuitry
(10) Schematics, wiring diagrams, mechanical layouts, and parts list for the specific unit as shipped
(11) Power requirements, heat dissipation, weight, dimensions, output current, output voltage, and other pertinent data

The instruction manual can be in two parts: one, primarily operating instructions, addressed to medical personnel; the other, detailed maintenance and repair instructions addressed to technical personnel, except that the separate maintenance manual should include essentially all the information included in the operating manual.

Manufacturers usually provide one copy of an operator and service manual with delivery of a device but might charge for additional copies. It can well be worth the investment to have a second copy retained in the biomedical engineering department (or its equivalent).

D.5.3.3 Physical Inspection.

D.5.3.3.1 Cables and Electrodes. Connectors, cables, and electrodes should be inspected for damage before each use of the apparatus.

D.5.3.3.2 Mechanical Damage. The apparatus should not be used if examination of the cabinet indicates that it has suffered mechanical damage. Dial markings should be clean and legible. At all times there should be evidence that the apparatus has been protected from liquid and electrolyte contamination.

D.5.3.3.3 Inspection. The governing body should provide training for user personnel and other appropriate personnel to detect externally evident damage. The apparatus should not be used if inspection of the cord, cabinet, switches, knobs, or dials discloses hazardous mechanical damage.

Specific procedures should be developed for reporting and repair of equipment found to be damaged.

D.5.3.3.4 Electrical Inspection.

D.5.3.3.4.1 Dispersive Cable Monitor. If the apparatus includes a continuity monitor for the dispersive cable, it should be checked for proper operation before each use of the apparatus.

D.5.3.3.4.2 Output Power. Provision for periodic measurement of the output power of the apparatus is essential. *(See Section D.8 in this annex.)*

D.6 The Effects of Electrosurgery on Tissue

D.6.1 Waveforms.

High-frequency electricity applied to tissue through a suitable electrode results in an arc that produces three different effects: dehydration, coagulation, or dissolution (cutting). Pulsed sine waveforms *[see Figure D.6.1(a) and Figure D.6.1(b)]* with a low duty cycle are com-

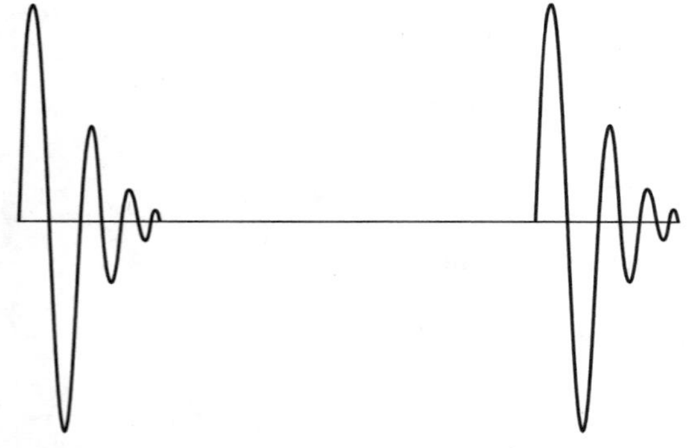

FIGURE D.6.1(a) *Typical Spark-Gap Waveform with a Low Duty Cycle.*

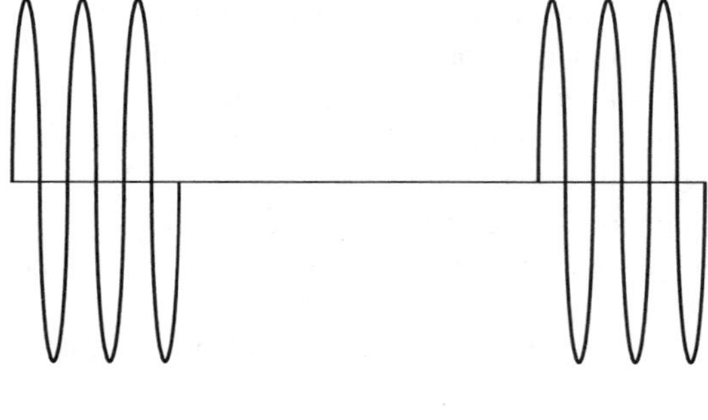

FIGURE D.6.1(b) *Typical Solid-State Waveform with a Low Duty Cycle.*

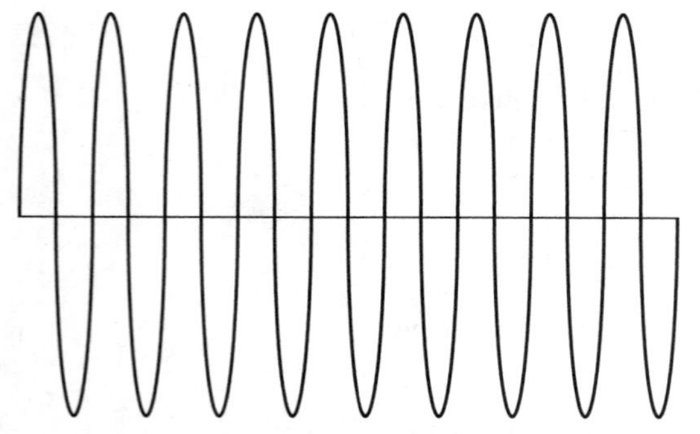

FIGURE D.6.1(c) *Continuous Undamped Sine Waveform.*

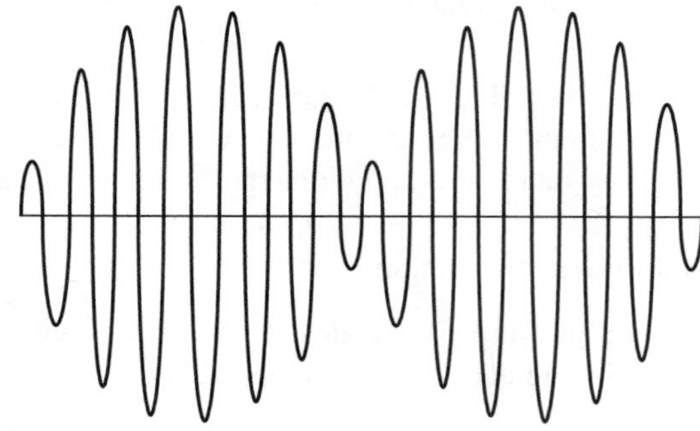

FIGURE D.6.1(d) *120-Hz Modulated Sine Waveform also Referred to as a Fully Rectified Waveform.*

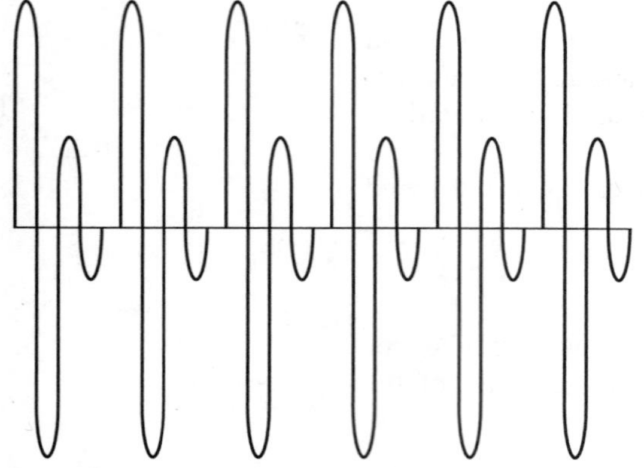

FIGURE D.6.1(e) *Typical Spark-Gap Waveform with a High Duty Cycle.*

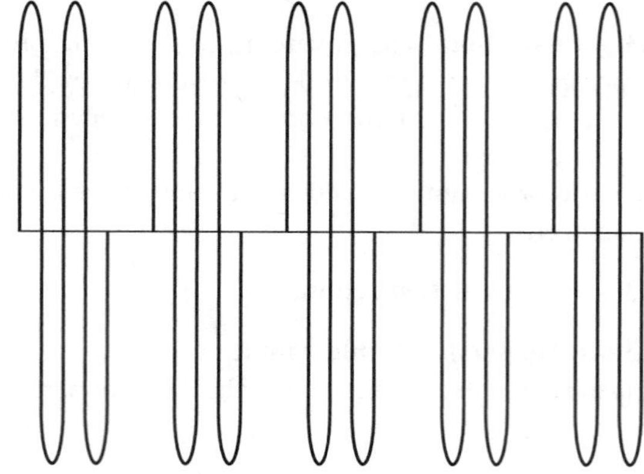

FIGURE D.6.1(f) *Typical Solid-State Waveform with a High Duty Cycle.*

monly used for dehydration and coagulation; for cutting, continuous undamped sine waveforms *[see Figure D.6.1(c)]* are used. If additional hemostasis is required while cutting, modulated *[see Figure D.6.1(d)]* pulsed sine waveforms are used with a high duty cycle *[see Figure D.6.1(e) and Figure D.6.1(f)]*. Some instruments use other related waveforms.

D.6.2 Fulguration.

This is a technique used for superficial dehydration or coagulation of the tissue. The electrode is held a short distance away and sparks jump to the tissue as shown in Figure D.6.2.

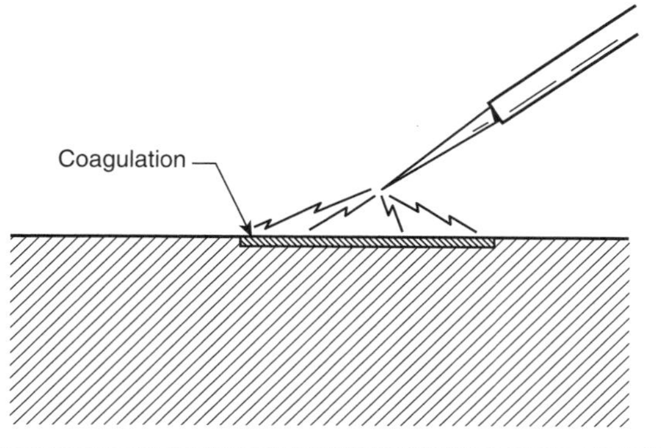

FIGURE D.6.2 *Fulguration.*

D.6.3 Desiccation.

This is a technique used for dehydration and deliberate destruction of tissue. The electrode is placed in contact with the tissue and left in to char the tissue as shown in Figure D.6.3.

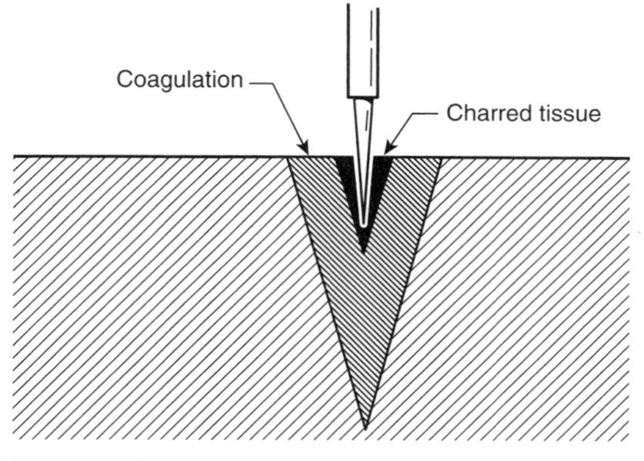

FIGURE D.6.3 *Desiccation.*

D.6.4 Coagulation.

This is the sealing of small blood vessels. The electrode is left in contact with the tissue for a period of time until a deep white coagulum is formed *(see Figure D.6.4)*. Time is an important parameter for proper coagulation. Excessive power is of questionable advantage, since it may actually cause the tissue to dissolve.

D.6.5 Cutting.

Dissolution (cutting) occurs when power is increased until arcing persists as the electrode is moved through the tissue. Dissolution of the molecular structure of tissue cells in the path of the arc makes it appear that the tissue is falling apart.

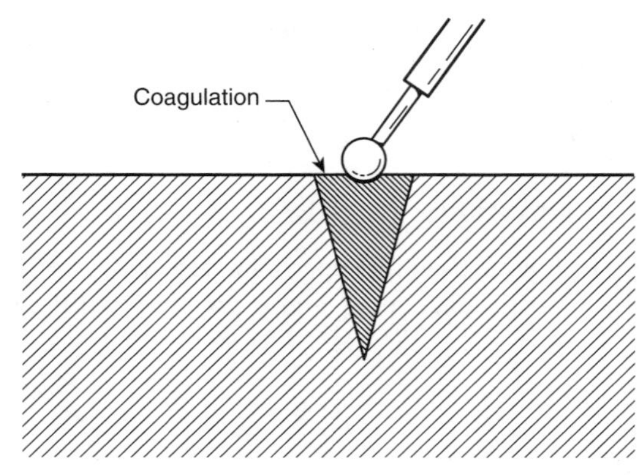

FIGURE D.6.4 Coagulation.

D.6.6 Hemostatic Cutting.

Although the preceding effects of high-frequency current are quite different, they are interrelated. The success of electrosurgery results from an appropriate combination of the pulsed and continuous modes to achieve the desirable degree of cutting and hemostasis. Maximal hemostasis is generally accompanied by complete coagulation of tissue. The depth of coagulation is dependent upon the kind of tissue, the power, the waveforms, the type of electrode, and the cutting speed.

D.6.7 Procedures.

D.6.7.1 Cutting. When primary healing is desired, a small flat blade or needle electrode is used to cut with sufficient power to part tissues cleanly with little hemostasis of small vessels. A wire loop is also used to skive tissue; it is the electrode commonly used in the resectoscope. When cutting with the resectoscope more hemostasis is usually required, and a hemostatic cutting waveform would normally be required. The effect on tissue of electrosurgery is a function of waveform, time, and energy. Energy transfer and necrosis extend radially from the electrode. Greater power leads to greater energy release and wider areas of cell death. Hence, power should be maintained at the lowest level that achieves the desired results. A large dispersive electrode is essential.

D.6.7.2 Monoterminal Technique. Small or shallow surface growths are often desiccated with a monoterminal technique. A fine needle is inserted into the growth and current is applied for several seconds until a mild blanching of tissue occurs. When small lesions are to be destroyed the capacitance of the body suffices for coupling to ground, and the use of a dispersive electrode is unnecessary.

D.6.7.3 Bipolar Technique. Both conductors of the high-frequency electrical circuit are applied to the tissue by paired electrodes so that the energy is dissipated between and around them. Tissue destruction is restricted to a controllable volume. The depth is controlled by the distance to which the electrodes are inserted into the tissue; the breadth by the space between the two active electrodes. This modality is used for coagulation of larger lesions. Tissue destruction extends beyond the ends of the electrodes to about the same extent as is visible around the electrodes. Bipolar current is also used to coagulate blood vessels. The bleeder is grasped in the forceps and current is applied momentarily to congeal the vessel. A dispersive electrode need not be used with bipolar electrodes.

D.6.8 Spark-Gap versus Solid-State Coagulation.

The principal clinical differences between spark-gap and solid-state coagulation lie in the ability of a spark-gap generator to develop higher peak powers, which results in a lower duty cycle for the same average power. This lower duty–cycle waveform results in less cutting or dissolution in the coagulation mode. In addition, spark-gap generators are able to produce higher open-circuit voltages, which results in a better ability to fulgurate.

D.6.9 Demonstration of Effect on Tissue.

The effects of the various modalities can be differentiated by holding a warm, moist, lean piece of beef in the hand while applying high-frequency current in various ways and strengths. The tester's body provides capacitance comparable to that of the patient at low powers. The meat should be placed on the dispersive electrode for higher power. The meat can be cut to reveal the extent of blanching that results from heating by the high-frequency current. Also, the amount of cutting in the coagulation mode between various units can be checked.

D.7 The Care and Use of Electrosurgery

D.7.1 General.

This section is for the indoctrination of operating room nurses, aides, and technicians in the care and use of electrosurgical equipment.

D.7.2 Purpose and Scope.

The indications for the use of high-frequency electrosurgery are described elsewhere in this annex. The purpose of this section is to promote safety for the patient and personnel and efficient operation of the unit. The steps detailed below for operating room personnel to follow for preparation, operation, and storage of the electrosurgical unit are designed to meet those ends.

D.7.3 Setting Up the Electrosurgical Unit.

The following procedures should be followed:

(1) Prior to the use of the electrosurgical unit, verify with anesthesia personnel the type of anesthetic to be used. Check B.6.1, Fires and Explosions, and the operating suite fire safety regulations as necessary.
(2) Prior to sterilization, inspect patient leads and fulgurating and coagulating tips for integrity and cleanliness and bits of tissue or carbon that would interfere with proper function. Test them for electrical continuity. Similarly, check when these leads and tips are removed from the sterile package by the instrument nurse.
(3) Make certain that the electrosurgical unit, together with its dispersive electrode and cable, foot switch and cable, and line cord, is free of dust and "operating room clean."
(4) Locate the electrosurgical unit on the operator's side of the table as far as possible from the anesthesia machine and monitoring equipment. Locate where the power cables and the active electrode and dispersive electrode leads hang naturally and are not stretched across traffic lanes.
(5) Position the leads and electrodes for physiological monitoring equipment as far as possible from the active cable and active electrode when it is in use.
(6) Utilize as large a dispersive electrode as practical, commensurate with the site of the operation and position and size of the patient. Locate electrode as close as possible to the operative site. If a plate is used, exercise care so that the patient's skin is not traumatized or folded. Provide contact with as great an area of skin as is possible. Note that if contact jelly is used on the dispersive electrode, use the correct type and spread uniformly over the electrode.
(7) Place the dispersive electrode against as large an area of soft tissue of the patient as practical. Avoid direct contact with bony prominences such as those of the scapula,

sacrum, ilium, or patella. Check for continued contact during a long procedure, or when changes in patient's position are necessary.

With many medical procedures lasting several hours, checking the placement and conditions of electrodes becomes very important not only to avoid thermal burns, but also to avoid chemical burns from the pooling of liquids, ischemic necrosis, and other effects that simulate thermal burns. These other lesions are commonly described as thermal burns.

(8) Attach the dispersive electrode securely to its cable, and check its mechanical and electrical integrity prior to preparing the operative site and draping the patient. Note that on an electrosurgical unit with a dispersive cable continuity alarm and automatic cutoff switch, follow the manufacturer's directions for preoperative testing. Also note that on electrosurgical units without a continuity alarm, the hospital should provide an external means for periodically testing the integrity of the dispersive cable.
(9) Do not employ electrosurgery without use of the dispersive electrode, unless the operator specifically orders monoterminal or bipolar techniques and directs the omission of the dispersive electrode.

D.7.4 Operation of the Electrosurgical Unit.

D.7.4.1 It is important that personnel adjusting the electrosurgical unit during the operative procedure be aware that if the surgeon needs currents in excess of those usually required for a comparable procedure, a fault might have developed in the active electrode or dispersive electrode cables.

D.7.4.2 If a flammable anesthetic agent has been employed for induction of inhalation anesthesia, even if followed by a nonflammable agent for maintenance, the electrosurgical unit should not be used on the neck, nasopharynx, and adjacent areas.

D.7.5 Electrosurgery with the Resectoscope.

The resectoscope should be maintained in top working order by periodical inspection and factory service. Discard loop electrodes, sheaths, and cords that show breaks, holes, or other evidence of deterioration.

Safe, effective use of electrosurgery for transurethral resections requires the following:

(1) The prevention of injury to the patient
(2) The prevention of injury to the user
(3) Minimizing electrical damage to equipment

D.7.5.1 Patient Burns. To minimize burns to the patient, perform the following procedures:

(1) Make sure the conductive surface of the dispersive electrode is in good contact with the skin.
(2) Do not make a large increase in power setting for an unexpected weak surgical effect.
(3) Keep metal parts of the resectoscope from contact with the patient.

D.7.5.2 Operator Burns. To minimize burns to the operator, perform the following procedures:

(1) Check to see that the control dials are set at the operator's minimum preferred settings.
(2) If the operator's hand touches some metal part of the resectoscope, as it often does, it should be with a firm, positive contact. Pinpoint contacts lead to burns even with low currents.
(3) Use only telescopes with fully insulated, nonmetal eyepieces.
(4) Avoid the use of eyeglasses with metal frames.

D.7.5.3 Telescope Use. To minimize damage to the telescope, perform the following procedures:

(1) Check to see that the loop is not bent. Guard against it touching or coming too close to the telescope.
(2) Avoid activating the electrosurgical unit when the electrode is not touching tissue.
(3) Use the minimum required power.
(4) Start each procedure with a new loop.
(5) Retract the telescope as far as possible to the point where the sheath is just visible under water to maximize the distance between the telescope and loop.
(6) Follow manufacturer's recommendations when using attached lenses.

D.7.6 Putaway and Storage.

After using an electrosurgical unit, do the following:

(1) Clean cutting and fulgurating tips of all blood, debris, carbon, and tissue prior to storage.

When electrodes, tips, wires, and so forth, are being sterilized after use, manufacturer's recommendations should be followed to ensure that there is no mechanical or electrical damage, particularly so that insulation is not compromised.

(2) Clean all electrical contacts.

Dirt on electrical contacts can increase their resistance. As a consequence of dirt buildup, more power than normal is necessary when the ESU is used. Because the resistance of dirty contacts can change with current flow, the operation of the device might become erratic.

(3) Coil lead cables neatly and store in appropriate locations.
(4) If the electrosurgical unit is stored other than in an operating room, select a dust-free location within the operating suite.

D.7.7 Repair of the Electrosurgical Unit.

D.7.7.1 The electrosurgical apparatus contains complex circuits that can develop malfunction after a period of operation. Prominently tag any item of electrosurgical equipment that is known or suspected to be defective and do not use again until it has been inspected and repaired by competent personnel.

D.8 Determination of Output Power

D.8.1 Output Power.

An approximate determination of output power of the electrosurgical device can be made using a radio-frequency ammeter of suitable range in series with a resistance. A simplified schema is shown in Figure D.8.1. Maintain spacing and insulation appropriate to the high frequency and high voltage involved. The power, *P*, in watts can be calculated as follows:

$$P = I^2 \times 500$$

where *I* is the rms current in amperes.

D.9 Informational and Referenced Publications and Articles in Annex D

D.9.1 NFPA Publication. National Fire Protection Association, 1 Batterymarch Park, Quincy, MA 02169-7471.

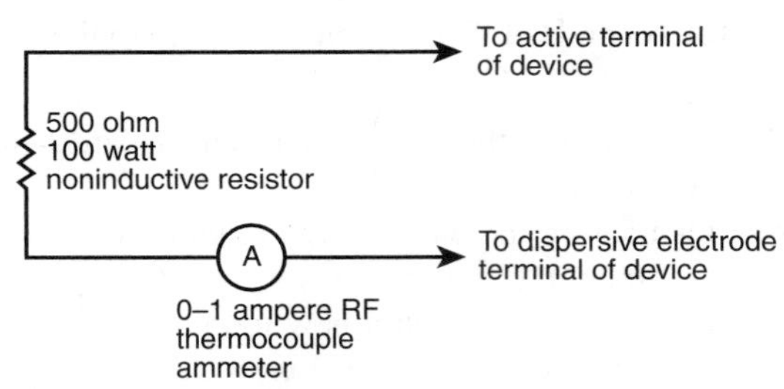

FIGURE D.8.1 *Simplified Apparatus to Measure Power Output of Electrosurgical Unit.*

NFPA 53, *Recommended Practice on Materials, Equipment, and Systems Used in Oxygen-Enriched Atmospheres*, 2004 edition.

D.9.2 ANSI Publications. American National Standards Institute, 25 West 43rd Street, 4th Floor, New York, NY 10036.

ANSI C95.1, *Safety Levels of Electromagnetic Radiation with Respect to Personnel*, 1991.

ANSI Z136.1, *Safe Use of Lasers*, 1993.

ANSI/Z136.3, *Safe Use of Lasers in Health Care Facilities*, 1988.

ANSI/AAMI HF 18, *Electrosurgical Devices*, 1993.

D.9.3 IEC Publication. (Available in U.S. through American National Standards Institute, 25 West 43rd Street, 4th Floor, New York, NY 10036.)

IEC 601-2-2, *Medical Electrical Equipment, Part 2: Particular Requirements for the Safety of High Frequency Surgical Equipment.*

D.9.4 U.S. Government Publications. U.S. Government Printing Office, Washington, DC 20402.

Federal Communications Commission Rules and Regulations, Part 18, *Industrial, Scientific and Medical Service*.

Food and Drug Administration, *Regulations for the Administration and Enforcement of the Radiation Control for Health and Safety Act of 1968.*

D.9.5 Articles on the Subject of High-Frequency Electricity. Battig, C. G., MD. Electrosurgical burn injuries and their prevention. *JAMA*, Vol. 204, No. 12, 17 June 1968.

Billin, A. G. *Electrosurgery in the Operating Room*. Ritter Company, Inc., 400 West Avenue, Rochester, NY 14611.

Bruner, J., and Leonard, P., "Electricity, Safety, and the Patient," Year Book Medical Publishers, Inc., 1989.

Chapter 8 of Bruner and Leonard [1] covers electrosurgery from its inception, including safety measures.

Conolly, W. B., Hunt, T. K., and Dunphy, J. E. The place of electrosurgery in abdominal operations. *Amer. J. Surg.*, 118:422–426 (Sept.), 1969.

Dobbie, A. K. The electrical aspects of surgical diathermy. *Biomedical Engineering*, pp. 206–216, May 1969.

Fein, R. L. Transurethral electrocautery procedures in patients with cardiac pacemakers. *JAMA*, Vol. 202, No. 2, pp. 101–103, 2 October 1967.

Hussey, J. L., and Pois, A. J. Bowel gas explosion. *Amer. J. Surg.*, 120:103, 1970.

Leeming, M. N. Low voltage direct current burns. *JAMA*, 214:1681–1684, 1970.

Mitchell, J. P., and Lomb, G. N. *A Handbook of Surgical Diathermy.* John Wright and Sons Ltd., Bristol, 1966.

Pearce, J. A., PhD, *Electrosurgery.* John Wiley & Sons, New York, 1986.

REFERENCES CITED IN COMMENTARY

1. Bruner, J., and Leonard, P., *Electricity, Safety, and the Patient,* Year Book Medical Publishers, Inc., Chicago, 1989, pp. 62–63, 231–232.
2. ANSI/IEEE C95.1, *Standard for Safety Levels with Respect to Human Exposure to Radio Frequency Electromagnetic Fields, 3 kHz to 300 GHz,* 1999.
3. NCRP Report No. 67, *Radio-Frequency Electromagnetic Fields — Properties, Quantities and Units, Biophysical Interaction, and Measurements,* 1981, National Council on Radiation Protection and Measurements, 7910 Woodmont Ave., Bethesda, MD 20814-3095.
4. NFPA 115, *Standard for Laser Fire Protection,* 2003 edition.
5. *Laser Safety Guide,* 1993, Laser Institute of America, 13501 Ingenuity Drive, Suite 128, Orlando, FL 32826.
6. *Guide for Control of Laser Hazards,* 1990, American Conference of Governmental Industrial Hygienists, 1330 Kemper Meadow Drive, Suite 600, Cincinnati, OH 45240.
7. ANSI Z136.1, *Standard for Safe Use of Lasers,* 2000 American National Standards Institute, 11 West 42nd Street, New York, NY 10036.
8. ANSI Z136.3, *Safe Use of Lasers in Health Care Facilities,* 1996, American National Standards Institute, 11 West 42nd Street, New York, NY 10036.

ANNEX E

Flammable Anesthetizing Locations

NOTE: The text of this annex is a compilation of requirements included in previous editions of NFPA 99 on safety practices for facilities that used flammable inhalation anesthetics. This material is being retained in this annex by the Technical Committee on Anesthesia Services for the following reasons: (1) The Committee is aware that some countries outside the United States still use this type of anesthetics and rely on the safety measures herein; and (2) while the Committee is unaware of any medical schools in the United States still teaching the proper use of flammable anesthetics or any health care facilities in the United States using flammable anesthetics, retaining this material will serve as a reminder of the precautions that would be necessary should the use of this type of anesthetics be re-instituted.

Annex E applies only to anesthetizing locations where flammable anesthetics are still used. Facilities that no longer use flammable anesthetics can find requirements for nonflammable anesthetizing locations, including those facilities where conductive floors are still present, in 13.4.1. Institutions that prohibit the use of flammable anesthetics in anesthetizing locations need not follow the requirements in Annex E.

As discussed in the commentary accompanying 13.4.1, the use of flammable anesthetics as general anesthesia in the United States has, for all practical purposes, ceased. (See "The Case for Abandonment of Explosive Anesthetic Agents" [1] and "Flammable Anesthetics Are Nearing Extinction" [2]. These papers remain the defining body of work on this subject.)

There are several reasons for the almost exclusive use of nonflammable anesthetics, the most obvious one being the elimination of the explosion hazard. This switch became possible when nonflammable anesthetizing agents became acceptable alternatives to the various flammable agents previously in use. The move has caused a debate in the U.S. medical community over whether to ban the use of flammable anesthetics.

Until the NFPA committee responsible for anesthesia safety or some authority having jurisdiction prohibits the use of flammable anesthetics in U.S. operating rooms, a set of procedures for the safe use of flammable anesthetics is necessary. In fact, the infrequent use of flammable anesthetics has been cited as a strong reason for the continued need for the requirements in this annex. Unfamiliarity with flammable anesthetics can be hazardous in and of itself. Because some countries still make use of flammable anesthetics, the guidance imparted in the code and in this handbook is beneficial to those health care providers who still employ these anesthetics.

E.1 Definitions

E.1.1 Antistatic.

That class of materials that includes conductive materials and, also, those materials that throughout their stated life meet the requirements of E.6.6.8.6.3 and E.6.6.8.6.4.

E.1.2 Conductive.

Not only those materials, such as metals, that are commonly considered electrically conductive, but also that class of materials that, when tested in accordance with this document, have a resistance not exceeding 1,000,000 ohms. Such materials are required where electrostatic interconnection is necessary.

E.1.3 Flammable Anesthetizing Location.

Any area of a facility that has been designated to be used for the administration of any flammable inhalation anesthetic agents in the normal course of examination or treatment.

E.1.4 Hazardous Area in a Flammable Anesthetizing Location.

The space extending 152 cm (5 ft) above the floor in a flammable anesthetizing location. *(See E.6.6.)*

Note that this definition is based on the following considerations:

(1) Available data and recent investigations indicate that under customary operating procedures, flammable anesthetic mixtures are diluted by air in the anesthetizing area to a nonflammable range before reaching a vertical height of about 30 cm (1 ft) from any source of leakage or spillage involving quantities of anesthetics used in anesthesia procedures. These findings corroborate the premises on which safeguards required in this standard were originally based and do not negate the need for any of the protective measures required; however, they do provide a sound basis for the statement that recirculation of air in ventilating systems serving anesthetizing locations does not increase the hazards of fire and explosions from flammable anesthetic vapors.

The references to investigations in E.1.4 are those by M. D. Vickers in "Explosion Hazards in Anesthesia" [3].

(2) The mobile character of the operating table and portable equipment and the variety of the surgeon's techniques and surgical positions that will alter the physical relationship of the anesthesia gas machine, the surgeon, the anesthetist, and the patient's head, and all of these with respect to their relative location within the room, must be considered in the determination of the electrical safeguards to be provided.
(3) The portion of the flammable anesthetizing location extending 152 cm (5 ft) above the floor as defined in Chapter 3 constitutes a "hazardous area." Because persons entering such anesthetizing locations may have accumulated electrostatic charges, the floors of corridors and rooms contiguous to the flammable inhalation anesthetizing location must be conductive and at the same potential as the floor in the flammable anesthetizing location. Patients should not be transported while flammable anesthetics are being administered. Rooms such as sterilizing rooms directly communicating with flammable anesthetizing locations are required by E.6.6.1.3 to be provided with conductive floors to equalize static charges. Such rooms, if not used as flammable anesthetizing locations, are not required to be served by explosionproof wiring specified in E.2.1. Where flammable anesthetizing locations open directly onto a passageway not a part of an operating room or delivery room, the conductive floor should extend 3 m (9.84 ft) from either side of the door frame and out from the frame (into the passageway) for 3 m (9.84 ft). It is desirable to demarcate the hazardous location of such a corridor by a physical barrier (doors) and cautionary signs to check smoking, use of open flame, wearing of improper clothing and shoes, and the application of insulating floor wax.
(4) Designated areas in which the use and handling of flammable anesthetic agents are prohibited by hospital regulations, such as corridors in the surgical suite, rooms adjacent

to flammable anesthetizing locations, and nonflammable anesthetizing locations, should be indicated by prominent signs permanently installed.

(5) Postoperative recovery units that are not immediately adjacent to flammable anesthetizing locations and in which the use of flammable anesthetic agents is prohibited are not considered to involve explosion hazards and therefore do not require the installation of static-dissipation systems nor explosionproof equipment required for explosive atmospheres. Prohibition of the use of flammable anesthetic agents by hospital regulation and the proper indication of such prohibition by prominent signs, as recommended in E.6.7.5, is recommended.

In the 1980s, a portion of the health care community heavily criticized the boundaries for the hazardous area in a flammable anesthetizing location. Much was written about changing the boundary, for example, to "2 feet from anesthetizing circuits." The following, taken from the newsletter of NFPA's Health Care Section *Code Red!* [4], is a summary of the position of the then Committee on Anesthesia Agents (now incorporated into the Committee on Gas Delivery Equipment), which is responsible for the definition:

> Anesthesia personnel have a multiplicity of responsibilities in the operating room, many of which must be carried out simultaneously, or almost so. Included are administering the anesthetic, monitoring the vital signs of the patient, administering blood, fluids, and medications other than anesthetic agents, and recording all of these events in a fairly detailed manner. It would be literally impossible to add to this burden the task of monitoring and policing a movable zone of risk, especially since the area in the vicinity of the head of the operating room table and gas anesthesia apparatus is one that visitors to the operating room frequently, but inappropriately, use to be able to look over the ether screen to view the site of the operation.
>
> The concept of a moving hazard makes accidental violation of safe practice more likely than when a fixed hazardous area is defined. For example, in the usual operation of some gas scavenging systems, and in a failure mode of some others, anesthetic gases are discharged through tubing that vents near the floor. If an explosive agent is being scavenged with such a device, a nonexplosionproof foot switch could easily be bumped into the zone of discharge of an explosive mixture.
>
> By retaining the *5-foot level,* one is able to keep flammable agents in the gaseous, vaporous, or liquid state well away from sources of ignition. The fact that the gas anesthesia apparatus can be moved widely around the operating room to accommodate operative requirements would make the role of a fire or building safety inspector infinitely complicated in any attempt to police a *zone of risks.* With the present 5-foot level, hospital inspectors are afforded a standard that is readily subject to inspection. Costs are not increased, since nonexplosionproof electrical outlets can be installed above the 5-foot level. Finally, anesthesia personnel who utilize flammable agents are afforded much peace of mind.

Arguments were submitted again during the 1984 revision of NFPA 99 to change the 1.5 m (5 ft) level requirement. The committee, however, still considered the current requirement necessary. In addition to the preceding arguments, the committee noted that the current requirements were necessary in light of the infrequency of use of flammable anesthetics and the concomitant decrease in familiarity with safety requirements involved in such use. The committee also cited the following: (1) the lack of control studies for a 0.61 m (2 ft) zone, (2) the litigious climate then prevailing in the United States, and (3) the cessation of teaching the use of flammable inhalation anesthetics in medical schools.

Clearly, the use of flammable inhalation anesthetics has fallen off to the vanishing point in the United States in a little more than the last decade. However, the use of flammable anesthetic agents might be continuing in other parts of the world. Facilities elsewhere might be built partly with U.S. funds, sponsorship, or architectural guidance and are, by implication, subject to U.S. standards of safety and liability. Paragraph E.6.6 provides a guide to prudent construction and conduct.

What was at issue in the 1980s was the necessity of some of the criteria developed for flammable anesthetizing locations, particularly the 1.5 m (5 ft) level.

E.1.5 Hazardous Location.

An anesthetizing location or any location where flammable agents are used or stored.

E.1.6 Mixed Facility.

A facility wherein flammable anesthetizing locations and nonflammable anesthetizing locations coexist within the same building, allowing interchange of personnel or equipment between flammable and nonflammable anesthetizing locations.

E.1.7 Storage Location for Flammable Inhalation Anesthetics.

Any room within a consuming facility used for the storage of flammable anesthetic or flammable disinfecting agents *(see* NFPA 30, *Flammable and Combustible Liquids Code)*, or inhalation anesthetic apparatus to which cylinders of flammable gases are attached.

Note that such a storage location is considered a hazardous area throughout the location.

E.2 Electrical System Criteria

E.2.1 Electric wiring installed in the hazardous area of a flammable inhalation anesthetizing location shall comply with the requirements of Article 501, Class I, Division 1 of NFPA 70, *National Electrical Code*. Equipment installed therein shall be approved for use in Class I, Group C, Division 1 hazardous areas.

E.2.2 Wiring for low-voltage control systems and nonemergency communications and signaling systems shall be installed in metal raceways unless located outside or above the hazardous area in the flammable anesthetizing location.

E.2.3 Electric switches installed in hazardous areas of flammable anesthetizing locations shall comply with the requirements of Section 501.6(a) of NFPA 70, *National Electrical Code*.

E.2.4 Receptacles in hazardous areas shall comply with the requirements of Section 501.12 of NFPA 70, *National Electrical Code*. They shall be a part of an approved unit device with an interlocking switch arranged so that the plug cannot be withdrawn or inserted when the switch is in the "on" position.

Note that it should be recognized that any interruption of the circuit, even of circuits as low as 8 volts, either by any switch or by loose or defective connections anywhere in the circuit, might produce a spark sufficient to ignite a flammable anesthetic agent.

The requirement for explosion-proof receptacles was applicable only up to the 1.5 m (5 ft) level. Above that height, normal straight-blade receptacles were acceptable because the hazardous area in a flammable anesthetizing location extended only up to 1.5 m (5 ft) above the floor. (See E.1.4.)

E.3 Ventilation — Flammable Anesthetizing Locations

E.3.1 Relative humidity of not less than 50 percent, at a temperature range of 18°C (64.4°F) to 27°C (80.6°F), shall be maintained in flammable inhalation anesthetizing locations.

See the commentary following 13.4.1 for a discussion of the relative humidity requirements in anesthetizing locations.

E.3.2 Requirements for ventilation and cooling set forth in 6.4.1.2 through 6.4.1.6 of NFPA 99 shall apply.

E.3.3 Ductwork for Air Handling.

It is not required that ductwork be fabricated of nonsparking material.

In the past, critical interpreters of requirements for flammable anesthetizing locations thought that the ductwork in such locations, perhaps because of the presence of some flammable vapors, should be constructed of nonsparking material (e.g., made out of stainless steel). The purpose of E.3.3 is to prevent further misinterpretation of this section.

The divider in a through-the-wall air conditioner that is designed to separate the indoors from outdoors should always be gasketed to prevent direct outdoor leakage. The room is at a higher pressure than at outdoors in order to maintain sepsis and thus cannot tolerate leaks. A divider without gasketing could not be depended on after many years to remain free of leaks.

E.3.4 If a window-type temperature regulating unit (air conditioner) is installed so that any part is less than 152 cm (5 ft) from the floor of a flammable anesthetizing location, such unit shall comply with the requirements set forth in E.3.5.

E.3.5 Such a window-type temperature regulating unit shall be provided with a vertical divider that effectively prevents airflow from the room side to the outside side, and all electric equipment on the room side of this divider shall meet the requirements of E.2.1 of this annex. The installed unit shall tightly fit the opening in the window or wall. Openings in the divider for shafts of fans, other moving parts, or wiring shall be gasketed unless the local air pressure on the room side of the opening when the unit is in operation is less than that on the outdoor side. A fresh-air port is permitted in the divider if it is automatically closed when the unit is not in operation. The rotating parts of fans on the room side of the divider shall not cause percussion sparks if they accidentally contact surrounding objects.

Note that for ventilation of anesthetizing locations, mechanical ventilation is required as a means of diluting flammable gases and maintaining the proper humidity. It is also the most effective and aseptic method of maintaining a uniform humidity within the area.

E.3.5.1 General. Anesthetizing locations used solely for the induction of anesthesia need only be ventilated at a rate sufficient to maintain the proper humidity.

The dilution of flammable and nonflammable gases is most effectively accomplished by ventilating with 100 percent fresh air (100 percent exhaust) through nonrecirculating air-conditioning systems. Now, however, some codes and standards allow the use of recirculating air-conditioning systems in anesthetizing locations. These systems reduce the gas-purging effect but increase the possibility of elevated gas concentrations, however. Thus, care should be taken to ensure that effective scavenging of the gases is available (and used) in these locations.

Anesthetizing locations in which clinical procedures are performed, such as operating rooms, delivery rooms, and certain treatment rooms, require special ventilation as described below. This special ventilation serves not only to maintain humidity but also to reduce the hazard of infection, which is accomplished by dilution and removal of airborne microbial contamination and dilution of flammable gases. It also contributes to odor control and comfort of personnel.

The Committee on Anesthesia Services recognizes that a hazard can be created by the chronic exposure of anesthesia and other operating room personnel to low concentrations of vapors or commonly employed volatile liquid inhalation anesthetic agents. For further information see the sources listed in E.3.5.1.1 through E.3.5.1.4.

E.3.5.1.1 Annex E Publications. Cohen, E. N., et al. Anesthesia, pregnancy and miscarriage: A study of operating room nurses and anesthetists. *Anesthesiology* 35:343, 1971.

Frey, R., et al. How strong is the influence of chronic exposure to inhalation anesthetics on personnel working in operating theatres? W.F.S.A. *Newsletter* No. 10, June 1974.

Whitcher, C. E., et al. Chronic exposure to anesthetic gas in the operating room. *Anesthesiology* 35:348, 1971.

Yanagida, H., et al. Nitrous oxide content in the operating suite. *Anesth. and Analg.* 53:347, 1974.

E.3.5.1.2 The Health Hazard. Bruce, D. L., and Bach, M. J. Psychological studies of human performance as affected by traces of enflurane and nitrous oxide. *Anesthesiology* 42:194–196, 1975.

Bruce, D. L., et al. Trace anesthetic effects on perceptual, cognitive and motor skills. *Anesthesiology* 40:453–458, 1973.

Chang, W. C., et al. Ultrastructural changes in the nervous system after chronic exposure to halothane. *Exp. Neurol.* 45:209–219, 1974.

Cohen, E. N., et al. A survey of anesthetic health hazards among dentists. *J. Am. Dent. Assoc.* 90:1291–1296, 1975.

Cohen, E. N., et al. Occupational disease among operating room personnel — a national study. *Anesthesiology* 41:321–340, 1974.

Cohen, E. W., and Brown, B. W. Comment on the critique. *Anesthesiology* 42:765–766, 1975.

Davison, L. A., et al. Psychological effects of halothane and isoflurane anesthesia. *Anesthesiology* 43:313–324, 1975.

Fink, B. R., ed. *Toxicity of Anesthetics*. Part Four, "Teratogenic Effects." Baltimore, Williams & Wilkins Co., 308–323, 1968.

Fink, B. R., and Cullen, B. F. Anesthetic pollution: What is happening to us? *Anesthesiology* 45:79–83, 1976.

Greene, N., Report on American Cancer Society study of causes of death amongst anesthetists. Annual Meeting, American Society of Anesthesiologists, New Orleans, LA, 18 October 1977.

Hazleton Laboratories America, Inc. Final Reports, CDC-99-74-46, National Institute for Occupational Safety and Health, 1014 Broadway, Cincinnati, OH. Long-term inhalation reproductive and teratogenic toxicity evaluation of nitrous oxide plus halothane. 14 November 1975. Cytogenic evaluation of spermatogonial cells in the rat following long-term inhalation exposure to nitrous oxide plus halothane. 17 November 1976.

Kripke, B. J., et al. Testicular reaction to prolonged exposure to nitrous oxide. *Anesthesiology* 44:104–113, 1976.

Lecky, J. H. Chronic exposure to anesthetic trace levels. *Complications in Anesthesia*, edited by L. H. Cooperman and F. K. Orkin. J. B. Lippincott Co., Philadelphia.

Quimby, K. L., et al. Behavioral consequences in rats from chronic exposure to 10 ppm halothane during early development. *Anesth. and Analg.* 54:628–633, 1975.

Smith, G., and Shirley, A. W. Failure to demonstrate effects of low concentrations of nitrous oxide and halothane on psychomotor performance. *Br. J. Anaesth.* 48:274, 1976.

Spence, A. A., et al. Occupational hazards for operating room-based physicians. *JAMA* 238:955–959, 1977.

Walts, L. F., et al. Critique: Occupational disease among operating room personnel. *Anesthesiology* 42:608–611, 1975.

E.3.5.1.3 Reduction and Control Methods. Lecky, J. H., et al. In-house manual for the control of anesthetic gas contamination in the operating room. University of Pennsylvania Hospital publication.

Lecky, J. H. The mechanical aspects of anesthetic pollution control. *Anesth. and Analg.* 56:769, 1977.

Muravchick, S. Scavenging enflurance from extracorporeal pump oxygenators. *Anesthesiology* 47:468–471, 1977.

Pisiali, R. L., et al. Distribution of waste anesthetic gases in the operating room air. *Anesthesiology* 45:487–494, 1976.

Whitcher, C. E., et al. Control of occupational exposure to N_2O in the dental operatory. HEW Publication No. (NIOSH) 77-171. Cincinnati, U.S. Department of Health, Education and Welfare, Public Health Services Center for Disease Control, National Institute for Occupational Safety and Health.

Whitcher, C. E., et al. Control of occupational exposure to nitrous oxide in the dental operatory. *J. Am. Dent. Assoc.* 95:763–766, 1977.

Whitcher, C. E., et al. Development and evaluation of methods for the elimination of waste anesthetic gases and vapors in hospitals. HEW Publication No. (NIOSH) 75-137, GPO stock no. 1733-0071. Supt. of Documents, Govt. Print. Off., 1975.

E.3.5.1.4 Dealing with Personnel. Lecky, J. H. Notice to employees on the potential health hazards associated with occupational exposure to anesthetics. University of Pennsylvania Hospital publication.

E.3.5.1.4.1 NIOSH — OSHA Publication. Criteria for a recommended standard: Occupation exposure to waste anesthetic gases and vapors. HEW Publication No. (NIOSH) 77-140. Cincinnati, U.S. Department of Health, Education and Welfare, Public Health Service Center for Disease Control, National Institute for Occupational Safety and Health.

E.3.5.1.4.2 ANSI Publication. American National Standards Institute, Committee Z79, SC-4 *Anesthesia Gas Scavenging Devices and Disposal Systems*, J. H. Lecky, M.D., Chairman, ANSI/Z79.11-1982.

A prudent course of action pending further data on this topic lies in the installation of a gas scavenging system for use when inhalation anesthetic techniques are employed with gas flows in excess of metabolic and anesthetic requirements. Care must be taken in the selection and application of any such system to a gas anesthesia apparatus or anesthesia ventilator to avoid exposing the breathing circuit to any pressure less than atmospheric, and also to avoid the dumping of any flammable vapors into a central suction system not designed for such operation.

E.3.5.2 Operating Rooms, Delivery Rooms, and Special Procedure Rooms. Ventilation air should be supplied from several outlets located on the ceiling or high on the walls of the location. Air should be exhausted by several inlets located near the floor on opposite walls. The air distribution pattern should move air down and through the location with a minimum of draft to the floor for exhaust.

Studies indicate that an air change rate equivalent to 25 room volumes of air per hour dilutes bacteria dispersed into the room by human activity. When properly filtered, 80 percent can be recirculated with no more microbial contamination than 100 percent outdoor air filtered in the same manner. *(See ASHRAE Handbook — HVAC Applications, 1982, Chapter 7, Table on Pressure Relationships and Ventilation of Certain Areas.)* A positive air pressure relative to the air pressure of adjoining areas should be maintained in the anesthetizing location. This is accomplished by supplying more air to the location than is exhausted from it. Such pressurization will eliminate the infiltration of contaminated air around perimeter openings of door closures or other wall openings during clinical procedures.

Ventilation systems should incorporate air filters with an efficiency of not less than 90 percent when tested in accordance with ASHRAE Standard 52, *Method of Testing Air Cleaning Devices Used in General Ventilation for Removing Particulate Matter.* (Summarized in ASHRAE *Handbook* — HVAC Applications, 1983, Chapter 10, Equipment.)

E.3.5.3 Humidity Control. The ventilation system must incorporate humidity equipment and controls to maintain a relative humidity of at least 50 percent. Although the high level of humidity is not sufficiently reliable for complete dissipation of electrostatic charges, this humidity does reduce the hazard of electrostatic spark discharges under many conditions. The control of airborne bacteria is facilitated in this range of humidity.

The classic reference on bacteria growth and infection versus humidity level is Dunklin and Puck, "Lethal Effect of Relative Humidity on Airborne Bacteria" [5]. Another good reference is McDade and Hall, "Survival of *Staphylococcus aureus* in the Environment" [6]. A third noteworthy article is Sonneland, "Does Operating Room Modernization Affect the Incidence of Infection?" [7].

E.3.5.4 Temperature. The temperature to be maintained in operating rooms should be chosen on the basis of the well-being of patient and operating teams. It is recommended that the equipment provide for a room temperature in a range of 20°C (68°F) to 24°C (75°F) with controls for selecting any desired temperature within this range.

E.4 Electrical Equipment Criteria

E.4.1 Wiring.

Wiring for fixed equipment installed outside the hazardous area of a flammable inhalation anesthetizing location shall comply with 4.3.2.1 in NFPA 99.

E.4.2 Installation.

All service equipment, switchboards, or panelboards shall be installed outside hazardous areas.

E.4.3 Control Devices.

Devices or apparatus such as motor controllers, thermal cutouts, switches, relays, the switches and contactors of autotransformer starters, and resistance and impedance devices, which tend to create arcs, sparks, or high temperatures, shall not be installed in hazardous areas unless devices or apparatus are of a type approved for use in Class I, Group C atmospheres in accordance with Sections 501.6(a) and 501.7(a), or Sections 501.6(b) and 501.7(b) of NFPA 70, *National Electrical Code.*

Note that it is recommended that control devices for such purposes be installed in a nonhazardous area and actuated by some suitable mechanical, hydraulic, or other nonelectric remote-control device that can be operated from any desired location. This recommendation applies particularly to foot and other switches that must be operated from a location at or near the floor.

E.4.4 Location.

Equipment in storage locations for flammable anesthetic locations shall comply with E.6.8.6.

E.4.5 Line Voltage Equipment — All Anesthetizing Locations.

E.4.5.1 Portable equipment shall be provided with a storage device for its flexible cord.

E.4.5.2 Flexible cord for portable lamps or portable electric appliances operating at more than 12 volts between conductors, intended for use in all anesthetizing locations, shall be continuous and without switches from the appliance to the attachment plug and of a type designated for extra-hard usage in accordance with Section 501.11 of NFPA 70, *National Electrical Code*. Such flexible cord shall contain one extra insulated conductor to form a grounding connection between the ground terminal of the polarized plug and metal lamp guards, motor frames, and all other exposed metal portions of portable lamps and appliances. Cords shall be protected at the entrance to equipment by a suitable insulating grommet. The flexible cord shall be of sufficient length to reach any position in which the portable device is to be used, and the attachment plug shall be inserted only in a fixed, approved receptacle. For correct use and maintenance of adapters, the provisions of 8.5.2.1.7 shall apply.

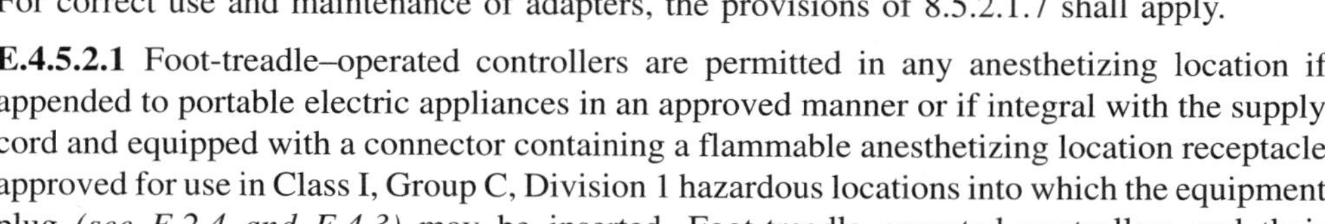

E.4.5.2.1 Foot-treadle–operated controllers are permitted in any anesthetizing location if appended to portable electric appliances in an approved manner or if integral with the supply cord and equipped with a connector containing a flammable anesthetizing location receptacle approved for use in Class I, Group C, Division 1 hazardous locations into which the equipment plug *(see E.2.4 and E.4.3)* may be inserted. Foot-treadle–operated controllers and their connector shall be splashproof.

E.4.5.2.2 Listed double-insulated appliances with two-wire cords shall be permitted.

E.4.5.2.3 Small metal parts not likely to become energized (e.g., nameplates, screws) shall not be required to be grounded.

E.4.5.2.4 Two or more power receptacles supplied by a flexible cord are permitted to be used to supply power to plug-connected components of a movable equipment assembly that is rack-, table-, or pedestal-mounted in a nonflammable anesthetizing location provided all of the following:

(1) The receptacles are an integral part of the equipment assembly, permanently attached.
(2) The sum of the ampacity of all appliances connected to the receptacles shall not exceed 75 percent of the ampacity of the flexible cord supplying the receptacles. Note that whole-body hyperthermia/hypothermia units should be powered from a separate branch circuit.
(3) The ampacity of the flexible cord is suitable and in accordance with the current edition of NFPA 70.

(4) The electrical and mechanical integrity of the assembly is regularly verified and documented through an ongoing maintenance program. *(See 13.4.1.2.6.3 for criteria of receptacles.)*

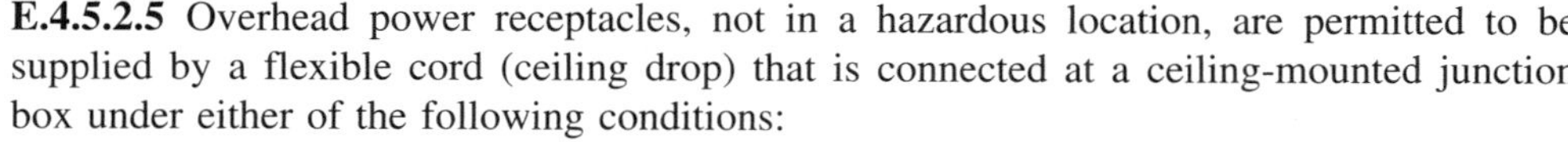

E.4.5.2.5 Overhead power receptacles, not in a hazardous location, are permitted to be supplied by a flexible cord (ceiling drop) that is connected at a ceiling-mounted junction box under either of the following conditions:

(1) Permanently
(2) Utilizing a locking-type plug cap and receptacle combination, or other method of retention. In either connection mode, suitable strain relief shall be provided. Note that the disconnection means is permitted only to facilitate replacement; as such, ceiling drop cords may not be disconnected for alternative usage. *(See 13.4.1.2.6.3 for criteria of receptacles.)*

E.4.6 Line Voltage Equipment — Flammable Anesthetizing Locations.

E.4.6.1 All equipment intended for use in anesthetizing locations shall be labeled by the manufacturer to indicate whether it is permitted to be used in a flammable anesthetizing location. Electric equipment presently in use shall be so labeled by the user. Labeling shall be permanent, conspicuous, and legible when the equipment is in the normal operating position *(see E.4.6.6)*.

E.4.6.2 Suction, pressure, or insufflation equipment, involving electric elements and located within the hazardous area, shall be of a type approved for use in Class I, Group C, Division 1 hazardous areas. Means shall be provided for liberating the exhaust gases from such apparatus in such a manner that gases will be effectively dispersed without making contact with any possible source of ignition.

Note that suction of pressure apparatus serving flammable anesthetizing locations but located outside such flammable anesthetizing locations need not be approved for Class I, Group C, Division 1 hazardous areas, providing the discharge from suction machines is kept away from sources of ignition.

E.4.6.3 Portable X-ray equipment intended for use in flammable anesthetizing locations shall be approved for use in Class I, Group C, Division 1 hazardous areas and shall be permitted to be provided with an approved positive-pressure system for the tube head and cables within the hazardous area *(see E.4.6.6)*. All devices and switches for X-ray equipment within the hazardous area shall conform to requirements of E.4.2 and E.6.6.5.6 and E.6.6.5.8 in this annex. X-ray equipment shall be provided with an approved method of eliminating electrostatic accumulation *(see 13.4.1.2.4 of NFPA 99 and E.6.6.5.6)*.

E.4.6.4 High-frequency equipment intended for use in flammable anesthetizing locations shall be approved for use in Class I, Group C, Division 1 hazardous areas.

Note that remote-control switches are recommended *(see E.4.3 and E.6.6.9.3)*.

Also note that for recommendations in connection with the use of cautery and high-frequency equipment in flammable anesthetizing locations, see E.6.6.8.10 and Sections E.7 and E.8; and Annex D.

E.4.6.5 Portable electric equipment, such as incubators, lamps, heaters, motors, and generators, used in flammable anesthetizing locations in which anesthesia equipment is present or in operating condition, shall comply with the requirements of Articles 500, 501, and 517 of NFPA 70, *National Electrical Code*, for Class I, Division 1 locations and shall be approved for Class I, Group C, Division 1 hazardous areas except as permitted in E.2.1 in this annex.

Note that the resistance and capacitive reactance between the conductors and the noncurrent-carrying metallic parts must be high enough to permit the use of the equipment on an ungrounded distribution system having a line isolation monitor specified in 4.3.2.6.3.

E.4.6.6 The following shall be considered exceptions to E.4.6.1 and E.4.6.5 in this annex:

(1) Equipment designed to operate on circuits of 10 volts or less. (Reserved)

(2) Portable electric or electronic equipment mounted within an enclosure and protected by an approved positive-pressure ventilating system that conforms with the following requirements shall otherwise comply with the standards of NFPA 70, *National Electrical Code*, for ordinary locations. The enclosure of such a system shall be supplied with air taken from a nonhazardous area and circulated to maintain within the enclosure a pressure of at least 1 in. (2.5 cm) of water above that of the hazardous area, and it shall be provided with means to deenergize the equipment if the air temperature exceeds 140°F (60°C) or if the pressure differential drops below 1 in. (2.5 cm) of water. The positive pressure shall be continuously maintained whether or not the equipment is in use, or means shall be provided to ensure that there are at least 10 changes of air within the enclosure before any electric equipment within the enclosure that does not comply with the requirements of E.4.4 is energized. The enclosure with its equipment shall be approved for use in Class I, Group C, Division 1 hazardous areas.
(3) Portable electric or electronic equipment, if it is mounted on a floor-borne movable assembly that will not overturn either when it is tilted through an angle of 20 degrees

or when in a normal operating position a horizontal force of 25 lb (11.3 kg) is applied at a height of 5 ft (152 cm) above the floor; and if the equipment, together with its enclosure, cannot be lowered within 5 ft (152 cm) of the floor without tilting the assembly, then the equipment need not be approved for use in Class I, Group C, Division 1 hazardous areas, but shall comply with the requirements of E.4.6.5. The entire assembly shall be approved for use in flammable anesthetizing locations as defined in E.1.3.

(4) Intrinsically safe electric or electronic equipment, which is incapable of releasing sufficient electric energy under normal or abnormal conditions to cause ignition of flammable anesthetic mixtures.

E.4.6.7 Photographic lighting equipment used in flammable anesthetizing locations shall comply with the provisions of E.4.6 to prevent ignition of flammable gases. Lamps used above the hazardous area shall be suitably enclosed to prevent sparks and hot particles falling into the hazardous area. Photoflash and photoflood lamps that are not suitably enclosed shall not be used within an anesthetizing location. Neither flash tubes nor their auxiliary equipment shall be used within the hazardous area.

Note that flash tube operation can be accompanied by sparking at switches, relays, and socket contacts, and by corona discharge of flashovers from high-voltage circuits.

E.4.6.8 The exposed metal parts of photographic lighting equipment shall be grounded as specified in 8.4.1.2.1 of NFPA 99.

E.4.7 Low-Voltage Equipment — Flammable Anesthetizing Locations.

(Specifications for portable equipment operating on low-voltage power supplies are stated in E.4.6.6 and E.6.6.)

E.5 Gas Equipment Criteria

Equipment capable of producing surface temperatures sufficient to cause chemical breakdown of the atmosphere within a patient enclosure shall not be permitted therein.

E.5.1 Where diethyl ether vapor is involved, surface temperatures shall not exceed 248°F (120°C).

E.5.2 Such a potentially hazardous atmosphere can be created by the placement in an incubator of a recently anesthetized infant or one whose mother received an inhalation anesthetic during delivery.

E.5.3 Diethyl ether vapor can produce formaldehyde upon contact with a heating element.

Section E.5 was necessary when flammable anesthetics, used for expectant mothers during delivery, caused flammable gases to find their way into the fetus' lungs through the mother's blood. This requirement also dates from the time when flammable anesthetics were used during surgery on infants.

In the late 1950s, M. K. Menderhall conducted a study unrelated to medicine on the thermal decomposition of ether [8].

E.6 Additional Criteria and Guidance

E.6.1 When this material was first published in 1941 as a separate document, the majority of inhalation anesthetics were administered with flammable agents, and fires and explosions in operating rooms occurred with disturbing frequency. Promulgation of this material by NFPA and the use of this material by hospitals has lowered the incidence of such tragedies significantly.

Since 1950, nonflammable inhalation anesthetics possessing relatively safe properties have been developed. The increasing use of these agents has curtailed, and in most institutions completely eliminated, the use of flammable agents. This change in anesthetic practice has made it desirable to delineate standards of construction and operation in facilities where flammable agents will never be used. It must be emphasized that many safety recommendations pertain to hazards other than those related to fires and explosions, e.g., electric shock. It must also be recognized that these agents might possess toxicologic hazards to patients and personnel.

One report from 1950, when flammable inhalation anesthetics were still used exclusively, listed 67 operating room explosions with a mortality rate of about 50 percent in U.S. hospitals.

This material has been formulated in the belief that, although materials and mechanical equipment must be relied upon to the fullest possible extent for the mitigation of fire, explosion, and electric shock hazards, such physical safeguards are most effective only when augmented by safety precautions conscientiously applied by operating room and supporting personnel. This section emphatically calls attention to the need for constant human diligence in the maintenance of safe practices because of the peculiar intermixing of flammable anesthetic hazards and electric shock hazards, together with the mental strain in the environment of surgical operations.

Studies of these operating room hazards by many investigators over more than 30 years have pointed to the conclusion that the greatest degree of safety possible within the limitations of our present knowledge is secured only through a completely coordinated program rather than by the application of individual and unrelated safeguards. Compliance with certain requirements of this section will be effective, or even permissible, only when accompanied by compliance with the full program of precautionary measures.

It is necessary that all personnel having any responsibility for safety in anesthesia collaborate in the precautionary program. In the case of hospitals, this will apply to members of the governing body, physicians, administrative personnel, nursing staff, and maintenance staff. Not only must such personnel achieve an understanding of the hazards involved, but, in addition, they must be reminded periodically of the dangers posed by electric shock, compressed gases and their cylinders, the explosive nature of all flammable agents, and the hazards created by oxygen-enriched atmospheres. *(See* NFPA 53, *Recommended Practice on Materials, Equipment, and Systems Used in Oxygen-Enriched Atmospheres.)*

For further discussion on the nature of the hazards, see C.13.1 in NFPA 99.

E.6.2 This section recognizes that some hospitals contain operating and delivery rooms designed and maintained for the use of flammable anesthetic agents. It also recognizes that there are some operating rooms and even entire operating suites designed for the exclusive use of nonflammable agents. A particular hazard exists where personnel elect to employ a flammable agent in a room not designed for it, or where a flammable agent is employed in a nonflammable anesthetizing location without taking the proper administrative steps.

Although the use of flammable anesthetics has been almost entirely eliminated in the United States, the first sentence of E.6.2 acknowledges that flammable anesthetics are still used in other parts of the world. This guidance could be required for foreign facilities, built with U.S. funds, that still use flammable anesthetic agents. An inquiry from India in 1993 confirmed that flammable anesthetics were still being used and that reference to NFPA 99 was still being made.

E.6.3 Sections E.7 and E.8 contain proposed regulations applying to specific types of inhalation anesthetizing locations.

Section E.7 contains regulations for flammable anesthetizing locations that can be adopted by hospitals for all anesthetizing locations designed for the safe administration of flammable inhalation anesthetic agents.

Section E.8 contains regulations for mixed facilities that can be adopted by hospitals in which flammable anesthetizing locations and nonflammable anesthetizing locations coexist within the same building, allowing interchange of personnel and equipment between flammable and nonflammable anesthetizing locations.

E.6.4 Identifying Flammable Anesthetizing Locations.

Anesthetizing locations shall be identified as listed in E.6.7.5.

E.6.5 Equipment Labeling.

All pieces of equipment used in flammable anesthetizing locations shall be labeled to indicate that they comply with applicable safety regulations.

Note that a generally recognized mark or symbol will meet the intent of this requirement.

E.6.6 Requirements for Flammable Anesthetizing Locations.

E.6.6.1 Areas Adjoining Flammable Inhalation Anesthetizing Locations and Flammable Anesthetizing Storage Locations.

E.6.6.1.1 An adjoining area connected by a closable doorway, such as a corridor, sterilizing room, scrub room, X-ray control room, or monitoring room, where it is not intended to store or administer flammable inhalation anesthetics, is not considered a hazardous area.

E.6.6.1.2 Areas described in E.6.6.1.1 above shall be permitted to be ventilated in accordance with the applicable sections of NFPA 70, *National Electrical Code*, for ordinary locations.

E.6.6.1.3 Conductive flooring is required in these adjoining areas to remove static charges from personnel or objects before they enter the flammable inhalation anesthetizing location or agent storage location *(see E.6.6.8.2)*.

E.6.6.1.4 Postanesthesia recovery rooms are not considered to be hazardous areas unless specifically intended for the induction of inhalation anesthesia with flammable anesthetic agents *(see E.6.6.9.2)*.

E.6.6.1.5 All doorways leading to flammable inhalation anesthetic agent storage locations shall be identified with NFPA 704, *Standard System for the Identification of the Hazards of Materials for Emergency Response*, symbols as appropriate.

E.6.6.2 Isolated Power Systems. A local ungrounded electric system shall be provided.

The installation of isolated power systems in anesthetizing locations was one of several measures instituted in 1941 to reduce the spark hazard in operating rooms. At that time, flammable inhalation anesthetics were generally used and the use of electrical equipment was starting to increase. Because these protective measures are believed to have reduced the number of incidents, they have been retained in flammable anesthetizing locations. For further discussion, see the commentary following A.3.3.85 for material on *isolated power system.* For performance criteria for isolated power systems, see 4.3.2.6.

Note that the isolated system reduces the ignition hazard from arcs and sparks between a live conductor and grounded metal and mitigates the hazard of shock or burn from electric current flowing through the body to ground. The latter hazard usually follows inadvertent contact with one live conductor or results from unrecognized failure of insulation.

Also note that such a system provides protection from spark and electric shock hazards due to the most common types of insulation failure. It does not, however, prevent all electric sparks or completely eliminate the possibility of electric shock from insulation failure. Patients and personnel often are wet with prepping solutions, blood, urine, and other conductive fluids that greatly reduce resistance to the passage of unintended electrical current. More than ordinary care is crucially necessary in the use and maintenance of all electric systems and equipment.

Finally note that the ungrounded electrical distribution system specified in this annex is intended to reduce the possibility of electric shocks and recurring arcs and sparks in the event of insulation failure of the electrical wiring system in anesthetizing locations. Because of the difficulty in achieving a sufficiently high level of insulation to permit operation of a line isolation monitor, and in recognition of evolving capabilities in medical care, an exception has been made so that permanently installed equipment as well as nonadjustable lighting fixtures in specified locations need not be supplied by the ungrounded system. *(See E.6.6.3 and E.6.6.4.)*

This last paragraph refers to material in E.6.6.3 and E.6.6.4 on fixed equipment and lighting. Prior to the 1984 edition of NFPA 99, only permanently installed X-ray equipment could be supplied by grounded power.

E.6.6.2.1 Hospitals complying with NFPA 56A, *Standard for the Use of Inhalation Anesthetics*, prior to 1970 shall not be required to change ground fault detectors to a line isolation monitor.

The committee has taken into consideration existing conditions by precluding the retroactive application of revised requirements on this subject that occurred subsequent to the 1970 edition of NFPA 56A.

E.6.6.2.2 The isolated electric system shall be required to be explosionproof only if installed in the hazardous areas of a flammable inhalation anesthetizing location.

It is not required or necessary that the isolated power system be installed in the hazardous area of a flammable anesthetizing location.

E.6.6.3 Power for Fixed Equipment. Approved, fixed, therapeutic, and diagnostic equipment, permanently installed outside the hazardous area of a flammable anesthetizing location, is permitted to be supplied by a grounded single- or three-phase system of less than 600 V with the following provisions:

(1) The equipment complies with 8.4.1.2.1 of NFPA 99
(2) Cord-connected accessories (such as positioning controls, aiming lights and fiberoptic light sources, slaved monitors, motorized cameras and video cameras, dosimeters, and exposure triggers) likely to come in contact with patients or personnel are supplied by isolated power at line voltage, or operate at 24 V or less, supplied by an isolating transformer

(3) Wiring is installed in accordance with NFPA 70, *National Electrical Code*, Section 517.61.

Note that it is intended that this section apply to positioning motors for patient tables associated with radiographic and other imaging equipment and to sometimes massive equipment for radiotherapy or for the delivery of other forms of energy.

Prior to 1978, only fixed lighting fixtures and permanently installed X-ray equipment were exempted from the requirement that electrical equipment in anesthetizing locations be supplied by an isolated power source. Certain fixed-type equipment was added to the exemption (originally TIA 56A-78-2) because of the difficulty in achieving a sufficiently high level of insulation to permit operation of line isolation monitors and because of the massive size of the line isolation transformers that would be required. In addition, allowance for 3-phase power was made (only single-phase power had previously been allowed in anesthetizing locations), with the committee noting (in TIA 56A-78-2) that conditions and state-of-the-art technology no longer warranted this exclusion.

E.6.6.4 Fixed Lighting. Branch circuits supplying only fixed lighting shall be permitted to be supplied by a conventional grounded system with the following provisions:

(1) Such fixtures are located at least 2.4 m (8 ft) above the floor
(2) Switches for the grounded circuits are wall-mounted and installed in accordance with NFPA 70, *National Electrical Code*, Article 517, Part D
(3) Wiring for grounded and ungrounded circuits is installed in accordance with NFPA 70, *National Electrical Code*, Article 517, Part D.

Note that wall-mounted remote-control stations for lighting control switches operating at 24 V or less can be installed in any anesthetizing location.

E.6.6.5 Ceiling-Suspended Fixtures.

E.6.6.5.1 Ceiling-suspended surgical lighting fixtures shall be supplied from an ungrounded electric distribution system *(see E.6.6.2 in this annex)*, which shall be monitored by a line isolation monitor as required by 4.3.2.6.3 of NFPA 99. Switching or dimmer devices shall control secondary circuit conductors only.

E.6.6.5.1.1 Where interruption of illumination is acceptable, as with single-filament lights, ceiling-suspended surgical lighting fixtures shall be permitted to be connected to a grounded source of supply, protected by approved individual ground fault circuit interrupters.

E.6.6.5.1.2 The secondary circuit of the ceiling-mounted surgical lighting fixture supplied by a step-down isolation transformer need not be equipped with a line isolation monitor provided that the step-down transformer is located in the same enclosure as the lamp fixture, or that the conductors carrying the current from the transformer to the lamp fixture are contained in metallic conduit that forms an integral electrical (ground) pathway between the transformer enclosure and the lamp fixture, and provided that the voltage in the secondary (lamp) circuit is not greater than 30 V.

Paragraph E.6.6.5.1.2 was added because some ceiling-mounted surgical fixtures include a step-down transformer mounted externally to the lighting fixture itself. The question arose whether this would constitute an isolated power system and thus require a line isolation monitor. The committee deemed it reasonable to address this configuration as similar to low-voltage signal and control circuits and as isolation transformers that are an integral part of an assembly of components. Although technically isolated, such secondary circuits are not required to be monitored.

E.6.6.5.2 The light source of ceiling-suspended surgical lighting fixtures installed above hazardous areas shall not enter the hazardous area, and, if in an enclosure, the enclosure shall not enter the hazardous area in its lowest position, unless it was approved for hazardous areas.

E.6.6.5.3 If installed above a hazardous area, fixtures with sliding contacts or arcing or sparking parts shall be installed so that in any position of use, no sliding contacts or arcing or sparking parts shall extend within the hazardous area.

E.6.6.5.4 Integral or appended switches, if installed on ceiling-suspended surgical lighting fixtures, shall be approved for use in Class I, Division 1 hazardous areas if a switch is installed in, or can be lowered into, the hazardous area.

E.6.6.5.5 Lamps installed in fixed position in hazardous areas shall be enclosed in a manner approved for use in Class I, Group C, Division 1 hazardous areas and shall be properly protected by substantial metal guards or other means where exposed to breakage. Lamps shall not be of the pendant type unless supported by and supplied through hangers of rigid conduit or flexible connectors approved for use in Class I, Division 1 hazardous areas in accordance with Section 501.9(A) or Section 501.9(B) of NFPA 70, *National Electrical Code*.

E.6.6.5.6 Tube heads and cable of permanently installed X-ray equipment in flammable anesthetizing locations shall be approved for use in Class I, Group C atmospheres.

E.6.6.5.7 Film viewing boxes in hazardous areas shall either comply with the requirements of Section 501.9(A) of NFPA 70, *National Electrical Code*, or they shall be of a type that excludes the atmosphere of the room. If located above the 5 ft (152 cm) level in a flammable anesthetizing location or mixed facility, or in a nonflammable anesthetizing location, the film viewing box shall be permitted to be of the totally enclosed type or so constructed as to prevent the escape of sparks or hot metal. Such viewing boxes shall be permitted to be connected to a conventional grounded supply circuit if the device is protected by an approved system of double insulation. Where such an approved system is employed, the equipment shall be distinctly marked.

E.6.6.5.8 Control units and other electric apparatus installed or intended for use in a flammable anesthetizing location shall comply with the requirements of NFPA 99 and Section E.4 of this annex *(see also E.6.6.5.4 and E.6.7.6)*.

E.6.6.6 Signaling and Communications Systems. All equipment of signaling and communications systems in hazardous areas, irrespective of voltage, shall be of a type approved for use in Class I, Group C, Division 1 hazardous areas in accordance with Section 501.14(a) or Section 501.14(b) of NFPA 70, *National Electrical Code*.

E.6.6.7 Piping. Subsection E.6.3 prohibits the piping of flammable anesthetic gases *(see 5.1.13.1.1)*.

E.6.6.8 Reduction in Electrostatic Hazard.

E.6.6.8.1 Purpose.

E.6.6.8.1.1 The requirements of this section have been promulgated to reduce the possibility of electrostatic spark discharges, with consequent ignition of flammable gases *(see E.6.6.8)*.

E.6.6.8.1.2 The prevention of the accumulation of static charges revolves about a number of safeguards that shall be complied with in flammable anesthetizing locations; in corridors and passageways adjacent thereto; in rooms connecting directly to anesthetizing locations, such as scrub rooms and sterilizing rooms; and in storage locations for flammable anesthetics located in an operating suite.

E.6.6.8.1.3 The methods employed to prevent such accumulation include the installation of conductive flooring *(see E.6.6.8.2)*, the maintenance of the relative humidity at 50 percent at least, and the use of certain items of conductive equipment, accessories, and wearing apparel.

E.6.6.8.2 Conductive Flooring. Note that a conductive floor serves as a convenient means of electrically connecting persons and objects together to prevent the accumulation of electrostatic charges.

A resistance not exceeding 50 megohms between objects or persons is generally sufficient to prevent accumulation of dangerous voltages. The upper limit of 1,000,000 ohms for the resistance of the floor has been chosen as meeting this requirement with a reasonable factor of safety and with reasonable provision for other resistances in the conductive path.

The resistance of some flooring materials changes with age. Floors of such materials should have an initial resistance that permits changes in resistance with age without exceeding the limits prescribed in E.6.6.8.2.3 and E.6.6.8.2.4.

Conductive flooring is just one of the safety precautions used to reduce the risk of electrostatic hazards when flammable anesthetics are used.

E.6.6.8.2.1 Conductive flooring shall be installed in those areas specified in E.6.6.8.1.2. Conductive flooring installed in corridors or passageways in compliance with E.6.6.8.1.2 shall extend the width of the corridor and along the corridor a minimum of 9.84 ft (3 m) on each side of door frames.

E.6.6.8.2.2 A conductive floor shall meet the resistance provisions through its inherent conductive properties. The surface of the floor in the locations specified by E.6.6.8.1.2 and E.6.6.8.2.1 shall provide a patch of moderate electric conductivity between all persons and equipment making contact with the floor to prevent the accumulation of dangerous electrostatic charges. No point on a nonconductive element in the surface of the floor shall be more than ¼ in. (6.4 mm) from a conductive element of the surface, except for insulated floor drains.

E.6.6.8.2.3 The resistance of the conductive floor shall be less than an average of 1,000,000 ohms, as measured in accordance with E.6.6.8.2.7.

This upper value (1 million ohms) for conductive floors in flammable anesthetizing locations was selected for several reasons. Part of the reasoning included balancing the need to dissipate static electricity (lowering floor resistance) with the protection against grounding personnel (raising floor resistance). Values of 20 million ohms or more are technically acceptable to discharge static electricity (see E.6.6.8.2 for further information). However, other factors influenced the committee's decision to reduce that value, including the long-term characteristics of conductive floors, the need for some safety factor, and the maintenance necessary to reduce resistance buildup due to dirt.

E.6.6.8.2.4 The resistance of the floor shall be more than an average of 25,000 ohms, as measured in accordance with E.6.6.8.2.7.

The lower limit of 25,000 ohms is necessary to limit the current flow that could occur under fault conditions.

E.6.6.8.2.5 A deliberate connection of the conductive floor to the room ground shall not be required.

The purpose of the conductive floor is to interconnect equipment and personnel in order to equalize static potentials. Connection is achieved whether or not the conductive floor is connected to the room ground.

E.6.6.8.2.6 The resistance of conductive floors shall be initially tested prior to use. Thereafter measurements shall be taken at intervals of not more than one month. A permanent record of the readings shall be kept.

E.6.6.8.2.7 The following test method shall be used *(see E.6.6.12)*:

(1) The floor shall be clean and dry, and the room shall be free of flammable gas mixtures.
(2) Each electrode shall weigh 5 lb (2.268 kg) and shall have a dry, flat, circular contact area 2½ in. (6.35 cm) in diameter, which shall comprise a surface of aluminum or tin

foil 0.0005 in. (0.013 mm) to 0.001 in. (0.025 mm) thick, backed by a layer of rubber ¼ in. (6.4 mm) thick and measuring between 40 and 60 durometer hardness as determined with a Shore Type A durometer (ASTM D2240-91).

(3) Resistance shall be measured by a suitably calibrated ohmmeter that shall have a nominal open circuit output voltage of 500 V dc and a nominal internal resistance of not less than 100,000 ohms, with tolerance defined as follows:
   (a) Short-circuit current of from 2.5 mA to 5 mA.
   (b) At any value of connected resistance, *Rx*, the terminal voltage, V, shall be

$$\frac{Rx}{Rx + \text{internal resistance}} \times 500\ \text{V} \pm 15\%$$

Revision for the 1978 edition of NFPA 56A took into account those existing test instruments that had an output resistance of approximately 200,000 ohms and a short-circuit current of 2.5 mA.

(4) Measurements shall be made between five or more pairs of points in each room and the results averaged. For compliance with E.6.6.8.2.3 in this annex, the average shall be within the limits specified and no individual measurement value shall be greater than 5 megohms, as measured between two electrodes placed 3 ft (91 cm) apart at any points on the floor. For compliance with E.6.6.8.2.4, the average value shall be no less than 25,000 ohms with no individual measurement's value less than 10,000 ohms as measured between a ground connection and an electrode placed at any point on the floor, and also as measured between two electrodes placed 3 ft (91 cm) apart at any points on the floor. There is no upper limit of resistance for a measurement between a ground connection and an electrode placed on the conductive floor.

Although E.6.6.8.2.5 does not require a deliberate connection between the conductive floor and room ground, if such a connection is made, the resistance value between the two electrodes on the floor still has to meet both requirements of the third sentence of E.6.6.8.2.7(4) — 25,000 ohms (average) with no value less than 10,000 ohms.

Note that if the resistance changes appreciably with time during a measurement, the value observed after the voltage has been applied for about 5 seconds can be considered to be the measured value.

Initial decay is generally quite fast. Settling out usually occurs within 5 seconds.

E.6.6.8.3 Accessories. Coverings of operating tables, stretcher pads, pillows and cushions, etc., shall be fabricated from conductive materials throughout. Conductive sheeting shall be tested on a nonconductive surface. The resistance between two electrodes placed 3 ft (91 cm) apart, or as close to this distance as the size of the material will permit, on the same surface, and between two electrodes placed in the middle of opposite surfaces, shall not exceed 1 megohm. Individual items covered with conductive sheeting shall be tested on a metal surface. The resistance between an electrode placed on the upper surface of the covered item and another electrode placed on the metal surface shall not exceed 1 megohm. The electrodes and ohmmeter used for these tests shall be of the type specified in E.6.6.8.2.7(2) and E.6.6.8.2.7(3), respectively.

E.6.6.8.4 Interconnecting Conductive Accessories.

E.6.6.8.4.1 All accessories that are required to be resilient or flexible on the anesthesia machine, and that form part of an interconnecting electrically conductive pathway, such as tubing, inhalers, rebreathing bags, headstraps, retainers, face masks, handbulbs, and similar items, shall be of conductive material throughout. Electric resistance of such accessories shall be not greater than 1 megohm when tested as specified in E.6.6.8.5.1.

E.6.6.8.4.2 High-pressure flexible tubing used to interconnect the gas anesthesia apparatus with the central piping station outlets shall be antistatic and shall be conductive throughout with a maximum resistance of 100,000 ohms per linear foot during the specified life of the material.

Note that when a nonconductive endotracheal catheter is in use, the conductive path from the patient to the anesthesia machine should be maintained by the use of a conductive headstrap.

E.6.6.8.4.3 Tubing and connectors used for suctioning shall provide a continuous electrically conductive pathway to the vacuum bottle and to the vacuum outlet. The materials used shall be conductive throughout or, where it is necessary for visual monitoring, shall be permitted to be of antistatic material with antistatic properties good for the specified life of the material provided the tubing or connector embodies a continuous integral conductive pathway designed so that in normal use the conductive pathway shall make and maintain conductive contact with conducting materials. Electric resistance of such tubing and connectors shall be not greater than 1 megohm when tested as specified in E.6.6.8.5 in this annex.

Note that specified life refers to the permanence of the antistatic property with respect to the stated life of the material, including storage, and is of particular importance if the material is expected to be used and cleaned (e.g., washed) several times.

The configuration for suctioning tubing shown in Exhibit E.1 was interpreted in July 1976 by the committee responsible for NFPA 56A as meeting the intent of "conductive throughout." The committee indicated, however, that the configuration was *not* acceptable for use elsewhere (e.g., on anesthesia machines).

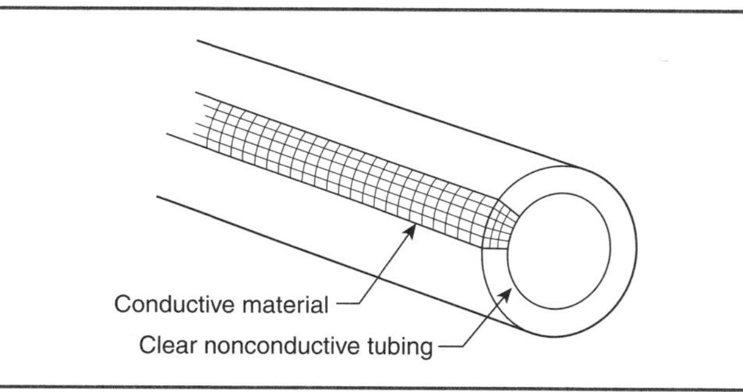

***EXHIBIT E.1** Suctioning tubing.*

E.6.6.8.4.4 All belting used in connection with rotating machinery shall have incorporated in it sufficient material to prevent the development of electrostatic charges. A conductive pulley shall be used.

Note that the conductivity of the path from the pulley to the ground should be considered. If ball bearings are used, the contact between the balls and the races will probably be sufficient when bearings are lubricated with graphitized oil or grease. If sleeve bearings are used, some means of conducting the charge from the pulley should be provided.

E.6.6.8.4.5 Wherever possible, items that are not parts of a machine shall be of conductive materials throughout, particularly where the item is depended on to provide a conductive pathway between other conductive items and/or the patient *(see second paragraph of E.6.6.8.4.2).*

Note that for essential elements in surgery, such as prosthetic and therapeutic devices, bacterial barriers, instruments, gloves (thermoplastic: for example, PVC), or biomechanical equipment, antistatic materials should be used if conductive materials are not available or are impractical. Any material can be employed if clearly nonhazardous owing to improbability of acquiring and holding a significant charge, e.g., suction catheter, endotracheal tube, plastic inserts in joint prostheses.

E.6.6.8.4.6 Nonconductive, nonantistatic parts shall be used where necessary as electric insulators or heat-insulating handles on approved devices. Where exposed metal parts of machines of necessity are insulated from each other by other nonconductive parts, they shall be electrically interconnected. The resistance of the grounding path between these metal parts shall not exceed 0.1 ohm.

E.6.6.8.4.7 Antistatic materials are not acceptable where they are relied upon to provide an interconnecting electrically conductive pathway.

E.6.6.8.5 Testing for Conductivity.

E.6.6.8.5.1 An ohmmeter of the type specified in E.6.6.8.2.7(3) shall be used for testing. Where possible, electrodes shall be of the type to make contact with metal positions across which it is desired to ensure a conductive pathway provided by the accessory, but care must be taken to ensure that the placing of the electrodes has not inadvertently provided an alternate conductive path to that under test; or, electrodes shall be of the type specified in E.6.6.8.2.7(2), where applicable; or, equivalent electrode contact shall be employed as practical. All items that are parts of a machine, such as tubing, bags, face masks, etc., shall be tested either in place or detached from the machine in accordance with one of the methods listed under E.6.6.8.5.2 through E.6.6.8.5.8.

E.6.6.8.5.2 When tested in place on the machine, it is first necessary to purge the entire system of flammable or explosive gases. The anesthesia jar and cylinders of flammable gases shall be removed from the machine and all the remaining parts purged by flowing air through them in sufficient quantity to assure that all residual anesthetic gases have been removed. All parts shall be tested and each part shall be tested separately.

E.6.6.8.5.3 For interconnecting parts that are to be classed as conductive throughout, one electrode shall be attached in a satisfactory manner to the metal frame of the machine, and the conductivity shall be determined by measuring the resistance between this first electrode and a second electrode consisting of a metal band snugly fitted around the midpart of the item being tested, or, for face masks and similar objects, between the first electrode and a second electrode *[see E.6.6.8.2.7(2)]* resting on the item.

E.6.6.8.5.4 For interconnecting parts that are to be classed as antistatic with a continuous integral conductive pathway, the conductivity test shall be performed as given in E.6.6.8.5.1 above except that, in place of the metal band electrode or the standard electrode of E.6.6.8.2.7(2), there shall be a suitable second electrode making contact with the part in a manner that simulates the actual second contact area made when the part is connected for use.

E.6.6.8.5.5 Metal parts of machines that are required to be apparently insulated from each other by other nonconductive parts shall be suitably tested for electric interconnection; this shall be permitted to be an ohmmeter test. The resistance of the grounding path between these metal parts shall not exceed 0.1 ohm.

E.6.6.8.5.6 When tubing and other accessories are tested for conductivity while detached from a machine, each part shall be fitted with a clean brass nipple of the same outside diameter as the connector by which the part is normally connected to the machine. A nipple shall be inserted into each such opening of the part. When two or more nipples are involved, satisfactory conductivity shall be determined by measuring the resistance between nipples. If only one nipple is involved, as in the case of a face mask or breathing bag, the resistance shall be measured between the nipple and another electrode suitably connected elsewhere (e.g., a standard electrode resting on the part).

E.6.6.8.5.7 While the above are given as standard test methods, where these methods cannot be applied, an equivalent test method is permitted to be used. Interconnecting conductivity is acceptable if the measured resistance is not greater than 1 megohm.

E.6.6.8.5.8 Conductive items containing antistatic material shall have the antistatic properties tested as described in E.6.6.8.6.3 and E.6.6.8.6.4.

A Formal Interpretation to NFPA 56A was issued in July 1976 to reaffirm the requirement that sheeting, film, and textiles needed to meet one of the two test methods listed, but not necessarily both.

Another Formal Interpretation was issued in January 1978 regarding a test specimen that could not be charged to the 5000 V prescribed by the Federal Test Method (FTM) Standard. If the specimen decayed as prescribed in the FTM Standard after being charged as high as possible, the specimen could be considered to have met the intent of the FTM Standard.

Another Formal Interpretation issued in January 1978 regarded the American Association of Textile Chemists and Colorists (AATCC) test method. The current test method [AATCC Test Method 76 Electrical Resistivity of Fabrics (current test dated 1995)] requires that the resistivity of the material be less than 10 ohms per unit square of material and that, for textiles, the measurement be made in several different directions parallel to the textile's yarn or thread. The less than 10-ohm value must be met regardless of direction or side. Additionally, this testing is applicable only to manufacturers, as noted in E.6.6.8.6.5.

E.6.6.8.6 Antistatic Accessories and Testing.

E.6.6.8.6.1 For conductive accessories containing antistatic material see E.6.6.8.4.1 and E.6.6.8.4.3; the antistatic material of these accessories shall be tested as given in E.6.6.8.6.3 and E.6.6.8.6.4. For other individual items that are permitted to be of antistatic material, see E.6.6.8.4.5.

E.6.6.8.6.2 Plastic sheeting, film, and other nontextile, nonmetal materials, if not required to form a conductive interconnecting pathway between machines, objects, and persons, need not be conductive but shall be of antistatic material except as given in E.6.6.8.4.5. They shall be of antistatic material throughout their specified life when tested as described in E.6.6.8.6.3 and E.6.6.8.6.4.

E.6.6.8.6.3 Antistatic sheeting, film, and textiles shall meet the specified requirements of at least one of the following test methods when preconditioned at 50 percent ± 2 percent RH at 23° ± 1°C for 25 hours or until equilibrium is reached, and tested at 50 percent ± 2 percent RH at 23° ± 1°C.

Method 4046 of Federal Test Method Standard 101B. After the specimen has received its maximum charge from the application of 5000 V, the time for the indicated specimen potential to drop to 10 percent of its maximum value shall not exceed ½ second.

Note that the static detector head should be of a type that is adequately shielded to minimize responses to potentials on the electrodes, and other stray pickup. The sample is held between electrically interconnected electrodes. The 5000 V are applied to the electrodes for 10 seconds after the indicated potential of the sample reaches equilibrium before the charge decay rate is measured.

Method 76 of the AATCC. Applied voltage should be 102 V per in. (40 V per cm) of interelectrode spacing. The measured resistivity shall be less than 1×10^{11} ohms per unit square of material.

E.6.6.8.6.4 Antistatic items other than sheeting, film, and textiles shall be tested in a manner as closely as possible equivalent to that given in E.6.6.8.6.3.

E.6.6.8.6.5 The supplier of conductive and antistatic accessories shall certify that the item or items supplied meet the requirements of one of the tests specified in E.6.6.8.6.3. The supplier shall certify the conditions of storage, shelf life, and, in the case of reusable items, the methods of repreparation necessary to allow the product or device to return to its antistatic or conductive properties.

E.6.6.8.7 Conductive Footwear.

E.6.6.8.7.1 The resistance of any static conductive footwear or any equivalent static conductive device used in conjunction with nonconductive footwear shall have a value before the item is first put in use not exceeding 500,000 ohms when tested in the following manner. The static conductive shoe or any equivalent static conductive device attached to a nonconductive shoe shall have clean contact surfaces. It shall be placed on a nonoxidizing metal plate wetted with water. A brass electrode having a contact area of 1 sq in. (6.5 sq cm) shall be placed on the inside of the sole or heel of the shoe after the surface under the electrode has been wetted by water. The resistance shall be measured between the plate and the electrode using a dc ohmmeter supplying a potential in excess of 100 V [e.g., see E.6.6.8.2.7(3)].

E.6.6.8.7.2 In the case of static conductive booties, the test shall be made as follows: The bootie shall be laid flat on an insulating surface. Two brass electrodes, each 1.5 in. (3.8 cm) long, having a contact area of 1 sq in. (6.5 sq cm), shall be used. One electrode shall be placed on the bootie near the toe and on the part of the bootie that normally comes in contact with the floor. The other electrodes shall be placed on the ankle section. The booties shall be wetted under the electrodes only.

E.6.6.8.7.3 If the tests as here described are not technically feasible for the device under consideration, an alternative equivalent means of testing shall be used. The static conductive footwear and any static conductive device used with nonconductive footwear shall also meet, during use, the requirements of E.6.6.10.1 through E.6.6.10.3 and E.6.6.13.3.

E.6.6.8.7.4 For protection of personnel against electric shock and high-frequency burns, static conductive footwear and equivalent static conductive devices shall not have any metal parts (nails, etc.) that normally come in contact with the floor.

E.6.6.8.8 Textiles. See also E.6.6.10.4 through E.6.6.10.6.

E.6.6.8.8.1 Silk, wool, synthetic textile materials, blends of synthetic textile materials with unmodified cotton or rayon, or nonwoven materials shall not be permitted in hazardous locations as outer garments or for nonapparel purposes, unless such materials have been tested and found to be antistatic by meeting the requirements of E.6.6.8.6.3.

In the case of reusable materials, the manufacturer shall certify that the antistatic properties shall be maintained through 50 wash-autoclave cycles or throughout the useful life of the material, whichever is greater.

In the case of nonreusable materials, the manufacturer shall certify that the antistatic properties shall be maintained throughout the useful life of the material.

Note that it is preferable to use only one textile material because static electricity is more readily generated by contact between articles of different materials than by contact between articles of the same material.

E.6.6.8.9 Furniture. Note that in its requirement for furniture in a flammable anesthetizing location to be constructed of conductive materials, the Subcommittee on Anesthesia Services specifically intends that any shelves within such furniture as well as the top also be conductive. Furniture is intended to include movable and permanently installed objects in the room, such as stools, tables, and cabinets. Wooden racks, however, are permitted for storage of cylinders of flammable as well as nonflammable gases.

E.6.6.8.9.1 If the furniture is conductive but not made of metal, then it shall have casters, tires, or legs of metal, conductive rubber, or equivalent conductive material with a floor contact surface having one dimension of at least ⅝ in. (1.58 cm). Approved equivalent means of making conductive contact between the piece of furniture and the floor is acceptable, provided the contact device is securely bonded to the piece of furniture and is of material that will not oxidize under conditions of normal use (so as to decrease the conductivity of the circuit), and that uninterrupted contact with the floor is at least ⅝ in. (1.6 cm) in one dimension *(see also E.6.6.13.4)*.

E.6.6.8.9.2 Surfaces on which movable objects are placed shall be without insulating paint, lacquer, or other nonconductive finish.

Note that an economical way to make painted furniture conform to this requirement is to attach unpainted sheet metal to the furniture's shelf or top with screws, rivets, or similar fasteners that provide electrical continuity to the frame and casters of the furniture.

E.6.6.8.9.3 The resistance between the conductive frame of the furniture referred to in E.6.6.8.9.2 and a metal plate placed under one supporting member but insulated from the floor shall not exceed 250,000 ohms, measured with an ohmmeter of the type described in E.6.6.8.2.7(3).

A two-part Formal Interpretation was issued on NFPA 56A in July 1976 relative to furniture used in flammable anesthetizing locations. The first part ruled that using insulating or nonconductive materials in furniture in such locations was permitted, provided the furniture's conductive frame met the requirements of E.6.6.8.9. The second part ruled that a vertical surface bulletin board did not constitute a surface on which movable objects could be placed such that E.6.6.8.9.2 would apply. In either case, the Interpretation Committee emphasized that these interpretations were not to be construed as allowing the use of nonconductive seats or cushions on stools and chairs in flammable anesthetizing locations.

E.6.6.8.10 High-Frequency Equipment. Potential sources of ignition, such as electrosurgical units, shall be prohibited during the administration of flammable anesthetizing agents.

The allowance of electrosurgical units (ESUs) in flammable locations under certain circumstances became a controversial issue in the 1980s. As a result of public comments in 1983, the former Committee on Anesthetizing Agents (now a part of the Committee on Gas Delivery Equipment) removed even the limited use of ESUs in flammable anesthetizing locations because of the lack of knowledge and training in the safe use of flammable anesthetic agents by operating room personnel due to the infrequent use of such agents.

E.6.6.9 General Requirements for Flammable Anesthetizing Locations.

E.6.6.9.1 Hospital authorities in consultation with others as noted in 7.2.2.1 shall adopt regulations to control apparel and footwear allowed, the periodic inspection of conductive materials, the control of purchase of static-conductive and antistatic materials, and the testing of conductive floors.

E.6.6.9.2 All required precautions shall apply to all anesthetizing locations in which flammable inhalation anesthetics are used.

E.6.6.9.3 Hospital regulations shall be established and enforced to control the use of electronic equipment such as television equipment, diathermy equipment, public address systems, monitoring equipment, and similar electronic and high-frequency apparatus in the presence of flammable inhalation anesthetic agents.

E.6.6.9.4 Hospital regulations shall prohibit the use of X-ray equipment in flammable anesthetizing locations if such equipment is not approved for operation in hazardous locations *(see E.6.6.5.6, E.6.6.5.7, and E.4.6.3)*.

E.6.6.9.5 Covers of fabric or of any form of sheeting shall not be used on anesthesia equipment capable of utilizing flammable anesthetizing agents because a cover will confine gas that could leak from a cylinder.

Note that when the cover is removed from the anesthesia machine under such conditions, a static charge might be created that could ignite the gas confined beneath the cover.

E.6.6.9.6 The use of rebreathing techniques in administering flammable anesthetic agents at all times is highly desirable. Through the use of these techniques, the escape of flammable mixtures is substantially limited.

E.6.6.9.7 Residual ether remaining in ether vaporizers at the end of each day shall be returned to its original containers for disposal or laboratory use only. The ether vaporizer, container, and such shall be thoroughly washed and dried before being returned to use *(see C.13.1.3)*.

E.6.6.9.8 Waste liquid ether and other flammable volatile liquid inhalation anesthetic agents shall be disposed of outside of the hospital building according to the recommendations of the authority having jurisdiction. One method is to allow the agent to evaporate in a shallow pan, well removed from possible sources of ignition under supervision.

Although it is acceptable to use the evaporative technique, it is very important that constant supervision be maintained when allowing the ether to evaporate in a shallow pan.

E.6.6.9.9 Members of the professional staff shall be required to submit for inspection and approval any special equipment they wish to introduce into flammable anesthetizing locations *(see 13.4.1.2.4.5)*. Such equipment shall be approved for use in Class I, Group C, Division 1 hazardous areas or comply with E.4.6.5. It shall be equipped with approved cords and attachment plugs *[see 8.4.1.2.4(1), 8.4.1.2.4(2), and E.2.4]*.

E.6.6.9.10 High-frequency electric and electronic equipment, such as electrosurgery amplifiers, monitors, recorders, television cameras, portable electrical tools, maintenance equipment, and certain sterilizing equipment that does not comply with the provisions of E.4.6.5 shall not be used when flammable inhalation anesthetic agents are being administered.

Cautery and electric surgical equipment shall not be used during procedures involving flammable inhalation anesthetic agents unless the equipment complies with the requirements of E.4.6.4.

See Annex D.

Readers are reminded that this section is applicable only to flammable anesthetizing locations.

E.6.6.10 Electrostatic Safeguards. Paragraph E.6.6.8 deals with the elements required to be incorporated into the structure and equipment to reduce the possibility of electrostatic spark discharges, which are a frequent source of the ignition of flammable anesthetic agents. The elimination of static charges is dependent on the vigilance of administrative activities in material selection, maintenance supervision, and periodic inspection and testing. It cannot be too strongly emphasized that an incomplete chain of precautions will generally increase the electrostatic hazard. For example, conductive flooring *(see E.6.6.8.2)* can contribute to the hazard unless all personnel wear conductive shoes and unless all objects in the room are electrically continuous with the floor.

E.6.6.10.1 All personnel entering flammable anesthetizing locations, mixed facilities, or storage locations for flammable anesthetics located in the surgical suite shall be in electrical contact with the conductive floor through the wearing of conductive footwear or an alternative method of providing a path of conductivity. The provision of conductive floors in corridors and rooms directly communicating with flammable anesthetizing locations *(see E.6.6.8.2)* will minimize the possibility of static discharge from patients or personnel entering such anesthetizing locations.

Note that one method for electrically connecting all persons to conductive floors is through the wearing of shoes conforming to the following specifications.

Each shoe having a sole and heel of conductive rubber, conductive leather, or equivalent material should be so fabricated that the resistance between a metal electrode placed inside the shoe and making contact with the inner sole equivalent in pressure and area to normal contact with the foot, and a metal plate making contact with the bottom of the shoe, equivalent in pressure and area to normal contact with the floor, be not more than 250,000 ohms.

E.6.6.10.2 Electric connection of the patient to the operating table shall be ensured by the provision of a high-impedance strap in contact with the patient's skin, with one end of the strap fastened to the metal frame of an operating table.

The term *high-impedance strap* is a misnomer in the sense that the strap has a high impedance compared to electric wire, but it actually has some conductive properties impregnated into it. A high-impedance strap could also be termed a *conductive strap.*

E.6.6.10.3 Because of the possibility of percussion sparks, shoes having ferrous nails that make contact with the floor shall not be permitted in flammable anesthetizing locations or mixed facilities or in storage locations for flammable anesthetic agents in the surgical suite.

E.6.6.10.4 Silk, wool, or synthetic textile materials, except rayon, shall not be permitted in flammable anesthetizing locations or mixed facilities as outer garments or for nonapparel purposes, unless these materials have been approved as antistatic in accordance with the requirements of E.6.6.8.6.3 and E.6.6.8.6.4.

Note that rayon refers to regenerated cellulose, not cellulose acetate. Cotton and rayon must be unmodified; i.e., must not be glazed, permanently starched, acetylated, or otherwise treated to reduce their natural hygroscopic quality. Fabrics of intimate blends of unmodified cotton or rayon with other textile materials are not acceptable unless tested and found to be antistatic.

E.6.6.10.5 Hosiery and underclothing in which the entire garment is in close contact with the skin shall be permitted to be of silk, wool, or synthetic material.

E.6.6.10.6 Undergarments with free-hanging skirts, such as slips or petticoats, shall be of cotton, rayon, or other materials demonstrated to be antistatic by the requirements of E.6.6.8.6.3 and E.6.6.8.6.4.

E.6.6.10.7 Antistatic materials for use in flammable anesthetizing locations shall be handled and used in the following manner:

(1) Antistatic materials shall be stored at the temperature and humidity required for flammable anesthetizing locations or they shall be allowed to equilibrate to the humidity and temperature of the flammable anesthetizing location prior to use.
(2) Antistatic materials shall be stored in such a manner that will ensure that the oldest stocks will be used first.
(3) Controls shall be established to ensure that manufacturers' recommendations as to use are followed in the case of antistatic materials.

E.6.6.10.8 All antistatic accessories intended for replacement, including belting, rubber accessories, plastics, sheeting, and the like, shall meet pertinent requirements for conductivity as specified in E.6.6.8.6.

E.6.6.11 Discretionary Use of Nonconforming Materials.

E.6.6.11.1 Suture material, alloplastic or therapeutic devices, bacterial barriers, instruments, gloves (thermoplastic), surgical dressings, and biologic interfaces of these otherwise prohibited materials shall be permitted to be used at the discretion of the surgeon.

E.6.6.11.2 Disposable supplies that contribute to the electrostatic hazard shall be so labeled on the unit package.

E.6.6.12 Maintenance of Conductive Floors.

E.6.6.12.1 The surface of conductive floors shall not be insulated by a film of oil or wax. Any waxes, polishes, or dressings used for maintenance of conductive floors shall not adversely affect the conductivity of the floor.

E.6.6.12.2 Floors that depend upon applications of water, salt solutions, or other treatment of a nonpermanent nature for their conductivity are not acceptable.

E.6.6.12.2.1 Treatment of the floor to modify conductivity shall be considered permanent provided the floor meets the requirements of E.6.6 for a period of not less than 2 years, during which no change or modification beyond normal washing is performed.

E.6.6.12.3 Cleaning procedures for conductive floors shall be established, then carefully followed to assure that conductivity characteristics of the floor are not adversely affected by such treatment.

E.6.6.12.4 Conductive floors shall be tested as specified in E.6.6.8.2.

A Formal Interpretation was issued on NFPA 56A in August 1977 that ruled that sealers or dressings intended to adjust the resistivity of a floor are acceptable. The only criterion for such items was that they not adversely affect the conductivity of the floor. A second question in the Formal Interpretation, on the permanence of sealers or dressings, subsequently resulted in an exception being formally adopted for the 1978 edition of NFPA 56A, which is now E.6.6.12.2.1.

E.6.6.13 Other Conductive Equipment.

E.6.6.13.1 The resistance of conductive accessories shall be tested prior to use as described in E.6.6.8.3 or E.6.6.8.4. Thereafter, measurements shall be taken at intervals of not more than 1 month. A permanent record of the readings shall be kept.

E.6.6.13.2 Antistatic plastics shall meet the requirements of E.6.6.8.6.2. It shall be the responsibility of the hospital to ensure that antistatic sheeting, etc., is used in accordance with the manufacturer's instructions. Failure to do so could in some cases lead to loss of antistatic properties. Antistatic materials that are reused (e.g., antistatic tubing incorporating a continuous conductive pathway as described in E.6.6.8.4.1) shall be tested *(see E.6.6.8.6.1)* periodically to ensure retention of conductive properties.

E.6.6.13.3 Conductive footwear and other personnel-to-floor connective devices shall be tested on the wearer each time they are worn. An approved resistance-measuring device having a short-circuit current not exceeding 0.5 mA shall be used.

Note that the reading may be taken between two insulated, nonoxidizing, metal plates so located that the wearer can stand in a normal manner with a foot on each, in which case the indicated resistance shall not exceed 1,000,000 ohms (1 megohm). *(See also the second paragraph of E.6.6.10.1.)*

E.6.6.13.4 The resistance of furniture *(see E.6.6.8.9)* and equipment shall be tested prior to use as described in E.6.6.8.9.3. Thereafter, measurements shall be taken at intervals of not more than 1 month. A permanent record of the readings shall be kept. The monthly tests can conveniently consist of measurements of the resistance between an electrode placed on the floor and an electrode placed successively on each article of furniture in the room. Additional tests of any individual item shall be made if the measured resistance exceeds 5 megohms.

E.6.6.13.5 Periodic inspection shall be made of leg tips, tires, casters, or other conductive devices on furniture and equipment to ensure that they are maintained free of wax, lint, or other extraneous material that insulates them and defeats the purpose for which they are used, and also to avoid transporting to conductive floors such materials from other areas.

E.6.6.13.6 Excess lubrication of casters shall be avoided to prevent accumulation of oil on conductive caster wheels and sides. Dry graphite or graphitized oil are preferable lubricants.

E.6.7 Requirements for Mixed Facilities.

A serious behavioral hazard exists in a "mixed facility," i.e., where there are some rooms where flammable agents are prohibited. In the latter situation, inadvertent use of a flammable agent in the "nonflammable" room could be disastrous. It is important to understand the regulations recommended in Section E.7.

The term *mixed facilities* was introduced by the committee for two reasons: (1) Although the use of flammable anesthetics diminished, many institutions wanted to retain some locations suitable for the use of such anesthetics; and (2) even if only a few locations were being maintained for flammable anesthetics, many enforcing authorities were requiring that all anesthetizing locations in a facility meet flammable requirements.

A mixed facility places an added burden on anesthesiologists and nurse anesthetists because these staff members usually are responsible for enforcing requirements for mixed facilities. Fixed equipment itself does not present a problem to the staff, as do movable items such as portable equipment, furniture, and supplies, which can be moved from nonflammable locations to flammable locations. Some items are not permitted to be moved in that direction. Although procedures can be established and followed under normal conditions, in an intense, life-threatening situation there is no guarantee that safety procedures will always be followed.

Items acceptable for use in flammable anesthetizing locations can safely be used in nonflammable anesthetizing locations, but the opposite is not always true. Although a facility could elect to make all movable items suitable for both locations, E.6.7 allows the two types of locations to exist independently in the same facility, as long as requirements peculiar to each location are observed.

E.6.7.1 General. The mixed facility is defined in E.1.6.

E.6.7.2 Construction of Anesthetizing Locations and Storage Locations.

E.6.7.2.1 Flammable anesthetizing locations shall be designed, constructed, and equipped as stated in 13.4.1.2 and E.6.6.

E.6.7.2.2 Nonflammable anesthetizing locations shall be designed, constructed, and equipped as stated in 13.4.1.2.

E.6.7.2.3 Storage locations for flammable anesthetics shall be constructed as provided in E.6.8. Storage locations for nonflammable medical gas cylinders shall be constructed as provided in 5.1.3.3.2 and 5.1.3.3.3.

E.6.7.3 Conductive Flooring in Posted Nonflammable Anesthetizing Locations Within a Mixed Facility. (Reserved)

E.6.7.4 Provision for Connection of Patient to Operating Table. Electric connection of the patient to the operating table shall be ensured by the provision of a high-resistance (conductive) strap in contact with the patient's skin, with one end of the strap fastened to the metal frame of an operating table.

Conductive straps are an example of an item that can be moved between the two types of anesthetizing locations because they are suitable for both flammable and nonflammable anesthetizing locations. Only one type of strap needs to be maintained. (See also the commentary on conductive straps following E.6.6.10.2.) An item suitable only for *nonflammable* anesthetizing locations, however, would not be acceptable in flammable anesthetizing locations.

E.6.7.5 Precautionary Signs.

E.6.7.5.1 The entrances to all anesthetizing locations shall be identified by prominently posted signs denoting individually whether the anesthetizing location is designed for flammable inhalation anesthetic agents or for nonflammable anesthetic agents.

Note the following suggested explanatory texts of such signs:

SUITABLE FOR USE WITH FLAMMABLE INHALATION ANESTHETIC AGENTS

or

RESTRICTED TO NONFLAMMABLE INHALATION ANESTHETIC AGENTS

E.6.7.5.2 In addition, a removable sign shall be posted to all entrances to the anesthetizing location indicating whether a flammable inhalation anesthetic agent is being employed.

Note the following suggested explanatory text of such a sign:

CAUTION
FLAMMABLE INHALATION ANESTHETIC IN USE
OBSERVE AND OBEY ALL SAFETY REGULATIONS

E.6.7.5.3 It shall be the responsibility of the anesthesiologist or nurse anesthetist to ensure that the room is suitably designated for use of the particular agent, whether flammable or nonflammable.

E.6.7.5.4 Regulations for the conduct of personnel, administration, and maintenance in mixed facilities shall be posted in at least one prominent location within the operating and, if applicable, delivery suite *(see E.6.2)*. Suggested text of such regulations is contained in Section E.8.

E.6.7.6 Movable Equipment and Furniture.

E.6.7.6.1 All equipment intended for use in both flammable and nonflammable anesthetizing locations shall meet the antistatic requirements of E.6.6.8.

E.6.7.6.2 Equipment intended for use only in nonflammable anesthetizing locations shall be labeled in accordance with E.4.6.1 and shall not be introduced into flammable anesthetizing locations. This equipment is not required to meet the antistatic requirements of E.6.6.8.

E.6.7.6.3 No portable equipment, including X-ray equipment, shall be introduced into mixed facilities unless it complies with the requirements of E.4.6.3 and is approved for use in Class I, Group C, Division 1 hazardous areas, or unless it is prominently labeled for use only in the presence of nonflammable anesthetic agents and then restricted to such use.

E.6.7.6.4 Portable electric equipment, such as incubators, lamps, heaters, motors, and generators used in mixed facilities in which flammable anesthetics are being employed shall comply with the requirements of Articles 500, 501, and 517 of NFPA 70, *National Electrical Code*, for Class I, Division 1 locations and shall be approved for Class I, Group C, Division 1 hazardous areas, except as permitted in E.4.6.6.

Note that the resistance and capacitive reactance between the conductors and the noncurrent-carrying metallic parts must be high enough to permit the use of the equipment on an ungrounded distribution system having a line isolation monitor specified in 4.3.2.6.3 of NFPA 99.

E.6.7.6.5 Furniture intended for use in both flammable and nonflammable anesthetizing locations of mixed facilities shall meet the antistatic requirements of E.6.6.8.9.

E.6.7.6.6 Furniture intended for use only in nonflammable anesthetizing locations of mixed facilities shall comply with E.6.6.8.9 or shall be conspicuously labeled and not be introduced into flammable anesthetizing locations.

E.6.8 Storage Locations for Flammable Anesthetic Agents (Any Quantity).

E.6.8.1 Enclosures in which flammable inhalation anesthetic agents are stored shall be individually and continuously ventilated by gravity or by mechanical means at a rate of not less than eight air changes per hour. The fresh-air inlet and the exhaust-air outlet within the enclosure shall be located as far apart as feasible consistent with the enclosure layout. The fresh-air inlet shall be located at or near the ceiling, and the bottom of the exhaust-air outlet shall be located 3 in. (7.6 cm) above the floor. The fresh-air supply shall be permitted to be heated. Exhaust air shall be discharged to the exterior of the building at least 12 ft (3.6 m) above grade in a manner to prevent its reentry into the building.

E.6.8.2 Exhaust fans shall have nonsparking blades. The fan motor shall be connected into the equipment system (either automatic or delayed restoration) *(see Chapter 4)*. All electric installations shall conform to NFPA 70, *National Electrical Code*, and, when inside the storage area or exhaust duct, shall be approved for use in Class I, Division 2, Group C locations. A visual signal that indicates failure of the exhaust system shall be installed at the entrance to the storage area.

Note that exhaust fans in all new installations, and whenever possible in existing installations, should be located at the discharge end of the exhaust duct.

E.6.8.3 Approved fire dampers shall be installed in openings through the required fire partition in accordance with the requirements of NFPA 90A, *Standard for the Installation of Air-Conditioning and Ventilating Systems*.

E.6.8.4 Enclosures shall not be used for purposes other than storage of flammable inhalation anesthetic agents.

E.6.8.5 Flooring shall comply with E.6.6.8.2.1.

E.6.8.6 Electric wiring and equipment in storage locations for flammable inhalation anesthetic agents shall comply with the requirements of NFPA 70, *National Electrical Code*, Article 500, Class I, Division 2, and equipment used therein shall be approved for use in Class I, Division 1, Group C hazardous areas *(see 4.3.3.1 in NFPA 99 for grounding requirements)*.

E.6.8.7 The provisions of E.6.6.2 for ungrounded electric distribution systems do not apply to storage locations for flammable agents.

E.6.8.8 Storage locations for flammable anesthetics shall meet the construction requirements stated in 5.1.3.3.2 and 5.1.3.3.3 and shall be ventilated as provided in E.6.6.8.

E.6.8.9 Flammable inhalation anesthetizing agents shall be stored only in such locations. Flammable inhalation anesthetizing agents shall not be stored in anesthetizing locations, except for cylinders of flammable anesthetic agents connected to a gas anesthesia apparatus.

E.6.8.10 Cylinders containing flammable gases (e.g., ethylene and cyclopropane) and containers of flammable liquids (e.g., diethyl ether, divinyl ether, ethyl chloride) shall be kept out of proximity to cylinders containing oxidizing gases (e.g., oxygen or nitrous oxide) through the use of separate rooms.

E.6.8.11 Storage locations for flammable inhalation agents shall be kept free of cylinders of nitrous oxide, compressed air, oxygen, and mixtures of oxygen.

E.6.8.12 Sources of illumination and ventilation equipment in storage locations for flammable inhalation anesthetic agents, wherever located, and especially in storage locations that are remote from the operative suite, shall be inspected and tested on a regular schedule. Such procedures shall determine that adequate ventilation is maintained under supervision.

E.7 Sample of Regulations for Flammable Anesthetizing Locations

REGULATIONS FOR SAFE PRACTICE IN FLAMMABLE ANESTHETIZING LOCATIONS

The following rules and regulations have been adopted by the medical staff and by the administration. Annex E, Flammable Anesthetizing Locations, of NFPA 99-2005 shall apply in all inhalation anesthetizing locations.

____

(Insert Date) (Insert Name of Hospital Authority)

By reason of their chemical compositions, the following flammable anesthetic agents present a hazard of explosion in anesthetizing locations:

Cyclopropane	Ethyl chloride
Ethyl ether	Ethylene

E.7.1 Flammable Anesthetizing Location.

E.7.1.1 Definition. The term flammable anesthetizing location shall mean any area of the hospital designated for the use of flammable anesthetizing agents.

E.7.2 Equipment

No electrical equipment except that judged by the Engineering Department of __________________________ Hospital as being in compliance with Annex E, Flammable Anesthetizing Locations, of NFPA 99-2005 shall be used in any flammable anesthetizing location.

When a physician wishes to use his or her personal electrical equipment, it shall first be inspected by the Engineering Department and, if judged to comply with Annex E, Flammable Anesthetizing Locations, of NFPA 99-2005, it shall be so labeled.

Portable X-ray equipment used in flammable anesthetizing locations shall be approved for use in hazardous areas.

Only approved photographic lighting equipment shall be used in flammable anesthetizing locations. Because of occasional bursting of bulbs, suitable enclosures shall be used to prevent sparks and hot particles from falling into the hazardous area.

Covers shall not be used on anesthesia machines designed for flammable anesthetic agents.

E.7.3 Personnel

Outer garments worn by the operating room personnel and visitors shall not include fabrics of silk, wool, or synthetic textile materials such as nylon, polyester, acrylic, or acetate unless such fabrics have been tested and found to be antistatic in accordance with the requirements of Annex E, Flammable Anesthetizing Locations, of NFPA 99-2005.

Silk, wool, or synthetic textile materials, except untreated rayon, shall not be permitted in anesthetizing locations as outer garments, or for nonapparel purposes, unless such fabrics have been tested and found to be antistatic in accordance with the requirements of Annex E, Flammable Anesthetizing Locations, of NFPA 99-2005. Hosiery and underclothing in which the entire garment is in close contact with the skin shall be permitted to be of silk, wool, or synthetic material.

All personnel and visitors entering flammable anesthetizing locations shall wear conductive footwear or other floor-contacting devices, that shall have been tested on the wearer and found to be satisfactorily conductive.

It shall be the responsibility of each individual entering a flammable anesthetizing location to determine at least once daily that he is in electrical contact with the conductive floor. Apparatus for testing shall be available.

Moving of patients from one area to another while a flammable anesthetic is being administered shall be prohibited.

Smoking shall be limited to dressing rooms and lounges with the doors leading to the corridor closed.

E.7.4 Practice

Flammable anesthetic agents shall be employed only in flammable anesthetizing locations.

Woolen and synthetic blankets shall not be permitted in flammable anesthetizing locations.

Electrical connection of the patient to the conductive floor shall be ensured by a high-impedance (conductive) strap in contact with the patient's skin with one end of the strap fastened to the metal frame of an operating table or shall be electrically interconnected by other means.

If cautery, electrosurgery, or electrical equipment employing an open spark is to be used during an operation, flammable anesthetics shall not be used. Flammable germicides or flammable fat solvents shall not be applied for the preoperative preparation of the field.

A visual (lighted red lamp) or audible warning signal from the line isolation monitor serving an anesthetizing location indicates that the total hazard current has exceeded allowable limits. This suggests that one or more electrical devices is contributing an excessively low impedance to ground, which might constitute a fault that would expose the patient or hospital personnel to an unsafe condition should an additional fault occur. Briefly and sequentially unplugging the power cord of each electrical device in the location will usually cause the green signal lamp to light, showing that the system has been adequately isolated from ground, when the potentially defective device has been unplugged. The continuing use of such a device, so identified, should be questioned, but not necessarily abandoned. At the earliest opportunity the device should be inspected by the hospital engineer or other qualified personnel and, if necessary, repaired or replaced.

E.7.5 Enforcement

It shall be the responsibility of ________________________ (name)

(an anesthesiologist or other qualified person appointed by the hospital authority to act in that capacity) to enforce the above regulations.

E.8 Sample of Regulations for Mixed Facilities

REGULATIONS FOR SAFE PRACTICE IN MIXED FACILITIES

The following rules and regulations have been adopted by the medical staff and by the administration. NFPA 99-2005, Annex E, Flammable Anesthetizing Locations, shall apply in all inhalation anesthetizing locations. This hospital is a mixed facility. Personnel are cautioned as to the existence of both flammable and nonflammable inhalation anesthetizing locations within the hospital building and the different practices that apply to each location.

____

(Insert Date) (Insert Name of Hospital Authority)

By reason of their chemical compositions, the following flammable anesthetic agents present a hazard of explosion in anesthetizing locations:

Cyclopropane	Ethyl chloride
Ethyl ether	Ethylene

E.8.1 Mixed Facility

E.8.1.1 Definitions. The term *mixed facility* shall mean a hospital wherein flammable anesthetizing locations and nonflammable anesthetizing locations coexist within the same building, allowing interchange of personnel and equipment between flammable and nonflammable anesthetizing locations.

Flammable anesthetizing location shall mean any area of the hospital designated for the administration of flammable anesthetic agents.

Nonflammable anesthetizing location shall mean any anesthetizing location permanently designated for the exclusive use of nonflammable anesthetizing agents.

E.8.2 Equipment

No electrical equipment except that judged by the Engineering Department of ____________________________ Hospital as being in compliance with NFPA 99-2005, Annex E, Flammable Anesthetizing Locations, shall be used in any flammable anesthetizing location.

When a physician wishes to use his or her personal electrical equipment, it shall first be inspected by the Engineering Department and, if judged to comply with NFPA 99-2005, Annex E, Flammable Anesthetizing Locations, it shall be so labeled.

Portable X-ray equipment used in flammable anesthetizing locations shall be approved for use in hazardous areas.

Only approved photographic lighting equipment shall be used in flammable anesthetizing locations. Because of occasional bursting of bulbs, suitable enclosures shall be used to prevent sparks and hot particles from falling into the hazardous area.

Covers shall not be used on anesthesia machines designed for flammable anesthetic agents.

All portable electrical equipment shall meet the requirements for flammable anesthetizing locations.

E.8.3 Personnel

Outer garments worn by the operating room personnel and visitors in mixed facilities shall not include fabrics of silk, wool, or synthetic textile materials such as nylon, polyester, acrylic, or acetate, unless such fabrics have been tested and found to be antistatic in accordance with the requirements of NFPA 99-2005, Annex E, Flammable Anesthetizing Locations.

Silk, wool, or synthetic textile materials, except untreated rayon, shall not be permitted in mixed facilities as outer garments, or for nonapparel purposes, unless such fabrics have been tested and found to be antistatic in accordance with the requirements of NFPA 99-2005, Annex E, Flammable Anesthetizing Locations. Hosiery and underclothing in which the entire garment is in close contact with the skin shall be permitted to be made of silk, wool, or synthetic material.

All personnel and visitors entering all anesthetizing locations in mixed facilities shall wear conductive footwear or other floor-contacting devices that shall have been tested on the wearer and found to be satisfactorily conductive.

It will be the responsibility of each individual entering an anesthetizing location of a mixed facility to determine at least once daily that he is in electrical contact with the conductive floor. Apparatus for testing shall be available.

Moving of patients from one area to another while a flammable anesthetic is being administered shall be prohibited.

Smoking shall be limited to dressing rooms and lounges with the doors leading to the corridor closed.

E.8.4 Practice

Flammable anesthetic agents shall be employed only in flammable anesthetizing locations.

The administration or the intended administration of a flammable anesthetic agent shall be brought to the attention of all personnel within the flammable anesthetizing location by verbal communication by the anesthesiologist and by posting prominent signs in the operating room and at all entrances to the operating room stating that a flammable anesthetic agent is in use.

Woolen and synthetic blankets shall not be permitted in anesthetizing locations.

Electrical connection of the patient to the conductive floor in a flammable anesthetizing location shall be assured by a high-impedance conductive strap in contact with the patient's skin with one end of the strap fastened to the metal frame of an operating table or shall be electrically interconnected by other means.

If cautery, electrosurgery, or electrical equipment employing an open spark is to be used during an operation, flammable anesthetics shall not be used. Flammable germicides and flammable fat solvents shall not be applied for the preoperative preparation of the field.

If, in the combined judgment of the anesthesiologist responsible for the administration of the anesthetic and the surgeon performing the operation, the life of the patient would be jeopardized by not administering a flammable anesthetic agent in a nonflammable anesthetizing location, the following steps shall be taken:

(1) Both surgeon and anesthesiologist involved in the case shall attest to the reason for administering a flammable anesthetic in a nonflammable anesthetizing location on the patient's record and in the operating room register.
(2) The hazard of static sparks shall be reduced by electrically connecting the patient, operating room table, anesthesia gas machine, and anesthesiologist by wet sheets or other conductive materials. Conductive accessories shall be used for the electrically conductive pathways from the anesthesia gas machine to the patient.

A visual (lighted red lamp) or audible warning signal from the line isolation monitor serving an anesthetizing location indicates that the total hazard current has exceeded allowable limits. This suggests that one or more electrical device is contributing an excessively low impedance to ground, which might constitute a fault that would expose the patient or hospital personnel to an unsafe condition should an additional fault occur. Briefly and sequentially unplugging the power cord of each electrical device in the location will usually cause the green signal lamp to light, showing that the system has been adequately isolated from ground, when the potentially defective device has been unplugged. The continuing use of such a device, so identified, should be questioned, but not necessarily abandoned. At the earliest opportunity the device should be inspected by the hospital engineer or other qualified personnel and, if necessary, repaired or replaced.

Interchange of personnel and portable equipment between flammable and nonflammable anesthetizing locations shall be strictly controlled.

Transportation of patients while an inhalation anesthetic is being administered by means of a mobile anesthesia machine shall be prohibited, unless deemed essential for the benefit of the patient in the combined judgment of the surgeon and anesthetist.

E.8.5 Enforcement

It shall be the responsibility of ________________________________ (name)

(an anesthesiologist or other qualified person appointed by the hospital authority to act in that capacity) to enforce the above regulations.

REFERENCES CITED IN COMMENTARY

1. Fineberg, H. V.,, et al., "The Case for Abandonment of Explosive Anesthetic Agents," *New England Journal of Medicine,* September 11, 1980.
2. Duncalf, D., M. D., "Flammable Anesthetics Are Nearing Extinction," *Anesthesiology,* vol. 56, no. 3, March 1982.
3. Vickers, M. D., "Explosion Hazards in Anesthesia," *Anesthesia,* 1970, vol. 25, pp. 482–492.
4. *Code Red!* April 1979 (newsletter of NFPA's Health Care Section).
5. Dunklin and Puck, "Lethal Effect of Relative Humidity on Airborne Bacteria," *Journal of Experimental Medicine,* vol. 87, pp. 87–101, 1988.
6. McDade, J. J., and Hall, L. B., "Survival of *Staphylococcus aureus* in the Environment," *American Journal of Hygiene,* vol. 78, pp. 330–337, 1963.
7. Sonneland, J. E., "Does Operating Room Modernization Affect the Incidence of Infection?", *Hospital Topics,* vol. 44, pp. 149–150, June 1966.
8. Menderhall, M. K., Paper on the study on thermal decomposition of ether, *Journal of the American Medical Association*, 173:123, 1960.

ANNEX F

Sample Ordinance Adopting NFPA 99

This annex is not a part of the requirements of this NFPA document but is included for informational purposes only.

F.1

The following sample ordinance is provided to assist a jurisdiction in the adoption of this code and is not part of this code.

ORDINANCE NO. _____

An ordinance of the *[jurisdiction]* adopting the *[year]* edition of NFPA *[document number]*, *[complete document title]*, and documents listed in Chapter 2 of that *[code, standard]*; prescribing regulations governing conditions hazardous to life and property from fire or explosion; providing for the issuance of permits and collection of fees; repealing Ordinance No. _____ of the *[jurisdiction]* and all other ordinances and parts of ordinances in conflict therewith; providing a penalty; providing a severability clause; and providing for publication; and providing an effective date.

BE IT ORDAINED BY THE *[governing body]* OF THE *[jurisdiction]*:

SECTION 1 That the *[complete document title]* and documents adopted by Chapter 2, three (3) copies of which are on file and are open to inspection by the public in the office of the *[jurisdiction's keeper of records]* of the *[jurisdiction]*, are hereby adopted and incorporated into this ordinance as fully as if set out at length herein, and from the date on which this ordinance shall take effect, the provisions thereof shall be controlling within the limits of the *[jurisdiction]*. The same are hereby adopted as the *[code, standard]* of the *[jurisdiction]* for the purpose of prescribing regulations governing conditions hazardous to life and property from fire or explosion and providing for issuance of permits and collection of fees.

SECTION 2 Any person who shall violate any provision of this code or standard hereby adopted or fail to comply therewith; or who shall violate or fail to comply with any order made thereunder; or who shall build in violation of any detailed statement of specifications or plans submitted and approved thereunder; or fail to operate in accordance with any certificate or permit issued thereunder; and from which no appeal has been taken; or who shall fail to comply with such an order as affirmed or modified by a court of competent jurisdiction, within the time fixed herein, shall severally for each and every such violation and noncompliance, respectively, be guilty of a misdemeanor, punishable by a fine of not less than $ _____ nor more than $_____ or by imprisonment for not less than _____ days nor more than _____ days or by both such fine and imprisonment. The imposition of one penalty for any violation shall not excuse the violation or permit it to continue; and all such persons shall be required to correct or remedy such violations or defects within a reasonable time; and when not otherwise specified the application of the above penalty shall not be held to prevent the enforced removal of prohibited conditions. Each day that prohibited conditions are maintained shall constitute a separate offense.

SECTION 3 Additions, insertions, and changes — that the *[year]* edition of NFPA *[document number]*, *[complete document title]* is amended and changed in the following respects:

List Amendments

SECTION 4 That ordinance No. _____ of *[jurisdiction]* entitled *[fill in the title of the ordinance or ordinances in effect at the present time]* and all other ordinances or parts of ordinances in conflict herewith are hereby repealed.

SECTION 5 That if any section, subsection, sentence, clause, or phrase of this ordinance is, for any reason, held to be invalid or unconstitutional, such decision shall not affect the validity or constitutionality of the remaining portions of this ordinance. The *[governing body]* hereby declares that it would have passed this ordinance, and each section, subsection, clause, or phrase hereof, irrespective of the fact that any one or more sections, subsections, sentences, clauses, and phrases be declared unconstitutional.

SECTION 6 That the *[jurisdiction's keeper of records]* is hereby ordered and directed to cause this ordinance to be published. [NOTE: An additional provision may be required to direct the number of times the ordinance is to be published and to specify that it is to be in a newspaper in general circulation. Posting may also be required.]

SECTION 7 That this ordinance and the rules, regulations, provisions, requirements, orders, and matters established and adopted hereby shall take effect and be in full force and effect *[time period]* from and after the date of its final passage and adoption.

ANNEX G

Informational References

G.1 Referenced Publications

The following documents or portions thereof are referenced within this standard for informational purposes only and are thus not part of the requirements of this document unless also listed in Chapter 2.

G.1.1 NFPA Publications.
National Fire Protection Association, 1 Batterymarch Park, Quincy, MA 02169-7471.

NFPA 10, *Standard for Portable Fire Extinguishers*, 2002 edition.

NFPA 30, *Flammable and Combustible Liquids Code*, 2003 edition.

NFPA 45, *Standard on Fire Protection for Laboratories Using Chemicals*, 2004 edition.

NFPA 49, *Hazardous Chemicals Data*, 1994 edition. (No longer in print; appears in NFPA *Fire Protection Guide to Hazardous Materials,* 13th edition, 2002.)

NFPA 50, *Standard for Bulk Oxygen Systems at Consumer Sites*, 2001 edition.

NFPA 53, *Recommended Practice on Materials, Equipment, and Systems Used in Oxygen-Enriched Atmospheres*, 2004 edition.

NFPA 54, *National Fuel Gas Code*, 2002 edition.

NFPA 70, *National Electrical Code®*, 2002 edition.

NFPA 80, *Standard for Fire Doors and Fire Windows*, 1999 edition.

NFPA 90A, *Standard for the Installation of Air-Conditioning and Ventilating Systems*, 2002 edition.

NFPA 90B, *Standard for the Installation of Warm Air Heating and Air-Conditioning Systems*, 2002 edition.

NFPA 99B, *Standard for Hypobaric Facilities*, 2002 edition.

NFPA *101®*, *Life Safety Code®*, 2003 edition.

NFPA 220, *Standard on Types of Building Construction*, 1999 edition.

NFPA 259, *Standard Test Method for Potential Heat of Building Materials*, 2003 edition.

NFPA 325, *Guide to Fire Hazard Properties of Flammable Liquids, Gases, and Volatile Solids*, 1994 edition. (No longer in print; appears in NFPA *Fire Protection Guide to Hazardous Materials,* 13th edition, 2002.)

NFPA 473, *Standard for Competencies for EMS Personnel Responding to Hazardous Materials Incidents*, 2002 edition.

NFPA 491, *Guide to Hazardous Chemical Reactions*, 1997 edition.

NFPA 701, *Standard Methods of Fire Tests for Flame Propagation of Textiles and Films*, 2004 edition.

NFPA 704, *Standard System for the Identification of the Hazards of Materials for Emergency Response*, 2001 edition.

NFPA 780, *Standard for the Installation of Lightning Protection Systems*, 2004 edition.

NFPA 801, *Standard for Fire Protection for Facilities Handling Radioactive Materials*, 2003 edition.

NFPA 1561, *Standard on Emergency Services Incident Management System*, 2002 edition.

NFPA 1600, *Standard on Disaster/Emergency Management and Business Continuity Programs*, 2004 edition.

NFPA *Fire Protection Guide to Hazardous Materials*, 2001 edition.

NFPA *Fire Protection Handbook*, 19th edition, 2003.

Introduction to Employee Fire and Life Safety: Developing a Preparedness Plan, 2001 edition (for evacuation of all types of occupancies).

G.1.2 Other Publications.
The following publications are available from the addresses listed.

G.1.2.1 AATCC Publication. American Association of Textile Chemists and Colorists, P.O. Box 886, Durham, NC 27701.

AATCC Test Method 76-1995, *Electrical Resistivity of Fabrics*, included in 1962 Technical Manual (ANSI/AATCC 76).

G.1.2.2 ASHRAE Publications. American Society of Heating, Refrigerating and Air Conditioning Engineers, Inc., 1791 Tullie Circle, NE, Atlanta, GA 30329.

ASHRAE Guide and Data Book (Annual).

ASHRAE Handbook of Fundamentals, 2001.

ASHRAE Handbook — HVAC Applications, 1982.

ASHRAE Handbook — HVAC Applications, 1983.

ASHRAE Handbook on HVAC Systems and Equipment, 1996 (Chap. 10, Steam Systems, 1996).

ASHRAE *Handbook — HVAC Applications*, 1999 (Chap. 7, Health Care Facilities, 1995).

ASHRAE Standard 52, *Method of Testing Air Cleaning Devices Used in General Ventilation for Removing Particulate Matter*, 1976.

G.1.2.3 ASME Publications. American Society of Mechanical Engineers, Three Park Avenue, New York, NY 10016–5990.

ASME B16.22, *Wrought Copper and Copper Alloy Solder Joint Pressure Fitting*, 2001.

ASME B16.50, *Wrought Copper and Copper Alloy Braze Joint Pressure Fitting*, 2001.

ASME *Boiler and Pressure Vessel Code*, Section IX, Welding and Brazing Qualifications, 1998.

G.1.2.4 ASTM Publications. American Society for Testing and Materials, 100 Barr Harbor Drive, West Conshohocken, PA 19428.

ASTM D 5, *Standard Test Method for Penetration of Bituminous Materials*, 1997.

ASTM D 56, *Standard Test Method for Flash Point by Tag Closed Tester* (ANSI), 1998.

ASTM D 92, *Standard Test Method for Flash and Fire Points by Cleveland Open Cup Tester*, 2002.

ASTM D 93, *Standard Test Methods for Flash Point by Pensky-Martens Closed Cup Tester* (ANSI), 1999.

ASTM D 2240, *Standard Test Method for Rubber Property — Durometer Hardness*, 1997.

ASTM D 2863, *Standard Test Method for Measuring the Minimum Oxygen Concentration to Support Candle-Like Combustion of Plastics*, 2000.

ASTM E 136, *Standard Test Method for Behavior of Materials in a Vertical Tube Furnace at 750°C*, 2004.

ASTM F 1288, *Standard Guide for Planning for and Responding to a Multiple Casualty Incident*, 1990. (Committee F 30, 1990)

ASTM G 63, *Standard Guide for Evaluating Nonmetallic Materials for Oxygen Service*, 1998.
ASTM G 88, *Standard Guide for Designing Systems for Oxygen Service*, 1990.
ASTM G 93, *Standard Practice for Cleaning Methods and Cleanliness Levels for Material and Equipment Used in Oxygen-Enriched Environments*, 1996.
ASTM G 94, *Standard Guide for Evaluating Metals for Oxygen Service*, 1992.

G.1.2.5 CGA Publications. Compressed Gas Association, Inc., 4221 Walney Road, 5th Floor, Chantilly, VA 20151–2923.

CGA E-10, *Maintenance of Medical Gas and Vacuum Systems in Health Care Facilities*, 2001.
CGA G-8.1, *Standard for Nitrous Oxide Systems at Consumer Sites*, 1990.
CGA P-1, *Safe Handling of Compressed Gases in Containers*, 1991.
CGA P-2, *Characteristics and Safe Handling of Medical Gases*, 1996.
CGA V-1, *Standard for Compressed Gas Cylinder Valve Outlet and Inlet Connections* (ANSI B57.1), 1994.
CGA V-5, *Diameter-Index Safety System (Noninterchangeable Low Pressure Connections for Medical Gas Applications)*, 2000.

G.1.2.6 JCAHO Publication. Joint Commission on the Accreditation of Healthcare Organizations, One Renaissance Blvd., Oakbrook Terrace, IL 60181.

Comprehensive Accreditation Manual for Hospitals.
Environment of Care, Emergency Management Standards Guide to Emergency Management Planning in Health Care.

G.1.2.7 Ocean Systems, Inc., Research and Development Laboratory, Tarrytown, NY 10591. Work carried out under U.S. Office of Contract No. N00014-67-A-0214-0013.

Ocean Systems, Inc., "Technical Memorandum UCRI-721, Chamber Fire Safety." (Figure A.3.3.14.3 is adapted from Figure 4, "Technical Memorandum UCRI-721, Chamber Fire Safety," T. C. Schmidt, V. A. Dorr, and R. W. Hamilton, Jr., Ocean Systems, Inc., Research and Development Laboratory, Tarrytown, NY 10591. Work carried out under US Office of Naval Research, Washington, DC, Contract No. N00014-67-A-0214-0013.) (G. A. Cook, R. E. Meierer, and B. M. Shields, "Screening of Flame-Resistant Materials and Comparison of Helium with Nitrogen for Use in Dividing Atmospheres." First summary report under ONR Contract No. 0014-66-C-0149. Tonawanda, NY: Union Carbide, 31 March 1967. DDC No. Ad-651583.)

G.1.2.8 UNECE Publications. UN Economic Commission for Europe, Information Service, Palais des Nations, CH-1211 Geneva 10, Switzerland.

UN *Recommendations on the Transport of Dangerous Goods, Model Regulations*, 11th, rev. ed.
Manual of Tests and Criteria, 3rd rev. ed.

G.1.2.9 U.S. Government Publications. U.S. Government Printing Office, Washington, DC 20402.

Biological Threat Interrogatories, http://www.va.gov/emshg/page.cfm?ID=BioThreatInterr.
Title 29, Code of Federal Regulations, Part 1910, Subpart 1030, *Bloodborne Pathogens*.
Title 29, Code of Federal Regulations, Part 910, Subpart 1910, *Occupational Exposures to Chemical Laboratories*.
Title 49, Code of Federal Regulations, Parts 171 through 190 (U.S. Dept. of Transportation, Specifications for Transportation of Explosives & Dangerous Articles). (In

Canada, the regulations of the Board of Transport Commissioners, Union Station, Ottawa, Canada, apply.)

Title 49, Code of Federal Regulations, Part 173, *Shippers — General Requirements for Shipments and Packagings*.

Commercial Standard 223-59, *Casters, Wheels, and Glides for Hospital Equipment*.

Environmental Protection Agency, Chemical Emergency Preparedness and Prevention, http://yosemite.epa.gov/oswer/ceppoweb.nsf/content/homelandSecurity.htm?OpenDocument.

National Research Council Publication 1132, *Diesel Engines for Use with Generators to Supply Emergency and Short Term Electric Power.* (Also available as Order No. O.P.52870 from University Microfilms, P.O. Box 1366, Ann Arbor, MI 48106.)

U.S. Department of Defense:

U.S. Army Medical Research Institute of Chemical Defense (USAMRICD), http://chemdef.apgea.army.mil/.

U.S. Army Medical Research Institute of Infectious Diseases (USAMRIID), http://www.usamriid.army.mil/general/index.html.

U.S. Army Soldier and Biological Chemical Command (SBCCOM), http://hld.sbccom.army.mil/ip/detectors.

U.S. Department of Health and Human Services:

Centers for Disease Control and Prevention: HHS Publication No. 93–8395, *Biosafety in Microbiological and Biomedical Laboratories*.

Centers for Disease Control and Prevention, Public Health Preparedness and Response for Bioterrorism Program, http://www.bt.cdc.gov/planning/continuationguidance/index.asp.

Health Resources and Services Administration, Hospital Bioterrorism Preparedness Program, www.hrsa.gov/bioterrorism.

National Institute for Occupational Health and Safety, Personal Protection Equipment, http://www.cdc.gov/niosh/topics/emres/ppe.html.

Protecting Building Environments from Airborne Chemical, Biologic and Radiologic Agents (page 9). http://www.cdc.gov/mmwr/PDF/wk/mm5135.pdf.

U.S. Department of Homeland Security:

Capability Assessment for Readiness, http://www.fema.gov/pdf/rrr/car.pdf.

Exercise Design Course, http://training.fema.gov/emiweb/IS/is120.asp.

Federal Response Plan/National Response Plan/National Incident Management System, www.fema.gov/rnr/frp.

Guide for All-Hazard Emergency Operations Planning, http://www.fema.gov/pdf/rrr/slg101.pdf.

Metropolitan Medical Response System, Resources, http://mmrs.hhs.gov/main/Resources.aspx.

National Disaster Medical System, Conference Library, http://ndms.dhhs.gov/NDMS%20Conference/conf2k3/previous_confe_03/previous_confe_03.html.

Strategic National Stockpile, http://www.bt.cdc.gov/stockpile/index.asp.

U.S. Department of Justice, Office of Domestic Preparedness, Publications Library, http://www.ojp.usdoj.gov/odp/library/bulletins.htm.

U.S. Department of Labor, Occupational Health and Safety Administration, Washington, DC:

Title 29, Code of Federal Regulations, Part 1910:

Employee Protection Plans, 1910.38

Hazardous Materials

Subpart H — *Hazardous Materials* (1910.101-126), specifically 1910.120 — *Hazardous Waste Operations and Emergency Response* (HAZWOPER) and Appendices A–E.

Subpart I — *Personal Protective Equipment* (1910.132-139 and Appendix B), specifically:

1910.132, *General Provisions*
1910.133, *Eye and Face Protection*
1910.134, *Respiratory Protection* (and appendices A-D)
1910.136, *Occupational Foot Protection*
1910.138, *Hand Protection*
Subpart Z — *Toxic and Hazardous Substances* (1910.1000-1450 and Appendix B), specifically 1910.1200 — *Hazard Communication* (and Appendices A–E).
Publication 3114, *Hazardous Waste Operations and Emergency Response*, http://www.osha.gov/Publications/OSHA3114/osha3114.html.
Publication 3152, *Hospitals and Community Emergency Response – What You Need to Know*, http://www.osha.gov/Publications/OSHA3152/osha3152.html.
U.S. Department of Veterans Affairs, Veterans Health Administration, http://www.va.gov/emshg/emp/emp.htm, *Emergency Management Program Guidebook*, Health Care Facility.

G.1.2.10 U.S. Pharmacopeia Publication. U.S. Pharmacopeia, 12601 Twinbrook Parkway, Rockville, MD 20852.

USP *Standard for Compressed Air*, Document No. XXII/NFXVII.

G.1.2.11 Other Publications.

DuPont Safety News, June 14, 1965.

Dasler and Bauer, Ind. Eng. Chem. Anal., Ed. 18, 52 (1964).
Hoeltge, G. A., Miller, A., Klein, B. R., Hamlin, W. B., *Accidental fires in clinical laboratories*.
Merriam-Webster's Collegiate Dictionary, 11th edition, Merriam-Webster, Inc., Springfield, MA, 2003.

G.2 Informational References

The following documents or portions thereof are listed here as informational resources only. They are not a part of the requirements of this document.

G.2.1 Published Articles on Fire Involving Respiratory Therapy Equipment, and Related Incidents.

Benson, D. M., and Wecht, C. H. Conflagration in an ambulance oxygen system. *Journal of Trauma*, vol. 15, no. 6:536–649, 1975.
Dillon, J. J. Cry fire! *Respiratory Care*, vol. 21, no. 11:1139–1140, 1976.
Gjerde, G. E., and Kraemer, R. An oxygen therapy fire. *Respiratory Care*, vol. 25, no. 3 3:362–363, 1980.
Walter, C. W. Fire in an oxygen-powered respirator. *JAMA* 197:44–46, 1960.
Webre, D. E., Leon, R., and Larson, N.W. Case History; Fire in a nebulizer. *Anesthesia and Analgesia* 52:843–848, 1973.

G.2.2 References for A.10.2.13.4.3.

Dalziel, C. F., and Lee, W. R., Reevaluation of lethal, electric currents effects of electricity on man. *Transactions on Industry and General Applications*, vol. IGA-4, no. 5, September/October 1968.
Roy, O. A., Park, G. R., and Scott, J. R., Intracardiac catheter fibrillation thresholds as a function of duration of 60 Hz current and electrode area. *IEEE Trans. Biomed. Eng.* BME 24:430–435, 1977.
Roy, O. A., and Scott, J. R., 60 Hz ventricular fibrillation and pump failure thresholds versus electrode area. *IEEE Trans. Biomed. Eng.* BME 23:45–48, 1976.

Watson, A. B., Wright, J. S., and Loughman, J., Electrical thresholds for ventricular fibrillation in man. *Med. J. Australia* 1:1179–1181, 1973.

Weinberg, D. I., et al., Electric shock hazards in cardiac catheterization. *Elec. Eng.* 82:30–35, 1963.

G.2.3 Addresses of Other Organizations that Publish Standards or Guidelines.

American Conference of Governmental and Industrial Hygienists, P.O. Box 1937, Cincinnati, OH 45201.

American Industrial Hygiene Assoc., 475 Wolf Ledges Parkway, Akron, OH 44311.

College of American Pathologists, 325 Waukegan Road, Northfield, IL 60003.

George Washington University, School of Engineering and Applied Sciences, Institute for Crisis, Disaster and Risk Management. *Medical and Health Incident Management (maHim) System: A Comprehensive Functional System Description for Mass Casually Medical and Health Incident Management*, http://www.seas.gwu.edu/~icdm/MaHIM%20V2%20final%20report%20sec%202.pdf.

National Emergency Management Association, Council of State Governments, Lexington, KY, Emergency Management Assistance Compact, http://www.emacweb.org/emac/index.cfm?CFID=5327&CFTOKEN=28115803.

Scientific Apparatus Makers Assoc., 1101 16th Street, NW, Washington, DC 20036.

University of Colorado, Natural Hazards and Information Applications Center, Disaster Research Clearinghouse, www.colorado.edu/hazards.

University of Delaware, Disaster Research Center, http://www.udel.edu/DRC/.

G.2.4 Addresses of Organizations and Agencies that Provide Health Care Emergency Preparedness Educational Materials.

G.2.4.1 Publications. National Fire Protection Association, 1 Batterymarch Park, Quincy, MA 02169-7471.

American Health Care Association, 1201 L Street, Washington, DC 20005.

American Hospital Association, 840 North Lake Shore Drive, Chicago, IL 60611.

American Medical Association, 515 N. State Street, Chicago, IL 60610.

American Red Cross, National Headquarters, 2025 E Street, NW, Washington, DC 20006.

American Nurses' Association, 8515 Georgia Avenue, Suite 400, Silver Spring, MD 20910.

American Red Cross:

Family Disaster Planning http://www.redcross.org/services/disaster/beprepared/familyplan.html Disaster Preparedness for People with Disabilities http://www.redcross.org/services/disaster/beprepared/disability.html

Association of American Railroads, 50 F Street, Washington, DC 20001-1564.

Charles C. Thomas Publisher, 2600 South First Street, Springfield, IL 62704.

Dun-Donnelley Publishing Corp., 666 Fifth Avenue, New York, NY 10019.

Federal Emergency Management Agency, 500 C Street, SW, Washington, DC 20472.

Florida Health Care Association, 307 W. Park Avenue, P.O. Box 1459, Tallahassee, FL 32301.

Helicopter Association International, 1635 Prince Street, Alexandria, VA 22314-2818.

Hospital Emergency Incident Command System, State of California Emergency Medical Services Authority, 1930 9th Street, Sacramento, CA 95814. http://www.emsa.ca.gov/dms2/heics3.htm

International Association of Fire Chiefs, 4025 Fair Ridge Drive, Suite 300, Fairfax, VA 22033-2868.

Joint Commission on Accreditation of Healthcare Organizations (JCAHO), One Renaissance Blvd., Oakbrook Terrace, IL 60181.

National Interagency Incident Management System, Incident Command System, National Interagency Fire Coordination Center, Boise, ID. http://www.nwcg.gov/pms/forms/ics_cours/ics_courses.htm
Pan American Health Organization, 525 23rd Street, NW, Washington, DC 20037 (Attn.: Editor, Disaster Preparedness in the Americas).
Standardized Emergency Management System, State of California Governor's Office of Emergency Services, 3650 Schreiber Avenue, Mather, CA 95655. http://www.oes.ca.gov/Operational/OESHome.nsf/Content/B4943535210895448825 6C2A0071E038?OpenDocument
University of Delaware, Disaster Research Center (Publications), Newark, DE 19716.
U.S. Department of Transportation (available from U.S. Government Printing Office, Washington, DC 20402).

G.2.4.2 Audio-Visual Materials. Many of the web links listed in G.2.4.1 contain PowerPoint presentations and/or streaming video.

National Fire Protection Association, 1 Batterymarch Park, Quincy, MA 02169-7471.
Abbott Laboratories, Audio/Visual Services, 565 Fifth Avenue, New York, NY 10017.
Brose Productions, Inc., 10850 Riverside Drive, N. Hollywood, CA 91602.
Federal Emergency Management Agency, Office of Public Affairs, Washington, DC 20472.
Fire Prevention Through Films, Inc., P.O. Box 11, Newton Highlands, MA 02161.
General Services Administration, National Audiovisual Center, Reference Section, Washington, DC 20409.
Helicopter Association International, 1635 Prince Street, Alexandria, VA 22314-2818.
Pyramid, P.O. Box 1048, Santa Monica, CA 90406.
University of Illinois Medical Center, Circle Campus, Chicago, IL 60612.

G.3 References for Extracts

The following documents are listed here to provide reference information, including title and edition, for extracts given throughout the nonmandatory sections of this standard as indicated by a reference in brackets [ ] following a section or paragraph. These documents are not a part of the requirements of this document unless also listed in Chapter 2 for other reasons.

NFPA 30, *Flammable and Combustible Liquids Code*, 2003 edition.
NFPA 45, *Standard on Fire Protection for Laboratories Using Chemicals,* 2004 edition.
NFPA 70, *National Electrical Code®*, 2002 edition.
NFPA 99B, *Standard for Hypobaric Facilities*, 2002 edition.
NFPA *101®*, *Life Safety Code®*, 2003 edition.
NFPA 1670, *Standard on Operations and Training for Technical Search and Rescue Incidents*, 2004 edition.

This list is neither an exhaustive list nor an endorsement of the materials mentioned.

PART TWO

Supplements

Part Two of this handbook is devoted to supplements that explore in detail the background of some topics related to NFPA 99. Supplements are not part of the standard but are included as additional information for handbook users.

Supplement 1

Overview of Fire Incidents in Health Care Facilities

Craig H. Kampmier

Craig Kampmier is a former staff liaison to NFPA's Technical Correlating Committee on Health Care Facilities.

INTRODUCTION

The application of codes and standards has contributed significantly to the continued decline of fire frequency and severity in health care facilities. To appreciate this accomplishment, it is necessary to examine some statistics from the recent past.

There are numerous dimensions to the classification of health care facilities and the statistical categories of *Facilities that Care for the Sick Excluding Nursing Homes and Residential Board and Care* and *Facilities that Care for the Aged Including Nursing Homes and Residential Board and Care.* A discussion would include hospitals, primary care clinics, diagnostic centers, physician group practices, nursing homes, assisted living, and group homes. However, the occupancy classifications might pose differences in the requirements of codes and standards and in the categorization of occupancies for the reporting and data compilation of incidents. Statistical representation is achieved through database continuity, allowing for some of the occupancy designations to suggest a variation from current health care vernacular, but the function of care delivery and risk from fire and other hazards remains within the established parameters.

THE STATISTICS

The first nationally representative statistics on U.S. reported fires became available in 1980. Since that time, between 1980 and 2001 the number of reported structure fires occurring in hospitals, sanatoriums, clinics, and hospital or clinic-type infirmaries has sharply declined. See Exhibit S1.1.

Although the number of reported fires occurring in facilities that care for the aged, with and without nursing staff, and in unclassified or unknown-type care of the aged care facilities declined between 1980 and 1998, there was an increase between 1998 and 2001. See Exhibit S1.2.

The number of fires, civilian deaths and injuries, and property damage associated with structure fires in facilities that care for the sick (excluding nursing homes and residential board and care facilities) decreased between 1980 and 2001. See Table S1.1.

NFPA statistical data in *Leading Causes and Other Patterns and Trends, Facilities that Care for the Aged and Sick* [1] does not differentiate between nursing homes and other occupancies that house the aged or infirmed. The relevance is that the number of incidents and risk involving this population has not diminished between 1980 and 2001. See Table S1.2.

MULTIPLE-DEATH FIRES

Common factors in the multiple-death fires in hospitals during the first two-thirds of the twentieth century include building construction; interior finish, contents, and decorative materials; absence of building compartmentation; means of egress; ignition sources; absence of detection and

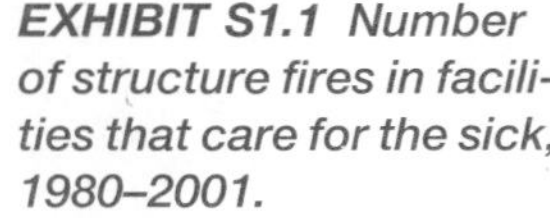

EXHIBIT S1.1 *Number of structure fires in facilities that care for the sick, 1980–2001.*

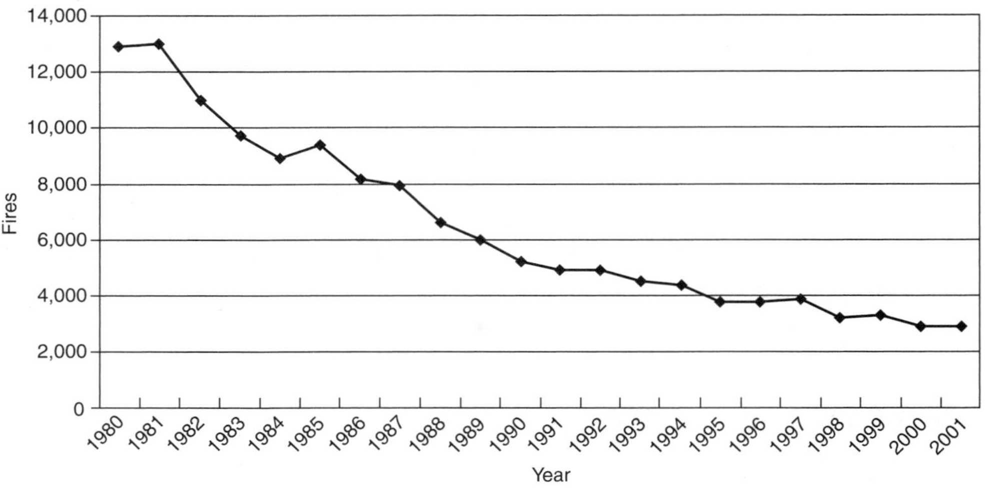

EXHIBIT S1.2 *Number of structure fires in facilities that care for the aged, 1980–2001.*

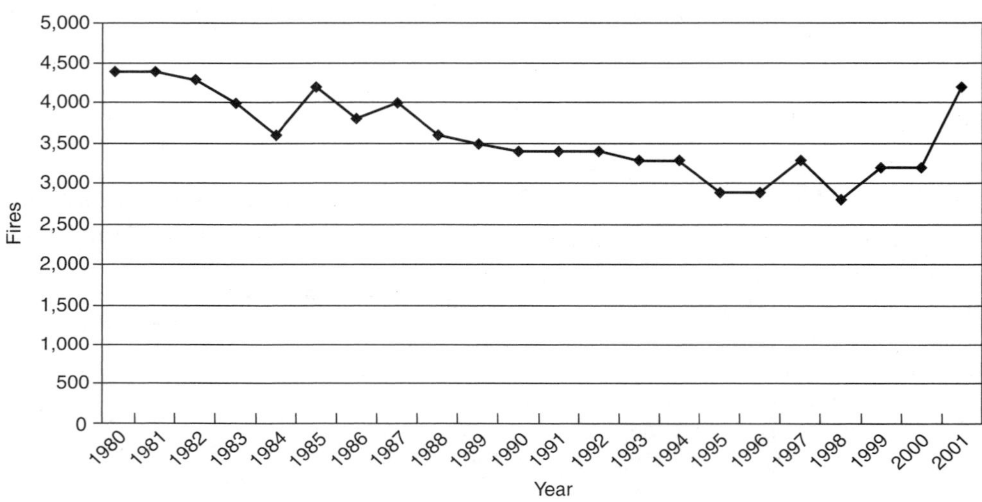

suppression systems; closing of room doors; staff training; and fire procedure rehearsal (drills). The last hospital fire to kill 10 or more people was the Hartford Hospital fire in 1961. Facilities that care for the aged sustained a loss of 12 patients in 1989 at a convalescent center, and in 2003 fires at a nursing home in Hartford and in Nashville sustained multiple deaths.

Although, statistically, residential board and care fires are included in facilities that care for the aged and have incurred loss of life to fire, they differ in their occupancy classification from health care occupancies. Fire incidents involving respiratory therapy (oxygen) and surgical procedures (cauterizing devices, oxygen, and alcohol-based agents) do occur but are absent from statistically representative data reporting; hence no representative conclusions can be drawn except to note their occurrence. Advances in health care have enabled many people to maintain themselves at home, and the media occasionally report incidents of smoking while on respiratory therapy (oxygen). Through the efforts of NFPA during the mid-1900s, the use of flammable anesthetics subsided in U.S hospital operating rooms, curtailing the explosions and losses that occurred prior to that time. See Table S1.3 for examples of life loss health care fires.

There are correlations among fires of the past, fires of recent history, and NFPA codes and standards. The common factors of multiple-death fires of the past transcend to NFPA *101*®, *Life Safety Code*® [2], and NFPA 99, *Standard for Health Care Facilities.* Provisions in NFPA *101* and NFPA 99 address building features, contents, hazards, staff, and procedures. A theme can be found between factors and sections within the NFPA documents and changes in the patterns and trends of fires and multiple deaths. See Table S1.4. Application of the most recent

***TABLE S1.1** Structure Fires in Facilities that Care for the Sick, Excluding Nursing Homes and Residential Board and Care Facilities by Year: 1980–2001*

Year	*Fires*	*Civilian Deaths*	*Civilian Injuries*	*Direct Property Damage $ (in millions)*	*Adjusted Loss for 2001 $ (in millions)*
1980	12,900	13	355	19.0	40.9
1981	13,000	8	362	12.5	24.3
1982	11,000	5	276	82.6*	151.3*
1983	9,700	23	307	8.4	14.9
1984	8,900	5	187	7.1	12.1
1985	9,400	13	284	9.3	15.3
1986	8,200	23	257	10.2	16.5
1987	7,900	13	220	12.9	20.1
1988	6,600	9	239	18.4	27.6
1989	6,000	17	237	14.7	21.0
1990	5,200	10	233	19.1	25.9
1991	4,900	3	170	28.2	36.6
1992	4,900	11	132	15.5	19.6
1993	4,500	4	255	18.1	22.2
1994	4,400	8	141	13.9	16.6
1995	3,800	9	188	11.3	13.1
1996	3,800	1	127	13.6	15.4
1997	3,900	9	162	9.4	10.4
1998	3,200	6	136	12.1	13.1
1999	3,300	0	124	12.6	13.4
2000	2,900	2	100	27.7	28.5
2001	2,900	0	68	17.9	17.9

*Direct property damage in 1982 was artificially inflated by a fire that was reported to have had a $30 million loss. This figure is believed to be in error. Actual loss for 1982 is most likely consistent with other fires in the 1980s.

Notes:

1. These are national estimates of fires reported to U.S. municipal fire departments and so exclude fires reported only to federal or state agencies or industrial fire brigades. National estimates are projections. Casualty and loss projections can be heavily influenced by the inclusion or exclusion of one unusually serious fire. Fires are expressed to the nearest hundred, deaths and injuries are rounded to the nearest one, and property damage is rounded to the nearest hundred thousand dollars.
2. The changes in NFIRS coding that accompanied the introduction of Version 5.0 in 1999 dictate special care in comparing statistics from before and after 1999. The proportion of data collected under these rules has been steadily increasing since 1999. Pay close attention to text discussions of how best to interpret trend data.

Source: NFIRS and NFPA survey. Inflation adjustments were based on purchasing power of the dollar information found at http://bls.gov/cpi/.

requirements and *grandfathering* could be a contributing factor to the fires that have sustained loss of life. Two human factors are prevalent throughout negative and positive outcome fires: staff training and procedure rehearsal (drills), and the closing of doors.

From 1999 to 2001 the leading causes of fire in facilities that care for the sick were *cooking equipment* (33.9 percent), followed by *appliance, tool or air conditioning* (12.4 percent), *intentional* (12.0 percent), *electrical* (9.4 percent), and *smoking material* (8.2 percent). See Table S1.5. During the same time period for facilities that care for the aged, the leading causes were *cooking equipment* (41.2 percent); *appliance, tool or air conditioning* (20.2 percent), *heating equipment* (9.8 percent), *smoking material* (8.3 percent), and *electrical* (6.7 percent). See Table S1.6.

The leading areas of fire origin from 1999 to 2001 in facilities that care for the sick were *cooking area or kitchen* (31 percent), *bedroom* (10.1 percent), and *laundry area* (7.6 percent). See Table S1.7. In facilities that care for the aged the leading areas of fire origin were *cooking area or kitchen* (37.9 percent), *laundry area* (15.8 percent), and *bedroom* (12.2 percent). See Table S1.8.

TABLE S1.2 Structure Fires in Facilities that Care for the Aged, Including Nursing Homes and Residential Board and Care Facilities by Year: 1980–2001

Year	Fires	Civilian Deaths	Civilian Injuries	Direct Property Damage $ (in millions)	Adjusted Loss for 2001 $ (in millions)
1980	4,400	19	138	1.9	4.1
1981	4,400	18	294	2.7	5.2
1982	4,300	29	150	2.5	4.6
1983	4,000	9	209	2.5	4.4
1984	3,600	24	176	4.0	6.8
1985	4,200	29	247	5.7	9.4
1986	3,800	11	209	3.5	5.7
1987	4,000	9	125	3.4	5.3
1988	3,600	24	262	14.8	22.2
1989	3,500	7	152	5.7	8.1
1990	3,400	12	301	4.2	5.7
1991	3,400	16	337	11.9	15.5
1992	3,400	4	218	6.7	8.5
1993	3,300	5	305	5.4	6.6
1994	3,300	9	286	9.8	11.7
1995	2,900	25	222	4.4	5.1
1996	2,900	10	170	7.4	8.4
1997	3,300	12	302	5.0	5.5
1998	2,800	2	225	7.2	7.8
1999	3,200	3	150	10.7	11.4
2000	3,200	11	170	6.4	6.6
2001	4,200	16	165	16.2	16.2

Notes:

1.These are national estimates of fires reported to U.S. municipal fire departments and so exclude fires reported only to federal or state agencies or industrial fire brigades. National estimates are projections. Casualty and loss projections can be heavily influenced by the inclusion or exclusion of one unusually serious fire. Fires are expressed to the nearest hundred, deaths and injuries are rounded to the nearest one, and property damage is rounded to the nearest hundred thousand dollars. Property damage figures have not been adjusted for inflation.

2. Version 5.0 of NFIRS, introduced in some jurisdictions in 1999, was the first version to contain a specific code that identified residential board and care facilities. In earlier versions, some board and care facility fires were captured in the care of aged category and some were captured under rooming, boarding, or lodging houses. Those captured under rooming, boarding, or lodging houses are not included here.

3. The changes in NFIRS coding that accompanied the introduction of Version 5.0 in 1999 dictate special care in comparing statistics from before and after 1999. The proportion of data collected under these rules has been steadily increasing since 1999. Pay close attention to text discussions of how best to interpret trend data.

Source: NFIRS and NFPA survey. Inflation adjustments were based on purchasing power of the dollar information found at http://bls.gov/cpi/.

SPRINKLERS

NFPA has no record of a fire killing more than two people in a completely sprinklered public assembly or educational, institutional, or residential building where the system was properly operating. (Health care occupancies used to be referred to as institutional.) In care of sick and aged facilities, sprinklers provided a 59 percent reduction in average direct property damage per fire versus in unsprinklered facilities in the period 1989 to 1998 [3]. The success stories of no lives lost to fire when there was sprinkler presence in hospitals and nursing homes to control or extinguish the fire span decades. See Table S1.9.

CONCLUSION

Fires remain a reality within our health care facilities and require continued vigilance in building construction, operational components, training, and rehearsal of emergency procedures through fire drills. The application of consensus

TABLE S1.3 Examples of Health Care Facilities Incurring Loss of Life During a Fire

Year	Facility	Civilian Deaths	Contributing Factor/Cause
1918	Grey Nunnery Montreal, CA	53 infants	Defective chimney
1929	Crile Clinic Cleveland, OH	125	X-ray film
1934	Kentucky Baptist Hospital Louisville, KY	1	Birthday cake with candle in oxygen tent
1949	St. Anthony's Hospital Effingham, IL	74	Undetermined
1950	Mercy Hospital Davenport, IA	41	Patient ignited window curtains
1961	Hartford Hospital Hartford, CT	16	Rubbish chute
1970	Harmer House Convalescent Home Marietta, OH	31	Smoking materials
1989	Hillhaven Rehabilitation and Convalescent Center Norfolk, VA	12	Smoking materials
1994	Petersburg Hospital Petersburg, VA	5	Smoking materials
2003	Greenwood Health Center Hartford, CT	16	Patient ignited bedding
2003	NHC Healthcare Center Nashville, TN	15	Undetermined

TABLE S1.4 Common Themes Among Past Fires, Hazards, the Ability to Sustain Patients in the Environment of Care, and NFPA 101® and NFPA 99

- Enclosed stairwells
- Exit access, exits, and exit discharge
- Length of travel
- Building divisions/smoke barriers/compartments
- Early detection
- Occupant warning
- Fire department notification
- Evacuation/fire procedure
- Sprinklers
- Furnishings/bedding/decorations
- Interior finish
- Combustible construction
- 1 ¾ in. solid bonded wood core doors
- Transoms
- Pipe chases
- Rubbish/laundry chutes
- Elevator shafts
- Training
- Fire procedure rehearsal
- Explosions
- Emergency power
- Electrical leakage
- Disruption of routine
- Influx (surge) of patients

codes and standards, as well as education, have contributed to health care facilities, as a whole, being safer locations in which to receive care than they were decades ago. Subjectively, the reduction or curtailment of smoking within health care facilities during the past twenty years has lessened its contribution as an ignition source.

Although changes and advancements in the provision of health care through technology and energy sources have enhanced our well-being, their role as one of the leading causes of fire remains relevant. The leading cause of fire and area of fire origin involves cooking equipment and cooking areas. Food preparation is not limited to the cafeteria or dining room area; stoves can still be found on nursing units. Microwave ovens have replaced the hotplates of yesteryear and can be found throughout a facility. Toasters, once common in nursing units for patients' toast, can be found in other areas of a facility for the breakfast or mid-shift bagel.

Automatic sprinkler systems have proven themselves as a means of saving lives, reducing the cost of property damage, and improving business continuity by minimizing the loss of resources and ensuring the ability to resume the normal routine of health care facility activities. The absence of sprinklers is reflected in the repetition of history.

TABLE S1.5 *Structure Fires in Facilities that Care for the Sick, Excluding Nursing Homes and Residential Board and Care by Cause, 1999–2001*

	Fires		*Civilian Deaths*		*Civilian Injuries*		*Direct Property Damage*	
Cause	*No.*	*%*	*No.*	*%*	*No.*	*%*	*$ (in millions)*	*%*
Cooking equipment	1,030	(33.9)	0	(0.0)	13	(13.6)	0.8	(4.0)
Appliance, tool, or air conditioning	380	(12.4)	0	(0.0)	15	(15.4)	1.2	(6.0)
Intentional	370	(12.0)	0	(0.0)	18	(18.7)	9.0	(46.2)
Electrical	290	(9.4)	0	(0.0)	14	(14.7)	3.9	(20.1)
Smoking material	250	(8.2)	1	(100.0)	11	(11.1)	0.8	(4.3)
Open flame, ember, or torch	230	(7.5)	0	(0.0)	12	(12.6)	1.8	(9.3)
Other equipment	230	(7.5)	0	(0.0)	3	(2.6)	0.7	(3.4)
Heating	180	(5.7)	0	(0.0)	6	(6.0)	0.5	(2.5)
Other heat, flame, or spark	70	(2.3)	0	(0.0)	2	(1.9)	0.1	(0.7)
Child playing	10	(0.5)	0	(0.0)	2	(2.5)	0.1	(0.7)
Natural causes	10	(0.4)	0	(0.0)	1	(0.8)	0.3	(1.5)
Exposure	10	(0.3)	0	(0.0)	0	(0.0)	0.3	(1.3)
Total	3,050	(100.0)	1	(100.0)	97	(100.0)	19.4	(100.0)

Notes:
1. Structure fires (incident type 11) in care of sick facilities (fixed property use 321–340) are included in this table. Fires of unknown cause or with cause not reported have been allocated proportionally as part of the calculation.
2. Fires are rounded to the nearest ten, casualties are rounded to the nearest one; direct property damage is rounded to the nearest hundred thousand dollars. Percentages are calculated on the actual estimates, so two figures with the same rounded-off estimates might have different percentages. Sums might not equal due to rounding errors. Damage has not been adjusted for inflation.
3. The changes in NFIRS coding that accompanied the introduction of Version 5.0 in 1999 dictate special care in comparing statistics from before and after 1999. The proportion of data collected under these rules has been steadily increasing since 1999. Pay close attention to text discussions of how best to interpret trend data.
4. The reporting of confined cooking fires (and certain other confined fires) has been simplified, which can result in an apparent increase in the number and share of these fires. The code "suspicious" has been eliminated. This may result in an apparent decline in the number of intentional (previously incendiary and suspicious) fires.
5. These are national estimates of fires reported to U.S. municipal fire departments and so exclude fires reported only to federal or state agencies or industrial fire brigades. National estimates are projections. Casualty and loss projections can be heavily influenced by the inclusion or exclusion of one unusually serious fire.
Source: National estimates based on NFIRS and NFPA survey.

TABLE S1.6 *Structure Fires in Facilities that Care for the Aged, Including Nursing Homes and Residential Board and Care by Cause, 1999–2001*

	Fires		*Civilian Deaths*		*Civilian Injuries*		*Direct Property Damage*	
Cause	*No.*	*%*	*No.*	*%*	*No.*	*%*	*$ (in millions)*	*%*
Cooking equipment	1,450	(41.2)	1	(6.4)	30	(18.6)	1.3	(11.8)
Appliance, tool, or air conditioning	710	(20.2)	0	(0.0)	36	(22.0)	2.5	(22.9)
Heating equipment	340	(9.8)	0	(0.0)	12	(7.7)	0.3	(2.5)
Smoking material	290	(8.3)	7	(66.8)	25	(15.5)	0.7	(6.2)
Electrical	240	(6.7)	1	(6.4)	19	(11.8)	0.8	(7.6)
Intentional	160	(4.5)	1	(6.8)	16	(10.0)	1.6	(14.1)
Open flame, ember, or torch	120	(3.5)	1	(13.6)	21	(12.7)	0.4	(3.4)
Other equipment	100	(2.7)	0	(0.0)	1	(0.5)	2.8	(25.0)
Other heat, flame, or spark	70	(2.0)	0	(0.0)	1	(0.6)	0.2	(1.5)
Natural causes	20	(0.5)	0	(0.0)	1	(0.5)	0.3	(2.8)
Exposure	10	(0.4)	0	(0.0)	0	(0.0)	0.2	(2.1)
Child playing	10	(0.2)	0	(0.0)	0	(0.0)	0.0	(0.1)
Total	3,530	(100.0)	11	(100.0)	162	(100.0)	11.1	(100.0)

Notes:
1. Estimated annual averages of unknown-cause fires are allocated proportionally.
2. Properties coded as facilities that care for the aged without nursing staff and children's homes or orphanages in earlier versions of NFIRS convert to residential board and care facilities in NFIRS Version 5.0. About 100 children's home or orphanage fires were reported, on average, per year during 1994–1998.
3. Structure fires (incident type 11) in care of aged facilities (fixed property use 311,459) are included in this table. Fires in which the cause was unknown or not reported have been allocated proportionally as part of the calculation.
4. Fires are rounded to the nearest ten, casualties are rounded to the nearest one; direct property damage is rounded to the nearest hundred thousand dollars. Percentages are calculated on the actual estimates, so two figures with the same rounded-off estimates may have different percentages. Sums may not equal due to rounding errors. Damage has not been adjusted for inflation.
5. The changes in NFIRS coding that accompanied the introduction of Version 5.0 in 1999 dictate special care in comparing statistics from before and after 1999. The proportion of data collected under these rules has been steadily increasing since 1999. Pay close attention to text discussions of how best to interpret trend data.
6. The reporting of confined cooking fires (and certain other confined fires) has been simplified, which can result in an apparent increase in the number and share of these fires. The code "suspicious" has been eliminated. This may result in an apparent decline in the number of intentional (previously incendiary and suspicious) fires.
7. These are national estimates of fires reported to U.S. municipal fire departments and so exclude fires reported only to federal or state agencies or industrial fire brigades. National estimates are projections. Casualty and loss projections can be heavily influenced by the inclusion or exclusion of one unusually serious fire.
Source: National estimates based on NFIRS and NFPA survey.

TABLE S1.7 *Structure Fires in Facilities that Care for the Sick, Excluding Nursing Homes and Residential Board and Care, by Area of Origin, 1999–2001*

	Fires		*Civilian Deaths*		*Civilian Injuries*		*Property Damage*	
Area of Origin	*No.*	*%*	*No.*	*%*	*No.*	*%*	*$ (in millions)*	*%*
Cooking area or kitchen	940	(31.0)	0	(0.0)	10	(10.3)	0.7	(3.8)
Bedroom	310	(10.1)	1	(100.0)	32	(32.8)	1.1	(5.7)
Laundry area	230	(7.6)	0	(0.0)	20	(20.5)	0.7	(3.5)
Bathroom, checkroom, lavatory, or locker room	150	(4.9)	0	(0.0)	8	(8.7)	0.5	(2.5)
Machinery room or area, or elevator machinery room	110	(3.6)	0	(0.0)	0	(0.0)	1.3	(6.5)
Office	90	(3.0)	0	(0.0)	1	(0.7)	0.6	(3.0)
Common room, den, family room, living room, or lounge	90	(2.9)	0	(0.0)	0	(0.0)	0.1	(0.7)
Corridor or hallway	80	(2.7)	0	(0.0)	2	(2.2)	0.2	(1.1)
Heating room or area, or water heater area	70	(2.4)	0	(0.0)	1	(1.5)	0.1	(0.7)
Bar area, dining hall area, or cafeteria	70	(2.3)	0	(0.0)	1	(0.8)	0.0	(0.2)
Exterior roof surface	60	(1.8)	0	(0.0)	0	(0.0)	0.9	(4.5)
Other known area of origin	840	(27.6)	0	(0.0)	22	(22.5)	13.2	(67.8)
Total	3,050	(100.0)	1	(100.0)	97	(100.0)	19.4	(100.0)

Notes:
1. Estimated annual averages of unknown-area fires are allocated proportionally.
2. Structure fires (incident type 11) in care of sick facilities (fixed property use 321–340) are included in this table. Fires in which the area was unknown or not reported have been allocated proportionally as part of the calculation.
3. Fires are rounded to the nearest ten; casualties are rounded to the nearest one; direct property damage is rounded to the nearest hundred thousand dollars. Percentages are calculated on the actual estimates, so two figures with the same rounded-off estimates might have different percentages. Sums might not equal due to rounding errors. Damage has not been adjusted for inflation.
4.These are national estimates of fires reported to U.S. municipal fire departments and so exclude fires reported only to federal or state agencies or industrial fire brigades. National estimates are projections. Casualty and loss projections can be heavily influenced by the inclusion or exclusion of one unusually serious fire.
Source: National estimates based on NFIRS and NFPA survey.

***TABLE S1.8** Structure Fires in Facilities that Care for the Aged, Including Nursing Homes and Residential Board and Care, by Area of Origin, 1999–2001*

	Fires		*Civilian Deaths*		*Civilian Injuries*		*Property Damage*	
Area of Origin	*No.*	*%*	*No.*	*%*	*No.*	*%*	*$ (in millions)*	*%*
Cooking area or kitchen	1,340	(37.9)	1	(5.6)	29	(17.9)	1.4	(12.5)
Laundry area	560	(15.8)	0	(0.0)	30	(18.8)	2.2	(20.1)
Bedroom	430	(12.2)	3	(28.8)	62	(38.1)	1.7	(15.2)
Bathroom, checkroom, lavatory, or locker room	120	(3.4)	2	(23.3)	1	(0.6)	0.3	(2.3)
Common room, den, family room, living room, or lounge	110	(3.1)	3	(27.0)	10	(6.3)	0.3	(2.8)
Heating room or area, or water heater area	80	(2.2)	0	(0.0)	1	(0.4)	0.0	(0.2)
Bar area, dining hall, or cafeteria	60	(1.7)	0	(0.0)	0	(0.0)	0.0	(0.3)
Corridor or hallway	50	(1.3)	0	(0.0)	3	(1.9)	0.0	(0.3)
Other known area of origin	790	(22.3)	2	(15.2)	26	(16.0)	5.1	(46.3)
Total	3,530	(100.0)	11	(100.0)	162	(100.0)	11.1	(100.0)

Notes:
1. Estimated annual averages of unknown-area fires are allocated proportionally.
2. Properties coded as facilities that care for the aged without nursing staff and children's homes or orphanages in earlier versions of NFIRS convert to residential board and care facilities in NFIRS Version 5.0. About 100 children's home or orphanage fires were reported, on average, per year from 1994 to 1998.
3. Structure fires (incident type 11) in care of aged facilities (fixed property use, 311,459) are included in this table. Fires of unknown cause or with cause not reported have been allocated proportionally as part of the calculation.
4. These are national estimates of fires reported to U.S. municipal fire departments and so exclude fires reported only to federal or state agencies or industrial fire brigades. National estimates are projections. Casualty and loss projections can be heavily influenced by the inclusion or exclusion of one unusually serious fire.
Source: National estimates based on NFIRS and NFPA survey.

TABLE S1.9 *Examples of Sprinkler Operation that Controlled or Extinguished Health Care Facility Fires.*

Year	*Facility Type*	*Sprinkler Heads Operated*	*Contributing Factor/Cause*
Pre-1920	Hospital Providence, RI	1	Mattresses
1920	Hospital N. Dartmouth, MA	1	Laundry
1940	Hospital Belmont, MA	1	Laundry
1949	Hospital Philadelphia, PA	1	Laundry chute
1961	Hospital Philadelphia, PA (day of Hartford fire)	1	Rubbish chute
1974	Nursing Home South Natick, MA	1	Patient set fire
1976	Nursing Home Niles, IL	1	Probable smoking materials
1985	Nursing Home IL	1	Laundry dryer & cotton mop heads
1992	Nursing Home Woburn, MA	21	Natural gas explosion
1993	Nursing Home Ashland, KY	1	Wiring for heat pump
1993	Hospital Weymouth, MA	2	Patient ignited mattress
1994	Nursing Home Knox County, TN	1	Smoking materials
1996	Hospital Hyannis, MA	2	Unattended electric stove ignited food tray left on stove

REFERENCES

1. *Leading Causes and Other Patterns and Trends, Facilities that Care for the Aged and Sick,* National Fire Protection Association, Quincy, MA, September 2004.
2. NFPA *101*®, *Life Safety Code*®, 2006 edition.
3. NFPA *U.S. Experience with Sprinklers,* 2003, Table 11.

Supplement 2

Regulatory Issues Affecting the Safety of Clinical Hyperbaric Medicine Facilities

W. T. Workman

Wilbur T. Workman, M.S., CAsP, CHT, is president of Workman Hyperbaric Services, Inc., in San Antonio, Texas. He has served on the NFPA Technical Committee on Hyperbaric and Hypobaric Facilities since 1984 and has been chairman since 1996. Mr. Workman specialized in Aerospace and Hyperbaric Physiology throughout his 23-year career in the United States Air Force. He holds dual board certifications in Aerospace Physiology and Hyperbaric Technology and now specializes in hyperbaric facility planning, staff training, operational safety, and regulatory compliance.

HISTORY AND DEVELOPMENT

The application of high atmospheric (or other gas) pressure for medical purposes dates back to 1650, when von Guericke developed the first practical air pump. It was not until nearly 180 years later, however, that this technology was used to provide compressed air for manned caisson work in the construction of bridges and underwater tunnels. Workers who spent long periods under increased pressure would often experience excruciating joint pain when returning to the surface (or decompressing). This condition was then called "compressed-air illness" or "caisson disease" and is now referred to as *decompression sickness*.

The technology and practical application of high air pressure for medical purposes (using hyperbaric chambers) continued to flourish throughout Europe in the 1800s. In 1854, Pol and Watelle reported what is thought to be the first account of the use of recompression to relieve the pain of compressed-air illness. This technique was endorsed by the renowned French physiologist Paul Bert, who, in 1878, stated that a combination of oxygen and recompression was a treatment for the illness. It was not until 1912, however, that a study of a large series of caisson disease cases clearly established the benefits of recompression therapy. Twelve years later, the U.S. Navy published its first standardized compressed air treatment schedules for decompression sickness.

The use of hyperbaric facilities to treat a variety of other medical conditions began to emerge in the late 1950s and early 1960s from the work of Dr. Borema and his colleagues in Amsterdam, with high-pressure oxygen for treating gas gangrene. Subsequently, high-pressure oxygen was found to be effective in the treatment of carbon monoxide poisoning, air embolism, and a variety of other conditions. Treatment was conducted in single-patient or multipatient hyperbaric chambers; some were even designed with operating room capability to allow surgical procedures to be performed on patients who would otherwise not receive enough oxygen if operated on at ambient atmospheric pressure.

SAFETY CONCERNS

Along with the treatment benefits, hyperbaric facilities brought to the medical community a host of new safety concerns. The very nature of a hyperbaric chamber — wherein a patient is confined in an atmosphere where the burning rate of materials is, generally, markedly enhanced and the ease of their ignition greatly increased — created the urgent need for safety requirements governing their use. In 1964, a Subcommittee on Hyperbaric and Hypobaric Facilities was appointed by NFPA to address the subject. Subcommittee membership included representatives from chamber and component manufacturers, chamber operators, fire service personnel, government personnel from the National Aeronautics and Space Administration and the military services, and others interested in hyperbaric chamber safety. The subcommittee's progress in drafting a standard was slow, however, because there were no previous publications on this topic.

A significant, but unfortunate, impetus for the development of the standard occurred on January 23, 1967. A fire erupted in the *Apollo 1* command module while on its launch pad at Cape Canaveral, Florida, and all three astronauts inside were killed. The fire, believed to be of electrical origin, broke out during a test in which the module was pressurized with 100 percent oxygen at 20 psia. A few days later another fire, proven to be of electrical origin, occurred in an Air Force hypobaric (altitude) chamber in San Antonio, Texas. The chamber contained pure oxygen at one-fifth of an atmosphere pressure. Two airmen were in the chamber at the time of the fire and both died of massive burns. These two tragic events spurred the development and adoption of NFPA 56D. Adopted as a tentative standard in 1968 and a full standard in 1970, NFPA 56D was incorporated into NFPA 99 in 1984. During this entire period, the document and its subject have undergone a process of continuous use, careful scrutiny, and regular review and revision.

The major changes of Chapter 20 in the last few revision cycles of NFPA 99 were a direct result of the continual input from both military and civilian representatives on the Technical Committee (TC) on Hyperbaric and Hypobaric Facilities. In preparation for the 1999 edition, membership of the TC was expanded to include representation from the U.S. Food and Drug Administration (FDA) and special expertise from the active fire research, fire sprinkler, and forensic communities. Their input proved invaluable to better understand the issues in support of the changes made for the 1999 edition. The most significant changes adopted for that edition were in the area of electrical requirements for Class A (multiplace) chambers. Support for these changes culminate many years of dedicated effort by committee members to update this portion of the standard and reflect an awareness of the technology now available to hyperbaric chamber designers that perhaps did not exist when the initial requirements were put into place. A better understanding of what constitutes an oxygen-enriched environment, the effects of hyperbaric conditions on the burning rate of materials, and the role that static electricity might play have also contributed to the ongoing revision process. It has been the committee's desire to reflect advances in technology and the ever-increasing understanding of the design and operation of hyperbaric facilities without compromising safety.

It is unfortunate that the majority of accidents involving hyperbaric facilities in the past 20 years have been the result of human error. Dr. Paul Sheffield and David Desautels reported information on 77 fatalities in 35 hyperbaric chamber fires from 1923 to 1996 [1]. These mishaps occurred in Asia, Europe, and North America. Information on mishaps from other regions was not reported. Of the 77 fatalities cited, none occurred in North American *clinical* hyperbaric chambers. Prior to 1980, the primary cause of hyperbaric chamber fires was electrical; after 1980, the vast majority was attributed to either prohibited materials allowed in the chamber or operator error. Careful analysis of these data clearly points to the success of engineering and fire safety codes and standards as applied in North America to clinical hyperbaric medicine facilities. Because of recent tragic accidents in other countries, there is a growing recognition of the need for comprehensive fire safety standards in developing countries. Also, setting minimum training standards on the safe operation of hyperbaric systems will have a positive effect on maintaining hyperbaric safety standards throughout the world. Additional information related to operational hyperbaric facility safety can be found in *Hyperbaric Facility Safety: A Practical Guide* [2].

In the early 1970s, there were fewer than 30 hyperbaric facilities in the nation. Today, there are an estimated 600 to 800. Most of this growth has occurred in the past 10 years as the role of hyperbaric oxygen therapy has been validated in comprehensive wound care. This trend is expected to continue. With any industry that experiences rapid growth, quality and safety standards must be established and rigidly enforced, as they are often vital to the success of the industry. Such is the case with hyperbaric oxygen therapy. As the use of hyperbaric therapy has become more widely accepted, there is a movement to promote hyperbaric oxygen therapy in nontraditional health care centers (freestanding), to use mobile-based systems that travel from one jurisdiction to another, and even to use hyperbaric chambers in the home. This trend is disconcerting because there are no training, staffing, or quality standards that hyperbaric operators in these environments must meet. According to NFPA *101®*, *Life Safety Code®*

[3], even hyperbaric facilities located in nonhealth care installations (freestanding) must comply with the basic hyperbaric safety standards as prescribed in Chapter 20 of NFPA 99. In addition to nonexistent training, staffing, and quality standards, there are no safety standards that mobile or home-based hyperbaric chambers must meet.

Although it is not the purpose of this introduction to describe the detailed requirements of organizations, such as the American Society of Mechanical Engineers' Committee on Pressure Vessels for Human Occupancy (ASME-PVHO), the FDA, and others related to hyperbaric facility safety, a short overview of the more prominent is warranted. A comprehensive appreciation of how collateral hyperbaric safety requirements are woven together with NFPA 99 will help to maintain the highest level of hyperbaric safety possible.

ORGANIZATIONAL INFORMATION

The American Society of Mechanical Engineers – Committee on Pressure Vessels for Human Occupancy

The ASME-PVHO *Safety Standard for Pressure Vessels for Human Occupancy* defines engineering parameters for the safe design, fabrication, testing, and installation of manned hyperbaric systems. Components covered are the actual pressure vessel, acrylic viewports, and related piping systems. In response to the growing need for educating the engineering community on the design requirements for clinical hyperbaric systems, the ASME-PVHO established the Medical Systems Subcommittee in 1991. The purpose of the subcommittee is to define the minimum design considerations that should be evaluated by engineers when designing a hyperbaric system intended for clinical use. Guidance developed by the subcommittee is to be integrated into the 2005 edition of the standard as a separate section. Input to this document has been provided by a cross section of experienced hyperbaric systems designers, clinical hyperbaric medicine physicians, and technical personnel.

Eleven U.S. states, three U.S. cities, and five Canadian provinces require that pressure vessels designed for human occupancy comply with ASME-PVHO. Currently, the states of Arkansas, California, Delaware, Georgia, Hawaii, Minnesota, North Carolina, Oregon, Tennessee, Washington, Wisconsin; the cities of Denver, Seattle, and the District of Columbia; and the Canadian provinces of Alberta, British Columbia, New Brunswick, Nova Scotia, and Ontario have mandatory PVHO laws.

Chapter 20 invokes compliance with ASME-PVHO for all hyperbaric chambers used in health care facilities, regardless of the state of installation. Therefore, if NFPA 99 is invoked in a particular state (or local jurisdiction), the requirement applies. It should also be noted that beginning with the 2000 edition of the *Life Safety Code* (NFPA *101*, 8.4.5, 2000 edition), all hyperbaric chambers used in a nontraditional health care facility (freestanding, office setting, etc.) must be designed, fabricated, tested, and stamped in accordance with the requirements of ASME-PVHO. It is important to know this requirement because hyperbaric chambers are being sold in this country that do not comply with ASME-PVHO and cannot be legally used in locations covered by either NFPA 99 or NFPA *101*.

See contact information at the conclusion of this supplement.

U.S. Food and Drug Administration

The Medical Device Amendments of 1976 (Public Law 91-295) established a comprehensive system for the regulation of medical devices intended for human use [4]. Specifically, it mandated that the FDA classify all medical devices into three categories: Class I, General Controls; Class II, Performance Standards; and, Class III, Pre-Market Approval. Devices in commercial distribution prior to May 28, 1976, are not required to comply with this law and are "grandfathered" as preamendment devices. However, devices developed after this date are required to establish either validated performance or substantial equivalency to devices already in commercial distribution.

The FDA Anesthesiology Panel categorizes hyperbaric chambers as Class II medical devices. As such, before placing these devices in commercial sales, the manufacturer must submit a 510(k) Pre-Market Notification request. This application can be based on an entirely new design or on substantial equivalency. The majority of clinical hyperbaric chamber manufacturers are in compliance with this requirement, but not all. Efforts are underway to ensure the compliance of all manufacturers.

In addition to being defined as a Class II medical device, clinical hyperbaric chambers are also considered as "prescription devices" by the FDA. A prescription device is one for which a physician must be involved in its procurement and must issue a prescription for the use of a hyperbaric chamber and the administration of oxygen.

The manufacture, packaging, storage, and installation of hyperbaric chambers must comply with the Quality Systems Regulations (QSRs) as described by the FDA. Failure to comply with any of the requirements of the QSR directives renders the device adulterated. Such a device, as well as the person responsible for the failure to comply, is subject to regulatory action. Any written or oral complaint under the FDA's mandatory Medical Device Reporting program or its voluntary MedWatch program concerning a hyperbaric chamber relative to its quality, reliability, safety, effectiveness, or performance shall be reviewed, evaluated, and documented. Oversight includes taking action on a hyperbaric chamber manufacturer for promotion and advertisement of its chamber for medical conditions not recognized by the Undersea and Hyperbaric Medical Society (UHMS) as indications for which the use of hyperbaric oxygen has been scientifically validated. Failure to comply with these requirements can result in the withdrawal of the hyperbaric chamber from commercial distribution.

See the contact information at the conclusion of this supplement.

The Joint Commission on Accreditation of Healthcare Organizations

The Joint Commission on Accreditation of Healthcare Organizations (JCAHO) is the organization that provides accreditation for all U.S. hospitals. Even though earlier editions of NFPA 99 stipulated that accreditation agencies, such as JCAHO, "establish and enforce appropriate programs to fulfill the provisions of this chapter," this requirement has not been universally applied. See the section on the Undersea and Hyperbaric Medical Society for additional information on clinical hyperbaric facility accreditation.

See also the contact information at the conclusion of this supplement.

The Occupational Safety and Health Administration

The Occupational Safety and Health Administration (OSHA) is the agency of the U.S. Department of Labor that promotes safe and healthful working conditions. Its chief responsibility is to develop and enforce job safety and health regulations. OSHA regulations deal with fire prevention, protective garments, railings, and many other safety matters. It has no direct program or regulations that deal specifically with hyperbaric facilities.

The Undersea and Hyperbaric Medical Society

The Undersea and Hyperbaric Medical Society (UHMS) is an international medical society with more than 2000 members and the following goals:

- Provide a forum for professional scientific communication among individuals and groups involved in basic and applied aspects of the undersea environment and hyperbaric medicine
- Promote cooperation between the life sciences and other disciplines with undersea activity and hyperbaric medicine
- Develop and promote educational activities and other programs that improve the scientific knowledge of undersea and hyperbaric environments and the accepted indications of hyperbaric oxygen therapy
- Improve the quality of care of the hyperbaric patient, as demonstrated through its hyperbaric facility accreditation program

In support of these objectives, the Hyperbaric Safety Committee of the UHMS has been very active in establishing a leading role in promoting hyperbaric facility safety. Practical guidelines on both monoplace and multiplace hyperbaric facility operations have been published and widely distributed. These commonsense documents should be required for every hyperbaric facility.

Recognizing the need for a comprehensive set of "Standards of Practice" for use throughout the U.S. hyperbaric medicine community, the UHMS developed consensus criteria on minimum training, staffing, skills verification for each specialty level, and overall facility safety. These criteria have provided a national set of guidelines for the appropriate and safe application of hyperbaric medicine. Compliance to these recommendations, and other appropriate standards or guidelines such as those developed by the JCAHO, the NFPA, the Compressed Gas Association, and other organizations, is assessed through a comprehensive clinical hyperbaric facility accreditation program offered by UHMS. The objectives of this voluntary program are to improve the quality of care provided to the hyperbaric patient and to further enhance patient safety.

At the time of this publication, more than 10 percent of hospital-based hyperbaric facilities in the country had been accredited through this program. UHMS is also working with JCAHO to become a formally recognized Complementary Accrediting Body. This effort is being facilitated by UHMS membership in the Joint Commission's Liaison Network. The accreditation program is specifically structured so that it can be applied to both hospital-based and freestanding hyperbaric facilities. Several state health departments are actively considering requiring that hyperbaric facilities be licensed in their state and that facility accreditation be used as the basis of licensure. In addition, at least one fire district is considering requiring that all hyperbaric facilities in the jurisdiction be accredited. Anyone interested in learning more of the accreditation program is encouraged to contact UHMS.

See the contact information at the conclusion of this supplement.

The American College of Hyperbaric Medicine

Unlike the UHMS with it broadly based membership, the American College of Hyperbaric Medicine (ACHM) is specifically for hyperbaric physicians. The college promotes and develops liaison with individuals and groups with similar interests in the field of hyperbaric medicine. A primary goal of ACHM is to enhance the exchange of scientific and therapeutic information related to the specialty of hyperbaric medicine in a manner that will encourage national and international goodwill as well as social and cultural exchanges.

See the contact information at the conclusion of this supplement.

CONCLUSION

While organizations such as NFPA, ASME, FDA, and others have done a superb job in ensuring that hyperbaric pressure vessels and related systems are safely designed, manufactured, and installed, it is up to the operator to ensure that the equipment is properly used and maintained. All personnel involved in hyperbaric medicine need to have a complete understanding of the safety requirements in this and other standards. An active, ongoing safety awareness and training program that involves the entire hyperbaric staff and local fire personnel must be in place. Prevention and training are key elements to any effective safety program. Much work is needed to ensure that all jurisdictional agencies fully understand how hyperbaric facilities are currently used, appreciate their rate of growth, and exercise their enforcement role as it exists today. Standards need to be uniformly applied across all venues to ensure that we continue to enjoy our safety record.

Today, hyperbaric medicine stands on the threshold of a major international expansion. Under the guidance of the Undersea and Hyperbaric Medical Society, the European Committee on Clinical Hyperbaric Medicine, the Japanese Hyperbaric Medicine Society, the British Hyperbaric Association, South Africa Undersea and Hyperbaric Medical Association, and a growing number of other international professional organizations, hyperbaric medicine practitioners throughout the world now use this powerful therapy for a growing number of conditions. A few medical conditions from this growing list are decompression sickness, problem wounds, air or gas embolism, carbon monoxide poisoning and smoke inhalation, gas gangrene, crush injury and other acute traumatic ischemias, necrotizing soft tissue infections, osteomyelitis, osteoradionecrosis of the mandible, non-healing diabetic wounds, failing skin flaps, and selected burns. Exciting research into new applications for hyperbaric medicine will help foster further expansion.

However, optimism for the future of clinical hyperbaric medicine must be tempered with a few words of caution. As with any rapidly growing specialty, there will be those who try to cut corners by purchasing hyperbaric equipment that has not gone through the rigors of regulatory review, install the equipment in nontraditional health care locations (such as regular business occupancies where NFPA 99 may not necessarily be applied if its citation by reference in NFPA *101* is not known), fail to receive adequate training in the safe and appropriate use of the equipment, and then use the equipment to treat medical conditions not recognized for hyperbaric treatment. There is a growing concern, due to these shortcomings, that the likelihood of a major hyperbaric accident occurring in North America is much greater. A mishap occurring in any type of hyperbaric facility will affect the entire community. Facilities can reduce their risk of mishap by seeking accreditation, which evaluates all aspects of hyperbaric facility safety and provides specific recommendations for improvement where necessary. Authorities having jurisdiction are encouraged to become more proactive in learning more about how these systems are being used and how existing safety standards can be appropriately applied.

CONTACT INFORMATION

American College of Hyperbaric Medicine
2901 West KK Parkway, Ste. 311
Milwaukee, WI 53125
(414) 385-1944
www.hyperbaricmedicine.org

American Society of Mechanical Engineers International
Three Park Ave.
New York, NY 10016-5990
(212) 591-8537
www.asme.org

U.S. Food and Drug Administration
Center for Devices and Radiological Health
Office of Device Evaluation
9200 Corporate Blvd. (HFZ-450)
Rockville, MD 20850
(301) 443-8609
www.fda.gov

The Joint Commission for Accreditation of Healthcare Organizations
One Renaissance Blvd.
Oakbrook Terrace, IL 60181
(630) 792-5000
www.jcaho.org

The Undersea and Hyperbaric Medical Society
10531 Metropolitan Ave.
Kensington, MD 20895-2627
(301) 942-2980
www.uhms.org

The Undersea and Hyperbaric Medical Society Satellite Office
18111 Copper Ridge Dr.
San Antonio, TX 78259-3612
(210) 404-1553
www.uhms.org

REFERENCES

1. Sheffield, P. J., and Desautels. D. A., Hyperbaric and Hypobaric Chamber Fires: A 73-Year Analysis, Undersea & Hyperbaric Medicine, 1997; 24(3): 153–164.
2. Workman, W. T., Editor, *Hyperbaric Facility Safety: A Practical Guide*, Best Publishing Company, Flagstaff, Arizona, 1999.
3. NFPA *101®, Life Safety Code®,* 2006 edition.
4. *Federal Register*, Vol. 44, No. 214, November 2, 1979.

Supplement 3

Disaster Recovery at Texas Medical Center from Tropical Storm Allison

Michael A. Crowley, P.E.

Michael A. Crowley, P.E., is vice president of engineering and the manager of the Houston office for Rolf Jensen & Associates, Inc., in Houston, Texas. He is a member of several NFPA committees, including the Technical Correlating Committee for NFPA 99, Standard for Health Care Facilities. He also has served on the NFPA 101 Technical Committee on Health Care Occupancies since 1985.

Tropical Storm Allison formed quickly over the Gulf of Mexico in early June 2001. The storm moved ashore with relatively low wind speeds but with torrential rains. On Wednesday, June 6, the storm passed over the Houston metropolitan area, moving north-northeast. On the first pass, the storm dumped enough rain to cause moderate flooding in some sections of the city and also saturated the ground. Due to a high-pressure system over the Midwest, the storm advanced north-northeast to approximately Lufkin, Texas, then it reversed course. The storm moved southwest, arriving over the Houston metropolitan area again on Friday, June 8. The rain began mid-afternoon on June 8.

Because of the storm's southwest direction of movement and the counterclockwise rotation of the tropical storm clouds, it appeared for some time that the storm did not move but was stationary over the Houston metropolitan area. Rain gauges recorded anywhere from two inches of rain on the far west side of the Houston area to 36 inches of rain east of downtown Houston. The amount of rain dropped from this storm system exceeded most records in the area. The storm tapered off its rainfall in the early morning hours of June 9. As the sun rose over Houston and Harris County, the massive damage and destruction that was caused by the flooding of Tropical Storm Allison became evident. The storm had left behind more than $2 billion in damage [1]. See Exhibit S3.1.

Storm Damage at the Texas Medical Center

One of the hardest hit sections of Houston was the Texas Medical Center, which is approximately 700 acres containing some forty medical facilities, including two medical schools, four nursing schools, thirteen hospitals, and two specialty hospitals. The Texas Medical Center contains only not-for-profit or state-operated institutions.

Although all the facilities were affected by the floods to some extent, the level of damage and destruction varied significantly based on their location within the Texas Medical Center. While there was ample warning that the tropical storm was passing over Houston for a second time, the intensity of the storm had not been anticipated. The facilities had been prepared for the tropical storm and possible flooding, but the high level of the floodwaters was not anticipated. The Texas Medical Center area has multiple electrical feeds from the Houston power grid. Early in the morning on June 9, floodwaters caused the multiple feed to fail, resulting in primary power loss to all the facilities.

EXHIBIT S3.1 *Aerial view of Tropical Storm Allison. (Courtesy of NASA)*

Contrary to press reports, none of the generator units were underwater. The generators initially started on the multiple facilities and began providing emergency power to the emergency circuits.

As the early morning of June 9 wore on, the floodwaters continued to rise. Water began entering the facilities from multiple roofs, over flood barriers at the drive entrances to parking garages, over flood barriers around the perimeters of the sites, and through backed-up storm sewers. The floodwaters also moved from area to area through the tunnel systems interconnecting the buildings within the Texas Medical Center. All of these institutions have had to deal with flooding in the past, and all have occasionally experienced minor flooding due to storms. The amount of water entering the facilities overwhelmed the normal sump pumps and filled the lower levels of the facilities. As the water rose, it began to come in contact with the electrical switchgear that controls the power distribution in many of the facilities. As the switchgear was affected, the facilities began to lose emergency power. As emergency power systems failed, patient care functions became critical.

Disaster Response

The health care facilities began their storm emergency procedures while handling the patients. Additional staff members from many facilities were notified to respond to the institution to assist.

Facility staffs rose to the challenge and became very innovative, taking actions to preserve and save patients' lives. By midday on June 9, most patient care issues had been stabilized. The next function became assessing damages to the facilities. Each facility took a slightly different approach in assessment and recovery; however, the following were common themes addressed by all.

The assessment phase began immediately. This phase lasted up to 10 days at some facilities due to the time frame necessary to remove the water safely from the facility and from access areas contaminated with hazardous chemicals. Along with the assessment phase was the initial recovery and *critical path evaluation* for the facilities. Each facility was affected differently by the flooding, and each facility had a different critical path to reach its recovery goals. Critical path items included emergency power for the following:

- Information management services
- Command and control areas
- Dehydration and air-conditioning units
- Temporary lighting
- Water removal systems

The early stages of the recovery also included assembling teams of consultants, contractors, and equipment suppliers to assist in damage evaluation and repairs. In the larger facilities, multiple general contractors were brought in and set up with construction trailers, and they functioned as an integral part of the assessment team. Consultants included mechanical, electrical, plumbing, med gases, building commissioning, fire protection, life safety, cost estimating, environmental health and safety, hygiene, asbestos, and architects. In addition to the consultants, the owners' representatives included architects, building construction managers, and insurance adjusters.

The Army Corps of Engineers, the Federal Emergency Management Agency (FEMA), the Houston Building Department, the Houston Fire Department, and the Texas Department of Health lent their input and support throughout the recovery effort. Their support included switchgear, onboard drawing reviews, expedited inspections, expedited drawing reviews, expedited permits, and disaster recovery funding.

The recovery goals for each institution varied, but in general, getting back to providing patient care at the prestorm levels was of paramount importance. This required drying the buildings including pumping, dehumidification, and repair of broken water mains and sewage lines due to the flood. The recovery process also included a massive cleanout of most of the facilities.

The removal of walls and other building materials covered in floodwater was not a major issue during the initial stages of the recovery. Some insurance adjusters questioned the level of demolition in some of the upper areas of the building that only experienced a couple of feet of flooding. However, in general, due to the infectious control concerns and mold concerns, a majority of the gypsum wallboard was removed in areas inundated with floods. Very little equipment that had been covered by floodwater was salvaged. However, some unusual size electrical motors and hard-to-get electrical components were refurbished for temporary use.

All the facilities approached the recovery similarly to a construction project needing a building certification prior to use. Almost every system in these facilities was affected in one way or another by the floods. Although not required by the authority having jurisdiction, recertification of the systems was conducted, including main power supply; emergency power and transfer switches; medical gas systems; water systems including deionized water systems and automatic sprinkler systems; stair pressurization systems; smoke control systems; fire detection and alarm systems; elevators; sump pumps; and foundation dewatering systems.

The floodwaters destroyed many of the support functions that needed to be rebuilt, including central sterile, labs, pharmacy, and bioengineering. These functions were critical to bring the hospitals back online. Other support areas that were damaged or lost, while critical to the research functions of the facilities, were not on the critical recovery path. Facilities such as research labs, vivariums, and engineering support shops were not included in the initial efforts to bring the facility back online. See Exhibit S3.2.

Recovery times varied from ten days to five weeks. The incident command function, although initially set up to deal with the flood, changed over time to become the project management and control functions for the recovery effort. Extensive meetings and tracking of goals and accomplishments were recorded to evaluate progress. Also, as the recovery progressed, damage assessments were re-evaluated as equipment was removed, replacement equipment delivery dates were tracked, and options and alternative solutions were constantly evaluated. Interim life safety measures were implemented that covered everything from changes in evacuation routes to completely revised fire department responses to the facilities due to the temporary emergency generator locations and other construction activities. Recovery resources, such as manpower and electri-

EXHIBIT S3.2 *Flood damage at Memorial Hermann Hospital in Houston after Tropical Storm Allison. (Courtesy of AP/Wideworld Photos)*

cal equipment, were limited in some instances. The recovery teams had to respond and develop alternative methods to meet their primary goals.

Lessons Learned

The disaster of Tropical Storm Allison is, in many ways, beyond description, due to the magnitude of its effect at the Texas Medical Center. Many of the individual stories of heroics and ingenuity might never be known. However, some of the lessons learned must be shared with all facilities to prepare them for the unthinkable. These lessons include the following:

- Maintain a good working relationship with a general contractor in the area, that is, someone who can be contacted in a moment's notice to provide the expertise and manpower to rebuild a major portion of the facility.
- Keep extensive records of the building systems, including manufacturers, model numbers, and dates of purchase. This file should include all of the life safety equipment, all of the major comfort equipment for the building, and all of the patient-related systems, ranging from nurse call to liquid oxygen.
- Keep a list of design professionals who know health care and, preferably, are located locally. Their opinions and engineering and design support can help the facility through critical recovery issues.
- Know the facility's insurance coverage, including limits, deductibles, and specialty clauses related to equipment loss due to floods, water, fire, and other hazards.
- Keep a working relationship with the authorities having jurisdiction, either directly through the hospital, through contractors, or through consultants. The authority having jurisdiction can be a great asset in helping navigate through the bureaucratic requirements of the recovery effort.

Conclusion

The challenges addressed during the post–flood recovery of Tropical Storm Allison were loss of fire protection systems, loss of fire detection and alarm systems, hazardous material contamination, removal of radioactive waste, removal of tons of debris, air quality control, management of combustible and flammable material, and removal and recovery of records. A single person or department cannot provide the talents needed to cover this wide range of challenges. It requires a team approach, with the facility operators managing the team and directing it toward reaching its goal.

Will a disaster like this happen at the Texas Medical Center again? Probably not. Each facility has assessed its vulnerabilities to flooding and has adjusted its building to protect it from floods and to respond to high water conditions in the area. These protections include floodwalls, flood doors to compartment the buildings, enhanced passive flood protection for the facilities, and relocation of vital equipment to above flood plain levels.

Other disasters can occur and can strike a critical blow to any facility, affecting its primary function of health care. With complete preplanning, all facilities can be prepared before the unthinkable disaster occurs.

REFERENCE

1. Paradise, J. R., "Atmospheric Pressure," *NFPA Journal* (July/August 2002): 49–52.

Index

D

E

G

H

M

Q

R

S

U

V

W

X

Z

About the Editor

Richard P. Bielen, P.E., is currently the Chief Systems and Applications Engineer for NFPA and serves as the Executive Secretary for the health care section. Bielen is currently responsible for the NFPA standards on health care, including NFPA 99, 99B, and 99C; the security standards NFPA 730 and NFPA 731; and mine fire safety.

Bielen holds a master's degree in fire protection engineering and a bachelor's degree in electrical engineering, both from Worcester Polytechnic Institute. He is also a registered professional engineer in fire protection engineering.

Bielen authored the *NFPA Pocket Guide to Medical Gas and Vacuum Systems Installation,* which contains the pertinent material from NFPA 99 as well as useful design and installation guidelines. In addition, he developed a seminar program on NFPA 99. He is the principal instructor for this seminar, both domestically and internationally.

Prior to joining NFPA, Bielen worked for the National Fire Protection Research Foundation, for several fire protection consulting firms, and in the electronics industry. He has published many articles on a variety of fire protection, health care, and security subjects.

Tentative Interim Amendment
NFPA 99
Standard for Health Care Facilities
2005 Edition

Reference: 13.4.1.2.2, A.13.4.1.2.2.2
TIA 05-2 (NFPA 99)
(SC-05-7-13)

Pursuant to Section 5 of the NFPA Regulations Governing Committee Projects, the National Fire Protection Association has issued the following Tentative Interim Amendment to NFPA 99, *Standard for Health Care Facilities,* 2005 edition. The TIA was processed by the Health Care Facilities Committee, and was issued by the Standards Council on July 29, 2005, with an effective date of August 18, 2005.

A Tentative Interim Amendment is tentative because it has not been processed through the entire standards-making procedures. It is interim because it is effective only between editions of the standard. A TIA automatically becomes a proposal of the proponent for the next edition of the standard; as such, it then is subject to all of the procedures of the standards-making process.

Revise section 13.4.1.2.2 & A.13.4.1.2.2.3 as follows:

13.4.1.2.2 Germicides and Antiseptics.
13.4.1.2.2.1 Medicaments, including those dispersed as aerosols, shall be permitted to be used in anesthetizing locations for germicidal and antiseptic purposes, for affixing plastic surgical drape materials, for preparation of wound dressing, or for other purposes.
13.4.1.2.2.2* Flammable liquid germicides or antiseptics used in anesthetizing locations, whenever the use of electro surgery, cautery, or ~~electrosurgery~~ a laser is contemplated, shall be ~~nonflammable~~ packaged to ensure controlled delivery to the patient in unit dose applicators, swabs, and other similar applicators.).
13.4.1.2.2.3 Whenever the application of flammable liquid germicides or antiseptics is employed in surgeries where the use of electro surgery, cautery, or a laser is contemplated, time shall be allowed to elapse between application of the germicide or antiseptic and:
(a) The application of drapes to permit complete evaporation and dissipation of any flammable vehicle remaining, and
(b) The use of electro surgery, cautery, or a laser to ensure the solution is completely dry and to permit thorough evaporation and dissipation of any flammable vehicle remaining.
13.4.1.2.2.4 Any solution-soaked materials shall be removed from the operating room prior to draping or use of electro surgery, cautery, or a laser.
13.4.1.2.2.5 Pooling of flammable liquid germicides or antiseptics shall be avoided; if pooling occurs, excess solution shall be wicked and the germicide or antiseptic allowed to completely dry.
13.4.1.2.2.6 A preoperative "time out" period shall be conducted prior to the initiation of any surgical procedure using flammable liquid germicides or antiseptics to verify that a flammable germicide or antiseptic:
(a) Application site is dry prior to draping, and use of electro surgery, cautery, or a laser, and
(b) That pooling of solution has not occurred, or has been corrected, and
(c) Any solution-soaked materials have been removed from the operating room prior to draping and use of electro surgery, cautery, or a laser.
13.4.1.2.2.7 Whenever flammable aerosols or antiseptics are employed, sufficient time shall be allowed to elapse between deposition and application of drapes to permit complete evaporation and dissipation of any flammable vehicle remaining.
13.4.1.2.2.8 Health care organizations shall establish policies and procedures outlining safety precautions related to the use of flammable liquid or aerosol germicides or antiseptics used in anesthetizing locations, as required in Section 13.4.1.2.10, whenever the use of electro surgery, cautery, or a laser is contemplated.

A.13.4.1.2.2.2 Some tinctures and solutions of disinfecting agents provide significant clinical benefits in reducing the risk of surgical infections. However, they can be flammable, and can be used improperly during surgical procedures. ~~Tipping containers, accidental spillage, and the pouring of excessive amounts of such flammable agents on patients expose them to injury in the event of accidental ignition of the flammable solvent~~. To control this risk, flammable germicides or antiseptics that are used when electro surgery, cautery, or a laser is contemplated should be packaged to ensure controlled delivery to the patient (e.g., unit dose applicator, swab, etc.) in small volumes appropriate for single application.